GRAMPIAN MOUNTAINS
GW01086809
R Spean
Fort William
A861
A82
Loch Treig
Loch Ericht
A93
Loch Leven
Kinlochleven
Ballachulish
A82
Loch Rannoch
A924
PERTH AND KINROSS
R Tay
A828
Aberfeldy
Blairgowrie
R Lyon
A923
A984
A827
A826
24
L Lyon
22
23
27
Killin
Loch Tay
A822
R Tay
A9
Tyndrum
Dalmally
A85
36
34
28
Crianlarich
Lochearnhead
A85
L Earn
Crieff
R Earn
Loch Awe
A819
A82
Loch Katrine
M90
Auchterarder
A822
A823
Inveraray
A815
A83
A821
Callander
A84
R Teith
A9
Loch Leven
STIRLING
CLACKMANNANSHIRE
A83
A81
A873
Dunblane
Kinross
63
Loch Long
Loch Lomond
R Forth
A91
Alloa
M90
WEST DUNBARTONSHIRE
A811
A977
A823
64
A817
Stirling
A907
Dunfermline
60
A886
A815
A875
EAST DUNBARTONSHIRE
A985
M876
M9
65
Helensburgh
A811
A809
M180
Kincardine Br
66
62
A814
A81
Kilsyth
Dunoon
Dumbarton
A891
A803
Falkirk
67
A8
A82
A80
FALKIRK
WEST LOTHIAN
M9
Colintraive
Greenock
A761
Cumbernauld
A886
INVERCLYDE
M80
M73
A73
A801
Bathgate
Glasgow
M8
A89
Rothesay
A78
A8
Airdrie
M8
A705
Livingston
Craig
61
A844
Firth of Clyde
Largs
Paisley
A71
Motherwell
A760
M77
A70
72
Island of Bute
East Kilbride
Hamilton
A706
NORTH AYRSHIRE
A737
A736
A726
A721
A702
Stewarton
A71
Kilwinning
A735
A77
Strathaven
M74
A72
A721
Ardrossan
Lanark
R Clyde
ISLE OF ARRAN
1 hr
A71
Kilmarnock
A73
S LANARKSHIRE
Brodick
Irvine
A78
Galston
A70
Biggar
Douglas
Lamlash
Troon
M74
A70
Prestwick
A719
A76
A701
A841
Ayr
A70
Cumnock
A719
EAST AYRSHIRE
New Cumnock
Sanquhar
A74(M)
Maybole
A713
A77
(catamaran)
Moffat
A702

Birds of Argyll

The editors dedicate this book to their
long-suffering wives and families,
in recognition of their remarkable
patience and support during the long
years of its preparation.

The Wild Swans at Coole

The trees are in their autumn beauty,
The woodland paths are dry,
Under the October twilight the water
Mirrors a still sky;
Upon the brimming water among the stones
Are nine-and-fifty Swans.

The nineteenth Autumn has come upon me
Since I made my count;
I saw, before I was well finished,
All suddenly mount
And scatter wheeling in great broken rings,
Upon their clamorous wings.

I have looked upon those brilliant creatures,
And now my heart is sore.
All's changed since I, hearing at twilight,
The first time on this shore,
The bell-beat of their wings above my head,
Trod with a lighter tread.

Unwearied still, lover by lover,
They paddle in the cold
Companionable streams or climb the air;
Their hearts have not grown old;
Passion or conquest, wander where they will,
Attend upon them still.

But now they drift on the still water,
Mysterious, beautiful;
Among what rushes will they build,
By what lake's edge or pool
Delight men's eyes when I awake some day
To find they have flown away?

W. B. Yeats 1919

Birds of Argyll

EDITORS

Tristan ap Rheinallt

Clive Craik

Paul Daw

Bob Furness

Steve Petty

David Wood

Argyll Bird Club

Scottish Charity No. 008782

http://www.argyllbirdclub.org

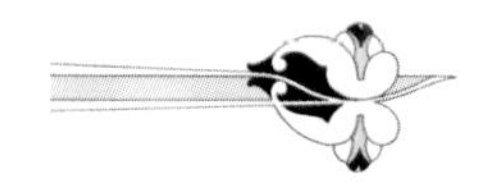

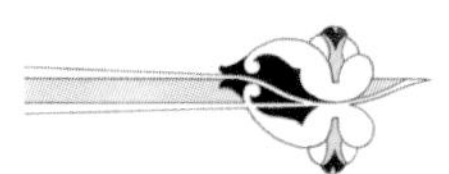

Birds of Argyll

Editors:
Tristan ap Rheinallt, Clive Craik, Paul Daw, Bob Furness, Steve Petty and David Wood.

Species account authors:
Tristan ap Rheinallt, Eric Bignal, John Bowler, Roger Broad, Paul Daw, Clive Craik, Bob Furness, Mike Gregory, Paul Haworth, David Jardine, David Merrie, Malcolm Ogilvie, Steve Petty, Michael Thomas and David Wood.

Artists:
Philip Snow and Margaret Staley.

Photographers:
John Anderson, Eric Bignal, Roy Blewitt, John Bowler, Sue Chattwood, Clive Craik, Jim Dickson, Iain Erskine, Bob Furness, Rob Jordan, Philip Kirkham, Iain Leach, Eddie Maguire, John McAvoy, David Merrie, David Palmar, Kelvin Pearce, Steve Petty, John Robinson, Hugh Venables, David S. Whitaker, David Wood, Louise Wood and Gordon Yates.

First published in 2007 by the Argyll Bird Club, Tigh-na-Tulloch, Tullochgorm, Minard, Argyll PA32 8YQ.
ISBN 978-0-9557777-0-7

Printed and bound by Ian Allan (Printing) Ltd., Riverside Business Park, Molesey Road, Hersham, Surrey KT12 4RG.

www.argyllbirdclub.org

Production of this book was supported financially by:

Front cover: Lunga, Treshnish Islands, by Margaret Staley.
Rear cover: Butterbridge, by Margaret Staley.

This publication should be cited as:
ap Rheinallt, T., Craik, J.C.A., Daw, P., Furness, R.W., Petty, S.J. & Wood, D. (eds.) (2007). *Birds of Argyll.* Argyll Bird Club, Lochgilphead.

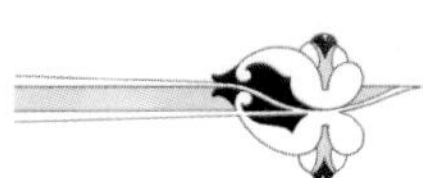

Contents

Argyll from space. This Landsat 7 image was captured in 2000.

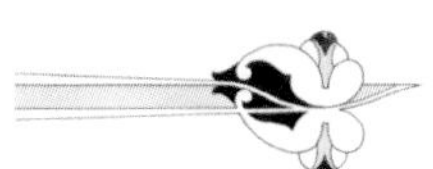

Foreword

The first meeting of the Argyll Bird Club was held in Inveraray on 30 March 1985. Presiding, the late Professor John Smyth from Paisley University noted that the best form of conservation tended to come from people living in the areas concerned. He encouraged us all to play an active role in supporting the Club, to encourage others to do so and to begin work on the documentation of numbers and distribution of the birds of Argyll in a systematic way. Before that meeting, data collection had been sporadic and documentation patchy. This book represents the culmination of a huge effort over the years and more than fulfils Professor Smyth's wise advice.

The years since the launch of the Club have, of course, seen increased pressure on birds and their habitats. Yet Argyll still has one of the most diverse and abundant avifaunas in the country. This book is a celebration of Argyll's birds and is an invaluable contribution to their conservation and to the effective management of their habitats. The birds' prospects depend so much on the goodwill and hard work of the people of Argyll; farmers, foresters, fishermen and others, some of who are already members of the Club. The information presented here will help to inform conservation practices and land management activities. This is important, as the many pressures, from developments on the coast to the increasing uses made of the uplands, progressively limit the habitats available for birds, and change the very nature of the landscape around us. Having this book available to those who take decisions about land-use planning and management will help stress the unique importance of birds and provide information on their particular habitat requirements.

Recent years have seen a huge growth in the popularity of bird watching as a hobby and a related increase in the time people devote to it. What begins as a hobby can become an all-consuming passion, and one that helps add valuable data and information, especially concerning species whose distribution or behaviour was previously poorly known. The efforts of the editorial team and the local County Recorder have shown what can be achieved by gathering together data collected over many years by an army of volunteers, and then turning it into a collective resource that hugely increases our knowledge.

I congratulate the editorial team on producing this book. It is a great testimony to their efforts, and to the work of all those volunteers who have submitted their records of bird sightings over the years. This is a unique publication, about a unique area, setting a new standard for regional avifaunas for years to come.

Professor Colin A. Galbraith

Founder member of Argyll Bird Club
and
Director of Policy and Advice,
Scottish Natural Heritage

Loch Feochan from the south-west, looking out towards the Grampian mountains of north-east Argyll. *John Anderson*

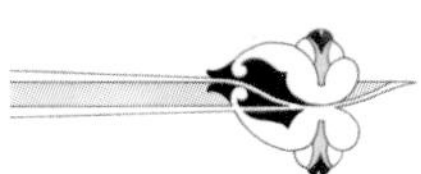

Preface

In *Birds of the West of Scotland* (1871), the Scottish naturalist Robert Gray gave an account of the White-tailed (Sea) Eagle. It opened with these memorable words:

"Being a much commoner bird in Scotland than the Golden Eagle, the Sea Eagle has never been at any time in the same danger of extinction. Even in 1867 and 1868 there were numerous eyries in places which have been occupied from time immemorial."

In fact, of course, it was the White-tailed Eagle that became extinct in Britain, while the Golden Eagle has persisted in fair numbers to the present day. Then, as now, expert opinion was fallible. However, Gray's words carry two more important messages - the danger of complacency and the speed at which changes in bird populations can occur. Gray died in 1887 but the formerly numerous White-tailed Eagle had been persecuted to near-extinction on the Scottish mainland by 1889. The last known breeding attempt by a pair of native Scottish birds was on Skye in 1916.

A more domestic insight into the wildlife of Argyll in the 1880s was given by William Anderson Smith, who lived at Rhugarbh, near Ledaig on the shores of Loch Creran in North Argyll. His two books, *Benderloch* (1882) and *Loch Creran* (1887), are fascinating diaries of local natural history and its changes with the seasons. He was a keen observer of birds and some of his most interesting accounts are of boat trips on Lochs Creran, Linnhe and Etive. He regularly visited one particular island where Peregrine, Raven, Black Guillemot and many gulls bred each summer. All these still breed there today and, nearby, the breeding sites of other birds also survive, such as the heronry on Eriska and the small Sand Martin colony in a bank at Ardentiny. Then, however, he and his sailing companions routinely set out with "...rifles for the seals, and fowling pieces for otters or peregrine falcons...". On a visit to the island in May 1880 they headed for the Ravens' nest, only to find that the gamekeeper had already "ruthlessly slaughtered the young birds as they lay: ay, and the mother too, on the top of them".

In *A Vertebrate Fauna of Argyll and the Inner Hebrides* (1892), Harvie-Brown & Buckley also gave many accounts of the persecution of raptors in Victorian times, including the widespread systematic killing of both species of eagle. They relate how a trap was set for a Golden Eagle in the north of Argyll. "Some days afterwards the trap and all disappeared. We heard a short time later that an eagle had been trapped (nearby) with a trap hanging to its leg." Elsewhere we are told of a White-tailed Eagle chick taken from its nest and kept as a captive. Its bill was grossly deformed, after being crushed in a gin-trap set at the nest for the adult birds.

Accounts like these may well prompt us to wonder how our own descendants will view the way that we ourselves are treating the wildlife that we hold in trust. From the viewpoint of nature conservation, some of the activities and events described here in the pages of *Birds of Argyll* are triumphs, but others are, in terms of nature conservation, disasters. Among the Scottish triumphs we may certainly list the successful reintroduction of White-tailed Eagles and the eleventh-hour rescue of Corn Crakes from local extinction; Argyll has played a large part in both. Among the disasters we must include, as part of widespread and continuing loss of habitats, the felling of native broadleaved woodlands that occurred in some areas in the 1970s and 1980s to make way for plantations of exotic conifers. Today, the few remaining western oakwoods are seen as jewels in the crown of Scottish biodiversity. Similarly, the almost total loss of mixed farming systems in Argyll has contributed to the collapse in populations of species which relied on the arable component, such as Corn Bunting and Yellowhammer.

Some changes were probably justified, in the sense that benefits may have outweighed losses. Certainly, there were powerful strategic and economic reasons underlying both the above examples. Other changes led to the destruction of habitats that arguably should have been saved. An example that appears repeatedly in this book is the draining in 1995 of Westport Marsh in Kintyre, once the haunt of breeding Garganey, Shoveler and Coot (all three are rare in Argyll), as well as Snipe, Lapwing and other valued wetland species. Another development, one that would not be permitted today, was the planting of conifers on Crinan Moss, adjacent to Moine Mhor, now recognised as an internationally important raised bog through its designation as a Special Area of Conservation. The extension of runways to Machrihanish RAF base in the 1980s also destroyed valuable peatlands - shortly before the base was abandoned. As this book nears completion (2007), a boggy area at Saulmore, near Oban, with breeding Lapwings, Snipe and Marsh Fritillary butterflies, is part of a site being developed as a golf course.

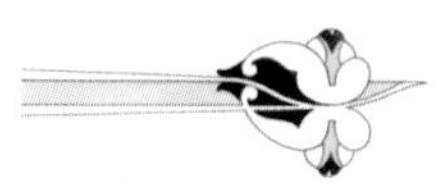

The developers, and organisations including SNH and Argyll and Bute Council, are preparing a detailed management plan for the course and the biodiversity of the land, including protection of the boggy area and its associated birds species. This case indicates how far the environment has climbed up the agenda; however, only time will tell, and our descendants judge, the extent to which this site can be safeguarded in perpetuity.

The story of Duich Moss on Islay injects a more positive note. In the mid-1980s, contractors began to drain this raised bog, an area of about six km², in preparation for large-scale digging of peat for whisky production. This would have destroyed a site which held the largest roost of Greenland White-fronted Geese in Scotland. Fortunately, after last-minute interventions by the (then) Nature Conservancy Council and European Union, the small amount of damage was made good and the site saved. The geese still roost there.

More generally, recent changes in agricultural subsidies and in forestry practices, away from maximum productivity and towards conservation, have already made their mark and offer some hope for the future. Nowadays, planning decisions take wildlife and conservation into account more than ever before. For their part, conservationists recognise that some of Argyll's most special habitats and species depend upon active management of the environment, particularly by traditional farming methods.

Past and present ornithological work in Argyll

There have been many long-term conservation and monitoring projects covering a wide range of bird species and bird communities. These have involved some of Argyll's most charismatic species, including Red-billed Chough, Corn Crake, White-tailed and Golden Eagles, as well as the geese that make islands like Islay such a fantastic winter birding experience. Many results of these projects are covered in the species accounts, particularly the work by members of Argyll Raptor Study Group (covering all raptor species and Raven) (http://www.scottishraptorgroups.org/areas/argyll.php). The successful re-introduction of White-tailed Eagles and the research leading to recovery in numbers of Corn Crakes both deserve special mention (RSPB, SNH). The steady increase in the number of RSPB reserves in the county, notably on Islay, Colonsay, Coll and Tiree, is an encouraging development that has led to valuable conservation measures and has greatly increased routine monitoring on all four islands. Several species of geese are monitored by annual counts in many parts of Argyll (SNH).

As would be expected from the rich avifauna of Islay, a great deal of research has taken place there, much of it again dealt with in the species accounts. The large numbers of wintering geese on Islay have been regularly counted since 1957 and with increasing frequency since 1990. SNH now make around 20 counts each winter as part of the Islay goose management scheme. Much work has been carried out on other aspects of goose ecology, including the colour-ringing of both Greenland White-fronted Geese by the Wildfowl and Wetlands Trust (WWT) and Barnacle Geese (Steve Percival). More intensive ecological studies have been made on both species through WWT and Glasgow University.

There have been many projects on Islay involving other bird species. These have included surveys and wing-tagging of Hen Harrier (Mike Peacock, Malcolm Ogilvie, Mike Madders, Clive McKay, Fiona Rout), Barn Owl ringing and monitoring of Rook (Ogilvie), and studies of Common Scoter (Ogilvie, McKay), Red-throated Diver (Aubrey and Edith Colling) and Lapwing and Redshank (RSPB/Stirling University). More generally, bird and invertebrate populations of Bridgend SSSI were studied during 1990-1991 (Ogilvie). On the Rinns of Islay, a full census of breeding birds, especially waders, was conducted by RSPB in 1994 and remains a rare example of a stock-take of the bird populations of such a large area. At Loch Gruinart, the visible migration and turnover of waders, geese and passerines were investigated by McKay and Tristan ap Rheinallt during 2000-2005.

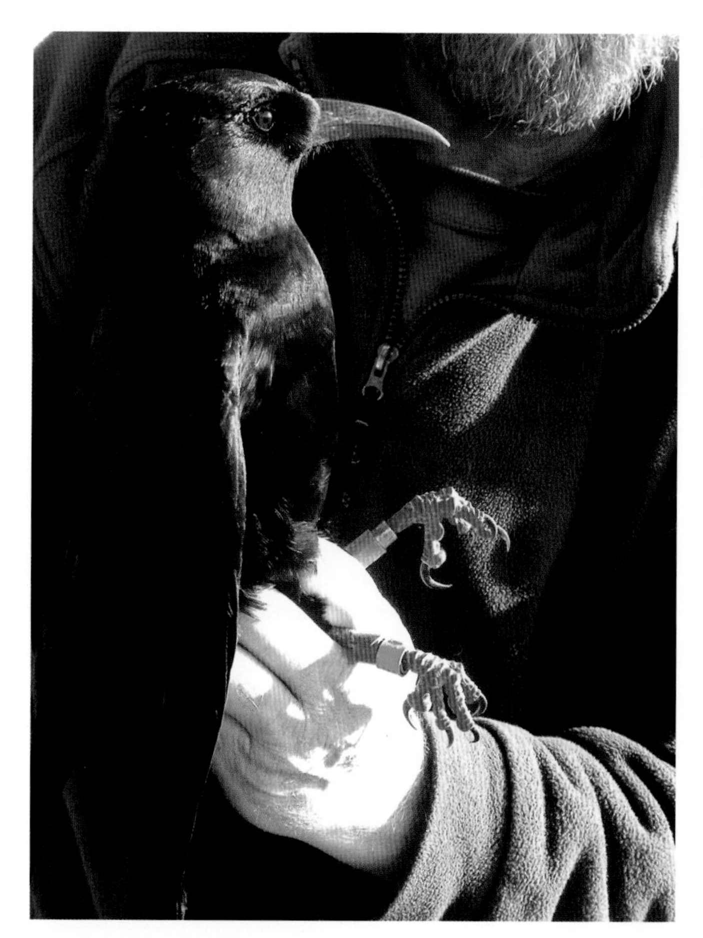

Chough have been studied intensively on Islay and Colonsay since 1979. *D.C. Jardine*

Eric Bignal has been involved in conservation and research on Choughs since 1979, when he moved to Argyll as the Nature Conservancy Council area officer. His work on Choughs in Argyll began with collaboration on Colonsay

Operating since 1993, Machrihanish Seabird Observatory has greatly enhanced our understanding of bird movements off the Kintyre coast. *Eddie Maguire*

with John and Pamela Clarke and on Islay with Judy Warnes, whose research built on the pioneering work in the 1960s and 1970s by Gordon Booth, C.J. Taylor and Ron Hickling. Colour-ringing, started by Judy Warnes in 1980 and continuing to the present (2007), allows individual birds to be recognised. This has led to various collaborative projects, notably with Pat Monaghan and students (McCracken, Thompson, Still, McKay) at Glasgow University as well as researchers from Italy and Spain, and to the formation of the Scottish Chough Study Group with Davy McCracken and Sue Bignal. In 1987 Eric started providing artificial nest sites for Choughs (with funding from JNCC, WWF and others). A high proportion (about 60%) of Choughs breeding on Islay now breed in specially provided nest sites.

Following Keith Verrall's pioneering observations at Frenchman's Rocks on the west coast of Islay in the 1970s (Verrall & Bourne 1982), Tristan ap Rheinallt carried out an intensive programme of seawatching at the same site from 1993 to 1997. Tristan made further observations there from 1999 to 2004, mostly in autumn. The main emphasis was on recording the movements of pelagic species, waders and wildfowl, and relating these to season and weather conditions. Regular seawatching has also been carried out for many years by Eddie Maguire at Uisaed Point in Kintyre. Here, in September 1993, he opened the Machrihanish Seabird and Wildlife Observatory, which he built and has since organised and developed. Its objectives are to record and photograph seabirds and other species in the area, and to encourage birdwatchers, local people, tourists and schools to visit and become involved. The observatory publishes annual or biennial reports.

In 1971, the late Barry Lawson organised an expedition which was the first of what has since become an annual pilgrimage by the Treshnish Island Auk Ringing Group (TIARG) to one of Argyll's best sites for breeding seabirds, the Treshnish Isles off the west coast of Mull. Most of one week of fieldwork is centred on Lunga and neighbouring Sgeir a Chaisteil, where a count of seabirds is made in late June. In recent years, TIARG have also been able to census the seabird colonies of the other Treshnish islands. As well as these annual counts, seabird productivity is measured on six permanent monitoring plots. The 4 -7 man TIARG team then turn their effort to ringing, concentrating on adults of the auk species, Storm Petrels, Kittiwakes and Shags. Shags are also colour-ringed as part of the BTO Retrap for Adult

Mist netting on Sanda. *David Palmar*

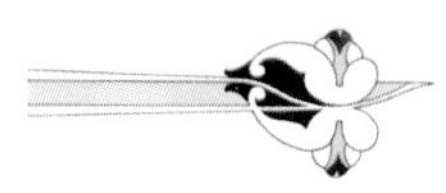

Survival (RAS) programme. During 1971-2006 TIARG ringed over 28,000 seabirds, including a high proportion of the national totals of some species. TIARG also record the numbers and productivity of all other breeding birds as well as other aspects of the wildlife. Their work has included an assessment of the impact of the many tourists who visit Treshnish (Willis 2000).

The Sanda Islands, off the tip of the Kintyre peninsula, also hold a notable seabird colony with an impressive range of pelagic species. Here Rab Morton and others have been monitoring and ringing seabirds and passerines, and recording other wildlife, since the 1990s. The work includes projects on European Storm-petrel, Manx Shearwater, Razorbill and Guillemot, as well as colour-ringing Lesser Black-backed Gulls. Both Treshnish and Sanda groups produce annual reports.

The island of Colonsay holds more breeding seabirds than any other site in Argyll (Jardine *et al.* 2002), arguably rivalling Treshnish as premier seabird spectacle of the county. John and Pamela Clarke studied the birds of Colonsay from the early 1980s to 1994. They recorded several species in detail, including the monitoring of Chough, Corn Crake, Heron, Raven, waders and raptors. They also worked on seabirds, carrying out the 1985-87 Seabird Census. They updated the botany of the islands and were responsible for much practical conservation work. David Jardine, continuing and expanding his earlier 1970s work on Colonsay, collaborated with the Clarkes in the 1980s and his long-term studies on the island have continued since then. He now visits Colonsay up to five times a year and his work has involved annual monitoring of the island populations of Chough (with Mike Peacock), Buzzard, Heron and Raven. He also monitors the seabird populations (making sample counts of Fulmar, Shag, Kittiwake, Guillemot and Razorbill and RAS studies of Guillemot and Kittiwake), as well as monitoring other raptors, waders, passerines and wildfowl. His work on Colonsay has included Long-eared Owl, an elusive tree-nesting species which otherwise receives almost no attention in Argyll.

The SAMS Mink-Seabird Project, organised by Clive Craik, has been running since 1990. It monitors seabirds breeding on some 150 small islands off the mainland coast of Argyll and neighbouring Lochaber. Most of these islands are close enough to the mainland (within 2km) to be affected by American Mink, which every year cause widespread whole-island breeding failures. Local removal of mink allows birds to breed normally, prevents colonies from disappearing and attracts birds back to former sites breeding sites. In 2006, 38 sites (with a total of 5,853 breeding pairs of 17 species of seabirds, wildfowl and waders) were protected in this way, 44 sites were unprotected but still occupied by breeding birds, but 72 sites had become empty after annual mink predation.

From 1990 to the present (2007), John Halliday (Reserve Manager, Argyll NNRs) has been undertaking a Common Birds Census at Taynish NNR. This unique and valuable long-term dataset for passerines in Argyll has recorded up to 40 species breeding in a range of habitats, from coastal grassland through scrub to mature oak woodland. There have been some interesting trends in the woodland. For example, since 2000 Wood Warblers and Tree Pipits have declined while Blackcaps have increased. Highlights were the appearance of Golden Oriole in 1992, 1997 and 2003. Willow Warblers are abundant at Taynish and, interestingly, their territories have doubled in number since the early 1990s. John's data have been used in many of the woodland passerine accounts in this book.

Argyll Bird Club's Nest Box Scheme (1987-1995) was organised by Steve Petty and the boxes were sited and monitored by members of Argyll Bird Club. Its aims were twofold: to find whether nest boxes would encourage Pied Flycatchers to increase their range in the county and to obtain information on the breeding performance of Blue and Great Tits in broadleaved woodlands in Argyll. Pied

Left: Mink predation of fully-grown chicks of Common Tern: Glas Eileanan, 1 August 1989.
Right: A mussel raft adapted for breeding terns at South Shian, Loch Creran. All the settled birds are large Common Tern chicks in their nest territories. Adults are flying in to feed them.
Clive Craik

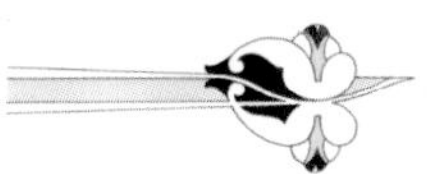

Flycatchers bred regularly in three of the 12 nest box areas, but after the initial success, numbers declined in common with populations elsewhere in Scotland. Blue and Great Tits were the most frequent species to breed in the boxes. Redstarts and Tree Creepers also nested in the boxes, but only rarely. Steve Petty, helped by David Anderson, also undertook a study of the population ecology of Tawny Owls in Cowal (1984-1996). The study area covered approximately 175km^2 of mainly coniferous forest and included around 140 nest boxes in which up to 50 pairs of owls bred each year. Breeding performance, survival and diet of the owls were compared with a similar population in Kielder Forest, Northumberland (see the Tawny Owl account). Other species to use the boxes in Cowal included Goosander, Mandarin and, surprisingly, Redstart and Great Tit. Red Squirrels frequently built dreys in the boxes!

In 1972 David Merrie started a survey of the distribution of Black- and Red-throated Divers throughout Scotland. This identified poor productivity in an area of Argyll beside Loch Awe. He built two nesting rafts in 1976, and six more followed in 1978. Six survive to date (2007) and monitoring has continued over the 30 years. Productivity has been considerably enhanced overall, but with wide variations between sites. From 1961 to 1971 David Merrie, together with Sandy Gordon, carried out an annual survey of nesting sites and breeding success of Golden Eagles in the area between Oban and the Mull of Kintyre, continuing a study begun by Charlie Palmar in the 1940s.

Deploying a raft for nesting Red-throated Divers on a Mid-Argyll hill loch. *David Merrie*

Mike Gregory's study of Golden Eagles in Argyll has been running longer than any of the other projects mentioned in this summary. Mike started his work in 1966 and, together with Sandy Gordon, has been monitoring the distribution and breeding performance of these birds in the southern part of mainland Argyll each year up to the present (2007). In 1993 he founded the Argyll Raptor Study Group and was its chairman for ten years.

Starting in the 1990s, Argyll hosted a string of novel projects which greatly extended our knowledge of Golden Eagle and White-tailed Eagle ecology (see the accounts for these species). Much of this work was driven by the need to understand the impacts on raptor populations of man-induced changes, particularly wind farm developments and landscape-scale shifts in patterns of afforestation. Recently, innovative technologies have been applied in Argyll, again in relation to proposed wind energy projects. For example, in 2004 an automatic radar station was deployed to detect and map flights of Greenland White-fronted Geese adjacent to a proposed windfarm in Kintyre.

From 1998 Simon Lawrence has been studying the environmental impacts of wind farms in Argyll, mainly at moorland sites. As well as monitoring bird collisions, he has examined the effects of the wind turbines on roost usage and flight lines of geese and on the activity of divers, raptors and waders.

The Wetland Bird Survey (WeBS) involves regular counts of non-breeding waterbirds at key locations. Sites recently covered in Argyll include Lochs Gruinart and Indaal on Islay, the four main freshwater lochs on Tiree (Lochs Bhasapol, a' Phuill, an Eilein and Riaghain), Holy Loch in Cowal, and Lochs Crinan, Gilp and Sween in Mid-Argyll.

The Breeding Bird Survey (BBS), organised by the BTO and begun in 1994, has increased our understanding of population trends for many of the commoner breeding birds throughout the UK. Many of the results given in this book come from this work. From 1994-2003 a total of 30 one-km squares in Argyll were surveyed at least once and 18 were surveyed in five or more years. All the Argyll recording areas, except Islay and Jura, were covered by at least one square in one year. By the nature of this survey, land-based species are covered most effectively (water birds are covered by the Waterways Breeding Bird Survey, which began in 1998). By 2003, a total of 122 species had been recorded at least once although a few of these, such as Whimbrel and Redwing, would have been late migrants. The following species were recorded in 10-19 squares: Mallard, Common Buzzard, Common Snipe, Common Gull, Lesser Black-backed Gull, Herring Gull, Great Black-backed Gull, Wood Pigeon, Barn Swallow, Tree Pipit, Pied Wagtail, Dunnock, Robin, Whinchat, Common Stonechat, Northern Wheatear, Blackbird, Mistle Thrush, Common Whitethroat, Goldcrest, Coal Tit, Blue Tit, Great Tit, Siskin and Lesser Redpoll. The following were recorded in 20 or more squares: Common Cuckoo, Sky Lark, Wren, Song Thrush, Willow Warbler and Common Chaffinch, while Meadow Pipit (27) and Hooded Crow (28) were recorded in almost every square.

Background to this book

Over the years, there have been several accounts of the birds of particular parts of Argyll - for example, Iona and Mull (Graham 1890), Mid-Argyll, Kintyre and Cowal (McLaren & Murray 1985), Mull (Madders & Snow 1987),

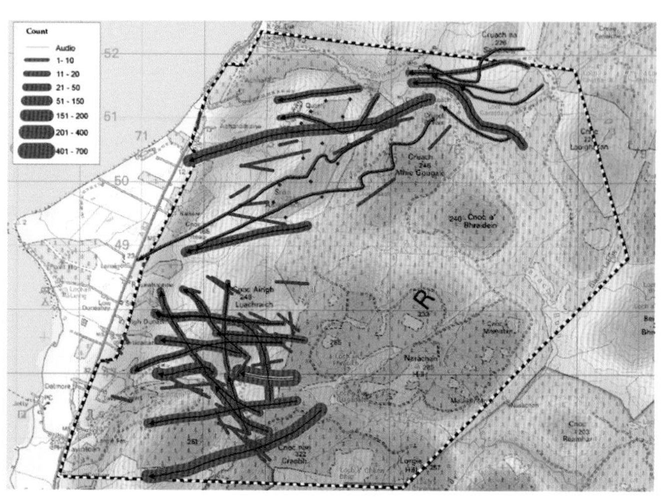

Left: mobile radar unit used to track Greenland White-fronted Geese in Kintyre.
Right: flights recorded around dawn on 2 November 2004, showing geese moving from roosting lochs to preferred feeding areas near the coast. *Central Science Laboratory*

Islay (Elliott 1989), Mid-Argyll (Madders *et al.* 1992) and Colonsay (Jardine *et al.* 1986, Jardine 2002). However, there have been no recent bird books devoted to Argyll as a whole. To find anything resembling a full avifauna, we must go back as far as *A Vertebrate Fauna of Argyll and the Inner Hebrides* by Harvie-Brown & Buckley (1892) and, before that, to *Birds of the West of Scotland* by Robert Gray (1871) and *A Tour in Scotland and a Voyage to the Hebrides* (1776) by Thomas Pennant. *Birds of Argyll* was conceived, written and produced by members of Argyll Bird Club in an attempt to meet this need.

The human population of Argyll is low and, as a result, there was comparatively little organised recording of birds in the county until recently. One has only to look at the changes in the contents of the *Argyll Bird Report*, from the first volume in 1984 to the 19th volume in 2006, to appreciate the huge growth that has taken place locally in bird recording. It is no coincidence that the numbers of both records and contributors have steadily increased since the Argyll Bird Club was formed in 1985. The County Bird Recorder's workload has grown correspondingly. The first holder of this position (as far as has been possible to trace) was Prof. M F M Meiklejohn (Clyde faunal area, North Argyllshire, Skye and Inner Hebrides) to 1970. He was followed by Mike Gregory (1971-1981) (Argyllshire, Inner Hebrides and Skye). The first recorder for the present Argyll area was Richard Coomber (1982-1984), followed by David Stroud (1985), Arthur Jennings (1986-1987), Mike Madders (1988-1992) and Tristan ap Rheinallt (1993-1996). Paul Daw, who has been Bird Recorder for Argyll since 1997, has introduced many innovations and improvements. In particular, he has been at the forefront in Scotland in developing suitable software and systems to manage such large amounts of data. At present (2007), he receives about 15,000 bird records each year, including the database of Islay records supplied by Malcolm Ogilvie.

The decision to produce this book was made in February 2001. From the beginning, it was clear that the project would have to involve the combined efforts of many people, all working on a voluntary basis. Some 328 wild bird species have been recorded in Argyll, and another 15 species are classed as escapes or introductions. To make best use of the expertise at our disposal, each species was assigned to one of a panel of 14 authors, although the division was far from equal. The following authors wrote the species accounts (with the number of accounts in brackets): Tristan ap Rheinallt (183, mainly scarce species and vagrants), Paul Daw (37, and 15 Category D and E species), Clive Craik (32), David Jardine (20), Malcolm Ogilvie (ten), Bob Furness (nine), David Wood (nine, with Michael Thomas as co-author for six of these), Roger Broad (eight), Steve Petty (seven), David Merrie (five), John Bowler (four), Paul Howarth (two), Eric Bignal (one) and Mike Gregory (one).

In the text, for simplicity, usually only the main author is named under each species, but many draft accounts were circulated to other authors or sent to specialists with relevant experience. Much useful new material was added at these stages.

For much of the lifetime of the project, Tristan ap Rheinallt acted as its planner, organiser and secretary, and it is undoubtedly to him that most of the credit goes for getting the project off the ground. The members of the rather informal editorial group at this stage were Tristan himself, Clive Craik, Paul Daw and David Wood. Throughout the project, a huge amount of work fell on the shoulders of Paul Daw. He had to fit the extra work for the book around his already considerable duties as County Bird Recorder. He also compiled and still maintains the Argyll Database of all bird records in the county since 1997, a resource which in January 2007 contained some 120,000 records. From that invaluable archive, Paul made an essential contribution by providing authors with all the Argyll records of each species. This, together with the full set of Argyll Bird Reports, was the main source of information for the book.

Regrettably, Tristan's many other commitments forced him to resign from the project late in 2005. Within a few weeks, an editorial committee of five was formed – Clive Craik, Paul Daw, Bob Furness, Steve Petty and David Wood. Steve took on the role of organiser and secretary. A commitment was made to complete the species accounts that were still unwritten and to see the book through to publication.

David Wood's gentle persuasion maintained much of the momentum of the project throughout its life. He also acted as its business manager, attending in particular to the essential matter of raising the necessary funds. He found and negotiated with a suitable printing firm and liaised with them at all stages of production.

After it had been decided to try to include pictures of most of the common bird species, preferably in a local setting, images were sought from as many photographers as possible. This process was started by Steve Petty and handed over to David Wood just before page-formatting began. Individual photographers are listed below and their names are also given under each photograph.

The completed species accounts were reviewed by three final editors (Craik, Furness, Petty). Bob Furness also collated and finalised the many references. David Wood undertook the huge task of page-formatting the entire book using Adobe's Creative Suite 2, which involved incorporating pictures and compiling tables, maps and charts. All five members of the editorial committee undertook final proof-reading, so the blame for any remaining errors is collective rather than individual!

Interpreting the Species Accounts

The species accounts are arranged using the sequence recently adopted by the British Ornithologists' Union (Dudley *et al.* 2006) using English and scientific names recommended by British Birds (Baker *et al.* 2006). Unless otherwise stated, records after 2003 have not been included in species' accounts. However, some of the more exciting or notable reports up to 2006 have been included, particularly of rare or declining species, as it was felt that this would be appreciated by readers.

Breeding totals of seabirds in Argyll and Bute are quoted from Seabird 2000 (Mitchell *et al.* 2004). These totals do not always agree with those obtained by adding the Seabird 2000 census counts made in the various parts of Argyll, some of which are given in the species accounts in this book. Differences may have arisen not only from the exclusion of Bute, but also from minor differences in the borders used for Argyll itself.

Familiar places, such as larger towns and lochs, are given without qualification. Less well-known place names are usually accompanied by the recording area in which they occur (North Argyll, Mid-Argyll, Cowal, Kintyre, Jura, Islay, Colonsay, Coll, Tiree, Mull; see map on p. 18). To help those in doubt about any locality, the whereabouts of all the place names used in this book are given in Appendix 5.

Acknowledgements

We are most grateful to Scottish Natural Heritage and to Argyll & Bute Biodiversity Partnership, who generously provided grants towards the production of this book.

We are greatly indebted to Margaret Staley and Philip Snow for kindly providing some really excellent pen-and-ink drawings that can be found throughout the book. Margaret also produced the two evocative paintings of Argyll landscapes and their birds that adorn the front and back covers. In addition, we are indebted to all photographers for their kindness in freely supplying the superb colour images: John Anderson, Eric Bignal, Roy Blewitt, John Bowler, Sue Chattwood, Jim Dickson, Iain Erskine, Bob Furness, Rob Jordan, Philip Kirkham, Iain Leach, Eddie Maguire, John McAvoy, David Merrie, David Palmar, Kelvin Pearce, Steve Petty, John Robinson, Hugh Venables, David S. Whitaker, David Wood, Louise Wood and Gordon Yates. You can find further examples of Philip's work online at http://www.birdphotographs.co.uk, and David Palmar's at http://photoscot.co.uk.

We are grateful for records from Tiree, the result of regular monthly systematic reports sent in by Alan Leitch from January 1998 until March 2001 and by John Bowler from June 2001 to the present. Records from Coll were supplied by Sarah Money and Simon Wellock, those from Islay by Malcolm Ogilvie, those from Colonsay by David Jardine and those from Machrihanish Seabird and Wildlife Observatory by Eddie Maguire. We are particularly grateful to all who read and commented on many of the species accounts, or provided additional information, including John Bowler, Jim Dickson, John Halliday, David Jardine, Clive McKay, Malcolm Ogilvie and Simon Wellock. Jim Dickson made valuable contributions and comments on the records of some of the rarer gull species. Claire McSorley and Blair Urquhart kindly assisted with preparation of the charts and maps respectively.

Tristan ap Rheinallt provided information on races of all relevant species. Another major source of information was the British Trust for Ornithology, who kindly supplied all the ringing and recovery records involving Argyll. Clive Craik and Malcolm Ogilvie condensed these computer-generated data into written summaries of recoveries for each species.

We thank A. P. Watt Ltd, on behalf of Gráinne Yeats, for permission to reproduce the poem "The Wild Swans at Coole" by W. B. Yeats.

We thank Ian Allan Printers for their helpful co-operation and efficient service, and we are grateful to Lyn Hedges for advice on marketing.

We are indebted to all those observers who, over many years, have submitted the bird records that constitute the Argyll Database, on which this book is based. Finally, we express our appreciation to all members of Argyll Bird Club, whose subscriptions have contributed towards the costs of producing this book.

Clive Craik

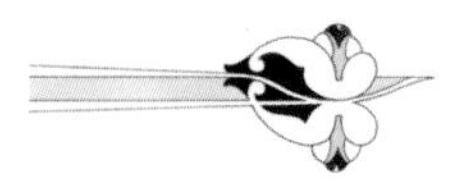

Abbreviations used in the text.

ABR	*Argyll Bird Report*. For a specific report, volume and page numbers are given (e.g., ABR 8:16).
Argyll Database	Bird record database held by the Argyll Bird Recorder
ARSG	Argyll Raptor Study Group data files
ASNH	*Annals of Scottish Natural History*. For a specific report, year and page number are given (e.g., ASNH 1893:16).
BB	*British Birds*. For a specific report, volume and page numbers are given (e.g., BB 1:8).
BBRC or BBRR	British Birds Rarities Committee *or* Report
BBS	Data from the BTO's Breeding Bird Survey (http://www.bto.org)
BOURC	British Ornithologists' Union Records Committee
B&R	Baxter, E.V. & Rintoul, L.J. (1953) *The Birds of Scotland: Their History, Distribution, and Migration*. Oliver and Boyd, Edinburgh.
BS3	Forrester, R.W., Andrews, I.J., McInerny, C.J., Murray, R.D., McGowan, R.Y., Zonfrillo, B., Betts, M.W., Jardine, D.C. & Grundy, D.S. (eds.) (2007) *The Birds of Scotland*. Scottish Ornithologists' Club, Aberlady.
BTO	British Trust for Ornithology
BTO Trend	BTO Trend data (http://www.bto.org)
BWP	Cramp, S., et al. (1977-1994) *Birds of the Western Palearctic, Volumes I-IX*. Oxford University Press, Oxford.
CBC	Data from the BTO Common Bird Census (http://www.bto.org)
CES	Constant effort ringing site
First Atlas	Sharrock, J.T.R. (ed.) (1976) *The Atlas of Breeding Birds in Britain and Ireland*. T. & A.D Poyser, Calton.
Garden BirdWatch	BTO Garden BirdWatch (http://www.bto.org)
Graham	Graham, H.D. (1890) *The Birds of Iona and Mull, 1852-1870*. David Douglas, Edinburgh.
Gray	Gray, R. (1871) *Birds of the West of Scotland, including the Outer Hebrides*. Murray, Scotland.
H&B	Harvie-Brown, J.A. & Buckley, T.E. (1892) *A Vertebrate Fauna of Argyll and the Inner Hebrides*. David Douglas, Edinburgh.
Historical Atlas	Holloway, S. (1996) *The Historical Atlas of Breeding Birds in Britain and Ireland: 1875-1900*. T. & A.D. Poyser, London.
IBNHR	*Islay Bird and Natural History Report*
McWilliam	McWilliam, J.M. (1936) *The Birds of the Firth of Clyde: including Ayrshire, Renfrewshire, Buteshire, Dumbartonshire and South Argyllshire*. H.F. & G. Witherby Ltd, London.
Migration Atlas	Wernham, C.V., Toms, M.P., Marchant, J.H., Clark, J.A., Siriwardena, G.M. & Baillie, S.R. (eds.) (2002) *The Migration Atlas: Movements of the Birds of Britain and Ireland*. T. & A.D. Poyser, London.
MSBO	Machrihanish Seabird and Wildlife Observatory, Kintyre
NEWS	European Non-estuarine Coastal Waterfowl Survey
NMS	National Museums of Scotland
NNR	National Nature Reserve
NSA	*New Statistical Account*
OSA	*Old Statistical Account*
Proc NHS Glasgow	*Proceedings of the Natural History Society of Glasgow*
RAS	Retrapping for Adult Survival (a BTO ringing project)
RM	*Ringing & Migration*. For a specific report, volume and page numbers are given (e.g., RM 16: 8).
SAMS	Scottish Association for Marine Science, Dunstaffnage, Oban
SB	*Scottish Birds*. For a specific report, volume and page numbers are given (e.g., SB 8:16)
SBR	*Scottish Bird Report*. For a specific report, year and page number are given (e.g., SBR 2001:16).
Seabird 2000	Mitchell, P.I., Newton, S.F., Ratcliffe, N. & Dunn, T.E. (2004) *Seabird Populations of Britain and Ireland: Results of the Seabird 2000 Census (1998-2002)*. T. & A.D. Poyser, London.
Second Atlas	Gibbons, D.W., Reid, J.B. & Chapman, R.A. (1993) *The New Atlas of Breeding in Britain and Ireland: 1988-1991*. T. & A.D. Poyser, London.
SN	*Scottish Naturalist*. For a specific report, year and page number are given (e.g., SN 1915:16).
SNH	Scottish Natural Heritage
SSSI	Site of Special Scientific Interest
Taynish CBC	Common Bird Census at Taynish National Nature Reserve (1990 onwards), undertaken annually by John Halliday, with support from SNH and the BTO
Thom	Thom, V.M. (1986) *Birds of Scotland*. T. & A.D. Poyser, Calton.
TIARG Reports	Ward, R.M. (compiler) *Treshnish Isles Auk Ringing Group Reports for 1998 onwards*. Privately Published
Trans NHS Glasgow	*Transactions of the Natural History Society of Glasgow*
WeBS	Wetland Bird Survey
WWT	Wildfowl and Wetlands Trust
Winter Atlas	Lack, P. (1986) *The Atlas of Wintering Birds in Britain and Ireland*. T. & A.D. Poyser, Calton.

An Introduction to Argyll

Location and landform

Argyll is not particularly big; a square with sides of 162km will contain it. At the northern tip, the Cairns of Coll reach out towards Ardnamurchan, while in the south, the island of Sanda guards one side of the Firth of Clyde's wide mouth. Argyll's western extremity, Skerryvore, is a remote rock in the Hebridean Sea, and on the east, the summit of Meall Buidhe forms part of the Grampian mountain chain. Within these relatively limited bounds lies one of the most physically and biologically diverse areas in Europe.

Within Argyll's land area of 6,890km^2 there are habitats ranging from tiny offshore skerries, islands with sweeping sandy bays backed by machair grassland, fertile lowland glens, fantastically rich ancient woodlands, extensive conifer plantations, freshwater lochs of all shapes and sizes, great tracts of moorland and peatland, and dramatic mountains. The county's convoluted shoreline runs for 4,800km. Below the waves, marine and coastal environments are equally diverse, ranging from shallow muddy sediments to reefs and ferocious tidal rapids.

The geography of Argyll is dominated by its coastline. There are 15 inhabited islands, around 180 smaller islands, and innumerable rocks and skerries. Mainland Argyll is heavily dissected by long sea lochs, of which Loch Fyne, at 68km, is one of the longest in Scotland. This loch, together with Lochs Etive, Creran, Long, Goil and Striven, penetrate deeply into the mainland. No land in the long peninsula of Kintyre is more than 7km from the coast.

Most land below 100m is distributed around the fringes of the coast and the sea lochs, but many of the smaller islands, including Gigha, Colonsay, Seil, Luing, Lismore, Iona, Coll and Tiree, are well below this height, or barely exceed it. Large areas up the spine of Kintyre, and in mid-Argyll, Cowal, Lorn, Jura, Mull and eastern Islay lie between 100m and 500m, while the real uplands are restricted to the Grampian hills and mountains in the north and east, the centre of Mull, and the Paps of Jura. Argyll has 21 Munros (mountains over 3,000 feet).

The topography of Argyll is extremely complex. In parts of south Kintyre, on Coll and on Tiree it is possible to walk for a few kilometres and experience little change in height, but across most of the county you are much more likely to encounter rapid changes of altitude and gradient. This reaches an extreme in the corrugated landscape of Knapdale in Mid-Argyll, with its succession of parallel ridges separated by shallow valleys. Alternatively, in Glen Creran, Glen Etive or in the Arrochar Alps, one may start at sea level and, after an unremitting ascent, reach a height of more than 1,000m having covered less than 5km of horizontal distance. The scale of the different landscapes varies widely, from extensive tracts of wild uplands through to intricate farmed and wooded landscapes on the coast. In all, 24 landscape character types have been mapped and described (Environmental Resources Management 1996).

Climate

Perched on Europe's western edge, the climate of Argyll is heavily influenced by the North Atlantic Drift and by the prevailing, moisture-laden south-west winds. The sea's impact on land temperatures is most pronounced on low-lying islands like Tiree, Coll and Colonsay, and on Atlantic facing coasts elsewhere. Here, the sea keeps temperatures rather cool in summer but mild in winter, compared with UK averages - a so-called hyperoceanic climate. Elsewhere in Argyll, land temperatures are determined mainly by altitude, with average temperatures dropping by around 0.6°C for every 100m rise in height. Thus, in January it is rare to see any snow lying across much of Islay, whereas the uplands of Mid- and North Argyll normally have over ten days of snow. With large local variations in altitude, neighbouring locations can have very different local climates. Argyll's mountains keep their snow and ice in sheltered pockets into late spring.

Rainfall across most of Argyll is over 200mm per month in winter and over 100mm per month in summer, well above the UK average. However, there is considerable local variation, and Argyll is not universally wet. The low-lying island of Tiree escapes with as little as 54mm in May (30 year mean, 1971-2000), and Tiree is significantly drier than Dunstaffnage, located near Oban on the mainland coast, in every month. Other relatively dry areas include Colonsay, Iona, The Oa (south-west Islay) and parts of Kintyre. However, even the driest parts of Argyll are much wetter than eastern Scotland and many parts of England.

Exposed Atlantic coasts of Argyll are very windy. Average windspeed across the year on Tiree is 14.5 knots, with January the windiest month (18.4 knots). Even in July and

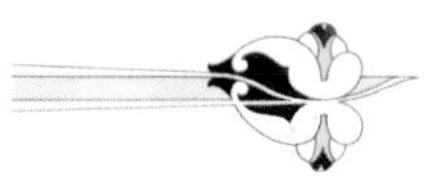

Overview of Argyll: major settlements, and the ten bird recording areas.

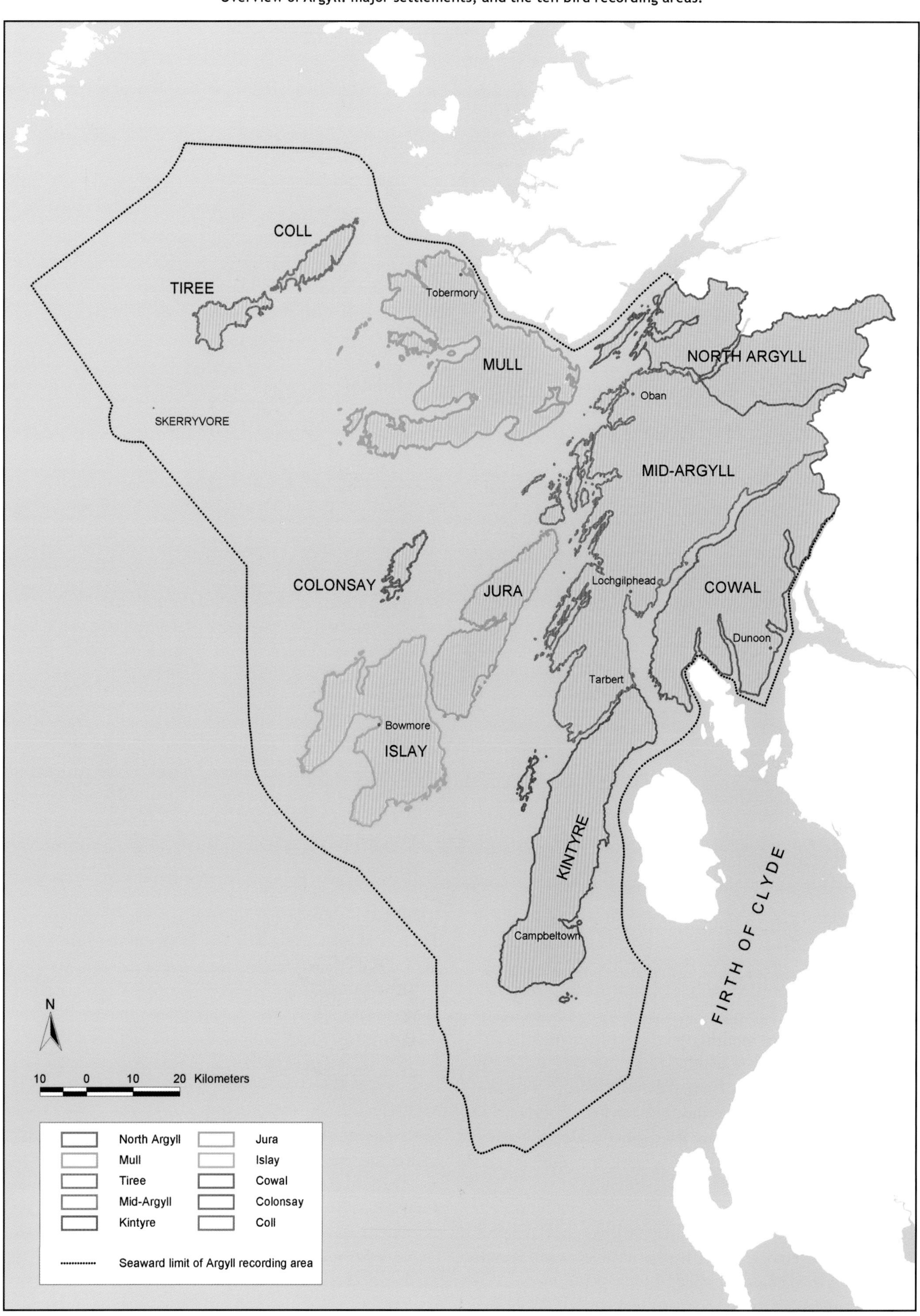

Topography of Argyll.

August, the 'calmest' months, the average windspeed is 10.9 knots. Tiree is therefore windier than Stornoway, Kirkwall and Lerwick at all times of year. However, in locations where the local landform provides moderate shelter, conditions are very much calmer; the average windspeed at Dunstaffnage is just 8.8 knots.

Geology

Argyll's turbulent human history is famous (Campbell 2001), but its geological past has been no less complex and violent. It is this geological story which largely underpins the physical appearance of the county today, and contributes to the diversity of its avifauna.

The oldest rock in Argyll, Lewisian gneiss, is also one of the oldest anywhere on Earth. It makes up parts of The Rinns on Islay, together with Iona, Coll and Tiree. This highly metamorphosed rock appears to be a survivor of the earth's crust from up to three billion years ago.

However, much of Argyll is composed of metamorphic rocks of the Dalradian sequence. These originally accumulated as great thicknesses of sandstone, limestone, shale and lava between about 800 and 600 million years ago. These layers also contained some significant igneous intrusions of about the same age. Then, between 550 and 430 million years ago, these rocks were caught up in one of the most dramatic geological events to have affected what is now Scotland: the collision of the great continental plate of Laurentia with a long island chain. Deeply buried and subjected to conditions of extreme heat and pressure, the Dalradian layers were transformed. Sandstone became quartzite, while siltstones and mudstones were transformed into phyllites, schists and slates. The volcanic rocks were also metamorphosed, and now outcrop in long, broken parallel bands from Tayvallich to Cladich on Loch Awe, in Kintyre and across Cowal. The collision thrust the newly-changed rocks, now much folded and broken, up into a vast mountain range in the episode known as the Caledonian Orogeny, and it is the weathered-down remnants of those mountains which now make up much of the Scottish Highlands. Three of the major geological boundaries involved in the collision occur in, or close to, Argyll: the Great Glen Fault, which runs through Mull, the Highland Boundary Fault, which cuts across the lower part of Loch Lomond, and the Moine Thrust, passing under the sea between Coll and Mull. The orientation of the faults imparted a strong 'grain' to the landscape, with lines of weakness following a pronounced south-west to north-east trend, which subsequently became the focus for erosion and weathering of the landscape by ice and water. The effect is reinforced at a smaller scale in much

Simplified geological map of Argyll.

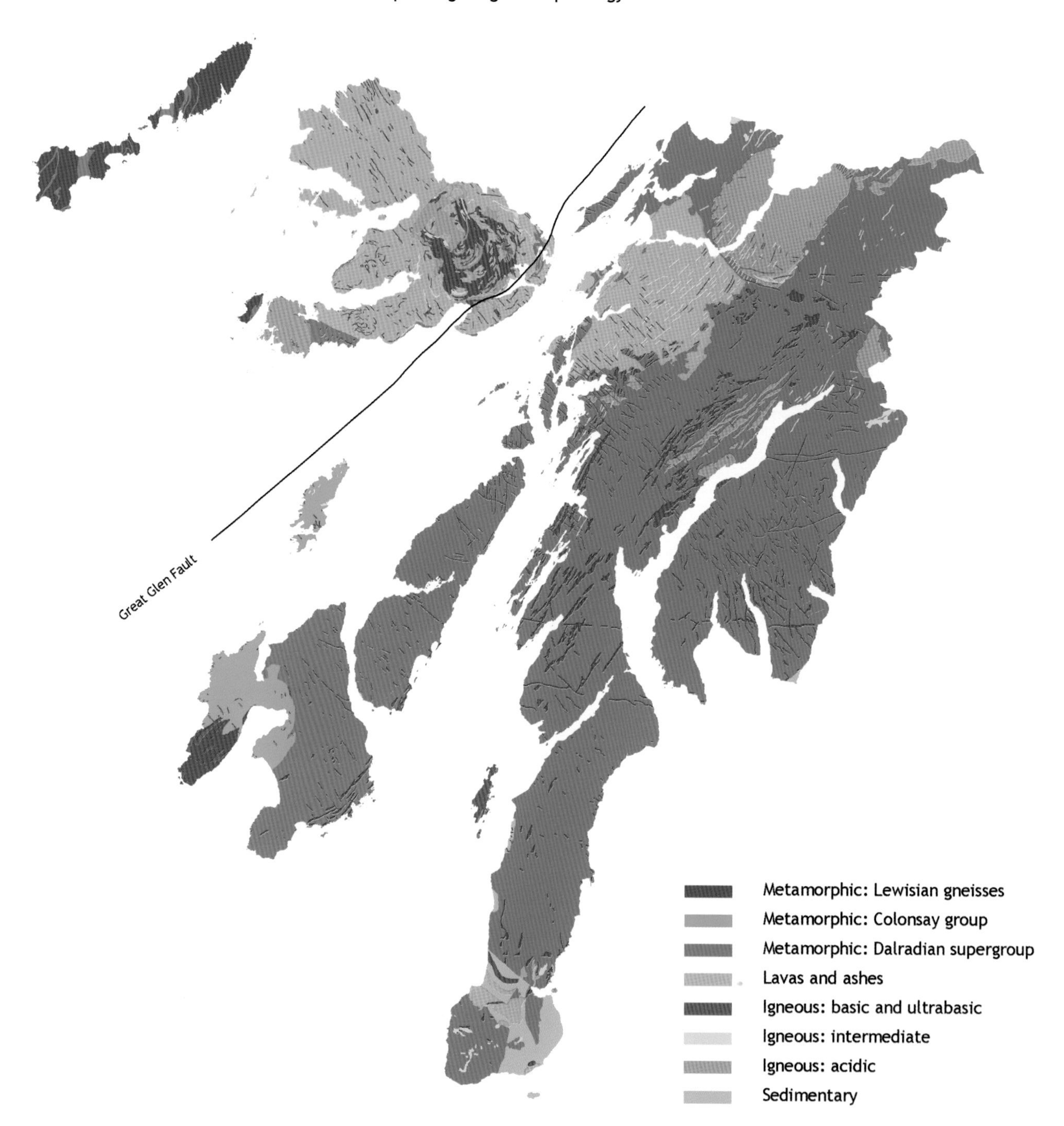

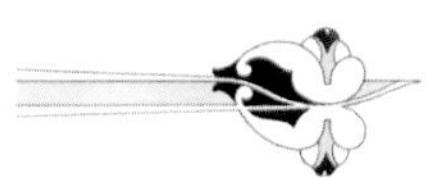

of Mid-Argyll, where alternating hard and soft layers of Dalradian rocks, highly folded along a south-west to north-east orientation, have eroded at different rates to produce a landscape of long parallel ridges and flooded valleys.

Igneous activity reached a new maximum towards the end of the period of uplift, and continued afterwards into the Silurian and Devonian periods. At this time, large quantities of magma were forced up through the existing rocks. Solidifying as granite and related rocks, these now form one of the largest igneous complexes in Britain. The mountains of north Argyll, including Ben Cruachan, Ben Starav and Ben Trilleachan, are made of these erosion-resistant, acid igneous rocks. Later, in the Old Red Sandstone period of the Devonian, large quantities of volcanic rocks were also deposited at the surface; these now form the more amorphous, lower-altitude plateau east of Oban, between Loch Melfort and Loch Etive.

Much of Mull is composed of the remains of a great volcano. It was part of an extended chain of vulcanism which stretched from St Kilda to Ailsa Craig, which became active as the earth's crust split apart to begin the creation of the Atlantic Ocean around 65 million years ago. The mountainous east of Mull is the weathered stump of the old volcanic vent, while much of the rest of the island is made up of sheet-like basalt layers, derived from successive lava flows. These have weathered to produce Mull's distinctive 'trap' landscape of wide, stepped terraces which can be seen particularly well in Ardmeanach, northern Mull and Ulva. Basalt also forms the famous columnar formations on the island of Staffa, along with Fingal's Cave. The Mull volcano was also responsible for many dykes and sills injected into surrounding metamorphosed rocks.

Sedimentary rocks have a very limited distribution in Argyll, being almost completely restricted to south Kintyre and to small areas of Mull, Kerrera and Lorn. Various ages and types of rock are present. Old Red Sandstones of the Devonian occur on Kerrera and south of Campbeltown, while younger, Carboniferous rocks make up the Machrihanish Coalfield. Nearby, there are three outcrops of Permian sandstones and conglomerates on the coast between Tayinloan and Bellochantuy. Lastly, conglomerates, limestones, sandstones and shales of the Jurassic and Triassic are found at a few coastal locations on Mull.

The final great force giving physical shape to Argyll's landforms was much more recent. Starting around 2.4 million years ago and ending just 10,000 years ago, Argyll was subjected to a complex succession of ice ages and warmer,

A diversity of habitats on Argyll's north-east edge. The glaciated valley of Glen Orchy, carrying the River Orchy, sweeps away from Loch Tulla. The central woodland is Doire Darach, one of the few native pinewoods in the county. The backdrop is formed by the Munros of Beinn an Dothaidh and Beinn Dorain, which are partly afforested with exotic conifers. Other mountains of the Grampian range lie beyond. *John Anderson*

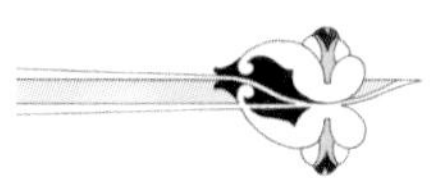

interglacial periods. During the cold periods, westward-moving glaciers and ice sheets gouged out great quantities of rock, deepening and reinforcing the existing grain of the landscape by creating dramatic U-shaped valleys such as Glen Kinglas and Glen Forsa, and the great sea lochs. The uplands were eroded down, and their contours smoothed. During warmer periods, the eroded materials were released from the melting ice and transported in torrents of meltwater, to be deposited as sands and gravels in river valleys, and offshore. A major complex of such outwash channels occurs around Ford and Kilmartin in Mid-Argyll. In many areas across Argyll, debris released from melting ice-sheets and glaciers also accumulated as poorly-sorted 'till', or as moraines, prominent examples of which occur around Loch Awe, on Mull and in Glen Kinglas. At the end of the last glacial period, the enormous quantities of water released caused sea levels to rise quickly. This flooded the land and created a new coastline, which was up to 35m higher than today's. Much more slowly, the land surface, relieved of the colossal weight of ice, rose back out of the sea. This left a sequence of raised beaches which today are prominent features in parts of Kintyre, Mid-Argyll and Jura.

After the ice

The final ice retreat occurred around 10,000 years ago. Left behind was a landscape largely wiped clean. Evidence for the recolonisation by plants comes from pollen and spores, preserved initially in lake sediments and later in peat. In the boreal period (between about 10,000 and 7,000 years ago), the climate was warming progressively, but was still very cold. The ice-scoured landscape was gradually colonised by ferns, willows and Crowberry, with birch first appearing about 8,800 years ago. Hazel and oak spread into Argyll from the south about 8,500 years ago. About 7,000 years ago, at the start of the Atlantic period, the climate warmed further and modern sea currents were established. This brought increased humidity and rainfall to the west coast. Oak woodland became the dominant habitat at low levels, with a tree line slightly higher than today, and there were probably very few open habitats except in lowland floodplains and basins and in the uplands, where peat began to accumulate. From about 5,000 years ago, at the start of the sub-boreal period, the climate became cooler and drier. Argyll's montane communities expanded at this time. Today's modern climate arrived about 2,000 years ago, with a return to warmer and wetter conditions.

Islands

The environment, ecology and culture of the western fringes of Argyll are defined by its island seascapes. This is simply one of the most spectacular and varied island groups anywhere in Europe. A trip to Argyll which omits an island itinerary is an impoverished visit.

Islay, Jura, Mull, Iona and Staffa are justly famous, whether for their whisky, their mystery, their rugged natural beauty, their cultural and historical heritage or for their archaeology.

One of many outstanding seascapes in Argyll: the island of Lismore in the Firth of Lorn. *John Anderson*

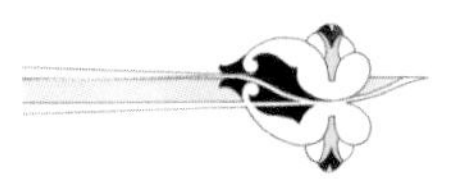

However, Argyll's islands are more even than this. There are 15 inhabited islands in Argyll, ranging from Mull at 87,000ha, down to tiny Lunga in the Firth of Lorn, with a land area of just 254ha. There are hundreds of uninhabited islets and skerries. From the low-lying machair plains of Tiree to the high top of Ben Mor on Mull, it is an extraordinary archipelago, and taken together, a hugely important resource for biodiversity.

The McCormaig Isles hold important colonies of Cormorants and Shags. The Paps of Jura lie behind. *David Wood*

The islands add greatly to the length of Argyll's already convoluted coastline. They also provide for varying degrees of shelter from the prevailing south-westerly Atlantic winds, increasing the range of coastal habitats present. The remoteness of islands like Coll and Tiree brings many challenges for their human populations, but the relative lack of agricultural intensification and pressure from built development has left more room for semi-natural habitats and their associated wildlife. The true conservation value of Argyll's islands is still quite poorly understood, except for their impressive bird populations, which have attracted amateur and professional ornithologists for many years. Fourteen island sites in Argyll have been designated as Sites of Special Scientific Interest, Special Protection Areas or RAMSAR sites for their nationally or internationally important bird populations.

The shallow, productive seas of the continental shelf, combined with freedom from mammalian predators and human disturbance, has led to the development of some spectacular seabird colonies on small islands such as Lunga in the Treshnish Isles, on west Colonsay and on Sanda. The effort required to reach such sites increases the eventual reward of seeing thousands of Kittiwakes, Common Guillemots, Razorbills, Puffins, gulls and Shags at close quarters. For those able to spend a summer's night on Sanda, there is the chance to hear and possibly see Storm Petrels and Manx Shearwaters. During the Seabird 2000 survey, the tiny island of Glas Eileanan in the Sound of Mull held 772 Common Tern nests, the second largest colony in Britain and Ireland. The absence of introduced mammalian predators from these islands is critical to their continued importance for seabirds. Since the 1970s, many Shag, gull and tern colonies have declined significantly, or disappeared, due to predation by American Mink. Nevertheless, small colonies of Arctic Skuas continue to thrive on Jura and Coll, and the Great Skua appears to be established as a breeding species on Coll. Undisturbed island shores, such as those on Tiree, can also hold significant bird interest in winter where large Tangle beds lie offshore. This seaweed, broken off by winter storms, is cast ashore in large quantities. Its rotting beds support large numbers of sandhoppers and other invertebrates, which in turn provide a crucial food resource for internationally important numbers of wading birds.

Argyll's islands, particularly Tiree, Coll, Colonsay and Islay, lie on the migration routes for many waterbirds, and are important staging posts for several species in autumn. The main species are Whooper Swan, European Golden Plover, Common Snipe, Northern Lapwing, Bar-tailed Godwit and Dunlin.

Coasts

The enormous length of coastline in Argyll is largely free of built development. Gently or steeply sloping rocky coastlines dominate, providing nesting opportunities for species such as Eider, Red-breasted Merganser, Rock Pipit and Common Sandpiper. However, many other coastal habitats occur, with a great deal of small-scale local variation. Tall cliffs occur on Mull, Staffa and in Kintyre, and those on Colonsay and Sanda provide nest sites for nationally important numbers of breeding seabirds. These hard rock coasts are backed by vegetation communities ranging from rock-crevices which are influenced by salt spray, to coastal grasslands and heaths, while exposed clifftops on Mull and the Garvellachs support

Two images illustrating opposite extremes of coastal environments in Argyll.

Above: John Anderson
Below: David Wood

Above: Loch Don, Mull. Shallow, sheltered inlet with extensive muddy intertidal areas, grading to saltmarsh and terrestrial habitats further inland. The land on the farther shore is part of a site of European importance for Golden Eagles, native oakwoods and other habitats.

Below: Staffa. Sheer basaltic sea-cliffs with full exposure to the Atlantic ocean. Puffins, Fulmars and Corn Crakes nest on Staffa. This island, with its famous cultural associations, is visited by thousands of tourists each year. Staffa is a Site of Special Scientific Interest, and was recently declared a National Nature Reserve.

arctic-alpine species at low altitudes. In sharp contrast, long sandy beaches backed by dunes and machair grassland occur in Kintyre and on Islay, Colonsay, Coll and Tiree. The heavily indented coast provides localised sheltered conditions, allowing the development of sediment shores. These reach their greatest extent at sites like Loch Indaal and Loch Guinart on Islay, and in mainland sea lochs including Riddon, Fyne, Caolisport, Sween, Craignish and West Loch Tarbert. Extensive intertidal mudflats at these sites host a typical fauna of lugworms, ragworms and cockles, which together with eelgrass beds, provide an important feeding resource for breeding Common Shelduck and for wintering waders and ducks. Beds of the unusual floating form of Knotted Wrack *Ascophyllum nodosum* f. *mackii* at the head of Loch Feochan support large populations of amphipods, a food resource exploited by large gull flocks at low tide (Paisley 2001).

Saltmarsh in Argyll occurs in a large number of rather small sites, mainly in sheltered locations at the heads of sea lochs and on the margins of bays. Although totalling less than 450ha (Bibby *et al.* 1987), saltmarshes are particularly important for coastal bird populations. They provide high-tide refuges for birds feeding on nearby mudflats, and breeding sites for gulls, terns and waders. In autumn and winter they provide important feeding grounds for passerines, ducks and geese. The few true estuaries in Argyll, such as Lochs Crinan and Riddon, show excellent transitions from maritime biotopes to coastal and terrestrial habitats.

There is a wide variation in tidal ranges across Argyll. An amphidromic point, or location of zero tides, is present between Kintyre and Islay, causing a very restricted tidal range in a zone between Rathlin Island and Jura. Nearby, in Loch Sween, this gives rise to a compressed zonation of plants and animals that live between high and low water marks. The tidal range increases to 3.5m off the west coast of Mull.

Away from settlements, much of Argyll's coast is relatively undisturbed, with farmed land often extending to the upper shore. Recreational use is increasing, particularly in the form of surfing and windsurfing on Tiree and at Machrihanish. Kelp harvesting and the cultivation of scallops and oysters occur on a very localised basis. Low intensity bait digging and winkle collection occurs at sites such as Loch Gilp and Loch Indaal, but no Argyll site supports an organised industry.

Part of Loch Sween, one of the richest areas for marine life in Britain. The pronounced 'grain' of this highly dissected coast runs south-west to north-east, a reminder of Argyll's geological past. The central peninsula is The Fairy Isles, which contains significant remnants of native broad-leaved woodland. It is managed by Scottish Wildlife Trust on behalf of Forestry Commission Scotland. *John Anderson*

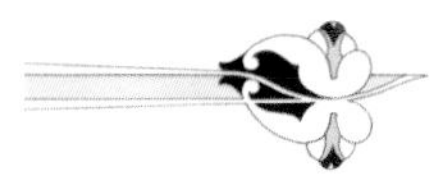

Disturbance to waterbirds from all these activities is probably quite limited.

Marine environments

Most marine areas in Argyll have not been surveyed in detail, including many areas which are potentially rich in marine life. However, assessments carried out through the long-running Marine Nature Conservation Review (Covey *et al.* 1998; Dipper & Beaver 1999) revealed enough to prove that marine environments in Argyll are extremely diverse. This is partly due to wide variations in substrate, degree of exposure, salinity and tidal flow. This complexity reaches an extreme in Loch Sween, one of the most exciting 'hotspots' for marine biodiversity in Britain. Biological richness across the county is further enhanced because Argyll's seas form a kind of biological transition zone, being the northern limit of distribution for many southern species, and the southern limit for many northern ones. In addition, many marine species occur in Argyll in much shallower waters than they typically do. Marine biotopes (away from sediment bottoms) are largely unmodified by human activities, while pollution levels are generally very low. Argyll's inshore waters support many nationally rare and scarce sea-bed organisms (Plaza & Sanderson 1997).

Sediment bottoms are widespread, with the sediment size determined by the degree of exposure and the strength of tidal currents. Sea-beds dominated by sands and gravels are commonest. The most species-rich sediment biotopes are those based on muddy gravels with full salinity, but high quality examples of these are scarce. Mud habitats in deep water are also common, and are home to large burrowing invertebrates such as Norway Lobster and sessile animals like sea pens and the spectacular Fireworks Anemone. Towards the heads of the major sea lochs, tidal exchange is greatly restricted, and salinity is progressively reduced due to inputs of fresh water from surrounding land. This reaches an extreme in Loch Etive, whose upper reaches are almost estuarine in character. Where tidal streams are stronger, dense beds of Horse Mussels are common, and the biological communities associated with them can be species-rich. However, the most diverse subtidal biotopes in Argyll are found on rocky reefs and steep cliff faces where strong tidal flows of up to 10 knots are funnelled, either by the shape of the coast, or by the presence of shallow sills in sea lochs. The strong tidal streams and rapids generated in locations such as the Firth of Lorn, Loch Sween, Loch Etive and Loch Creran support an abundant marine fauna which typically includes sponges, hydroids, soft corals, bryozoan mats, anemones, mussels and brittlestars, together with a wide range of seaweeds.

Ferocious tidal rapids, whirlpools and overfalls in the Gulf of Corryvreckan, north of Jura. *David Wood*

The North Atlantic Drift not only keeps Argyll's coast mild throughout the year. It also interacts with other ocean currents flowing north out of the Irish and Clyde Seas, forming a boundary zone just north of Ireland. This area, the Islay Front, together with similar areas which sometimes form north and south of Islay, are often rich in plankton. In turn this makes them productive areas for fish and for the higher predators that feed on them: seabirds, seals, Harbour Porpoises, dolphins and Minke Whales.

The importance of marine environment for seabirds varies according to species and time of year. During the breeding season, waters within 1-2km of seabird colonies are used, particularly by Common Guillemots, Razorbills, Puffins, Kittiwakes, Black Guillemots and Shags, for preening, displaying and feeding. The main feeding areas in Argyll's waters have not been mapped accurately, but based on studies at other British sites, may be located over 20km from the colonies they support (review in McSorley *et al.* 2003). In spring, autumn and winter, inshore areas like the Firth of Clyde, Firth of Lorn and Sound of Gigha provide sheltered foraging for Eider, Common Scoter, Red-breasted Merganser, Slavonian Grebe and Long-tailed Duck, while Loch Indaal hosts a diverse winter assemblage which can also include Scaup, Teal, Wigeon, and Shelduck.

Intertidal and marine habitats and species in Argyll have been intensively studied since the 1930s, continuing to the present day with innovative technologies, such as broadscale seabed mapping by remote sensing (Davies 1999). Much of this work has been facilitated by the presence of the Scottish Association of Marine Science research facility at Dunstaffnage, and latterly by the Hebridean Whale and Dolphin Trust, based on Mull. Paisley (2001) and Barne *et al.* (1997) summarize the extensive literature.

Fishing is still a diverse and important industry in Argyll, albeit on nothing like the scale seen in the 19th century (Martin 1996). Traditional fisheries for Herring, Whitebait and Mackerel are now much reduced due to depleted stocks, and Tarbert's famous ring net fishery is long gone. Instead, many boats now dredge or trawl for Scallops, Queen Scallops and Norway Lobsters, which are common and widely distributed in Argyll's coastal waters wherever the seabed is sandy or muddy. Soft sea bottoms around Argyll's coasts are heavily modified by the use of such mobile fishing gear, but the severity and significance of this is disputed. The setting of 'pots' for crabs and lobsters is very common, with some larger boats setting thousands of creels, and there is an increasing use of SCUBA divers to gather scallops. Recent years have also seen the introduction of static, bottom-set tangle nets, which are intended to catch crayfish but which may also trap and kill seabirds, seals and cetaceans ('ghost' fishing). However, seabirds can also benefit from the fishing industry, as witnessed by the large gull flocks often seen around boats, feeding on offal and other discards.

The combination of high water quality, relatively sheltered conditions and rapid tidal exchange is found in many locations across Argyll, and has promoted the development of fish farming as an important economic activity. Until recently the industry was dominated by salmon, but Trout, Cod and Halibut have also been explored. The industry provides important employment in rural Argyll, but its scale has also raised a number of concerns due to impacts on the seabed, the likely connection with sea lice in wild salmonids,

Lobster fisherman. Fishing is still an important economic activity in Argyll. *Eddie Maguire*

the uncertain effects of chemicals on marine wildlife, and the genetic contamination of wild fish by escapes of farmed stock. In the more sheltered sea lochs, shellfish farming, particularly of Common Mussels, has increased dramatically since the 1980s, providing an irresistible food resource for Eiders. This has caused some localised problems for fish farmers, particularly in Loch Etive (Ross & Furness 2000).

In 2005, the Firth of Lorn and Loch Creran became marine Special Areas of Conservation, and in 2006, Argyll emerged as a likely area to become Britain's first marine National Park. These initiatives engaged conservationists in what was already a long-running, and at times heated, debate between different sectors of the fishing industry about the sustainable management of marine resources in Argyll.

Ecotourism in Argyll's coastal and marine environments is an expanding economic activity, but the sector is still relatively under-developed. However, the spectacular animal life of Argyll's underwater cliffs, reefs and tidal rapids, combined with its clear waters, have long made the county popular with sports divers. In addition, a number of boat tour businesses have recently been established, focussing on 'seabird islands' such as Treshnish, and on watching cetaceans, Basking Sharks and seals. The coastal waters of Argyll are also extremely popular with with sea anglers and with recreational boat users, from dinghies right up to large yachts.

Two of the many varied faces of farming in Argyll.

Above: Philip Kirkham
Below: John Bowler

Above: On Islay, improved grassland attracts thousands of Greenland White-fronted Geese and Greenland Barnacle Geese every winter. Safeguarding these internationally important flocks, while managing the damage to grass crops, has been one of the toughest conservation challenges in Argyll.

Below: Traditional agricultural systems, especially low-intensity cattle grazing, are important in maintaining the condition of habitats and their associated wildlife in many parts of Argyll, including, as here, on Tiree. Subsidy packages for farming increasingly reflect this linkage.

Farmland

The first signs of humans in Argyll date from about 9,000 years ago, soon after the final ice retreat. At this time, bone tools were in use around Oban. Many of Argyll's early human inhabitants probably lived around the coast as hunters and gatherers; they made good use of coastal food resources, as shown by the presence of shells and seabird bones in middens on Oronsay, dating from about 6,000 years ago. However, from about this time, man first began to modify the landscape, with the establishment of farming and settled communities. Woodlands were gradually felled, creating a diverse mosaic of habitats. As the human population grew, Argyll's natural environments were progressively modified. Driven by the need to feed a growing population, cultural landscapes based mainly on food production developed across Argyll, in which almost all of the habitats and species present were affected in some way by human activities, rather than by natural processes alone (Butter 1999).

The development of farming in Argyll has always been influenced by the county's relative geographic isolation, the patchy distribution of good soils, and adverse climatic conditions. For many centuries, a low-intensity mixed farming system existed. This was largely subsistence-based, but was supplemented by cattle export. However, from the mid-18th century the radical agricultural innovations sweeping across Scotland began to impact Argyll (Ascherson 2002). Large estates started to carry out diverse "improvements" to increase productivity and profitability. The enclosure of fields began on a large scale, poorer land was limed, and wetlands and lowland peat bogs were drained. Sheep began to replace cattle as the predominant livestock. Populations of mammalian predators, raptors and corvids were reduced by intensive culling, and wild bird species deemed to be more desirable, such as Black Grouse, Red Grouse and Pheasants were encouraged to increase. The human population reached a peak in Argyll around the 1840s. However, the farming scene was still diverse, with arable crops an important component, and large-scale mechanisation and pesticides were still some way in the future. The complex patchwork of man-modified habitats provided for a diverse farmland bird community.

After World War Two, economic and social factors put increasing pressure on mixed, low-input farming systems in Argyll. Small farms amalgamated into larger units, and the importance of cattle declined steadily to the extent that there are now 11 ewes for every beef cow, and 33 ewes for every dairy cow (Anon 2005a). Arable crops are now rarely grown, leading to significant declines in previously common farmland birds such as Sky Lark, Corn Bunting and Yellowhammer. To remain economic, farms in Argyll today tend to be much more intensively managed than before. On poorer land, subsidy structures have rewarded large sheep flocks, leading in places to a loss of habitat quality and diversity through over-grazing. On better land, intensive cattle production, with its associated silage crops, is most profitable. Thousands of Greenland White-fronted Geese and Greenland Barnacle Geese are attracted to feed on these fields in winter, particularly in Kintyre and Islay. These impressive flocks are simultaneously one of Argyll's most famous wildlife spectacles, and an economic threat to those farmers affected by damaged grass crops.

Low-input, low-output farming continued in some of Argyll's outlying areas and on some of the islands until quite recently. This allowed the persistence of relict populations of several bird species, which are now recognised as being of international importance. For instance, cattle grazing helps to maintain year-round populations of Red-billed Chough on Islay and Colonsay, at the northern limit of its range, while less intensive farming on Coll and Tiree allows the survival of small numbers of breeding Corn Crake, which are now increasing and recolonising other islands with the help of targeted habitat management. Seasonally-flooded, semi-improved grazing marshes on Tiree, combined with traditionally managed coastal grasslands known as machair, provide ideal conditions for high densities of breeding waders such as Dunlin, Oystercatcher, Ringed Plover and Common Redshank.

Today, agriculture remains one of Argyll's most important economic sectors, and farmland is still one of Argyll's foremost wildlife habitats. Since the 1980s, government money has been available to encourage farmers to enhance land for wildlife, through a variety of agri-environment schemes. Uptake has been limited by the relatively small budgets allocated to these schemes. In the future, reform of the Common Agricultural Policy will mean that farmers and crofters will be rewarded for delivering a wider range of social, environmental and economic benefits on farmland. New subsidy structures will reinforce the concept of "good agricultural and environmental condition" and promote biodiversity as a legitimate land use in its own right, rather than simply encouraging the maximum headage of stock. This will present significant new opportunities to expand and diversify wildlife habitats on farms.

Woodlands

Woodlands are hugely important habitats in Argyll, if only because of the large areas involved. Woodland of some kind covers about 200,000ha of Argyll, some 29% of the land area. The climax community across much of Argyll is upland broadleaved woodland, characterised by the dominance of oak and birch in the canopy and with varying amounts of Holly, Hazel and Rowan in the shrub layer. In areas with more alkaline soils, typically at the base of slopes or along burnsides, Ash and Wych Elm may also be common. High rainfall, varied substrates and clean air make these woodlands exceptionally rich in ferns, bryophytes and lichens, many of which grow on the trees themselves. Invertebrate species diversity can also be very high. These native woodlands have a distinctive breeding bird population which includes Common Redstart, Tree Pipit and Wood Warbler (Amar *et al.* 2006). In North Argyll, a handful of small Caledonian pinewoods occur at the

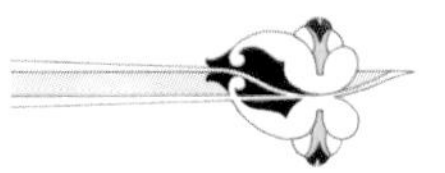

The changes brought about by afforestation with non-native conifers are profound, and typically affect whole landscapes.

Both photos: Steve Petty

Above: Moorland freshly ploughed for new planting, Carradale, Kintyre, May 1983.

Below: The canopy takes just a few years to close up in Argyll's mild, humid climate. After the radical habitat shift, entirely different bird communities are supported. Powder Dams, Cowal, October 2003.

south-western extremity of their Scottish range. Sometimes intermixed with other woodland types, these pinewoods are significantly different from the more extensive Caledonian forests of north and east Scotland, and some of Argyll's pinewoods are partly of plantation origin. Unfortunately, Crested Tit, Scottish Crossbill and Capercaillie are absent from Argyll's native pinewoods. Native woodlands nowadays contribute a modest 20,000ha to the total woodland area in Argyll, but this is increasing.

In common with the pattern across Scotland, nearly all native woodlands had already been felled by the time historical records began. Woods which survived were either useful, or inaccessible. Many of today's remaining large oakwoods, such as Taynish and Glen Nant, were intensively managed for charcoal production and as part of the tanning industry until the late 19th century. These woodlands are now easily recognised by the uniform age-structure of their oak trees. Other woods were retained for hazel coppice or as shelter for livestock. Some of the least modified and botanically rich native woodlands now occur in ravines, the steep ground giving protection from felling and stock grazing. Over-grazing by deer and farm stock, and invasion by Rhododendron, are major issues affecting the condition of native woodlands in Argyll. Fragmentation is also a serious problem, with remaining woodlands often so small and isolated that they cannot host the full range of native species and habitats. Increasingly, locations for new native woods are planned to increase the connectivity of existing ancient woodlands, based on the dispersal capabilities of a range of characteristic native woodland organisms.

From the 18th century onwards, landowners started to plant trees to provide a timber resource for their estates. In 1909, the Office of Woods carried out trial plantings along Loch Awe, and in 1919 Argyll was identified as suitable for the commercial planting of woodlands by the newly-formed Forestry Commission. However, the main era of planting occurred after 1945, driven by the perceived need to provide the country with a strategic timber resource. It reached a peak in the 1970s and 1980s. Between the 1940s and the 1980s, some 22% of Argyll's remaining native woods were converted into conifer plantations (National Countryside Monitoring Scheme data). However, most of the planting was on poor agricultural land in the uplands, as post-war farm economics became increasingly bleak and Argyll's farmers sold land to the Forestry Commission as their way out of farming. Independent forestry companies also flourished, taking advantage of generous government grants to establish new woodlands on private land. By the late 1990s, large areas of mainland Argyll had been afforested with conifers, particularly in Mid-Argyll, Kintyre and Cowal. Extensive plantations were also established on Mull and Islay. By this time, forestry had become a significant employer in Argyll. However, the extent of coniferous planting across the county prompted widespread concern about the reasonable balance of land use and the extent to which forestry was prejudicing other land management activities. Since 2000, the rate of new planting has slowed, partly because less open land suitable for planting is now available, and partly because the industry has moved to harvesting and restructuring existing forests. Nowadays, new native woodlands are increasingly being established instead of new conifer plantations.

The effect of coniferous afforestation on bird communities is dramatic, but perhaps surprisingly, a wide range of species can be found in these novel habitats (Patterson *et al.* 1995). Species more normally associated with broadleaved woodland and open ground can thrive in the various growth stages present in many older forests. For instance, Meadow Pipits, Tree Pipits and Whinchats breed on clear-felled areas, Dunnocks, Lesser Redpolls and Willow Warblers are to be found in crops before canopy closure, while Song Thrushes, Blackbirds, Woodcocks and several species of raptors occur in older tree stands. In addition, species that are conifer-dependent have greatly extended their range in Argyll, including Siskins, Common Crossbills, Goldcrests and Coal Tits. Once conifers are clear-felled, a flush of ground vegetation soon afterwards is often associated with a sudden jump in small mammal numbers, particularly those of the Field Vole. These rodents and shrews provide an abundant

A surviving fragment of ancient oakwood on the shore of Loch Eck. The large oak has a Tawny Owl nestbox, in which Mandarin Ducks have also bred. *Steve Petty*

The number of wind energy developments in Argyll has increased dramatically in recent years. This one is Beinn Ghlas, 10km east of Oban. It was one of the first in Argyll, and is modest compared with some current proposals. *John Anderson*

food supply for raptors, such as Common Buzzard, Common Kestrel, Tawny Owl and Short-eared Owl.

The area of publicly-owned woodland in Argyll amounts to around 80,000ha. As the economics of commercial timber production in Scotland become uncertain, Forestry Commission Scotland is seeking alternative or additional uses for this enormous estate (Anon 2006). Large areas are now being zoned to revert to native broadleaved woodland or semi-natural open habitats, and existing forests are being managed more sympathetically, with smaller coup sizes and the introduction of wildlife-friendly practices such as continuous cover and long-term retentions. More controversially, state-owned conifer forests have recently been targetted by windfarm developers.

Older conifer stands, which often include some large-diameter dead wood, are attractive habitats for a wide range of birds, but particularly for Spotted Flycatcher, Great Spotted Woodpecker and Tree Creeper. In addition, the mild, oceanic climate of Argyll led to the establishment of numerous botanical gardens in Argyll in the 19th century, including Benmore Botanic Garden and Ardkinglas Woodland Garden in Cowal, Achamore Garden on Gigha, Arduaine Garden (Loch Melfort), Crarae Gardens (near Inveraray) and Colonsay House Garden on Colonsay. Nowadays these contain interesting and diverse stands of old conifers and a wide range of other exotic plants, shrubs and trees, where large quantities of seeds and fruits are seasonally available, which together provide suitable conditions for a wide range of birds associated with mature, open woodlands.

Upland and montane habitats

The uplands of Argyll are dominated by unimproved acidic grassland, blanket bog and wet and dry heath, with smaller, localised areas of unimproved calcareous grassland and true montane vegetation. Large areas of a single vegetation type are uncommon. Instead, there is a great deal of fine-grained habitat diversity, with mosaics, flushes and transitions the norm. A complete survey of upland vegetation in Mid-Argyll, Kintyre and Cowal in the late 1990s identified several hotspots of botanical interest (Dayton 2000). These include the montane areas around Beinn Buidhe and many of the south-western Breadalbane summits, which have outstanding calcareous tall-herb ledge and diverse sub-montane communities, including many nationally scarce and rare plants. The remote, sub-montane upland areas on the Ellary and Ormsary Estates are also notable for their intact blanket mires. Additional base-rich communities occur on the Eredine uplands and in North Knapdale. Mesotrophic fens roughly coincide with areas of calcareous grassland, with additional areas at Carn Ban and Beinn Bheula. On the islands, the landscape of blanket bog and nutrient-poor lochans of north-east Coll stands out, while the cliffs, screes and high tops of Ardmeanach on Mull support notable arctic-alpine communities.

Breeding birds of Argyll's uplands include common and widely distributed species, such as Meadow Pipit, Sky Lark, Whinchat, Northern Wheatear, Stonechat and Twite. Nesting seabirds, including Great Skua, Arctic Skua and Common Gull, increase the species diversity of heathland sites on

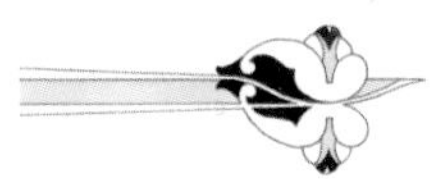

Coll and other islands. Uncommon breeding species include European Golden Plover, Dunlin and Ptarmigan, while the raptors include Hen Harrier, Golden Eagle, Peregrine Falcon and Merlin. The Ring Ouzel is very rare in Argyll, and may only occasionally breed in these habitats. Golden Eagles and White-tailed Eagles occur at high densities on Mull, where they form an important attraction for a growing ecotourism industry.

Few moorlands in Argyll have been managed for driven grouse. Instead, the uplands were traditionally used as summer grazings for cattle and, more recently, as ranches for large sheep flocks. The combination of high stocking densities and large numbers of Red and Sika deer has led to some areas becoming overgrazed, and so becoming poorer habitats with fewer plant species. Large areas of upland vegetation have also been lost to coniferous afforestation. Since the late 1990s, an increasing number of wind farms have been built or proposed for Argyll's uplands. The long term effects of wind energy developments on upland bird populations are uncertain. Potential impacts include direct mortality of birds due to collisions with turbine blades or towers, displacement of birds from around wind farms, disturbance to sensitive breeding species during construction and operation, and damage to habitats caused by the installation of access tracks and other infrastructure. Considerable effort has been invested in trying to model these risks, and a range of mitigation measures has recently been attempted, including large-scale habitat modification (Walker *et al.* 2005). Windfarms are increasingly affecting the landscape character of Argyll's uplands, as 'wild land' (Anon 1999) is progressively replaced with semi-industrialised vistas.

Freshwater habitats

Despite high rainfall, large rivers are rare in Argyll. With a few exceptions, catchments are small and watercourses short and steep. Rapid runoff following heavy rain generates spate conditions very quickly, and water quality is generally very high. The many small burns provide nesting habitat for Grey Wagtail, Dipper, Goosander and Common Sandpiper. Trout, salmon and eel occur throughout, but the reduction in the abundance of migratory salmonids seen elsewhere in Scotland has also affected populations here. Nonetheless, rod-and-line fisheries are still important economic components of estate management on Mull and on parts of the mainland. Argyll has over 300 freshwater lochs, generally small but with the notable exceptions of Lochs Ba and Frisa on Mull and Lochs Awe and Eck on the mainland. Loch Eck is unique in Britain for containing the full range of native salmonid fish species; it is also one of only two British sites to contain Powan and Arctic Charr together. Nutrient-poor upland lochs occur extensively across Mid-Argyll, Coll and Jura, providing important breeding sites for Red-throated Diver, Black-throated Diver and Greylag Goose, while more nutrient-rich sites such as Lochan Taynish support nesting Mallard and other ducks. In contrast, lochs of the machair on Tiree are influenced by blown shell sand. This alkaline influence, combined with nutrient inputs from surrounding agricultural land, means these lochs support more diverse plant and animal communities than their moorland counterparts. Rare waterfowl such as Pintail, Gadwall and Shoveller occur in such habitats.

Loch Awe is by far the largest body of fresh water in Argyll. *John Anderson*

Most individual marshes and wetlands in Argyll are small, and typically occur as part of habitat suites or mosaics. At their edges, they often grade into freshwater or coastal communities. Many previously extensive wetlands, such as the Laggan in Kintyre, have been much reduced or lost altogether due to drainage and agricultural improvement. With appropriate management, however, sites can be recovered. For instance, through careful control of grazing and water levels, wetlands at the RSPB reserve of Loch Gruinart on Islay have been developed into superb habitats for nesting and wintering ducks and waders.

Settlements and industry

Argyll is one of the less populated areas of Scotland. At the time of the 2001 national census, about 80,000 people lived in the county, less than 2% of Scotland's total. Around 8,600 live on islands, and there are just three towns with over 5,000 inhabitants: Dunoon (9,300), Oban (8,100) and Campbeltown (6,100) (Jones 2004). Industrialised areas are largely restricted to small ports such as Oban, Tarbert, Tobermory and Campbeltown, and to whisky distilleries (especially on Islay). Power generation is increasingly important in Argyll. Facilities include the pumped-storage hydro-electric scheme at Cruachan, and an increasing number of windfarms. So, although almost all of Argyll's land has been modified in some way by human activities, built development itself is still relatively sparse. Jackdaws, Rooks and gulls have adapted successfully to the limited town centre areas of Argyll.

All major settlements in Argyll are coastal. Oban, seen here, is one of the principal hubs of a growing tourism industry, of which ecotourism is an important component. *John Anderson*

Gardens, both suburban and rural, are important habitats for birds that have been able to adapt to their semi-open landscapes and moderate levels of human disturbance. These species were once found mainly in woodlands and at woodland edges. The widespread use of bird tables in gardens has increased the winter survival of species like Blackbird, Song Thrush, Robin, Siskin and Coal Tit, while nestboxes are readily adopted by Blue Tits and Great Tits, especially in areas with few natural holes suitable for nesting.

The limits of acceptable change

The history of radical changes to wildlife habitats, and the populations of birds they support, has been a common thread running through this chapter. Modification began as soon as humans came to live in Argyll, picked up pace with the advent of settled communities and farming, and has continued right up to the present day. It culminated in massive and rapid shifts in just the past few decades, linked to two key processes: widespread afforestation, and fundamental alterations to agricultural systems.

We all make different subjective judgements about change. A hillwalker might mourn the loss of an expansive "wild" moorland, with its distinctive but species-poor bird assemblage, to a Sitka Spruce plantation. A forester would argue that the plantation supports more jobs than the moor ever did, and may produce a useful timber crop, whereas the economic value of the moorland was effectively zero. The forest tracks now bulldozed up the hill may be loathed as eyesores by local residents, but appreciated by mountain bikers. A woodland ecologist will enjoy studying the newly-expanded populations of Siskins, Coal Tits and Common Crossbills, all species which have proved able to utilise the exotic conifers.

If we find it difficult to reach consensus about recent transformations which are plain for all to see, we find it still harder to agree how we want our county to look in the decades ahead. However, getting better at doing so has never been more urgent. Global warming, driven by our emissions of greenhouse gases, now threatens to bite hard, and Argyll will not be exempt. The effects of climate change cannot be predicted with certainty, but may include substantial rises in sea level, an increase in the number and severity of storms, and even shifts in the ocean currents that determine Argyll's climate and support its amazing marine life. Major change now appears inevitable; we may well ponder the fate of very low-lying coastal areas of Argyll as the century unfolds. Yet perhaps still, for a short while, we can influence the extent of change by altering how we live our daily lives. Very soon now, we must all decide on the limits of acceptable change, both for our own behaviour, and for the habitats and birds of Argyll that we value.

David Wood

Where to watch birds in Argyll

There are many superb birdwatching opportunities in Argyll. This chapter lists a selection of localities, some well known, others less visited. It provides a spread of sites across the county to give a representative taste of the options available; the list is not exhaustive. Sites are grouped by Recording Area, and map reference numbers are plotted on the inside covers of the book. For large sites, the grid reference gives an approximate centre, or where possible, a point of convenient access.

The bird list for each site covers the whole calendar year. Many of the birds listed are only present seasonally. If your interest is in particular species, check the relevant accounts in this book, or the bird sighting updates which are regularly posted at www.argyllbirdclub.org.

Some sites are managed explicitly for nature conservation, including the RSPB's Reserves and SNH's National Nature Reserves. These tend to provide opportunities for more structured birdwatching, including a wide range of access options and dedicated interpretation facilities, including maps and leaflets. The web sites of these organisations can be very informative (see Appendix 4). Prospective visitors are strongly recommended to obtain as much information as possible in advance. A little forward planning will result in a more rewarding visit, and is almost essential for visits to some island sites.

For those wanting some assistance to develop their birdwatching skills, a range of guidance is available. The Machrihanish Seabird Observatory in Kintyre (map ref 69) is particularly relevant for shorebirds and seabirds, but is not restricted to these species. Check opening times before you visit (www.machrihanishbirds.org.uk). Staff at the Loch Gruinart RSPB reserve centre (map ref 54) can explain the year-round importance of this flagship site to birds and other wildlife. The Wildlife Information Centre, run by the Islay Natural History Trust and located at Port Charlotte, provides some excellent resources on Islay's rich wildlife. Family activity sessions are organised during the summer. Check the opening times of the Centre before visiting (www.islaywildlife.freeserve.co.uk). You could come on a local field trip organised by the Argyll Bird Club (details at www.argyllbirdclub.org), or take advantage of the expert guided services now provided by several companies, especially on Mull. Assisted viewing by telescope of a pair of White-tailed Eagles at a nest on Mull is provided in most years; check availability with the Mull Tourist Information Centre at Craignure. Lastly, Forestry Commission Scotland runs a range of wildlife events in its woodlands. Check their web site.

Most sites listed here may be viewed from roadsides or other public locations, but in some cases you may need to cross privately-owned land. Legislation passed by the Scottish Parliament in 2003 gives everyone a right of responsible access to most land and inland water in Scotland. The word "responsible" here is very important. Argyll's countryside is the place of work for many people, so please remember to act considerately. The Scottish Outdoor Access Code, available at www.outdooraccess-scotland.com, contains all the information you need on this important topic.

Paul Daw and David Wood

Map ref number	Location	Recording Area	Grid Reference	Habitat	Birds
1	Coll RSPB Reserve	Coll	NM150541	White shell sand beaches, sand-dunes and machair grassland	White-fronted Goose, Barnacle Goose, Great Northern Diver, Manx Shearwater, Hen Harrier, Merlin, Corn Crake, Sanderling, Dunlin, breeding Lapwing and Common Redshank, Purple Sandpiper, Turnstone, Arctic Tern, Little Tern, Razorbill, Common Guillemot, Stonechat, Grasshopper Warbler, Twite
2	Balephetrish Bay	Tiree	NM005471	Wide shallow bay with sandy beach	Great Northern Diver, Long-tailed Duck, Ringed Plover, Grey Plover, Sanderling, Dunlin, Purple Sandpiper, Turnstone
3	Gott Bay	Tiree	NM043469	Large sandy bay in east Tiree, with muddier south-west corner	Great Northern Diver, Brent Goose, Common Shelduck, Ringed Plover, Sanderling, Dunlin, Red Knot, Bar-tailed Godwit, Eurasian Curlew, Turnstone, gulls, Arctic Tern, Little Tern, Northern Wheatear
4	Loch a' Phuill	Tiree	NL956418	Large freshwater machair loch in south-west Tiree	Mute Swan, Whooper Swan, Greenland White-fronted Goose, Greylag Goose, Wigeon, Gadwall, Eurasian Teal, Pintail, Shoveler, Tufted Duck, Greater Scaup, Goldeneye, Peregrine Falcon, Ringed Plover, European Golden Plover, Northern Lapwing, Red Knot, Curlew Sandpiper, Dunlin, Little Stint, Ruff, Black-tailed Godwit, Whimbrel, Eurasian Curlew, Common Redshank, Greenshank, Black-headed Gull, Kittiwake, Arctic Tern, Little Tern, Sand Martin, rarities
5	Loch an Eilein	Tiree	NL984436	Freshwater loch in west Tiree	Mute Swan, Whooper Swan, Greylag Goose, Pintail, Tufted Duck, Red-breasted Merganser, Northern Lapwing, Ruff, Black-tailed Godwit, Common Redshank, Greenshank, Rock Dove, Sand Martin
6	Loch Bhasapol	Tiree	NL971469	Freshwater machair loch with marshes and reedbeds in north-west Tiree	Whooper Swan, Greenland White-fronted Goose, Greylag Goose, Eurasian Wigeon, Mallard, Shoveler, Tufted Duck, Pochard, Goldeneye, Merlin, Moorhen, Common Coot, Corncrake, European Golden Plover, Northern Lapwing, Common Snipe, Eurasian Curlew, Black-headed Gull, Arctic Tern, Sedge Warbler, Twite, Reed Bunting
7	Sorobaidh Bay	Tiree	NL995425	Sandy bay in south-west of Tiree with stream outlets at each end	Great Northern Diver, Brent Goose, Common Shelduck, Merlin, Ringed Plover, Sanderling, Purple Sandpiper, Dunlin, Bar-tailed Godwit, Eurasian Curlew, Turnstone, gulls, Arctic Tern, White Wagtail, Northern Wheatear
8	Traigh Bhagh / The Reef	Tiree	NM006438	Sandy bay, backed by dunes and machair (there is no access to The Reef itself but the machair plain can be viewed from the road and dunes)	Great Northern Diver, Greenland White-fronted Goose, Greylag Goose, Eurasian Teal, Mallard, Hen Harrier, Merlin, Peregrine Falcon, Ringed Plover, European Golden Plover, Northern Lapwing, Sanderling, Dunlin, Common Snipe, Whimbrel, Common Redshank, Turnstone, Arctic Tern, Little Tern, Skylark, Northern Wheatear, Common Raven, Twite, Snow Bunting
9	Calgary	Mull	NM370511	Enclosed, isolated bay in north-west of Mull	Greylag Goose, Red-throated Diver, Great Northern Diver, White-tailed Eagle, Peregrine Falcon, Ringed Plover, Rock Pipit, Grey Wagtail, Whinchat
10	Carsaig & Bay	Mull	NM537215	Open bay on south side of Mull	Divers in winter, Peregrine Falcon, Common Raven
11	Glen Bellart	Mull	NM454482	Largely uninhabited glen in north of Mull with mountains, moorland and conifer forest	Hen Harrier, Golden Eagle, Merlin, Short-eared Owl, Snow Bunting
12	Grasspoint	Mull	NM747309	Headland overlooking Firth of Lorn towards island of Kerrera	Manx Shearwater, Gannet, White-tailed Eagle, Hen Harrier, Sparrowhawk, Black Guillemot, Tree Pipit, Common Stonechat, Grasshopper Warbler, Common Whitethroat, Wood Warbler, Willow Warbler, Common Raven, Twite, Lesser Redpoll
13	Iona	Mull	NM277243	Island west of Mull with sandy bays, and cliffs and stacks to the south	Shelduck, Fulmar, Cormorant, Shag, Corn Crake, Ringed Plover, Dunlin, Snipe, Whimbrel, Common Sandpiper, Black Guillemot, Sky Lark, Stonechat, Northern Wheatear, Sedge Warbler, Spotted Flycatcher, Common Raven, Linnet, Twite

Map ref number	Location	Recording Area	Grid Reference	Habitat	Birds
14	Loch a' Chumhainn ('Loch Cuin')	Mull	NM422518	Freshwater loch at the north of Mull	Greylag Goose, Little Grebe, Common Snipe, Eurasian Teal, Common Redshank, Greenshank
15	Loch Beg	Mull	NM531290	Sea loch with mud flats at low tide	Greylag Goose, Red-breasted Merganser, Goosander, Ringed Plover, European Golden Plover, Northern Lapwing, Eurasian Curlew, Common Redshank, Greenshank
16	Loch Don	Mull	NM739319	Enclosed sea loch	Mute Swan, Whooper Swan, Common Shelduck, Eurasian Wigeon, Eurasian Teal, Red-breasted Merganser, Little Grebe, White-tailed Eagle, Peregrine Falcon, Ringed Plover, European Golden Plover, Northern Lapwing, Dunlin, Bar-tailed Godwit, Whimbrel, Common Redshank, Greenshank
17	Loch na Keal	Mull	NM496380	Large sea loch with many large and small islands. Bays backed by meadow and woodland	Common Eider, Black-throated Diver, Slavonian Grebe, White-tailed Eagle, Hen Harrier, Golden Eagle, Ringed Plover, Greenshank
18	Loch Scridain	Mull	NM461258	Large sea loch with area of tidal mud flats at head (Loch Beg)	Eurasian Wigeon, Common Goldeneye, Red-breasted Merganser, Red-throated Diver, Black-throated Diver, Great Northern Diver, Common Redshank, Greenshank
19	Lochbuie	Mull	NM604233	Open sea loch	Red-throated Diver, Black-throated Diver, Great Northern Diver, Golden Eagle, Northern Wheatear
20	Mishnish Lochs	Mull	NM477525	Chain of freshwater lochs in the north of Mull	Greylag Goose, Common Goldeneye, Goosander, Little Grebe, Grasshopper Warbler
21	Treshnish Isles	Mull	NM278419	Collection of small uninhabited islands off the west coast of Mull with rocky shores and low cliffs in places. Contain important seabird colonies	Greylag Goose, Common Eider, Fulmar, Manx Shearwater, European Storm Petrel, Northern Gannet, Shag, Peregrine Falcon, Corn Crake, Oystercatcher, Ringed Plover, Common Snipe, Common Sandpiper, Arctic Skua, Great Skua, Lesser Black-backed Gull, Herring Gull, Great Black-backed Gull, Kittiwake, Common Tern, Arctic Tern, Common Guillemot, Razorbill, Black Guillemot, Puffin, Rock Dove, Sky Lark, Meadow Pipit, Rock Pipit, Wren, Northern Wheatear, Hooded Crow, Common Raven, Common Starling, Twite
22	Ledaig Point & Ardmucknish Bay	North Argyll	NM895350	Promontory at the mouth of Loch Etive and the broad sandy bay north from there	Common Eider, Red-breasted Merganser, Red-throated Diver, Great Northern Diver, Oystercatcher, Ringed Plover, Red Knot, Dunlin, Sanderling, Common Redshank, Eurasian Curlew, Turnstone, Common Tern, Sand Martin, Linnet, Twite
23	Loch Etive, Outer (Connel Bridge-Taynuilt)	North Argyll	NM951347	Large enclosed sea loch with many islands	Mute Swan, Greylag Goose, Greater Canada Goose, Eurasian Wigeon, Mallard, Common Eider, Common Goldeneye, Red-breasted Merganser, Goosander, Little Grebe, Great Cormorant, Grey Heron, Ringed Plover, Northern Lapwing, Eurasian Curlew, Common Gull, Common Tern, Arctic Tern, Sand Martin
24	Loch Tulla	North Argyll	NN294426	High altitude freshwater loch	Eurasian Wigeon, Black-throated Diver, Greenshank
25	Add Estuary	Mid-Argyll	NR798933	Estuary and saltmarsh with extensive mud flats at low tide. Public hide on canal towpath at NR803925.	Mute Swan, Greylag Goose, Wigeon, (returning American Wigeon), Eurasian Teal, Common Eider, Common Goldeneye, Red-breasted Merganser, Goosander, Little Grebe, Shag, Heronry, Hen Harrier, Common Buzzard, Osprey, Peregrine Falcon, Oystercatcher, Ringed Plover, Dunlin, Red Knot, Black-tailed Godwit, Common Redshank, Greenshank, Common Sandpiper, White Wagtail, Twite
26	Danna Island	Mid-Argyll	NR692778	Island at end of Loch Sween connected to manland by causeway	Greenland White-fronted Geese and Barnacle Geese in winter

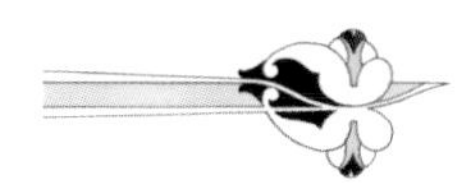

Map ref number	Location	Recording Area	Grid Reference	Habitat	Birds
27	Kilchurn Castle (Loch Awe)	Mid-Argyll	NN131276	North end of large freshwater loch	Common Pochard, Tufted Duck, Goldeneye, Osprey, Sand Martin
28	Loch Awe	Mid-Argyll	NN025195	Long narrow freshwater loch with conifer forest and oak woodland along the shores	Mute Swan, Greater Canada Goose, Mandarin Duck, Common Pochard, Tufted Duck, Goosander, Osprey, Great Spotted Woodpecker, Sand Martin, Common Redstart
29	Loch Caolisport	Mid-Argyll	NR740749	Large sea loch with sandy bays	Eurasian Wigeon, Mallard, Common Eider, Common Goldeneye, Black-throated Diver, Great Northern Diver, Oystercatcher, Purple Sandpiper, Dunlin, Eurasian Curlew, Common Redshank
30	Loch Crinan	Mid-Argyll	NR804924	Open sea loch at mouth of Add Estuary	Greylag Goose, Common Shelduck, Eurasian Wigeon, American Wigeon, Eurasian Teal, Mallard, Red-breasted Merganser, Goosander, Osprey, Oystercatcher, Northern Lapwing, Dunlin, Bar-tailed Godwit, Eurasian Curlew, Common Redshank, gulls
31	Loch Feochan (Head)	Mid-Argyll	NM873245	Enclosed sea loch	Common Goldeneye, Red-breasted Merganser, Goosander, Common Sandpiper, gull roosts
32	Loch Gilp	Mid-Argyll	NR858877	Small sea loch	Whooper Swan, Common Shelduck, Eurasian Wigeon, Mallard, Common Eider, Common Goldeneye, Goosander, Oystercatcher, Ringed Plover, Dunlin, Bar-tailed Godwit, Eurasian Curlew, Common Redshank, Common Tern
33	Loch na Cille (Loch Sween)	Mid-Argyll	NR696802	Sea loch at the mouth of Loch Sween	Greenland White-fronted Goose, Barnacle Goose, Greylag Goose, Eurasian Wigeon, Eurasian Teal, Red-throated Diver, Great Northern Diver, Buzzard, Common Kestrel, Ringed Plover, Grey Plover, Northern Lapwing, Dunlin, Eurasian Curlew, Common Redshank, Common Stonechat, Common Raven
34	Loch Nell	Mid-Argyll	NM893274	Large freshwater loch	Tufted Duck, Common Pochard, Common Coot, gulls
35	Moine Mhor (National Nature Reserve)	Mid-Argyll	NR827958	One of the last wild raised bogs in Britain	Greenland White-fronted Goose, Greylag Goose, Mallard, Red-breasted Merganser, Goosander, Hen Harrier, Common Buzzard, Osprey, Common Kestrel, Peregrine Falcon, Common Snipe, Common Redshank, Common Sandpiper, Common Cuckoo, Barn Owl, Short-eared Owl, Sky Lark, Sand Martin, Tree Pipit, Whinchat, Common Stonechat, Grasshopper Warbler, Garden Warbler, Willow Warbler, Eurasian Jay, Common Raven, Reed Bunting
36	Oban (including harbour)	Mid-Argyll	NM858300	Harbour and bay with shingle beach	Mute Swan, Mallard, Common Eider, Shag, Turnstone, Ring-billed Gull, Common Gull, Lesser Black-backed Gull, Herring Gull, Iceland Gull, Razorbill, Common Guillemot, Black Guillemot, Common Swift, Rock Pipit
37	Seil Island	Mid-Argyll	NM768175	Island south of Oban connected to mainland by roadbridge. Sea cliffs on west coast, estuarine habitat to east and north	Mute Swan, Greylag Goose, Greater Canada Goose, Common Shelduck, Eurasian Wigeon, Eurasian Teal, Mallard, Tufted Duck, Common Eider, Red-breasted Merganser, Red-throated Diver, Little Grebe, Great Cormorant, Shag, Grey Heron, Hen Harrier, Common Buzzard, Common Kestrel, Oystercatcher, Ringed Plover, Eurasian Curlew, Common Redshank, Greenshank, Common Sandpiper, gulls, Common Tern, Black Guillemot, Common Cuckoo, Tawny Owl, Long-eared Owl, Sky Lark, Sand Martin, Barn Swallow, House Martin, Grey Wagtail, Whinchat, Common Stonechat, Northern Wheatear, Grasshopper Warbler, Sedge Warbler, Common Whitethroat, Willow Warbler, Goldcrest, Common Raven, Linnet, Twite, Bullfinch, Yellowhammer, Reed Bunting

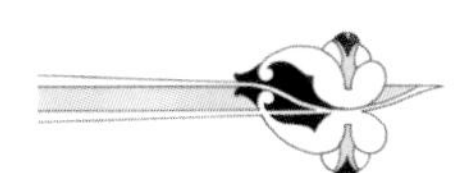

Map ref number	Location	Recording Area	Grid Reference	Habitat	Birds
38	Taynish NNR (National Nature Reserve)	Mid-Argyll	NR733845	Ancient oak woodland on a peninsula in Loch Sween	Whooper Swan, Mallard, Tufted Duck, Little Grebe, Eurasian Sparrowhawk, Common Buzzard, Common Kestrel, Woodcock, Common Sandpiper, Common Cuckoo, Common Redstart, Grasshopper Warbler, Sedge Warbler, Common Whitethroat, Garden Warbler, Blackcap, Wood Warbler, Willow Warbler, Goldcrest, Spotted Flycatcher, Long-tailed Tit, Coal Tit, Blue Tit, Great Tit, Eurasian Treecreeper, Common Chaffinch, Goldfinch, Linnet, Lesser Redpoll, Common Crossbill, Bullfinch, Reed Bunting
39	Ulva Lagoons (Loch Sween)	Mid-Argyll	NR711820	Salt-water lagoons	Mute Swan, Whooper Swan, Greenland White-fronted Goose, Greater Canada Goose, Common Shelduck, Eurasian Wigeon, Eurasian Teal, Common Buzzard, Hen Harrier, Common Kestrel, Ringed Plover, Eurasian Curlew, Common Redshank, Greenshank, Common Sandpiper, Common Stonechat, Common Raven, Reed Bunting
40	Craighouse & Small Isles Bay	Jura	NR527673	Sandy bay and off-shore islands	Shag, Hen Harrier, Buzzard, Common Kestrel, Black-headed Gull, Common Gull, Herring Gull, Common Tern, Arctic Tern, Black Guillemot, Common Raven, Starling
41	Ardnave Loch	Islay	NR283727	Freshwater loch close to the sea	Whooper Swan, Greylag Goose, Eurasian Wigeon, Eurasian Teal, Tufted Duck, Goldeneye, Red-breasted Merganser, Water Rail, Little Grebe, Hen Harrier, European Golden Plover, Black-tailed Godwit (in spring), Turnstone, Red-billed Chough, Twite, Reed Bunting
42	Ardnave Point	Islay	NR296748	Headland on west coast	Barnacle Goose, Common Scoter, Black-throated Diver, Great Northern Diver, Manx Shearwater, European Storm Petrel, Ringed Plover, Grey Plover, Sanderling, Dunlin, Whimbrel, Turnstone, Red-billed Chough, Common Raven, Twite, Snow Bunting
43	Bowmore	Islay	NR311600	Township on eastern shore of Loch Indaal	Winter :Brent Goose, Great Northern Diver, Slavonian Grebe, Whooper Swan, Greater Scaup, Common Goldeneye, Red-breasted Merganser, Purple Sandpiper, Iceland Gull
44	Bridgend	Islay	NR330622	Wide sandy bay with saltmarsh at head of Loch Indaal	Goose Roost viewpoint : Greylag Goose, Brent Goose, Common Shelduck, Eurasian Wigeon, Pintail, Greater Scaup, European Golden Plover, Dunlin, Red Knot, Bar-tailed Godwit, Greenshank, Iceland Gull
45	Bridgend Woods	Islay	NR344625	Deciduous woodland at head of Loch Indaal	Tawny Owl, Grey Wagtail, Dipper, Blackcap, Wood Warbler, Common Chiffchaff, Long-tailed Tit, Eurasian Treecreeper, Bullfinch
46	Bruichladdich	Islay	NR265613	Township on western shore of Loch Indaal	Whooper Swan, Common Scoter, divers, Ringed Plover, Purple Sandpiper, Turnstone, White Wagtail
47	Claggain Bay	Islay	NR465534	East-facing bay in east of Islay	Red-throated Diver and other divers, Common Sandpiper, Turnstone
48	Frenchman's Rocks	Islay	NR158538	West-facing sea-watching site in far south-west of Islay	Autumn passage: Brent Goose, Greater Scaup, Common Scoter, Red-throated Diver, Great Northern Diver, Sooty Shearwater, Manx Shearwater, Balearic Shearwater, European Storm Petrel, Leach's Storm-Petrel, Peregrine Falcon, Whimbrel, Grey Phalarope, Pomarine Skua, Arctic Skua, Great Skua, Sabine's Gull, Kittiwake, Arctic Tern, Black Guillemot, Rock Pipit
49	Islay Ferry (Kennacraig-Port Ellen/ Port Askaig)	Islay	NR701563	Sea crossing from Kennacraig, Kintyre, to Islay	Common Scoter, Goldeneye, Red-throated Diver, Black-throated Diver, Great Northern Diver, Fulmar, Sooty Shearwater, Manx Shearwater, Balearic Shearwater, European Storm Petrel, Leach's Storm-Petrel, Gannet, Arctic Skua, Great Skua, Kittiwake, Common Guillemot, Razorbill, Black Guillemot, Little Auk
50	Kilchoman	Islay	NR213635	Moorland and farmland close to the sea	Hen Harrier, Merlin, Peregrine Falcon, Rock Dove, Whinchat, Northern Wheatear, Red-billed Chough, Common Raven, Twite

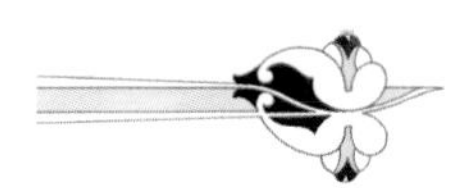

Map ref number	Location	Recording Area	Grid Reference	Habitat	Birds
51	Kilnaughton Bay	Islay	NR346454	Large bay on south side of Islay	Common Shelduck, Goldeneye, Red-breasted Merganser, Red-throated Diver, Great Northern Diver, Shag, Woodcock, Common Tern, Arctic Tern, Guillemot, Razorbill
52	Loch Ballygrant	Islay	NR405661	Freshwater surrounded by woodland	Mute Swan, Common Pochard, Tufted Duck, Little Grebe, Common Coot
53	Loch Gorm	Islay	NR232657	Large freshwater loch	Whooper Swan, Greylag Goose, Eurasian Teal, Common Pochard, Tufted Duck, Common Scoter, Common Goldeneye, Hen Harrier, Barn Owl, Grasshopper Warbler, Sedge Warbler, Twite, Reed Bunting
54	Loch Gruinart - including RSPB reserve	Islay	NR286687	Sea-loch with mud flats at low tide, saltmarsh, wetland, farmland, moorland and flooded fields nearby in winter	Whooper Swan, Greenland White-fronted Goose, Greylag Goose, Barnacle Goose, Brent Goose, Common Shelduck, Eurasian Wigeon, Gadwall, Eurasian Teal, Green-winged Teal, Pintail, Shoveler, Hen Harrier, Eurasian Sparrowhawk, Golden Eagle, Merlin, Peregrine Falcon, Water Rail, Spotted Crake, Corn Crake, Ringed Plover, European Golden Plover, Grey Plover, Northern Lapwing, Red Knot, Sanderling, Curlew Sandpiper, Dunlin, Ruff, Common Snipe, Black-tailed Godwit, Bar-tailed Godwit, Whimbrel, Eurasian Curlew, Common Redshank, Greenshank, Turnstone, gulls, Common Tern, Arctic Tern, Rock Dove, Barn Owl, Short-eared Owl, Sky Lark, Whinchat, Common Stonechat, Grasshopper Warbler, Red-billed Chough, Linnet, Twite, Yellowhammer, Reed Bunting
55	Loch Indaal	Islay	NR293614	Large sea-loch	Barnacle Goose, Brent Goose, Common Shelduck, Eurasian Wigeon, Eurasian Teal, Pintail, Greater Scaup, Common Eider, Long-tailed Duck, Common Scoter, Goldeneye, Red-breasted Merganser, Red-throated Diver, Black-throated Diver, Great Northern Diver, Slavonian Grebe, Great Cormorant, Shag, Oystercatcher, Ringed Plover, European Golden Plover, Grey Plover, Northern Lapwing, Red Knot, Dunlin, Bar-tailed Godwit, Whimbrel, Eurasian Curlew, Common Redshank, Turnstone, gulls, Common Tern, Arctic Tern, Black Guillemot, Rock Pipit
56	Oa Peninsula	Islay	NR311438	Coastal cliffs, open moorland, freshwater lochs, coastal grassland and heath	Red-throated Diver, Golden Eagle, Hen Harrier, Common Kestrel, Peregrine Falcon, Common Guillemot, Razorbill, Black Guillemot, Short-eared Owl, Grasshopper Warbler, Red-billed Chough, Snow Bunting
57	Kiloran Bay	Colonsay	NR401980	Sandy bay at the north end of Colonsay	Fulmar, Shag, Ringed Plover, Turnstone, Kittiwake, Rock Dove, Red-billed Chough
58	Oronsay	Colonsay	NR348889	Island accessible at low tide from Colonsay. RSPB reserve	Whooper Swan, Greenland White-fronted Goose, Greylag Goose, Greater Canada Goose, Barnacle Goose, Brent Goose, Common Shelduck, Eurasian Wigeon, Eurasian Teal, Mallard, Common Eider, Red-breasted Merganser, Red-throated Diver, Great Northern Diver, Great Cormorant, Shag, Grey Heron, Hen Harrier, Eurasian Sparrowhawk, Common Buzzard, Golden Eagle, Common Kestrel, Merlin, Peregrine Falcon, Corn Crake, Oystercatcher, Ringed Plover, European Golden Plover, Northern Lapwing, Dunlin, Black-tailed Godwit, Whimbrel, Common Redshank, Greenshank, Rock Dove, Sky Lark, White Wagtail, Common Stonechat, Northern Wheatear, Sedge Warbler, Red-billed Chough, Common Raven, Linnet, Twite, Lapland Bunting, Snow Bunting
59	The Strand	Colonsay	NR369902	Area of sand, mud and saltings between Colonsay and Oronsay, exposed at low tide	Greater Canada Goose, Common Eider, Common Buzzard, Oystercatcher, Ringed Plover, Dunlin, Whimbrel, Eurasian Curlew, Greenshank, Common Sandpiper, gulls

Map ref number	Location	Recording Area	Grid Reference	Habitat	Birds
60	Benmore Gardens	Cowal	NS139855	Botanical garden, with an impressive collection of conifers (with some very large trees), rhododendrons, etc.	Goosander, Common Buzzard, Peregrine, Eurasian Sparrowhawk, Tawny Owl, Woodcock, Great Spotted Woodpecker, Green Woodpecker, Grey Wagtail, Tree Pipit, Dipper, Common Redstart, Blackcap, Wood Warbler, Willow Warbler, Goldcrest, Spotted Flycatcher, Long-tailed Tit, Coal Tit, Blue Tit, Great Tit, Eurasian Treecreeper, Common Chaffinch, Lesser Redpoll, Siskin, Common Crossbill, Bullfinch
61	Firth of Clyde (Dunoon-Toward Point)	Cowal	NS154708	Road along the coast passing through various habitats, and with good views over the Clyde estuary	Common Eider, Manx Shearwater, Shag, Ringed Plover, Purple Sandpiper, Turnstone, Black Guillemot
62	Holy Loch	Cowal	NS160815	Large sea loch with extensive mud flats at low tide	Shelduck, Wigeon, Eurasian Teal, Common Goldeneye, Little Grebe, Oystercatcher, Eurasian Curlew, Common Redshank, gulls, Kingfisher
63	Loch Eck and Glenbranter Forest	Cowal	NS139921	A large freshwater loch, extensive conifer forests with some large oakwoods on the lower ground and heather and grass moorland above the trees	Mandarin Duck, Goosander, Mallard, Heron, Golden Eagle, Common Buzzard, Peregrine, Eurasian Sparrowhawk, Tawny Owl, Common Kestrel, Woodcock, Common Sandpiper, Common Cuckoo, Great Spotted Woodpecker, Grey Wagtail, Tree Pipit, Dipper, Common Redstart, Grasshopper Warbler, Common Whitethroat, Blackcap, Wood Warbler, Willow Warbler, Goldcrest, Spotted Flycatcher, Long-tailed Tit, Coal Tit, Blue Tit, Great Tit, Eurasian Treecreeper, Common Raven, Jay, Common Chaffinch, Lesser Redpoll, Siskin, Common Crossbill, Bullfinch, Reed Bunting
64	Loch Long (Ardentinny-Strone Point)	Cowal	NS189873	Sea loch with shingle shoreline	Common Eider, Common Goldeneye, Red-breasted Merganser, Red-throated Diver, Sandwich Tern, Common Swift, Magpie
65	Loch Riddon	Cowal	NS007782	Estuary and sea loch with extensive mud flats at low tide	Mute Swan, Shelduck, Wigeon, Eurasian Teal, Shelduck, Oystercatcher, Eurasian Curlew, Common Redshank, gulls
66	Otter Ferry	Cowal	NR929844	Shoreline with long sandy and rocky spit stretching out into Loch Fyne	Common Shelduck, Common Eider, Common Goldeneye, Red-breasted Merganser, Red-throated Diver, Black-throated Diver, Great Cormorant, Shag, Hen Harrier, Eurasian Sparrowhawk, Peregrine Falcon, Common Guillemot, Razorbill, Black Guillemot, Oystercatcher, Ringed Plover, Dunlin, Eurasian Curlew, Common Redshank, Common Sandpiper, Turnstone, Northern Wheatear
67		Cowal	NR975722	Coastal area with woodland (broadleaved and coniferous), golf course and unimproved wet grasslands/ peatlands	Manx Shearwater, Northern Gannet, Red-throated Diver, Hen Harrier, Golden Eagle, Common Buzzard, Sandwich Tern, Common Sandpiper, Eurasian Curlew, Snipe, Common Cuckoo, Grasshopper Warbler, Sedge Warbler, Common Whitethroat, Blackcap, Willow Warbler, Goldcrest, Spotted Flycatcher, Long-tailed Tit, Coal Tit, Blue Tit, Great Tit, Eurasian Treecreeper, Common Raven, Jay, Common Chaffinch, Goldfinch, Linnet, Lesser Redpoll, Siskin, Common Crossbill, Bullfinch, Reed Bunting
68	Campbeltown Loch	Kintyre	NR723204	Large enclosed sea loch and harbour	Little Grebe, Common Eider, Goldeneye, Red-breasted Merganser, Peregrine Falcon, Oystercatcher, Ringed Plover, Eurasian Curlew, Turnstone, Iceland Gull, Glaucous Gull, Common Tern, Black Guillemot

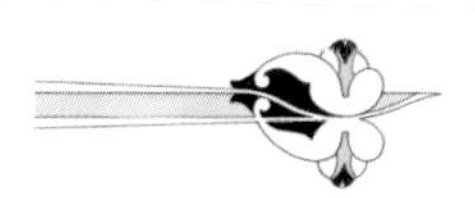

Map ref number	Location	Recording Area	Grid Reference	Habitat	Birds
69	Machrihanish SBO (Seabird Observatory) and Machrihanish Bay	Kintyre	NR628209	Bird observatory on promontory just west of Machrihanish village. To the north, Machrihanish Bay is an extensive sandy beach backed by dune systems	Whooper Swan, Greylag Goose, Brent Goose, Common Shelduck, Eurasian Wigeon, Eurasian Teal, Pintail, Greater Scaup, Common Eider, Common Scoter, Common Goldeneye, Red-throated Diver, Black-throated Diver, Great Northern Diver, Fulmar, Sooty Shearwater, Manx Shearwater, Balearic Shearwater, European Storm Petrel, Leach's Storm-Petrel, Gannet, Ringed Plover, European Golden Plover, Red Knot, Sanderling, Little Stint, Curlew Sandpiper, Dunlin, Ruff, Black-tailed Godwit, Whimbrel, Eurasian Curlew, Common Redshank, Greenshank, Common Sandpiper, Turnstone, Pomarine Skua, Arctic Skua, Great Skua, Sabine's Gull, Glaucous Gull, Kittiwake, Sandwich Tern, Common Tern, Arctic Tern, Common Guillemot, Razorbill, Little Auk, White Wagtail, Common Raven, Linnet, Twite, Snow Bunting
70	Ronachan Point	Kintyre	NR740555	Coastal viewpoint overlooking north end of Sound of Gigha and mouth of West Loch Tarbert	Common Scoter, Velvet Scoter, Shag
71	Sanda Islands	Kintyre	NR725045	Group of islands off the south coast of Kintyre with bird observatory and important seabird colonies	Common Shelduck, Mallard, Common Eider, Red-breasted Merganser, Fulmar, Manx Shearwater, European Storm Petrel, Great Cormorant, Shag, Common Buzzard, Peregrine Falcon, Oystercatcher, Ringed Plover, Whimbrel, Eurasian Curlew, Common Redshank, Greenshank, Common Sandpiper, Common Guillemot, Razorbill, Black Guillemot, Puffin, Sky Lark, White Wagtail, Wren, Common Stonechat, Northern Wheatear, Sedge Warbler, Common Whitethroat, Willow Warbler, Common Raven, Linnet, Twite, Lesser Redpoll, Reed Bunting
72	Skipness & Bay	Kintyre	NR902575	Sand and shingle bay looking across to Arran with woodland behind	Common Eider, Red-breasted Merganser, Red-throated Diver, Black-throated Diver, Great Northern Diver, Northern Gannet, Common Buzzard, Eurasian Sparrowhawk, Oystercatcher, Ringed Plover, Dunlin, Purple Sandpiper, Common Sandpiper, Turnstone, Razorbill, Black Guillemot, Common Raven
73	Sound of Gigha	Kintyre	NR673477	Stretch of sea between Kintyre and Isle of Gigha including sandy headland at Rhunahaorine Point (NR6949)	Common Shelduck, Mallard, Common Eider, Long-tailed Duck, Common Scoter, Velvet Scoter, Common Goldeneye, Red-breasted Merganser, Fulmar, Red-throated Diver, Black-throated Diver, Great Northern Diver, Slavonian Grebe
74	Tayinloan	Kintyre	NR692465	Sandy beach with meadowland behind and ferry terminal for Gigha	Mute Swan, Whooper Swan, Greenland White-fronted Goose, Greylag Goose, Barnacle Goose, Common Shelduck, Eurasian Wigeon, Eurasian Teal, Mallard, Common Eider, Long-tailed Duck, Common Scoter, Common Goldeneye, Red-breasted Merganser, Red-throated Diver, Great Northern Diver, Slavonian Grebe, Hen Harrier, Common Buzzard, Common Kestrel, Peregrine Falcon, Oystercatcher, Ringed Plover, European Golden Plover, Northern Lapwing, Red Knot, Dunlin, Common Snipe, Bar-tailed Godwit, Eurasian Curlew, Common Redshank, Turnstone, gulls, Sandwich Tern, Black Guillemot, Sky Lark, Rock Pipit, Common Stonechat, Northern Wheatear, Common Raven, Goldfinch, Twite, Reed Bunting, Snow Bunting
75	West Loch Tarbert	Kintyre	NR842663	Large sea loch with areas of tidal mud flats	Mute Swan, Whooper Swan, Common Scoter, Common Goldeneye, Red-breasted Merganser, Red-throated Diver, Black-throated Diver, Great Northern Diver, Hen Harrier, Osprey, Dunlin, Eurasian Curlew, Common Redshank, Greenshank, Black-headed Gull, Common Tern, Black Guillemot

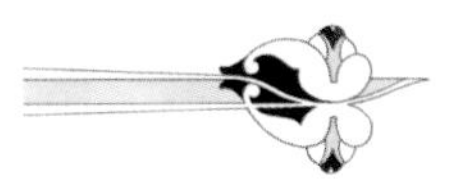

Mute Swan

Cygnus olor

This is a widespread resident, fairly common on the mainland and on Tiree, but scarcer on other large islands and not recorded from Colonsay until 1999. Traditional sites on the coast are used by flocks throughout the year, especially during moult in late summer and in decreasing numbers through autumn and winter.

This is the largest regularly breeding bird of the British Isles. The body mass of the male averages about 12kg, that of the female about 10kg, much the same as a male and female badger and over two thousand times as much as a Goldcrest. This enormous body mass has important biological implications. Take-off and landing need a runway of several tens of metres of unobstructed and reasonably calm water, affecting where swans breed as well as where they live for the rest of the year. Equally important for these herbivores is young, rapidly growing vegetation in large quantities, exposed at low tides or growing no more than neck-deep. At Loch Indaal, and probably elsewhere, besides up-ending to feed on submerged vegetation, fully-grown birds also graze on land like Whoopers (M.A. Ogilvie pers. comm.).

For much of the 19th century the Mute Swan was regarded as an edible, semi-domesticated species that was slowly spreading, both naturally and by regular introductions. Neither Graham, nor Gray nor H&B recognised it as a wild bird.

The history of the species on Tiree probably illustrates what happened over large parts of Scotland. Single birds were recorded there in 1891 and 1898 (H&B, Irby 1899). In 1908 17 arrived on Loch Bhasapol in early June and were expected to leave before winter, suggesting that then, as now, the site was used by a moult flock. In 1909 a pair nested, in 1911 a flock of 75 were on Loch Bhasapol in late July (Anderson 1911), and by 1950 the species was breeding in numbers on Tiree (mostly from B&R, who also give records from Islay, Jura, Coll and Gigha). Writing in 1953, B&R also noted that Mute Swans had increased enormously in Scotland "in recent years" and commented on the large assemblies of non-breeding birds that occurred in summer.

As in many long-lived species, non-breeders consistently outnumber breeding birds. In the Scottish surveys of 1955, 1978 and 1983, the ratio was respectively 2.5, 1.8 and 1.6 to one (Thom) and in 1990 and 2002 it was 1.3 and 1.6. In Argyll this ratio has varied between 0.15 in 1983 and 3.75 in 1955 (Table).

There were heavy losses of Mute Swans in the cold winter of 1962-63, but decreases in southern Britain in the 1970s and 1980s due to ingestion of lead weights used by anglers were less serious in Scotland. The First Atlas showed that, apart from a well-established population on the Uists and a very few squares on the north-west mainland of Scotland, Argyll forms a fairly sharp northern limit to the range of this species in western Britain. Breeding was confirmed along the coast of Cowal and North and Mid-Argyll and also on Gigha, Coll and Tiree, but not on Colonsay or on much of Kintyre and south and west Mull. There were only small changes by the time of the Second Atlas, when breeding was recorded in 25% of 10-km squares in the county, with the highest densities on Tiree, southern Jura, Holy Loch, Loch Etive and southern Mid-Argyll. Single Mute Swans recorded on

Mute Swans at the Kyles of Bute. Wintering groups like these are often surprisingly tolerant of human disturbance. *Philip Kirkham*

Oronsay on 8 May 1999 and 6 February 2001 were the first Colonsay records for over 50 years, possibly reflecting better coverage after the arrival of a resident warden (ABR).

Nests are by fresh water and along the seashore, both on the mainland and on small islands. One pair often nests by a small stream next to a busy car-park near the centre of Oban. Territories are set up early in the year and eggs are laid in April and May, although one early pair at Ardnave Loch began laying on 24 March in 1989 and 19 March in 1990 (ABR). Incubation lasts 36 days and the small young are led to the water soon after hatching. Adults and young stay on the fairly large territories all summer and, when the young grow slowly, sometimes all winter. The young of many pairs disappear while still small, presumably because of predators such as fox, otter, mink and large gulls. In the SAMS study, mostly in Mid and North Argyll, 20 pairs were monitored in late summer 2001. Ten were known to have nested, 16 had no young and four had a total of ten young (1.0 young/pair known to have nested, or 0.5 young/pair seen in late summer). Comparison of areas where mink were and were not controlled showed that mink removal gave a productivity increase of 4.8 times in 1999 and 1.3 in 2000, suggesting that mink may be having considerable effects. Annual data suggest low productivity over most of Argyll with considerable variation among years, but synthesis of such records is difficult as the dates of brood counts vary (ABR). Broods of five or more large young in autumn are uncommon.

Rapidly growing young are able to fly in late autumn and the mobile family group, usually led by the still-aggressive male, may then fly considerable distances, presumably in search of food. A colour-ringed pair that nested on an island off Fort William in May 1998 flew into Dunstaffnage Bay with four young on 31 October 1998, a distance of c.50km, but all were driven off by the male of the resident pair with young of their own. The Table shows the numbers of breeding and non-breeding swans found in Argyll during national surveys, usually in April-May. Results from areas such as Argyll are best regarded as minima; indeed, coverage of mainland Argyll in the 1990 survey was considered by the organiser to have been "a disaster" (Brown & Brown 1993), while the same authors described coverage of Argyll in 2002 as "good".

Period	Breeding birds	Non-breeding birds	Total	Source
1955-56	48	180	228	Rawcliffe 1958
1978	80	106	186	Ogilvie 1981
1983	124	18	142	Brown & Brown 1985
1985	70	63	133	Stroud & Newton 1986
1988-89			135	ABR:6
1990	90 (+46[1])	80 (+12[1])	170 (+58[1])	Brown & Brown 1993
2002	54	109	163	Brown & Brown 2005

[1]Additional estimates to compensate for incomplete coverage.

Numbers of Mute Swans in Argyll, 1955-2002.

Some pairs stay on their breeding territories all year, while others undertake a usually short migration in mid to late summer to traditional moult sites. Smaller numbers remain at these sites through winter, and immature and non-breeding birds are found there throughout the year, so that overall there is little change between summer and winter distributions.

As in other wildfowl, all the flight feathers are moulted together (rather than sequentially as in most birds). Individuals are flightless for *c.*6-8 weeks, although birds may be found in this condition from late May to October (Migration Atlas). The numbers at these gatherings in Argyll do not approach the several hundred-strong assemblies found elsewhere in Scotland (detailed by Thom). The largest moult flock in Argyll is on Tiree (50-70 birds), mostly on fresh water, especially Loch a' Phuill. Other moult and wintering sites in the county are coastal, such as Lochs Craignish, Gilp, Etive, Sween and elsewhere.

Newton & Newton (1991) found the species fairly widespread in winter in Argyll and counted maxima of 174 in September 1988 and 146 in October 1989. Swans were usually in small flocks, rarely more than 30 birds, at 25 sites of the 34 that were counted monthly. Winter maxima of more than ten birds occurred at ten sites (the head of West Loch Tarbert, Holy Loch, Keills Peninsula, Lochs Craignish, Crinan, Feochan, Don, Etive, Laich and Loch a' Phuill). Counts at most sites decreased in late winter as pairs moved to breeding territories. More recent counts reported annually in ABR confirm this decrease during winter, counts at all sites being smaller in the first half of the year than in the second. The survey of mid-January 2000 found at least 149 birds in the county (ABR). Besides showing little change since 1988-1989 (above), these winter counts are similar to those in the breeding season (Table), suggesting that most birds are included. As in late summer, the largest winter numbers are on Tiree, typically 40-70 birds, although 100 with three juveniles were recorded there in September 1987. Other important areas include Loch Craignish (20-50 birds) and Outer Loch Etive (10-35). Maxima in lower double-figures are counted regularly at 15 other sites on the mainland and several sites on Mull, Jura and Islay. Regular feeding by humans probably caused growth of the well-counted flock in Oban Bay, where winter maxima increased from 15 in 1988 to 60 or more in 2001, 2002 and 2003 (ABR).

Ringing has shown that established pairs are sedentary but younger birds may move longer distances, often to or between distant flocks. The following, mostly ringed as cygnets and recovered in their first few years, show this well. Nine ringed in the Uists were found in Argyll (five of them on Tiree), and two cygnets ringed at Oban in September 1987 were found dead below overhead wires in South Uist on 19 November that year. Swans ringed near Oban were found on the Firth of Forth (five), in the Solway Firth area (three), Lochwinnoch (one) and Tiree (one). Three ringed as cygnets in the Firth of Forth area were recovered in Argyll, including the most distant of all 182 ring recoveries involving Argyll, 228 km from Lothian to Islay. Sixty birds were recovered 2-6 years after ringing, eight at 6-7 yrs, three at 7-8 yrs, seven at 8-9 yrs, six at 9-10 yrs, five at 10-11 yrs, two at 11-12 yrs and four at 12-13 yrs. Fifty-five were seen or released when alive; and of 127 found dead, 16 hit overhead wires, two hit buildings and one was shot.

More detailed histories shown by colour-ringing include, as well as the example already quoted, one ringed at Ardfern on 16 November 1995 and seen in Ayr on 24 January 1996. The most revealing was the history of FJ8, the only Argyll bird found outside Scotland. Ringed as a cygnet on South Uist in October 1978, it appeared 210 km to the southeast in West Loch Tarbert (Kintyre) from July to November 1979. It was seen regularly in Ulster from April 1980 to April 1982 before being recorded at the south end of Gigha in June 1985 (ABR).

Clive Craik

Bewick's Swan

Cygnus columbianus

Rare autumn and spring migrant. Once a common winter visitor, especially to Tiree.

The Bewick's Swan of the race *bewickii* is a high-Arctic breeder that winters mainly in the Netherlands, England and southern Ireland. According to H&B, this species was not rare on the west coast and islands of Argyll, especially Tiree. Gray gives a record of two shot at Barnashalag [probably meaning Barnashaig], Argyllshire, in February 1871. B&R, whilst regarding it as rare in mainland Argyll, referred to its past abundance on Tiree, where about two hundred were recorded in 1899 and "crowds" in November 1908, with several hundred birds also reported more recently by Seton Gordon. B&R also mentioned records from Mull, Jura and Islay, where a flock of 98 was present on 6 December 1903. There are also some pre-1935 records from Colonsay (Jardine *et al.* 1986).

During the first half of the 20th century, Bewick's Swans became very much scarcer in the Inner and Outer Hebrides (B&R, Thom). Although this species shows high site-fidelity, it is known to respond rapidly to new feeding or roosting opportunities, and there are many examples of major shifts in concentrations throughout the wintering range. Such shifts can happen over periods of just a few years and can lead to almost complete abandonment of traditional wintering sites, as has happened in Northern Ireland in recent years (J. Bowler pers. comm.).

As a result of such behaviour, the Bewick's Swan has become a rare visitor to Argyll. There were four published records in the 1960s, nine or more in the 1970s, five in the 1980s, and ten in the 1990s. With the exception of three adults at Ardnave Loch on Islay on 13 November 2003, the most recent record dates back to 1996, and the most recent double-figure count was of 14 birds flying south over Islay on 24 October 1976 (SB 10:89). Over-wintering was last recorded in 1990/91, on Islay; all records since then concern birds present briefly in autumn (October-November) or spring (April-May). Interestingly, all but four of the records from 1970 to 2003 came from Islay or Kintyre. The exceptions were one at the River Ruel in Cowal on 10 January 1971 (SB 7:125), one on Tiree in April 1971 (Ogilvie & Atkinson-Willes 1983), four at Loch Shira in Mid-Argyll on 11 December 1984 (SBR 1984:15, ABR 2:10), and two at Loch Fada on Colonsay on 3 May 1991 (SBR 1991:12, ABR 8:27).

A swan seen at Loch an Eilein on Tiree on 6 December 1989 appeared to be a hybrid Whooper x Bewick's (ABR 6:15).

Tristan ap Rheinallt

Bewick's Swan. Its distinctive bill pattern separates this species from the Whooper Swan. *David Palmar*

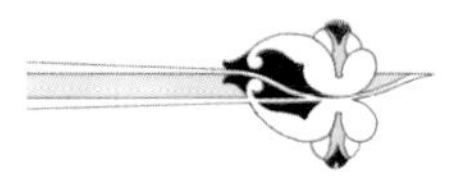

Whooper Swan

Cygnus cygnus

A common passage migrant with smaller numbers wintering. Loch a' Phuill on Tiree is a site of national importance for wintering birds. A few birds summer in the county in most years and breeding has been recorded.

Although the Whooper Swan breeds throughout northern Eurasia, nearly all those wintering in Britain and Ireland are believed to belong to the Icelandic breeding population. Seven birds ringed in Iceland have been recovered in Argyll over the years, and neck-collared or leg-ringed swans from Iceland are also regularly seen on Tiree.

Both Gray and Graham recorded the species as a visitor to Iona and Mull, the latter author looking back to a time in the first half of the 18th century when they were abundant and occurred in large flocks. Gray also stated that Whooper Swans were found in small flocks on Islay every winter, being much more numerous in hard weather. H&B gave more detailed information on its status, emphasising the importance of Tiree as a wintering location, with more than 140 birds being recorded there in the winter of 1891/92. However, their comments suggest that Whooper and Bewick's Swans may not always have been reliably distinguished by early naturalists.

According to H&B, Whooper Swans preferred the islands to the Argyll mainland, although swans were seen on wintering on Tiree may have increased in the 19th century, since the NSA merely stated that "a few swans occasionally frequent the lakes [of Tiree and Coll] in winter." A substantial increase on Tiree between the end of the 19th century and the middle of the 20th was noted by B&R, who contrasted this with an apparent decrease on Mull and Iona.

The first birds of the autumn can arrive in Argyll as early as the beginning of September, though widespread arrival is not usually recorded until around the second week of October or later. The first small flocks are usually seen on the islands, but this is not always the case and it appears that migration takes place across a broad front. Satellite tracking has shown that some birds fly directly from Iceland to Ireland, and direct flights to Argyll presumably also take place, though some individuals may make landfall further north in Scotland and continue overland. The sea crossing, a minimum of 800 km, can take as little as 12 hours, though adverse weather can increase this significantly (Migration Atlas).

According to B&R, Tiree and Islay were the species' main strongholds in the Inner Hebrides. This is still true, though only small numbers are usually present on Islay in midwinter. Numbers on both islands generally peak in October or November and, although some flocks remain only briefly, others appear to stay for several weeks, often feeding in stubble fields. Feeding in agricultural fields is a habit that apparently began in the 1960s (Migration Atlas). Peak counts of 100-200 birds are typical for Islay and Tiree in autumn, but totals passing through are clearly much higher. For example, nearly

Whooper Swans are a distinctive part of the winter scene in Argyll, especially on Islay and Tiree. *Philip Kirkham*

the major mainland sea lochs in unusually hard winters. This association with severe weather echoes comments made about certain mainland parishes in the OSA and NSA. Numbers

500 swans were estimated to have been seen at Loch Gruinart between 12 and 29 October 1989.

Away from these two islands, Whooper Swans are regular

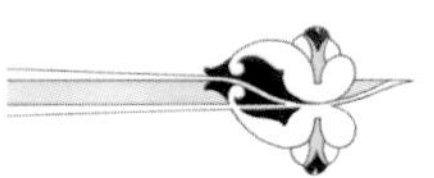

autumn visitors to Mull, Colonsay and Oronsay, though counts on these islands rarely exceed 50 birds. There are few records from Coll and even fewer from Jura. On the mainland, by far the largest numbers are recorded in Kintyre, with The Laggan holding a flock of more than 100 in some autumns. Elsewhere, birds can be found on scattered coastal and inland lochs throughout the mainland, though such flocks rarely contain more than 40 individuals. Generally speaking, most migrants have moved on by the end of November. In some years, numbers on Islay remain high into December, although this is perhaps less true now than it was in the 1980s. Only on Tiree do numbers remain high throughout the winter (Figure). In recent years, up to around 100 have been recorded on the island during December, January and February, though the total is not always so high. This represents around two per cent of the British wintering population of some 5,000 birds. Elsewhere in Argyll, numbers at this time of year are very much lower. In December 1998, for example, up to 129 were present on Tiree but no other site in Argyll produced a count of more than 16 birds. There appears to be no recent evidence of significant immigration during cold weather in midwinter.

Satellite tracking has shown that some of the birds migrating through Argyll go to the Solway Firth, a major wintering area. Ringing recoveries and sightings of marked birds show that wintering Whooper Swans from Northern Ireland, Lancashire and the Ouse Washes (Cambridgeshire) also use Argyll as a staging post on their southward or northward journeys.

There is usually a significant return migration between mid-March and mid-April although, as in autumn, its timing, duration and intensity vary from year to year. This movement may be concentrated within just a few days, with flocks present only briefly. Often, they are recorded flying overhead in a northerly or north-westerly direction. As in autumn, migration obviously takes place across a broad front, with frequent records from the mainland. The highest numbers are usually on Tiree, where spring counts of 100 or more are not unusual, with a particularly high total of 263 on three lochs on 24 March 1998. Elsewhere, flocks typically total 30 or fewer. A few late birds remain into May, particularly on Tiree, though as the month wears on it becomes difficult to distinguish late migrants from birds that will stay the summer.

Summering Whooper Swans are not infrequently reported in Argyll, mostly on Tiree and Islay but sometimes on Mull, Colonsay and the mainland. It has long been realised that some are injured and unable to migrate. H&B, for example, describe one that summered on Tiree in 1879. Breeding records are unusual, however. In 1978 and 1979 a pair reared three and two cygnets respectively on Tiree (Thom). Only two to five pairs are thought to breed in Britain each year, some of these probably being feral (Second Atlas).

Tristan ap Rheinallt

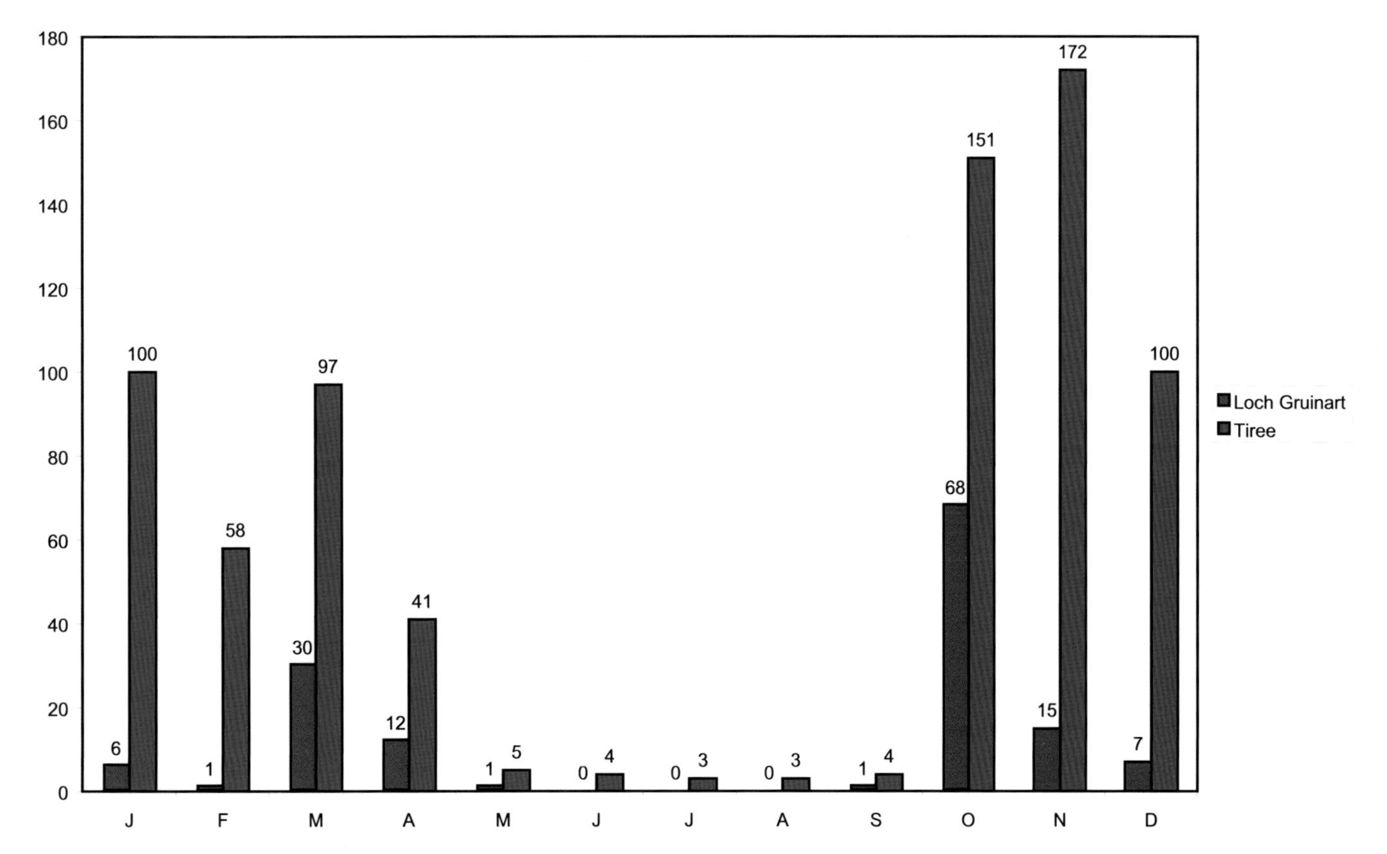

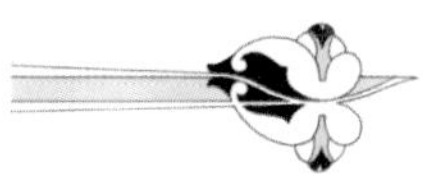

Bean Goose

Anser fabalis

This species is now a vagrant which has occurred in small numbers (1-18) in six winters since 1981-2. All but one of the identified birds were of the race *A. f. fabalis*.

In the 19th century, this was apparently the commonest 'grey' goose over much of Scotland, but there is known to have been confusion with both the Pink-footed and, especially, the Greylag Goose. There is also the problem that it is relatively easy to misidentify lone first-winter Greenland White-fronted Geese as Bean Geese. Gray was informed by an Islay resident that the species was not uncommon in parts of the island, but did not arrive until January or February, and that the flocks were not large and the birds were very wary. Graham said that it frequented the islands of Iona and Mull in winter, but, as H&B pointed out, Graham's illustration of a Bean Goose was in fact of a Greylag, which he does not include as present on Mull. B&R reported that the species was occasionally recorded in Argyll in winter and on passage.

In recent times, there have been just nine records of the species in Argyll, as follows: 30 March 1962 a flock of 30 on Islay, of which five were the last seen on 7 April; 14 November 1981 a flock of 13 on Islay, which stayed about four days, coinciding with a small influx of birds into Scotland at that time; 17 March 1982 a single bird on Islay; 18 October 1985 two on Islay; 20 October 1993 one with two Pinkfeet at The Laggan, Kintyre; 4 October 2002 two (race undetermined) flew south off Craignish Point; 28 October 2003 five, usually with Greenland Whitefronts on Islay stayed to at least 15 February 2004; 27 March 2004 six at Arinagour, Coll; 20 March 2004 one on Oronsay (race *rossicus*) stayed until 4 June 2004.

The Bean Goose is a vagrant to Argyll. *David Palmar*

Malcolm Ogilvie

Pink-footed Goose

Anser brachyrhynchus

A passage migrant, especially in autumn. A very small number winter.

Confusion with other 'grey' geese, especially Bean and Greylag, means that published comments on their status in earlier times cannot always be relied on. Thus, Graham described the species as "by no means a rare one" on Iona and Mull, but "the general colour of the grey geese is so similar that you cannot tell one kind from another at a distance". Neither Gray nor H&B had anything to add, while B&R reported that it was a regular winter visitor to Islay and that it was said to be fairly common there, though they gave no numbers. They repeat Graham's comment that it was by no means rare on Iona and Mull, and comment that this was still its status on those islands. They publish just one record in full, of a "small flock" on The Laggan, near Campbeltown, on 22 January 1933, describing it as an unusual occurrence.

The autumn passage of Pinkfeet, from their Iceland breeding grounds to their winter quarters in Scotland and England, begins in mid-September and lasts into October. The great majority of the population heads for north-eastern and eastern Scotland, but small numbers regularly come down the west side of the country and are seen passing over, and occasionally landing, on islands such as Islay, Mull and Tiree, and on the mainland. Flocks are mostly fairly small, under 100, with a maximum of just over 300. Of the flocks that do land, it is rare for them to stay for more than a day or two, or even just an hour or two, before moving on. Considering the total Icelandic Pink-footed Goose population has increased from 100,000 to over 250,000 in the last 20 years, it is perhaps surprising that the numbers visiting Argyll are so small and have shown little change over the same period. The small numbers of wintering birds are often in flocks of other goose species. Scattered singles and groups of two to five, rarely more, are seen every winter on Islay (with a usual island total of up to ten), and also in small numbers on Tiree and Kintyre, occasionally elsewhere. Spring passage is much smaller than in autumn, with no reports in some years and small flocks, maximum 30, seen in others over-flying, usually above one of the islands.

Malcolm Ogilvie

Flocks of Pink-footed Geese occur regularly on Islay in Autumn. *Philip Kirkham*

White-fronted Goose

Anser albifrons

The Greenland race *A. a. flavirostris* winters in a small number of traditional haunts, and is also a passage migrant. The European race *A. a. albifrons* is a vagrant.

Greenland race

The Greenland subspecies of this goose was only described in 1948, but there is no reason to doubt that this has always been the wintering Whitefront of Argyll. With the proviso that identification of 'grey' geese was not always accurate in past times, the Whitefront has long been regarded as a regular wintering species in Argyll. Gray called Islay its headquarters, and quotes from his main source of information on the island, Mr H. Elwes. The latter was clearly a careful observer and it is fascinating to read comments about the species that are still true today: they usually arrived in the first week of October and stayed until the second week of April; they were in smaller flocks than other geese "from three or four to one hundred or more"; were not difficult to approach by a good stalker when on the fields; they preferred marshy places, though came onto stubble and grass fields later in the season; and they showed "a great partiality for particular fields". Gray describes the goose as only a straggler elsewhere, a statement confirmed by Graham who reports a single bird being shot on Iona. H&B mention an arrival on Tiree in October 1887, though with the unlikely comment, from the observer they quote, that all the first arrivals were young ones, whereas geese travel in family parties and adult and young Whitefronts are among the easiest species to tell apart. In 1889, the goose was described as common on Tiree, with some very early arrivals, 21 September, compared to the usual first week of October. They were said to remain all winter and depart in March, while another observer commented that they stayed until the end of April.

Berry (1939) says that Whitefronts on Islay had "increased enormously" and that they had supplanted the Greylag, though it has to be said that this supposition seems somewhat unlikely today, especially as the two species occur apparently harmoniously in the same localities on Kintyre. B&R had little to add to the above authors, except to say that the species was common and numerous on Tiree in 1898, but had decreased again by 1950.

In the last *c.*50 years, there have been 13 or 14 known regular haunts of the Greenland White-fronted Goose in Argyll. They have been described by Ruttledge & Ogilvie (1979) and Fox *et al.* (1994) and are shown in the Table together with counts over three periods since 1955.

The current world population of Greenland White-fronted Geese is about 26,500. In nature conservation terms, the numbers wintering in Argyll (particularly Islay) are therefore of global significance. Unfortunately, they show a strong preference for feeding on improved grassland, a critical economic asset to Argyll's farmers. Large numbers of geese can cause real economic damage, both by trampling and by delaying growth of the grass in early spring. In the 1980s, the need to fulfil the UK's nature conservation obligations, while protecting farmers' livelihoods, led to intense and at times acrimonious debates between conservation and agriculture. Today, farmers and ecologists actively participate in goose management schemes which aim to achieve both objectives. Separate schemes are in place for Islay, also covering Barnacle Geese (q.v.), and for Kintyre, resulting in direct payments to

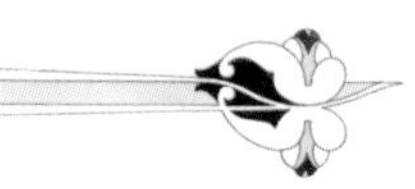

farmers in these areas of £636,000 and £73,000 respectively in 2003/04 (Madsen *et al.* 1999, Anon 2005a, b).

In autumn, Greenland Whitefronts migrate from their West Greenland breeding grounds to Iceland where they spend most of September, before completing their migration to Scotland and Ireland. The first arrivals are in the very last few days of September, but more usually in the first or second

Internationally important numbers of Greenland White-fronted Geese winter in Argyll. *Philip Kirkham*

week of October, with continuing migration until the end of the month. Precise timing of movement is dependent on weather conditions, the largest movements taking place when northerly weather reaches Iceland, producing snow and frost on the feeding grounds but providing a helpful north wind to aid them on their journey south. Birds are seen passing over some of their regular Argyll wintering haunts, while others, as shown by ringing and individual colour-marking, may pause for a few days or a week or two, before continuing to haunts in Ireland. Ringing has shown a very strong degree of site-faithfulness with some individuals only ever being seen in the same small area of farmland (with a radius of 1-2 km) in up to 20 successive years. Other birds are more peripatetic and there are a number of records of birds wintering in Ireland for one or more years then switching to Islay.

Return migration normally takes place from early to mid-April and may continue to the end of the month. Exact timing depends to an extent on the weather conditions with the birds leaving early in southerly winds and delaying movement if the wind is northerly.

Away from the regular haunts, the Greenland Whitefront can best be described as a straggler, turning up occasionally in unusual places on the mainland.

A small, feral, breeding population occurs on the southern end of the Rinns peninsula, Islay, escapes from a captive waterfowl collection established in the 1970s and 1980s, though since dispersed. Up to six pairs are present, with no more than three to five young being seen each year. There is a wintering flock of Greenland birds in the area which may attract away some of the young birds, as the feral flock has not changed significantly in size in the last 15-20 years.

Numbers of Greenland White-fronted Geese wintering in Argyll, 1955-2005. nc = no counts.

Site	1955-1979	1982-1994	1995-2005
Tiree	150-200	900-1,100	1,000-1,300
Coll	c.50	600-850	500-1,000
Benderloch Peninsula and Lismore Island	50-100	100-300	250-450
Ross of Mull (2 sites)	nc	50-80	40-50
Colonsay and Oronsay	10-25	100-250	80-200
Islay	3-4,000	3,500-11,000	8,000-13,000
Lowlandman's Bay, Jura	c.50	20-40	0-40
Loch a'Chnuic Bhric, Jura	c.25	100-120	80-120
Keills and Danna	nc	250-350	250-400
Moine Mhor	nc	25-60	20-40
Clachan, Kintyre	nc	100	0-230
Rhunahaorine	500-600	900-1,500	800-1,500
Machrihanish, Kintyre	350-450	1,000-1,200	800-1,400

Notes to the table:

1. Numbers increased steadily from the early 1980s, when the goose was given protection in both Scotland and Ireland, until about 2000-2001. Since then, the population has gone into decline, partly because of a run of poor breeding seasons and partly, and perhaps linked, to changes taking place on the breeding grounds. Thus, the higher total in the final column refers to about the middle of the ten-year period.

2. The site 'Benderloch Peninsula and Lismore Island' have been counted separately in the last few years, with the birds on the Benderloch Peninsula also visiting Eriska. Recent counts have suggested up to 250 on Lismore and 150 on Benderloch/Eriska.

3. The site 'Loch a'Chnuic Bhric, Jura' is known to hold birds that roost on Islay, but they are not normally included in the Islay count unless, as does happen, they have not bothered to fly across the Sound on a count day.

4. The site 'Lowlandman's Bay, Jura' appears to have become abandoned in recent years, the last count being of nine birds in winter 2002-3.

5. Birds that feed around Rhunahaorine during the day normally roost on hill lochs in central Kintyre.

European race

The following are all known records:

One, shot in snowstorm, Islay, January 1955.

Flock of 40, near Bridgend, Islay 26 March 1962 and 42, same area, 7 April the same year.

Flock of 20, Bridgend, February 1972.

Adult, Octovullin, Islay, 11-15 March 1986, paired to Lesser White-fronted Goose.

Malcolm Ogilvie

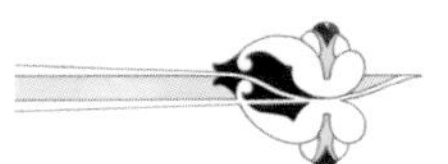

Lesser White-fronted Goose

Anser erythropus

Vagrant.

Most of the 12 apparently wild Lesser White-fronted Geese recorded in Scotland have been in Dumfries & Galloway. However, this declining species, whose nearest breeding grounds are in northern Scandinavia, has twice been recorded in Argyll, both on Islay. One was seen at Bridgend on 15 March 1980 (BB 74:459), and another was at Loch Skerrols from 11 to 15 March 1986 (BB 81:545). The former accompanied two dark-bellied Brent Geese, while the latter was paired with a European White-fronted Goose (Elliott 1989). Both these species, whose breeding distribution overlaps with that of the Lesser White-fronted Goose in northern Russia, are relatively rare in Argyll.

Tristan ap Rheinallt

Greylag Goose

Anser anser

Resident and increasing breeder. Small numbers of migrants pass through, some staying to winter.

As with the Bean and the Pink-footed Goose, early accounts of Greylag Geese in Argyll are subject to caution because of identification confusions. Gray says he was told that small flocks were found in various parts of Islay during the winter, arriving after the more numerous Whitefronts and departing about the middle of April. Graham writes about 'wild geese', by which, it can be assumed, he means Greylags, but he elsewhere makes the point that the grey geese are very difficult to tell apart. At any rate, he describes the small isles near Staffa, presumably the Treshnish, as being the winter home of large numbers, in company with Barnacle Geese. He had no reports of them in the summer.

H&B include a number of interesting observations beginning with a quote from the 1791 Statistical Account, that "wild geese hatch around Lismore, Argyle". At the time they were writing, they thought it was uncommon and rarely seen to land anywhere along the coastline, but more often observed flying over in small flocks. They report that it was a rare visitor to Tiree and that it had bred both on Colonsay and Islay. On the latter island, they say that the last taken nest was in 1825.

B&R state that "about 70 years ago" (so in the late 19th century), a considerable number wintered on Islay. It is difficult to know whether this is their interpretation of Gray or the result of new information. They go on to say that they subsequently decreased with only a few now wintering. Their only other report from Argyll is that the species wintered fairly commonly on Coll.

The Greylag is now a common breeding species on some of the islands, especially Tiree and Coll, and to a lesser extent Colonsay, Islay and Jura, while small numbers of pairs are now appearing on the mainland coast of Argyll. The first breeding on Coll and Tiree was reported to have taken place prior to 1932 (Boyd 1958), but it subsequently occurred only irregularly on either island until probably sometime in the 1960s or 1970s. The first survey of breeding waterfowl on the islands took place in 1987, when there were an estimated 20 pairs of Greylags on Tiree, together with 20-40 non-breeding birds in April, and 30 breeding pairs on Coll, with a similar number of non-breeders (Stroud 1989). Estimates on Tiree during 1998-2005 were in the range 200-300 pairs, peaking at 317 pairs in 2001. There were *c.*60 pairs on Coll in 2004 and 20 on Gunna in 2001. These are all minima.

Madders (1992) gives annual winter counts from 1981 to 1991 on Coll and Tiree, showing the start of a rapid and sustained increase in this period, notably on Tiree (from 57 to 1,198 birds). By November 1995, there were nearly 2,000 birds (1,451 Tiree, 428 Coll), and in December 2001, just over 4,000 birds (3,674 Tiree, 334 Coll), with virtually all, as far as is known, belonging to the resident breeding population. Ringing has shown this increase stems originally from the native west of Scotland population of Greylags, which has its headquarters on the Uists.

On Colonsay, there is an old breeding record, but in modern times breeding commenced in 1986 with three pairs nesting. Since then, numbers have increased to some tens of pairs, which favour the many skerries and islets around the Strand and Oronsay (Jardine 2002). In 2006, 30 broods with 115 young were counted on Colonsay itself. On Islay, too, breeding apparently took place in the 19th century, but the next breeding would appear to be by two pairs in 1997. They were on a freshwater loch, but over the next few years they spread out to breed on wet flushes in moorland and, in particular, on islets off the north and south-east coasts. The present population (2005) is certainly 50 pairs and could be more.

When regular winter counts of geese in Scotland began in the 1950s and early 1960s, there were four Argyll localities holding Greylags, Moine Mhor/Crinan Moss, Islay, and Rhunahaorine and Machrihanish on Kintyre. An average 120 were present at Moine Mhor in the 1950s and 1960s, but they increased through the 1970s to levels of 4-500 by the 1980s, which have been maintained, though with some fluctuations, ever since. Small numbers started nesting on islands off the mainland coast in 1995, increasing to 21 pairs on 11 islands in 2002 (Craik 2002a) and 46 pairs on 23 islands by 2005 (Argyll Database). From being very scarce on Islay in the 1930s and 1940s, a wintering flock built up from about the mid-1950s, with up to 500 by the early 1960s, peaking at 665 in November 1964, before a rapid decline which saw only 2-

Numbers of breeding Greylag Geese continue to increase on Argyll's islands and mainland coast. *Philip Kirkham*

300 in the late 1960s and early 1970s, and no more than 100 through the 1980s (Ogilvie 1992c) and barely that until the late 1990s, when a slow increase recommenced, associated with the establishment of a breeding population. There are now close to 200 wintering on the island again, most, though not quite all, local breeding birds. However, two different birds wearing neck collars put on birds of the Icelandic population in the Moray Firth, have been seen on Islay in recent years. The origin of the Islay Greylags that wintered in the 1950s to 1970s has never been explained. The increase took place at the same time as it did on Kintyre and Bute, which undoubtedly hold birds from the Icelandic breeding population, which winters almost entirely within Scotland, but those other sites, as well as the total population, continued to increase as Islay was declining. The alternative, that they were birds from the resident population of the Western Isles, is a possibility, but no more than that.

The two wintering flocks on Kintyre increased from low numbers, less than 50, in the 1950s and 1960s, to 300-500 in each by the 1980s and have continued at roughly this level to the present time. Elsewhere in Argyll, wintering Greylags were always fairly uncommon until the great increase in breeding on Tiree and Coll, leading to wintering totals of up to 3,000 on the former island and up to 1,000 on the latter. Numbers wintering on Colonsay, too, have increased, to around 200 (Jardine 2002). Birds spreading from these islands are now breeding in small numbers along the mainland coast.

Compared with the migratory Icelandic population, the native Greylag is relatively uncommon: numbers in Scotland increased from around 10,000 birds in 2000 to about 15,000 in 2004. The numbers resident on Coll and Tiree represent about 37% of this total, and are now the subject of a management scheme which seeks to address the twinned issues of nature conservation and agricultural damage caused by geese. This is a separate scheme to those operated in Islay and in Kintyre for Greenland White-fronted and Greenland Barnacle Geese.

Malcolm Ogilvie

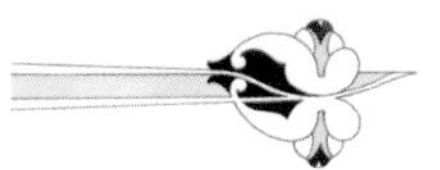

Snow Goose

Anser caerulescens

A small population, derived from escaped birds, breeds on Mull and Coll. This species is also a winter vagrant from North America, mainly to Islay.

A small resident breeding population, containing both white and blue phase birds, has become established on north-west Mull and on Coll since the 1950s-1960s (exact date unknown), when birds in a waterfowl collection at Treshnish Point were allowed to go full-winged. By the early 1970s, the population had increased to 40-50, rarely more, at which level it has remained ever since, with the highest count being of 57 on Mull in January 1981. Initially, all breeding is thought to have taken place in and around the collection area on Mull, with the birds often being seen in winter on Coll. The first known breeding on Coll took place in 1985 (but could have occurred in earlier years), and since then there seems to have been a shift of most, perhaps all, of the breeding pairs to that island. Counts of breeding pairs and young have been infrequent, with recent totals from Coll of five pairs rearing at least 16 young in 1997, four young reared in 1998, nine pairs raising at least 28 young in 2000, and 24 adults and ten young present in 2002. Catches of flightless birds took place on Coll in 1998 (seven birds) and 2002 (34 birds, including six retraps). The distribution of colour-phases of the 24 adults caught in 2002 was six white and nine blue males and seven white and two blue females. The failure of this apparently self-sustaining population to increase in the last 30+ years suggests relatively high mortality or else emigration, though there is no evidence for the latter. There have been no records from the Mull breeding area since 1993 (Argyll Database).

Snow Geese have been quite regularly recorded as vagrants with flocks of wintering Barnacle or Greenland White-fronted Geese, mostly on Islay (Table). Occasional records, mainly summer and autumn, of single birds in North Argyll, are assumed to be from the Mull/Coll population and are not included. The probability is that most, if not all, birds in the Table are genuine transatlantic vagrants, especially those wintering with Greenland Whitefronts, as Snow Geese have increased within the breeding range of the former species in West Greenland in the last 10-20 years.

Malcolm Ogilvie

Records of vagrant Snow Geese in Argyll, excluding feral birds on Mull and Coll.

Winter	Count	Locality	Comments
1927-28	3	Islay	With Barnacle Geese
1928-29	2	Islay	With Barnacle Geese
1931-32	3	Islay	With Barnacle Geese
1933-34	2	Islay	-
1971-72	1	Islay	-
1973-74	1	Islay	Juvenile seen on one day only
1974-75	1	Islay	With Whitefronts
1975-76	1	Islay	Same bird as previous winter
1976-77	1	Islay	Same bird as previous winter
1977-78	1	Islay	Same bird as previous winter
1978-79	1	Islay	Same bird as previous winter
1983-84	2	Islay	With Whitefronts
1983-84	1	Crinan Moss	With Whitefronts
1986-87	1	Islay	For a single day
1987-88	2	Islay	With Barnacle Geese
1988-89	2	Islay	With Barnacle Geese
1993-94	1	Islay	With Whitefronts
1994-95	1	Islay	Same bird as previous winter
1995-96	1	Islay	Same bird as previous winter
1995-96	2	Islay	Present for one day in November
1995-96	3	Islay	Present January
1995-96	3	The Laggan, Kintyre	Present February to April and assumed same 3 as on Islay
1996-97	1	Islay	Same bird as previous winter
1997-98	1	Tiree	October-December, with Whitefronts
1998-99	1	Tiree	With Whitefront to 7 February
1998-99	1	Islay	With Whitefronts from 9 March, presumed Tiree bird
1999-2000	1	Tiree	With Whitefronts
2000-01	1	Islay	With Whitefronts
2000-01	1	Tiree	With Whitefronts
2001-02	1	Islay	With Whitefronts
2002-03	1	Islay	With Whitefronts

Bill Allan found this Snow Goose feeding with Greylag Geese near Ardfern in January 2007. *Jim Dickson*

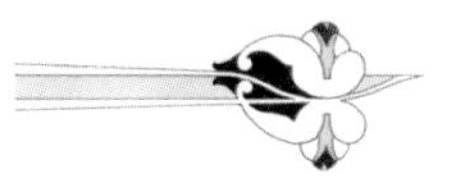

Greater Canada Goose

Branta canadensis

Greater Canada Goose *B. canadensis*: this long-time introduced resident on Colonsay has recently colonised parts of the Argyll mainland coast. These birds all appear to be of the nominate race *canadensis*, introduced to Britain in the 17th century.

Lesser Canada Goose *B. hutchinsii*: a few birds of smaller appearance occur annually on Islay and occasionally elsewhere. They have been ascribed to several different races, most if not all of which belong to this species.

Greater Canada Goose

The first record for Argyll appears to be one that was shot on Tiree some time before 1913. Another was shot in Kintyre in October 1932. Nothing appears to be known about their size or whether or not they were with other geese of their own or another kind (B&R). In 1934, the gamekeeper on Colonsay, at the request of his laird, introduced two pinioned pairs of the nominate race to the island. The aim appeared mainly to improve the sport available to visiting shooting parties, both by adding another sporting quarry and in the hope that the Canada Geese would attract passing flocks of geese on their way to Islay or Ireland to land there and stay. By 1968, the population had increased to 65, since when it has been

Canada Geese: still increasing in Argyll. *David Wood*

above 100 and back down again to 80-90 in 2005. The recent decline can be attributed to control by local people. The birds have spread out to breed quite widely round the island, including on coastal moorland whence they lead their young to freshwaters or the sea. In the late summer of recent years, the bulk of the population has moved to Oronsay to feed on the arable fields of the RSPB's reserve there where an abundance of grain is made available.

Breeding on small islands close to the Argyll mainland coast was first recorded in 1995. A recent rapid increase there has led to the establishment of many scattered pairs and several small colonies, some of ten pairs or more. This has resulted in a new phenomenon in mainland sealochs – the unfamiliar sight of large flocks of adult and young Canada Geese in late summer, for example, a single flock of 115 birds, including about 15-20 broods, in Loch Melfort on 24 June 2006, and 269 in Loch Crinan on 7 August 2006. There were at least 32 pairs on 15 islands by 2002 (Craik 2002a) and 57 pairs on 28 islands by 2005 (Craik, pers. comm.). All these birds probably stem either from Colonsay, or from the long-established colony of some 50 pairs or more on Eilean Balnagowan, just outside the Argyll recording area in Loch Linnhe, where a moult flock of 245 flightless adults was swimming within Argyll on 2 July 2006 (Craik, pers. comm.).

Most of the birds breeding on the mainland coast disappear in July and do not appear again at breeding sites until February or March, when they immediately display and compete for territories on small islands. Flocks of up to 100 occur in winter, feeding in coastal fields in North Argyll and Mid-Argyll. On Coll and Tiree, Canada Geese are absent in the breeding season and rare vagrants in winter.

Lesser Canada Goose

Small numbers of birds winter, the great majority on Islay, with very occasional records from Tiree and Kintyre, invariably among the flocks of Barnacle and, occasionally, Greenland White-fronted Geese. There are records on Islay of one or two in several years from 1958 to the early 1980s, since when they have been more or less annual, and with some increase in numbers to the present 6-10. These birds are presumed to be from the wild populations breeding in the Canadian Arctic and in west Greenland, which normally move south in winter to more temperate parts of Canada and the USA. The smallest birds are smaller than Barnacle Geese, the largest about the size of a Whitefront, while there can be very pale to very dark birds in all the sizes. It is believed that several of the 11 named races are involved. BOURC, which is responsible for maintenance of the British List and has recently followed the American Ornithologists Union in splitting the former Canada Goose into Greater and Lesser species, say that racial assignment is impossible from field descriptions and therefore these birds are best treated as belonging to 'race or races undetermined' (http://www.bou.org.uk/recnews.html). Much work has been done in the USA on mitochondrial DNA separation of the different races, but it is not possible to apply the results to individuals found in Britain without some means of obtaining samples from them. The situation is not made any easier by the fact that, on Islay at least, birds of very different sizes and colours can associate closely together, behaving as if a pair. Hybrids with Barnacle Goose have also been reported occasionally, e.g. Islay 1972 and 2002-3 – 2005-6 (the same family).

Malcolm Ogilvie

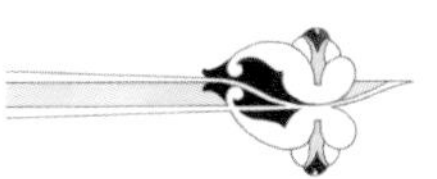

Barnacle Goose

Branta leucopsis

A large wintering population is found mainly on islands, especially Islay, and has shown a four-fold increase in the last 45 years.

Gray described this species as a well-known winter visitor to the Inner Hebrides wherever there were suitable feeding grounds and that it frequented Islay in "very large flocks". H&B said that it was the most plentiful of the wild geese and that "there were thousands in Islay, Jura, Colonsay and on the Treshnish Islands". They also said that it was found on most of the suitable islands, including being abundant on Mull, though it only seldom appeared on Tiree. More resonantly, they stated that the geese "do great damage to grass". It is clear, looking at past and present farming practices on the islands, that the word "thousands" should apply to all the islands combined and not to each separately, as only Islay could ever have supported as many as a thousand, let alone more. However, B&R not only say that, "in 1892 there were thousands wintering on Jura", which is an inaccurate quote from H&B, but also quote Pennant's "vast flocks" on Colonsay and that it is "abundant at times" on Coll, to the extent of causing serious damage.

The first counts on Islay, and the first attempts at a population survey throughout western and northern Scotland took place in the late 1950s. Annual or more frequent counts have taken place on Islay ever since and on Coll, Tiree and Colonsay for at least the last 10 years. Aerial surveys of the whole range have occurred at roughly five-year intervals. During the last 45-50 years, the whole of the Greenland population has grown from around 14,000 birds to the present 55,000. For a long time, the increase was more or less confined to Islay, but in the last ten years, substantial increases have also occurred on, in particular, Tiree, Coll and Colonsay, with some apparent decline on the smaller islands like the Treshnish. This is a reflection of improved farming taking place on the larger islands and the decline in the essential sheep-grazing on the outliers.

Movements within Argyll have been studied through individual marking of birds both on the breeding grounds and in winter on Islay and in Ireland. This commenced in 1961 and has continued intermittently ever since (Pettifor *et al.* 1999). These studies have shown that the Barnacle Geese adopt a range of wintering strategies. The large majority on Islay (about 75%) are highly site-faithful, using the same areas both within and between winters. At other sites within Argyll site-fidelity is also high, though these birds often exhibit more within-winter movements. One particularly well-observed strategy is to visit Islay during the early part of the autumn, then move to their main site for the remainder of the winter. As many as half of the ringed birds observed on Tiree, for example, have usually also been seen on Islay earlier in the winter. A minority of the population, however, is much more mobile, moving sites between years and within a winter. These include both small-scale movements between different sites within Islay, and larger-scale changes in wintering area. Generally these more mobile birds tend to be the same individuals, though some change strategy in occasional years. A ringed pair that was amongst the most site-faithful birds of all (using only a few fields within the RSPB reserve at Loch Gruinart) changed completely one year and moved to Orkney. The next year they returned to Islay and continued their previous strategy. Movements of Barnacle Geese have not been restricted to within Argyll but occur to and from all parts of the wintering range (though generally occur at a lower level between more distant sites). Regular movements, but in

Large flocks of Barnacle Geese are one of Argyll's most dramatic wildlife spectacles. *Philip Kirkham*

only small numbers, are recorded to and from wintering sites in Ireland and more northerly Scottish sites (including the Outer Hebrides, Orkney and Sutherland).

The overall patterns of site use within Islay have been studied over nearly 20 years, and have shown a remarkable degree of consistency. Five major feeding ranges were identified in a study in the 1980s (Percival 1991), each of which is linked to a specific night roosting area. These groupings of ringed birds are still highly apparent now, and have been maintained through several major changes in goose management on Islay.

The numbers of Greenland Barnacle Geese wintering in Argyll, and particularly on Islay, are of international importance. In spring 2003, the total world population was *c.*56,400 birds, about two-thirds of which winter on Islay. Greenland Barnacle Geese are included in the Islay goose management scheme, which provides payments to farmers for a range of measures to offset the agricultural damage caused by these exceptional flocks (see White-fronted Goose).

There has also been a very low level of population interchange with the Svalbard Barnacle Goose population, with 70 ringed birds from that population being seen on Islay. Many of these return quickly to their usual wintering area on the Solway, but some (about half) remain with their 'new' population, and a handful have bred successfully, confirming there is a degree of gene flow between the populations (albeit at a very low level). As with most ringing studies, there have been several exceptional movements well outside the birds'

Numbers of Greenland Barnacle Geese wintering in Islay and elsewhere in Argyll, 1959-2003.

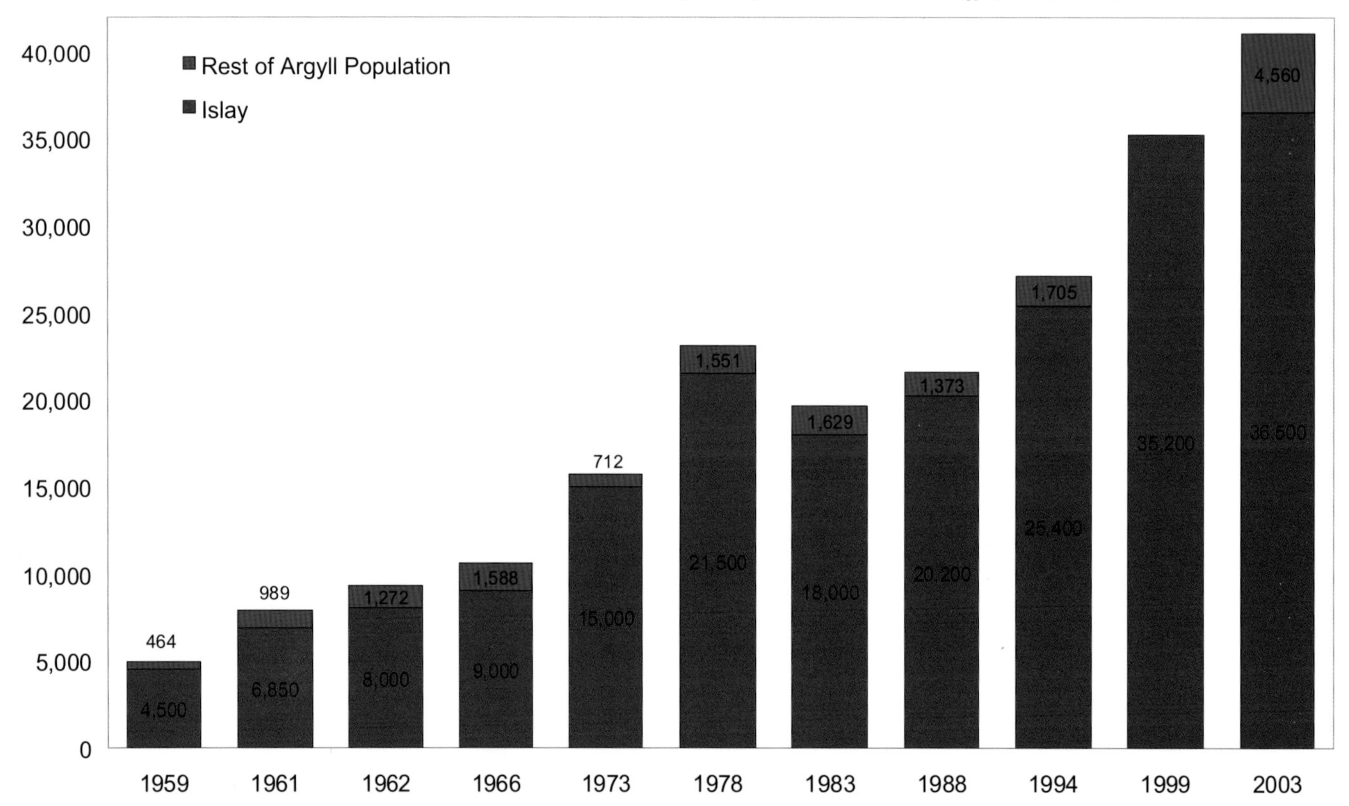

Numbers of Greenland Barnacle Geese wintering in Argyll (excluding Islay), 1959-2003.

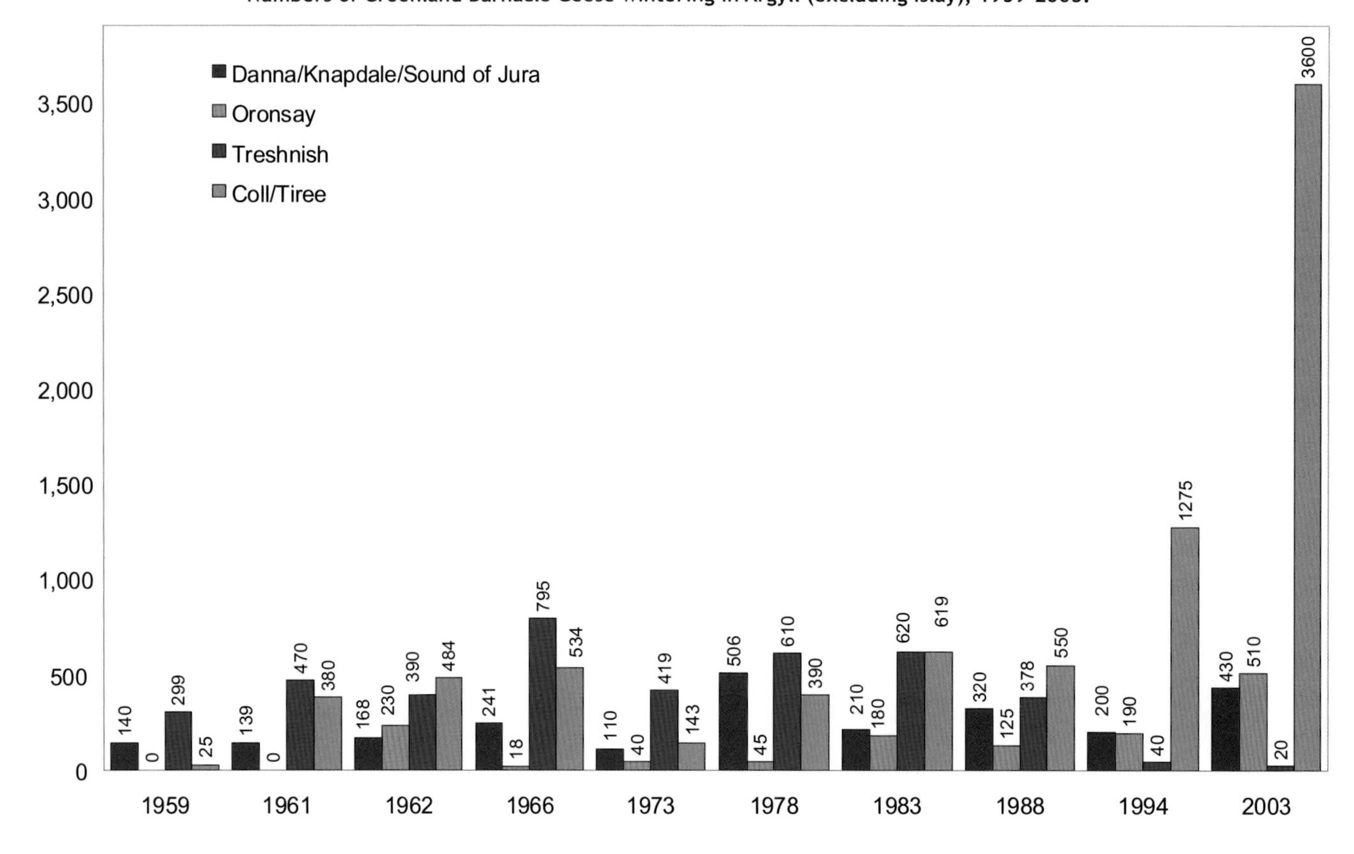

usual range. The geese generally seem well able to return to their usual sites; a ringed pair went to Pentire Head in Cornwall in November 1990, but were back on Islay two months later, whilst one bird briefly visited the Farne Islands off the Northumberland coast in April 1997 during its spring migration, but returned as usual to Islay the following November.

Malcolm Ogilvie

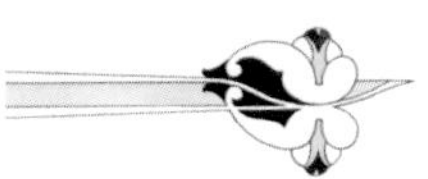

Brent Goose

Branta bernicla

The light-bellied race *B. b. hrota* is a regular passage migrant, mostly in small numbers, and possibly used to winter. The dark-bellied race *B. b. bernicla* is a vagrant, as is the Black Brant *B. b. nigricans*.

Light-bellied race

The birds seen in Argyll belong to the population which breeds in the north-east Canadian Arctic and winters almost exclusively in Ireland. A small number of birds have been seen on Islay in the last 30 years that had been colour marked either in Canada, Iceland (on passage) or Ireland. Gray described Islay as the best known haunt in the Inner Hebrides, with a large flock observed annually in Loch Indaal, and quoted an Islay resident as saying that the geese spent the entire winter there. In complete contrast, just 21 years later, H&B wrote that the species is "as rare on the coasts of the isles of Argyll as the Bernicle is abundant". They noted that it was so rare on Islay that it was included in a case of stuffed birds shot on one of the estates, though admittedly the one furthest from Loch Indaal. Graham reported it as frequenting the Treshnish Islands, though this seems unlikely given the species' preference for mudflats.

Berry (1939) quotes the three authors above and, despite repeating what H&B said, adds that there had been no change in status in the last fifty years and quotes from an unnamed correspondent that the species was still "very numerous" in at least one part of Islay and "occasional" in others. B&R add little of substance and muddy the waters even more by saying that "they are still numerous on this island [Islay], we saw a party of six on 12 September 1937". Booth (1981) quotes sources which state that none were seen between 1938 and 1948, and just one flock was seen in 20 years up to 1959. He also mentions what must have been an astonishing sight, the arrival of 3-4,000 birds in Loch Indaal in April 1971, which stayed overnight and flew on the next morning. This represented perhaps 20% of the then total population. It has to be assumed that they had set off from Ireland in the late afternoon and had been forced down, presumably by bad weather. By the late 1970s, small flocks of up to 50 were appearing in October and November and up to 60 in April and May (Booth 1981).

Islay now has a marked autumn and spring passage and the addition of very small numbers of wintering birds. The number of birds passing through, especially in the autumn, has increased, just as the total population has increased, from c.9,000 in the 1960s to the present 20,000. Flocks of 100-150, occasionally 200, are seen mainly in Loch Gruinart from mid-September onwards. The largest passage was of 590, in several flocks, seen on 2 October 2001. The flocks often land on the sandflats in the loch, but usually move on again within hours. There is only very limited *Zostera* in Loch Gruinart. Perhaps surprisingly, there are very few records of flocks landing in Loch Indaal, despite that site having quite extensive *Zostera* beds exposed at low tide. However, it is presumably these that attract a small number of birds to winter there. This has been a regular event for at least the last ten years, with a slow increase in numbers from 5-6 in the mid-1990s to the present 20-25. In addition to these birds, there are generally from one to three stragglers among the flocks of Barnacles feeding out on the pastures. The spring passage seems to have reduced in recent years, with reports in most, but not every year, of a few small flocks of 15-30 seen flying north in April and the very beginning of May, but rarely touching down.

Up to 200 Light-bellied Brent Geese can be seen at Loch Gruinart, Islay, on autumn passage. *Philip Kirkham*

Elsewhere, the light-bellied Brent Goose is also seen on migration in the autumn, in varying numbers presumably according to whether the prevailing conditions either bring the birds down within sight or allow them to fly direct to Ireland. They are regularly recorded passing over, e.g. Tiree, Mull, Colonsay and Machrihanish. On 2 October 2001, the day of Loch Gruinart's largest passage, 575 were counted over-flying Tiree, while Machrihanish had 160 in four groups on 10 October that year.

Dark-bellied race

Single birds, rarely two and once four were seen on Islay during the winters of 1980-1, 1982-3, 1985-6, 1986-7, 1987-8, 1991-2 (this or another bird was seen on Jura on one day), 1992-3, 1993-4 and 1994-5. There have been no acceptable records since. The only known record away from Islay is one on Tiree in 1988 on the extraordinary date of 6 June.

Black Brant

One was present at Loch Gruinart, Islay, from 20 October 1989 to 17 May 1990. This record has been accepted by BBRC.

Malcolm Ogilvie

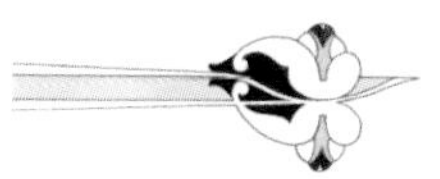

Red-Breasted Goose

Branta ruficollis

Vagrant.

Only one individual of this attractive goose species has ever been recorded in an apparently wild state in Argyll. However, it was present on Islay for three consecutive winters and was widely admired by locals and visitors alike. It was first seen at Loch Gruinart on 27 October 2001 (BB 95:484), having arrived in company with the main influx of Barnacle Geese. It remained for the winter and was last seen on 3 April 2002 (TapR, pers. obs.), before reappearing on 18 October and remaining until at least 9 April 2003 (BB 96:555) and then again from 10 November 2003 to at least 28 March 2004 (BB 97:562). Red-breasted Geese breed on the Taymir Peninsula in Siberia and winter on the Black Sea, although a few are regularly seen in winter as far west as the Netherlands. Thus, there is no overlap in their distribution with the population of Barnacle Geese that winters on Islay, leading some to question the origin of the above individual.

Tristan ap Rheinallt

Common Shelduck

Tadorna tadorna

A widespread but not very numerous breeding species around sandy coasts.

Most Shelducks are absent from mid-August to late October, when they migrate to moulting grounds outside Argyll. In winter they are mostly found in estuarine habitats. While the major concentrations in Scotland are on larger estuaries such as the Forth, Eden, Solway and Clyde, within Argyll birds are relatively numerous on the sheltered sea lochs of Islay, Tiree and Colonsay.

Historical accounts of the status of the Shelduck in Argyll seem to provide a satisfactory summary of the present situation too. Gray described Common Shelldrake as "also numerous in ...Mull, Islay, Jura, Colonsay, ...Tyree and Coll, and indeed on nearly all of the smaller islands of any consequence in the inner group, where it is found breeding. On the mainland ... very numerous in the breeding seasons, frequenting sandy pasture lands near the shore, where it generally takes possession of rabbit-holes". H&B described it as "breeding in the smaller islets round Iona and Mull, and indeed on most suitable places along the coast, in holes scraped in sand or peaty soil... Breeds in Islay and Jura. On the mainland nests also in suitable places, but it appears to prefer islands where possible. Resident in Tiree. Breeds on one at least of the Treshnish Isles."

The Shelduck is on the Amber List of species of medium conservation concern in the UK because the majority of the non-breeding population congregates on less than ten sites, and because more than 20% of the north-west European non-breeding population occurs in the UK (RSPB web page). Nevertheless, numbers have been increasing over recent decades, not only in Britain and Ireland, but also throughout Europe (Second Atlas). The population in the UK is now around 11,000 breeding pairs, with probably about 1,500 pairs nesting in Scotland (Thom). However, the assessment of breeding numbers is complicated by the presence of large numbers of non-breeding birds, and by a particular tendency in this species for the proportion of non-breeders to be greater in areas with high breeding densities (Ingold 1991).

In Scotland, it is widespread on sandy or muddy coasts, and is found on most island groups, although it is scarce in Shetland where sandy habitat is very limited. Research in England has demonstrated that densities vary in relation to the detailed characteristics of sediment composition, with these sediment qualities affecting food supply for the birds (Yates *et al.* 1996). Within Argyll, Shelduck distribution also tends to reflect the availability of suitable sandy and muddy habitat, but numbers are low compared to the concentrations found in the larger Scottish estuaries such as the Moray Firth, Tay, Forth, Solway and Clyde. This is probably because sands of the Argyll coastline tend to be relatively large-grained and less rich in invertebrates than the muddier sediments of sheltered estuaries. Shelducks also breed at inland freshwater sites in a few areas (Linton & Fox 1991, Thom), but are rarely known to do so in Argyll, although in 1987, three pairs with young were seen inland on Tiree (Stroud 1989).

Although the total number of breeding pairs in Argyll is not known, there have been counts in some areas that can be used to extrapolate towards a likely total figure. On Islay, Elliott (1989) suggested there were about 30 feeding territories, which together with non-breeding birds amounted to around 130 resident adults. In 2001, eight pairs bred at the RSPB's Loch Gruinart Reserve and three pairs at Bridgend Merse (Loch Indaal). In the same year, 25 pairs bred on Colonsay, six pairs on Sanda, three on Tiree

The effects of mink predation on Common Shelducks nesting in Argyll are unknown. *Philip Kirkham*

(where at least seven broods were seen in 1999), and scattered pairs were reported from Loch Fyne, Machrihanish Bay, Campbeltown Loch, Coll and Loch Sween. In the previous year there were also reports of three pairs breeding on Iona, two pairs at Loch Beg, Mull, and one or two broods at Loch Crinan. So the Argyll population is likely to be rather more than 70-80 breeding pairs, but perhaps does not exceed one or two hundred pairs. This would seem to be consistent with it forming only a small part of the Scottish total.

Much research was done between the 1970s and 2000 on the breeding, winter feeding, and moult-migration of Shelducks in Scotland, but with this research based on east coast estuaries (Thom) its applicability to the situation in Argyll is uncertain. Shelducks are burrow-nesters, often using holes dug by Rabbits. Very recent research has shown that breeding success can be severely affected by American Mink (Bartoszewicz & Zalewski 2003), which is a matter of concern in Argyll given the continued spread of mink across the region. However, the relatively low breeding density of Shelducks in Argyll, and the presence of plenty of suitable habitat and potential nest sites in areas where food supplies are adequate to support breeding, suggests that this species may be able to find sufficient safe nest sites despite the widespread presence of mink along Argyll coasts. Shelduck broods are frequently attacked by large gulls, and duckling survival tends to be low. However, research on estuaries on the east coast of Scotland found that isolated pairs tended to have much higher breeding success than those in areas with high concentrations of breeding pairs. So, the more scattered nature of breeding in Argyll may favour higher productivity than seen in estuaries.

Shelducks can also be quite sensitive to human disturbance on their wintering grounds, with numbers tending to decrease in areas close to new footpaths (Burton *et al.* 2002). However, in Argyll, winter concentrations tend to be in areas where human disturbance is likely to be slight.

Seasonal variation in numbers on Loch Gruinart and Loch Indaal has been reported regularly (ABR). Numbers peak in January-March in most years, with a decline from April to July as birds move to breeding sites. In most years there are very few Shelducks seen at these sites in August to early October when the birds are away at moulting grounds, and then numbers build up again from late October to mid-winter (Figure).

Shelducks undertake a moult migration in late summer and many join the huge assembly on the Waddensea off north-east Germany (Thom). However increasing numbers now moult closer to home especially in the Forth Estuary and, recently, the Solway Firth (SBR 1998-2001). The only recovery of a Shelduck ringed in Argyll was of a duckling ringed on Loch na Keal (Mull) in June 1981 and reported alive at Seal Sands (Teesmouth) in December 1983. Birds found dead in Argyll had been ringed on the estuary of the River Weser, Germany (2), in Denmark (1), Seal Sands (1), South Uist (1) and Aberlady Bay, Lothian (1). The last had been ringed as a duckling in 1979 and was found dead in 1994. Several of these recoveries in Argyll seem likely to be examples of movements related to the moult migration, but there may also be dispersal of birds between different breeding areas. Apart from the dramatic long-distance moult migration, there is little evidence of extensive movements between breeding and wintering areas, and it is likely that most Shelducks winter fairly close to where they may breed. Moser *et al.* (1986) looked at the mid-winter distribution of coastal birds from the Clyde to the north-west tip of Scotland. They found that the greatest concentration of Shelducks was in 'area C', which included Islay, Jura and Colonsay. On Islay, Lochs Indaal and Gruinart hold the largest winter numbers in Argyll, with very few other sites, apart from The Strand on Colonsay, ever having more than 20 birds. However, WeBS counts on Loch Sween since 1998 have shown that 30 or more (maximum of 74 in 2003) gather regularly at Ceann an t-Sailein from January to March (ABR, Argyll Database).

Bob Furness

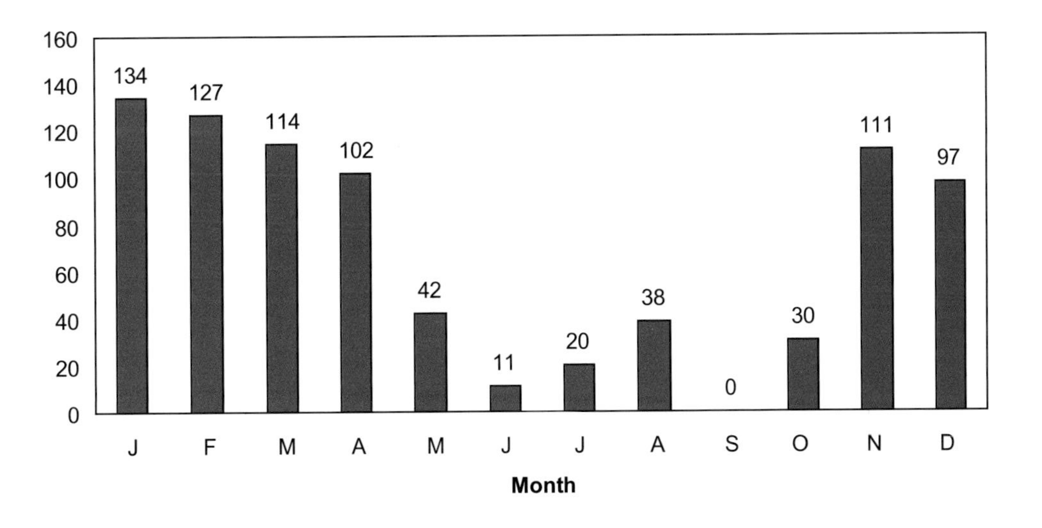

Monthly variation in numbers of Shelducks at Loch Gruinart, Islay, in 1999.

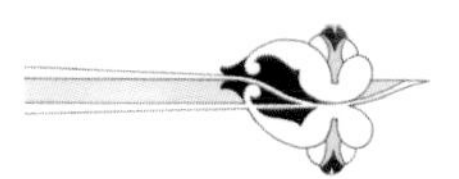

Mandarin Duck

Aix galericulata

This duck, a native of east Asia, is a recent colonist in Argyll, having established a breeding population from escapes from wildfowl collections in the 1990s.

There are no historic records of this introduced species. Indeed, there are no known records until the last decade of the 20th century when in 1991 evidence of breeding was found in a nest box provided for Tawny Owls at Loch Eck in Cowal (Petty & Anderson 1994). This was confirmed during spring 1992, when breeding was again found in the same area. The female was caught and ringed and she also bred each year until at least 1996. There were no other marks on the duck to indicate her origin, and checks of wildfowl collections in south and Mid-Argyll did not locate any that admitted to losing Mandarins. The nearest known breeding population is in Perthshire, which also became established through escapes.

Mandarin Ducks have nested in Argyll since 1991. *Jim Dickson*

The Lock Eck population was monitored closely at first (Table), but information on this population has been lacking in recent years.

In some nest boxes Mandarin eggs were found alongside those of Goosanders, and Anderson & Petty (1996) noted occasions when both species hatched eggs of the other species.

Mandarins can be shy, retiring and easily under-recorded. However, Anderson & Petty (1996) believed the first breeding attempt was in 1991 as there had been many suitable nest boxes in the area since 1983. They confirmed breeding in natural nest sites in 1996, when two females were seen with newly-hatched ducklings. One brood was seen in Glenbranter when all pairs in nest boxes were still incubating, while the other brood was in the grounds of Strachur House, some 5km from the Glenbranter nest box population.

Mandarins have now spread, either through dispersal from Cowal (although there have been no movements recorded from birds ringed in the Loch Eck study) or through further escapes in other parts of Argyll. In 1998 breeding was reported at Creggans in Cowal and in 1999 two males and two females were seen on the River Shira, 15km north of the Loch Eck breeding area. In 2000, a pair with two young was reported at Braevallich on Loch Awe and a female was seen as far away as Tobermory on Mull in June. The highest count of birds reported was at least 50 coming to a pond in Glenbranter in March 1998. Thus, the Argyll birds probably comprise the largest free-flying population in Scotland.

In its natural range, the Mandarin is a bird of broadleaved forests and fresh water habitats. The seeds of trees and shrubs, including acorns and beech mast, form an important part of their diet in late summer and autumn, as do amphibians, insects and aquatic vegetation during the breeding season. The extent of similar habitats and foods in Argyll, combined with recent breeding performance and population growth in Cowal, suggests that the Mandarin is set to become a permanent and more widespread part of Argyll's avifauna. The establishment of non-native species can provide conservation problems, but the development of free-flying populations of Mandarins in Britain has usually been thought of as acceptable, given the endangered nature of the native population in China and Japan (Davies 1988).

David Jardine

Year	Number of nesting females	Number of eggs laid	Number of unhatched eggs	Number of ducklings hatched
1991	1	nd	4	nd
1992	1	14	4	10
1993	1	13	8	5
1994	1	13	3	10
1995	5	42	25	17
1996	4	55	8	47
1997	nd	nd	nd	nd
1998	18	nd	nd	nd

Adapted from Anderson & Petty (1996). nd = no data.

Breeding data from a population of Mandarin Ducks at Lock Eck (Cowal).

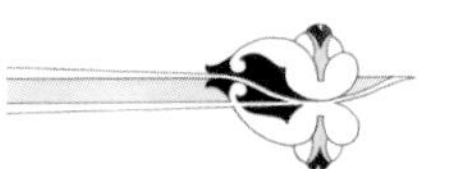

Eurasian Wigeon

Anas penelope

Resident, passage migrant, and winter visitor.

The Eurasian Wigeon has a palearctic breeding distribution, and is largely migratory, wintering as far south as the Equator. In Argyll, it is widespread and common from autumn through to early spring, mainly in saltwater locations, where it feeds on aquatic plants such as *Zostera marina* and on salt marsh vegetation. It is a scarce breeder. The greatest numbers occur from September through November, when flocks of 400-500 are regularly found at Loch Indaal, Loch Gruinart or the Gruinart RSPB reserve, and the mouth of the River Add by Crinan (ABR). Often the flocks draw attention to themselves by their continual whistling, hence the old name of "Whew Duck". The Winter Atlas shows flocks of more than 300 occurring in Islay, West Loch Tarbert, Mid-Argyll, Loch Don, Mull and Loch Creran. Flocks of a similar size now also occur regularly on Loch a' Phuill, Tiree (ABR, Argyll Database). It is possible that flocks break up into smaller more scattered entities during the winter, or that birds disperse south and west. However they may be found in most sheltered coastal bays throughout the winter, and inland on shallow lochs such as Tangy Loch. Flock numbers decrease markedly from March onwards. The Wigeon is highly migratory. About 70% of the European population breeds in Finland, and most of the remainder in Sweden, Norway and Iceland (where thousands are to be found around Lake Myvatn). Recoveries in Argyll of Wigeon ringed in summer include three from Iceland, one from Finland, one from Astrakhan and one from Loch Leven in Fife. It is likely that the greater part of the Argyll winter population comes from Iceland.

A small number remain throughout the breeding season, though at Loch Gruinart they appear not to have bred. In recent years breeding has been reported from Tiree, and Loch Tulla in the Black Mount (ABR). The First and Second Atlases show confirmed breeding near the head of West Loch Tarbert, near Crinan and in Cowal. It has been reported as having formerly bred in Bute (Saunders & Eagle Clarke 1927). It would appear that Argyll may hold up to ten pairs of the estimated 350 that breed in Britain. Wigeon appear to have colonized Scotland comparatively recently, with nesting first recorded in Sutherland in 1834 (B&R). The expansive phase seems to have ended about 1950, with fewer breeding instances in marginal areas, such as Argyll (First Atlas). The nest is usually under grass tussocks, beside or near waters of low acidity (Second Atlas). The young and adults graze marginal vegetation and feed on insects. In Iceland the hatching of chironomid midges is a crucial factor in duckling survival. Is the apparent reduction in breeding pairs in Argyll related to increased acidification due to commercial forestry

Eurasian Wigeon: widely distributed on sheltered coastal waters in Argyll in winter. *David Palmar*

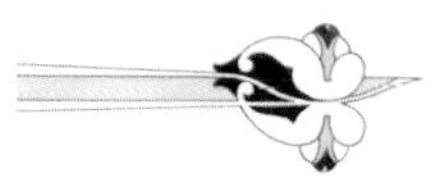

and a lower midge count? The former has certainly occurred, but is there any evidence for the latter?

In common with Mallard and Eurasian Teal, the Wigeon is commonly taken for sport or food. It was "much esteemed for the table" (Morris 1903). Large numbers used to be taken in decoys near the sea (Saunders & Eagle Clarke 1927). Jardine, writing in a slightly earlier period, states they "furnish a plentiful supply to the southern markets". However, it is unlikely that shooting has had any significant impact on numbers in recent years in Argyll, and the numbers wintering today are consistent with those recorded in the early to mid 1960s.

David Merrie

American Wigeon

Anas americana

Vagrant

Given that Thom described this North American species as an almost annual visitor to Scotland, it is perhaps surprising that the first Argyll record did not occur until 1989, when a male was seen on Islay at Loch Indaal on 15 and 16 November (BB 83:448). The bird, which associated with the Wigeon flock at Gartmain, near Bowmore (G. Jackson pers. comm.), apparently stayed until at least 10 February 1990 (ABR 6:19, 7:17).

A long-staying male was at Campbeltown Loch from 2 February to 14 April 1992 (BB 88:501), and another was seen at An Fhaodhail on Tiree on 21 May 1992 (BB 86:460). Following a gap of several years, there followed a sequence of records from Loch Craignish and the nearby Add Estuary, all presumably involving the same male. It was first seen at Loch Craignish on 1 October 1998 (BB 92:563), and then on the Add Estuary from 3 to 18 April 1999 (BB 93:520, ABR 16:35) and on 30 April 2000, before returning to Loch Craignish on 8 October and the Add Estuary on 27 October 2000 (BB 94:461), and the Add Estuary once more on at least 5 October 2001 (BB 95:485). Further records, all assumed to be of the same bird, followed in the winters of 2002/03, 2003/04 and 2004/05 (Argyll Database). A male was at Loch a' Phuill on Tiree from 3 to 9 October 2001 (BB 95:485) and finally, a first-winter male was at Ardnave Loch, Islay from 13 February to 3 March 2004, bringing the total number of Argyll records to the end of 2006 to six.

A male American Wigeon was a regular visitor to the Add Estuary between 1998 and 2005. *Eddie Maguire*

The recent increase parallels the trend seen over Britain and Ireland as a whole, with October arrivals in the west being typical of North American vagrants, even though numbers of wintering Eurasian Wigeons do not peak until much later. The scarcity of records of unaccompanied females and immatures is also a generalised phenomenon, reflecting identification difficulties (Votier *et al.* 2003).

A hybrid Eurasian x American Wigeon was reported from Islay on 20 March 2000 (ABR 17:36). Other birds that have borne some degree of resemblance to male American Wigeon include an apparent hybrid Eurasian x Chiloe Wigeon *A. sibilatrix* on Islay at Loch Gruinart on 21 October 2001 (TapR, pers. obs.).

Tristan ap Rheinallt

Gadwall

Anas strepera

Scarce but regular passage migrant and winter visitor in small numbers, particularly to Islay and Tiree, less frequently to Kintyre and Mid-Argyll. Breeds sporadically on Tiree and on Islay.

The Gadwall is a dabbling duck which favours nutrient-rich shallow wetlands with emergent vegetation. Within the British Isles it is most numerous in southern and eastern England where such habitats are more common. Argyll lies towards the north-west edge of the species' range within the British Isles but the shallow base-rich machair lochs and winter floods of the islands provide suitable feeding and potential breeding habitat, as they do further north on the Uists (First Atlas, Second Atlas).

B&R could find no breeding records for the species in Argyll. However, breeding may have occurred on Tiree in 1913 when two adults were noted with ten fledged young in late August (Anderson 1913) and was proven in 1955 when a duck was observed with three unfledged young in late July (Boyd 1958). No birds were observed anywhere in Argyll in 1968-72 (First Atlas). Breeding was again suspected on Tiree in 1983 and there was a further spate of breeding records in the late 1980s. These included a female with a brood of ten in 1986 and females with broods of three and six in 1987 following records of one to six birds at several sites between May and July (Stroud 1989), and females with broods of two and three at Loch Bhasapol in June 1989. Odd birds and pairs have subsequently appeared almost annually at suitable breeding locations on Tiree in March-June and especially in May, but there have been no further breeding records. On Islay, up to two pairs attempted to breed in 1992, and breeding was again suspected at Loch Gruinart in 1993 and 1994. Breeding was finally proven at Loch Gruinart when a female was seen with two young on 21 May 1996. The species has remained an almost annual spring visitor to the Gruinart floods, with breeding by one pair thought possible in 2002 and by three pairs in 2003, whilst a female was seen with one duckling in June 2004.

The species was apparently a numerous winter visitor to Tiree in the late nineteenth century. Elsewhere in Argyll, it was considered a rarity, with one shot out of a flock of six on a pool near Poltalloch (Mid-Argyll) in August many first-winter birds. Anderson (1898) reported the species as "very common" in winter on Tiree, although by 1913 his description of its status there had changed to "common enough" in winter and spring, with records from August to April.

Subsequently, Gadwall seem to have become much scarcer in winter. They were said to be scarce on Tiree after 1913, although they were apparently "numerous" on Loch a' Phuill in January 1949, and 12 were counted during the 1956/57 winter (Ogilvie & Atkinson-Willes 1983). Newton (in Stroud 1989) noted few recent winter records on Tiree, citing a single male on Loch a' Phuill in February 1985, with two more there in September 1987 and males at Clachan in January 1987 and on 30 March 1990. Boyd (1958) only noted odd birds seen at five sites over four days on Tiree in early April 1954. The species remains an annual winter visitor to Tiree, with up to ten birds frequenting the main lochs, particularly Loch a' Phuill in July to January, with a

Loch a' Phuill on Tiree and Loch Gruinart on Islay are two of the best sites to find Gadwall in Argyll. *Philip Kirkham*

years earlier being the only record quoted by H&B. H&B were the first to mention the abundance of Gadwall on Tiree in winter, noting that birds were shot there in winter since 1870 or earlier, and that numbers steadily increased, so that it was abundant by 1891. They described the occurrence of large flocks at sea beyond the Balephetrish reefs during the day, sheltering inside the reefs only in very heavy weather and flighting all over the island at night to the mosses. The species often made up a large portion of hunters' bags at that time, with for example 30 or 40 being shot by one party in the 1878/79 winter. Interestingly, these were almost invariably peak of 13 there on 27 July 1992. Six were observed to fly towards Tiree from Coll on 19 October 2002, but there are no records to date from the latter island. On Islay, the species has become a regular winter visitor, since being regarded only as a straggler as recently as 1981 (Ogilvie 1983). Typically, up to six birds arrive on Islay in October, visiting the floods at Loch Gruinart, and occasionally other sites such as Ardnave Loch and Loch Gorm, then remaining to March or April. The peak count for Islay was 23 at Loch Gruinart on 14 October 2000.

The species is scarce elsewhere in Argyll, although birds

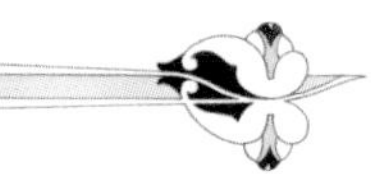

were recorded with some regularity at Glen Lonan between 1986 and 1992, with a peak count of seven on 2 November 1996. Gadwall have also been seen flying south past Uisaed Point (Kintyre) in the autumn, with the highest day-counts being eight birds on 19 October 1989 and 12 on 17 October 1995. Records became rather more widespread in the late 1990s, with the most notable count being one of seven birds at Loch Crinan on 17 September 1999. Odd birds and pairs have been recorded on passage at lochs on Mull and at scattered other sites, including Sanda Island, Loch Caolisport (Mid-Argyll), Tayinloan, Loch Leathan (Mid-Argyll) and Loch Gilp.

John Bowler

Eurasian Teal

Anas crecca

Widespread but uncommon breeding species. Common passage migrant and winter visitor.

The Eurasian Teal occurs across Argyll at all seasons. It is found in all open country habitats, except montane, providing there are small areas of open water. It is a common breeder on hill lochs and lowland waters, but very much under-recorded, so that one can only make a guess of the order of 100 pairs in Argyll, representing a very small proportion of the British breeding population of 1,500 to 2,600 pairs (Second Atlas). Outside the breeding season numbers have been meticulously counted during WeBS and other counts at the main areas of congregation, when flocks ranging from 15 to 300 have been recorded (ABR). By far the largest gatherings occur at Gruinart on Islay, where numbers regularly reach 700 from September to March, with a peak of 2,453 occurring in November 2004. However smaller parties may be found almost anywhere where there is sheltered coastal water or shallow inland water.

Breeding often occurs at waters where large winter concentrations occur, but it is not known whether breeders form part of the winter population. There are only six ringing records of Teal in Argyll. Five were recovered in Argyll after being ringed elsewhere in the British Isles at distances of 162-581km. The sixth was ringed as a duckling on Tiree in June 1927 and shot there in October of the same year. It has been said that some of our breeders are summer visitors, departing in autumn for more southern quarters (Saunders & Eagle Clarke 1927). On migration it is said "they travel, for the most part, in large flocks, a 'plump' so called, and chiefly by night, though large numbers are also seen moving in the day-time; in either case at a high elevation" (Morris 1893).

It has been estimated that the number of Teal that winter in UK lies between 100,000 and 200,000, but, due to their widely dispersed nature, organized counts only record between 64,000 and 88,000 (Winter Atlas). It is likely that the same or greater margin of error exists in relation to Teal in Argyll. Migrants are estimated to form 85% of the total. Breeding declines have been attributed partly to upland afforestation, particularly in Kintyre (Second Atlas). Experimental creation of open water in peatland habitat may increase the number of Teal breeding successfully. It would be nice to see this tried

The Eurasian Teal is widespread but uncommon as a breeding species in Argyll. *Philip Kirkham*

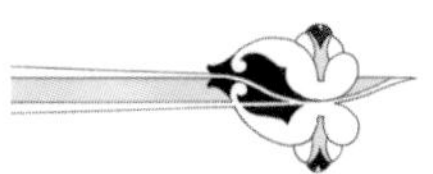

out in afforested areas of Argyll. The nest is always close to the ground and well hidden, contains from eight to 15 eggs, but broods seen in Argyll are rarely more than six (ABR). The nest is often a considerable distance from water, to which the young are led soon after hatching.

David Merrie

Green-winged Teal

Anas carolinensis

Rare visitor during the winter months, with returning birds possibly accounting for a high proportion of records.

Until recently this transatlantic visitor was considered to be conspecific with Eurasian Teal *Anas crecca*. Since 2001, however, it has been regarded as a separate species. The first Scottish record was in 1938, and records have been annual in the country since 1972 (Thom). The first occurrence in Argyll involved a drake at Loch Gorm on Islay from 7 to 9 May 1978 (BB 75:491)[1]. Another was seen at Loch Don on Mull on 12 February 1984 (BB 78:537); this bird apparently returned the following winter (ABR 8:65), but supporting details were not provided.

From 1989, drake Green-winged Teals were seen regularly on Islay (Table). Although most sightings were on the floods at Loch Gruinart, birds were seen in several different locations in the winters of 1988/89, 1989/90 and 1990/91. Since there was no overlap in dates between locations, all the sightings in the first two of these winters were considered to relate to the same individual (BB 84:461). This individual could also have been responsible for the sightings in the winters of 1990/91 and 1991/92, failing to return in 1992/93. Similarly, it is possible that the records between 1996 and 2003 involved just two individuals, seen together at Loch Gruinart on 22 April 1999 (SBR 1999:28, ABR 16:36), and present simultaneously at two locations (Loch Gruinart and Bruichladdich) in late 2001. The absence of records in 2000/01 may be a result of access difficulties related to the foot-and-mouth epidemic.

Other than Islay, the only records come from Tiree, where single drakes were at An Fhaodhail from 27 November 1996 to 4 March 1997 (SBR 1997:20, SBR 1998:26, ABR 15:35), Loch Bhasapol from 19 to 21 December 1999 (SB 1999:28, ABR 16:36), Heylipol on 1 and 2 June 2002, at various locations on the island from 26 May to 4 June 2003 (Argyll Database), and on Loch Bhasapol on 6 June 2005 (Argyll Database).

The true number of individuals involved is impossible to assess. All Islay records since 1988 could be accounted for by just three drakes, though the true total is likely to be considerably higher, late spring birds having perhaps wintered elsewhere. Assuming that the sightings in different winters on Tiree involved three or more birds, it seems that there have been at least eight individuals in all.

Although many of the sightings have involved drakes that were apparently unpaired, the 1996/97 Tiree bird was paired with a female Eurasian Teal towards the end of its stay. A drake Green-winged Teal at Loch Gruinart on 2 December 2001 was accompanied by an apparent hybrid drake Eurasian Teal x Green-winged Teal (TapR, pers. obs.).

[1] Wrongly stated to be in 1979 in SB 1981:52 and in Elliott (1989).

Tristan ap Rheinallt

Winter	First date	Last date	Minimum number of birds	Reference
1988/89	25-26 March	3 April	1	BB 83:450
1989/90	25 December	10 February	1	BB 84:461, SBR 1990:14, ABR 7:18
1990/91	24 January	2 March	1	SBR 1991:18, ABR 8:31
1991/92	24 April	28 April	1	SBR 1992:15, ABR 9:19
1993-1995	no records	-	-	-
1996/97	15 October	1 December	1	SB 1996:17, SB 1997:20, ABR 15:35
1997/98	20 January	26 January	1	SB 1998:26, ABR 15:35
1998/99	9 January	3 May	2	SBR 1999:28, ABR 16:36
1999/2000	13 January	17 May	1	ABR 17:38
2000/01	no records	-	-	-
2001/02	18 November	21 April	2	Argyll Database
2002/03	4 November	30 March	1	Argyll Database
2003/04	12 November	31 January	1	Argyll Database
2004/05	1 November	20 December	2	Argyll Database
2005/06	no records	-	-	-

Records of drake Green-winged Teals on Islay from winter 1988/89 to the end of 2006.

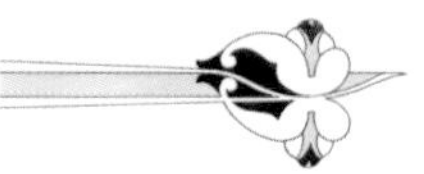

Mallard

Anas platyrhynchos

The Mallard is Argyll's commonest duck. It is resident in coastal and lowland freshwaters throughout the county.

Circumpolar and holarctic in distribution, the Mallard is able to exploit a wide range of habitats (Fuller 1982). It needs water less than 1m deep in which to forage, but will feed in crop fields, especially stubble or potatoes. Although they are largely vegetarian, eating an extremely wide range of plants and seeds, a small part of their diet consists of shrimps, molluscs and crustaceans.

In Argyll it breeds in moderate numbers on or by waters up to 450m asl, but mainly on lowland waters. Saunders & Eagle Clarke (1927) had it breeding to 606m asl. At the time of the Second Atlas it was found breeding in 67% of 10km squares in Argyll. Even in winter, occasional birds may be seen on the higher hill lochs, but all large flocks occur between sea-level and 150m. Generally the autumn/winter maxima occur in September, when migrant birds swell the flocks of residents. The largest flock recorded in recent times was 662 on Loch Gruinart, Islay, in 1999, but flocks of around 200 are regularly seen in Islay, Tiree, and Loch Caolisport (ABR), or where they are fed for shooting, as at Rhunahaorine (D. Merrie pers. obs.). More usually one encounters parties of between 20 and 40, very often in the company of Eurasian Wigeon and Eurasian Teal. In October and November maximum flock size reduces to an average of *c.*180, before rising again in December to 270. Thereafter flock size reduces sharply (ABR).

Mallards are early nesters, broods being recorded in early April. In May birds start to congregate again, presumably with failed or non-breeders grouping, and then from June onwards, young broods join the flocks. The input of fledglings seems to be balanced by mortality of young birds throughout May to July as average maximum flock size stays about 70. In August the first migrant birds arrive and maximum flock size increases to an average of *c.*170 (ABR).

It is unlikely that shooting has a significant impact on the numbers of wintering Mallard in Argyll. Also, the number of hand-reared Mallard introduced to the wild population is a very small proportion of the total. The Mallard is reported as not infrequently interbreeding with the Pintail, (which has bred in both Tiree and Islay), and in captivity with almost any duck.

The nest is made of grass and lined and edged with grey down and is usually on the ground close to fresh water. Many other locations such as hedgerows, forks or hollows of trees,

Mallards: common and familiar year-round across Argyll. *Louise Wood*

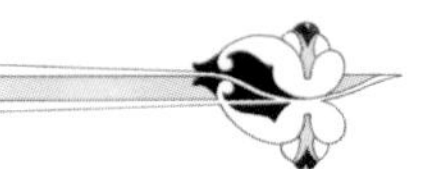

and even the deserted nests of other birds may be used. Saunders & Eagle Clarke (1927) report a nest 18m above the ground and the author has found such a nest on a cliff face used by Peregrines.

There are only three ringing recoveries of Mallard in Argyll, two of movements within Argyll, and one of a bird ringed in Lincolnshire.

A famous shooting man stated "I have seen these birds during the breeding-season very far up among the hills; a few hatch and rear their young about the rough ground and mosses near the sea, but these get fewer every year, in consequence of draining and clearing which goes on in all the swamps and wild grounds." Charles St. John (1924). So, the effects of habitat change are not that new. In recent years there has been considerable reduction in the amount of arable crops grown in Argyll, and the qualities of inland waters are changing due to afforestation, and of coastal waters due to fish farming, amongst other things. Although there does not seem to be any significant change over the last 40 years in year-round abundance of the Mallard, regular monitoring of this common species would be likely to provide reliable evidence of changes resulting from climate or habitat.

David Merrie

Black Duck

Anas rubripes

Vagrant

This transatlantic vagrant, which is occurring with increasing frequency in the British Isles, has been recorded once in Argyll. A drake was present briefly on Tiree at Loch a' Phuill on 15 June 2001 (BB 95:486). This was the 25th British and 7th Scottish record. All the previous Scottish records involved birds first seen in autumn or winter, with most staying at the same location for several months.

Tristan ap Rheinallt

Pintail

Anas acuta

Scarce breeder on Tiree; wintering and passage birds are seen in small numbers in a few localities.

There appear to be no 19th century records of this species in Argyll, while the first 20th century reference is a somewhat cryptic, and unhelpful, comment by Berry (1939): "it may be becoming less uncommon on Islay and in a few other districts [of Argyll and the Inner Hebrides]". B&R report that a young female with down on its back and several primaries still in sheaths was sent to the British Museum from Tiree in 1938, which could amount to a possible breeding record for the island. Otherwise, they merely say that the species is recorded irregularly on passage on some of the Inner Hebrides, including Tiree, and that a few winter in the Inner Hebrides. Breeding was confirmed on Tiree in 1951 and possibly in 1952 and 1955. It took place again in 1969 (Stroud 1989), and then, during the 1980s, the species gradually became established as a more or less regular breeder with usually one to two pairs present and breeding proved in some years. This pattern has continued to the present day. Since the early 1990s, pairs have stayed well into the summer on Islay, particularly since the

The Pintail is Argyll's rarest regularly-breeding duck. *Philip Snow*

RSPB created shallow flooded areas from 1992 onwards, but breeding has yet to be proved.

Islay is the main wintering haunt in the county. Prior to 1982-3, the species was a casual visitor with small numbers being seen from time to time, but rarely staying for more than days or a few weeks. After 1982-3, Pintails became regular winterers in Loch Indaal, increasing steadily from an average maximum (mean of three highest counts in a winter) of seven in 1982-3, to 28 in 1987-8, 44 in 1991-2. In summer 1992, the RSPB created a flooded marsh on its Loch Gruinart reserve and Pintail immediately started wintering there. Coordinated counts suggest that the birds are moving between the two lochs. Combining the totals shows a further, if slower, increase to 60 in 1996-7, followed by some levelling out, though January 2006 produced a new record count of 73. Small numbers winter on Tiree, rarely more than ten, and using several lochs, though with some preference for Lochs a'Phuill, Riaghain and an Eilean. Elsewhere in Argyll, the Pintail is a rare bird. In many years, there are no records of the species away from Islay and Tiree other than very small numbers (1–3) seen on autumn passage at the Machrihanish SBO (ABR).

Malcolm Ogilvie

Garganey

Anas querquedula

Regular spring visitor to Islay and Tiree. Has bred in Argyll on at least two occasions.

The Garganey, which is the only duck species to occur in Britain as a summer migrant, has been known as an irregular summer visitor to Scotland since the middle of the 19th century (Thom). According to Gray, the only Argyll record involved a pair on a small moorland loch in Upper Loch Fyne. No date was given for this record. Using information from Henry Evans, H&B stated that the species had occurred on Jura. B&R appeared sceptical about the authenticity of these and other older records, including claimed occurrences on Islay in winter. The first fully acceptable record, therefore, appears to be of a bird shot at Machrie on Islay on 10 September 1964 (SB 3:199). Then, in May 1976, the remains of a bird were found at a Peregrine eyrie, again on Islay (SB 10:83, Elliott 1989). These were the only records until 1989, since when birds have been reported annually in Argyll. Nearly all records during 1989-2003 fell between mid-April and mid-June, with the earliest on 1 April 2003 at Loch Gruinart and a peak of arrivals in mid- to late May. All spring records have come from Islay and Tiree, with five exceptions: up to three birds at Westport Marsh in Kintyre from 19 May 1994 (Maguire 1995); a male at Coll RSPB reserve on 21 May 1995 (ABR 12:31); two on Oronsay on 13 May 2000 (ABR 17:39); a pair at Ederline on 21 April 2002; and a pair at Breachacha on Coll in May 2002. The Ederline sighting is the only mainland record to date.

Breeding was confirmed at Westport Marsh on 24 June 1994, when a brood of three was seen (Maguire 1995, SBR 1994:18, ABR 11:32). This was apparently only the third instance of proven successful breeding in Scotland. It was followed three years later by the sighting of a female with nine young at Loch Gruinart on 27 May 1997 (ABR 14:34). Although birds continue to be seen regularly at the latter site and breeding is suspected to have occurred on at least one other occasion, sadly Westport Marsh has since been drained. However, there were frequent sightings at multiple locations on Tiree during 2002 and 2003. In both years, juveniles or probable juveniles were seen during August, suggesting that breeding may have occurred. Breeding was confirmed on Coll in 2004, when a pair were seen with five small young on 1 July.

As elsewhere in Scotland, this species is recorded much less frequently in autumn than in spring. Other than the above records from Tiree, there have only been three autumn records in the period 1989-2003: a pair at Loch a' Phuill on Tiree on 7 August 1998 (ABR 15:37); two birds on Oronsay on 27 August 2000 (ABR 17:39); and one at Loch Gruinart on 2 September 2000 (ABR 17: 39).

Tristan ap Rheinallt

The Garganey nests sporadically in Argyll, close to the limit of its European range. *Hugh Venables*

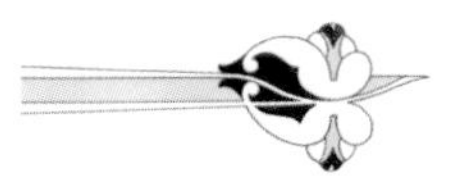

Blue-winged Teal

Anas discors

Vagrant.

The Outer Hebrides and the Northern Isles account for most Scottish records of this attractive North American duck. There are three accepted records from Argyll, all in spring. A pair was at Loch Riaghain on Tiree from 26 May to at least 3 June 1986 (BB 80:528). Twelve years later, single drakes were seen at Loch a' Phuill on Tiree on 19 May and at Loch Gruinart on Islay on 24 and 25 May 1998 (BB 92:564). Although treated by the BBRC as different birds, it seems possible that they were one and the same. The latter apparently remained at Loch Gruinart until at least 30 May (ABR 15:37). In Scotland overall, there have been more records in autumn than in spring. Many of the autumn records have involved females or immatures, which may be overlooked in Argyll.

[A claimed sighting of a female at Bridgend Merse on Islay on 19 October 1974 (Elliott 1989, Ogilvie 1992a, Evans 1994) was apparently not submitted to BBRC.]

Tristan ap Rheinallt

Shoveler

Anas clypeata

Scarce and localised breeder, with annual breeding only on Islay and Tiree; more numerous as a winter visitor and passage migrant, although still largely confined to Islay and Tiree.

Like the Gadwall, the Shoveler favours nutrient-rich shallow wetlands with emergent vegetation, and within the British Isles it is most numerous in southern and eastern England where these habitats are more common. Argyll lies towards the northwest edge of the species' range, but the shallow base-rich machair lochs and marshes provide suitable breeding and wintering habitat, as they do further north on the Uists and Benbecula (First and Second Atlases).

The species colonised Scotland from the 1840s onwards, with its main breeding focus in the south-east lowlands (First Atlas). It was first recorded breeding in Argyll in 1866, when a nest was found on Loch Awe (B&R), followed by Tiree in 1887 when young were shot on the island (H&B) and then on Islay where it bred at Loch Eighinn in 1918 (B&R). Only on Tiree did the species fully establish itself as a breeding species at this time; it was reported to be fairly common, with a few pairs breeding in 1898. By 1908, the Shoveler was said to be increasing yearly as a breeding species on Tiree, with "a great many" nesting there in 1913 (Anderson 1913). Boyd (1958) recorded a pair on Tiree and another on the islet of Gunna in June 1949, several in May-June 1952, flocks of up to six and pairs in April 1954, and at least 20 young birds in July 1955, with nesting proved "in recent years" at Loch Garradh nan Capull. Breeding has continued to occur on Tiree, with records from 1968-72 (First Atlas) including two nests in 1969. Numbers appear to have then increased further with up to 16 nesting pairs noted annually on the lochs and scattered marshy pools since 1986. Nest success appears to be high, with annual records of broods and a maximum of some nine to twelve broods in 1986.

On Islay, breeding was once regarded as irregular and involved very small numbers (Booth 1981), but has subsequently become more frequent and is concentrated on the floods at Loch Gruinart, where there were 11 broods in 1999 plus two more pairs on the old canal, six broods in 2000, and 8-13 pairs breeding annually in 2001-04. Breeding has also been recorded from Coll, where a brood was noted near Grishipoll in summer 1989 and two pairs nested in May

Both breeding and wintering numbers of Shovelers have increased in Argyll in recent years. *Philip Kirkham*

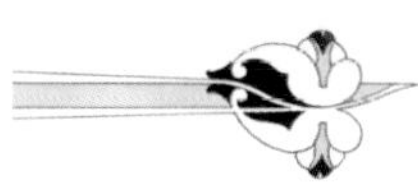

2004, but the species is otherwise very rare on the island with the only other records in May 1937, June 1992 and June 1994. Elsewhere, a female with a brood was reported from Machrihanish (Kintyre) in 1972 (SB 7: 337), and breeding was also reported from the Machrihanish area in 1992, at Westport Marsh. Birds were present at Westport Marsh in subsequent springs, but the species' occupation of this site came to an abrupt end in 1995 when the marsh was drained. On Colonsay, two pairs were present at Ardskenish in early May 1993, and at least one pair nested on the island in 1994. The Argyll breeding population of 20-30 pairs represents some 1-3% of the UK total of 1,000-1,500 pairs (Second Atlas).

The Shoveler is more numerous on passage and in winter, but remains largely restricted to Islay and Tiree. Wintering birds are present from October to March, typically reaching a maximum in mid-winter, although with a hint of a further peak in numbers in March on Islay. Count totals increased on both islands in the 1990s. On Tiree, Anderson (1913) reported that only a few birds remained all winter, whilst Boyd (1958) reported birds wintering in flocks of up to six from September to April. Ogilvie & Atkinson-Willes (1983) noted that up to 20 birds had been counted in winter on Tiree, but numbers appear to have dropped after 1983 with only up to half a dozen birds recorded in the mid 1980s (Newton in Stroud 1989). More recently, counts have increased again, with 24 in late November 1991, 31 in March 1998, 36 on 17 December 2000 and a record 41 on 6 January 2001. On Islay, the Shoveler was regarded as a rare winter visitor in the late 19th century by Gray and it was only recorded in groups of up to five in most months of the year in 1983 (Ogilvie 1983). However, wintering numbers have subsequently steadily increased with peaks of 54 in November 1998, 62 in March 1999, 70 in March 2000, 81 in December 2001, 85 in December 2002 and a record 92 in December 2003. On Islay, the majority of the birds occur on the floods at Loch Gruinart and small numbers appear only briefly at other sites such as Loch Gorm and Loch Indaal, whereas the species occurs more widely on the scattered machair lochs of Tiree, including Loch a' Phuill, Loch Riaghain, Loch Bhasapol, Loch an Eilein and Loch Earblaig. Early observers apparently never recorded the species away from the lochs, but Boyd (1958) noted birds on the shore of Tiree in 1954 and 1955, and Shoveler are now regularly seen in winter along more sheltered stretches of the Tiree coast. Elsewhere in Argyll, odd birds have been recorded recently on passage and in winter at scattered locations including the Add Estuary, Moine Mhor, Loch Caolisport, Loch Crinan, Oronsay and Colonsay. Very few of these records have involved more than two birds, but eight were seen at Holy Loch on 13 January 2001, with five there on 6 October the same year. Also, a total of 22 flew south past Uisaed Point (Kintyre) on five dates between 13 September and 29 October 2001.

John Bowler

Red-crested Pochard

Netta rufina

Vagrant.

As a breeding species, the Red-crested Pochard has a scattered distribution in central Europe, though its main stronghold is in central Asia. In recent years, a feral population has become established in southern Britain, and probable escapes are recorded with increasing regularity in Scotland.

Argyll appears to be the only county in Scotland with pre-20th century records. A male was shot on a freshwater loch at Craignish on 7 January 1862, apparently by Captain McDougall of Luing. The skin was sent to Henry Graham and then kept in the collection of Captain J. P. Orde of Kilmory, who exhibited it to the Zoological Society of London (Gray, Graham, H&B, B&R). At the time this was the only Scottish record of the species, then regarded as an accidental visitor to the British Isles (Gray).

[Millais (1913) records that "two young males were shot near Oban in the winter of 1898, as I am informed by Mr Bishop, the Oban taxidermist, who mounted them". No additional details appear to have been published anywhere and, although the record was quoted by B&R and Thom, there is no evidence that the specimens were seen by Millais or by any other ornithologist of the time.]

Tristan ap Rheinallt

Common Pochard

Aythya ferina

Scarce but regular passage migrant and winter visitor in small numbers, particularly to Tiree, Islay and a few Mid-Argyll lochs.

The Common Pochard favours nutrient-rich fresh-waters less than 6m deep and on the continent is essentially a dweller of open steppes. It is predominantly vegetarian, diving to feed on submerged plant matter (Winter Atlas). In Britain, it breeds mostly on fertile lowland lakes and gravel pits in the east of England. There has been a slow increase in numbers to around 400 pairs (Second Atlas), although there has been a contraction in the Scottish range since 1972. Argyll lies on the northwest edge of the British breeding range but, like other parts of Britain, probably receives additional passage and wintering birds from the Baltic countries to Russia (Migration Atlas).

The first record of breeding in Argyll was at Loch Awe in 1871 (B&R). Breeding also occurred at Loch Bhasapol (Tiree) in 1891 (H&B). Both Anderson (1898) and Irby (1899) recorded a few pairs breeding on Tiree, particularly at Loch Bhasapol, but Anderson (1913) described the species as occurring there mostly in winter, with a few remaining all summer but not nesting every year. Breeding appears to have

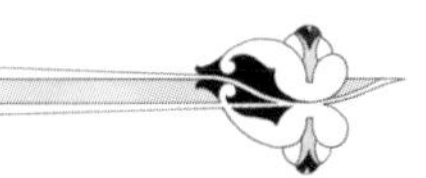

discontinued around 1913, and the next summer record was not until 1957 when a drake was noted at Loch Bhasapol in June (Boyd 1958). There have been further occasional records during May to August of up to two drakes and single females appearing on the larger lochs on Tiree and, more rarely, on Islay and some of the mainland lochs. However, the only reported occurrence of breeding was on an unnamed loch in Mid-Argyll in 1983 (ABR 1: 24).

Gray considered the Pochard to be a familiar species in western Scotland in winter, describing it as common on many of the Inner Hebrides and noting that it was frequently shot on the freshwater lochs of Islay and Mull. H&B thought the Pochard only an infrequent winter visitor to Argyll, noting a small wintering flock at Loch Bhasapol, and occasional records from Mull and Jura. Anderson (1898) considered the Pochard to be numerous on Tiree in winter but numbers appear to have declined there after 1913, with Boyd (1958) noting just one drake in December 1953 and another in early April 1954. A high count of 115 was recorded in January 1965, and by the mid 1980s there was a regular wintering population of around 40-75 birds centred on Loch Bhasapol, peaking at 116 in January 1986 (Stroud 1989). Numbers have subsequently been lower, rarely exceeding 50 in the 1990s, and considerably more variable, with only one bird present in January 2001 but up to 38 in December 2003-January 2004. Birds are still seen most often at Loch Bhasapol, although in some winters, as in 2002-03, they favour Loch a' Phuill and Loch Riaghain, with very occasional records from Loch an Eilein. The first birds typically arrive in late October-November and stragglers remain until late April. There are just three records to date from the neighbouring island of Coll.

On Islay, the species wintered in good numbers on most of the larger and more fertile freshwater lochs in the 1970s, with the largest and most regular numbers at Loch Skerrols. A maximum of 320 was counted at Loch Skerrols in the 1970s with an annual mean of 149 birds, whilst groups of 20-90 birds were recorded at other large lochs on the island (Ogilvie 1983). High numbers of birds continued to visit Loch Skerrols until the early 1990s with peaks of 250 birds

The Common Pochard is mostly found on nutrient-rich freshwater lochs, but is now declining in Argyll. *Philip Kirkham*

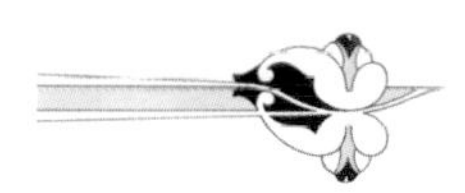

there on 29 November 1989, 330 in November 1992, and 220 in October 1993. Subsequently, wintering numbers have been rather lower, with 105 at Loch Skerrols on 31 October 1996, but counts of around 30 are more typical. Occasional counts of 30 or more birds have also been made recently at Loch Gorm in autumn, and at Ardnave Loch.

Elsewhere in Argyll, the species has also experienced a decline. On the mainland, counts of 218 at Tangy Loch, near Campbeltown on 6 November 1971 (SBR), and 82 further north in Kintyre at Loch nan Gad on 21 December 1975 (SBR), have not been matched since. Recent regular records come from Loch Awe, Loch Leathan and Loch nan Druimnean in Mid-Argyll, with counts of 20 or more birds in the mid-1990s. Single birds and small groups have been noted, particularly in January and February, at other scattered freshwater lochs in the same general area. In Cowal, there are very few recent records away from Loch Restil, though there was an isolated count of 52 at Loch Melldalloch on 10 November 1971 (SBR). On Mull, a regular wintering flock at Loch Assapol peaked at 89 birds in December 1985 (ABR) but now seems to be absent. On Jura, 64 birds were counted on 23 February 1984 (ABR) but there are no recent records. Some 15 to 20 birds wintered on Colonsay in the mid 1950s (Owen & Atkinson-Willes 1984), with exceptional counts of 150 in autumn 1973 and 97 on 6 February 1977 (Jardine *et al.* 1986), but the species is now present in very small numbers if at all.

During the autumn, particularly in October, occasional southbound birds have been noted passing offshore at Machrihanish and at Frenchman's Rocks (Islay). Singles and small groups are also sometimes encountered on salt water during the winter months. Overall, it is clear that the Pochard has declined substantially as a winter visitor to Argyll over the past 20 to 30 years. The reason for this is unknown. However, large fluctuations are apparently not unusual at Scottish sites (Thom), even though numbers have been stable in Britain and Ireland as a whole since the 1970s (Migration Atlas).

John Bowler

Ring-necked Duck

Aythya collaris

Vagrant.

This North American duck is an annual visitor to Scotland in small numbers, occurring mostly in the north and west. All nine Argyll records involved single males, some of which were long-stayers as is often the case with this species.

Interestingly, all but two of these records were in winter or spring. In Scotland as a whole, autumn records are relatively more frequent, though still less numerous than spring records. There has been a general decline in records since the early 1990s. As with American Wigeon, it seems possible that female and immature birds have been overlooked in Argyll.

Tristan ap Rheinallt

Records of Ring-necked Ducks in Argyll, 1982-2006.

Date	Location	Comment	Reference
6 - 7 Mar 1982	Loch Leathan	To 14 Mar (SBR, ABR)	BB 76:487, SBR 1982:18, ABR 1:24
15 - 17 May 1982	Loch Ba		BB 76:487
23 Jan - 15 Feb 1984	Easter Ellister	To at least 11 Mar (SBR, ABR)	BB 78:538, SBR 1984:19, ABR 2:16
27 Jan to at least 22 Apr 1991	Ardnave Loch		BB 85:515
14 Feb to at least 16 Feb 1991	Loch Nell		BB 85:515
30 May - 2 Jun 1993	Loch an Torr		BB 87:516
23 October 1997	Ardnave Loch		SB 1997:21
3 - 18 Oct 2001	Tiree		SBR 2001:27
20 - 21 Apr 2004	Loch Bhasapol		Argyll Database

Even small areas of wetland can be havens for wildfowl in winter. *David Wood*

Ferruginous Duck

Aythya nyroca

Vagrant.

A drake was on Loch Bhasapol on Tiree from 21 to 29 April 2003 (Bowler 2003, BB 97:563). This was the 14th Scottish record of this attractive and declining species, which breeds patchily in southern and eastern Europe and is now classified as endangered. Most individuals occurring in Britain are thought to have a genuinely wild origin (BB 95:488). All but two of the previous Scottish records came from the mainland, the exceptions being an immature drake on Rum in October 1979 and a drake on Orkney in May 1981.

The Tiree individual was the first to be seen in Scotland since 1992. Only a few months later, from July to September 2003, one was present in Fife and then in Kinross – perhaps the same individual?

Tristan ap Rheinallt

Tufted Duck

Aythya fuligula

Widespread winter visitor to freshwater lochs, with largest numbers on Tiree and Islay. Breeds in small numbers on these islands and also on Colonsay and Mull, with scattered pairs found throughout mainland Argyll.

The Tufted Duck is a migratory species that breeds in sheltered lowland freshwater habitats across most of northern Europe and winters further south and west. In much of Europe introduced freshwater zebra mussels form a key part of the diet, and have been an important factor in a marked range expansion in the late 19th and early 20th centuries. Breeding was first recorded in England in 1849. The Tufted Duck has increased and spread as a breeding bird over much of Britain in the last 100 years, and at the same time has become more common in winter. The species was first recorded breeding in Scotland in 1872 (First Atlas) and has subsequently become widespread, although it remains less common in the west because suitable breeding habitat is not so widely available. Many Scottish breeding birds are believed to winter in Ireland, whilst winter numbers are increased by immigrants from Iceland, northern Scandinavia and Russia (Winter Atlas).

The earliest information about the breeding of this species in Argyll comes from Tiree, where more than one pair was said to be present in 1891, and nesting occurred again in 1892

Largely a bird of freshwater lochs, the Tufted Duck is seldom seen on the open sea or in sea-lochs. *David Palmar*

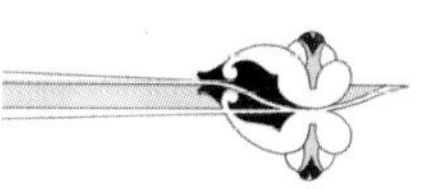

and 1895. Anderson (1898, 1913) described the species as a common visitor to Tiree in winter and spring, but otherwise could only report that a few pairs had nested "some years ago" at Loch Bhasapol. Breeding appears to have ceased some time before 1913, and was not suspected to have occurred again until 1946-52, when birds were present in summer. Breeding was confirmed at Loch a' Chlair in June 1957. In 1986, eight broods were noted, increasing to nine in 1987 (Stroud 1989) and to a peak of 13 broods from 19+ pairs in 1989 (SBR 1989), but the number of broods recorded subsequently has not exceeded eight.

In 1985, a survey of 493 freshwater lochs, mostly in mainland Argyll, revealed the Tufted Duck to be the third commonest duck species, though it was only found on 21 water bodies. Of these, the ones holding most birds were Loch Awe, Tangy Loch (Kintyre) and Loch Gorm (Islay). Overall, Tufted Ducks were widely but thinly distributed, mainly on larger lochs at low altitudes, with an estimated total of 60 breeding pairs (Broad *et al.* 1986). This survey did not cover Tiree, Coll, Colonsay or Mull, though selective coverage of Islay led to the discovery of 14 pairs there. Breeding was first recorded on Islay in the early 1950s (B&R), with up to ten pairs breeding there by the 1970s (Ogilvie 1983). Currently, the known breeding population appears to be around six pairs, though this may be an underestimate. Two or three pairs were found breeding on Colonsay in 1939 and 1942, increasing to five pairs in 1989. On Mull, breeding was suspected to have occurred at the time of the BTO Atlas survey in 1968-72 (First Atlas), and two pairs were recorded there in 1985 (Broad *et al.* 1986) but none in 1988-91 (Second Atlas). Though coverage was incomplete, the 1985 survey was the most recent attempt to estimate the breeding population of Tufted Ducks in Argyll. With the inclusion of Tiree and the other islands, a total population of some 100 pairs seems likely. Given the possible declines since then on Tiree and Islay, the current total may be lower. Loch Nell, near Oban, was once a regular site for a moult flock of males in late summer. As many as 60 birds were recorded there in early August 1992, but only small numbers have been seen since the mid-1990s.

H&B documented an increase in the winter occurrence of the Tufted Duck in Argyll, noting a westward spread of records from eastern Scotland to the Argyll watershed and the larger islands by 1891. The record of a bird shot on Tiree in January 1887 was regarded as notable (H&B), perhaps indicating the scarcity of the species on the island at that time. However, wintering numbers apparently increased rapidly, with Tufted Ducks described as common on the island a few years later (H&B, Anderson 1898) and again as common in winter 1953-55, with flocks not usually exceeding 70 birds frequenting both sea and fresh water (Boyd 1958). A very high count of 615 was recorded on Tiree in the 1956-57 winter but typically numbers peak at around 100-220 birds in mid-winter, including 221 on 23-25 November 1985, 173 on 7 February 2003 and 178 on 19 December 2003. Birds frequent all four main lochs on the island, with largest numbers at Loch Bhasapol and Loch a' Phuill.

While Tiree remains the stronghold of this species in Argyll during the winter months, it occurs in most areas. Good numbers wintered on Islay in the 1960s and 1970s, with peak counts of 16-40 on several freshwater lochs, regularly as many as 50 at Loch Skerrols with a peak count of 100, and a high count of 200 at Loch Allan in February 1969 (Ogilvie 1983). Numbers have subsequently declined, with typical maximum winter counts of 20-30 birds from six main sites over the past five years. The only loch regularly recording larger numbers is Loch Gorm, where a recent high count of 96 on 4 October 2001 indicates an influence of passage birds. Elsewhere in Argyll, the species is a widespread winter visitor with small flocks reported from many freshwater lochs. There is little direct evidence for migration through Argyll, other than occasional records – which may involve birds of Icelandic origin – during autumn seawatches. Some wintering Tufted Ducks in Argyll come from further east, as shown by the recovery, at Loch Fyne on 11 January 1969, of a bird ringed at or near Loch Leven (Fife) the previous August.

John Bowler

Greater Scaup

Aythya marila

Winters regularly at Loch Indaal, where the flock averages about 1,000 birds. Occurs irregularly and in much smaller numbers elsewhere, with small flocks of migrants sometimes seen during autumn seawatches.

Gray described the Scaup as a regular winter visitor to Iona and Mull, that was also occasionally seen on the shores of Islay, while Graham said that it occurred in small numbers on both sea and freshwater in Iona and Mull. According to H&B, it was seen frequently on Tiree, where Eagle Clarke reported a large flock in Hynish Bay on the unusual date of 12 June 1891. Anderson (1898) reported considerable numbers on Tiree in winter. More than half a century later, B&R had very little to add to these early accounts, although they did describe the species as uncommon on the Argyll mainland.

Today, the main site for Scaup in Argyll is Loch Indaal on Islay. Indeed, this is now one of the three most important wintering sites of this species in the British Isles, with some eight per cent of the UK wintering population of just over 12,000 birds (Gregory *et al.* 2002). This followed a decline in numbers in the Firth of Forth and a recovery in the Icelandic breeding population, leading to Lough Neagh becoming the main wintering site in the British Isles. Although it seems certain that the bulk of the Loch Indaal flock consists of Icelandic birds, it is likely that wintering flocks anywhere in

Britain and Ireland include birds that breed in Fennoscandia and further east (Migration Atlas).

Regular counting of birds in Loch Indaal began in the early 1970s, with 1,500 birds present in January 1973 (IBNHR 1991:6). Since then, peak winter counts have fluctuated considerably, though rarely falling below 500, but there has been no long-term change. Counts exceeding 1,400 were made in 1986, 1991 and 2000, the highest to date being 1,505 in January 1986 (IBNHR 1991:6). The birds are most frequent in the north-eastern part of the loch between Bowmore and Black Rock. In the past, they also occasionally used the nearby freshwater loch, Loch Skerrols (Elliott 1989), but only small numbers have been recorded there recently.

Loch Indaal, Islay, holds about eight per cent of the UK's wintering population of Scaup. *Jim Dickson*

Almost all the peak counts have been in December, January or February. From about February onwards there is a progressive decline in numbers, with a few birds still present in mid-May and stragglers sometimes into June. Generally, returning birds are first reported in late August or early September, with numbers continuing to rise steeply through to November or December. At Uisaed Point in Kintyre, small flocks are regularly seen flying south in the second half of September and October, and smaller numbers are seen on occasion at Frenchman's Rocks on Islay; at the former site, the highest count at that time of year was 70 in 8 hours on 30 September 1996 (ABR 13:38).

These observations tally with the statement in the Migration Atlas that the main arrival of Scaup in Britain and Ireland starts late in October, with some birds arriving at wintering sites as early as September. However, in some years at least, migration through Argyll begins as early as mid-July. Thus on 22 July 1996, a total of 51 flew south past the Portnahaven area of Islay and six past Uisaed Point (ABR 13:38); most of these were drakes. In 1997, 33 flew south past Uisaed Point on 9 August and 90 on 12 August (ABR 14:36). The only comparable recent record from elsewhere in Scotland appears to be a count of 87 birds (all but three of which were drakes) at Annan (Dumfries & Galloway) on 9 July 1998 (SBR 1998:29). Although this was a one-off count, birds might be undetected there in other years (P. Collin pers. comm.). Recent arrival (rather than over-summering) could also account for the occurrence of 15 birds in Loch Indaal on 15 July 1988 (ABR 5:18) and 36 on 4 August 1999 (ABR 16:39), as well as a scattering of records of mainly single birds from Mull and Kintyre at the same time of year.

Away from Loch Indaal, there appear to be no wintering flocks of any size, though small numbers are regularly recorded on Tiree and at Loch Torr on Mull. The largest winter count was of 32 birds on West Loch Tarbert in mid-January 1981 (ABR 1:25). Generally speaking, most records away from Loch Indaal have been in autumn or spring. Singles and small groups, rarely exceeding five birds, have been recorded in recent years on Mull, Tiree, Coll and Oronsay, as well as on the mainland at Loch Etive, Oban, Loch Feochan, Loch Crinan, Loch Fyne and Loch Gilp. An isolated record from Cowal involved one flying down the east Kyle of Bute on 17 May 1985 (ABR 3:21). Some of these records involve single birds or pairs present briefly in late May or early June, arousing suspicions that breeding might occur. For example, two males and a female were at a suitable breeding site in Mid-Argyll in late May 1985, though they had departed by June (ABR 3:21). Given that Scaup have occasionally nested in the Outer Hebrides (e.g. Thom), it seems possible that the species may one day be recorded as a breeder in Argyll.

Tristan ap Rheinallt

Lesser Scaup

Aythya affinis

Vagrant.

Since the first occurrence in 1987, this North American duck has been recorded with increasing frequency in Britain and Ireland. There is one accepted record from Argyll. A first-winter female was at Ardnave Loch on Islay from 6 November 1998 to 9 January 1999. It also visited Loch Gruinart during this period (BB 92:566, 94:465). This was the sixth Scottish record and coincided with the occurrence of three birds together (the first British multiple record) in Shetland.

Tristan ap Rheinallt

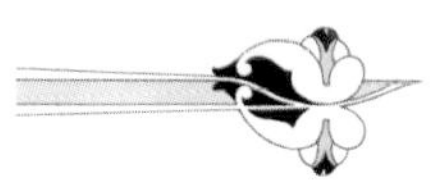

Eider

Somateria mollissima

A widespread breeding species. Common on most coasts of Argyll, but especially on the Clyde.

Numbers have increased considerably over many decades and flocks of over 1,000 birds occur in some areas in late summer. It is a partial migrant, with some birds from exposed coasts moving into the Firth of Clyde for the winter. The Eider is a significant predator at mussel farms with the potential to bankrupt businesses.

The Eider Duck occurs throughout the coastal fringes of Argyll, where it feeds in shallow marine and brackish waters on the Blue Mussel and to a smaller extent on other invertebrates. Eiders nest on the ground in secluded places away from predators and human disturbance. This can include moorland at considerable altitudes (occasionally up to 200m asl) as well as small islands. They often nest in small groups, but large colonies may develop on safe sites such as secluded predator-free islands. Nests may be on open heather or grass, but can also be under thick cover of brambles, bracken or even in dense scrubby woodland or young conifer plantations. Outside the breeding season, Eiders tend to remain close to the shore and often aggregate into feeding or roosting flocks of hundreds, sometimes thousands, of birds. Most feeding is in water less than 10m deep.

In Argyll, Eiders often congregate around mariculture developments, military piers, harbours and marinas as well as at natural mussel beds. They will feed at mussel farms, where they can be a serious economic pest (Ross *et al.* 2001), and at salmon cages. It is unclear whether Eiders at salmon farms are feeding only on fouling invertebrates on the ropes, chains and cages, or whether they also feed on surplus aquafeed pellets that sink out of the cages. Because salmon farms are closed to the public to avoid risks of disease transmission, Eiders often roost on shore where they have learned that disturbance is rare. Secluded rocky shores or gravel beaches are also used as daytime roosting areas, especially when the birds have a stomach full of mussels. At night, Eiders roost in offshore flocks, flying in to the coast at first light to start feeding. The present distribution and number are remarkably different from the historical status of the species in Argyll.

There are records of Eiders in Argyll from as far back as the 16th century, when Dean Munro reported many on Gigha. Pennant (1789) found Eiders on Colonsay and Oronsay in 1768 and it is thought that these islands provided a centre of dispersal for the expanding population in the Argyll islands in the 19th century. This increase was the start of an expansion of range and numbers all over Scotland that began around 1850 (B&R). Before 1900, Eiders could be found around many islands in north-west Argyll, but nowhere in the Clyde area. Gray reported "The extraordinary number of Eider Ducks found on the island of Colonsay has gained for this bird the local name of *Lach Cholonsa*. It is likewise very numerous around Mull and Iona. Quantities of Eider eggs are sent to Glasgow poulterers from Islay, and occasionally from Tiree and Coll. South of Islay the Eider is but a winter straggler".

McWilliam reported "The Eider was a rare winter visitor to the Clyde till recent years...In the course of about 15 years the Eider has succeeded in establishing itself as a common Clyde species". Small numbers began to appear in Loch Fyne from the 1890s, where it was first found nesting in 1908. However, the first nesting record on a Clyde island was in 1928, when it nested on Bute (B&R). B&R also reported "rapid spread of the Eider in the Firth of Clyde closely connected with the distribution of the mussel. Recently there was a sudden invasion by this mussel on the shores of the Cumbraes and in the Holy Loch and other localities". It is quite likely that this spread of the mussel in the Clyde was related to levels of organic (predominantly sewage) pollution. At the end of the 19th century the Clyde estuary was so severely polluted that mudflats became devoid of oxygen and animal life was wiped out. Development of sewage treatment has progressively reduced the amount of sewage in the Clyde since then. Blooms of mussels may have resulted when pollution levels were reduced, but still high enough to maintain large bacterial populations supporting these filter feeders. Certainly, since 1900 the proportion of Argyll Eiders found within the Clyde has increased dramatically. Chris Waltho has found evidence that local distribution varies in relation to mussel availability across years. There were about 1,000 fewer Eiders in the area from Coulport to Rhu in 2001 than in 2000. In 2000, only about 5% of the diet of these birds was not mussels, but in 2001 about 20%-30% of the diet was not mussels, suggesting lower availability of mussels in this area in 2001 (Waltho 2002). Ring recovery data show that movements of Argyll Eiders tend to be very local. Of 24 Argyll-ringed birds, only 11 were found more than 9km from the ringing site, and none had moved more than 99km.

In recent years, Eiders in the Clyde have been counted each September, and in 1998 this census was extended to the whole of Argyll. Total numbers in the Clyde ranged from 14,500 to 19,400 birds in the years 1996-2002, and the lack of any clear trend in the total over this period suggests that the prolonged increase in Eider numbers in this area may have ceased. However, this now represents the largest regional population of Eiders in Scotland, greatly exceeding numbers on the Tay, Firth of Forth, Shetland or Orkney. Many birds are on the Ayrshire coast or inner Clyde rather than in the Argyll parts of the Clyde, but high concentrations (often over 1,000 birds) occur in Holy Loch, and at Otter Ferry in Loch Fyne. By contrast, in 1998 the total for the whole of Argyll outside the Clyde (west coast of Kintyre and northwards including the islands) was 1,900. So the Clyde holds about ten times as many Eiders in autumn as found in the outer part of Argyll. The highest counts from the islands were 528 around Mull and 283 around Islay. Almost all birds around Mull were at mussel or salmon farms, as were many of those in sea lochs on the Argyll mainland. This suggests local distribution is strongly influenced not only by the availability of mussel beds in the Clyde but also by feeding opportunities created by the mariculture industry.

Counts of Eiders in early April 1999 throughout Argyll and the Clyde were used to gain an impression of the likely distribution of breeding birds since this was thought to be just before laying begins. This spring census found 18,000 Eiders, of which 12,750 were in the Clyde and 5,250 were in the much larger area west and north of Kintyre up to Ardnamurchan. The higher spring than autumn numbers in outer Argyll supports the widely held view that some Eiders from the more exposed coasts of western Argyll move into the Clyde for the autumn and winter. However, the numbers also show that Eiders are far more abundant as breeders in the Clyde than in outer Argyll. Counts of nests at major colonies support this.

The largest colonies of Eiders in the Clyde are on Horse Island, Ardrossan (just outside Argyll) which held about 500 nests in 2001 (Waltho 2001), and the Burnt Islands, off Bute, which held about 400 to 600 nests in 2000-02 (estimated by mark-recapture by Bob Furness). The Faslane military base hosts about 100 Eider nests (Waltho 2001). Breeding aggregations in central mainland Argyll sea lochs have been surveyed by Clive Craik in 1999-2002. Seven islands in Loch Fyne held a total of at least 190 nests, seven sites in Loch Linnhe held at least 70 nests and six sites in Loch Etive held at least 60 nests. The April 1999 counts of adult females may be indicative of breeding numbers on the larger islands; 170 at Gigha, 190 at Islay, 8 at Jura, 140 at Colonsay, 80 at Kerrera, 85 at Lismore, 260 at Mull, 130 at Coll and 280 at Tiree.

At Argyll colonies the average clutch size is about four eggs, with occasional clutches of seven or eight eggs probably the result of two ducks laying in the same nest. The earliest eggs start hatching around 18 May, with most hatching at the end of May. A few females may incubate during early July, and there is an exceptional record of a brood of newly hatched chicks at Otter Ferry on 19 August 2000 (ABR). As is typical of the species, duckling survival at Argyll colonies is very low. Many chicks are eaten by large gulls. The large crèches of Eider ducklings seen in estuaries on the east of Scotland do not normally form in Argyll. Most females take their brood to feeding areas independently and mixing of broods is relatively infrequent.

More Eiders occur on the Clyde in autumn than anywhere else in Scotland. *David Wood*

It is characteristic of Eiders, and of most other ducks, that numbers of males exceed numbers of females. In the Clyde and outer Argyll in 2000-02, adult males formed about 63% of the population, rather consistently across sites. This is a higher excess of males than in most other parts of Scotland. The reasons are not clear, but may relate to higher levels of nest predation. In recent years predation by American Mink has become an increasing problem at some colonies, where numbers of incubating ducks have been killed. After such predation, two large colonies in Loch Fyne have recently disappeared while, at sites near Oban where mink are controlled, nesting numbers have increased. Eiders of both sexes may be killed at mussel farms. Small numbers are shot under licence and uncertain numbers are shot illegally. Some birds drown as a result of becoming entangled in anti-predator nets set around mussel lines or rafts to protect the stock against depredations by the ducks (Ross & Furness 2000). The only two recoveries of Eiders ringed at nests on the Burnt Islands in 1999-2001 have been birds that were drowned in nets at mussel farms.

Bob Furness

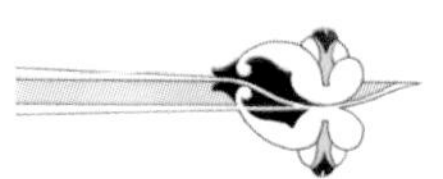

King Eider

Somateria spectabilis

Vagrant.

The King Eider breeds in the High Arctic and regularly winters, in Europe, as far south as Iceland and north Norway. As long ago as the end of the 19th century, H&B described it as occurring in Scotland "here and there, now and then, if not regularly at all seasons." At the time, there was one Argyll record, described by them as follows:

... Mr. Henry Evans of Jura, who, after careful searching many days amongst troops of Eider Ducks, at last spotted the rare relative amongst the crowd, on the 4th of October 1889. All present, including Mr. H. Evans and his brother, and all of whom had telescopes, saw the bird distinctly, a magnificent male... Later on, having seen this bird five times, Mr. Evans "saw him alight on the sea, steered for him, and flushed him twenty yards off, so saw his red or orange-red legs before he rose and tucked them up;"...

Not long afterwards, one was seen from the cliffs near Kintra on Islay on 25 July 1906 (ASNH 1907:198, B&R, see BB 2:86). There were no more reports until the early 1970s, when the first of eleven recent records occurred. These recent records are considered by BBRC to relate to no more than eight birds, with one returning individual believed to account for all the 1970s records (Suddaby *et al.* 1994).

However, the true total is unknown and it seems likely that the 1993, 1995 and 1998 Kintyre records could all refer to the same individual, as could the 2000 and 2002 records from the north mainland. All the records refer to males, and it seems possible that females and immatures have been overlooked, although males are thought to move much further from their natal breeding sites than females (Suddaby *et al.* 1994). Most of the Argyll records have been in spring (late March to early June), suggesting northbound migrants.

Tristan ap Rheinallt

Date	Location	Comment	Reference
18 - 24 Dec 1972	Clachan (Kintyre)		BB 66:338, SB 7:340
5 Jun 1974	Innellan	Same bird as Clachan	BB 68:314, Suddaby *et al.* (1994), SB 8:414
3 Jun 1979	Tayinloan	Same bird as Clachan	BB 73:501, Suddaby *et al.* (1994)
26 Apr - 7 Jun 1993	Salum Bay (Tiree)		BB 87:517
13 Oct 1993	Port Ellen (Islay)	Possibly same bird as Salum Bay, but counted as different by BBRC	BB 87:517
3 Nov 1993	Machrihanish	Same bird as Port Ellen	BB 93:525
26 Mar - 1 Apr 1995	Uisaed Point, nr Machrihanish		BB 91:469
2 - 10 Jun 1998	Ballochantuy		BB 93:525
8 Apr - 1 May 2000	North Ledaig		BB 94:466
6 Apr 2002	Dunstaffnage		BB 96:559
25 May - 21 Jun 2003	Toward and Cluniter		Argyll Database

Records of King Eiders, 1972-2003.

Harlequin Duck

Histrionicus histrionicus

Vagrant.

There is one accepted record of this species in Argyll. A female was at Claggain Bay on Islay during 20 to 30 October 1987 (BB 81:549, 82:518), and apparently also on 31 October (SBR 1987:16, ABR 5:6). This was only the fifth acceptable Scottish record (Andrews & Naylor 2002) and it attracted a large influx of twitchers to the island.

The breeding range of this attractive duck includes Iceland, Greenland and eastern North America. Icelandic birds are apparently only short-distance migrants, and the Islay bird may therefore have come from Greenland or eastern Canada.

[An earlier record quoted by Elliott (1989) concerned a male shot on Islay in November 1954. This record was recently reviewed by a BBRC subcommittee and is no longer considered acceptable (Wallace *et al.* 2006).]

Tristan ap Rheinallt

Long-tailed Duck

Clangula hyemalis

Uncommon winter visitor, occurring regularly in small numbers at specific locations in Coll, Tiree, Islay and Kintyre. Numbers appear to peak in spring at some sites. Occasional summer records.

Long-tailed Ducks wintering in Britain and Ireland are believed to originate from northern Fennoscandia and north-west Russia. It is thought that the peak winter population exceeds 20,000 birds, most of these being in the Moray Firth

(Migration Atlas). Argyll holds only a tiny fraction of this population.

Large parts of the Argyll coastline are unsuitable for Long-tailed Ducks, which prefer areas with extensive offshore shallows and soft substrates. Gray reported that they occurred "in considerable numbers" off the coasts of Mull and Islay in the winter months. The species was very familiar to Graham, who described the arrival of the first wintering birds in early November, followed by fresh arrivals in severe weather during December and January to give peak numbers in late winter. However, Iona's regular wintering flock apparently vanished some time between 1852 and 1867 (Graham, H&B), a phenomenon attributed by Graham to "some occult change in the growth of the submarine vegetation, which forms the pasturage of these creatures". H&B described the species as common off Tiree, with records from Colonsay, Oronsay and Jura.

Today, birds normally arrive off the coast of Argyll from mid-October onwards, but a few may turn up as early as mid-September. The only site where migrating birds are seen with any degree of regularity is Uisaed Point in Kintyre, where almost all records of southbound birds are in October and day-counts rarely exceed single figures. The most regular wintering sites today appear to be Feall Bay on Coll, the Sound of Gigha, Balephetrish Bay on Tiree and Loch Indaal on Islay. The last three sites accounted for most of the birds recorded in Argyll during the Winter Atlas survey. All four hold 20 or more birds during some winters.

The main wintering sites for Long-tailed Ducks are the Sound of Gigha and waters around Tiree, Coll and Islay. *Philip Kirkham*

Flocks of fewer than 20 birds are not infrequently reported from several other sites on Tiree, though movement between sites could lead to duplication. Apart from some isolated double-figure counts from a few other sites in Kintyre and Islay, the remaining records consist mostly of scattered reports of one to four birds from Mull, Colonsay, Oronsay, Mid-Argyll and North Argyll, in addition to the areas already listed. Long-tailed Ducks appear to be rare in Cowal, though single birds were on Holy Loch on 1 February 1986, 9 February 1992 and 16 May 1992. Similarly, the only recent records from Jura are of 20 west of the island on 8 April 1972 (SB 7:338) and six at Corpach Bay on 30 March 1991. It is known that wintering Long-tailed Ducks may stay well offshore (Migration Atlas), as in the case of Tiree (H&B). This suggests that shore-based counts may be underestimates, and also that some locations in Argyll where birds are irregularly sighted might hold wintering flocks. An aerial survey of waters around Coll and Tiree on 18 February 2004 found 61 Long-tailed Ducks in transects totalling 416km (Wilson 2006). There are occasional records on fresh water, not only close to the sea on the islands but also on lochs such as Loch Leathan, Loch Awe and Loch nan Druimnean in Mid-Argyll.

While it is likely that numbers at some sites peak in

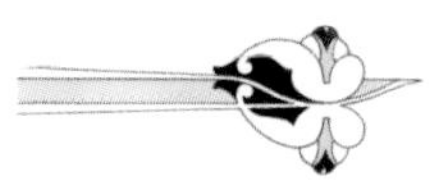

Peak counts of Long-tailed Ducks at four sites in Argyll, 1988-1997.

Site	Peak count	Date of peak count
Feall Bay	125	8 December 1991
Sound of Gigha	73	19 April 1992
Balephetrish Bay	21	11 November 1988
Loch Indaal	20	15 April 1997

midwinter, there is a suggestion of an April peak at other sites, such as the Sound of Gigha. This suggests that Argyll's wintering population is augmented by northbound migrants in spring, as may be the case elsewhere in Britain (Winter Atlas). On the other hand, birds may simply be more conspicuous at that time. Although return to the breeding grounds begins in February (Migration Atlas), the main departure from Argyll seems to occur in April, the last individuals remaining at regular sites into early May. A few are observed later in May and there is a small number of summer records. A female remained at Ganavan Bay, Oban from 10 July to 14 August 1995.

It has been suggested that some of the Icelandic population, which is only partially migratory, may winter in Scotland. Although there is no direct evidence (Migration Atlas), Argyll-based seawatchers report occasional Long-tailed Ducks with influxes of mainly Icelandic wildfowl during October.

Tristan ap Rheinallt

Common Scoter

Melanitta nigra

Very small breeding population in two localities. Present year round in Loch Indaal and the Sound of Gigha, less regular in winter elsewhere.

H&B record a probable breeding record from Tiree in 1889, but breeding in the county was not proved until 1954 when Meiklejohn & Stanford found at least five pairs (including two nests with eggs) at Loch Gorm, Islay. Although the next proven breeding record there was not until 1970, there is no reason to believe it was not taking place annually, as has been the case ever since. Determining the maximum number of pairs takes several visits, preferably early or late in the day. This has happened annually since the mid-1980s, but not in earlier years, so counts of five nests in 1970, 6-7 pairs in 1973, eight males in 1975, ten males and seven females in 1978 are not certainly maxima. Since 1986, high counts have included 14 pairs and three males in 1987 and 14 pairs and two males in 1989, while throughout the 1990s, numbers varied between a low of six males and seven females in 1998 and a peak of 12 pairs, two males and a female in 1996. Although there were up to seven or eight pairs in 2000-2002, in 2003 there were only two pairs and two males, while in 2004 there were just two pairs. The possible causes for this sudden decline are unknown. Also in the 1990s, a single pair was seen in at least six years on a small lochan a few hundred metres from Loch

Maximum counts of Common Scoter at Loch Indaal and Sound of Gigha, 1986-2003.

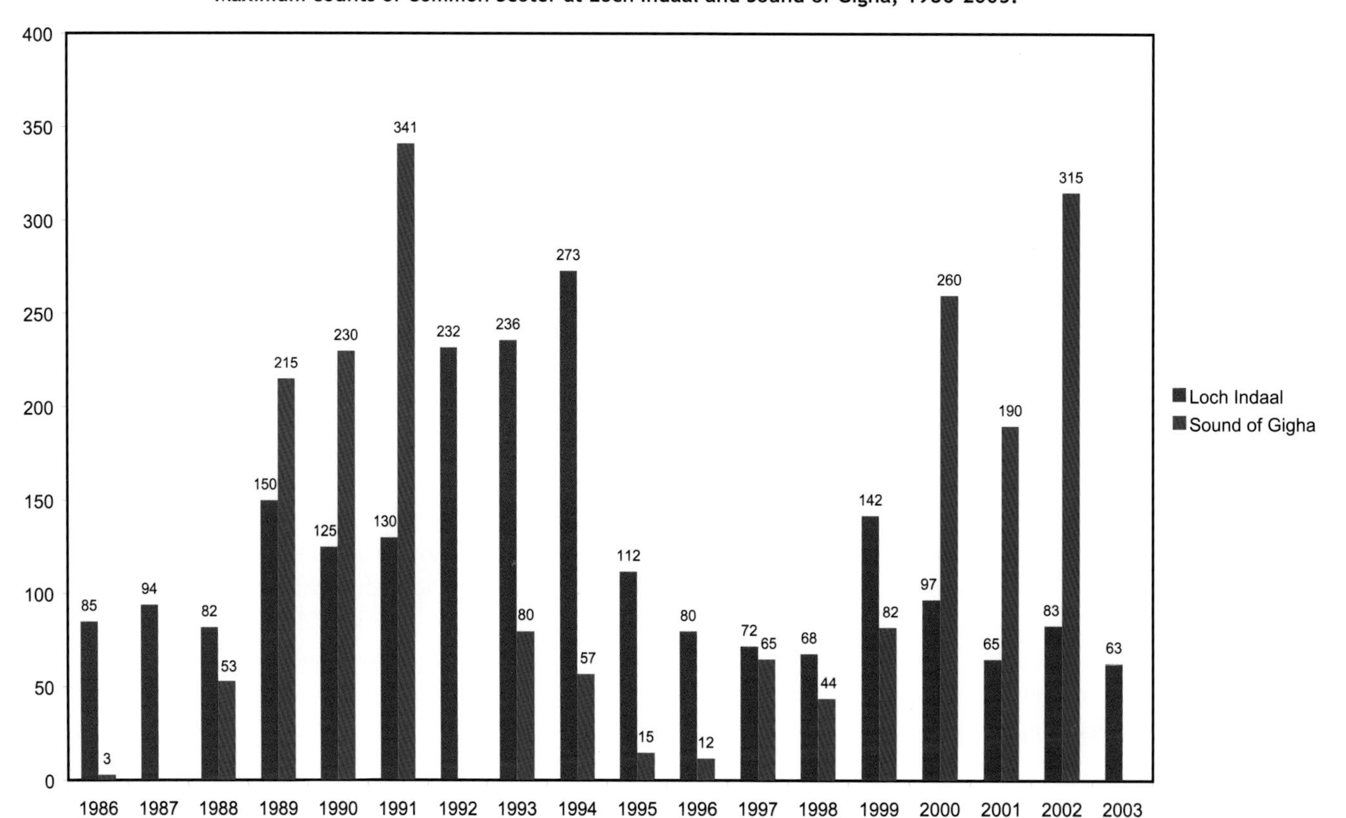

No counts from Sound of Gigha in 1987, 1992 and 2003.

Gorm. Nests have only been searched for in a few years, with the majority found on one or more of the three small islands in the loch, though in one year when otters were breeding on the principal island, three nests were found around the shores of the loch. Ducklings have only been reported in eight years since 1970, with one sighting of a family on the sea off the adjacent west coast of Islay suggesting that, as elsewhere, the females take their broods to the sea when they are quite small. Breeding took place on Loch Awe in the early 1980s (one pair in 1982 and at least one in 1985), and then in most years since 1992, usually one or two pairs, but five males and three females in 1994 and five pairs in 1999. There was only one pair in 2000 and none in 2001. In addition, a pair bred on a loch in North Argyll each year between 1997 and 2000, a single pair bred at a site in Mid-Argyll in 2002 and a female with a half grown chick, together with other adults possibly with young were at a site on Jura in June 2002 (ABR).

Common Scoters are present throughout the year on the sea in Loch Indaal and in the Sound of Gigha. Numbers fluctuate in both areas, often peaking during the migration periods in spring and late summer. The Figure shows the maximum counts each year, but these should be interpreted cautiously because frequency and duration of observations varied between years.

Sea-watches at adjacent points (Frenchman's Rocks, Islay, and Machrihanish, Kintyre) regularly record up to 50 birds passing in a few hours, especially in autumn. Elsewhere in the county, the Common Scoter is an occasional visitor in groups from 1-10, rarely to 50, mainly to sheltered sea lochs such as West Loch Tarbert and Loch Caolisport, but also to waters around Mull and Tiree.

Malcolm Ogilvie

Surf Scoter

Melanitta perspicillata

Rare visitor, mostly in spring.

Breeding in North America, the Surf Scoter has long been known as an occasional visitor to Scottish waters. It has occurred annually since 1974, with the majority of records from the east coast where small numbers are now present all year round. The situation in the west is somewhat different, with generally fewer records. Ayrshire, for example, did not record its first bird until 1999 (SBR 1999:34).

The first Argyll record involved a male at Ballochroy and Achanadriane in Kintyre from 16 to 21 April 1977 (BB 71:495). This was followed less then a month later by a group of five birds flying south past Frenchman's Rocks on Islay on 15 May (BB 71:495). Over the next 18 years, there were only three more records, all from the islands: Islay in 1982, Tiree in 1983, and Islay in 1990.

From 1996 to 2001, Surf Scoters were seen annually in Argyll, although several records are likely to have involved returning birds. However, there were no records in 2002 or 2003. The nine records between 1996 and 2001 came from Islay (four), Mull (two), Kintyre (two) and Tiree. Most were of singles, but five birds were at Ronachan Point in Kintyre on 2 May 1997 (ABR 14:38). Of these 14 records, nine were in spring (March to May) and four in October; no fewer than six came from Loch Indaal on Islay.

Tristan ap Rheinallt

Velvet Scoter

Melanitta fusca

Scarce but regular in and around the Sound of Gigha and, in much smaller numbers, at Loch Indaal on Islay. The wintering population at the former location has declined substantially since the 1970s, when it numbered more than 50 birds.

Velvet Scoters, thought to be from populations in Norway, Finland and perhaps Northern Russia, moult and winter in large numbers on the east coast of Britain, including Scotland (Thom, Migration Atlas). However, numbers in the west are very much lower. In Argyll, the first mention is from Craignish (NSA). H&B refer to a sighting on Loch Gilp. However, they ignore a statement by Gray that several flocks were at Loch Indaal in 1867. Given that Common Scoters had apparently not been recorded from Islay at this time, there must be some doubt over which species was involved. The same applies to Henry Evans' claim that Velvet Scoters occurred on Jura (quoted by H&B). In his list of Jura birds (Harvie-Brown papers, NMS), Evans claimed that the Velvet

The Sound of Gigha is the most reliable place to find Velvet Scoters in Argyll. *Philip Snow*

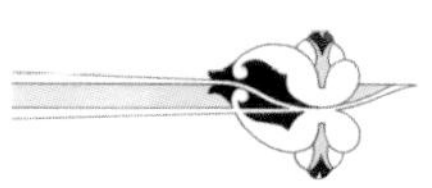

Date	Location	Count	Comment	Reference
20 April 1964	Machir Bay (Islay)	7	-	Booth 1975, Elliott 1989
30 October 1993	Uisaed Point	6	Flying south	ABR 10:34
24 April 1994	Frenchman's Rocks (Islay)	7	Flying north	ABR 11:36
10 October 1997	Uisaed Point	5	Flying south	ABR 14:38
27 May 1999	Croig (Mull)	8	In flight	ABR 16:42

Counts of five or more Velvet Scoters at locations other than Sound of Gigha and West Loch Tarbert.

Scoter was far from rare on the island, being known locally as the "sea blackcock". Again, it may be significant that the Common Scoter does not feature on this list. B&R refer to a record of a pair on Loch Scridain on Mull on 16 June 1876; curiously, Harvie-Brown claimed to have seen a pair of Common Scoters at the same location, presumably in 1880 (H&B). In fact, the only fully documented pre-1950 record of Velvet Scoter involves a female off Port Askaig on Islay on 17 July 1931 (SN 1932:8, B&R).

Following a few records from Kilberry in the first half of the 1950s (Rainier 1975), it became apparent that the mouth of West Loch Tarbert was a regular haunt of this species, with up to three birds in November 1956, one in November 1957, and eight on 28 March 1959 (SB 1:130). After 15 years when no further sightings were reported, counts in the 1970s revealed large numbers south of West Loch Tarbert, with a maximum of more than 80 off Tayinloan on 7 April 1976 (SB 10:85). This made the Sound of Gigha one of only two nationally important areas for Velvet Scoters in the west of Scotland, the other being the Outer Hebrides (Thom). However, a count of 18 off Tayinloan on 29 November 1981 (SBR 1981:21) was the only one to reach double figures in the whole of the 1980s, and the situation has shown little change since then, the highest count being 18 off Rhunahaorine Point on 10 April 1994 (ABR 11:36). Regular counts in 2000 peaked at 16 on 5 April (ABR 17:43), showing clearly that the decline was real. Birds have been recorded in the Sound of Gigha in every month of the year, some apparently summering and others arriving to moult from about July onwards. Males reach their moult sites in late summer, females and young joining them later (Migration Atlas).

Elsewhere in Argyll, the only location where birds are known to winter regularly is Loch Indaal. However, numbers here are very much smaller, no count having exceeded three. Birds were noted in Machrihanish Bay in the winters of 1993/94, 1994/95 and 1996/97, with two individuals wintering in 1993/94 (ABR 11:36). Uisaed Point, at the southern end of the bay, has also produced several records of migrating birds in spring and autumn. Away from the Sound of Gigha and West Loch Tarbert, all counts of five or more in Argyll have occurred during the migration seasons (Table).

Single birds and groups of up to four have been noted sporadically at several other locations, primarily on Mull, Islay and Tiree. Away from Kintyre, there appear to be only two recent mainland records: two birds at Lochgilphead on 21 January 1984 (ABR 2:17) and four in Loch Etive on 11 February 1986 (ABR 4:15). A female on Loch Gorm on Islay on 17 May 2000 (ABR 17:43) was apparently the only bird ever seen on freshwater in Argyll.

Tristan ap Rheinallt

Goldeneye at Loch Uisg, Mull. *Philip Snow*

Common Goldeneye

Bucephala clangula

A common winter visitor. Birds are regularly present in all areas from early October to late April, with occasional summer records.

This is a common and widespread passage migrant and winter visitor to Scotland that has bred in Inverness-shire, and elsewhere in small numbers, since 1970. The wintering population is largely from Scandinavia. It is most numerous in sea lochs, and estuaries, with the largest numbers in the Firth of Clyde and Firth of Forth, and smaller numbers inland (Thom, SBR). Concentrations are often linked to sites of sewage outfalls or other discharges of organic material. There are sometimes marked differences in the sex composition of flocks, with males more numerous than females, but the reason for this is unknown (Winter Atlas).

The Common Goldeneye has been known as a winter visitor to Scotland for at least 200 years (NSA). In the mid 19th century Gray described it as 'commonly distributed over the whole of western Scotland', although H&B said it was 'common yet hardly to be called abundant'. Among the localities specifically mentioned were the waters around Islay, Jura, Tiree, Iona and Mull (H&B). In the mid-20th century it was said to be common on the sea lochs of Argyll and on Islay and, in flocks normally of fewer than 20 birds, on Coll and Tiree. It was also reported from Iona and Mull in small numbers (B&R, Boyd 1958). The Winter Atlas shows the highest numbers in the sea lochs of Cowal, along the west coast of the mainland from Gigha northwards, in Lochs Creran and Etive and in the west of Mull, Islay and Tiree. Apart from in Campbeltown Loch there were few in southern Kintyre and only small numbers on Coll, Colonsay and Jura.

A few birds start to appear in Argyll from early September onwards, but the majority do not arrive until mid to late October. These may include some males from the Scottish breeding population (Second Atlas). Numbers are at their highest from late December to early March and most have left by the end of April, with a few lingering into May. The great majority are found in the sea lochs and off the coast of the mainland and, to some extent, the islands. Significant numbers occur on freshwater lochs of Tiree, but on the mainland they are scarce away from saltwater. The present distribution is still much as shown in the Winter Atlas except that only two counts of more than 20 birds have been reported from Mull in recent years. Most sites hold less than 20 birds, but a few favoured localities support much higher numbers (Table). Since 1990 Loch Caolisport has regularly held 100 or more birds, with a maximum count of 197 in January 2001. From 2003, similar numbers have gathered on Loch Fyne at the mouth of Leacann Water, Furnace. The highest count to the end of 2005 was 236 on 20 November 2005.

There have been isolated records of summering birds in some years but no evidence of breeding.

Paul Daw

Location	Date	Count
Holy Loch, Cowal	13 December 1997	33
Otter Ferry, Cowal	24 February 2001	28
Kilnaughton/Port Ellen Bay, Islay	25 December 1995	75
Loch Indaal, Islay	27 February 1993	38
Sound of Gigha, Kintyre	28 December 2001	85
Furnace (Loch Fyne), Mid-Argyll	20 November 2005	236
Loch Craignish, Mid-Argyll	11 December 1995	27
Loch Feochan, Mid-Argyll	5 March 1999	56
Loch Gair, Mid-Argyll	7 March 1999	35
Loch Gilp, Mid-Argyll	12 February 2003	57
Loch Caolisport, Mid-Argyll	January 2001	197
Loch Sween, Mid-Argyll	29 February 2004	51
Outer Loch Etive, North Argyll	14 March 1998	34
Inner Loch Etive, off Glennoe Jetty	5 December 1998	82
Loch Spelve, Mull	17 November 2001	65
Loch a' Phuill, Tiree	1 December 2004	66

Maximum counts at sites holding more than 25 Goldeneyes from 1990 to the end of 2005.

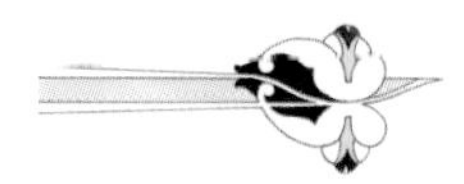

Smew

Mergus albellus

Rare winter visitor.

In Europe, the Smew breeds mainly in northern Sweden, northern Finland and Russia. Birds begin to leave breeding sites in September and pass through Sweden and the Baltic countries from mid-October to early November. Bad weather during winter drives them westwards, peak arrivals in the UK usually being in January (BWP, Migration Atlas). Against this background, the apparent regular presence of this species in Tiree towards the end of the 19th century, when birds were recorded in autumn, winter and spring, seems anomalous to say the least. H&B state that it is recognised "on the sea here [i.e. on Tiree] both in winter and summer", whilst B&R add that it is one of the earliest migratory ducks to arrive in Tiree, pairs having been recorded as early as 30 July 1898 and 19 August 1896. Although occasional individuals are said to remain well into summer at sites far to the south of the breeding range (Migration Atlas), these early reports from Tiree are so much at variance with current knowledge that they must be regarded with suspicion.

Other authors appear to have regarded the Smew as a rare visitor to Argyll. The sole mention in the NSA comes from Inveraray, where it is included without comment in the list of birds for the parish. Gray describes it as a very rare winter visitor to Islay, while H&B mention a report of a young male at Taynish at the beginning of January 1861 and a mounted specimen shot on Colonsay and displayed in the hotel. Elliott (1989) mentions an 1892 record from Islay.

At least four records exist for the first half of the 20th century: a female between Coll and Tiree on 16 January 1901 (SN 1914:43); one at Skipness on 10 December 1922 (McWilliam); one dead at Kilchoman on Islay on the unusual date of 9 June 1924 (SN 1928:123); and one at Bruichladdich on Islay in December 1925. On 1 January 1954, six (three males and three females) were reported from the head of West Loch Tarbert at the time of a minor influx nationwide (Glasgow and West of Scotland Bird Bulletin 3:14); this record may be responsible for the statement in Gibson & McWilliam (1959) that the Smew is probably "regular in winter in small numbers, particularly in the Tarbert lochs", as there appears to be no other published evidence for this.

All other records fall between 1978 and 2004. In addition to a presumed returning female at Loch Indaal on Islay from winter 1984/85 to winter 1988/89, individuals were reported from Campbeltown Loch (February 1978), Mull (winter 1982/83), Cairndow (February 1984), Colonsay (February 1994), Loch Gilp (November 1998), Oban Bay (November 1999), and Loch Seil (January 2000) (all ABR) and Loch Poit na h-I, Mull (May 2004) (Argyll Database). Clearly, therefore, the Smew is now no more than a very rare winter visitor to Argyll.

Tristan ap Rheinallt

Red-breasted Merganser

Mergus serrator

This is one of the more numerous and widespread resident ducks of the coast, smaller numbers being found on fresh water. Moult flocks form at coastal sites in late summer, those in the Sound of Gigha and Loch Indaal being the best known. Most birds winter along the coast singly, in pairs or in small groups.

Gray reported this species breeding on rocky islets off Islay, Jura, Colonsay and Tiree and considered it a "well known native of nearly all the lakes of any importance north of Loch Lomond". Graham recognised that it was more abundant than Goosander. H&B found it abundant "...in almost all the (Argyll) area, both sea and fresh water, mainland and isles".

B&R described the expansion in its range during 1885-1920. By *c.*1950 the species was common in north-west Scotland south to Argyll and Dunbartonshire and "very common in the Argyll sealochs in winter and early spring".

The First Atlas took the view that "in marine habitats in south-west Scotland, this is often the most numerous breeding duck". Recent counts, however, have suggested that this is not true now in Argyll. Mergansers are outnumbered by several other duck species in winter (see below); and most observers would agree that they are less numerous in summer than Common Eider and possibly Mallard.

Birds return to breeding grounds from late February to April, and nesting occurs along the shore of the mainland and on small islands, particularly in sealochs, as well as on rivers and freshwater lochs. Males play no part in nest-building, incubation or rearing. The female usually lays her 8-10 eggs in nests under an arch of dense vegetation or in a short burrow or other shallow cavity.

The main breeding concentration in the British Isles is in western Scotland. In the Second Atlas, breeding was recorded in most coastal and some inland squares of Argyll; 52% of 10-km squares were occupied, the highest densities being in Mid-Argyll, Cowal, Jura, southern Islay and along the Sound of Mull.

Incubating birds are not flushed until an intruder almost treads on them, so that nests are difficult to find. In 1899, Paterson & Renwick (1900) found nests on several islands in Loch Fyne, including two "within a couple of feet of each other" on Sgat Mor (*cf.* report of colonial nesting by Martin 1988), and one with 16 eggs on Eilean Aoghainn. In the SAMS study, mostly of small islands in mainland sealochs, not more than ten nests are found each year, very few compared with the numbers of adults seen. Similarly, although females with young are reported annually, they seem to occur nowhere in numbers that might be expected for such a widespread and common bird. Single females with broods of 18-23 small young were seen in 1998, 1999 and 2001 (ABR) and crèches of 40-50 young have been reported elsewhere in Scotland

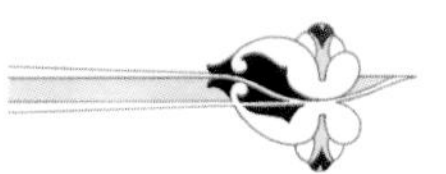

(B&R). These presumably result from more than one female laying in a single nest or from combination of two or more broods.

In their survey of freshwater lochs in Argyll, Broad *et al.* (1986) found 73 Red-breasted Mergansers, or 34-46 pairs, on 23 of 493 lochs, with rarely more than one or two pairs per loch. Most lochs with the species were of medium size. Birds were present in 19 10-km squares and there were about one to three pairs per 10-km square. An overall county total of 150 pairs was estimated (ABR for 1989).

Most of the British population is sedentary, moving only short distances to nearby coasts to moult and winter. Birds gather in large moult flocks at coastal sites from June and numbers peak in August. Thom gave the three most important moult flocks in Scotland as the Sound of Gigha, Kincardine and Angus, and Tentsmuir. The Sound of Gigha still holds the largest moult flock in Argyll with recent counts as follows: 1,070 in August 1990, (765 off "Kintyre" in September 1991), 580 in July 1994, 420 in July 2000 and 395 in July 2002 (ABR). These are all considerably less than the 1,700 cited by Thom and suggest long-term decline. The Sound of Mull has also held an important moult assembly, but with few recent counts: for example, Scallastle Bay held 224 in Aug 1992 and 412 in July 1994. Another large moult flock forms in Loch Indaal, with maxima of 100-200 birds in 1997-2003, again fewer than in the past (240 in August 1989, 336 in September 1991, 560 in August 1992, 265 in July 1993 and 220 in September 1996) (ABR).

In autumn small numbers pass seawatching sites such as MSBO as birds disperse from moult areas to wintering grounds, and those wintering in west Scotland are joined by migrants from Iceland. In Argyll the Winter Atlas showed only small differences from the breeding distribution, probably both because movements are short and because most Argyll squares are coastal and dispersal from rivers correspondingly less apparent.

Newton & Newton (1991) counted wildfowl monthly from September to March at 34 sites in Argyll. In winter 1988-89, the maximum and minimum monthly totals were 299 in September and 118 in January, while in 1989-90 counts were similar, 256 in September and 123 in January. The pattern each winter was the same: from September to March, Mergansers were outnumbered by Common Eider, Eurasian Wigeon, Mallard and Teal. From October to March they were also outnumbered by Scaup, and in February and March also by Shelduck and Goldeneye, becoming only the eighth most numerous duck. In the NEWS count in Argyll in Dec 1997-Jan 1998, 470 Mergansers were counted making them the fifth most abundant duck, less numerous than Eider (3,283), Wigeon (1,488), Mallard (1,160) and Teal (1,107), but exceeding Goldeneye (362) and Shelduck (156).

In a study of sawbills and fishfarms, Carss (1989) recorded all sawbills seen from November 1986 to May 1987 in an area that comprised Lochs Creran, Etive, Feochan, Melfort and Awe and their associated fresh waters. Of 336 sightings of Mergansers, 97% were on sealochs, the others on fresh

Red-breasted Mergansers feed on a range of fish, including, as here, Wrasse. *Philip Kirkham*

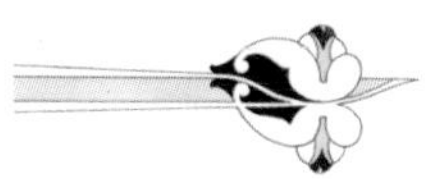

water. Mergansers differed from Goosanders by being more numerous, almost all on sealochs and present all year round. Unlike Goosanders, Mergansers were not considered a threat to farm stock, so were not killed at fishfarms.

However, Mergansers are regularly killed on rivers because they feed on the small young of wild salmon and trout. Marquiss *et al.* (1998) examined corpses of fish-eating birds shot in Scotland under licence during 1991-1996. The stomachs of 185 Mergansers contained the remains of 669 salmon and 499 trout. Among these were 27 birds from Argyll, all from the river Laggan on Islay and containing the remains of 95 salmon and 88 trout.

In Scotland between 1983 and 1991, 3,134 Mergansers were shot under licence, a mean of 348 per annum, varying from 204 in 1988 to 523 in 1983 (Carss 1994). The numbers killed illegally are unknown.

Clive Craik

Goosander

Mergus merganser

Goosanders are usually found on larger freshwater lochs and on fast-flowing rivers and their associated sealochs. They are rarely found in groups of more than a few birds and are most frequent on the mainland and on Mull.

The Goosander is primarily a freshwater species that breeds by upland lochs and rivers. Its present breeding stronghold in the British Isles is in southern Scotland and northern England. Despite much persecution, Goosanders have steadily increased their range and numbers over the last 130 years. Nowadays in the west of Scotland, Mergansers are much more abundant than Goosanders along the sea shore, while Goosanders outnumber Mergansers on fresh water. Surprisingly, Gray considered the Goosander to be the more numerous in west Scotland, while Graham described the Merganser as the commoner, at least on Iona and Mull.

The first successful breeding in the British Isles was on Loch Awe in 1871 when "a female and seven young birds were well identified by Mr James Graham of Liverpool as they sailed out past his boat within twenty yards" (H&B). These authors recorded the species from "so many places in the west of Sutherland, West Ross-shire and Argyllshire" (they mentioned Torcastle, Lochbuie, the north-west of Mull, and Tiree) that they considered it "one of the most rapidly advancing amongst breeding species of Anatidae in Scotland".

B&R concluded that colonisation of Scotland had been rapid from 1870 onwards, driven both by local breeding and by successive immigrations from Europe, including a notable invasion in winter 1875-1876. By 1892 Goosanders were abundant on the west coast from Edrachillis to Loch Awe, having colonised "a good many places in N Argyll", and by 1913 they were breeding as far south as Craignish.

By 1978 breeding had been recorded in all mainland counties of Scotland north of the Tay and Clyde, and numbers were steadily increasing in the Borders. Scotland held about 1,000 pairs, or 75-80% of the British Isles total, with Argyll and the Inner Hebrides holding about 50 pairs, mostly on the mainland (First Atlas, Thom). By the time of the Second Atlas, the British population was estimated at *c.*2,700 pairs and breeding was recorded in 7% of 10-km squares in Argyll, mostly in North and Mid-Argyll, with smaller numbers in Mull, Cowal and Kintyre. None was found in Coll, Islay or Jura, while two squares showing probable breeding on Tiree in 1968-72 were unoccupied in 1988-91.

In a survey of freshwater lochs in May-June 1985, 493 lochs were visited in North and Mid-Argyll, Cowal, Kintyre, Islay and Jura (not Mull). Goosanders were seen only in North and Mid-Argyll, mainly on Loch Awe with smaller numbers in the Rannoch Moor area. In May, 48 were recorded on 326 lochs (21 male, 27 female; eight in North Argyll and 40 in Mid-Argyll) and, in June, 28 were seen on 307 lochs (one male, 27 females; six in North Argyll and 22 in Mid-Argyll), most males having by then left on moult migration. Of 68 10-km squares visited, 12 held Goosanders (Broad *et al.* 1986).

Goosanders become most conspicuous when they arrive as small groups and pairs early in the year. Females nest in natural holes and cavities close to rivers and freshwater lochs, and a small population breeds in Tawny Owl nest-boxes around Loch Eck, Cowal. The usual clutch is 8-11 and, as with Mergansers, clutches or broods much greater than this are almost certainly the combined offspring of more than one bird. Females and half-grown young move downriver to sealochs and estuaries in late summer. Few adult males are seen in Scotland in June-October during their remarkable moult migration to the far north of Norway (Little & Furness 1985). Most of the males in Europe, an estimated 35,000 birds, gather there for annual moult in late summer, although the report of 13 males in Loch Feochan on 29 July 1991 (ABR) suggests that not all do so. Males begin to return to Scotland in late August and most have returned by November.

Observations suggest that many females may also gather at traditional sites to moult although, unlike those of the males, these are within the British Isles and probably close to the breeding areas. By far the two largest gatherings of Goosanders recorded were of redheads, probably moulting females, at or near the head of Loch Fyne: there were 32 in August and 65 in September 1997 (Argyll Database). A similar-sized all-redhead moult flock may be seen in the northern part of Loch Linnhe (C. Craik, pers. obs. 2005). Reports of both sexes become less frequent in late summer, possibly because these concentrations lead to many areas becoming empty of males and females.

By midwinter, both sexes are present in the breeding areas or in nearby river mouths and sealochs. Most British

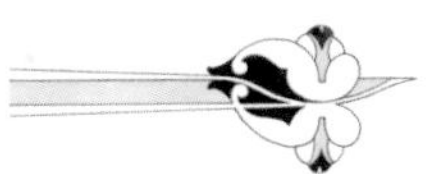

breeders winter within 150km of the breeding site and most of those seen in lowland Britain outside the breeding areas are migrants from Europe. The British winter population consists of *c.*8,900 birds, only about 6% of the 150,000 in north-west Europe (Migration Atlas). The distribution in Argyll in the Winter Atlas differed only slightly from that found in both Breeding Atlas surveys. Most of the occupied squares were in North Argyll, Mid-Argyll and Mull, with small numbers in Cowal, Islay and Tiree but none in Kintyre, Jura or Coll.

Although Goosanders can be seen all year round, numbers in the county have never been high. In monthly counts during September-March at 34 sites in Argyll, Newton & Newton (1991) found two, zero, nine, seven, zero, seven and 15 goosanders in 1988-89, and three, one, three, five, six, five and zero in 1989-90. In the NEWS count (December 1997-January 1998) 20 were recorded in Argyll, all on Mull.

Most Goosanders ringed as chicks are recovered within 20km of their natal site, but some disperse much further (Migration Atlas). There is only one recovery involving Argyll. A female ringed in Glenbranter Forest in April 1996 was found dead in Glencoe in 1998, a movement of 63km.

While young salmon and trout can form up to 80% of Goosander diet on some rivers, the need for and effectiveness of the shooting of this species are still debated. Marquiss *et al.* (1998) found that most of the salmon were small (<89 mm long) and considered that shooting could reduce the numbers of sawbills locally but that any effect was short-lived as new birds moved in. They examined the carcasses of 1,082 Goosanders shot under licence in Scotland, most from salmon rivers. The stomachs contained the remains of 2,010 salmon and 2,044 trout. (Among these were five from the river Awe and the river Laggan (Islay) containing 15 salmon and 13 trout.)

Carss (1994) recorded that, in Scotland from 1983 to 1991, 3,443 Goosanders were shot under licence, a mean of 383 per annum varying between 175 in 1987 and 673 in 1990.

As well as damaging stocks of wild salmon, Goosanders have been reported to cause damage at fishfarms in fresh water, particularly those rearing trout and salmon. Carss (1989) studied sawbills at 12 salmon and trout farms between Loch Creran and Loch Melfort, including Loch Awe where most of the Goosanders were found. He considered that Goosanders were responsible for repeated damage to nets on a fishfarm at Loch Awe, allowing up to 7% of the fish to escape, while Mergansers were not implicated in predation of farm stock or damage to nets. He recorded 83 sightings of Goosanders during 1 January-31 July 1986, and 42 in the same period in 1987 (*cf.* 336 sightings of Mergansers during 1 November 1986-31 May 1987). Ninety percent of the Goosanders were on fresh water. Carss suggested that Loch Awe was a gathering point for male Goosanders before their moult migration.

Clive Craik

Large numbers of Goosanders have been shot in Scotland to protect salmon and trout fisheries. *David Palmar*

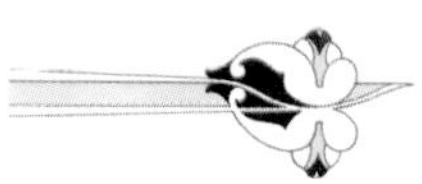

Ruddy Duck

Oxyura jamaicensis

Vagrant.

Despite breeding at 15 sites in the Clyde area in recent years, this introduced North American duck remains a rare vagrant in Argyll. There are only four records, all involving single birds (Table).

It has been suggested that the British population is largely resident, but more recent work suggests that the species may be developing a migratory strategy similar to its American relatives (Migration Atlas). Overshooting migrants and post-breeding wanderers have turned up all over Scotland. The Scottish breeding population has expanded markedly in recent years, and it seems possible that records from Argyll will become more frequent in the future unless culling halts or reverses this expansion (Smith *et al.* 2005).

Tristan ap Rheinallt

Records of Ruddy Ducks in Argyll to the end of 2006.

Date	Location	Comment	Reference
15 May 1984	Loch na Beiste, Clachan (Kintyre)	Female	SB14:100, ABR 3:24
8 & 13 May 1987	Loch Bhasapol and Borrapol (Tiree)	[Also, wrongly, in 1988 ABR systematic list and 1988 SBR]	ABR 5:6
25 October 1993	Duntrune Castle, Loch Crinan	Eclipse male	ABR 10:35
12 May 1999	Claddach, near Portnahaven (Islay)	Male	ABR 16:44

The Add Estuary in Mid-Argyll, looking out towards Jura and Scarba. It is a good location to see Red-breasted Mergansers, Goosanders, other ducks and waders, Hen Harriers and Ospreys. The central native woodland is Crinan Wood, which hosts a typical west coast assemblage including Common Redstart, Wood Warbler and Eurasian Jay. *John Anderson*

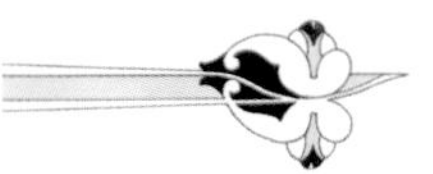

Red Grouse

Lagopus lagopus

Resident in relatively small numbers.

The Red Grouse is a resident British sub-species of the Willow Ptarmigan, which has a circumpolar distribution from the high Arctic down to the latitude of northern France (BWP). In addition to the Red Grouse, 13 or 14 other sub-species have been described. In Finland and the Baltic countries the Willow Grouse occurs mainly in bogs deep in forests, whereas the Red Grouse in Britain requires mostly treeless heather moors (Hagemeijer & Blair 1997). It is highly territorial in summer, but flocks in winter. On the heavily managed moors of eastern Scotland, high densities occur and flocks (packs) may reach several hundred birds. Flocking occurs in response to snow cover (Winter Atlas).

In Argyll, where the moors are wetter, the heather of poorer quality, and the snow cover less frequent, the Red Grouse is thinly distributed. Flocks seldom exceed 10-20 birds, although there is one recent record from Mull of 48 (ABR). It is very much under-reported in Argyll out of, and also probably during, the breeding season. A survey between Carradale and Glenbarr in central Kintyre, covering 1.6 km^2, found cock grouse at a mean density of 6.9 km^{-2} (Central Kintyre Habitat Management Plan, Scottish Power). There is very little seasonal movement of birds, but they may seek lower ground in hard winters. The only ringing recovery in Argyll is of a bird ringed and recovered at Bridge of Orchy. Red Grouse were introduced for shooting to Coll in 2001-02 and to Colonsay in 2003 (ABR).

Breeding has been reported from Islay, Mid-Argyll, Mull and Jura, but it undoubtedly occurs more widely. Red Grouse throughout Britain have decreased markedly since 1930, and more especially in the north and west of the country. Numbers shot have fallen by 50% overall (Second Atlas). The current population in Argyll cannot be more than a few hundred pairs, compared to the estimate of 250,000 pairs in Britain. In areas where they are numerous, Red Grouse exhibit a cyclic fluctuation in numbers. In Britain, peaks occur about every six years, and numbers in peak years may exceed the lowest population levels fourfold. There is some evidence of population cycles from the Torosay Castle (Mull) game records, which note that over 150 birds were shot in seven years during the first two decades of the 20th century (Petty 2004). The factors relating to population fluctuations and response to disease and moorland management have been studied for many decades, but arguments still rage as to whether their numbers are intrinsically or extrinsically regulated (Jenkins 2003).

Jardine (1866) writes that, in winter, the Red Grouse "have learned to depend on the labour's of the husbandman for his winter's food" and "before the grain is removed, [they] find a plentiful harvest. Hundreds crowd the stooks in the upland corn-fields, while in the lower countries they seek what has been left on the stubble or ploughed fields." Could the changes in agriculture in Argyll in the last six decades, where corn crops have almost ceased, and other arable crops greatly reduced, have affected the winter survival, and thus the breeding population? However, it is more likely that populations are restricted by over-grazing of Argyll's remaining heathlands.

David Merrie

The Red Grouse is a decreasing species of heather moorland. *Kelvin Pearce*

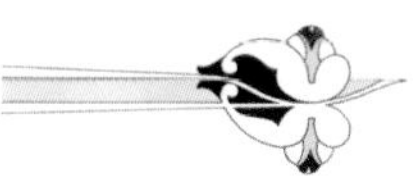

Ptarmigan

Lagopus muta

Resident breeder at high altitudes, mainly in north and east Argyll and Mull.

The Ptarmigan is one of the few British birds whose English name is derived from the Gaelic, the original in this case being *tàrmachan*. The first published report for Argyll appears to be that of Thomas Pennant (1776), who stated that the species occurred on Islay and the Paps of Jura. The Statistical Account of Scotland (1791-95) lists it for Lochgoilhead and Kilmorich on the mainland, and for Torosay, and Kilfinichen and Kilvecuen, on Mull. In the NSA, Ptarmigan are again said to occur in Kilfinichen and Kilvecuen, as well as in adjacent Kilninian and Kilmore (though this information seems to have been copied from the earlier Kilfinichen and Kilvecuen account). They are also reported from Jura. On the mainland, they are said to occur in Inveraray, Ardchattan, Glassary, and Dunoon and Kilmun. The species is also listed for Lismore and Appin in both accounts, but the location specified in the NSA is outside the area covered by this book.

The entry for Dunoon and Kilmun states that "Ptarmigan are found in the highest hills in the parish, though their number is but small, and their race thought to be almost extinct." The entry for the parish of Inverchaolain records that "Ptarmigan used to be found in two of our highest mountains, but were said to have been extirpated some years ago by the gamekeeper of a neighbouring proprietor." There is therefore some suggestion of a decline in the years prior to 1845. H&B commented on the "decrease, death and disappearance" of Ptarmigan from many insular localities, predicting its extinction on Mull – where it still occurred on Ben More, Ben Buie and Craig Baan – and referring to a decline on Jura over the previous half-century. Only in the north of Argyllshire, outside the area treated in this book, were Ptarmigan described as common. On Islay, as on Jura, it was said to be very rare.

By the time of B&R, there was little evidence for any further change in its status. Birds apparently persisted on Islay (where a brood was said to have been found on the summit of Glas Bheinn in 1936), Jura, and (though in very small numbers) on Mull. B&R present no recent information about distribution in mainland Argyll, except to remark in a wider Scottish context that north of Ben Lomond and North Angus, Ptarmigan were found on most hills of more than 2,000 feet. More information was given by Watson (1965), who presented a map of distribution in Scotland, showing Ptarmigan to occur along the northern and eastern boundaries of Argyll, extending as far south as Cowal, as well as on Mull. Elsewhere, the only location was Scarba, where a pair with young was said to have been seen in 1959. Although more detailed in its coverage, the First Atlas presented much the same picture. Altogether, the species was recorded in twelve 10- km squares that were wholly within Argyll, together with another twelve squares along the northern and eastern edge of the area. Thus Ptarmigan appeared to be widespread in north-cast Argyll adjacent to upper Loch Etive, Glen Orchy, the head of Loch Awe and the head of Loch Fyne, extending as far south as Loch Eck. However, the only records from the islands came from Mull, where the species was recorded in three squares. However, in 1977, eight were reported from

Ptarmigan are found in small numbers on a few high mountains in Argyll. *Philip Snow*

the Paps of Jura in December (SB 10:128).

The Second Atlas showed an unchanged distribution on Mull but an apparent contraction of range in north and east Argyll, with six previously occupied squares wholly within Argyll producing no records. This was part of a more general negative trend across Scotland, where there was an 11 per cent decrease in the number of squares with records between the two Atlas periods. However, records since 1991 (ABR) have confirmed the continued presence of birds in two of the squares apparently "lost" between the Atlas periods (NN03, NN23). Interestingly, the Second Atlas shows a single occupied square in the northern half of Jura: a bird was heard calling on Rainberg Mor on 21 May 1988 (ABR 5:20), suggesting that the species still held on in the island.

It is clear that the Ptarmigan has indeed disappeared from the periphery of its Scottish range (including the Outer Hebrides and south-west Scotland) over the past two centuries or so (First Atlas, Thom). Its apparent extinction on Islay and probably Jura can be seen as part of this trend, which may be related, in some areas at least, to habitat deterioration following overgrazing by sheep (Second Atlas), and climate change. Nevertheless, and despite predictions to the contrary, the Ptarmigan seems to be holding its own on Mull and continues to be widely, if thinly, distributed on the higher summits of the mainland.

Tristan ap Rheinallt

Black Grouse

Tetrao tetrix

Scarce breeding resident. Population is in sharp decline and, in 2004, Argyll was found to hold fewer than 180 lekking males. Very thinly distributed in all mainland areas with a few on Islay and Jura.

Generally, numbers have fallen throughout mainland Argyll. B&R referred to nearly 100 being shot in one small cornfield near Taychreggan, Loch Awe, in the severe winter of 1878-79. In 2004, the whole mainland population was unlikely to have much exceeded 150 lekking males. This decline was despite localised increases following colonisation of young forestry, for example at Cloanaig, Kintyre, where in 1989 it was described as more numerous than in the previous 15 years. There has been attrition in all mainland areas with substantial declines in numbers of males at leks. A few leks, especially in Mid-Argyll, held 10-15 males until 1991. Since 1992, no reports have exceeded double figures. Three male Black Grouse-Capercaillie hybrids were seen together near Loch Awe in 1998, presumably reflecting dwindling numbers of both species. On Cowal, Haysom (2001) surveyed Black Grouse south of a line from Strachur to Carrick. Within this study area of 630 km^2, she identified 68 leks during 1996-98. All were visited in 1998, when 106 males were present at 46 leks and the largest lek held eight males (average 2.4 males). Re-survey of this area in 2003 found just 29 males and the largest lek held three (average 1.3), a decline of almost 23% a year. During the Argyll Black Grouse Recovery Project (2002-04) a systematic survey in 2004 was thought to have been complete on the mainland, except in North Argyll where a few small leks may have been missed. In 2004, 127 males were found and the largest lek held seven, but this was exceptional and most leks held only single males (Table). At 43 lek sites where counts were made in both 2002 and 2004, the total number of males decreased from 73 to 45, a decline of 21.5% a year (calculated from results in Lek Report for 2004 [Black Grouse Recovery Project, Argyll & Bute]).

On Mull, according to Gray, Black Grouse were much commoner than Red Grouse and Graham thought that they outnumbered Red Grouse by 10 to 1 in south-west Mull. At the north of the island, H&B found that Black Grouse not infrequently made the crossing from Mull to Ardnamurchan. The game records for one sporting estate showed that double figures were shot annually almost every year at Torosay between 1899 and 1917 with the highest bags in 1900-01 and 1912-13 when 101 and 71 were shot respectively. Thereafter, the numbers shot declined substantially. The maximum shot in any year since the First World War was seven and in many years none were taken (Petty 2004). Unlike on the mainland, the decline seems to have continued across the whole island, without any obvious resurgence during extensive afforestation in 1960-80. Breeding was suspected in one isolated 10-km square during work for the First Atlas. In the last 20 years there have been just 1-2 reports in five separate years.

Jardine *et al.* (1986) reviewed the historical data for Colonsay where the species was described as plentiful in 1898 and 1899 when 64 and 68 were shot respectively (Gathorn-Hardy 1914). It became extinct in the First World War (Loder 1935) but it was successfully reintroduced in 1933 with some remaining until the last two were shot in 1953. There have been no records since with the exception of confirmed breeding in one 10-km square during work for the First Atlas, for which no supporting evidence has been found.

On Islay, historical records were reviewed by Booth (1981) who noted that Pennant saw some in 1772. Thompson (1850) reported great numbers of greyhens in 1849. Gray found it increasing rapidly in the north part of the island despite lack of cover and in autumn it regularly came to feed in stubbles. It remained numerous until about 1914 with 100 shot in a season. Thereafter, following an outbreak of disease, it rapidly declined and was almost exterminated between 1918 and 1920. With a voluntary shooting ban until 1924 numbers apparently recovered to levels previously seen in the last 50 years. It was common in 1939 although few were now shot. During the First Atlas it remained widespread and breeding was confirmed in seven 10-km squares. Substantial numbers were still found in 1982 when 30 were present near Loch Gruinart, but it was reported as becoming rare by 1987 and

The crash of Black Grouse populations throughout Scotland, including Argyll, has been well documented. Targeted conservation effort is now aiming to secure a long-term future for this iconic bird of the woodland edge. *David Palmar*

very scarce by 1988. In 1994, when information was available from a survey of traditional lek sites on the south Rinns (Stanbury & Campbell 1994), not more than five males were reported on the whole island. Since then reports of 1-3 birds have come from not more than 2-3 areas in any one year. There appears to be no evidence of recent reintroductions or restocking on Islay or elsewhere in Argyll.

Historical information for Jura is sparse. During work for the First Atlas, breeding was confirmed in the south of the island. Thom thought that small numbers survived here after restocking or reintroductions. Small numbers were present in the south of the island during the Second Atlas and are still found regularly at Craighouse where three males were seen in May 2003. A few more may hang on in association with new broadleaf forestry blocks (W. MacDonald pers. comm.). The species appears to be very scarce in the northern half of the island, where lekking birds were formerly regular and more numerous at Kinuachdrach. Only two have been seen here since 2000 (M. Richardson pers. comm.) when one was also flushed near An Carn, Lealt.

Gray described it as common on all mountain ranges, hilly districts and patches of upland heath in western Scotland and plentiful on many of the Inner Hebrides. There have since been marked changes with a general long-term decline and contraction of range, temporarily offset by shorter-term local increases. Changes in population levels have not always been gradual. Occasional major fluctuations have occurred in the space of a few years. Rintoul & Baxter (1927) noted a period of increase in Scotland in the late 1880s-1890s. This was followed by a more dramatic decline in the 20th century that is reflected in declining game bags on sporting estates which fell by more than 95% after 1900. In Argyll, particularly during 1960-80, with the establishment of extensive tracts of new forestry plantations on formerly heavily grazed moorland, Black Grouse numbers increased dramatically and at times were considered a pest, eating tops of newly planted trees (Petty 2004). Most of these gains were temporary and reversed following canopy closure. The overall situation in Argyll mirrors that in many other parts of the UK and along the southern limit of its range on the continent in Holland, Belgium and much of Central Europe (Second Atlas). Estimates indicate that the British population had fallen to 6,510 lekking males in 1995-96 (Hancock *et al.* 1999). Information gathered since 2002 by the Argyll Black Grouse Recovery Project shows that the current Argyll population is a tiny fraction of its former numbers and is still falling. Also, the range of Black Grouse in Argyll appears to be in danger of fragmentation. Recruitment from adjacent regions would appear to be unlikely. To the north of Argyll, numbers in Lochaber are equally low. To the north-east the population in Tayside, still considered to be a major stronghold, is rather too distant. Numbers around Loch Lomond are generally at a low ebb. Only in the Roseneath-Garelochhead area is there a modest population, including a lek of more than 10 birds since 2002, conveniently close to the depopulating Cowal peninsula.

Black Grouse associate with habitats up to 600m asl, principally on the moorland-woodland fringe. Both broadleaved and coniferous woodland are frequented, especially where they are sufficiently open and have a well-developed ericaceous ground flora. Young forestry plantations can be attractive for a few years until the canopy closes. Scrub, wet flushes and marginal agricultural land provide additional habitat elements but it is the resulting mosaic rather than the individual habitats that appear to be most important. Fragmentation and habitat degradation due to overgrazing have been identified as significant threats. Black Grouse have been shown to be vulnerable to collisions with deer fences and population decline may be hastened by increased predation from crows and foxes (Baines & Summers 1997).

In the UK, Black Grouse are relatively sedentary. Robel (1969) found that males range over an area of 303-689 ha around their lekking site. There is a tendency for immature males and females to wander a little more widely; for example, three immature males moved up to 5 km and one moved 17 km (Johnstone 1967). In northern parts of the continent, the species is known to be capable of much longer movements with journeys of more than 1,000 km recorded from Sweden (Migration Atlas).

The Black Grouse is protected under the Game Acts (close season 11 December-19 August) and listed on Annex II/2 of EC Directive. There is now a voluntary ban on shooting.

Roger Broad

	Number of leks surveyed	Number of leks with males	Number of males at leks	Mean number of males/lek
Kintyre	21	11	28	2.5
Mid-Argyll: Knapdale	10	8	12	1.5
Mid-Argyll: north of Crinan	42	31	47	1.5
North Argyll	10	10	18	1.8
Cowal	25	12	22	1.8
Total	108	72	127	1.8

Numbers of Black Grouse males at leks in mainland Argyll in 2004.

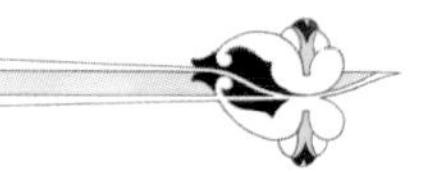

Capercaillie

Tetrao urogallus

Very rare. A few records from Mid-Argyll and Cowal in recent years.

The Capercaillie, whose name derives from the Gaelic *capull coille*, or horse of the woods, became extinct as a native Scottish breeding bird in the latter half of the 18th century, apparently as a result of extensive felling of pine woods (Harvie-Brown 1879, Ritchie 1920). There is little evidence of its occurrence in Argyll in early times, but birds were said to be at Muckairn, on the southern shore of Loch Etive, around 1690, disappearing some 75 years later (B&R). Hugh Fraser, in the NSA, stated that none had been seen in Muckairn for sixty or seventy years. He also commented that the Capercaillies that once frequented the birchwoods tasted better than those from the fir woods. The past occurrence of this species in Glen Etive was also referred to by H&B.

The current population is the result of a series of introductions of birds from Sweden, the largest and most successful being at Taymouth Castle in Perth in 1837-38 (B&R, Pennie 1950). Although the Capercaillie is a highly sedentary species, there was a fairly rapid spread from this and other centres of introduction, whose success was attributed in large part to replanting of woodland (B&R). Gray made no mention of Argyll, but H&B provide a detailed list of sightings. The first was a single bird on the Black Mount in 1867 or 1868. Birds arrived at Ardkinglas, at the northern end of Loch Fyne, in 1875, 12 being seen there on one day in 1878. In 1876 or 1877 they made their appearance at Inveraray, but disappeared after a few years. None were shot, but several were killed when they flew into wire fences. Capercaillie eggs were also brought to Inveraray in 1876 but they failed to hatch, as did eggs imported to the Black Mount at an earlier date. Finally, a bird was shot near Poltalloch in 1883.

Females were pioneers in range expansion, and when first occupying new areas would sometimes mate with Black Grouse, producing hybrid offspring (First Atlas, Thom). Hybrids were shot at Ardkinglas in 1878 and 1879, and birds seen at Inveraray in the 1870s were later thought to include

The magnificent Capercaillie may be extinct in Argyll. *Margaret Staley*

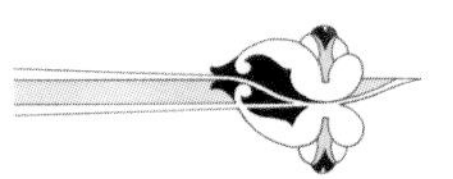

hybrid offspring (H&B). A hybrid was also shot at Glen Finart in Cowal in 1912 (SN Extra Publication 2:13).

By the early years of the twentieth century, Capercaillies were said to have penetrated Argyll "almost to the line of the Crinan Canal" (B&R). However, they were not considered to be widespread or plentiful, though there were records at that time from Ardkinglas, Glen Finart and Dalmally. It is possible that the maritime climate of the western seaboard limited their spread, which reached its maximum extent in 1914, before contracting once more as a result of extensive felling during the two World Wars (First Atlas). Thus felling was thought to have almost exterminated the Cowal population during 1920-30, and by 1949 the species was apparently absent from Argyll once more, with the possible exception of the Barcaldine and Kilberry areas (Pennie 1951) and Tayvallich (Rainier 1975). However, they had reappeared in the eastern part of Cowal by the time of the First Atlas, at the south-western extremity of their Scottish range. Birds were also recorded in two 10- km squares in the north-east of Argyll at this time, one including the extensive forestry plantations of Glen Orchy and Glen Lochy. Away from these areas, one was seen near Lochgair in February 1974 (SB 8:422) and another at Achnamara, at the inner end of Loch Sween, in February 1976 (SB 10:90).

No Capercaillies were recorded in Argyll during the Winter Atlas survey. The Second Atlas showed that birds had apparently disappeared from the north-east though were now recorded further south and west in the vicinity of Loch Awe and Loch Avich (SB 1991:27), where they had been seen in the past (ABR 1:35). The range in Cowal had contracted, though birds were still being recorded in good numbers on the nearby Loch Lomond islands. This range contraction was associated with a major decline in the Scottish population, arising from a variety of factors.

Most records in recent years come from the two core areas occupied in 1988-91, the only exception being a female at Loch Tulla, well outside the normal range, on 19 October 1996 (ABR 13:45, SBR 1996:26). In 1993, the sighting of a female with a brood of three young in Cowal, at a lek where two males had been seen earlier in the year, constituted the first confirmed breeding record since the First Atlas (SB 1993:22). At a regular lek site in the Loch Awe area, three males observed in 1998 appeared to be hybrids with Black Grouse rather than pure-bred Capercaillies (SBR 1998:40). Females were also seen at three sites that year, confirming that the species still held on in both areas. However, given that Scottish Capercaillies are now failing to hold their own even in the native pine forests that constitute their optimal habitat, it seems only a matter of time before this magnificent bird becomes extinct in Argyll once again, as the lack of records during 2000-2006 would suggest.

Tristan ap Rheinallt

Red-legged Partridge

Alectoris rufa

Widely introduced and breeding in the wild, but populations may not be self-sustaining.

An early attempt to introduce Red-legged Partridges to Scotland was reported by H&B. One of an unspecified number released at Barcaldine was shot in 1889 at Kilmarouag, just east of Connel. Presumably this introduction, like all others prior to the second half of the 20th century (B&R), met with no success. Another attempt, on Islay in 1953 or 1954, fared no better: of 18 birds hatched from imported eggs and released, none could be found a few weeks later (Elliott 1989). By the time of the First Atlas, birds were breeding in many localities in eastern Scotland but still almost completely absent from the west.

The first recent sightings in Argyll were in 1977, when single birds were at Ford and at Loch Riddon in Cowal (SB 10:128). Since this species is highly sedentary (Migration Atlas), it seems likely that they derived from local releases. There were no further reports until 1985, when birds were said to have been released in south Mull (ABR 4:19) and Islay (Elliott 1989). During 1987 to 1990, there were releases in Colonsay, Islay, Mull, Kintyre and Mid-Argyll. However, survival in at least one of these areas was poor: of 100 released in Mull in 1990, none were thought to remain alive at the end of the year (ABR 7:25). The map in the Second Atlas shows occupied 10-km squares in Cowal, Kintyre, Colonsay and Islay, as well as around Ben Lui. More recently, birds were released at new sites such as the island of Shuna, near Luing, in 1993, Lochorodale in Kintyre in 1997, and the Otter Estate in Cowal, while there were yet more releases on Colonsay and Islay. Birds were also seen on Tiree (1997) and at Ardchonnel (2003).

Although there is little evidence, it seems likely that many of the birds released were hybrids between this species and the closely related Chukar *Alectoris chukar*. Hybrids were certainly released on Islay in 1987, together with at least one pure-bred Chukar (ABR 5:7), and hybrids were reported there in 1991 (ABR 8:38). The licensing of releases of hybrids came to an end in 1992 (Second Atlas), so any releases from 1993 onwards should have involved only pure-bred Red-legged Partridges.

It seems unlikely that any populations in Argyll are self-sustaining. One Islay gamekeeper commented recently to the author that, whilst pairs breed readily in the wild, survival of young to adulthood is very poor. Nevertheless, continued releases may ensure that the Red-legged Partridge, unlike the Grey, remains a familiar sight in parts of Argyll for years to come.

Tristan ap Rheinallt

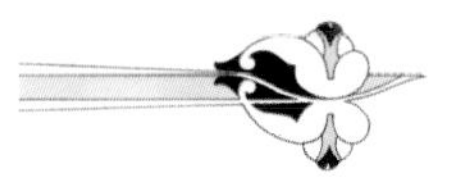

Grey Partridge

Perdix perdix

Once widespread but now very localised. Introductions have taken place in several areas but do not appear to have resulted in self-sustaining populations.

The Grey Partridge was once the most numerous gamebird in the British Isles. Indeed, in many areas it was the most abundant bird of any species on farmland (Migration Atlas). Although there is no evidence that this was ever the case anywhere in Argyll, there are frequent mentions from mainland parishes in both statistical accounts. Alexander Campbell, writing about the parishes of Kilcalmouell and Kilberry in 1794 (OSA), complained that partridges damaged the corn, but that farmers were not allowed to protect their crops without the landlord's permission and payment of a heavy tax to the Government. In 1845, they were described as abundant in Kilmartin and "pretty numerous" in Dunoon and Kilmun. In Saddell and Skipness, on the other hand, they were "still scarce" (possibly a reference to the hard winter of 1837-38?) but increasing rapidly. Gray described the species as being plentiful in all cultivated tracts of Scotland, while H&B stated that it was generally distributed in mainland Argyll, with numbers "naturally accommodating themselves to various-sized areas of cultivated land." It was, however, believed to have declined in the Ledaig area as a result of failing root crops and close-cutting of stubbles.

Writing some 60 years later, B&R could still describe this species as common in all the agricultural districts of Scotland, although declining in some parts, including the Argyll mainland. It had become extinct in the area around Skipness about 1898 (McWilliam) and there had been a serious decline in the number shot on the Largie Castle estate at Tayinloan. Further north, Taynish Estate near Tayvallich, once very good for partridges, had apparently become less so by 1940. The First Atlas points to a continued decline, with records from only eight mainland 10-km squares, scattered across south Kintyre, Cowal, and the Lochgilphead and Oban areas. By the time of the Second Atlas, only one occupied square remained on the mainland, near Loch Melfort, where a bird was seen at Eleraig in June 1991 (ABR 8:38). Since then, there have been no mainland records and it seems that the Grey Partridge is now extinct in mainland Argyll, as in some other areas of Scotland where it was common in the past. The overall decline in Britain and Ireland has been ascribed to reduced chick survival associated with the use of herbicides in cereals (Second Atlas), but other factors, related to climate and habitat, may also be important.

The situation in the larger Argyll islands warrants separate treatment (Tables). Grey Partridges are known to have occurred on Islay, Jura, Gigha, Colonsay, Mull, Tiree and Coll. For all except Islay and Coll, there is evidence that the species

Records of Grey Partridges on Islay, Jura and Colonsay, c.1794-2003.

Island	Date	Comment	Reference
Islay	1794*	Present Kilchoman	OSA
	1842	Plentiful	B&R
	1871*	Common in all cultivated parts	Gray
	1912-1926	Many introduced	Booth 1975
	1953*	Common	B&R
	1954	Only about nine coveys on one estate	Meiklejohn & Stanford 1954
	1968-72	Not recorded	First Atlas
	1969	Bred well in the dry spring	Elliott 1989
	1971-75	Series of failed introductions; last bird seen in 1979	Elliott 1989
	1984	One report	ABR 2:21
	1988-91	Breeding evidence from one 10-km square	Second Atlas
	1988-2003	Several releases and presumed releases, birds reported widely	ABR
Jura	1794*	Absent	OSA
	1844*	Recently introduced	NSA
	1890	About ten coveys present; sudden increase	H&B
	1968-72	Not recorded	First Atlas
	1988-91	Not recorded	Second Atlas
Colonsay	1794*	Absent	OSA
	1836	A few present	Jardine *et al.* 1986
	1891*	Abundant	H&B
	1898-99	Total of 155 shot	Jardine *et al.* 1986
	1935*	Small numbers on most farms	Loder 1935
	1939	Breeding	B&R
	1940-41	Two shot; probably became extinct around this time	Jardine *et al.* 1986
	1968-72	Not recorded	First Atlas
	1988-91	Not recorded	Second Atlas

*Dates of publication where no exact date of record is available.

The Grey Partridge is extinct on the Argyll mainland, but introduced birds occur on some of the islands. *Margaret Staley*

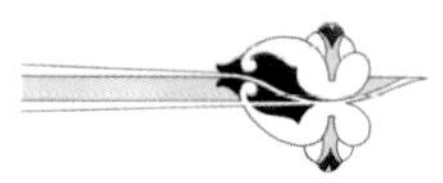

Records of Grey Partridges on Mull, Gigha, Tiree, Coll and Shuna, *c.*1840-2003.

Island	Date	Comment	Reference
Mull	1843*	Absent	OSA
	c.1840	Introduced	H&B
	1871*	Present	Gray
	1888	Small numbers Glenforsa	H&B
	1953*	Very scarce	B&R
	1968-72	Not recorded	First Atlas
	1988-91	Not recorded	Second Atlas
	1990	100 released at two sites, with some surviving to the end of the year	ABR 7:26
Gigha	c.1860	Introduced	H&B
	1891*	Dying out after former abundance	H&B
	1953*	Extinct	B&R
	1968-72	Not recorded	First Atlas
	1988-91	Not recorded	Second Atlas
Tiree	1888-9	Introduced	H&B
	1890	Introduced; bred well but young mostly drowned in heavy rains; others preyed upon by Peregrines	H&B
	1899*	Not breeding - but this believed by B&R to be an error	Irby 1899
	1912	Extinct; young eaten by cats and rats	Anderson 1913, B&R
	1968-72	Not recorded	First Atlas
	1988-91	Not recorded	Second Atlas
	1997	One seen, thought to be recently released	ABR 14:44
Coll	1899	Breeding	B&R
	1937-39	Breeding commonly on sand hills, bags of 200-300 obtained	B&R; Boyd 1958
	1945	Covey seen	Boyd 1958
	1968-72	Present in all three 10- km squares, with breeding confirmed in one	First Atlas
	1983	Considered extinct	ABR 1:36
	1988-91	Not recorded	Second Atlas
	2002-3	Several sightings of up to five birds, derived from a recent release	Argyll Database
Shuna (nr Luing)	1994	One seen; release of Red-legged Partridges known to have taken place on the island in 1993	ABR 11:42

*Dates of publication where no exact date of record is available

was introduced. Populations on the different islands have lasted for varying periods, being particularly short-lived in the case of Tiree and Gigha but more persistent on Colonsay and Islay. On Islay at least, it was maintained by continued introductions, almost to the present day. Indeed, almost all records since 1990 come from Islay and recently Coll, except for single birds seen on Tiree and, closer to the mainland, on Shuna. It is likely that factors contributing to decline on the mainland also drove well-established populations such as those on Colonsay and Coll to extinction.

Tristan ap Rheinallt

Common Quail

Coturnix coturnix

Irregular summer visitor, mainly to Kintyre and the islands. Breeding not proven.

The Quail was probably common in Britain and Ireland until the end of the 18th century, declining in the first half of the 19th (First Atlas). In Scotland, it was once much more plentiful than it is today (B&R), but there is little evidence that this was the case in Argyll. Although it was described as common in the county about 1845 (B&R), the species received only a single mention in each of the two sets of statistical accounts for the Argyll parishes. Gray made no reference to Quail in Argyll, whilst H&B quoted no specific records, referring only in general terms to occurrences in Kintyre and Jura. Anderson (1898, 1913) stated that there had been just one record in Tiree.

Through most of the 20th century, only scattered records were published. The First Atlas contained no records from Argyll or indeed for almost the whole of western Scotland, although one was on Islay on 18 June 1970 (SB 6:365). Thus a record of eight to ten birds calling in an area of 2km^2 at Campbeltown in June and July 1978 (SBR 1978:22) was exceptional, all the more so because only a few singles were reported elsewhere in Scotland that year. However, information from the last two decades shows that, as a rule, numbers reported in Argyll do not reflect overall trends in Britain particularly well.

In Britain as a whole, both 1983 and 1989 were "Quail years", with numbers higher than normal as a consequence of high breeding success, adverse conditions in other parts of the range, or southerly winds (Migration Atlas). In 1989, numbers recorded in Scotland were more than ten times those recorded in any previous year (Murray 1991a). However, there was little evidence of increase in Argyll, with no records in 1983 and two or three in 1989 (ABR 6:27, Murray 1991a, Second Atlas), only one more than in 1987 and 1988. In 1997, on the other hand, no fewer than 16 birds were recorded in Argyll, in a year when numbers in Scotland were again high but not approaching 1989 levels. Birds were reported, mostly in June, from Coll (8), Tiree (3), Islay (3), Mull (1) and Kintyre (1) (ABR 1997:44). The following year, five were reported from Coll (S. Money pers. comm.), two from Tiree and one from Colonsay, making this the second best year in Argyll, although it was a poor year in Scotland.

Overall, Quails were recorded in Argyll in 14 of the 26 years from 1980 to 2005, with only one or two birds reported in eight of those years. Most records came from Kintyre and the islands, the exceptions being birds near Ford in 1992, at Moine Mhor NNR in 1996 and in Kilmartin Glen in 1999 (ABR). Dates ranged from 29 May to 20 August, and most records were in June. Thus the occurrence of Quail in Argyll, as in Britain and Ireland generally, is associated with an onward wave of migration following breeding earlier in the year in the Mediterranean region or North Africa (Migration Atlas). Birds are thought to leave our shores from September onwards (Migration Atlas), but there are no recent autumn records from Argyll. One was caught on Skerryvore on 24 October 1899 (ASNH 1900:83, B&R), and one was shot at West Ardow [West Ardhu] on Mull on 29 October 1904 (ASNH 1905:221, B&R).

Almost all Argyll records refer to calling males. Since persistent calling may indicate a local shortage or absence of females, and birds call only occasionally once mated, such records do not provide evidence of breeding (Migration Atlas). Proof of breeding is rarely obtained and has not yet been produced for Argyll.

Tristan ap Rheinallt

Common Pheasant

Phasianus colchicus

Pheasants are abundant in those parts of Argyll where they are reared and released for shooting. They are rarely reported from Jura and North Argyll.

The average resident of Argyll probably sees more Pheasants dead on the road near shooting estates than alive in their usual woodland habitat. Some figures will illustrate the unnatural history of the species. The wild population of Britain in winter is thought to number about eight million birds (making this one of our most numerous species). Every year fifteen million are released. In autumn 2001 about 450 reared birds were released at High Lossit and another 450 at Peninver, two typical Argyll estates (ABR). Overall stocking densities in Argyll are perhaps 0.5-1 birds/acre, but in favoured areas may rise to around five. About 45% of released birds are shot and about half of the rest die in their first winter (Winter Atlas). Numbers in Britain in summer are estimated at 850,000 territorial and 650,000 non-territorial cocks and 1,600,000 hens (Second Atlas).

Pheasants are thought to have been introduced to Britain by the Normans or, possibly, the Romans, and numerous subspecies are now found. The first introductions were apparently *P. c. colchicus*, which occurs in the wild in the Western Palearctic. From the 1700s other races were introduced from further afield, including *torquatus* whose plumage characteristics include a white collar (BWP). As a result "hybrids" are now present in feral populations. This can be seen in Argyll, where birds occur with collars of varying thickness or none. Gray found that Pheasants were "not uncommon and increasing" on Islay, where they had been introduced about 1840. B&R reported that Pheasants were plentiful on Islay in 1842 where, as today, they were found in "most unexpected places" such as "open moor, miles from any covert or cornfields, as well as in wet bogs". B&R found Pheasants common on Islay in 1913-1914 and not uncommon there in 1948. Nowadays about 20 male Pheasant territories are counted at RSPB Loch Gruinart each summer (ABR) and birds occur in other parts of the island. B&R state that, in 1844, Pheasants had "lately" been introduced to Jura, where they were very common in 1939 after being reared and released; and Thom makes special mention of a feral population apparently thriving in unusual habitat of rough moorland on the west coast of Jura. B&R quoted Graham's record of Pheasants on Colonsay around 1890 and said that they were common there in 1942. More recently, between six and ten calling males were counted on Colonsay in the summers of 1991-1993, and between 14 and 20 in 1994-1999, but a large increase was noted after about 150 had been released there in 2000 (ABR). B&R also recorded that Pheasants were introduced to Gigha sometime during 1862-1892 and to Coll in 1937-1938. A small but apparently self-sustaining population of about 5-10 pairs on Coll in 2003-2004 had probably been there since before 1989 (S. Wellock, pers. comm.); Pheasants were described as "very common" on Coll in 1984 (ABR). Thom quoted a 1983 report that Pheasants had recently died out on Tiree. In 1985 they were reintroduced to Tiree where they have since been widespread, although there have been no further introductions. At least ten were counted there during the goose count of March 1999 (ABR) and broods of young are seen in most summers, although there is no organised shooting of Pheasants on Tiree. H&B mention Pheasants at Glenforsa on Mull, where they had been introduced "many years" earlier, and at Benderloch and Poltalloch on the

Many Pheasants are released in Argyll each year for shooting. *Margaret Staley*

mainland. Six territories were counted at Taynish NNR in 1996. An all-black Pheasant was seen at Esknish on Islay on 25 Feb 2001 (Argyll Database), and two albinos were dead on the road by the Kilmaronag estate near Oban in January 1998.

Breeding was recorded in 41% of 10-km squares in Argyll during 1988-1991 (Second Atlas). The resulting map showed a distribution that was almost continuous over most of the British Isles, including most of Kintyre and Islay and parts of Colonsay, Jura, Coll, Tiree and Mull. However, the species was absent from a large part of north-west Scotland, including the mountainous areas of central Mull, North Argyll and part of Mid-Argyll. Islay was the most densely populated part of the county. There were only small differences in distribution from the First Atlas or from the Winter Atlas.

Cock Pheasants set up territories in early spring, usually at

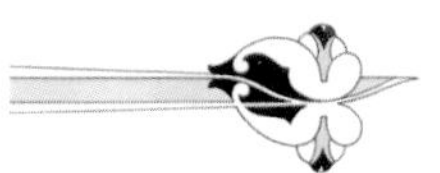

the edge of woodland or near other dense vegetation. Nests are in dense ground vegetation and the large clutches of about eleven eggs are laid in late April or May. Hens on nests with eggs have twice been found on islets in Loch Etive, close to the Pheasant-rearing estate at Kilmaronag on the south shore (C. Craik, pers. obs.). Chicks leave the nest soon after hatching and are dependent on the hen until after fledging. Hens with small or large young have been recorded on many occasions in Argyll showing that successful wild breeding occurs in most parts of the county. However, it is not clear to what extent birds of the rather ill-defined wild population are replaced each year by releases. The 1983 report of extinction on Tiree (above) suggests that, in certain areas, feral populations may sometimes depend on regular restocking for continued existence.

Flocks form during October-March and the largest numbers of birds are seen in early winter. The highest single counts from the Argyll Database were 105 on 28 November 1999 and 66 on 5 November 1997, both feeding in stubble at RSPB Loch Gruinart.

Clive Craik

Red-throated Diver

Gavia stellata

Summer breeder on moorland lochs, passage migrant, and winter visitor offshore.

The Red-throated Diver is circumpolar and holarctic in distribution. Argyll lies at its southern breeding limit. The British population of 1,200 to 1,500 pairs breed mostly in Orkney and Shetland. In Argyll about 80 pairs breed on moorland lochs with low banks or islands. About 35 pairs are on the Argyll islands and 45 pairs on the mainland. Early records suggest lower numbers and more restricted distribution. H&B excluded it from Argyll except Mull. Baxter & Rintoul (1928) stated that it had bred in North Argyll and Islay. Witherby *et al.* (1945) stated that it bred in Argyll south to Kintyre and in several of the Inner Hebrides (south to Islay). The Second Atlas indicated an expansion in Argyll even since the First Atlas. Whilst there had undoubtedly been some increase, it is possible that some breeding sites were missed by earlier fieldworkers due to their remoteness.

The nest is always very close to the water, usually on a bank no more than 20cm high, and generally on a small lochan or corner of a larger loch. Islands are preferred to the perimeter. It is very unusual for any Argyll loch to hold more

The Red-throat is the commonest diver in Argyll throughout the year. *Bob Furness*

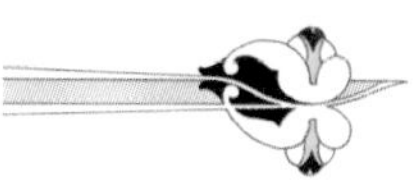

than a single pair. The breeding lochs vary in size from 0.2ha to 30ha, with most less than 5ha. Such lochs cannot provide an adequate food supply, so adults fish in larger lochs and in the sea. Each pair requires about 2km² of shallow water within 8km of the nest (Merrie 1978). Breeding success in Argyll from 1973 to 1978 averaged 0.35 young per breeding pair (Merrie 1996), and in South Argyll in 1988, 0.27 (RSPB unpublished data). Some areas produced almost no fledged juveniles over many years.

In 1976 a project commenced to provide nesting rafts on two estates in Mid-Argyll (Merrie 1979). The concept was adopted by the RSPB for Black-throated Divers, and later by Forest Enterprise for Red-throated Divers. Productivity of pairs for which rafts had been provided increased to 0.75 chicks per pair. However, only about 15% of the Argyll population has been provided with rafts, and the population may currently be in slow decline. The possible reasons for this include human disturbance, water level fluctuation, natural predation, reductions in available fish stocks, and increased afforestation of moorland. Rafts eliminate the risk due to water level fluctuation, and reduce those due to human disturbance and natural predation from foxes, which are main causes of nest failure. Fish stocks are not as yet implicated. In the last few years some adult fatalities at nest sites have been recorded and some egg losses have occurred, both of which suggest predation by feral mink. Forestry Commission (Scotland) is now careful to avoid planting trees too close to the edge of lochs and is active in putting out new rafts.

Adults arrive on breeding lochs from late March and leave by early September. Fledgling young have been seen on their natal lochs into the first week in September. Outside the breeding season birds move offshore and disperse. The British population increases to perhaps 20,000 by early October (Winter Atlas), mostly on the east coast, but about 6,000 to 7,000 are estimated to pass between the west coast of Britain and the coast of Ireland. Observations from mid-September to mid-October at Frenchman's Rocks (Islay) and at Machrihanish have averaged from 0.5 to 8 birds per hour (ABR). In the winter this bird is regularly seen in small numbers off the Argyll coast, but is more common in eastern coastal waters of Scotland and England. The scale of winter dispersal is not well known, but recoveries of Scottish ringed birds have been made from the French coast. Two birds ringed as chicks in Shetland were recovered in Argyll, in June and September, indicating that interchange in the breeding season is possible.

Formerly these birds were widely killed by collectors, especially in the winter quarters (Morris 1903). Divers are also known to have been taken for food by the inhabitants of western Scotland. In Jardine's day, as now, birds were caught in fishing nets, particularly fixed nets close inshore. Thus, in balance, old threats have been replaced by new ones, but so far the gains from reduction in human persecution outweigh losses due to other causes. The situation remains critical for this, one of Argyll's most special birds.

David Merrie

Hill lochs are important breeding sites for Red-throated and Black-throated Divers in Argyll. *John Anderson*

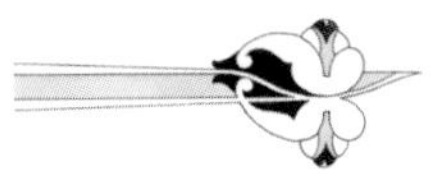

Black-throated Diver

Gavia arctica

Very scarce, breeding at about ten freshwater lochs in Mid and North Argyll. Scarce and localised in coastal areas in winter where it is a little more numerous in passage periods.

Black-throated Divers breed on undisturbed and unpolluted fresh water lochs, where stretches of shoreline or islands are easily accessible and provide level vegetated nest sites, within about a metre of the water's edge. Extensive shallow water fringes are important when feeding small chicks. Even where nesting lochs are close to the coast, breeding Black-throated Divers apparently feed exclusively in fresh water. Outside the breeding season they are found almost entirely on the sea, generally within 1-2km of the shore. Passage and wintering concentrations occur at favoured sheltered, shallow, coastal waters.

Argyll is at the south-west limit of the breeding range in the UK with the exception of a very small and isolated population in South Ayrshire and Galloway where sporadic breeding has occurred since 1956. H&B found that Kintyre, Islay, Jura and Mull were outside the breeding range and did not know of any nesting attempts in Ireland where it was relatively rare, even as a migrant. Black-throated Divers apparently bred on Coll in or around 1899 (Irby 1899). Rumours of breeding on Islay could not be confirmed by Meiklejohn & Stanford (1954) who visited 54 lochs in 1954. McWilliam (1931) recorded breeding in Kintyre and it was confirmed here again during the First Atlas when it was apparently more widespread, also breeding on Islay, Jura, Mull and Cowal. Occupation of these peripheral parts of its range appears to have been short-lived. A review of historical records up to the 1980s indicated a decline in the Scottish population and contraction of range, especially in these peripheral areas (Mudge *et al.* 1991).

The first systematic Black-throated Diver survey found 150-160 summering pairs in Scotland in 1985 (Campbell & Talbot 1987). The majority of fresh water lochs in Argyll, large enough to support a breeding pair, were visited as part of this census. There were no breeding records from Mull, Jura, Islay, Kintyre or Cowal. Since 1985, breeding has been confirmed at ten separate sites all in Mid- and North Argyll and the majority have since been monitored annually by the RSPB. The same lochs are generally used year after year, although breeding is occasionally attempted on adjacent lochs. Many sites are occupied annually, but occupation at several sites between 2000-2004 was more irregular. A second Scottish survey in 1994 estimated about 200 summering pairs (Whyte *et al.* 1995). With the very recent discovery of additional breeding pairs in north-west Scotland and the Outer Hebrides, the population may be closer to 220 summering pairs (D. Butterfield pers. comm.). Argyll has supported 5-6% of the Scottish population since 1985. There is reliable evidence that Black-throats have bred, at some time or other, at more than double the number of lochs in recent usage in Argyll.

Breeding Black-throated Divers are strongly territorial and one pair normally requires 50-150ha open water, but in fish-rich areas territories may be 5-10ha (BWP). Nine of the Argyll lochs in recent usage are relatively small, averaging 24ha of open water (range 7-55ha) and neighbouring freshwater

The Black-throated Diver is a very scarce breeding species in Argyll. *John McAvoy*

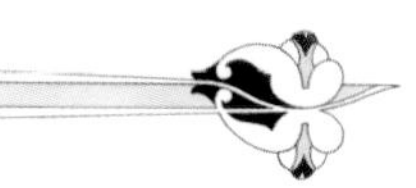

lochs provide associated feeding areas. Breeding attempts could have gone undetected at some of the largest lochs where there has been little extensive monitoring. Partial surveys at Loch Awe have sometimes found "summering pairs" but have provided little evidence that breeding still regularly occurs at this former multiple-breeding locality. The diet is principally salmonids 12-24cm in length and European Eels up to 35cm. Chicks are fed smaller fish, less than 24cm long, especially salmonids, sticklebacks and minnows, or invertebrates where fish are in short supply (Jackson 2003).

Some adults return to visit freshwater breeding sites from mid-March and the first eggs are laid in early May. Natural nests, usually within a metre of the loch shore or on islands, are very prone to flooding. Artificial rafts have been used successfully to overcome problems associated with fluctuating water levels. The first rafts were used by Black-throats in Argyll in 1976 (Merrie 1979). In the mid 1980s rafts were provided by the RSPB and Forestry Commission at another five traditional sites as part of a larger programme in Scotland. Results from the Scottish Black-throated Diver raft programme have shown that the production of chicks from rafts has been at least twice as good as the production of chicks from natural sites (Hancock 2000). In Argyll, 116 monitored breeding attempts reared 49 young during 1985-2004. It is unlikely that many successful breeding attempts occurred undetected at other sites in Argyll. While it was not unusual to find two chicks hatching, only three broods of two survived to fledging, all at the same loch. Overall, 56 breeding attempts at natural sites fledged 19 young (0.34 young/breeding attempt) and 60 breeding attempts at raft sites fledged 30 young (0.50 young/breeding attempt).

On four out of five occasions, chicks hatched on a raft on a particularly small loch moved at least 150m to an adjacent larger loch well before they were capable of flight. Unlike some sites in north Scotland (Mudge & Talbot 1993), replacement clutches are rarely recorded in Argyll if the first is lost. As well as reducing the threat of flooding, rafts reduce human disturbance along the shore and remove the risk of predation by foxes. However, otters have been identified as predators of eggs (McWilliam 1931) and feral mink were suspected of killing an adult breeding on a raft in 1993 and causing the failure of several diver clutches and neighbouring Common Gull nests. Canada Geese have begun to colonise Argyll hill lochs and may compete for nesting rafts.

In Mid-Argyll and North Argyll additional birds in adult plumage occasionally associate with breeding birds, but more than three to four on the same water body is infrequent except at the largest lochs such as Loch Awe. Single birds in breeding plumage are recorded almost annually from fresh water in the breeding season on Mull but are rarely reported from other areas. There have been no more than one to two sightings reported from fresh water on Coll, Colonsay, Islay, Jura, Kintyre and Cowal in the last 20 years.

Very little is known of the movements of Argyll's Black-throats after they leave their breeding lochs, which are deserted by August. Small post-breeding gatherings have been recorded occasionally on inland waters before they move to the coast. For example, there were five birds at Loch Nell on 28 July 1991 and seven adults Loch Tulla on 9 August 1995.

Black-throats are generally less gregarious than Red-throats around the British coastline and in winter are the rarest of the three wintering divers, with estimated autumnal peaks of 1,400-1,800 birds and a wintering population of about 1,300 (Lack 1986). These numbers, far exceeding the total Scottish population, indicate winter immigration, with Fennoscandia the most likely source. Since 1989, substantial gatherings have been found off Kintyre with concentrations somewhat smaller on the east side, particularly in the Skipness area, than on the west. Large concentrations have been regularly identified in the shallow coastal areas in the Sound of Gigha-West Loch Tarbert area and further north at Loch Caolisport (Table). Around the major islands, important numbers have occurred at Loch Indaal and to a lesser extent around the coast of Mull. Away from these favoured areas, records are scarce. Black-throats are recorded in Argyll coastal waters in all months and some of the summer records are of immatures.

There are no ringing recoveries and it is not known whether passage and wintering birds originate from Argyll, other parts of Scotland or further afield. A programme of co-ordinated surveys would be needed to determine whether, as seems likely, the birds found in winter in Loch Caolisport gather earlier in the Sound of Gigha.

Largest numbers are recorded in Argyll waters during the passage months of March-May and October (Table) but few are seen on passage from well-watched sea-watching sites. Recent records off MSBO include 17 flying south between September-October 1989 and four heading south and four heading north in September-October 1993. Four were heading south off Frenchman's Rocks, Islay in autumn 1993.

The concentrations of divers on inland coastal waters are vulnerable to pollution and are particularly at risk when the birds are temporarily flightless during moult into summer

Maximum monthly counts of Black-throated Divers, 1982-2000.

	J	F	M	A	M	J	J	A	S	O	N	D
Campbeltown to Skipness	0	0	12	21	21	8	0	0	12	10	0	0
Sound of Gigha to West Loch Tarbert	0	0	27	66	46	37	8	55	42	49	22	0
Loch Caolisport	22	16	44	28	0	0	0	0	0	0	10	41
Loch Indaal	0	0	0	0	20	6	0	0	0	31	7	11
Coastal Mull	0	0	7	0	11	0	0	0	0	0	6	0

plumage. On the breeding sites, fluctuating water levels remain the single largest threat if rafts are not available. Artificial stocking of lochs for angling or changes to the hydrological regime may alter plankton and invertebrate levels and reduce the food, including small fish, required by Black-throated Divers. Lastly, wind farms may present new risks for Black-throated Divers, which are unsuited for aerial avoidance manoeuvres.

Roger Broad

Great Northern Diver

Gavia immer

Present in coastal waters throughout the year, though scarce in summer. Numbers peak in spring and autumn, when 20 per cent or more of Europe's wintering population may be in the sea off Argyll.

The Great Northern Diver has long been known as a common winter visitor to northern and western Scotland (Gray, H&B, B&R). Pennant's account of his 1772 tour of Scotland drew attention to its occurrence around Gigha, stating that: "The great Arctic diver, of the British Zoology, sometimes visits these seas: and is styled in the Erse, *murbhuachaille*, or 'the herdsman of the ocean'; because, as is pretended, it never leaves that element, never flies, and hatches the young beneath its wing" (Pennant 1776). Today, more than two centuries later, we know the Sound of Gigha to be the main stronghold of the species in the county.

Great Northern Divers are present in Argyll waters all year round. It has been known since the time of H&B that small numbers are found in the summer, mostly immature but including some adults. Numbers are normally small but an unprecedented 46 were in a raft offshore at Machrihanish on 6 August 2001 (ABR 18:23). The main arrival from breeding grounds in Iceland, Greenland and possibly Canada takes place from late September or October to mid-November, with the main departure in May. Numbers appear to peak in autumn and spring, suggesting that birds wintering further south may stop off *en route*. At Argyll's two main sites, Loch Indaal and the Sound of Gigha, peak midwinter counts are much lower than peak spring or autumn counts. The same is true for most, though not all, of the other major sites (Table). However, interpretation of the data is not straightforward. The Great Northern Diver is found further offshore than its smaller congeners (Migration Atlas). Moreover, birds may flock at times of migration, so that spring and autumn peaks could be artefacts. Above all, accurate counting of divers demands perfectly calm conditions and good visibility, and these are rare in Argyll, especially in winter.

For such reasons, it is impossible to know whether these maximum counts are genuinely seasonal or whether they represent exceptional influxes. However, there are other records of large numbers at these sites in autumn and spring (260 in the Sound of Gigha in October, and two more counts exceeding 100 in Loch Indaal in April and November), together with a count of 417 birds along the west coast of Kintyre on 6 May 2001 (ABR 18:22), suggesting that the spring and autumn peaks in the table are not atypical. Recent aerial surveys found 175 Great Northern Divers in transect lines totalling 416km in the waters around Coll and Tiree (18

Many Great Northern Divers are seen close inshore on spring passage. *Philip Snow*

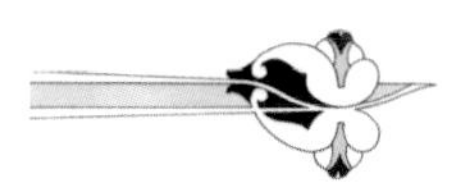

Maximum counts of Great Northern Divers, 1983-2000.

Location	Max. count	Max. midwinter count (Dec-Feb)	Date of max. count	Reference
MAINLAND				
Sound of Gigha	268	107	25 October 1991	ABR 8:23
West Loch Tarbert	80	67	18 May 1990	SBR 1990:5
Machrihanish	60	31	18 May 1990	SBR 1990:5
Loch Caolisport	50	50	19 February 2000	ABR 17:23
ISLAY				
Loch Indaal	157	35	27 April 1995	ABR 12:18
TIREE				
Crossapol/Hynish Bay	62	28	18 November 1983	SBR 1983:8
Gott Bay	30	-	Late April 1989	ABR 6:10
COLL	54	-	Mid-April 1999	ABR 16:21
COLONSAY	45	30-35	18 May 1989	SBR 1989:3
ORONSAY	34	-	16 April 1994	ABR 11:16
MULL				
Loch na Keal	28	28	3 February 1983	SBR 1983:8
Loch Scridain	26	-	7 April 1997	ABR 14:20

The Sound of Gigha and West Loch Tarbert could be regarded as one extended site. However, most of the counts from West Loch Tarbert refer to birds seen from the Islay ferry near the north end of Gigha, and are thus unlikely to be counted from land.

February 2004) and 104 in transect lines totalling 225km in the Sound of Gigha (9 March 2005) (Wilson 2006). Smaller numbers are present elsewhere along the coast at these times, so the total in Argyll waters may well exceed 1,000 during the migration seasons, but it falls substantially in midwinter. Given that birds wintering in western France or Iberia may be involved, this total cannot be compared directly with the UK wintering population. However, it represents 20 per cent of the European wintering population, estimated to be 5,000 birds (Gregory *et al.* 2002).

The Table does not include an exceptional count of 217 divers, thought to be mainly Great Northern, flying north past Frenchman's Rocks on Islay on 4 May 1975 (SB 9:179, Verrall & Bourne 1982). These authors believed that, on that date, birds flying inconspicuously overhead in fine weather were forced to descend by locally overcast skies and fog. No such phenomenon has been witnessed since, though a steady southward passage of small numbers of Great Northern Divers is recorded during autumn seawatches.

Most reports come from the islands, Kintyre and the western coast of the mainland. Isolated records from Cowal include single birds at Loch Long on 12 December 1988 (ABR 5:15) and 18 January 1991 (ABR 8:23), and at Carry Point on 30 May 1990 (ABR 7:10). The only freshwater record seems to have been at Loch Gorm on Islay, where one was present on 24 May 1991 (ABR 8:23).

Tristan ap Rheinallt

White-billed Diver

Gavia adamsii

Vagrant.

Until recently, the Northern Isles and northern Scotland accounted for most British records of this Arctic breeder, whose winter distribution remains poorly known. However, there is recent evidence for a regular spring migration through the Hebrides, peaking in late April and early May. The pattern of the eight Argyll records to 2005, of which six have been in spring, reflects this (Table). Interestingly, one of the spring birds, an immature, apparently summered. Summer records of White-billed Divers in Scotland are rare but not unknown.

The timing of the spring records corresponds well with

Records of White-billed Divers in Argyll.

Date	Location	Comment	Reference
27 Mar 1986	Loch Indaal (Islay)	Oiled adult found moribund	BB 80:519
21-24 Apr & 4-6 Jul 1987	Loch Sween	2nd-summer; Apr & Jul records probably the same bird	BB 81:538
5 May 1991	Machrihanish Bay	Adult	BB 85:510
21 Sep 1999	Machir Bay (Islay)	1st-summer	BB 93:515
21 May 2000 (at least)	Loch na Keal (Mull)	1st-summer	BB 94:455
15 May 2003	Between Iona and Treshnish Isles	Adult	BB 97:567
22-23 May 2004	Sorisdale (Coll)	2nd-summer	BB 98:639
5 Feb 2005	near Inverneil (Loch Fyne)	Probably adult	BB 100:24

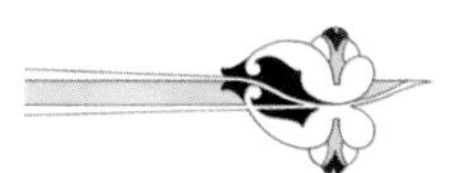

the peak in numbers of Great Northern Divers in Argyll, suggesting that the two species possibly migrate together. On the other hand, recent information from the Isle of Lewis indicates that their habitat preferences differ to some extent, White-billed Divers preferring rocky coasts with cliffs, away from the main concentrations of Great Northern Divers. Thus visits to the more remote coasts of Argyll at the right season might produce more records.

Tristan ap Rheinallt

Pied-billed Grebe

Podilymbus podiceps

Vagrant.

There is one record of this species in Argyll. One was seen at Loch Peallach (Mishnish Lochs) on Mull on 8 and 15 June 1998 (BB 92:557). This was the sixth Scottish record and came hot on the heels of another bird (possibly the same one) at Airthrey Loch in the Forth recording area, last seen on 7 June 1998. These were the first records in Scotland since 1987.

Tristan ap Rheinallt

Little Grebe

Tachybaptus ruficollis

Breeds locally on shallow, well vegetated, freshwater bodies. Widespread in sheltered coastal waters in winter.

According to Gray, this species was well known in Mull, Islay, Jura, Gigha, Colonsay, Tiree, Coll and Iona. Towards the end of the 19th century, it was said to breed commonly throughout Argyll, and to be found "universally along the coasts and in the sea-lochs" during winter. Loch Creran, Loch Linnhe and the surrounding waters held particularly large numbers (H&B). In the first half of the 20th century, breeding occurred on Mull, Islay, Jura, Gigha, Colonsay, Tiree, Lismore and possibly Coll. Increases were reported from south-west, south-east and east Scotland and the Outer Hebrides during this period, but there was no suggestion of a similar trend in Argyll (B&R).

In the last 30 years there seems to have been a slight extension in range and possibly in numbers. In addition to the main breeding areas in Mid-Argyll and on Islay and the few pairs on Mull and Colonsay identified during 1968-72 (First Atlas), there are recent breeding records for Cowal, Kintyre, North Argyll and Tiree. There are none, however, for Coll or Jura. On Mull the breeding population is apparently confined to the north-west of the island and the only recent confirmed breeding records relate to the Mishnish Lochs. The Second Atlas showed breeding in 14% of 10-km squares in Argyll. Confirmed breeding records came from more than 20 sites during 1991-2000.

Although quite scarce as a breeding species, Little Grebes are often encountered just off-shore in winter. *David Palmar*

At the end of the breeding season, which may finish as late as August, most of the freshwater breeding sites are deserted. On Islay and Tiree, however, a few Little Grebes are present on inland lochs throughout the winter and Loch Ballygrant on Islay regularly holds up to six birds. Although there is little direct evidence, there is undoubtedly some autumn migration across the North Sea to Scotland and some of these birds may reach Argyll.

In winter, one or two birds may be found at many coastal locations. Sheltered waters of sea-lochs and estuaries are especially favoured. Numbers usually amount to no more than four or five individuals but regular monitoring as part of the WeBS programme has revealed that a few favoured sites regularly hold larger concentrations. In particular, Loch Etive has recently been shown to regularly hold more than 20 birds and on 15 January 2000 no less than 42 were counted there. It is not clear whether this represents a real increase in numbers or is simply a result of more systematic surveying. Other sites that regularly record counts in double figures include Loch Sween, where 25 were counted on 13 November 2005, and Campbeltown Loch. Other than these, the only counts of more than nine birds since 1980 were: ten at Lochdon, Mull on 10 October 1982, 14 at Lochdon on 19 January 1985, 16 at Lochdon on 6 March 1986 (more than the known breeding population of Mull at this time), 12 at Ardentallen (Loch Feochan) on 29 November 1990, 11 at Loch Feochan on 5 February 1991 and 11 at Loch Gair on 7 March 1999.

Paul Daw

Great Crested Grebe

Podiceps cristatus

Uncommon migrant and winter visitor, with several records annually. A small number of favoured sites account for a high proportion of Argyll records.

In the latter part of the nineteenth century, the Great Crested Grebe was regarded as the scarcest of the five grebe species in Scotland (Gray). At the time, there were very few records from Argyll (Gray, H&B), although it was at one time said to occur in Ardchattan (NSA). There were a few reports from Tiree at the end of the 19th century and a record in 1952 (Boyd 1958). The species began to be recorded more regularly in the 1960s, probably because of increased observer activity and its well-documented expansion into Scotland as a breeding species (B&R).

The report of a pair with young at Ardnave Loch on Islay in June 1969 (SB 6:68) is the only record of breeding in Argyll. The map in the First Atlas is otherwise blank north and west of a line from Helensburgh to Lossiemouth. Nevertheless, the sighting of two pairs in breeding plumage on a Tiree loch on 22 May 1900 (B&R), if authentic, suggests that breeding might have occurred in Argyll around the time that Great Crested Grebes were beginning to colonise the Clyde. With the exception of one or two isolated instances such as these, however, the shortage of suitable habitats in the Highlands appears to have halted the species' northward expansion, as is shown by comparison between the First and Second Atlases.

Since about 1980, Great Crested Grebes have been seen annually in Argyll outside the breeding season. Counts of more than a hundred are regularly made at Ardmore Point on the Clyde, not far from Helensburgh, so it is surprising that no more than two have ever been seen together in Argyll itself. A small number of sites account for a large proportion of the county records, suggesting that Great Crested Grebes, like other grebe species, are reluctant to stray far from their regular wintering areas. At Loch Indaal on Islay, Great Crested Grebes were seen in 17 of the 23 winters between 1980/81 and 2002/03. Most of those records were in autumn or spring, but it is difficult to be certain whether the birds were migrants or wintering individuals that escaped notice in the coldest months. Other regular sites are West Loch Tarbert (seven winters), Blairmore/Long Long (seven), Machrihanish Bay/Uisaed Point (six), Loch Gilp (three), and Lochs Crinan/Craignish (three). Some older records also come from these sites, suggesting that they have a long history of occupation. Thus Gray reported sightings on Loch Indaal, while one was seen at Craignish on 8 November 1909 (ASNH 1910:211) and another just north of the entrance to West Loch Tarbert on 18 June 1926 (McWilliam).

Post-1979 records away from the main sites are divided between Islay, Mull and scattered locations on the mainland. Most of these birds were seen only once and few occurred during December to February, suggesting that the majority were migrants. Only four records between 1980 and 2005 fell outside the period 1 August to 1 May. Interestingly, two of these were at freshwater sites: single birds were seen on Loch Awe on 20 July 1987 (ABR 5:4) and Loch Gorm on Islay on 24 July 1989 (ABR 6:10). Loch Gorm was also the site of the only other freshwater record, on 4 April 1991 (ABR 8:24).

Seawatching has produced only two records of migrating Great Crested Grebes, past Uisaed Point on 8 August 1993 (ABR 10:16) and past Frenchman's Rocks on 1 May 1994 (ABR 11: 17). It is believed that most passage of this species is nocturnal (Migration Atlas).

Tristan ap Rheinallt

Red-necked Grebe

Podiceps grisegena

Scarce visitor, mainly in winter.

Although present in good numbers in the Firth of Forth in winter, this east European breeder has always been regarded

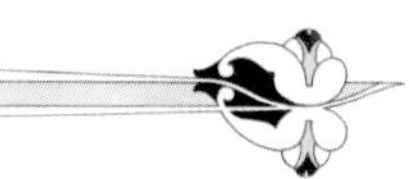

as a scarce visitor to western Scotland. H&B did not include the Red-necked Grebe in their systematic list for Argyll. B&R stated that it had occurred in Argyll but gave no details, and they knew of no recent records from the Inner Hebrides. Wilson's statement in Boyd (1958) that it was "common and not breeding Tiree" seems highly improbable.

The earliest dated record seems to be of a bird photographed on Loch Sween on the rather unusual date of 22 June 1968 (SB 5: 309). Records then became more frequent, with seven in the 1970s, seven in the 1980s, 13 in the 1990s, and five during 2000-03. All these involved single birds.

A Red-necked Grebe is always an exciting find in Argyll. *Philip Snow*

Of the 33 records to the end of 2003, 14 came from the mainland and 19 from the islands. Most of the mainland records came from Kintyre but birds were also recorded at Loch Awe, Gairletter and Ardrishaig in addition to Loch Sween. Of the island records, 12 were on Islay, four on Mull, two on Colonsay and one on Tiree. Certain sites in Argyll are favoured, in particular Loch Indaal, West Loch Tarbert and the Sound of Gigha. Almost all records come from the coast, but birds have also been seen on Loch Gorm, the Mishnish Lochs and Loch Awe.

The records show a wide scatter of dates, with a peak in late winter and early spring (late January to early April). Only six of the 33 records were outside the period 29 September to 8 April (Figure).

Seasonal variation in records of Red-necked Grebes in Argyll.

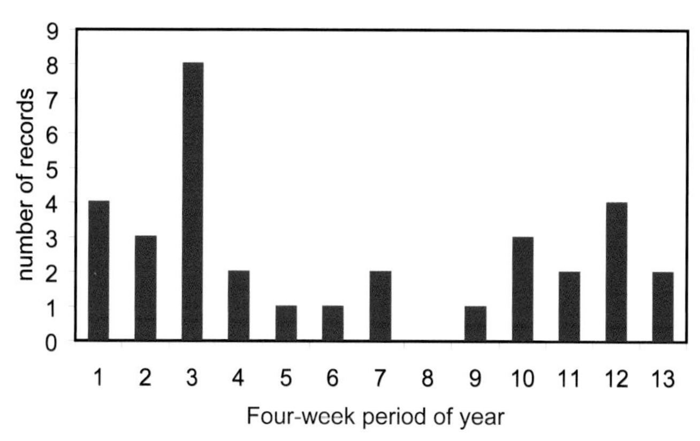

Interestingly, only three of these records involve sightings of the same bird over a period of more than a day. This suggests that many of the birds in Argyll are transient visitors or are mobile over a large area, perhaps spending much of their time well offshore. It is not inconceivable that some records involve misidentifications of other grebe species.

Tristan ap Rheinallt

Slavonian Grebe

Podiceps auritus

Regular winter visitor to traditional sites. Argyll holds a nationally important wintering population.

About 400 Slavonian Grebes are thought to winter off British coasts. The most impressive concentrations occur on the east coast of Scotland and in the Northern Isles, where numbers peak in midwinter. A few breed in Scotland.

According to Graham, Slavonian Grebes migrating north occurred in small parties at Lochgilphead, and during bad weather they remained there through March and into early April. A male and female in breeding plumage were shot at Loch Caolisport on 20 June 1860, a date that prompted speculation about breeding (Gray). Although there were few confirmed records, H&B believed Slavonian Grebes to be "not uncommon" around the islands in winter. This view was repeated by B&R, who quoted regular sightings in Loch Indaal and on Tiree, where birds were to be found more on fresh water than on the sea. Nowadays the winter distribution is better known, and it is clear that mainland sites are also important. Birds normally arrive on wintering grounds in late August or September, departing in April, and most of them presumably belong to the Icelandic breeding population.

In a comprehensive review of the period 1986/87-1992/93, Evans (2000) concluded that the main sites in Argyll were Loch Indaal on Islay, Loch na Keal on Mull and the Sound of Gigha, all of which he classed as "nationally important" because they held at least seven birds, or one percent of the UK population. He found that Argyll held larger mean numbers during September to April than any other coastal "site" in Scotland except the Firth of Forth. Mean counts from Evans (2000), together with maximum counts (ABR and Argyll Database) are given in the Table.

Evans attributed the difference between the December-February mean and the September-April mean at two of the sites to the presence of migrants this fits well with the dates of the maximum counts. At Loch na Keal, targeted surveys between winter 1994/95 and winter 1998/99 produced a considerably higher five-year mean of 27 birds. The means for the other two sites in the Table may likewise

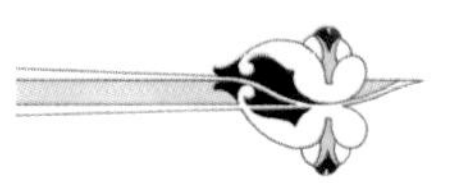

be underestimates.

Smaller numbers have been recorded at many other locations in recent years. There are a few records from freshwater lochs, usually near Loch na Keal or Loch Indaal in autumn or spring. Most of the subsidiary sites are on the mainland or Mull, but Islay, Tiree, Colonsay and Oronsay are also represented. The most regular sites seem to be Loch Spelve and Loch Ba on Mull, and Loch Caolisport and Ardmucknish Bay on the mainland. Of these, only Loch Ba has produced a count exceeding ten birds. However, there was an isolated count of 11 on Loch Sween on 2 February 1986 (ABR 4:9), whilst adjacent Linne Mhuirich held nine in November 1985 (ABR 4:39) and 16 in February 1987 (ABR 5:4).

Mean and maximum counts of Slavonian Grebes in Argyll.

Location	Dec-Feb mean	Sep-Apr mean	Max count	Date of max count
Loch Indaal	17	30	50	19 Apr 1992
Loch na Keal	11	12	38	20 Jan 1997
Sound of Gigha	4	13	51	30 Oct 2002

Slavonian Grebes are normally present at their wintering sites in Argyll between the end of August and April. There are also a few summer records. In addition to the 1860 record above, two birds remained in the Sound of Gigha through the summer of 1990 (ABR 7:11), and one was there on 7 July 1997 (ABR 14:21). On fresh water, a bird was on Loch Staoisha on Islay on 24 June 1988 (ABR 5:15). There is an unpublished record of a juvenile at Loch Leathan on 7 August 1981, but breeding was not thought to have occurred there. The only birds to have been seen apparently migrating were two that flew south past Uisaed Point on 11 September 1996 (ABR 13:21).

Slavonian Grebes wintering in Argyll probably belong to the race *arcticus*, which breeds in Iceland, northern Norway and Scotland (Migration Atlas).

Tristan ap Rheinallt

Black-necked Grebe

Podiceps nigricollis

Rare migrant and winter visitor.

The Black-necked Grebe occurs in Scotland as a rare breeder and as a very scarce migrant and winter visitor to coastal areas. Most non-breeding records come from a few favoured localities such as Loch Ryan (Dumfries & Galloway) and Ruddon's Point (Fife). On the west coast, the numbers of records decline as one moves north. The first Outer Hebrides record was not until 1982, but there were 14 records in Argyll between 1936 and 2003. The first of these was a bird in "winter plumage", so presumably a juvenile, at Inveraray on the seasonally early date of 14 August 1936 (Campbell 1937). The other 13 records were between mid-October and mid-April (Table).

There were no Argyll records during the period 1990-2002. This lack of records coincided with a decline at the important Loch Ryan wintering site. The bird on fresh water at Loch Gruinart in October 2003 was presumably a migrant, as perhaps were the others seen in autumn and spring.

Tristan ap Rheinallt

Date	Location	Number of birds	Comment	Reference
22 December 1963	Loch Creran	1		SB 3:85
18 January 1964	Strachur	1		SB 3:85
17 February 1968	Strachur	5	one stayed until 2 March	SB 5:309
18 March 1976	Loch Indaal	1		SB 10:80
28 October 1976	Campbeltown	1		SB 10:80
16 October 1978	Campbeltown	2		SBR 1978:12
10 April 1981	West Loch Tarbert	1		SBR 1981:13
20 January 1982	Loch Cuin (Mull)	1		SBR 1982:13
31 March 1982	West Loch Tarbert	1		SBR 1982:13
11 December 1982	Loch Indaal	1		SBR 1982:13
20 February 1990	Loch Ederline	1		SBR 1990:6
19 October 2003	Loch Gruinart floods	1	stayed until 20 October	Argyll Database
2 December 2003	Loch na Keal	1	stayed for at least 2 days	Argyll Database

Records of Black-necked Grebes in Argyll, 1963-2003.

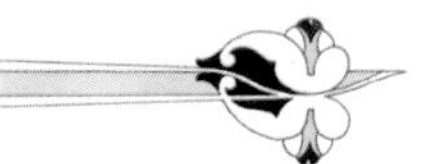

Fulmar

Fulmarus glacialis

The Fulmar is now a common breeding seabird occurring on most of the Argyll islands with over 8,000 breeding pairs.

The Fulmar was an extremely rare bird in Argyll during the 19th century. Graham never remembered seeing one alive but they were occasionally picked up dead about Soay, Iona, and Mull (H&B). They did report a small group which had been seen at sea at the Hawes Bank to the west of Coll and Tiree. It was certainly scarce, as specimens at the time were sent for taxidermy, including one that died after being injured on telegraph wires in October 1888 on Tiree, and another from Jura on 10 June 1886.

Fisher (1952) describes the spread of the Fulmar in his Collins New Naturalist monograph which was updated by further surveys (Fisher 1966 and Table). He suggests, on the basis of date of first prospecting and distance to nearest known breeding station, that Argyll was colonised from the south, *via* Ireland, rather than from the Outer Hebrides to the north. The first confirmed breeding was on the Sanaig cliffs in north-west Islay in 1924, following prospecting birds being seen there in 1918. Breeding was recorded on the Mull of Oa in 1926 and during the next 15 years Fulmars colonized sites on the Rinns at Kilchiaran, Lossit Point and Portnahaven.

Colonisation then followed on Colonsay with birds prospecting in 1924, but breeding was not proved until 1927 (Loder 1935). In 1925, prospecting birds were found on the Treshnish Isles and Tiree and breeding was confirmed on both in 1929. Fulmars were also prospecting at Caliach Point and Treshnish Point in north Mull in 1932 and 1933, but breeding was not confirmed. Further spread around Mull took place in the late 1940s; Iona (breeding 1947), Staffa (breeding 1947), Soa (prospecting 1947) and Inch Kenneth (prospecting 1949).

Spread also occurred, probably from Northern Ireland, into the Kintyre peninsula. A few birds were seen as early as 1921, and prospecting was noted from 1937; breeding was confirmed in 1940. On Sanda prospecting started in 1938 and breeding was recorded in 1942.

Numbers of Fulmars prospecting and nesting in Argyll, 1919-1959.

Year	Prospecting	1-9 pairs	10-99 pairs	100+ pairs
1919	1 site			
1929	2 sites	4 sites		
1939	9 sites	2 sites	3 sites	1 site
1949	7 sites	7 sites	6 sites	1 site
1959	8 sites	7 sites	9 sites	1 site

Colonisation has continued, with breeding now occurring on Gigha (first noted in Operation Seafarer 1969-70), on Coll (Operation Seafarer), the Garvellachs (first noted in the Second Atlas), and on Jura (Second Atlas). There have been no breeding records in North Argyll or the inner Firth of Lorne.

The dramatic range expansion of Fulmars during the 20th century now seems to have slowed. *Louise Wood*

Distribution and abundance of breeding Fulmars (apparently occupied sites) in Argyll during Seabird 2000.

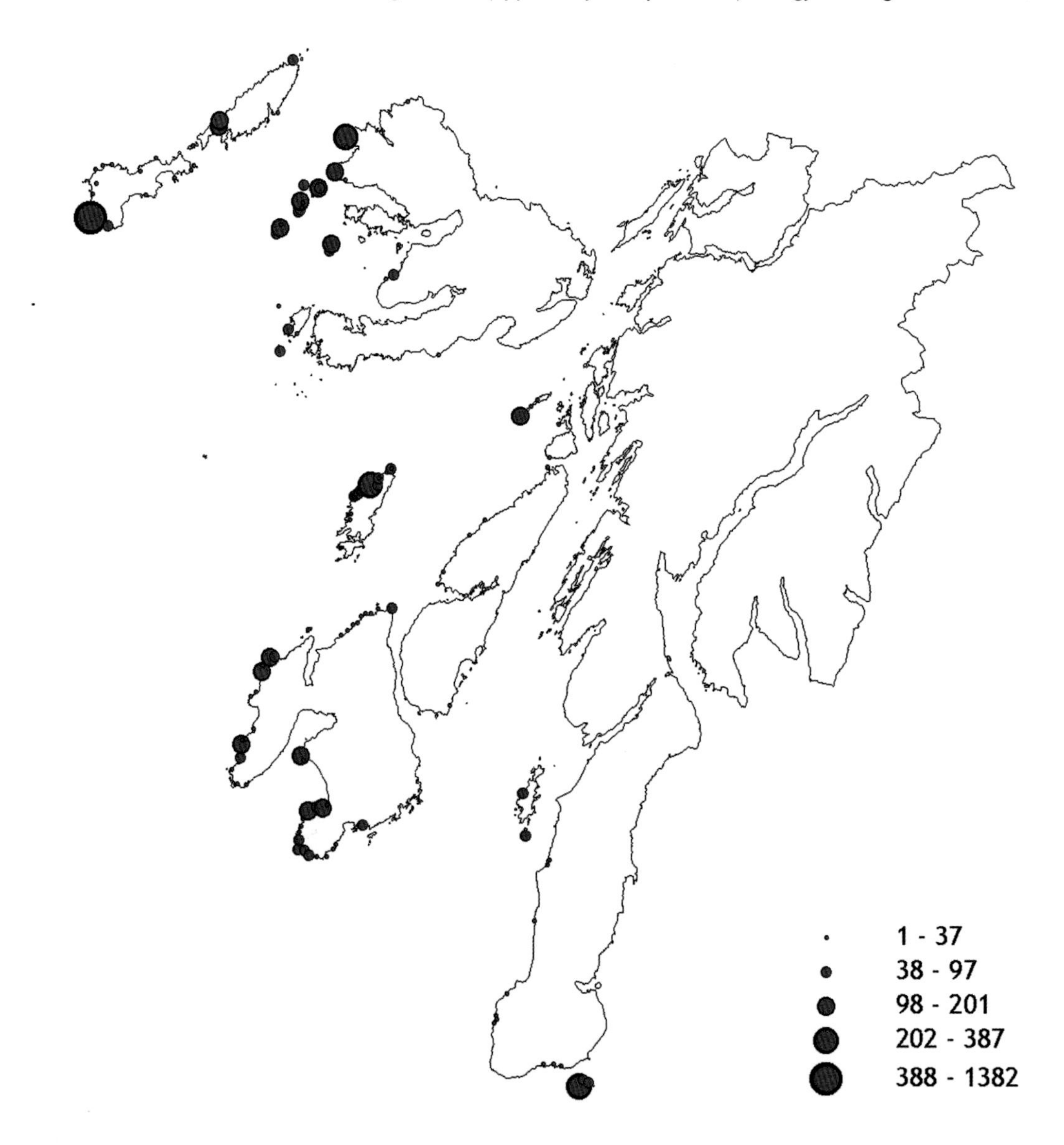

Operation Seafarer (1969-70) recorded 3,804 pairs in Argyll and Bute and this increased rapidly to 7,172 pairs in the next census in 1985-87 (Lloyd *et al.* 1991). Following this, the rate of increase slowed and the Seabird 2000 census found 8,467 apparently occupied sites (AOS) in Argyll & Bute (essentially equivalent to 'pairs' though this term recognises that some sites are held by unpaired birds so is technically more correct). Much of the population is confined to the islands, with four islands holding more than 1,000 AOS in 2000: Mull (including the Treshnish islands) 2,091, Islay 1,957, Tiree 1,664 and Colonsay 1,323. The only birds breeding in mainland Argyll are on the Kintyre peninsula.

Fulmar populations in Britain increased at 7% per annum through most of the second half of the 20th century (Lloyd *et al.* 1991) and counts at three sample sites on Colonsay from 1975 showed a similar increase until the early 1990s, when the population started to decline slightly and then stabilised (Jardine 1998). The causes of this decline are not known but may be related to food supplies, or to increased mortality through predation. Fulmars have been found as regular prey items in the recently re-established White-tailed Eagle population on Mull (Marquiss *et al.* 2003).

Fulmars may travel long distances to feed, and will scavenge at fishing vessels as well as taking zooplankton and small fish. Adult survival rates are very high. There have been few studies of the breeding success of Fulmars in Argyll; this would be a useful area for future study in the context of changing fisheries, fish stocks and oceanography.

Sea-watching at Frenchman's Rocks on Islay and at Uisaed Point in Kintyre has demonstrated that the peak passage is in autumn. Interpretation of records, however, is difficult because of variation in effort, but numbers are usually higher at the former location. The peak passage is usually in July, August or September, but usually diminishes quickly during October (ABR). Fulmars can be seen offshore in most months of the year. Maximum counts on single days were 3,809 flying south in nine hours on 28 August 1994 and 2,532 flying south on 25 August 1995, both at Frenchman's Rocks.

Small numbers of Fulmars can be seen offshore in winter months with adults returning to the breeding cliffs as early

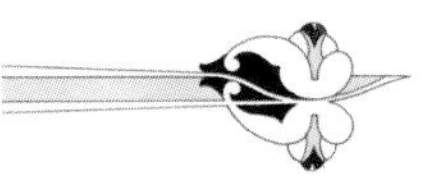

as February. Fulmars ringed in Argyll have been recovered in Iceland (two young birds, one two-years, and the other 18-months old), Sweden (one three-years old), France (one ten-years old) and on the shores of the Irish Sea (three on the Isle of Man, three in North Wales and one in Cumbria). Fulmars ringed on Canna (two) and in the Firth of Forth, Sutherland and Orkney (one each) have been recovered in Argyll.

Dark or "blue" phase birds have been recorded on 15 occasions during the last 20 years. Most dark individuals have been recorded from the main sea-watching sites on Islay and Kintyre, but they have also been reported from Tiree, west of Mull, and Colonsay. They have been noted in eight months of the year, with most during February-April and again in August-October.

David Jardine

Cory's Shearwater

Calonectris diomedea

Vagrant.

Although sometimes recorded in large numbers off the coasts of Ireland and south-west England following northward dispersal from breeding grounds further south, this large shearwater is only a scarce visitor to Scotland. Indeed, the first record occurred as recently as 1947 (B&R). In most years, only a few scattered individuals are seen, some as early as May. There were nine records in Argyll to the end of 2005, all between mid-August and early October. All but three of these were made during intensive seawatching over several years at two sites (Machrihanish and Frenchman's Rocks). The species does therefore appear to be a true rarity in Argyll, although birds could be present more regularly further offshore.

[A few other published records, including one in the 1989 SBR, were rejected by or not submitted to SBRC. These included a sighting at sea south of Tiree in September or October by the Seabirds at Sea team (Stone *et al.* 1995).]

Tristan ap Rheinallt

Great Shearwater

Puffinus gravis

Irregular autumn visitor.

This species, like Cory's Shearwater, is mainly an autumn visitor to Scotland. Unlike Cory's, however, it appears regularly in some numbers in Scottish waters as part of its clockwise migration around the north Atlantic from breeding grounds in Tristan da Cunha. Thus B&R stated that: "When we get to the Outer Hebrides we find the Great Shearwater occurring in considerable numbers, especially about St. Kilda and North Rona". The timing of the main movement through British and Irish waters suggests that the birds involved are largely non-breeders (Migration Atlas).

Within Argyll, the Great Shearwater is very much a bird of the northern islands. Up to the end of 2005, 15 of the 23 dated records were off Tiree, Coll and Mull. These include the third Scottish record and the first for Argyll, a bird found dead after gales on Tiree on 14 or 15 October 1891 (H&B). Until fairly recently, the largest number seen at once was six, between Coll and Mull on 5 September 1981 (SBR 1981:13, ABR 1:12). However, on 3 October 1999 a flock of at least 70 was seen near Hawes Bank, 10km north of Coll (SBR 1999:12, ABR 16:23). This is apparently by far the largest number seen together in Scottish waters.

Unlike further north, intensive seawatching off Kintyre and Islay in recent years has produced only three records: two birds off Machrihanish on 21 September 1993, five there on 9 September 1994 (ABR 13:22), and three on 31 August 2001 (SOC website). Earlier, however, there were records from Colonsay in 1936 and 1976 and from Kintyre in 1969.

Away from Kintyre, the only mainland record concerned two birds in the Firth of Lorne, two miles from Oban Bay, on the seasonally early date of 22 June 1923 (B&R; see BB 17:87). Apart from a single bird between Coll and Tiree on 18 May 1988 (SBR 1988:9, ABR 5:15), all other Argyll records have been between mid-July and early November. The latest was one found dead in the sprat nets of a boat that had been fishing at Loch na Keal on 7 and 8 November 1995 (SBR 1995:9, ABR 13:22).

[As with Cory's Shearwater, a small number of published records, including one in SBR 1989, were rejected by or not submitted to SBRC. No details exist of an undated August 1963 record from Islay.]

Tristan ap Rheinallt

Date	Location	Number of birds	Reference
19 August 1973	Frenchman's Rocks	1	BB 67:313
14 August 1975	Machrihanish	1	BB 69:327
28 August 1992	Machrihanish	3	SBR 1994:9
20 September 1993	Frenchman's Rocks	1	SBR 1993:8
5 October 1996	Coul Point (Islay)	1	SBR 1996:9
20 September 1997	Oban - Colonsay ferry, *c.*10 km off Scarba	1	SBR 1997:11
29 August 2002	Frenchman's Rocks	1	Argyll Database
8 September 2003	Machrihanish	1	Argyll Database
24 August 2005	Aird (Tiree)	1	Argyll Database

Records of Cory's Shearwater in Argyll to the end of 2006.

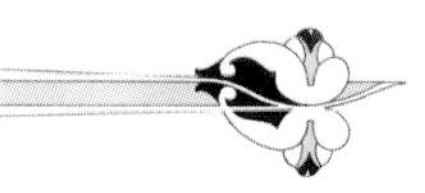

Sooty Shearwater

Puffinus griseus

A regular autumn visitor, observed mostly from west-facing coasts, islands and ferry crossings.

Sooty Shearwaters breed in the Southern Hemisphere, migrating to spend the austral winter in North Atlantic waters. In the past, there was apparently some confusion between this species and the Great Shearwater, so that older records of larger shearwaters in Argyll cannot be assigned with certainty to any species (H&B). The first acceptable Argyll records of Sooty Shearwaters come from the 1930s, with singles off the Mull of Kintyre on 2 September 1932 and three miles from Islay on 10 September 1935 (B&R).

The species began to be recorded with increasing frequency from 1970, although this may reflect observer effort rather than increase in numbers. In the mid-1970s, Sooty Shearwaters were found to be regular off the west coast of Islay. A total of 496 birds was recorded at Frenchman's Rocks in 404 hours' observation during 1973 to 1977, with sightings between 11 August and 17 October (Verrall & Bourne 1982).

More recently, regular seawatching at this site and at Uisaed Point has confirmed that the largest numbers consistently occur in late August and September, with birds also seen in October and, to a lesser extent, July. At both sites, nearly all birds fly south, with average numbers over the autumn period exceeding one individual per hour (SBR 1994:9).

There is an obvious association with early-autumn southward passage of Manx Shearwaters, although peak counts of the two species do not necessarily coincide. Unlike pelagic species such as Leach's Petrel, Sooty Shearwaters do not require strong onshore winds to appear close inshore. Indeed, some of the highest counts have occurred in calm or near-calm conditions. There is substantial year-to-year variation in abundance.

Away from these two sites, most records in Argyll come from islands and ferry crossings, especially the crossing from the mainland to Coll and Tiree. Three-figure counts are infrequent (Table). Much larger numbers have been recorded in areas such as Orkney, Shetland and the east coast of Scotland (Rivers 2002).

There are few records from Argyll between November and June. Spring records include one at Ballochroy in Kintyre on 23 April 1977 (SB 10:119), one off north-east Colonsay on 29 April 1983 (ABR 1:13, SBR 1983:9), and one in the Sound of Mull on 31 May 1998 (ABR 15:23, SBR 1998:12).

Birds occasionally occur in November: singles were seen at Frenchman's Rocks and at Machrihanish on 3 November 1996, and one was at the former site on 16 November 1996 (ABR 13:22). In Scotland as a whole, there are records from nearly every month (Thom).

Because adults normally return to the breeding colonies by early October, it has been suggested that, like Great Shearwaters, most birds seen in the British Isles in autumn are non-breeders (BWP).

Tristan ap Rheinallt

Location	Count	Date
Frenchman's Rocks	159	8 September 1975 (Verrall & Bourne 1982)
Between Mull and Tiree	120	29 August 1977 (SB 10:119)
Frenchman's Rocks	115	4 September 1977 (SB 10:119)
Between Mull and Coll	300	29 August 1979 (SBR 1979:12)
Uisaed Point	277	27 August 1993 (ABR 10:18)
Uisaed Point	143	9 September 1994 (ABR 11:18, SBR 1994:9)
Frenchman's Rocks	102	15 September 1995 (ABR 12:20, SBR 1995:9)
Frenchman's Rocks	109	26 September 1996 (ABR 13:22, SBR 1996:9)
Frenchman's Rocks	320	2 September 2001 (ABR 18:24)
Frenchman's Rocks	379	29 August 2002 (Argyll Database)
Kennacraig - Islay ferry	180	10 September 2002 (Argyll Database)

Counts of more than 100 Sooty Shearwaters in Argyll waters to the end of 2006.

Manx Shearwater

Puffinus puffinus

The Manx Shearwater is a rare breeding seabird in Argyll, being restricted to two or three sites (Treshnish, Sanda and possibly the Garvellachs) comprising around 1,500 pairs. Large numbers are seen on passage, especially during the autumn.

The presence of Manx Shearwater as a breeding species in Argyll has been sketchily known since the 19th century. It is only in very recent years that standard methods have been used to establish the size of the breeding population of this pelagic species that only comes ashore during the short hours of darkness of the summer months.

In 1852, Graham spoke of it as common to Iona and Mull and appearing in large flocks swimming near Staffa, and he reported finding eggs there, on Lunga (Treshnish Isles) and seeing them around the small isles around Iona. H&B were not convinced of its regular breeding on Staffa as they state that Graham never reported finding another there on all his egg hunting tours.

Operation Seafarer recorded this species breeding on the Treshnish Isles in 1969-70, but the size of the population was not established. This survey also repeated records of past breeding near Iona and Ulva (Cramp *et al.* 1974). The next seabird survey (Lloyd *et al.* 1991) again recorded it breeding on the Treshnish Isles in 1986 with no indication of the size of the colony. This survey also reported that there were 50-100 pairs breeding on Sanda in 1987, where breeding was first reported in 1977 (Maguire 1978). Seabird 2000 found 1,283 apparently occupied burrows (AOB) on the Treshnish Isles in 2000 and 200 AOB on the Sanda Isles in 2001. There may indeed be some small breeding colonies of Manx Shearwaters in Argyll not yet discovered. Dusk-time rafts, sometimes numbering hundreds of birds, have regularly been seen near the Garvellachs in the late evening during summer as long ago as 1889 (H&B). Carcasses of depredated Manx Shearwaters were found on the island on 29 June 1991, and birds on Garbh Eileach were heard calling in early June 2005 (Mavor *et al.* 2006), suggesting that they might breed here, as indeed they could on one of the many other small islands to the north of Scarba, or on the cliffs of south-east Mull. This congregation, however, may only be a group that gathers to feed by night in the tidal rips of this area. Establishing exactly why this group regularly gathers in this area, and has done so since the 19th century, would be a useful contribution to the understanding of the Argyll avifauna.

Manx Shearwaters breed at just a handful of sites in Argyll, but can be regularly seen in coastal waters, particularly in August. *Philip Snow*

The Manx Shearwater is regularly seen on passage at key sea-watching sites in Argyll. Most birds are seen travelling south and are regularly seen between mid-April and late September (Verrall & Bourne 1982). Passage is greater off more westerly points close to pelagic waters such as Frenchman's Rocks on Islay, and Tiree, than more inshore areas such as Uisaed Point on Kintyre. It usually peaks during August, when a westerly gale can lead to huge numbers of birds being seen. The largest movement involved 11,364 birds passing north-west Tiree in an hour on 12 August 1998 and, on 13 August 1999, 12,500 passed Frenchman's Rocks in 2.5 hours. While these movements are exceptional, it is not unusual for over 5,000 birds to be seen moving on a single day each year.

Very small numbers have been seen during the winter months, when most Manx Shearwaters, as shown by ringing studies, are usually in the South Atlantic Ocean. Manx Shearwaters ringed in Argyll have been recovered off Brazil (two) and on the Scilly Isles (one). An adult ringed in Finistère (France) in 1966 was found dead on Treshnish in 1983; and birds ringed in Ireland (17), Wales (15) and elsewhere in Scotland (seven) have been found in Argyll.

At their breeding colonies, Manx Shearwaters are extremely vulnerable to introduced mammalian predators, notably American Mink and rats. Preventing these species from reaching the islands is therefore an important priority. There have been several close calls on Sanda: a single adult mink was recorded there in 1996, and an adult female with young made it ashore in 2005. Both adults were trapped before serious mortality to Manx Shearwaters or other seabirds could occur.

David Jardine

Balearic Shearwater

Puffinus mauretanicus

Scarce autumn migrant.

The Balearic Shearwater is a regular visitor to British and Irish waters during the summer months, with around 1,000 individuals currently reported annually (Fraser *et al.* 2000, Fraser & Rogers 2001). Birds leave their Mediterranean breeding grounds from May onwards and gather to moult as far north as the southern North Sea (Migration Atlas). The peak months for British records are July, August and September.

A bird flying north past Saligo Bay on Islay on 11 September 1976 was only the seventh Scottish record (SB 10:81). The next Argyll record was not until 1989, when one passed Furnace on 14 August (SBR 1989:5, ABR 6:12). Since 1992, however, records in the county have been annual.

Regular seawatching at Uisaed Point and Frenchman's Rocks gave a total of 195 birds during the years 1992-2003 (possibly including repeated sightings of the same birds on different days). From 1995 onwards, birds were reported from other locations. Up to the end of 2005, there were six records from the Kennacraig to Islay ferry, two from Coull Point on the west coast of Islay and one from Coll. Ten records from from Tiree over the same period included records from Hynish, West Hynish, Balevullin, Aird and Gott Bay.

Almost all records have been in August, September and October, peaking in mid-September. The earliest was on 1 August, and late birds were seen on 3 November and 19 December. With the exception of those seen in the latter half of October, most Balearic Shearwaters occur in association with substantial movements of Manx Shearwaters.

The increase in British records since the mid-1980s is said to reflect increased popularity of seawatching as well as improved identification skills (Migration Atlas). The Scottish records show a similar increase, although there is considerable year-to-year variation (Fraser & Rogers 2001)[1]. However, intensive seawatching at Frenchman's Rocks during the mid-1970s produced no records of Balearic Shearwater, even though the observer was familiar with this form (K. Verrall pers. comm.) and was responsible for the first Argyll record. This suggests that the increase is real rather than apparent.

[1]But note that the unusually high total for 1996 in Fig. 1 of Fraser & Rogers (2001) may be incorrect, given that Fraser et al. (1999) reported a total of 64 records for Argyll that year, rather than 42 (see above).

Tristan ap Rheinallt

North Atlantic Little Shearwater

Puffinus baroli

Vagrant.

This species breeds on Madeira, the Canaries and the Azores, and is a rare visitor to British waters. The sole accepted record from Argyll involves a bird seen by Keith Verrall from Frenchman's Rocks on Islay on 30 June 1974 (BB 68:310, Verrall 1977a). This was the first of four Scottish records to date.

The relatedness of this species to other small shearwaters is not yet fully understood. Formerly known as the Little Shearwater, the latest taxonomic revision recommends that Macaronesian Shearwater would be a better common name for *P. baroli* (Onley & Scofield 2007).

[Several additional Argyll records have been rejected by the British Birds Rarities Committee. It appears that brief sightings during seawatches are unlikely to gain acceptance, especially if only one observer is involved.]

Tristan ap Rheinallt

Wilson's Storm-petrel

Oceanites oceanicus

Vagrant.

This southern-hemisphere breeder is now known to occur regularly in the Western Approaches, but Scottish records remain very few. The only accepted Argyll record concerns one on Jura on 1 October 1891.

Evans (ASNH 1892:18) wrote: "A specimen of Wilson's Petrel was found alive by the keeper's children at Inner Jura, on the western side of the island, on the first of October last. The bird had become entangled in a net used to keep poultry out of a kitchen garden, and was brought to me in perfectly fresh condition. Fortunately I was there at the time or it would have been lost. There is no doubt as to the species: the colour of the wings, the length of the tarsus (one and a half inches), and yellow patches on the webs of the feet, make the identity of the bird certain. The net in which the Petrel was captured is about fifty yards from the sea. Unfortunately the sex of the specimen was not noted, for I did not examine the bird carefully until after it had been skinned by the keeper. The weather was fine at the time of its capture, but there can be little doubt its appearance is to be associated with the heavy gale on 26 September."

According to H&B, the bird was stuffed by McLeay of 65 Church Street, Inverness. It was the fourth British record of this species, the first three also involving dead or dying birds. Almost a hundred years passed before the second Scottish record, off Harris in 1988.

Tristan ap Rheinallt

White-faced Storm-petrel

Pelagodroma marina

Vagrant.

An immature female was caught alive at the edge of a roadside stream between Kiloran and Kilchattan on Colonsay on 1 January 1897, following a period of severe south-westerly gales. It was sent for identification to W. Eagle Clarke, who wrote (ASNH 1897:88):

"A specimen of this stranger to European seas was captured alive on the margins of a stream on the west side of the island of Colonsay on 1 January of the present year. It was forwarded in the flesh to Edinburgh, where I had the pleasure of examining it and determining its identity. On dissection, the bird proved to be a female, and an inspection of its bones indicated that it was quite a young bird... The weather immediately preceding this bird's visit to the West Coast of Scotland was characterised by severe gales from the south-west, and these may, perhaps have been instrumental in driving it from its accustomed haunts..."

This, the only accepted British record of White-faced Storm-petrel, was assigned to the race *P. m. hypoleuca*, which breeds in the Selvagen Islands off the Canaries. The skin is now in the National Museums of Scotland.

Tristan ap Rheinallt

European Storm-petrel

Hydrobates pelagicus

This summer visitor returns to its main Argyll breeding grounds on Sanda and the Treshnish Isles in May and June. A few pairs nest on Soa and Staffa. Most sightings are offshore during July to September.

This tiny seabird fascinated the Victorian naturalists and its discovery as a breeding species on the islets around Iona and Staffa in 1852 was described in considerable length by Graham. He first found them in burrows on Soa, to the south of Iona, and also recorded them breeding in boulder fields on Staffa and the Treshnish Isles. The habit of the European Storm-petrel to nest underground and only to return to its nesting area at night has made study of this species rather awkward and two of the three seabird censuses conducted in the late 20th century added little to the understanding of its distribution and abundance in Argyll. Cramp *et al.* (1974) reported its previous breeding on the Treshnish Isles and that it was suspected of still doing so. They also reported previous breeding near Iona and on Mull, but added that its current status remained unknown. Lloyd *et al.* (1991) could provide little further information on its status in 1985-87.

The Treshnish Auk Ringing Group started ringing European Storm-petrels on the Treshnish Isles, catching them with mist nets after dark, and eventually evaluated the size of the population. An early tape response survey in 1996 suggested there may be as many as 5,040 breeding pairs but during Seabird 2000, using refined methods, it was estimated that there were 1,200 apparently occupied burrows (AOBs). A further five AOBs were found on Staffa and there were three AOBs on Soa in 1999.

The discovery of breeding European Storm-petrels on Sanda did not occur until 1977 (Maguire 1978), although Gray hinted at its presence in the area by noting that it occurred on numerous other rocks and islands from Ardnamurchan to the Mull of Kintyre. An initial estimate of the number of breeding pairs on Sanda was 100-500 pairs in 1980, refined to 50-100 pairs in 1987. Two hundred AOBs were located there during Seabird 2000. It is quite probable that there remain unrecorded colonies of this delightful seabird and, like several of the other nocturnal species occurring in Argyll, further research into its breeding status is needed. Fortunately, all known storm-petrel colonies in Argyll have, so far, remained free of mammalian predators such as American Mink and rats. Indeed, European Storm-petrels seem to be unable to sustain breeding populations on Scottish islands once rats colonize (de Leon *et al.* 2006).

The very small size of the European Storm-petrel and its nocturnal and pelagic habits mean that only the small numbers which come close to the shore are seen during sea-watches; indeed it has often been on foggy and misty days that the largest numbers have been reported. The very highest daily counts have been in August and September; 180 flew south past Frenchman's Rocks, Islay, in two hours on 21 August 1989 and 178 flew south past Uisaed Point, Kintyre, in seven hours on 13 August 1998. They can be seen off western headlands from late May through until late October and occasionally into early November. There have been a few sightings of single birds in Loch Fyne.

The use of tape lures to attract storm-petrels to mist-nets was first developed in Argyll (Maguire 1978) and this transformed the understanding of movements of this species. Interpretation of results is problematical as they are influenced by the distribution of ringing effort and by the fact that tape luring tends to attract non-breeding birds and can draw birds into mist nets far from breeding colonies. European Storm-petrels ringed in Argyll have been recovered in Norway (1),

The diminutive European Storm-petrel spends almost all of its life at sea. *Sue Chattwood*

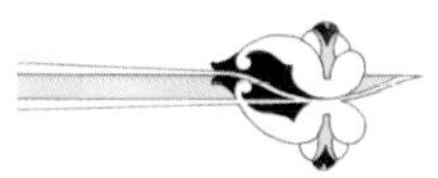

Portugal (3), Liberia (1) and at sea off Western Sahara (1) and South Africa (1), as well as Ireland (217), Wales (11), northern England (186), southern England (3), Wales (11) and elsewhere in Scotland (171). Birds recovered in Argyll had been ringed in Portugal (9) and Norway (6), as well as Ireland (387), Wales (22), northern England (286), southern England (10) and elsewhere in Scotland (287).

David Jardine

Leach's Storm-petrel

Oceanodroma leucorhoa

Autumn migrant, seen mainly off exposed coasts and headlands in severe weather or wrecked after storms. Occasionally reported in spring and summer.

Leach's Storm-petrel, which breeds in Britain only on a few remote Scottish islands, has long been known as an autumn visitor to Argyll during periods of severe weather. Lawrie (1891) described vividly his encounter with these birds in early October of that year:

"During the recent severe weather we were driven for shelter into Kames Bay, Loch Melfort. The gale was very stiff, and for several days we were surrounded by a large number of Fork-tailed Petrels. Often a dozen at a time would be flying close to us. During the lulls in the squalls I shot five as specimens, and sent them to be stuffed... At last the storm moderated; the petrels had then become very tame. I touched one with a broom as he flew over; another settled on the bowsprit. After we were under weigh, one of the crew caught another for a moment in his sou'-wester, but it escaped..."

This occurrence followed a succession of westerly and north-westerly gales. Birds were also reported in other parts of Argyll around this time, and large numbers of petrels, most probably this species, were recorded in Loch Indaal on Islay (H&B, ASNH 1892:75). Some years previously, Gray commented that specimens had been obtained in the Firth of Clyde as far up as Dunoon. Another major wreck of this species occurred in late October and early November 1952, when large numbers were seen in Mull and along the coast of mainland Argyll, including Cowal (Wynne-Edwards 1953). On 26 October, hundreds were sheltering in Oban Bay (Glasgow and West of Scotland Bird Bulletin 1:14). According to the Migration Atlas, numbers in western Europe during such influxes are sometimes so large that birds from the other side of the Atlantic, where there are millions of breeding pairs, must be involved.

Recently, intensive seawatching has shown that Leach's Storm-petrels occur off the western mainland and islands of Argyll almost every year. The passage of fast-moving depressions to the north, followed by a switch in wind direction from south-west to north-west, often heralds their appearance close inshore. Even moderate westerlies or north-westerlies can produce sightings of small numbers between late August and early November, either during seawatches or from ferry crossings. Daily counts of birds flying south past Uisaed Point and Frenchman's Rocks at this time of year have exceeded 50 on a few occasions. A count of 466 at Uisaed Point in a five-hour period on 15 September 1992, however, was exceptional (ABR 10:19), and 143 at Frenchman's Rocks in nine hours on 21 September 2004 was a record count for this site (Argyll Database). Some seen at this time of year are clearly exhausted and may fall prey to marauding Peregrines. Occasionally, birds are seen over land or found injured away from the coast.

In recent years, there have also been a few spring records associated with north-westerly gales in March and May. The highest counts at this time have been 11 flying south past Uisaed Point on 11 May 1992 (ABR 10:19) and 18 flying south past Frenchman's Rocks on 22 May 1999 (ABR 16:25). Occasional individuals are seen in the summer months, e.g. one off Tiree on 28 June 1978 (SBR 1978:13) and one off Uisaed Point on 21 July 1999 (ABR 16:25). Midwinter records appear to be very unusual. A bird was found dead at the head of Loch Fyne on 15 December 1998 (ABR 15:24), and there were at least three birds in Mid-Argyll between 4 and 12 December 2006, at a time when many Leach's Storm-petrels were reported throughout Britain (Argyll Database).

Tristan ap Rheinallt

Northern Gannet

Morus bassanus

The rich waters around the Argyll islands provide good feeding for Gannets and parties of birds can be seen plunge-diving in many locations, often in the company of other seabirds. However, there are no breeding colonies in Argyll.

The earliest record of the Northern Gannet in Argyll comes from Mesolithic excavations on the island of Oronsay. While the presence of bones in the shell middens does not indicate the breeding status of the species at the time (*c.*4,000 years BC), it does show the species has a long history in Argyll waters (Bishop 1913).

In the 19th century, the Gannet was recorded from time to time in considerable feeding parties, but there were no known breeding colonies (Graham, H&B). Sightings were mainly from around the islands and around the Firth of Clyde and H&B report that it was rarely recorded from Loch Linnhe and Loch Creran. Gray believed that most of the birds seen in Argyll waters were from the colony on Ailsa Craig as there were records of birds rounding the Mull of Kintyre on their return to the breeding colony in the Clyde.

B&R noted that Gannets were said to possibly have bred at one time on Islay, but they could find no corroboration of this report. James Fisher (in Bannerman 1961) suggested this was in 1703, but the record remains doubtful and is only mentioned here for completeness. The three surveys of seabirds in 1969-70 (Cramp *et al.* 1974), in 1985-87 (Lloyd *et al.* 1991) and in Seabird 2000 found no evidence of breeding in Argyll. The nearest sites are at Ailsa Craig (32,456 AOS in 1995) and Scar Rocks (1,952 AOS in 1995) to the south, St Kilda (60,428 AOS in 1994) to the north (Murray & Wanless 1997), and Clare Island, Mayo (two AOS in 1986) to the west.

Gannets can be seen plunge-diving in many of Argyll's sheltered waters, but their nearest breeding colony is on Ailsa Craig, 21km south of Arran. *Philip Kirkham*

Despite the long distances from the breeding colonies (100km to the south-east and 300km to the north-west), Verrall & Bourne (1982) indicated that Gannets were the third most frequent seabird recorded around Islay. They noted that they could be seen in all months of the year with peak occurrences during June to September. Over 1,000 have been seen from Frenchman's Rocks on a number of occasions, with a peak of 2,489 flying south on 13 August 1995. Numbers passing Uisaed Point on Kintyre were fewer. Careful recording showed that most of these birds were in adult plumage. Of 6,260 birds logged between March and September in 1994, 87% were adults, 7% sub-adults and 6% young immatures; only 0.2% were birds of the year. In other years a similar age distribution has been found and the scarcity of juvenile birds suggests that young from Ailsa Craig do not disperse westward into the southern Hebridean waters in their first autumn.

Two nestlings ringed in Norway have been found dead in Argyll during their first year, and 34 birds ringed at British colonies have been found in Argyll, one from Wales and the rest from Scotland.

David Jardine

Great Cormorant

Phalacrocorax carbo

Numbers of Great Cormorants nesting have increased to around 230 pairs in recent years. It is found on freshwater lochs and around the coasts of Argyll in small numbers; in all coastal areas it is greatly outnumbered by the Shag.

Evidence that Cormorants were hunted by Mesolithic man in Argyll, some 6,000 years ago, was provided by the discovery of bones of this species by Victorian archaeologists in the shell middens on Oronsay (Bishop 1913). Victorian naturalists reported the Cormorant throughout Argyll, including inland waters such as Loch Awe. H&B discuss some of the difficulties they had in determining its status because of confusion between Great Cormorants and Shags.

The Cormorant has never been a numerous breeding species in Argyll. Operation Seafarer (Cramp *et al.* 1974) recorded breeding sites in the Sound of Mull, the Torran Rocks off Mull and the Mull of Kintyre totalling 61 pairs. The 1985-87 survey (Lloyd *et al.* 1991) reported 164 pairs plus ten birds at seven sites (Sanda, McCormaig Isles, southern Jura, Coll, Iona, Torran Rocks and Ulva). It is not known whether this represented a real increase in the population following improved protection for the Cormorant, or the results of a more thorough survey.

A further increase in the number of breeding pairs was reported during Seabird 2000 when 231 apparently occupied nests (AON) were found. This increase is more likely to be real and several new colonies have become established: North Argyll 3 AON, Sound of Jura 54 (two sites), Loch Fyne 65 (two sites), Sanda 28, Gigha 10, Jura 11, and Mull 42 (two sites).

The SAMS seabird study conducted on the small offshore islets of Mid- and North Argyll has given some information

Distribution and abundance of Great Cormorant breeding colonies (apparently occupied nests) in Argyll during Seabird 2000.

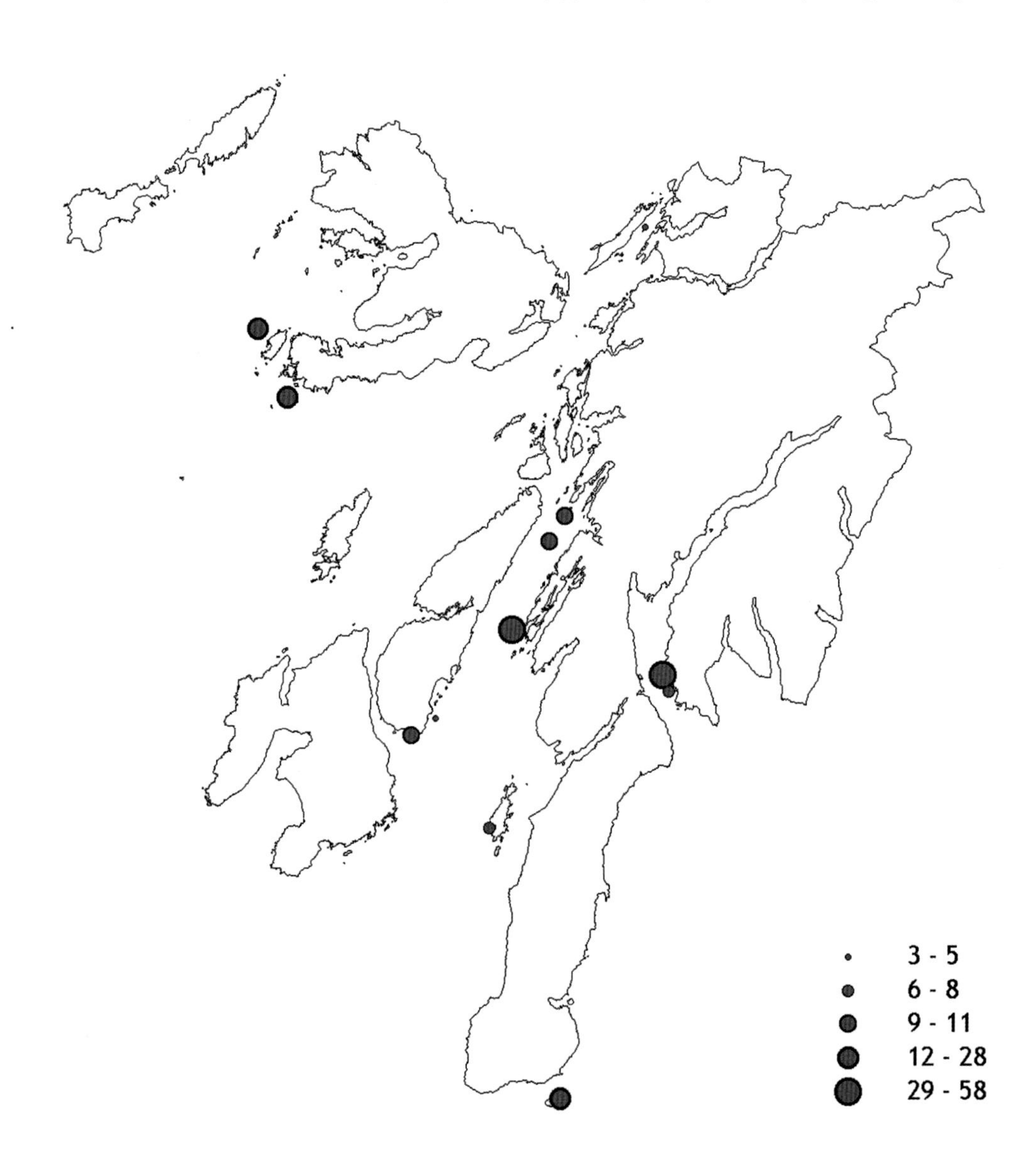

on the annual breeding performance of Cormorants since 1992. This suggested that the number of chicks reared each year varied between 1.0 and 2.3 young per nest, although there was variation between sites.

Cormorants are rarely found in large gatherings in Argyll, with few reports of over 30 birds together outside the breeding season. They are usually found in groups of fewer than ten, or single birds. They can be found throughout the coastline and are regular feeders on freshwater lochs, though usually singly rather than in groups. The record of six on Loch Awe at the Pass of Brander on 11 February 1986 was therefore exceptional, but they were probably attracted by the fish farm.

Cormorants ringed in Argyll have been recovered in Spain (two), France (three) and Ireland (six), but most recoveries are of birds shot for "protection" of fisheries or fish farms. Many of the 18 recoveries within Argyll, 58 elsewhere in Scotland and 13 in England were on trout and salmon rivers such as the Test and the Tweed or at salmonid farms in Scotland. Other Cormorants recovered in Argyll had been ringed in Ireland (four) or elsewhere in Scotland (79). These recoveries suggest considerable seasonal movement of Cormorants into, and out of Argyll, but it is unclear whether birds from the continental subspecies reach Argyll; plumages of birds seen in Argyll suggest that the vast majority are birds of the nominate subspecies *P. carbo carbo* and not the continental *P. c. sinensis*. This is supported by a recent study of mitochondrial DNA of Cormorants in Europe, which included samples from Argyll (Marion & Le Gentil 2006).

While it seems that Cormorant numbers have increased in Argyll, the conflict between Cormorants and fish farming has resulted in some culling of this species in Argyll, and the continued growth of fish farming may represent a threat to Cormorants in some parts of the county.

David Jardine

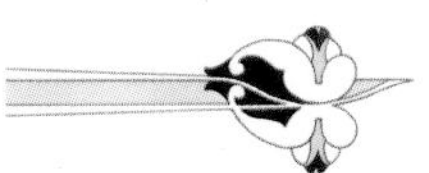

Great Cormorants often roost on man-made structures, such as this disused pier. *Philip Kirkham*

Shag

Phalacrocorax aristotelis

The Shag is a very common resident that breeds on the coast and on islands in sea-lochs. It is widespread in coastal waters in winter but rare inland at all times.

Bones of Shags were found by Victorian archaeologists in the shell middens on Oronsay (Bishop 1913), suggesting that this species was hunted by Mesolithic man some 6,000 years ago in Argyll. Victorian naturalists reported it as common and confirmed it has long been shot for the larder (Graham) a practice that continued well into the 20th century.

The three seabird censuses conducted in the late 20th century have shown some changes in the numbers and distribution of Shags in Argyll. Operation Seafarer (Cramp *et al.* 1974) recorded it as widespread around the coasts, including small colonies of 1-10 pairs on Lismore and in Cowal. These colonies were not reported in 1985-87 (Lloyd *et al.* 1991), when breeding was not reported further up the Firth of Lorne than the Garvellachs, or on the Argyllshire coast of the Firth of Clyde. They did report a significant increase in the breeding population, from 1,774 pairs in 1969-70 to 4,883 pairs and 254 birds in 1985-87. The reason for this increase is not known, but it could reflect a number of possibilities. Shag populations suffer periodic crashes when birds die in prolonged storms, or through poor food supplies. It is possible that the population in 1969 was at a low ebb following such a crash, although these population crashes tend to be a feature of east Scotland rather than the west, where the coast provides more shelter. Shags also received additional protection in the 1981 Wildlife & Countryside Act and this may have led to some reduction in persecution through shooting. Alternatively, and perhaps most likely, the apparent increase may reflect improved survey coverage or methods.

A significant reduction in the total population in Argyll was reported by the Seabird 2000 survey, when a total of 3,341 apparently occupied nests (AON) were found. The largest breeding stations were on the Treshnish Isles (601 AON), Sanda (565) and Gigha (240). Small numbers were found in Loch Fyne (30) and in North Argyll (50).

The study conducted by the Scottish Association for Marine Science on seabirds on the small offshore islets of Argyll has provided some information on the annual breeding performance of Shags since 1992. This suggested that the number of chicks reared each year varied between 0.92 and 1.6 young per nest, although there was variation between sites. The study found that American Mink took eggs and chicks of Shags and killed breeding adults; the cessation of breeding at the colony on Eilean Fraoich and Eilean nan Coinean in the Sound of Jura in 1996, which had held around 1,200 pairs in 1981, was clearly due to this predator. All other breeding seabird species also disappeared from this once-notable colony after successive years of complete breeding failures caused by mink.

Distribution and abundance of breeding Shags (apparently occupied nests) in Argyll during Seabird 2000.

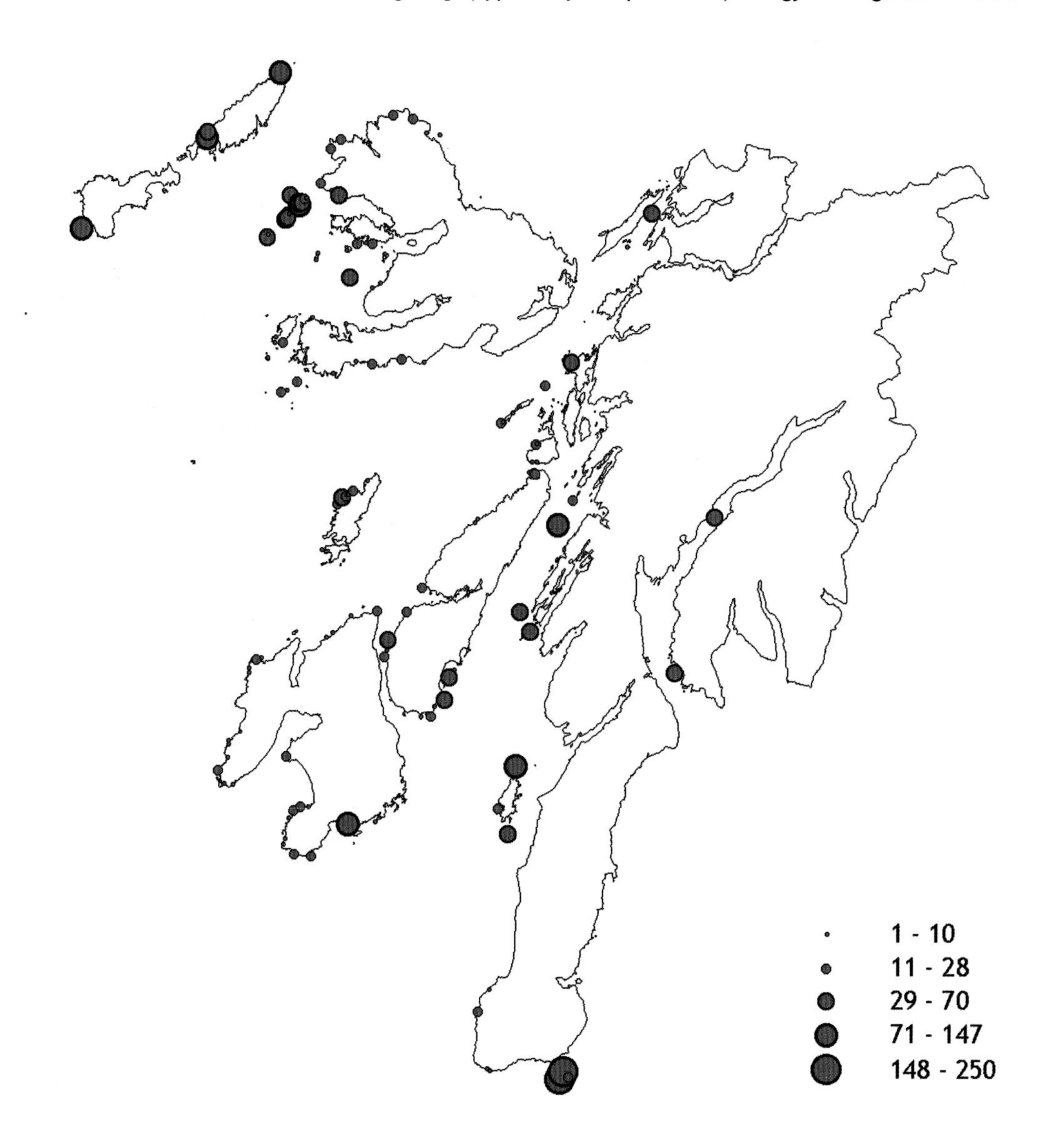

The Shag is not a strongly migratory species and few large movements have been reported other than to and from local feeding areas, which can involve large congregations of birds. The largest reported in recent years have been post-breeding congregations in the tidal waters of the Sound of Gunna, between Coll and Tiree, where 1,000 birds were reported on 11 September 2000 and 1,126 were there on 7 August 1998. Ringing has confirmed that Shags in Argyll are much more sedentary than Cormorants. No Shags ringed in Argyll have been recovered outside the British Isles, but there have been recoveries in Ireland (15), Wales (one), northern England (two) and elsewhere in Scotland (215). However, very few of these birds moved to the east coast. Generally, Argyll Shags seem to stay in west Scotland. Shags recovered in Argyll had been ringed in Ireland (18), Wales (one), northern England (27) and elsewhere in Scotland (142).

David Jardine

Ascension Frigatebird

Fregata aquila

Vagrant.

An immature frigatebird was found exhausted at Loch a' Phuill on Tiree on 10 July 1953 and caught in a landing-net (Anon. 1954). The bird died later that day and the skin is now in the National Museums of Scotland.

At the time, the bird was identified as an immature female Magnificent Frigatebird *Fregata magnificens*. However, as part of the BBRC's review of records for the period 1950 to 1958, the skin was recently re-examined. This resulted in the sensational discovery that the bird was in fact an Ascension Frigatebird in "juvenile" plumage. Confined as a breeding bird to a tiny islet off Ascension Island in the tropical eastern Atlantic, this species has never otherwise been recorded in

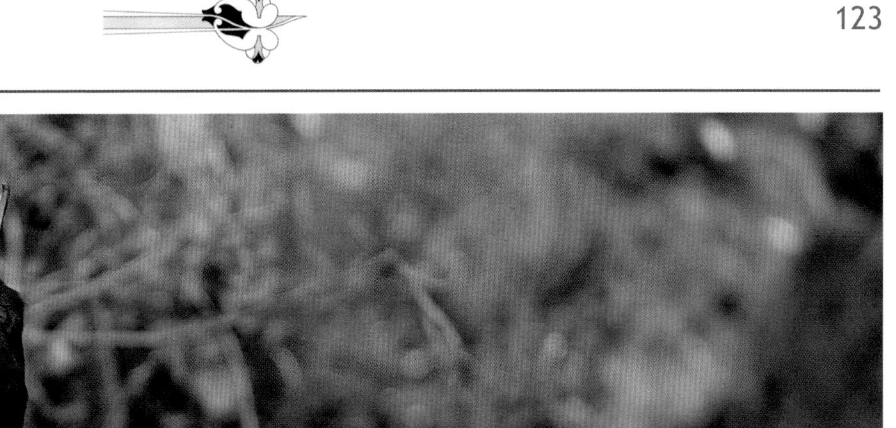

The Shag is another seabird species that has declined in Argyll following predation of its colonies by mink. *David Wood*

the Western Palearctic. Indeed, the only other records away from Ascension come from western Africa (McGowan 2003, Waldbridge *et al.* 2003).

Undoubtedly, this is Argyll's most remarkable rarity. There are, in fact, very few records of frigatebirds of any kind from Britain and Ireland. Until very recently, an adult female Magnificent Frigatebird taken into care on the Isle of Man in 1998 was the only other individual identified to species (Waldbridge *et al.* 2003).

Tristan ap Rheinallt

Eurasian Bittern

Botaurus stellaris

A rare visitor, mostly during winter. Apparently bred in the past, but became extinct by the end of the eighteenth century or shortly afterwards.

The history of this species in Scotland is unclear (Thom). According to B&R, it was said to have nested in a good many parts of the country before reclamation of the marshes. It seems likely that, as in other parts of Britain, its disappearance

All dated records of Eurasian Bitterns in Argyll to the end of 2006.

Date	Location	Comment	Reference
2 Feb 1864	Islay	Shot	Booth 1975
Late Dec 1878	River Eachaig (Cowal)	Shot	H&B
1887/1888	Taynish (Mid-Argyll)	Killed	H&B
17 Jan 1912	Oban	Found dead on pier	SN 1912:67, SN Extra Publication No. 2 (1913):11
12 Jan 1971	Oban		SB 7:118
14 Jan - 22 Mar 1982	Dervaig (Mull)		ABR 1:15, SBR 1982:14
4 Dec 1982	Tayinloan		ABR 1:15, SBR 1982:14
23 Dec 1983	Dervaig		SBR 1983:10
19 Sep 1999	Appin	Adult male hit by car	ABR 16:26

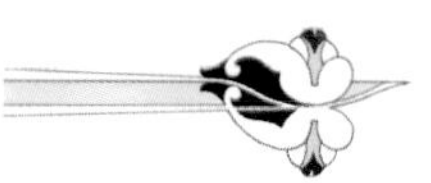

from Argyll coincided with the major drainage works that took place in the latter part of the eighteenth and early part of the nineteenth centuries (Shrubb 2003). Thus the NSA for Inveraray states that the species had disappeared by 1843, although it had apparently been common 40 years previously (B&R). Bitterns were believed to have been common in the Benderloch district before bog reclamation (H&B). They may have nested in Kintyre at the beginning of the 19th century (Gibson & McWilliam 1959). Specimens had been shot on Islay and Mull before 1870 (Gray).

By the second half of the nineteenth century, the Bittern had become a noteworthy rarity in Argyll. Since then, its status has not changed. Dated records, all of single birds, are listed in the Table.

The Argyll records show a similar pattern to occurrences in the rest of Scotland, where most sightings occur between August and February and the birds are often dead or dying (Thom). The December-January peak in sightings away from breeding areas is characteristic of Britain and Ireland as a whole, and may reflect influxes from north-west Europe as a consequence of hard weather (Migration Atlas).

Tristan ap Rheinallt

American Bittern

Botaurus lentiginosus

Vagrant.

The only Argyll record of this rare transatlantic vagrant concerns a bird shot on Islay in 1875. Lumsden (1876a) wrote:

"At the November meeting of the Society Mr Lumsden placed on the table a Bittern, which had been killed in Islay in the previous month. At the time he could not confidently state to which species the bird belonged, not having had an opportunity before the meeting of comparing it with other specimens, or of consulting any work on the subject. Since then, however, he had carefully examined the bird, and he could now state that it is a specimen of American Bittern. Mr Harvie-Brown and Dr Dewar also identified the specimen. It was killed about the last week of October on the shore at Islay, and is the fifth or sixth specimen from Scotland."

H&B added that: "Harvie-Brown saw this bird in MacCulloch's shop in Glasgow along with Mr Lumsden. It was shot by a visitor to the island, stuffed by MacCulloch, but has been quite lost sight of since."

Four pre-1875 Scottish records are now considered acceptable, and there were two further records in the twentieth century, both from western Scotland (Outer Hebrides in 1932 and Clyde in 1981) (Andrews & Naylor 2002).

Tristan ap Rheinallt

Night Heron

Nycticorax nycticorax

Vagrant.

The Night Heron is a widespread summer visitor to southern Europe, several individuals being recorded in southern Britain in most years. However, it remains rare in Scotland.

The first Argyll record concerns a bird said to be an immature female, which was captured in an exhausted condition at Loch Creran in early November 1884. The specimen was presented to Kelvingrove Museum [Zoologist 9 (1885): 69]. Writing seven years later, H&B refer to two further records: a locally shot bird preserved at Barcaldine House, and another seen on Loch Creran. B&R repeat this information, but Naylor (1996) gives only the first record. The origin of the information in H&B seems to be a list of the birds of Benderloch, sent to Harvie-Brown by W. Anderson Smith on 4 May 1887. This mentions all three records, without more detail other than that the bird in the Kelvingrove Museum was shot at Ledaig. In a later letter, dated 20 January 1891, Anderson Smith states: "But I know of at least three Night Herons which are otherwise rare in Scotland having been shot or absolutely recognised in the district."

Given the distinctive nature of this species, the two specimen records are probably acceptable, even though there is no evidence that Harvie-Brown himself saw the bird in Barcaldine House. However, since the sight record from Loch Creran seems to lack supporting evidence, it is not considered acceptable.

In more recent years, a probable adult was at Loch a' Phuill on Tiree on 20 April 1987, and an adult was at Lonban on Coll about 21 April to 6 June the same year (BB 81:542). Although BBRC did not suggest that the two individuals were the same, this is highly likely in view of the coincidence of dates (SBR 1987:10).

In Scotland as a whole, the status of the Night Heron over the past half-century has been clouded by the existence of a colony of free-flying birds at Edinburgh Zoo. This colony is believed to account for most of the apparently wild birds seen in the Lothian area, but the provenance of those further afield is less certain. However, the year 1987 featured a major influx of Night Herons into many parts of Britain between mid-April and early May (BB 81:542), making it likely that the Coll and Tiree records refer to a genuine vagrant.

[A single-observer report of an immature accompanying the Coll bird (ABR 5:4) was not accepted at the time.]

Tristan ap Rheinallt

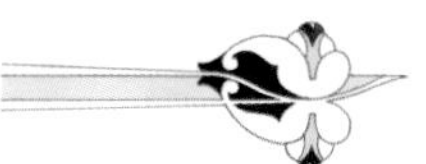

Snowy Egret

Egretta thula

Vagrant.

The sighting of a Snowy Egret at Balvicar on Seil island on 5 November 2001, by local birdwatchers Bill Jackson and Jim Dickson, led to a major invasion of Argyll by twitchers from all over the UK. This transatlantic vagrant had never previously been recorded in the British Isles. Full details of the sighting were published by Jackson (2001, 2004) and the bird also graced the front cover of the October 2002 issue of *British Birds*. It remained in the Balvicar area (where it had apparently been present since 30 October) until 25 November, before moving to Ayrshire (BB 95:481-482). It was then resident on Arran for more than two months in early 2002, before returning to Argyll and visiting Loch Fyne (twice), Seil (twice), Loch Riddon and Lochgilphead between 3 April and about 7 June, with a brief visit to Bute in mid-May. After apparently disappearing in early June, the same individual reappeared in Dumfries & Galloway in mid-August and remained until mid-September 2002 (BB 96:551).

Snowy Egret was a long-awaited addition to the British list, having been recorded on six previous occasions in the Western Palearctic, thrice in Iceland and thrice in the Azores.

Tristan ap Rheinallt

Little Egret

Egretta garzetta

Rare migrant, mainly in late spring.

It seems hard to believe today that this species did not feature in B&R; the first Scottish record was in 1954, a year after their book was published. Another 15 years passed before Argyll recorded its first birds, a group of four at Lochdonhead on Mull on 12 October 1969. Three of these stayed until at least 20 November 1969 (BB 63:270). Following one at Loch Feochan on 1 February 1970 and another on Islay between 25 May and 4 July the same year, there was a gap of 18 years until the next record. However, Little Egrets were then recorded in Argyll in 12 of the 19 years between 1988 and 2006, reflecting a general increase followed by their establishment as a breeding species in southern Britain (Musgrove 2002).

In all, there have been 19 accepted records in Argyll (to the end of 2006), with ten of these in May. The May peak, typical of Mediterranean vagrants, has given way further south in Britain to an autumn maximum (Musgrove 2002), and it will be interesting to see whether this also becomes the pattern in Argyll. Unlike many other vagrants, Little Egrets have been recorded relatively often in mainland Argyll, with nine records from Mid-Argyll and Kintyre. The ten island records come from Colonsay, Islay, Mull and Tiree.

Tristan ap Rheinallt

This Snowy Egret, first seen on Seil in late 2001, was one of Argyll's most exciting recent rarities. *Iain Leach*

The Little Egret, though still rare in Argyll, has been seen more frequently in the county since the late 1980s. *Philip Kirkham*

Great White Egret

Ardea alba

Vagrant.

Once a major rarity in Britain, the Great White Egret is occurring here with increasing frequency. The upsurge in records is associated with a growing breeding population in the Netherlands and the recent establishment of a colony in northern France. Thus more than half of the 25 accepted Scottish records to the end of 2001 occurred in the twelve-year period from 1990.

Although there were only six accepted records in Argyll to the end of 2004 (Table), these reflect the general trend in that four have occurred since 1998. All six records involve single birds seen on islands in late spring, between late April and mid-June.

Tristan ap Rheinallt

All records of Great White Egrets in Argyll to the end of 2006.

Date	Location	Comment	Reference
15 June 1986	Gruinart Flats (Islay)		BB 81:544
29 April 1988	Ballachuan Loch (Seil)	Location given wrongly as Mull in *BB Rarities Report*	BB 82:513
18 May 1998	Loch Gruinart (Islay)		BB 93:519
18 May & 18 June 2000	Loch an Eilein and Loch Bhasapol (Tiree)		BB 93:515
28 May to 2 June 2002	Loch a' Phuill and Cnoc Bhirceapol (Tiree)		BB 96:551
16 to 17 May 2004	Loch Gorm (Islay)		BB 98:642

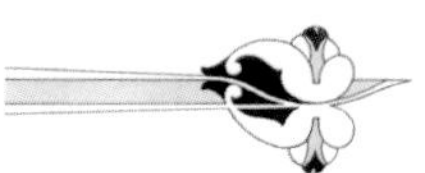

Grey Heron

Ardea cinerea

The mild climate and the long indented sheltered coastline of Argyll provide ideal habitat for Grey Herons. It is one of the commoner marine predators with over 500 pairs distributed throughout much of the county.

In the 19th century the Grey Heron was not widely distributed in Argyll, as Graham knew of none breeding on Mull, with the nearest reported nest being at Kilmory, Lochgilphead. This contrasts with the 15 heronries found on Mull in 1989 containing a total of 69-76 nests. It is possible that a number of factors such as reduced persecution, more woodlands for nesting, and milder winters leading to reduced mortality, may all have played a part in the increase in numbers of Grey Herons in recent years.

The national heronry survey began in 1928 and is the longest running bird survey in Britain. While it does provide some early records of breeding Grey Herons in Argyll, they pose some difficulties of interpretation, as the survey may not have been complete (Garden 1958). Some of these difficulties have, however, been overcome in later surveys (Marquiss 1989). Twenty-two heronries were reported in Argyll in the 1928/29 survey. These were estimated to have between 101 and 127 breeding pairs (average colony size of 5.2 pairs). This figure included three heronries in Morvern. The largest heronry reported was of 20 nests at Saddell in Kintyre. There were two other heronries with ten or more nests, at Kildalton on Islay and at Loch Riddon in Cowal. This survey recorded breeding on the larger islands of Mull, Islay and Jura and also on Coll. In 1954, 33 heronries were reported and were judged to have between 270 and 289 pairs, including three sites in Morvern (average colony of 8.5 pairs) (Garden 1958). This may have reflected improved reporting of heronries during the 1954 survey, or a real increase following improved weather conditions or reduced persecution. The largest reported heronry was of 22 occupied nests at Calgary on Mull, with a further nine sites with ten or more nests at Coilessan (Mull), Loch Spelve, Ulva, Inver (Jura), Ardentallen Point (Loch Feochan), Tayvallich, Rudha nan Eoin (Loch Long), Largie Castle (Kintyre) and Torrisdale Castle, Kintyre. The 1954 survey also reported nesting in reed-beds on Colonsay,

Herons suffer high mortality in harsh winters, but in recent years they appear to have done well in Argyll. *Roy Blewitt*

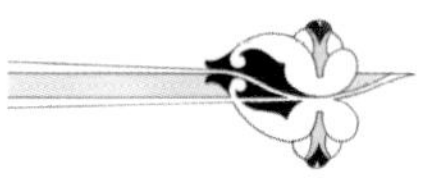

a phenomenon still found to this day in an isolated willow bush in the reed-bed at Loch Fada.

The 1964 heronry census appears to have been poorly supported with only 12 heronries recorded in Argyll with 59 nests (average 4.9 pairs). This low count, however, may reflect a real drop in the population following the harsh winter in 1963 (Marquiss 1989). The most comprehensive assessment of the Grey Heron population in Argyll is provided by Marquiss (1989). This is based on the 1985 survey, when a total of 36 heronries were surveyed at which 259 nests were found (average 7.2 pairs). Marquiss (1989), however, corrected for heronries that had been recorded as occupied during the previous decade which were not counted during the census. He included Bute (21 nests reported in heronries counted), and after correcting for 17 uncounted heronries concluded that the population for the area was around 600 pairs.

The influence of a fish farm on the breeding performance of Grey Herons in Mid-Argyll was studied by Carss & Marquiss (1996) during 1986 and 1987. They found that regurgitations from birds at two heronries feeding in natural habitats and one near a fish farm on Loch Awe contained similar numbers of fish; those, however, from nestlings at the fish farm colony were four times heavier. They also found that the Grey Herons at the fish farm colony started laying earlier and produced more young per egg laid than did birds at other heronries, although this was only significant in 1986 when breeding was probably affected by poor weather. However, they concluded that the widespread killing of Grey Herons at fish farms probably outweighed the increased productivity.

The mild winter weather experienced in Argyll is ideal for this species that suffers increased mortality during prolonged cold spells. It is therefore not surprising that the Winter Atlas showed that the county has a greater concentration of Grey Herons than many other parts of Scotland. No estimate of the population that winters in Argyll has ever been suggested, but evidence from ringing suggests that it may be larger than during the summer months. Such a study would be a useful contribution to our understanding of the Argyll avifauna. There is evidence of Scandinavian herons escaping the winter frosts by migrating to Argyll, with nine records of birds ringed as chicks in Norway being found dead in Argyll during December to March, and two further recoveries of long dead birds in April and May. Other Grey Herons ringed outside Argyll have come from Ireland (one), northern England (two) and elsewhere in Scotland (25). Perhaps more surprising was the recovery of a young Grey Heron ringed on Colonsay in May 2000, which was found dead after much snow in Rogaland, Norway, in February 2001. This was only the third recovery of a British-ringed heron in Norway (the other two were from Shetland) and it is surmised that the Colonsay bird dispersed via the Northern Isles before heading east to Norway. Other Grey Herons ringed in Argyll have been found in Ireland (three) and elsewhere in Scotland (12).

David Jardine

White Stork

Ciconia ciconia

Vagrant.

The White Stork is a rare visitor to Scotland from the Continent, occurring less than annually, most often in April, May or June. Some of those seen in the wild are probably escapes from captivity or wandering semi-feral birds. The species' rarity on the west coast of Scotland is illustrated by the fact that the first confirmed record for the Outer Hebrides was not until 1998 (SBR 1998:17). Nevertheless, there are three accepted Argyll records, all dating from the 1970s.

One at Benderloch on 22 April 1971 was later seen in Ardnamurchan (BB 65:327, SB 7:118). Another at various sites on Islay between 25 April and 8 May 1978 was thought to be the same individual as one in Ayrshire on 23 and 24 April (BB 72:511, Elliott 1989). One at Campbeltown from 1 to 3 May 1978 was considered to be a different bird (BB 73:497).

[Besides these accepted records, there were four reports of single birds on Islay between 1975 and 1981 (Elliott 1989, and elsewhere). Although possibly genuine, these records appear not to have been submitted to the BBRC.]

Tristan ap Rheinallt

Glossy Ibis

Plegadis falcinellus

Vagrant, with no records since 1958.

Over the past century or more, this exotic species has experienced a marked contraction of its breeding range in western and central Europe and North Africa (BWP). As a result, records in Scotland, as in Britain as a whole, have become much less frequent. The pattern of occurrence in Argyll reflects this situation, with a total of six records between 1901 and 1958, and none since (Table). All but the last of these records are in B&R. At least four were in autumn, reflecting the general pattern for this species.

Tristan ap Rheinallt

Records of Glossy Ibis in Argyll from 1901 to the end of 2006.

Date	Location	Comment	Reference
21 February 1901	Tiree	One shot after being present for some time	SN 1914:43, Boyd 1958
30 October 1902	Kildalton (Islay)	Immature female shot	ASNH 1903: 50, 83, 151
13 October 1913	Lismore	Immature killed in a ditch by a boy	SN 1913:284, SN Extra Publication No. 3, pp. 14, 69
6 September 1920	Gruinart Flats (Islay)	Two birds (joined by a third on 13 September, according to Elliott)	SN 1921:108, Elliott 1989
1926	Islay	Two birds	SN 1921:108
October 1958	Tiree	One present from early in month to 26 October	BB 53:160, SB 1:66

Eurasian Spoonbill

Platalea leucorodia

Vagrant.

Spoonbills are regular visitors to Britain and Ireland, arriving in small numbers during spring and autumn and almost all presumed to be of Dutch origin. At one time rare visitors to Scotland, they have been recorded with increasing frequency since the beginning of the 1970s. Most recent years have produced several records, although it is difficult to know exactly how many individuals are involved.

In Argyll, there have been seven records, all but one of single birds and two probably involving the same one (Table). The strong bias towards autumn does not reflect the situation in Scotland as a whole, where spring records are frequent.

[A record of one at the Strand on Colonsay on an unspecified date in September 1977 (Jardine *et al.* 1986) was apparently not submitted to or not accepted for publication in SBR.]

Tristan ap Rheinallt

Records of Spoonbills in Argyll from 1907 to the end of 2006.

Date	Location	Comment	Reference
Nov 1907	Inchkenneth, Loch na Keal (Mull)	Shot, specimen preserved in Royal Scottish Museum	ASNH 1908:199, B&R
May (?) 1936	Nr Bowmore (Islay)	Caught, preserved at Bowmore School	B&R, Booth 1975
28 Oct 1975	Tayvallich		SB 9:183
17 Sep 1978	Portnahaven (Islay)		SBR 1978:14
16 Oct 1978	Campbeltown	Probably same as Islay bird, subsequently seen Arran and Ayrshire	SBR 1978:14
4 Sep 1994	Dervaig (Mull)		SBR 1994:12, ABR 11:22
8-12 Oct 1998	Bridgend (Islay)	Four juveniles, one remaining to 19 October	SBR 1998:17, ABR 15:27

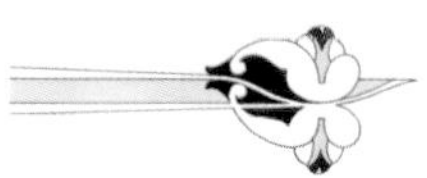

Above: Loch Gilp, Mid-Argyll, supports locally important numbers of wintering ducks, waders and gulls.

Below: Loch Crinan is a favourite foraging area for Grey Herons.

Above: Jim Dickson
Below: David Wood

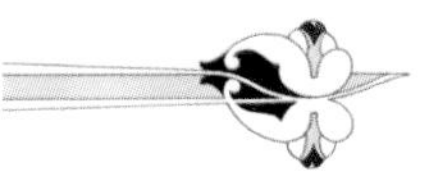

Honey Buzzard

Pernis apivorus

A rare migrant, which may have been overlooked, with fewer than 12 recorded, all between June and early October.

The first record of this enigmatic raptor is of a young male shot at Kilberry on 20 September 1875 (H&B), although there is also an undated record of one on a keeper's vermin board, probably in the Kildalton area of Islay. In keeping with the traditions of the era, the third record was of an immature female shot at Kilfinan, Loch Fyne, on 9 October 1902. There were no further records until one was seen at Langamull, Mull, on 13 September 1959. There were six further records up to 1999, with two in June, one in July, two in August and one in September. These were from Islay (two), Kintyre (one), Crinan (one) and Connel (two). Some of these individuals are likely to have been migrating or non-breeding birds from the small Scottish population.

In 2000, two young from a nest in Highland Region were fitted with satellite tags which showed that a south-westerly route was taken on migration, with one bird being recorded near Ardpatrick in Knapdale on 14 September and the other over Bunessan on Mull on 25 September, though neither was seen by birdwatchers.

Reforestation in Argyll, and elsewhere in Scotland, during the last half-century has provided increasing habitat for this elusive raptor. The possibility of breeding should not be ruled out, although it may take experienced and patient ornithologists to find this secretive species in the county.

[In addition to these accepted records there are four further records that have been published for Argyll. Two (Islay, 1 March 1975 and Mull, 18 April 1979) are well outside the normal dates when this migratory species is recorded in Britain and should certainly be viewed with considerable caution. The record of one at Calgary, Mull, on 28 June 1990 was not accepted by SBRC and the record of one on Colonsay in August 1975 has never been scrutinised.]

David Jardine

Black Kite

Milvus migrans

Vagrant.

The only Argyll record concerns a bird seen at Vaul on Tiree on 16 May 1997 (BB 93:526). This was the fifteenth Scottish record of this rare visitor from the Continent. Of the 16 birds recorded in Scotland to the end of 2001, seven were first sighted in May and three in June, reflecting the species' status as mainly a late spring vagrant to Britain.

Tristan ap Rheinallt

Red Kite

Milvus milvus

Scarce visitor from recent re-establishment projects in Highland, central and south-west Scotland. A regular breeder in the early part of the 19th century.

"When the curers retired to their meals six or seven of these birds would frequently sail down from the neighbouring wood and, uttering a shrill squeal, carry off the cleanings. We are aware of no part where these birds are more abundant than on both sides of Loch Fyne."

Thus wrote Sir William Jardine (quoted in B&R), describing the Red Kite's habit of consuming refuse left on the shoreline near Inveraray's herring-curing stations. Although once common and widely distributed in Scotland, the Red Kite was exterminated as a breeding bird in the 19th century (B&R). According to the OSA, it was very abundant in the parishes of Lochgoilhead and Kilmorich, and was also reported from Mull. In the NSA, it is listed, without additional comment, in the parish accounts for Ardchattan, Inveraray, Killean and Kilchenzie, and Saddell and Skipness. It is also named in two of the parish accounts for Mull, but the ornithological content of these is obviously copied directly from the earlier version.

Birds apparently continued to breed in many areas of mainland Argyll until the late 1850s, becoming extinct in the 1860s (Gray). However, H&B reported Red Kites at an undisclosed location in Argyll in 1884, and nesting was said to have taken place in the Campbeltown area as recently as 1905, at least one bird being present to 18 June 1911 (Zoologist (4th series) (1911) 15:317). B&R quoted the 1911 record without reference to earlier breeding, suggesting that they had doubts, while McWilliam rejected the breeding record outright. In June 1919, two years after the last documented breeding attempt in Scotland (Thom), one was seen on several occasions at Ardkinglas, Loch Fyne (Stewart 1938; B&R).

For several decades there were no further records. One was then seen at Easter Ellister on Islay on 17 March 1984 (SBR 1984:21; ABR 2:18), and the same or another at various sites on Islay between 30 November and 1 December 1985 (SB 14:100; ABR 3:24). This bird (or birds) may have originated in Wales or in another part of the species' European range.

In 1989, a bird was reported from Carradale in Kintyre on 19 October; the next day, what may well have been the same individual was seen at Gruinart on Islay and remained on the island until 10 March 1990 (ABR 6:24). A few days later, this wing-tagged bird was back at the site in Highland Region where it had been released in 1989 as part of a re-establishment project. It was the first of many Argyll records involving wing-tagged birds and, later, their offspring. Between 1990 and 2004 there were more than 50 records from all parts of mainland Argyll as well as Coll, Mull, Islay,

This group of Red Kites was photographed in Central Scotland. The birds were wing-tagged as part of the Scottish re-introduction programme. *David Palmar*

Jura, Gigha and Tiree. Some may have been wintering birds seen at intervals in the same or different locations, so that the number of birds could have been considerably less than 50. A dead bird found at Machrihanish in November 2001 was thought to have been released in Dumfries & Galloway three months earlier (ABR 18:45).

Most Argyll records have involved single birds but two have been seen together on several occasions, and three were at Lochdon on Mull for at least a week in September 1992. Although there have been more sightings in autumn than at any other time of year, Red Kites have occurred in Argyll in every month.

As the Scottish population expands, it seems likely that the Red Kite will revert to its former status as a breeding bird in Argyll. However, the fact that the species is highly philopatric (Migration Atlas) suggests that this may take some time.

Tristan ap Rheinallt

White-tailed Eagle

Haliaeetus albicilla

Very rare breeding resident, with five to ten pairs in 2004; wandering immatures occur more widely in all seasons. All are derived from re-establishment projects in north-west Scotland since 1975.

The White-tailed Eagle has been described as a generalist predator and scavenger without stringent habitat requirements (Helander & Stjerberg 2002), but throughout much of its range it has strong associations with coastal areas and lowland freshwater wetlands and, in Scotland, with the adjacent upland areas. Before its extermination in Scotland and more recently, since recolonisation, it has found suitable locations to build its nests on crags and in trees. Love (1983) documents the decline and extinction of the White-tailed Eagle in Britain and Ireland. In 1918 the last bird was shot in Shetland, two years after the last recorded breeding attempt in Skye. Reports of breeding appear to have persisted in Argyll until the 1890s (B&R) and a pair, which may have been breeding, was seen as late as 1913 just beyond the Argyll recording area at Ardnamurchan Point, Highland Region. Persecution and collecting for trophies played a large part in the final chapter of decline, which destroyed a population that had once been more numerous than Golden Eagles (Gray).

Love (1983) identified more than one hundred previous eyrie sites in Scotland. The majority of these were in the Hebrides with another fifty in Ireland (Usher & Warren 1900) including sites at Fair Head, Co Antrim and other sites along the north Irish coast, just a short flight from Argyll. Nine sites were identified in Argyll including reference to this species "frequenting the mainland hills of Creran and Etive" and, further inland, breeding in a small tree on a tiny island at Loch Tulla, near the edge of Rannoch Moor. Other nest sites are known from just outside the Argyll recording area in the Highland and Tayside sections of Rannoch Moor. They also nested at the Mull of Kintyre, on inaccessible pinnacles on Jura's west coast and at the Mull of Oa and Bolsay on Islay. On Mull, a pair with a chick was seen near Scallastle and pairs were present at Burgh, Loch Tuath and Gruline. The Gaelic names of Sgeir na h-Iolaire, Treshnish Isles, and Nead na h-Iolaire, on the Ross of Mull opposite Iona, suggest further sites around Mull.

The first of two unsuccessful, small-scale attempts at reintroduction took place in July 1959 when an adult and two juveniles captured in Norway were released in Glen Etive. The adult appeared rather tame and was recaptured after attacking chickens at Appin. The two juveniles quickly learnt to fend for themselves and remained in the area for several months, but in January 1960 one was killed in a fox trap near Otter Ferry (Sandeman 1965). The second attempt, on Fair Isle in 1968, involved the release of four chicks from Norway (Dennis 1968). Lessons from these attempts proved useful in the Nature Conservancy Council project that initially released 82 Norwegian chicks on Rum between 1975-85 and, in a second phase, another 59 Norwegian birds on the mainland of north Scotland between 1993-98. Wandering immatures from Rum began to appear in Argyll from the early 1980s with some becoming resident on Mull, where nest building was first noticed in 1982 and the first breeding attempt was confirmed in 1983. After a gap of 70 years, the first chick to fly from a Scottish eyrie fledged on Mull in 1985. Breeding has occurred every year since and, in 2004, the Argyll population of five to ten breeding pairs represented 15-30% of the Scottish population.

The spectacular White-tailed Eagle is a regular sight on Mull, and recently also in other parts of Argyll, particularly around the coast. *Iain Erskine*

In two separate areas, during 1983-86 and again in 1989-96, the resident male associated with two females, pairing with both in some years and favouring one of them in others. Breeding was unsuccessful on the occasion when both females laid in the same nest, but one of the pairings was generally successful when the females laid in separate nests. The first successful breeding female disappeared, presumed dead, when she was 21 years old. During her life she reared 15 chicks. She was replaced by another female within two months. The original male disappeared two years later at 23 years of age and was also quickly replaced. Breeding success of the Mull birds has been reduced on a number of occasions by egg collectors and major efforts, assisted by the local community, have been made to reduce these illegal activities. In response to a steadily growing interest from the general public, a site at Loch Frisa, Mull, has been opened by a partnership of RSPB Scotland, Scottish Natural Heritage, Forestry Commission Scotland and Mull and Iona Community Trust, for public viewing every year since 2000.

Many of the White-tailed Eagles released or reared in Scotland have been ringed and individually wing-tagged. Sightings have shown that, in addition to the resident breeding birds, steadily increasing numbers of wandering birds, mainly immatures, have occurred throughout the year, giving hope that further areas of Argyll will soon be recolonised. A minimum of 23 immatures, including locally fledged young, were identified in Argyll in 2004. The majority of records come from the western coastal areas and islands, with regular sightings from Mull, Jura, Islay, Lismore and Kerrera but also, less frequently, from more land-locked water bodies, for example Loch Awe and lower Loch Fyne. Birds up to two or three years old can be particularly itinerant; for example, within two years of fledging on Mull, one was seen on Jura, Islay, coastal Mid-Argyll, inland North Argyll and Morvern. This wide dispersal of young birds, which readily take carrion, makes them particularly vulnerable to indiscriminate use of poisons. A second-year bird hatched in North Scotland in

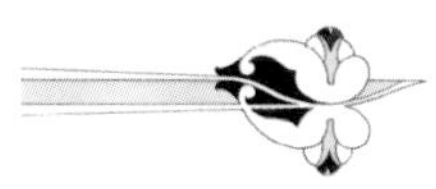

2000 and found dead on a farm near Kilmartin, Mid-Argyll, on 1 May 2002 was a victim of carbofuran poisoning.

Where Golden Eagles now occupy coastal areas that historically were the haunt of White-tailed Eagles, there has been speculation about the impact of recolonising White-tailed Eagles and which species will be dominant. An examination of competition between the two, where they live side by side on Mull, concluded that there were no consistent effects of White-tailed Eagles on the productivity or occupancy of Golden Eagles (Whitfield *et al.* 2002). Data from breeding pairs in Argyll have contributed important insight into the diet of White-tailed Eagles in Scotland. Comparative investigations, where Golden Eagles occurred in the same area, drew heavily on information from the early breeding attempts in Argyll. The findings indicated that the diet of White-tailed Eagles was very diverse, with items either taken as live prey or scavenged from land and sea. Prey included Mountain Hares, Rabbits, deer, sheep, goats, seabirds, ducks, waders and other items including some fish. While there were more Rabbits and Mountain Hares in the diet of Golden Eagles, White-tailed Eagles took more seabirds and ducks (Watson *et al.* 1992). More recently, detailed research in Argyll and elsewhere in Scotland has confirmed the diversity of prey and identified variation in diet between pairs and occasional incidence of lambs taken live or scavenged (Marquiss *et al.* 2003). The overall impact of eagles on farming was judged to be small, but it was important at some farms. Since 1998, management schemes have been available to farmers on Mull, providing payments for a range of measures to reduce vulnerability of lambs to eagle predation. White-tailed Eagles are red-listed, protected under Schedule 1 of the Wildlife and Countryside Act 1981 and listed on Annex 1 of the EC Birds Directive. The Nature Conservation (Scotland) Act 2004 provides year round protection for their nests.

Roger Broad

Marsh Harrier

Circus aeruginosus

Scarce spring migrant, with a few records in summer and autumn. Occasional long-staying birds.

Having dismissed the claim by Gray that this species was common in the Appin district of Argyll, B&R do not have any more recent records to add. Indeed, a female or immature seen on Jura on 27 July 1962 was said to be the first record for the Inner Hebrides (SB 2:256, 344). The first record for mainland Argyll followed on 18 May 1964, when an adult female was seen at Loch Sween (SB 3:268, 4:288). Marsh Harriers remained rare in Argyll until the mid-1980s, with just four more records. From 1985 to 2004, however, there were records in every year except two (1992 and 2003).

Of the 45 records to the end of 2004, more than half (25) came from Islay, ten from other islands (Mull, Tiree, Coll, Colonsay and Jura) and ten from the mainland. Half the mainland records came from Kintyre, and birds were also seen at Loch Sween, Loch Arail, St Catherine's and Moine Mhòr. Most arrivals were in spring, peaking in mid-May, with a few records from mid-June onwards but no sign of an increase in numbers during the autumn.

The earliest dated record in spring involved a female at Loch Gruinart on Islay on 19 April 1988 (SBR 1988:17, ABR 5:19), and the latest in autumn was an immature male that stayed at Loch Gruinart from 3 August to 27 October 1998 (ABR 15:44). Long-staying, wandering birds may have been responsible for some series of sightings published as separate records.

The growing number of records in Argyll since the 1980s reflects the situation in Scotland as a whole, where the increase reported by Thom has continued to the present. Indeed, the Marsh Harrier is now established as a breeder in Scotland. Unfortunately, the reed beds in which it prefers to nest are in rather short supply in Argyll.

In compiling this account, it has been assumed that several records of a female on Islay between 22 May and 26 June 2002 all involved the same bird. In addition, the Figure contains fewer records than the 43 total because not all were dated.

Tristan ap Rheinallt

Marsh Harriers have been seen more regularly in Argyll since the mid-1980s, particularly on the islands. *Philip Snow*

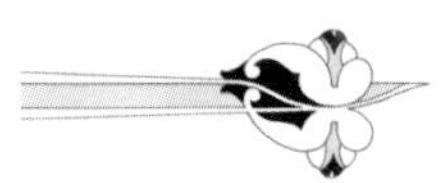

Hen Harrier

Circus cyaneus

Sparse but widespread breeding species, with Argyll holding around one-quarter of the Scottish population. On migration and in winter, seen regularly on islands such as Tiree, where breeding does not occur.

During the breeding season, the Hen Harrier in Britain is largely a bird of heather moorland and newly afforested uplands (Watson 1977). Its history as a breeding species in Britain is one of decline due to human persecution, followed by increase as persecution was relaxed around the time of the Second World War. Although it remains a rare breeder in England and Wales, it is once again widespread, but uncommon, over much of Scotland (Sim *et al.* 2001), although numbers and range are still limited by persecution (Etheridge *et al.* 1997).

In the early part of the 19th century, the Hen Harrier was still a common breeding bird throughout much of Scotland. However, by the middle of the century, it had become decidedly scarce owing to intense persecution (B&R). Although Gray made no mention of its occurrence in mainland Argyll, he described it as very common throughout the Inner Hebrides, including Mull, Islay and Jura. Here it was known by the Gaelic name *Clamhan luch*, or mouse-hawk. Graham described the Hen Harrier as a common non-breeding visitor to Iona and Mull. H&B claimed it once bred commonly on Mull, but had become much scarcer, as it had in mainland areas such as Inveraray. In 1887 it was thought to be common in Benderloch, and birds were still regular on Islay during the autumn at this time (B&R).

At one time the Hen Harrier may have been eliminated from the whole of mainland Britain with the possible exception of Kintyre (Watson 1977, Thom). However, the reduction in gamekeeping during and after the Second World War, coupled with a decrease in heather-burning and the establishment of conifer forests, encouraged recolonisation (First Atlas, Thom). B&R provided no recent breeding records from the Argyll mainland or islands, but Watson (1977) gave evidence of nesting on the mainland in 1949. This was in young conifers at Minard Forest in Mid-Argyll, after which breeding became more widespread in such habitat. In Kintyre, 20 pairs were present in 1973, but few bred successfully and by 1975 this population was down to about ten pairs. There is some doubt whether birds continued to breed on the Inner Hebrides throughout (Thom). Elliott (1989) believed Hen Harriers became extinct as breeding birds on Islay late in the 19th century and recolonised the island during the 1960s.

Of late, Hen Harriers in Argyll have certainly suffered less from persecution than in other parts of Scotland, largely because Argyll lacks managed grouse moors. By the time of the First Atlas, breeding was widespread in Kintyre, Cowal and Mid-Argyll, with several 10-km squares on Islay and Mull also occupied. Although Thom described the species as "scarce or sporadic" on Islay and Mull, the Second Atlas provided evidence for a substantial expansion on Islay, with confirmed breeding from nearly every 10-km square. There was some consolidation of the range on Mull, with birds also starting to breed in the western half of Jura. The situation on the mainland showed little change, with birds absent from much of the northeast where the habitat was less suitable. At least four active nesting areas were located in young conifers in Kintyre in 1983 (Petty 1985).

In 1998, a national survey by the RSPB and local raptor groups (Sim *et al.* 2001) found 52 territorial pairs at a sample of sites in Argyll and Bute. It was estimated that complete coverage would have recorded 124 pairs (95% confidence limits 66-189 pairs), representing 25% of the Scottish breeding population. Much of the Argyll population was

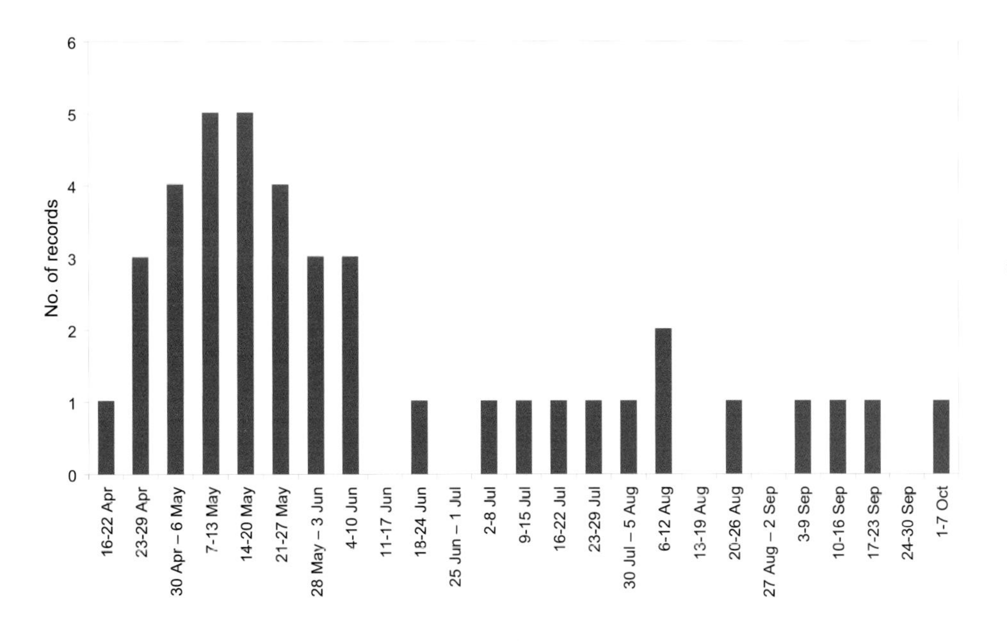

Weekly distribution of dated Marsh Harrier records, 1962-2003.

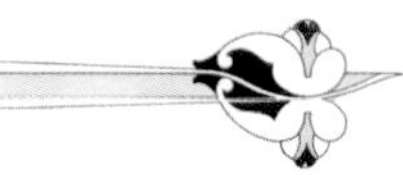

Hen Harriers have proved adept at foraging in young conifer plantations. *Philip Snow*

on Islay, where 24 occupied territories were located in 2001, though only 22 of these held pairs (ABR 18:46). Mull was also important, with 22 occupied territories found during a complete survey in 2002 (Argyll Database). In 2004, two pairs held territories on Coll and one pair bred (Wellock 2004). In 2006, the first successful breeding occurred on Colonsay.

There have been detailed studies of habitat preference and feeding ecology in Argyll. Long heather is strongly preferred for nesting, either on moorland or in first-rotation conifer forests before the canopy closes (Redpath *et al.* 1998). Hen Harriers forage successfully in young plantations because of the abundance of Field Voles and Meadow Pipits (Madders 2003). Although birds forage in young second-rotation conifer crops, they rarely breed in this habitat (Petty & Anderson 1986, Petty 1996).

Young conifer plantations clearly constitute an important breeding habitat in Argyll. In 1988 and 1999 respectively, 63% and 35% of nests were in plantations, most of which were less than five years old. Numbers of birds attempting to breed fluctuate from year-to-year due to changes in Field Vole abundance. Voles are an important food source early in the breeding season before the harriers switch to bird prey. Cold, wet weather in early spring can lead to late laying and nest failure, while heavy rainfall in summer makes it difficult for adults to hunt. For example, in 1993, 1994 and 2002, poor breeding success (Table) was attributed to adverse weather. Moorland fires can destroy nests, as at Loch Gruinart RSPB Reserve on Islay in 1994 and again on Islay in 1996. Nests also fail because of fox predation although foxes are absent from the Argyll islands. On the whole, breeding success in Argyll was found to be higher than in areas of Scotland with managed grouse moors (Etheridge *et al.* 1997).

Data for 1988-2005 show that the mean number of fledged young per nest varies from only 1.5 to more than three (Table). Because some nests are unsuccessful, the mean number of fledged young per successful nest is higher and also less variable, ranging from 2.19 to 3.43. Polygyny occurs regularly in Argyll, single male harriers being paired with as many as three successfully breeding females. Thus in any year, the number of males is likely to be less than the number of nests.

Of ten sites checked annually in Mid-Argyll and north Kintyre, only two have been occupied in recent years. At Moine Mhor, up to three pairs bred in the early 1990s, but there has been little evidence of breeding since 1997. On the east of Kintyre between Tarbert and Skipness, up to five pairs bred in 1998, but only one pair remains. The reason for this decline is uncertain as there has been little change in the breeding habitats of open mire, heathland and conifer edge at these sites. However, of 20 breeding attempts between Tarbert and Skipness over the years 1997-2006, only eight have been successful with a large proportion of failures attributable to predation, possibly by foxes. Similarly, of 14 breeding attempts at Moine Mhor between 1988 and 2006, eight were successful, the failures being largely due to predation. Interestingly, a female reared and tagged at Moine Mhor in 1992 bred successfully at Moine Mhor in 1993. For four consecutive years, this female then bred with a male reared and tagged at Moine Mhor in 1991. They were unsuccessful in 1994, 1995 and 1997, but reared three young in 1996.

In the Winter Atlas survey, Hen Harriers on the mainland were more scattered in winter than in summer, though they remained concentrated on Islay and to a lesser extent Mull.

At least some of the change reflected a tendency for birds to forsake moorland in winter for farmland, marshes and conifer plantations at lower altitudes. This tendency is stronger in males than in females (Migration Atlas). During winter, Hen Harriers roost communally, and several traditional sites are known on mainland Argyll and the islands. Among the largest (maximum counts in parentheses) are roosts on Islay (18), Mull (ten) and Aros Moss (nine). Numbers at these roosts seem to have fallen in recent years, though they fluctuate considerably from year to year. Roosts are occasionally used by non-breeders during summer. At Moine Mhor, roosting birds were counted monthly from October to March from 1984 to 2006. Numbers remained at a relatively high level during 1988-1995 with a winter average of 7-13 birds and a peak count of 17 in November 1994. Then there was gradual decline to a winter average recently of only 2-5 birds.

British Hen Harriers are described as partial migrants and some young birds, especially males, undertake long movements into south-western Europe during their first autumn. Ireland appears to be an important wintering area for young Hen Harriers from Argyll (Migration Atlas), as shown by five ringing recoveries between October and March. In south Kintyre, apparent passage migrants have been observed over the sea on several occasions during August, September and October, presumably heading towards Ireland. However, birds may also wander further afield as shown by two recoveries of chicks ringed in Argyll and recovered along the west coast of France. The first was ringed in Kintyre in June 1961 and was recovered not far from the Spanish border in January 1962. The second, ringed on Islay in June 1984, was recovered near the Loire estuary at the age of about 18 months. Wing-tagged birds have given more evidence of migration, with chicks tagged in Argyll being seen as far afield as Cornwall and the Isles of Scilly. Closer to home, Argyll-ringed birds have been recovered elsewhere in Scotland, especially in Dumfries & Galloway, as well as in northern England. Most of these recoveries are during winter months, the few exceptions involving birds in their second calendar year that may have been non-breeders.

Following autumn movements, numbers in some areas of Argyll, such as Mull, seem to fall considerably in winter, but numbers may be greater in those winters with peak numbers of voles. The presence of immigrants is supported by a small number of recoveries of birds ringed elsewhere in Scotland, the furthest being two birds from Orkney. Interestingly, few ringed in Argyll have been recovered in the county in winter, suggesting that the proportion of residents here may be small. Even adults can move considerable distances from one breeding season to the next, as shown by a female that bred in Orkney during 1975-1981 and in Argyll in 1984 (Thom).

Migrants occur on some islands where breeding does not take place, for example on Tiree. Most sightings are in autumn, but wintering is regular and may involve several individuals. Up to six were on Colonsay during winter 1990/91 (ABR). Less frequently, birds are recorded from these islands in summer, most of them probably immature.

Tristan ap Rheinallt

Mean breeding success of Hen Harriers in Argyll, 1988-2005.

Year	No. of nests monitored	Fledged young per nest	Fledged young per successful nest
1988	39	2.59	3.12
1989	47	3.06	3.43
1990	68	2.63	3.29
1991	78	2.17	nd
1992	64	2.67	3.00
1993	57	2.04	2.19
1994	48	1.50	2.81
1995	24	2.13	2.88
1996	30	2.27	3.40
1997	nd	nd	3.16
1998	nd	nd	2.88
1999	21	1.86	2.44
2000	28	2.07	2.63
2001	37	2.38	3.26
2002	21	1.52	2.46
2003	43	2.49	2.97
2004	60	1.63	2.28
2005	50	1.28	2.65

Survey effort, and criteria for nest outcomes, have varied since 1988.

Northern Goshawk

Accipiter gentilis

Sporadic visitor of uncertain status. Breeding may have occurred following releases in Mid-Argyll in 1969-73 and 1980, but a self-sustaining population was not established.

The Goshawk is possibly the least-known member of the Argyll avifauna. Gray mentioned occurrences in Mull (two shot in the late 1850s), Glenorchy (one killed in 1848) and Appin (a female shot during the 1860s). Although all these records were apparently backed up by preserved specimens, H&B made no reference to this species, a clear indication that they did not believe Gray's records. Writing more than half a century later, B&R did not include Argyll among the Scottish mainland counties where Goshawks at one time bred. However, they referred to a record of a presumed migrant on Mull, probably the bird seen by Buckley at Glenforsa on 9 November 1892 (Buckley 1893).

The next record involved a bird seen at Loch Ballygrant on Islay on 28 April 1959, said at the time to be the first for the Inner Hebrides (SB 1:144, Greenwood 1960). Not long afterwards, one at the Mull of Kintyre on 15 September 1963 was said to be the first record for "South Argyll" (Gordon & Merrie 1964). This marked the beginning of a slow increase that gathered pace in the 1970s.

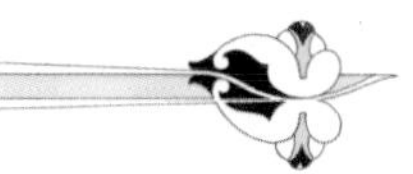

If genuine, these records are likely to relate to birds of imported origin rather than migrants from the Continent (Petty 2007). Indeed, it has recently come to light that Goshawks were introduced to mainland Argyll on two occasions around this time. A total of eight birds were released in Knapdale Forest, near the head of Loch Sween, between 1969 and 1973, and a further three birds were released in the same area in 1980 (Petty 2007). The former releases may well account for a sequence of records from the same area of Mid-Argyll between 1974 and 1979 (Rainier 1975, 1983), and for an unconfirmed report of successful breeding in 1973 (Rainier 1975), while the latter releases may be responsible for an unconfirmed report of breeding in the early 1980s (Petty 2007).

In contrast to some other parts of Scotland, released birds did not establish a self-sustaining population, possibly due to a lack of food (Petty 2007). No Argyll records feature in the Second Atlas, and there appears to be no firm evidence to back the view that Goshawks were "almost annual" on Islay in the mid-1980s (Elliott 1989). Nonetheless, the Second Atlas showed birds to occur in several squares around Sunart, barely 20km from the northern border of Argyll, as well as further north. Expansion into Argyll seemed to be only a matter of time.

Since then, the population in Highland Region has declined. In 1993, concerns about the uncritical acceptance of records led the Argyll Bird Records Committee to add Goshawk to the list of species for which a supporting description was required. Only one record has subsequently been accepted: an adult was seen by an experienced observer in Knapdale in March 2006 (Argyll Database). Some though certainly not all of the other reports may be genuine and relate to wandering individuals from elsewhere in Scotland. Therefore it is still possible that breeding will occur in Argyll in the future. With only a few pairs currently breeding in Highland Region, founder birds are perhaps most likely to come from the increasing population in southern Scotland. However, it may take a considerable time to recruit enough birds to establish a viable breeding population (Petty 2007).

Tristan ap Rheinallt

An adult female Goshawk perched in a Larch tree. Female Sparrowhawks are often misidentified as Goshawks. *David S. Whitaker*

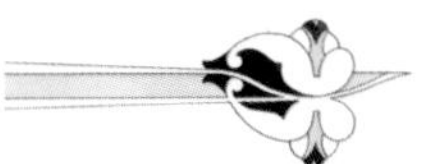

Eurasian Sparrowhawk

Accipiter nisus

A widespread resident.

This elusive bird-eating raptor breeds in woodland but hunts over a wide range of habitats. Outside the breeding season, dispersing birds can be seen throughout much of mainland Argyll and its islands. There are no breeding records for Tiree due to a lack of suitable habitat, but it has bred recently on Coll.

During the 19th and early 20th centuries, numbers in Argyll would have been low for two reasons. First, tree cover reached its lowest point after many centuries of deforestation (Forestry Commission 2005), although some new planting was initiated at this time around some large country houses. Second, gamekeepers ruthlessly shot, trapped and poisoned predators, including Sparrowhawks, which were often eradicated from the remaining suitable habitat (Newton 1972a). However, unlike some larger raptors, Sparrowhawks did not become extinct, largely due to their secretive nature and high reproductive rates. In earlier literature there was sometimes confusion between species of small raptors. Thus, all records of Sparrowhawks nesting on crags and rocks should be treated with caution, as these probably relate to Kestrel, or even Merlin.

Gray noted that "in the remoter districts of the West of Scotland this daring and destructive bird is not nearly as numerous as the Merlin or the Kestrel". Graham said that Sparrowhawks were as rare as Buzzards on Mull in the mid 19th century, although they may have been more frequent on the mainland side of the island, where there were more trees. H&B found that they were not uncommon in many of the more wooded parts of the mainland, and that they bred on some of the "better-wooded islands" such as Mull, Islay and Jura. B&R recorded three nests on Islay as long ago as 1875, and a nest with eggs was found on Colonsay in 1939.

By the mid 20th century their fortunes had improved due to both a decline in gamebird rearing and the increasing area of suitable breeding habitat provided by state reforestation schemes, which commenced in the 1920s (Petty & Avery 1990). However, this was short-lived as numbers declined rapidly throughout most of the UK following the introduction of DDT and other more toxic organochlorine pesticides used as seed dressings in agriculture (Newton 1986). Numbers reached their lowest level in the 1960s and 1970s. However, areas such as Argyll, where pesticide use was not widespread, probably experienced only a minor decline in numbers. Following restrictions on the use of these pesticides, numbers increased rapidly (Newton & Haas 1984, Newton 1992).

Currently, numbers and breeding range of Sparrowhawks in Argyll are probably greater than at any time in the last 400-500 years, due largely to extensive reforestation in the last 80 years. The 'change map' in the Second Atlas indicates that range expansion is still in progress, particularly in Kintyre and Mull and to a lesser extent on Islay, all with large areas of forest that reached a suitable age for breeding in the period between the First and the Second Atlases. Greenwood *et al.* (2003) estimated the Scottish population to be 7,000 pairs, but there is no estimate for Argyll.

Sparrowhawks are widely distributed across Argyll, breeding in deciduous and coniferous woodlands. However, they are probably seen most often in or near gardens. *R.J.C. Blewitt*

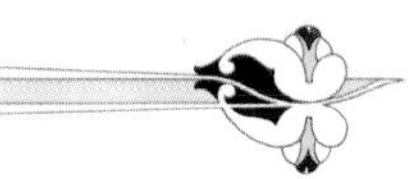

In any one area, breeding numbers of Sparrowhawks vary little among years, largely because their bird prey collectively exhibit little change in abundance from one year to another (Newton 1986). However, in conifer forests in northern England, pulses of high breeding productivity have been related to bumper cone crops and the associated abundance of conifer seed-eating finches (Petty *et al.* 1995). Similar events may occur in Argyll in good cone years.

Sparrowhawks prefer to nest in conifers rather than broadleaved trees, probably because conifers offer better protection from adverse weather and predators. They breed in conifer forests as soon as they can fly between the trees, usually when stands are at least 20 years old. Birds often abandon stands when they become too open and move into younger crops nearby. They frequently return to the same area of forest each year to breed, but typically build a new nest. However, in the absence of conifers, they breed in broadleaved woods and even in scrub-filled gullies in otherwise treeless landscapes. For example, on Islay, Gordon Yates found a nest on the ground in ferns at the base of a Rowan and another in a Gorse bush just 1m above the ground (photos of both nests appear in Newton 1986, illustrations 18 lower and 21 lower) (Yates 2005).

Sparrowhawks hunt mainly in woodlands, but they also forage over open habitats. Females hunt more over open ground than males (Marquiss & Newton 1981). Sparrowhawks exhibit the largest sexual size dimorphism of any British raptor; females weigh around twice as much as males. This enables a pair to take a wider range of prey. Woodpigeons are about the largest prey taken regularly by females. Thus, in any area Sparrowhawks kill individuals of most bird species present, although they concentrate on the most abundant small-to-medium sized songbirds.

This is one of the latest raptors to breed, usually starting to lay in May, with chicks hatching around the middle of June (Newton 1986). This timing coincides with the peak availability of fledging songbirds, on which the chicks are largely fed. Clutches of four to six are the most frequent. The only data on breeding success in Argyll come from a study area in Cowal (Table). Here, 89% of breeding pairs were successful (rearing at least one chick). The mean annual brood size of 3.2 was high compared to a mean brood of 2.9 from a population in eastern England, which was recovering from the pesticide era (Newton 1992).

British Sparrowhawks are non-migratory but can disperse over a wide area. The main movement of fledglings away from nesting areas takes place in August and September, when they can be seen almost anywhere in Argyll. At this time they are rapidly developing their aerial agility and are often to be seen jousting high in the sky with other raptors. Generally, Sparrowhawks that breed in the uplands disperse over greater distances than those in the lowlands, undoubtedly due to fast-reducing prey populations at this time of year. Six Sparrowhawks ringed in Argyll have been recovered elsewhere in Scotland, but only two travelled more than 100km; one at Glencarse, near Perth (Tayside, 107km) and one at Kingussie (Highland, 114km). A female ringed as a chick at Peterculter, Aberdeen, in July 1984 was found dead at Tarbert (Kintyre, 241km) in October the same year. Most British Sparrowhawks settle to breed within 20km of where they were reared (Newton 1986, Migration Atlas).

Mean breeding success of Sparrowhawks in Cowal (ARSG).

Year	Total pairs	Successful pairs	Young per nest	Young per successful nest
1995	10	10	4.10	4.10
1996	7	7	-	
1997	8	6	2.25	3.00
1998	12	10	2.75	3.30
1999	9	8	3.78	4.13
Mean			3.22	3.63

During winter they are rarely seen in upland areas, due to the lack of suitable prey (Migration Atlas). Instead, they can be found in low-lying agricultural areas, where thrushes, Starlings and finches are abundant, and along the coast and islands where waders and songbirds abound. They frequently visit gardens with bird feeders. In 2004, this was the 16th most frequently recorded bird in gardens in Argyll, with a reporting rate of 26% (BTO Garden BirdWatch). However, exploiting such feeding opportunities has its drawbacks, as some Sparrowhawks are killed when they fly into windows!

The current healthy population level in Argyll gives no cause for concern. In fact, the population is likely to increase further as forests established during the last 20 years become suitable for breeding. However, there is a lack of quantitative data on breeding performance in a range of habitat types. In the past, Sparrowhawks have been shown to be an excellent indicator of environmental contaminants. They may well do so in the future, providing baseline data are available.

Steve J. Petty

Common Buzzard

Buteo buteo

The Common Buzzard is the most abundant raptor in Argyll. It is a resident breeding bird found throughout the county.

B&R noted that at the start of the 19th century Common Buzzards "bred plentifully over the greater part of Scotland". They noted that from around 1830 persecution of this species became intense and this included the population in Argyll as they report by 1850 it was exterminated from Kintyre. Graham did not find any breeding on Iona, but B&R report it was still breeding on Mull in 1865. Gray noted that it could be found in some numbers in the Inner Hebrides, but on the mainland it was only met with sparingly. H&B give the impression little had changed by the end of the 19th century as they only noted breeding in the larger and remoter cliffs.

The 20th century recovery of Buzzards in Argyll came as a result of changing trends in sport shooting (and fewer gamekeepers), through changes in legislation and changes in land-use, such as the increase in forestry where control of "vermin" was less vigorous. B&R noted that Buzzards re-established in Kintyre in the first half of the 20th century. They report that Buzzards were breeding on Islay, Jura and Colonsay and that breeding was first recorded on Tiree in 1950 and on Coll in 1938. Fraser Darling (1940) found it on Lunga, in the Treshnish Isles, in 1937 and in 1929 it was well distributed in Mull (B&R).

The First Atlas gave the first comprehensive survey of its distribution in Argyll. Breeding was recorded throughout Argyll except on Islay, where it was restricted to the Kildalton area. At this time persecution persisted on Islay and only declined during the 1980s with the introduction of Larsen traps for crow-control. The Second Atlas found Buzzards in 78% of 10-km squares in Argyll; unoccupied squares were largely coastal with small land areas. An estimate based on returns from the first year of Atlas fieldwork suggested that there were between 1,200-1,950 Buzzards in the county (Jardine 1989). This work mentioned that Buzzards were still at lower densities on Islay than other low-lying parts of Argyll, although breeding was more widespread here than in the First Atlas. Given that densities on Islay have risen since the Second Atlas, the Argyll population is currently thought to be in the range 1,500-2,250 birds during the breeding season.

While Buzzards are widespread in Argyll, they are out-competed by Golden Eagles and injured birds have been found in eagle territories; in another study area five pairs of Buzzards were replaced by one new pair of Golden Eagles. The large population of Buzzards in Argyll has encouraged a number of breeding studies. The earliest of these was included in a national analysis of breeding Buzzards (Campbell 1947). Local studies have been reported for Kintyre (Maguire 1979), Mid- and North Argyll (Austin & Houston 1997) and Colonsay (Jardine 2003) (Table). There are ongoing studies on Mull and in Kintyre.

Most Buzzards in Argyll lay two to four eggs, but in 1988 a clutch of six was found at Taynish. In the Kintyre study two-thirds of nests were in trees, while on Colonsay less than 25% were in trees and most were on small crags. The studies suggest that the most common number of young fledged per nest was two, then one young, with a few nests rearing three young in years of good weather and food supply. Nests rearing four young are rare but do occur occasionally. Austin & Houston (1997) found that there were differences in breeding performance in different habitats in Mid- and North Argyll. Birds breeding in sheep-walk laid earlier (mean 12 April) and were more productive (2.2 young/successful nest) than those using forests (mean 22 April and 1.7 young/successful nest).

Buzzards are omnivorous, but their principal prey during the breeding season is Rabbits. On Colonsay over 80% (by

Buzzards are a familiar raptor across Argyll. They often use exposed perches by the roadside, and can be fairly tolerant of human presence. *R.J.C. Blewitt*

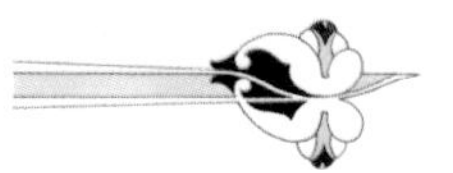

	Kintyre (Maguire 1979)	Mid & North Argyll (Austin & Houston 1997)	Colonsay (Jardine 2003)
Years	1977-78	1989-91	1990-2000
Number of pairs	34-55	34-43	17-24
Density (pairs 100km^{-2})	29.5	38-53	14.4-18.2
Laying period	27 March - 5 May	2 April - 7 May	7 April - 10 May
Mean first egg	20 April	14 April	21 April
Mean clutch size	2.58	2.2	n/a
Mean fledged young (successful nests)	2.36	1.75	1.75

The breeding performance of Buzzards in Argyll from three studies.

weight) of the prey remains were young Rabbits. They also prey on other small mammals such as Field Voles and, in some areas, Brown Rats. During the breeding season they take a lot of young birds, the Colonsay study finding remains of 20 species, including Corncrake, at the nest. During wet weather, when soaring is restricted, Buzzards are often seen feeding on earthworms; a congregation of 32 birds were feeding in this manner in one field at Campbeltown on 8 October 1989.

The breeding studies of Buzzards in Argyll have led to many nestlings being ringed. There have been over 70 recoveries that confirm the largely sedentary nature of this species in the county. Only eight birds were recovered outside Argyll; two were found in both Antrim and Tayside, and one each in Ulster, Central, Bute and Ayrshire. The longest movement was of a bird ringed on Colonsay and recovered 92km away near Fairlie (Ayrshire). Around a third of recoveries were within 5km of their birthplace, another third between 5-20km and only 13% beyond 50km. Recoveries were in all directions of the compass, with no evidence of any directional movements. Eleven percent of recoveries were within three months of ringing, another 44% were within one year and only 7% were over five years. The oldest recovery was of a bird ringed in 1979 in Kintyre which was found 5km away over 18 years later at Campbeltown.

David Jardine

Rough-legged Buzzard

Buteo lagopus

Rare visitor, mostly in autumn.

As would be expected for a species whose nearest breeding grounds are in Scandinavia, Rough-legged Buzzards are recorded much more frequently on the east coast of Scotland and in the Northern Isles than they are in the west. The first known Argyll record concerns six specimens sent for preservation by a gamekeeper in Mull in February 1886, following a major immigration of the species in autumn 1885 (Proc NHS Glasgow 3:30, H&B). Prior to 1973, there were only two further records: one at Loch Fyne on 9 October 1902 (ASNH 1903:83, 150), and two near Strachur on the very early date of 9 September 1963 (SB 2:487, SB 3:171).

Between 1973 and 1988, about ten birds were recorded, some being seen repeatedly over periods of up to two months. Four of these birds were seen on the mainland, at Loch Sween, Glenkinglass, Glen Lochy and near Inveraray. The remaining six were equally divided between Islay and Mull. With the exception of one on Islay from January to March 1975, and one near Inveraray in March 1983, all were first reported between 4 October and 15 November. These dates correspond to the main autumn arrival of the species in Scotland, these birds having apparently come direct from breeding populations in Norway and Sweden (Migration Atlas).

Over the past decade and a half, the species has become rarer once more. Indeed, there is only one accepted Argyll record since 1988, involving a bird seen at Moss on Tiree on the early date of 17 September 1997 (ABR 14:42). This decline reflects the overall trend in Scotland, where there were about 16 records a year on average in the 1980s, falling to fewer than five in the 1990s. However, some of the apparent decline, in Argyll at least, may be due to a more rigorous approach to record assessment. In Britain as a whole, mean annual totals were considerably higher in the 1990s than in the 1980s (Fraser & Rogers 2001).

[Several additional records were published by Elliott (1989) but, since no details are available and the records were not published in SB, they are considered unacceptable. The same applies to the 1965 Colonsay record published by Jardine *et al.* (1986).]

Tristan ap Rheinallt

Golden Eagle

Aquila chrysaetos

Widespread resident breeder; affected by changes in land use, particularly afforestation.

Argyll holds about 20% of the Scottish population of Golden Eagles. These are regularly distributed throughout the mainland and the larger islands, being absent only where there is extensive low-level agricultural land such as in the vicinity of Campbeltown and parts of Islay. Mainland Argyll holds

About 40 pairs of Golden Eagles nest in Argyll. *Iain Erskine*

about 40 breeding pairs, and another 40 or so pairs are shared among Islay, Jura, Mull and the other islands. Even quite small islands can hold one or two pairs of Golden Eagles. Territories tend to be evenly spaced but the density of breeding pairs on Mull is about twice that on mainland Argyll. Some pairs have alternative eyries up to 12km apart, while neighbouring pairs may have eyries within 1km of each other although not recorded as being used in the same season.

Eagles usually nest well away from human activity but a few pairs regularly breed successfully within sight of a public road or close to occupied habitation. Nest sites can be almost at sea level or as high as 650m asl but are usually in the 250-350m range. In Argyll nests are usually on crags or small rocks or in gullies. There have even been one or two nests on sloping ground. Tree nests are unusual but have been found in Scots Pine, Oak, Birch, Alder and Ash. Some coastal eyries were probably once used by White-tailed Eagles. Breeding adults can roam within a range of 20km diameter and wandering immature birds can be seen almost anywhere in Argyll. One mainland pair occasionally nests on the island of Bute.

Early historical records often did not differentiate between Golden Eagles and White-tailed Eagles and there are no figures for comparison with modern population data. Pennant (1771-1776) mentioned 'eagles' as being resident in Islay. The OSA referred to 'eagles' from the Borders up to Shetland, and either or both species were clearly common at that time. Macgillivray (1836) stated that the Golden Eagle was less common than the White-tailed Eagle and that vast numbers had been destroyed lately due to sheep farming. He further remarked that Golden Eagles were more common in the west than the east of the country. The NSA also commented that sheep farming had resulted in a seriously diminished eagle population but they were still recorded breeding from the Borders northwards. Graham said that 'eagles' were much less numerous than a generation ago, judging by the number of empty eyries pointed out to him by the older natives on cliffs of south and west Mull. H&B referred to 50 Golden Eagles killed in a period of only six years on Jura and stated that none of the eyries on the island had been occupied since 1887. In 1953, B&R said that several pairs were then breeding on Islay, quoted six pairs as breeding on Jura, and referred to three pairs on Mull. These data from B&R are probably much lower than numbers actually present at that time.

Anecdotal evidence suggests that persecution of eagles continued during the first half of the 20th century, and occupancy and productivity would only have started to improve after the 1954 Protection of Birds Act. Soon afterwards, the RSPB started to build up a data bank of the Scottish Golden Eagle population, and it was only then that

Golden Eagle monitoring data for Argyll, 1992-2005.

Year	Territories checked	Territories occupied	Territories where eggs laid	Territories known to have fledged young	% of occupied territories that fledged young	Minimum number of young fledged	Number of young per successful pair
1992	96*	84	59	27	32.1%	28	1.03
1996	57	54	37+	25	46.2%	29	1.16
1997	58	53	?	25	47.1%	31	1.24
1998	61	54	?	22	40.7%	27	1.22
1999	61	57	28	16	28.0%	17	1.06
2000	62	59	28+	19	32.2%	22	1.15
2001	54	54	27	18	33.3%	21	1.16
2002	62	57	36	15	26.3%	15	1.00
2003	100*	80	52	29 (30)	36.3% (37.5%)	30 (31)	1.03 (1.03)
2004	61	56	38	28 (29)	50.0%	32 (33)	1.14 (1.13)
2005	65	59	40	17 (18)	28.8%	19 (20)	1.11

Figures in brackets include chick half grown on last visit.
* 1992 and 2003 were national survey years with full coverage of all known territories. In other years, a sample of territories was monitored.

Most Golden Eagles nest on crags, but a few use trees. *Iain Erskine*

anything like a reliable total, and an idea of distribution within the country, became available. Since the 1960s, samples of the Argyll population have been monitored annually by the Argyll Raptor Study Group (Table), showing that most territories have been occupied almost continuously but that at least four historic areas in Cowal were deserted by 1964 and at least three more vacated in Knapdale and Kintyre by 1980. Breeding success varies considerably, some pairs consistently rearing young and others rarely or never doing so. Overall productivity seems to have peaked in the 1970s and declined steadily since then, mainly because more pairs are not laying eggs.

Nowadays there is still evidence of regular persecution in a few places. For example, three Golden Eagles and one White-tailed Eagle were found dead in suspicious circumstances near Kilmelford during 1997-2002, including two confirmed poisoned. In addition, there have been several cases of egg collectors raiding eyries on Mull, and there was a period in the 1980s when eaglets were regularly removed from one inland glen by suspected falconers or bird traders. Nevertheless, changes in land use are more likely to be having a greater adverse effect on the eagle population. The most obvious change has been the removal of sheep from much of the hill ground and their replacement with extensive conifer plantations. Whilst this sometimes provides more secluded nesting sites, there is no doubt that the thick tree cover eventually reduces the amount of hunting land available to Golden Eagles. In an attempt to determine the effect of forestry on eagles, RSPB and Forest Research carried out a radio-tracking project on the Argyll mainland between 1991 and 1996, supplemented by direct observations of birds on the Ross of Mull. These studies produced data on ranging behaviour which have been used in subsequent conservation planning, including a model which goes some way to predicting how resident eagles use different parts of their territory for foraging (McLeod *et al.* 2002; Haworth *et al.* 2006). More recently, eagle monitoring data from 1970 to 2000 was analysed in relation to land use change in mainland Argyll (Whitfield *et al.* 2007). This study suggested that afforestation was very likely to be responsible for an overall decline in productivity over this period, but effects on individual pairs were complex. The more productive pairs of eagles, and those pairs able to shift their territory-use to exploit different areas, were least affected by afforestation.

The construction of wind farms within or close to eagle territories might also have adverse effects, although habitat improvements are often proposed as attempts to mitigate these. The results to date (2007) at two sites in Argyll have not been encouraging. At Beinn an Tuirc in Kintyre, a pair has failed to breed successfully since the wind farm was built in 2001-02. At Beinn Ghlas near Taynuilt in Mid-Argyll, where a wind farm was built in 1999-2000, the resident pair has abandoned the territory. At Beinn an Tuirc, the eagles' ranging behaviour was studied both before and after wind farm construction, and attempts at habitat improvement elsewhere in this pair's home range were also made (Walker *et al.* 2005). Even the human activity at the shore facilities of a badly sited fish farm can cause a particular eyrie to become unusable, as occurred at a site in Seil Sound, Mid-Argyll, in 1984 (Gregory, unpublished records).

Variation in Rabbit numbers can affect Golden Eagle productivity. Pairs with a long history of good productivity can suddenly fail to breed if there is a crash in the local Rabbit population; equally, pairs with a poor breeding record can improve when Rabbit numbers suddenly increase. Rabbits, if available, are the principal prey of Golden Eagles in Argyll, probably because they are easier to catch than many other species. In winter the birds are likely to be more reliant on sheep and deer carrion. Red Grouse are certainly taken, even though these are only sparsely distributed in Argyll, and other avian prey recorded includes Meadow Pipit, Song Thrush, and Curlew. On one visit to an eyrie in an inland glen some 8km from the sea, an observer was surprised to find a freshly killed Gannet.

Between 1970 and 2000 over 250 Golden Eagle chicks were ringed, mostly in mainland Argyll, Mull and Islay. Fewer than 10% have been recovered. The most distant recovery was of a bird ringed near Colintraive in 1973 and killed on a power line some 80km away near Pitlochry one year later. One bird was recovered at 20km three years after ringing and another at 15km after five years. This suggests either that Golden Eagles do not travel far from their natal area, or that young birds may travel widely and return. There have been only three island recoveries, including one ringed as a nestling on Mull in 1984 and found dead in the sea just off the coast of Rum in 2000. Almost half of the birds recovered were found dead beneath power lines. There were two recoveries of birds ringed as adults in 1993 during the Argyll radio-tracking study. These two were a breeding pair and both were later found dead within their territory. There has been only one recovery in Argyll of a bird ringed elsewhere. This was ringed in Wester Ross in 1988 and found later that year on East Lochaweside.

The Golden Eagles which recolonised the Antrim coast of Northern Ireland from 1953 to 1960 almost certainly came from Argyll. They were reputed to hunt in Argyll and take prey back to Antrim, although the evidence for this was somewhat tenuous. The low productivity of those now nesting in Kintyre and Islay makes it unlikely that natural recolonisation of Ireland will occur, and a project to reintroduce birds to Donegal was started in 2001 using eaglets obtained from Scotland.

Mike Gregory

Osprey

Pandion haliaetus

Summer migrant occurring in small but increasing numbers. Recent breeding re-colonist on mainland Argyll with nine pairs in 2004.

Brown & Waterston (1962) reviewed the status of Ospreys and their extinction as a breeding species in Scotland by 1916. In Argyll, former breeding sites were documented on an island in Loch Avich in 1794 (B&R) and in 1833 at the Pass of Brander and on the ruins of Kilchurn Castle, Loch Awe (Selby 1833). Both Loch Awe sites were mentioned by McGillivray (1836). Selby (1833) noted that the nest at the Pass of Brander "was usually robbed" and another clutch was taken at Loch Awe in 1850 (B&R). Repeated use of traditional breeding sites undoubtedly hastened their downfall and Gray noted in 1871 that "Ospreys had long since ceased to breed" in the West of Scotland. At the end of this long decline, the last recorded breeding record anywhere in Scotland was in 1916. Re-colonisation by immigrants from Scandinavia occurred in 1954. Unlike historical eyries, of which 90% were in the west, more than 90% of recent eyries have so far been in the eastern half of Scotland (Dennis 1995).

With Ospreys capable of foraging up to 10km from nests, many places in Argyll appear to provide their habitat requirements - a combination of fresh water or shallow, coastal areas where adequate stocks of suitably-sized fish can be caught and with suitable trees for nesting. Natural nests have usually been built in conifers with an open aspect, but artificial sites in trees have been readily accepted. To date, Ospreys have not attempted to nest on other man-made structures in Argyll, for example electricity pylons, as happens at a small number of sites elsewhere in Scotland.

Re-colonisation of Argyll occurred at an artificial site constructed by Ralph Clough early in 1987 in a 25m conifer

Ospreys are now firmly re-established as a breeding species in Argyll. Numbers are increasing slowly. *Philip Kirkham*

near Loch Awe. A pair adopted the platform in May of the same year and laid two fertile eggs. This first breeding attempt in more than 100 years also attracted 1-2 additional birds on occasions before the nesting attempt failed and the site was deserted. This extended the range by more than 70km west from the nearest breeding locality in Central Scotland and even further south-west from the nearest site in Highland Region. The leap in range, and the discovery of more Ospreys migrating over Argyll than had previously been suspected, provided the impetus to build further artificial nest platforms. In 1988 birds returned to the original nest site, but a breeding pair was not established. However, a second platform was used and three young raised. Re-colonisation of mainland Argyll, using both natural tree sites and artificial platforms put up in trees, has continued at a slow rate to reach five breeding pairs by 2001 and nine pairs with nests, all in Mid-Argyll, in 2004. This represents about 5% of the Scottish population that was estimated to be more than 169 pairs in 2004.

The average success for the 60 breeding attempts in Argyll during 1987-2004 was 1.56 young per clutch laid. This compares favourably with breeding success of the total Scottish population (Morton 2001) and with many suitable sites available, Argyll seems poised for further re-colonisation. Non-breeding birds are increasingly reported in small numbers from all areas of the Argyll mainland and one or two birds have recently summered on Islay and Mull.

One at Ballygrant (Islay) on 3 March 1981 was early for Argyll. Usually, with favourable weather, the first returning birds appear near their nest sites from the last week of March to early April, and established pairs whose eyries have survived the winter may be incubating by mid-April. In autumn most have departed by early September, but the estuary at Crinan has become a regular place for fishing Ospreys in August to mid-September. Late birds were recorded on 4 October 1990 at Blackmount (North Argyll), 11 October 1998 at Lochdon (Mull), 26 October 1990 at Bellanoch (Mid-Argyll) and 9 November 1990 at Torrans (Mull).

Scottish Ospreys generally migrate south or south-west to winter in West Africa (Migration Atlas). The small number of Argyll ringing recoveries conform to this pattern and indicate the timings of migration to and from the area. A chick ringed near Loch Awe was shot and injured near Saumur, south-west France during its first southward migration in early October and another was reported from a typical wintering area for Scottish Ospreys in the Gambia in November of its second year. Its recovery from inside a crocodile was far from typical! A juvenile fitted with a radio tag in Highland Region was tracked by satellite passing Jura and heading for Northern Ireland on 10 September and had reached Portugal by 17 September. Two Ospreys found dead or dying in their second year, on Mull in late April and Colonsay in July, had been ringed as chicks in Speyside and Morayshire. Ospreys spend their first year in southern latitudes (Migration Atlas) so both these were presumed to have succumbed towards the end of their first return journeys to Scotland. Ospreys are Amber-listed, protected under Schedule 1 of the Wildlife and Countryside Act 1981 and listed on Annex 1 of the EC Birds Directive.

Roger Broad

Common Kestrel

Falco tinnunculus

A widespread but uncommon resident; numbers fluctuate from year to year.

Kestrels are confined mainly to extensive areas of rough grassland, where they hunt small mammals (Village 1990). This food varies in abundance from year to year, and so do Kestrel numbers. They are partial migrants, with many Argyll birds moving south when rodent numbers are low during autumn/winter. In contrast, many birds overwinter when food is abundant. Kestrels benefited from the creation of vast areas of open ground through the destruction of native forests over many centuries, with numbers reaching a high level in the 18th and 19th centuries (Historical Atlas). Although many must have been killed by gamekeepers in the 19th and early 20th centuries, overall numbers would probably have been little affected, due to their abundance and high reproductive rates (Newton 1972a). During this period, this was the only raptor that was tolerated by some gamekeepers because of its diet.

Gray noted that during the late 19th century this was "by far the commonest bird of prey in the western counties of Scotland, ranking even more numerous than the Merlin" and that it was "abundant on all the Hebrides". Similarly, Graham said it was "by far the most abundant of the hawk tribe" on Mull during 1852-1870 where it nested on "almost every precipitous sea cliff". He also noted that one pair nested "among the old cathedral ruins of Iona". These comments were reinforced by H&B who considered it the "most abundant bird of prey, not only on the mainland, but also on many of the isles" including Mull, Islay and Jura, and even on Colonsay. They also noted that "it is nowhere perhaps more abundant than amongst the cliffs south of Oban Bay, Kerrera, and the Isles of the Sea". B&R say that "in 1899 Kestrels were breeding on both Coll and Tiree and they still breed on these islands". However, H&B noted that "it is occasionally seen in Tiree in autumn and winter, and still frequents, in limited number, the outlying Treshnish Isles", implying that on the small isles it was scarcer than indicated by B&R. In 1982, Thom claimed it was still the "most widespread and abundant of thc raptors" in Scotland.

Nowadays it is quite a different story. In Argyll, Kestrels are far less abundant than Buzzards, and probably than Sparrowhawks. Their decline was due to a number of factors. The most important was the impoverishment and reduction of suitable foraging habitat by reforestation, grassland 'improvement' (reseeding and draining) and increasing grazing pressure from domesticated herbivores and rising numbers of Red, Sika and Roe Deer. Competition with increasing numbers of Buzzards (for food and nest sites) and Peregrines (for nest sites) may also adversely affect Kestrel numbers.

The change map in the Second Atlas clearly documents the contraction of range in north-west Scotland in the period between the two breeding atlases, with Mid- and North Argyll particularly affected. Even on the islands (Mull, Jura and Islay) there were more losses than gains. Furthermore, BBS data indicate a 31% decline in Scotland during 1994-2004. Recently, there have only been sporadic breeding attempts on Colonsay (ABRs, Argyll Database). For many years there was no confirmed breeding on Coll and Tiree, until one pair bred successfully on Coll in 2004 and 2005 (J. Bowler pers. comm.). Perhaps their scarcity on these small islands is linked to the absence of Field Voles and other small mammals (Corbet & Harris 1991), a fact noted by H&B. The

Common Kestrel hunting at the Highland Mary statue, Dunoon. *Margaret Staley*

size of the breeding population in Argyll is unknown, but the estimated Scottish population is 7,765 pairs (BTO data).

Grassland habitats are particularly important to Kestrels because of the small mammal populations they sustain. In Argyll, the Field Vole is the main prey of Kestrels, although they also take other small mammals, small birds and arthropods, including earthworms (Village 1990). Field voles are most abundant in rough, unimproved grassland subject to light grazing from low densities of sheep, cattle and deer (Charles 1981, Corbet & Harris 1991). In such habitats vole numbers fluctuate considerably from year to year. Areas where trees have been planted recently, and from where large herbivores have been excluded by fencing, are noted for dramatic increases in Field Vole numbers, which can attract high breeding densities of Kestrels, as long as nest sites are available (Village 1990).

There have been no specific studies of Kestrels in Argyll. A few nest sites are monitored annually by the ARSG, but these data are patchy and based on small samples (ABR). The only published estimate of breeding density comes from counts of scarce breeding birds made in two newly-afforested areas of Kintyre in 1983 (Petty 1985). In one area, 1.2 active nesting areas per 10 km square were located, a much lower density than recorded in other newly-afforested areas in Scotland (Village 1990). Kestrels do not build a nest themselves, but are dependent on some existing structure in which they form a scrape for their eggs (Village 1990). The most frequently used site is on a crag ledge, but they also use old tree nests of other birds, such as crows and Buzzards. Nest sites are invariably in open or semi-open habitats or along a forest edge facing out onto open country. They sometimes use suitable nest boxes when natural sites are lacking.

There is concern over the decline of Kestrels throughout the UK, where they are now classed as an amber species (Greenwood *et al.* 2003). In Argyll, their future is closely linked to how grassland habitats are managed. Current trends of increasing stocking densities of sheep and rising deer numbers will have detrimental effects on small mammal densities in these important habitats, and must be a cause of concern. However, without any long-term data on breeding performance and density it is not possible to quantify population trends accurately.

In Europe, northern populations are more migratory than those in the south (Migration Atlas). In Argyll, Kestrels are partial migrants, with dispersal away from nesting areas occurring from July-August. More birds overwinter when Field Vole populations are high in the autumn. Outwith the breeding season, Kestrels occur regularly in areas where they do not breed, including Coll and Tiree (Migration Atlas, Argyll Database). Seven birds ringed in Argyll have been recovered away from the area where they were ringed. All moved in a southerly direction (ESE-SSW). Four were recovered less than 100km from the ringing site while three moved greater distances; 109km to Ireland (Co. Down), 593km to Cornwall (Bude) and 1,260km to France (Dordogne). Six birds recovered in Argyll had been ringed as nestlings elsewhere. One from Sweden was recovered in October at Dalmally (1,762km). The others were all ringed in Scotland and came from Inverness (208km), Perth (113km), Northumbria (230km and 233km), Ardross, Highland Region (153km) and Dumfries & Galloway (114km). The last bird was ringed at Kirkconnel in 1926 and recovered at Inveraray the same year.

Steve J. Petty

Red-footed Falcon

Falco vespertinus

Vagrant.

The Red-footed Falcon, which breeds patchily in eastern Europe and more widely in the former Soviet Union, is an annual visitor to Scotland. Most birds are seen in the Northern Isles and spring occurrences are typical, with fewer than a quarter of the Scottish records being in autumn. The only record of this species in Argyll concerns a female at Macharioch in south Kintyre on 19 August 1990 (BB 88:506; SBR 1990:23).

Tristan ap Rheinallt

Merlin

Falco columbarius

Breeds locally on open moorland and bogs. Widespread on low coastal ground, including farmland, in winter.

The Merlin is a very sparsely distributed breeding bird across mainland Argyll and the larger islands (Table). Merlins are apparently absent as breeding birds from Lismore, Kerrera, Seil, Luing, Gigha, Colonsay and Tiree.

Although little systematic work is currently undertaken on breeding Merlins in Argyll, it is reasonably clear that only a proportion of the known ranges are occupied in any one year. Breeding success is also quite variable, although again data are very limited. In North Mull, one site failed to hatch eggs in 1990 and 1991 yet fledged four young in 2003, whilst another fledged five young in 1991 but appears to have been unoccupied thereafter. Successful ranges in the Oban to Lochgilphead area fledged between two and four young in 1990 and 1991. The generally low population and low rates of occupancy are difficult to explain, bearing in mind the widespread availability of nest sites and a reasonably abundant supply of passerine prey. Nest sites utilised include

Probably no more than 15-20 pairs of Merlins nest in Argyll. *R.J.C. Blewitt*

typical rolling heather moorland on Islay, the tops of small heather-clad crags on Mull, and old crow nests in Rowans on mainland Argyll. Crow nests on the edge of conifer forests have yet to be utilised in Argyll. The diet mainly consists of small moorland passerines especially Meadow Pipit, Skylark and possibly Twite in some locations. Although considered elusive, it seems unlikely that substantial numbers of breeding Merlins remain to be discovered in Argyll. There are probably no more than 30-40 distinct ranges and in any one year the population is unlikely to exceed 15-20 pairs. Argyll Merlins therefore account for perhaps only 2% of the British population.

The First Atlas shows three confirmed, three probable and ten possible breeding squares in mainland Argyll, with six confirmed, three probable and 11 possible on the islands. The Second Atlas shows eight mainland and nine island squares with evidence of breeding. Merlins were present in 14 mainland and nine island squares with no evidence of breeding. There appears to have been relatively little change in overall numbers but a small reduction in known breeding pairs in Knapdale and Kintyre and a slight increase in Cowal and hills of Lorn, south of Oban and on Islay. The decline in Knapdale and Kintyre may reflect increased afforestation whilst increases of proven breeding elsewhere can probably

Location	Number of known ranges	Comment
North Argyll	3	
Oban to Lochgilphead	4	In early 1990s
Knapdale & Kintyre	3-6	
Cowal	2-3	
Coll	6	1986; since much reduced due to moorland fires (Stroud 1989)
Mull	8	
Islay	4-6	
Jura	1-2	
Total	30-40	

Number of known Merlin home ranges in Argyll.

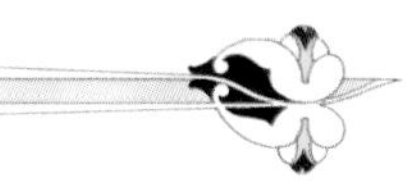

be attributed to increased survey effort.

During autumn and winter Merlins are commonly encountered in low lying coastal and farmland habitats throughout mainland Argyll and the islands. The first migrants tend to arrive on coastal or farmland habitat during early August, the last ones apparently leaving in late April or early May. Some of these birds may be from local breeding areas, whilst others presumably arrive from Iceland where there is a large breeding population. In general, there appears to be an autumn peak followed by lower numbers in mid-winter.

Only two Merlins ringed in Argyll have been recovered outside the county: a chick ringed in Kintyre in 1988 was found dead near Lisburn, Co. Antrim in November 1989. A chick ringed on Coll in 1987 was found dead on Anglesey in April 1989. A chick ringed on Rum in July 1966 was recovered alive on Tiree in September of that year. These recoveries fit the general pattern of mainly southerly movements in autumn (Migration Atlas).

Paul Haworth

Hobby

Falco subbuteo

Rare visitor in spring and autumn.

The Hobby, which is the only British falcon to migrate to winter quarters in Africa, is currently an expanding species in southern Britain. In Scotland, it was until recently regarded as an irregular visitor, but it now breeds in small numbers. The Hobby does not feature in H&B, but B&R describe it as an occasional visitor to Argyll. This statement is presumably based on Walter Stewart's record of one in upper Loch Fyne in September 1920 (Stewart 1938), since there appear to be no other published older reports. After one was shot near Foreland on Islay in 1966 or 1967 and retained in the collection at Islay House (Booth 1975), there was a spate of records in the 1970s and early 1980s. Between 1973 and 1985, a total of 11 birds were reported, from Mull (six), Islay (two), Coll, Kintyre and the Oban area. Since then, there have been just six accepted records, all of single birds: Sanda in May 1988, Dubh Artach in June 1994 (see photograph in ABR 11), Islay in September 1994, Tiree in June 2004, Coll in July 2004 and Islay in May 2005.

The decline since the mid-1980s mirrors a similar decline for Rough-legged Buzzard. Unlike Rough-legged Buzzard, however, there has been an increase over Scotland as a whole during the same period, from about 11 records a year on average in the 1980s to about 18 records a year in the 1990s. Thus the situation in Argyll – where seven of the 11 records in the peak period were reported by just two observers – appears anomalous. As with Rough-legged Buzzard, a more rigorous approach to record assessment in recent years has contributed to the apparent decline.

[Gibson & McWilliam (1959) give a record of an injured bird found in Kintyre on 16 November 1927. This record, which was apparently not published at the time, falls well outside the known period of occurrence of this species in Scotland in autumn. It is therefore considered unacceptable.]

Tristan ap Rheinallt

Gyr Falcon

Falco rusticolus

Vagrant.

This Arctic species once occurred much more commonly in the British Isles than it does now. Scotland accounts for most of the British records, with Shetland being the most favoured location. It is thought that most or all Gyr Falcons occurring here come from Greenland (Thom).

The analysis of older Argyll records is difficult because of apparent errors in dates, which have been repeated by more recent authors. The fact that the different colour morphs were once regarded as different species, then more recently as different races, introduces additional complications. B&R, for instance, dismissed the records of Gray on the basis that they did not distinguish between *F. r. rusticolus* and *F. r. candicans*, which are no longer regarded as valid subspecies. Ten of these older records are regarded as acceptable, on the basis that specimens were procured or, in the case of white-phase birds, the records were published in the ornithological journals of the day (Table 1).

Whilst incomplete, these dates suggest a tendency for records to occur in late winter and spring (February to April), in accordance with the statement of B&R that by far the greatest number of records (of "Greenland Falcon") had occurred in March. There were no more records between the 1920s and the early 1970s. Since the first recent record in 1973, five have been accepted by BBRC (Table 2), although several others are listed by Elliott (1989).

[The following older records are regarded as unacceptable or erroneous: an undated specimen shot on Islay and said to be in Islay House collection (Gray); an immature male killed on Islay in February 1838 (Evans 1994); two more said to have been shot on Islay in 1867 but probably repetition of the above 1867 birds by confusion of dates (Elliott 1989); one seen by P. Robertson in Black Mount Deer Forest, possibly in Argyll, in September 1868 {Gray; H&B; ascribed incorrectly to Islay by Evans (1994) and by Naylor (1996)}; one "fired at" by gamekeeper James Brown on Islay in winter 1888, but with no evidence of a specimen (H&B); one seen by Austin Mackenzie in January 1907, location uncertain {ASNH 1907 report:198; The Field 109 (1907):149}; and several sight records, all undated, from The Laggan in Kintyre during 1908-1919 (Gibson & McWilliam 1959)].

Tristan ap Rheinallt

Table 1. Records of Gyr Falcons in Argyll, 1862-1913.

Date	Location	Morph	Comment	Reference
Autumn 1862	Kildalton	White	Male shot by P. Mackenzie, Kildalton gamekeeper, exhibited to Glasgow Nat. Hist. Soc.	Gray, H&B where season given incorrectly as summer
Sep 1866	Glendaruel	Grey	Caught in pole trap but then "lost"; said to have been identified "beyond doubt"	Gray, H&B where date given incorrectly as 1876
1867	Islay	White	Procured, per Mr Elwes	Gray, H&B where date given (incorrectly?) as 1866
Early Mar 1867	Kilchoman Glen	Grey	Trapped by G. McTaggart	H&B
Apr 1876	Islay	Grey	Shot; specimen later owned by E. Crawshay	H&B; date given as 1867 by Booth (1975)
20 Apr 1876	Kintyre?	White	Trapped and sent alive to Clifton Zoological Gardens	McWilliam, Gibson & McWilliam (1959), Zoologist (2nd Series) 11 (1876): 4954
6 Feb 1901	Tiree	White	Seen chasing a Lapwing, which saved its life by going into the water	SN 1914:43
15 Feb 1903	Tiree	White	Struck down a Lapwing	ASNH 1904:143, 211
Winter 1910	The Laggan	Grey	Immature female shot, mounted by R. Ward	Gibson & McWilliam 1959, The Field 140 (1922): 839
31 Mar 1913	Colonsay	White	Adult female caught in rabbit trap, specimen retained in RSM	SN 1913:116, S N Extra Publication No. 3:13

Table 2. Records of Gyr Falcons in Argyll, 1973-2002.

Date	Location	Morph	Comment	Reference
27 - 31 Dec 1973	Tiree	?	Record fully assessed but details no longer available	BB 67:318, BB 87:520
22 Dec 1978 - 2 Mar 1979	Easter Ellister & Loch Tallant	White	Female; found dead of alphachlorate poisoning at Dun Nosebridge on 19 March	BB 73:503, SBR 1979:23
17 Apr 1990	Loch Gruinart & Sunderland	White	First-summer male	BB 86:474
3 Nov 1991	Port Charlotte	White	Juvenile female, taken into care having flown into a window. Released the next day but found dead MacArthur's Head on 10 November; skin at RSM	BB 86:474, SBR 1991:26, ABR 8:36
22 - 24 Feb 2002	Loch Gruinart & Loch Gorm	White	Adult	BB 96:563

Peregrine Falcon

Falco peregrinus

Widespread but scarce breeding species in all areas of Argyll, with about 70 occupied territories in 2005. Found throughout the year in most areas.

Ratcliffe (1993) documents the long association of man and Peregrines. The Peregrine's resilience to recover after successive onslaughts is well known. The earliest records of Argyll nest sites result from early falconry interests and were reported from Coll, Tiree and Colonsay in 1343 and Treshnish Isles in 1549 (Ritchie 1920). During the 18th and 19th centuries Peregrines figured in the records of sporting estates during an era of persecution. Ratcliffe referred to one keeper near Lochgoilhead who killed one or both Peregrines at a breeding haunt in 17 successive years. Gray noted that considerable numbers of Peregrines were sent to the 'bird stuffers' of Glasgow, from the mountainous districts at the head of Loch Long, both to the north and west, and other parts of Argyll. Despite such widespread killing, Gray found that the Peregrine maintained a good hold and, in the Inner Isles and mainland of Argyll, was found commonly in pairs, each frequenting a radius of *c.* 10km. It was described as about equally distributed on Islay, Mull and Jura. Graham reported that it was also frequently seen on Iona, although no nest had ever been found there. Also at this period, it is likely that some sites suffered the repeated attentions of egg collectors. During 1940-46, Peregrines were open to legal destruction in certain parts of the UK including Argyll. These measures were to protect carrier pigeons released by airmen who had ditched when on sea patrol around the north and west coasts. No figures exist for the numbers killed, but Ratcliffe (1993) considered any losses were local and temporary.

After 1950, with the introduction and use of synthetic

organic pesticides, the Peregrine population tipped into steep decline. With the exception of some parts of the Scottish Highlands, all areas of the UK were affected. By 1963 the UK population had declined to its lowest point, 44% below its pre-crash level. Decline was evident in Argyll in 1961 with coastal Peregrines showing greater declines than those inland but, compared with other areas, Argyll was lightly affected. Following the introduction of measures to curb the use of the most harmful substances, national surveys carried out at ten-yearly intervals charted a remarkable recovery (Ratcliffe 1984, Crick & Ratcliffe 1995, Banks *et al.* 2002). Numbers bounced back throughout the UK in all but some coastal areas. By 1991, the UK population had risen to levels that were higher than previously recorded, although perhaps the only part of Argyll to show an elevated population was Cowal. Here, annual monitoring by Argyll Raptor Study Group found that, as well as pairs in the usual places, crags at two sites, previously considered to be alternative nest sites, were also occupied by singles or pairs. However, any elevated level appears only to have been short-lived. By 2002 numbers in Cowal were a little lower than in 1991. Despite the new sites in Cowal and another six identified in other, well-worked parts of Argyll, the results of the most recent survey in 2002 showed a substantial overall reduction in the number of occupied sites (Table 1). Future monitoring will be needed to determine whether this latest decline in Argyll persists and becomes of real concern.

Numbers of nest locations known in different parts of Argyll were given by Ratcliffe (1993). These are updated to 2002 and have been revised to conform to the Argyll recording areas (Table 1). By 2002, 123 territories had been recognised in Argyll and all, bar three, were visited during this national survey. While a few of the more remote locations received only a single visit, most were checked two or three times. During 2003-04, with the identification of an additional pair on Coll and an increase to four territories on Colonsay and Oransay, the total number of territories recognised in Argyll has risen to 125.

Argyll Peregrines generally form a scrape for their nests on suitable ledges on inland and coastal cliffs. Many such sites are traditional with a long history of use, often with alternative nest sites nearby. They also use the disused nests of crag-nesting Raven and occasionally Golden Eagle. There is generally no shortage of suitable natural crags for nesting

Although relatively little affected by pesticides in the 1960s, Argyll's Peregrine population has declined since 1990. *R.J.C. Blewitt*

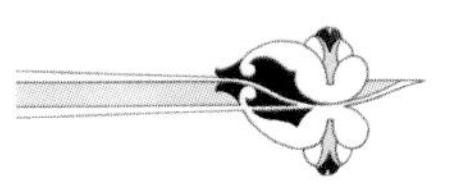

pairs in Argyll, so it is unsurprising that perhaps only one or two disused quarries have been regularly used by Peregrines. One pair regularly nests on a worked-out cliff in an active quarry. To date, examples of other nest sites found in very small numbers elsewhere in UK, including buildings, disused tree-nests of other species and the ground, have not been recorded in Argyll. However, a non-breeding pair on Islay behaved territorially in early spring for three successive years (1994-6) where their best choice of nest site would have been little more than a heathery slope on the ground.

A summary of breeding data (Table 2), collected from sites across Argyll by the Argyll Raptor Study Group, masks more local variation. Breeding data from systematic monitoring on Cowal, where many sites have been monitored annually, shows a wide variation, both in the number of breeding attempts and the breeding success between years. For example, in 1986 some pairs apparently did not attempt to breed during extended inclement spring weather; 1998 was particularly good with an average of 2.7 young per successful pair and 1999 was exceptionally poor with only two successful breeding attempts averaging 1.54 young per successful pair. During the 1980s and early 1990s there was evidence of interference and robbery of eggs or young at up to two or three sites in some years, but this has not been proven since 1995.

Most British Peregrines winter below 400m asl, but many bleak hill breeding sites are still held during winter, at least for roosting (Ratcliffe, in Lack 1986). In Argyll, Peregrines are apparently widespread, especially on lower ground, around the coasts and islands throughout the winter months. However, there is scant information from any Argyll nesting crags at this season. Most nest crags are below 400m asl and have easy access to islands and lower ground where there appears to be no shortage of prey during winter. Whether the few, more land-locked upland sites, especially in the north-east of the county, are vacated during the winter is not known. Such movement has been suggested for birds in north-west Scotland to account for their apparent winter scarcity and fits with the idea that birds may leave these less hospitable areas as prey declines in the autumn (Ratcliffe, in Lack 1986). Occasional birds are noticed when they temporarily roost elsewhere, including one that joined a communal Raven roost near Tobermory in February 1986 and a female that roosted on a church in Campbeltown in January 1989.

British Peregrines are not considered regular migrants, although there may be local movements by young and some adults away from high ground sites during winter. Birds that have dispersed from breeding sites, all originally ringed as chicks, have produced 27 recoveries involving Argyll. Eight were reported within one year of ringing and the oldest was ten years old. There were 11 movements less than 50km, nine travelled up to 100km and seven moved further, the longest movement being 349km. Such dispersal is similar to movements elsewhere in the UK for which Ratcliffe (in Migration Atlas) calculated a median distance of 45km. The majority of movements are within Argyll and among the 11 in or out of the county, only one from Benbecula, Outer Hebrides, originates from north or west of Argyll. The rest involve locations south and east of Argyll and include Central Region (one), Lothian (one), Ayrshire and Arran (six), Dumfries and Galloway (four), Co Mayo, Republic of Ireland (one) and Cumbria (one).

Area	No. checked in 1991	No. occupied in 1991	No. checked in 2002	No. occupied in 2002
Coll	2	1	2	2
Tiree	1	1	1	1
Mull & satellites	18	11	18	6
Colonsay & Oronsay	1	1	3	2
Jura	7	7	7	4
Islay	19	16	18	12
Kintyre & Gigha	16	13	16	10
Mid-Argyll	21	17	23	11
North Argyll	6	4	10	6
Cowal	18	17	22	15
Total	109	88	120	69

Table 1. Number of occupied Peregrine territories (singles or pairs) in Argyll in 1991 and 2002.

Year	Sample size	Failed pairs	Successful pairs	Young fledged	No. fledged per breeding pair	No. fledged per successful pair
1980-89	88	25	63	128	1.45	2.03
1990-99	87	20	67	145	1.66	2.16
2000-04	59	18	41	75	1.27	1.82
Total	234	58	171	348	1.48	2.03

Table 2. Breeding success of Peregrines in Argyll, 1980-2004.

Ratcliffe (1993) describes Peregrine feeding strategies and gives a comprehensive list of prey species. Coastal Peregrines undoubtedly take a range of seabird species but there are few locations in Argyll where seabirds occur in sufficient number to provide the majority of prey taken during the breeding season. In recent years, this has only been noted on Colonsay where a pair apparently concentrated on Kittiwakes. Observations at Argyll seawatch sites have documented opportunistic behaviour involving unusual prey species, some apparently taken from the sea. These included Leach's Storm-petrels driven close inshore by bad weather at Machrihanish in September 1990. An adult, having caught one offshore, passed it to an accompanying juvenile. Subsequently, two juveniles each killed a Leach's Storm-petrel on 19 September. An adult was again seen hunting Leach's Storm-petrels here in September 1994. On Islay in 1993 a young Peregrine was seen carrying a Little Auk on 12 December, and on 31 December an adult lifted another Little Auk from the sea.

Peregrines are Amber-listed, protected under Schedule 1 of the Wildlife and Countryside Act 1981 and listed on Annex 1 of the EC Birds Directive.

Roger Broad

Most of Argyll's raptor species can be found on Mull. This dedicated facility for viewing White-tailed Eagles at Loch Frisa was provided through a partnership between RSPB, Scottish Natural Heritage, Mull and Iona Community Trust and Forestry Commission Scotland. *Iain Erskine*

Several raptor species, including Peregrine, Merlin and Golden Eagle, occur at low density in the uplands of North Argyll. This is Loch Etive, looking north-east to Ben Starav and Glen Coe. *Iain Erskine*

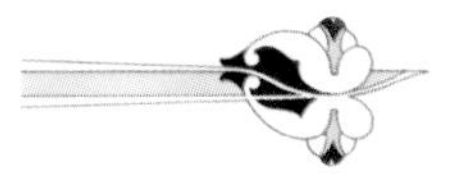

Water Rail

Rallus aquaticus

A secretive and under-recorded resident found at low density on the mainland but in larger numbers on the outer islands. In winter its numbers are thought to increase by immigration.

Normally solitary or forming small groups, Water Rails seldom stray from their habitat of dense aquatic plants. They are much more often heard than seen and an observer is lucky to catch sight of one as it flies across a road or runs between thickets. However, when the watersides are frozen, Water Rails are driven into the open to seek alternative food.

Water Rails breeding in the British Isles are almost certainly all resident. However, many birds from Europe migrate to Britain for the winter, presumably to escape the frozen winters; thus birds ringed while wintering in Britain have been recovered on the continent, mainly in Germany. The race found over most of the British Isles is *R. a. aquaticus*, which breeds through most of Europe. The Icelandic race *hibernans* has been recorded on passage on some Scottish islands (Migration Atlas).

H&B mention it on Tiree in winter ("often seen by the snipe shooter") and during a fall of migrants on the Rinns of Islay in November 1888. B&R record that "a few" summered and bred on Tiree in 1913, that they were fairly numerous in winter on Islay and Tiree, that they occurred on Mull and that they were frequent at lighthouses during passage movements along both coasts in September-November and February-May. Thom recorded possible breeding on Tiree in 1977 and on Colonsay in 1983. As recently as 1984 the County Recorder had received no proof of breeding in Argyll and the introductory sentence to the species in the Systematic List was "Rare migrant and winter visitor. Some may stay to breed". Most breeding season records involve calling males or pairs in suitable habitat and successful breeding has been confirmed only twice: a chick caught by a cat at Cornaigmore on Tiree on 1 July 2000 was released unharmed; and an adult with at least two chicks was seen at Jura Manse on Jura on 5 July 2006 (ABR, Argyll Database).

The Second Atlas showed Water Rails to be present over much of England and parts of Scotland, especially in the Borders and the Clyde Valley, but absent from most of the north-west Highlands. They were found in ten of the 10-km squares of Argyll (four on Islay, three in Mid-Argyll and one each on Colonsay, Gigha and Mull). In only four of these ten squares was there evidence of breeding (two in Mid-Argyll and one each on Islay and Colonsay). The highest density was at Loch Gruinart. Notably, the species was not recorded on Coll and Tiree.

Work since then has shown that Water Rails may occur at fairly high density throughout the year at the most favoured sites, especially on Islay (one to four calling males each year at RSPB Loch Gruinart during 1989-2002) and on Tiree (1-10 sites on the island during many of the years 1985-2000 and nine in 2004) (ABR). On Colonsay, six calling birds were recorded at two sites in 1992 but since then counts have

The Water Rail is a secretive bird that has probably been under-recorded in the past. *Philip Kirkham*

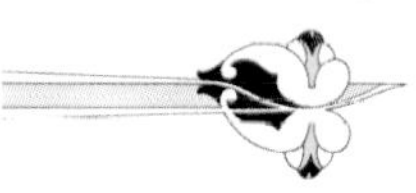

been lower. On Coll, one or two pairs breed annually on the RSPB reserve and another three or four pairs elsewhere on the island. Three or four calling birds were heard on Iona in June 2001 and on Gigha in October 2002, and small numbers are regularly heard or seen at several sites on Mull and the mainland (ABR).

A more intensive survey was undertaken by Clive McKay on Islay in 2003. The main habitat there is *Phragmites* swamp but Water Rails also occupy swamps dominated by Bog Bean and *Carex* spp. McKay considered that favourable features of islands such as Islay and Tiree are abundant small lochs, reedy areas, mires and overgrown ditches, all of which are less frequent on the mainland. Using responses to taped calls, he detected eight pairs and four singles (probable pairs) at RSPB Loch Gruinart and one pair just outside the reserve. He concluded that Water Rails were widespread on Islay and estimated the island total to be 50-100 pairs. In June 2006, 19 territories were counted on Colonsay by the same method (David Jardine pers. comm.).

Numbers wintering at these sites are often higher than in summer, suggesting some immigration. Reflecting the bird's sedentary nature, the Winter Atlas showed little difference in distribution from the Second Atlas, except that a few more coastal squares were occupied in winter. Birds were found in only 12 squares in Argyll, including five squares on Islay, three on Mull, and one each in Coll, Mid-Argyll, Kintyre (Machrihanish) and Gigha. All records were of single birds except two at Machrihanish. Again, closer study suggests that these were underestimates. For example, three or four winter on Coll RSPB reserve and several more elsewhere on the island (up to six at Cliad).

Water Rails sometimes enter gardens to feed or to join hens and ducks at feeding time. This happened on Mull in the winters of 1981/82 and 2002/03 and on Tiree in August 2002 (ABR). Water Rails sometimes enter waterside traps set for mink, as one did at Taynish NNR in December 1997 (ABR), and another at Crinan in about 1990 (per JCAC). One was ringed at South Shian on 2 December 1994 and one was shot on Gigha on 29 January 1987 (ABR). Because of their scuttling habit and reluctance to fly, Water Rails are often killed by cats (one at Portnahaven, Islay, in September or October 1995; one at Kintaline Mill, Benderloch, in November 2003, and at least two on Tiree in March 2002 and February 2003: Argyll Database). This echoes a much earlier account from Iona where, in deep snow on 9 January 1852, Graham's dog chased and caught the first Water Rail Graham had seen on the island. He kept the unharmed bird in a box and fed it on chopped meat, which it took from his hand. It became so tame that, according to his friend Robert Gray, it was "amusing to see it unconcernedly stalking through the apartments, picking its steps enquiringly among the dogs and cats basking on the hearthrug, and with as much apparent freedom as if it were merely reconnoitring the banks of a duck pond".

Clive Craik

Spotted Crake

Porzana porzana

Rare and irregular summer visitor, also recorded as an autumn migrant in the past. Most recent records come from the islands, especially Islay. Breeding may occur.

The Spotted Crake, a bird of extensive wetlands, is notoriously secretive and normally attracts attention only because of its loud, characteristic song. As a breeding bird, it appears to be very thinly scattered in the British Isles, with Scotland accounting for a substantial proportion of recent records (Second Atlas). The British breeding population is thought to number only about 75 to 80 pairs (Gilbert 2002). For most birdwatchers, the only opportunity to observe this species comes when autumn migrants, perhaps from Scandinavia or elsewhere in northern Europe, stop off on their way to their African wintering grounds.

Prior to the major wetland drainage activities that took place in the 18th and 19th centuries, the Spotted Crake is thought to have bred much more widely in Britain (Second Atlas), though it seems to have been at best uncommon in western Scotland (B&R). Gray knew of no occurrences in Argyll, and the only records quoted by H&B were a bird shot on Lismore in September 1870 and another at Ederline, Loch Awe, in autumn 1891. In mid-August 1893 a young bird was shot in a marsh by the River Add (ASNH 1896:60, McWilliam), and one was shot in Foreland Marsh on Islay on 29 September 1896 (ASNH 1897:45,148). One was also killed at Dubh Artach in August 1900 (ASNH 1901:140).

Thus, around the start of the 20th century, it appears that the Spotted Crake occurred in Argyll only as an autumn migrant. This may have remained the case until recently, although it is possible that territorial birds were overlooked. The first published record of a singing bird involved one at Glen Lonan in Mid-Argyll on 1 and 2 July 1974 (SB 8:422). No Spotted Crakes were recorded in Argyll during work for the First Atlas, and the next summer record was of a bird at Dalintober, Benderloch, for two weeks in June 1982 (ABR 1:37). The Second Atlas shows occupancy of a single 10-km square in north-west Islay, where a bird was singing at Loch Gorm for around a week in June 1989 (SBR 1989:18, ABR 6:28). A singing bird was also present at Taynish for a month from 10 June 1990 (SBR 1990:26, ABR 7:26), although this record is absent from the Atlas.

From 1991 to 2006, birds were heard singing or, more rarely, seen in every year except 1992 and 1998. All the records during this 16-year period came from four islands: Islay, Coll, Colonsay and Tiree. On Islay, birds were recorded in 10 of the 16 years, with a maximum of three singing males in the Gruinart area in May 1996 (SBR 1996:26, ABR 13:45). Spotted Crakes were reported from Coll in 1995, 1999 and every year from 2002 to 2006. Singles also occurred on Colonsay in 1994 and Tiree in 2002. From 30 May until

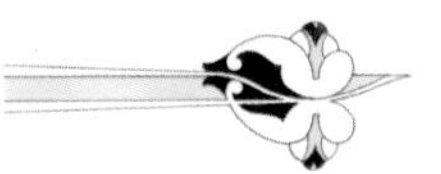

at least 7 July 2006 a bird sang continuously at night at a site on Tiree. All but two of the dated records fell between late April and the end of June, the earliest being 27 April 1999 at Loch Gruinart (ABR 16:49).

Loch Gruinart RSPB Reserve has had the most records in recent years. In 1993, birds were calling into July and a juvenile was sighted on 10 September (SBR 1993:23, ABR 10:40). This strongly suggests that breeding occurred, although the possibility that the September bird was a migrant cannot be ruled out.

Other than this individual, there appear to be no recent autumn records. However, on Colonsay one was seen crossing the road between Mid Loch Fada and East Loch Fada on 16 December 1976 (SB 10:91, Jardine *et al.* 1986), and on Islay an even later bird was reported from Bridgend on 31 December 1973 (SB 9:235). These are two of several Scottish records in November and December (B&R, Thom).

Tristan ap Rheinallt

Sora

Porzana carolina

Vagrant.

This transatlantic vagrant has been recorded in Argyll on one occasion, on Tiree in 1901 (Gunnis 1902, The Field 98 (1901): 907).

Gunnis (1902) wrote: "On 25 October last my brother-in-law, Mr E. Lort Phillipps, while shooting snipe with me in Ronnach bog, at the west end of the Island of Tiree, Inner Hebrides, obtained a specimen of the Carolina Crake. This bird was examined by Dr. Bowdler Sharpe, and was exhibited by Mr. Lort Phillipps at the meeting of the British Ornithologists' Club on 26 November last. It was a young male which had completed its first autumn moult, and was very fat – indeed I have seldom seen a bird in better condition, showing that it had been for some time either on the Island, or in some other locality well suited for its feeding habits. When on the wing it resembled a diminutive Landrail, with its laboured flight and hanging legs."

The location, Ronnach bog (=Runnach Beag), does not appear on today's Ordnance Survey maps but is situated at Ceann a' Mhara (J. Bowler pers. comm.).

This was the third British record. The species has since been recorded in Scotland on two further occasions, in Shetland and the Western Isles.

Tristan ap Rheinallt

The RSPB reserve at Loch Gruinart on Islay is probably the best place to find Spotted Crakes in Argyll. *Margaret Staley*

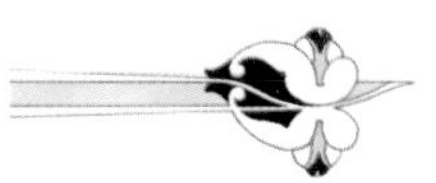

Little Crake

Porzana parva

Vagrant.

The only record of this species in Argyll concerns a bird caught near Loch Scammadale in Mid-Argyll on 29 September 1911 (SN Extra Publication No. 1, pp. 70, B&R). It was the third of five Scottish records to date of this rare visitor from the Continent.

Tristan ap Rheinallt

Corn Crake

Crex crex

A summer visitor now mainly confined to Coll and Tiree where long-term decline in numbers has been reversed following recent conservation action. There were at least 654 calling males in Argyll in 2006.

Historically, Corn Crakes were once common and widespread and Gray thought that perhaps no Scottish bird was more generally distributed. The population in Britain and Ireland in the 19th century must have been many tens of thousands. By the late 1930s its decline was already well advanced, being absent from much of England, South Wales and large parts of Scotland (Norris 1947). By 1969-71 the species was only common in parts of Ireland and western Scottish islands and the total population of Britain and Ireland was in the order of 2,640 calling males (Cadbury 1980). Where they remained most common, Sharrock (1976) estimated that some 10-km squares held 20-30 calling males. Within the next twenty years withdrawal towards the north and west continued apace. The Argyll mainland was almost deserted and the remaining strongholds became confined largely to the Hebridean islands. Regular breeding ceased in Northern Ireland in 1988 (Second Atlas) and total extinction from Great Britain seemed a real possibility. This continuing long-term decline was considered largely a result of changes in agriculture. Mechanisation, intensification and the development of new strains of grasses allowed faster and earlier mowing of crops and increasing conversion of hay to silage. Together these resulted in the destruction of eggs, chicks and adults and the deterioration and loss of suitable Corn Crake habitat. The decline has been closely correlated with average grass mowing dates. The most rapid declines occurred where the mean mowing date was earlier than late July-early August (Green & Williams 1994). Further habitat loss resulted from the conversion of hay meadows to permanent sheep pasture and from the abandonment of large areas to "sheep ranching".

Corn Crakes reached their lowest point in Argyll in 1993 with 158 calling males (Table). Conservation measures, implemented largely since the early 1990s, began to stem the decline and reverse the downward trend in numbers. The results of national surveys (Cadbury 1980, Hudson *et al.* 1990, Green 1995) emphasised the importance of the Argyll islands, which have held an increasingly large proportion of the population in Great Britain (Table). Recent increases in the Argyll population have been greater than in other Scottish strongholds where similar conservation measures are being implemented. The increase of almost 50% in Argyll between 2003 and 2004 was exceptional, numbers jumped from 345 to 511 and density reached a recent high on parts of Tiree with 182 calling males in one 10-km square.

On Tiree, although historical numbers would have been higher, Cadbury (1980) found Corn Crakes fluctuated from 51-100 during 1969-87 and he concluded that there was no recent sign of decline. He associated this with plenty of grass grown to feed over-wintered cattle, much not cut until late July. Almost everywhere else in Argyll, field sizes were larger and more easily adapted away from the traditional farming practices associated with late cutting of grass. There is less historical information for Coll, but numbers had declined to less than 20 before the RSPB established a reserve for Corn Crakes and began a substantial reversal in numbers that now extends to the whole island (Table). Since 1988 there have

Number of calling male Corn Crakes in Argyll, 1978/79 - 2006, during the survey period of 20 May - 10 July.

	1978-9	1988	1993	1998	2003	2004	2005	2006
Coll	28	20	20	40	90	134	159	171
Tiree	85	101	111	136	184	262	310	316
Mull (main island only)	1	3	1	2	0	3	5	7
Iona	25*	3	4	12	24	24	29	39
Colonsay & Oronsay	22	18	10	14	32	46	53	62
Islay	23	19	9	4	10	31	52	59
Other areas Argyll	3	5	3	3	5	11	6	?
Argyll total	**187**	**169**	**158**	**211**	**345**	**511**	**614**	**654+**
Total GB and Isle of Man	723	574	480	589	830	1066	1107	1145
Argyll total as % of Total GB and Isle of Man	26%	29%	33%	36%	42%	48%	55%	c.57%

*Figure for 1977.

By 2006, the number of calling male Corn Crakes in Argyll had increased to at least 654, including 39 on Iona. *Margaret Staley*

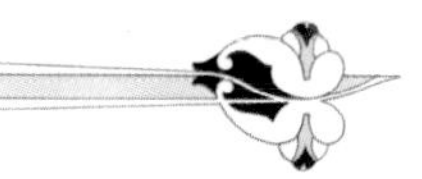

been few reports from mainland Mull and rarely have birds returned to the same site in successive years. One or two additional birds have been reported from the nearby islands of Gometra, Staffa and Little Colonsay since 2000. The Treshnish Isles have attracted 1-2 birds in most years since 1993, but there were nine in 1999 and, while the majority have been on Lunga, others have been on Fladda and Cairn na Burgh. The latter may well have been the sort of site that Gray had in mind when he found them widespread "on all the rocky islets on the west coast". Iona appears not to have completely lost its Corn Crakes, although numbers fell to 3-4 for several years. A steady recovery in the last decade followed the onset of conservation measures. The first suggestion of overspill may have been seen in 2004 when there were three reports from the adjacent Ross of Mull.

Records reviewed by Jardine *et al.* (1986) for Colonsay and Oronsay indicate the height from which numbers have fallen since 1947, when G.L. Sandeman suggested that there were at least a pair or two to every field in cultivated areas. Following the establishment of an RSPB reserve principally for Corn Crakes on Oronsay, there have been signs of a recovery across the whole island (Table). On Islay, Meiklejohn & Stanford (1954) heard birds calling in 31 different fields in June; Booth (1981) reported that the first machines for cutting silage were introduced to the island in the early 1960s, spraying of herbicides on corn and grass began in the mid 1970s and a serious decline in Corn Crakes was reported in 1978 and 1979. Stroud (1986), using a combination of survey and local information, compiled a list of 82 sites on Islay where Corn Crakes had been reliably heard since 1960. Only 35% were occupied in 1985 when Stroud located 20-29 calling males. The decline appeared to be least at Portnahaven where crofting and traditional farming practices were largely unchanged. Elsewhere, the greatest losses coincided with the switch from hay to silage production made possible by the introduction of new machinery.

The last records of Corn Crakes returning annually to Jura and Gigha were in 1988. The recent upturn in numbers has not yet reached Jura and, despite one or two records on Gigha since 2000, annual occupation has not been re-established. The same applies for the whole of mainland Argyll. Very recent records, for example on Lismore in 2001 and on Easdale Island in 2004, promise range extension but can only be viewed as tentative, unless birds return in successive years. Elsewhere on the mainland since 1978-79, reports have averaged not more than one or two per year. In North Argyll the most recent records were clustered around Oban, Connel and Achnacreemore until 1991. Tayvallich, Taynish, Kilmelford and Balvicar provided the most recent reports from Mid-Argyll until 1994, although the McCormaig Islands, off the mouth of Loch Sween, have attracted 1-2 in several years since 1993. In Cowal, the last record was Glendaruel in 1993 with others near Tighnabruaich. Records from Kintyre, with the exception of one at Tarbert, were clustered south of Campbeltown until the latest in 1997, but some of these are late season records and probably include some post-breeding dispersal or early migrants.

The first Corn Crakes generally arrive in Argyll in late April-early May, although the earliest recent spring arrival is 17 April. The majority arrive from early May and males begin calling, persistently at night and occasionally during the day, from their arrival through until July. Systematic surveys are carried out in suitable weather to coincide with the peak night time calling period, between midnight and three o'clock from 20 May-10 July. The proportion of males and females in a population is not well known and census figures are given as calling males. When the female begins to incubate, its mate takes no further part in this breeding attempt and continues calling to attract a further female. Females may attempt to rear two or more broods and can be successively polyandrous. First broods are deserted at 10-15 days old and chicks then have to fend for themselves until they are capable of flight at around 5-6 weeks. Young reared from early clutches are probably capable of migration by late July. When suitable conditions prevail, late broods with small young have been seen in early September, and in 2004, an adult with four attendant middle-sized chicks on 24 September was exceptionally late. Chicks from later broods, and adults when they have completed their moult, depart in September-October. The dispersal of some birds from mid-July probably explains the occurrence at new localities at this time of year.

Research carried out by RSPB has identified five critical elements for the survival of breeding Corn Crakes. On arrival in spring they require (1) suitable vegetation, e.g. nettles, irises and umbellifers, sufficiently tall to give them refuge in early cover, (2) adjacent extensive areas of ungrazed meadow (hay or silage) of sufficient height to provide cover for second clutches, and through which they can move freely to feed and yet remain concealed. These meadows need to be (3) mown or grazed after 1 August, and preferably later, to allow second broods to be reared and (4) hay and silage should be cut slowly and in such a way that young birds and adults do not become trapped and killed by machinery. The final element (5) is tall vegetation to provide late cover, where Corn Crakes can remain concealed and feed after adjacent hay and silage fields have been cut or grazed. A variety of measures have been progressively implemented in the Argyll islands to provide these critical elements since the early 1990s. These have included habitat development and management on existing and new RSPB reserves, and management agreements with co-operating farmers and crofters. This has reversed the downward trend on the Argyll islands and led to some large increases in numbers (Table). Re-colonisation of other parts will perhaps be slower, given the Corn Crakes' faithfulness to natal areas and the expectation that re-colonists on the mainland will rarely be able to avoid intensive agricultural practices.

In addition to these threats from agricultural change and intensification, other perils account for several Corn Crakes each year in the Argyll islands. They fall prey to Buzzards on

Tiree, where remains have occasionally been found in nests. Cats, both domestic and feral, account for several Corn Crakes each year, and a similar number die on the roads. Unfortunately, there have been reports of prime breeding habitat being irresponsibly trampled by bird watchers searching for birds at a couple of Argyll sites.

Both adult and juvenile Corn Crakes have been ringed on Tiree and Coll. Recaptures in subsequent years suggest that the majority are site-faithful and there have been no distant inter-island movements. However, a chick ringed on Canna in 1980 was caught and released on Islay in June 1981. Corn Crakes are generally short-lived with few surviving to breed for more than one year. The oldest known is an adult trapped on Tiree in 1996 and found dead in 1998.

B&R refer to historical records of Corn Crakes wintering in the UK. Thom traced the latest date to 3 November, but on Tiree, one was seen well on 1 March 2006 and several people heard a male calling at night on 3 March 2007. It is presumed that these were over-wintering birds (J. Bowler pers. comm.). The onset of migration towards winter quarters may be protracted, with some reaching continental Europe before later broods are fledged. A juvenile recovered 19 days after ringing and an adult, both from Argyll, were shot in September on migration through Tarn and Dordogne in west France. These indicate the route of Scottish Corn Crakes through France and Morocco and across the Sahara to wintering areas that are imprecisely known but are thought to be in the Tanzania-Mozambique area of south-east Africa (Migration Atlas). Hazards on migration and in the wintering quarters are thought to have played only a minor part in the decline (Stowe & Becker 1992).

Roger Broad

Moorhen

Gallinula chloropus

This resident and highly sedentary species is sparsely distributed in the county, usually by freshwater ponds or slowly running streams, always near suitably tall and dense vegetation.

The BTO Atlases, both breeding and winter, show the Moorhen to be widely distributed over lowland Britain but with a striking absence from north-west Scotland. Argyll lies on the fringe of its distribution. The Second Atlas found the species present in 16% of 10-km squares in Argyll, but the relatively small number of records in ABR implies that its density within these squares is low. Most ponds and streams in the county are acid and oligotrophic, and a lack of lush waterside cover alongside productive, eutrophic water may well limit its distribution. A survey of 493 freshwater lochs and lochans in May-June 1985 did not find a single Moorhen (ABR). It is very scarce in brackish or marine habitats, and the report of breeding "on an island in Loch Fyne" in 1983 was unusual (ABR).

Graham recorded that two pairs bred regularly on a small marshy pond on Iona, while H&B said that it was "often seen by the snipe-shooter" on Tiree and likely to be breeding there. Unless its range and numbers have since decreased, the assertion by Gray that the Moorhen was "abundant everywhere on the western mainland" was too general. Commenting on its scarcity from Argyll northwards, B&R recorded that it was breeding on Islay "in some numbers" and that it bred on Gigha in 1949, on Colonsay in 1939 and 1942, and on "all the reedy marshes on Tiree". They stated that it was uncommon on Mull, and that a single pair bred on Coll in 1937-38. Thom, while also noting that the species was "uncommon and very local" in Argyll, believed that it had "recently ceased to nest on Colonsay" (but see below).

Many authors have mentioned the reluctance of Moorhens to move far from their favoured haunts, even in freezing weather, so that populations may fall considerably after severe winters. However, numbers are usually restored rapidly, as one-third of pairs attempt a second brood each year, and a

The Moorhen is sparsely distributed in Argyll, close to the northern limit of its British range. *David Palmar*

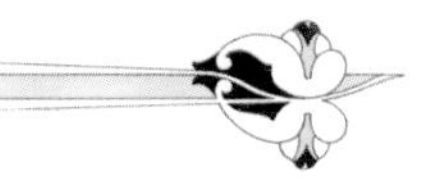

small number produce third and even fourth broods (Second Atlas). Indeed, a pair with three successive broods occurred at Easter Ellister in 1999; and a double-brooded pair was recorded at Silvercraigs, near Lochgilphead, in 2001 (ABR).

Despite the low overall density in Argyll, there are several sites that seem to hold the species permanently, or almost so, and breeding probably takes place regularly at most of these. The highest numbers have been at Loch Gruinart RSPB Reserve (17 birds on 28 November 1984 and 17 in January 1986; eight broods in 1993; six pairs bred in 1995; 5-6 pairs bred in 2000; and four pairs with at least one brood in 2001) (ABR). For the years 1997-2002, the Argyll Database holds records from some 19 sites in Mid-Argyll, 17 sites on Tiree, 12 on Islay, seven in Kintyre (including Gigha), three in North Argyll (including Lismore), three on Mull, two on Colonsay, one on Coll and none from Cowal or Jura (although some of these figures may reflect the distribution of recorders as much as of Moorhens). Birds were reported fairly regularly on Colonsay up to 1997 (especially from Loch Fada and Ardskenish), but none was recorded on the mainland of Colonsay during 1998-2002. One in May 2000 was "the first on Oronsay since the 1970s", a single bird was on Colonsay through the summer of 2004, and three were on East Loch Fada in March 2005. A record of an adult with three juveniles near Breachacha in June and September 2002 was the first report from Coll for many years, and a survey of the whole of Coll in 2004 found a minimum of four pairs. Only one record was traced from Cowal (two at Kilbride Bay on 26 March 1994) (ABR). The most recent record from Jura seems to be that of a single bird on the Lussa River in February 1975 (M.A. Ogilvie pers. comm.).

Ringing has shown that there is some migration into Britain from the Netherlands, Denmark, Germany and France, but almost all recoveries have been in south-east England, the short sea crossing reflecting the reluctance to fly (Migration Atlas). There have been no recoveries of any ringed birds either to or from Argyll but few, if any, have been ringed here.

Clive Craik

Common Coot

Fulica atra

Irregular breeder and scarce winter visitor, the only regular wintering flock being at Loch Bhasapol on Tiree. More numerous and widespread in the past.

The Coot is a species that has declined rapidly in Argyll in recent years, for reasons that are not clear. Although common in the south of Scotland, it has always been scarce in the Highlands. This is due to its preference for shallow eutrophic waters: as a breeding bird, it favours lowland freshwater habitats with plenty of submerged and emergent vegetation.

Its past status as a breeding bird in Argyll is not entirely clear. In the NSA, the Coot was listed for only two Argyll parishes, Inveraray and Glassary. Nevertheless, Gray claimed that it was found commonly throughout the inner islands, breeding in suitable places, with considerable numbers in Islay and Mull. H&B, on the other hand, believed that it was not common anywhere in Argyll and stated that there were no positive records from Islay, though they commented that it bred on "the more important lochs" of Tiree. Anderson (1898) went as far as to describe it as an "abundant resident" on Tiree. Whether scarce or common, the Coot was clearly widespread in the first half of the 20th century, nesting on Islay, Colonsay, Coll and Lismore, as well as in small numbers on the mainland (B&R).

However, the early part of the 20th century saw the beginning of a range contraction across Scotland, with breeding ceasing in some peripheral areas such as Lewis and Harris (Thom). This contraction was tentatively linked to a lowering of mean summer temperatures (First Atlas). It is not possible to say when Argyll began to be affected, but the situation in Tiree seems to have changed by the time of the First Atlas survey, which produced evidence of possible breeding from just one square. There were no records from Coll, where three pairs had been found in 1937-38 (B&R).

Comparison of the maps in the First and Second Atlases shows a clear decline. The Coot was lost from eleven 10-km squares in Argyll, only three squares being added. It disappeared as a breeding species from Mull and Gigha but persisted on Colonsay and Islay. Although there was no evidence of breeding on Islay during 1988-91, the Coot had been described as resident on Lochs Ballygrant, Finlaggan and Skerrols in 1985 (ABR 3:28). Both the Second Atlas and a survey of larger lochs in 1985 (Broad *et al.* 1986) confirmed that the Coot had become very scarce on the mainland.

From the beginning of the 1990s, there was further decline to the point where the Coot became practically extinct as a breeding species. At Westport Marsh near Machrihanish, breeding occurred in 1989, 1993 and 1994 but the site was abandoned in spring 1995 when the marsh was drained. At East Loch Fada on Colonsay, the only other site with positive evidence of breeding during 1988-1991, there have since been no summer records, although birds have been seen in March and August. The only other confirmed breeding since 1991 occurred at Kilmory, Lochgilphead, in 1998; courtship was also observed at this site in March 2003. A pair were present at Loch Bhasapol (Tiree) during April 2004 and breeding was suspected though no young were seen. In May-July of 2002 and 2003, sightings of single birds or pairs at Loch Ederline in Mid-Argyll, at Loch Ballygrant on Islay, and at Loch Poit na h-I and Loch Assapol on Mull hint at a possible revival of fortunes.

In winter as in summer, the Coot appears to have undergone a substantial decline in Argyll over the past 30 years or so. Its earlier history is rather unclear, but H&B reported the exceptional presence of hundreds of birds on Loch Awe for a few days in January 1879. On Tiree, numbers in the early 20th century were apparently even higher in winter than in summer (Anderson 1913). In March 1939, it was "plentiful" on Islay (B&R), and as recently as the early 1970s, this island held a wintering population that sometimes exceeded 100 birds. In the winter of 1973/74, for example, numbers at the main site, Loch Skerrols, peaked at 136 on 2 February.

The Winter Atlas survey of 1981-84 was the first systematic attempt at mapping the Coot's winter distribution. As in summer, Argyll lies at the northern edge of the range in western Britain, apart from the healthy population in the southern Outer Hebrides. The survey showed the Coot to be thinly distributed across Argyll in small numbers, most records coming from the northern part of the mainland. Of the major islands, only Islay and Mull were found to have birds. Although it is difficult to compare this picture with the few data from earlier years, it seems likely that there had already been a decline. No birds at all were recorded from Tiree.

Since then there have been further changes. On Islay, for example, the wintering population may be as few as one or two individuals in most winters, the highest recent count being six birds on Loch Ballygrant on 27 December 2002. Elsewhere on the islands, one to three birds are still occasionally recorded from Gigha, Colonsay and Mull, while on Tiree there is a regular small wintering flock on Loch Bhasapol, apparently first recorded in 1986 and typically peaking at around 7 to 13 individuals. On the mainland, another small flock occurs on Loch Nell, with up to six birds in winter 2002/3, but there have been no more recent reports. Elsewhere, single birds are sometimes seen on Mid-Argyll lochs such as Loch Awe, Loch Ederline and Loch Sween, as well as occasionally in Kintyre.

From autumn through to spring, birds sometimes occur on the sea in sheltered locations. Although a small number of sites account for most Argyll records throughout the year, the distribution is more scattered in autumn. This indicates the presence of passage migrants that probably move on

The Coot has declined as a breeding bird in Argyll throughout the 20th century. *Philip Kirkham*

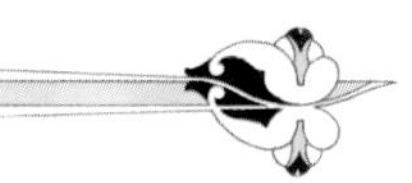

after a few days. Although the resident British population is said to be supplemented in winter by birds from north-west Europe (Migration Atlas), there is no evidence that these have occurred in Argyll. The movements of Coot are poorly known, making it difficult to draw any conclusions about the origin of birds in Argyll in winter.

Tristan ap Rheinallt

Common Crane

Grus grus

Vagrant.

B&R considered this species, which nests in northern Europe, rare enough to warrant a full listing of all acceptable Scottish records. However, from the late 1960s there was a large increase in occurrences, most birds being in spring in the north and east of the country (Thom). This trend has continued to the present, although sightings in western Scotland remain few and far between. There are eight accepted Argyll records of single birds, all but one in spring and all but two staying for at least four days (Table).

Records of Common Cranes in Argyll to 2006.

Date	Location	Reference
10 - 28 May 1966	West Loch Tarbert	BB 60:316
19 Dec 1966 - 19 Mar 1967	Glenbarr (Kintyre)	BB 61:339
9 - 12 May 1975	Bunessan (Mull)	BB 69:334
18 May 1985	Port Askaig (Islay)	BB 79:542
13 - 25 May 1986	Ballinaby (Islay)	BB 81:554
29 Apr - 12 May 1993	Tiree	SBR 1993:23, SBR 1994:26, ABR 11:44
17 - 20 May 1995	Bowmore (Islay)	SBR 1995:29, ABR 12:41
3 May 2004	Breachacha (Coll)	Argyll Database

A full account of the 1966 records, accompanied by a photograph of the bird at Glenbarr, was published by Macmillan (1967).

Tristan ap Rheinallt

Oystercatcher

Haematopus ostralegus

This unmistakeable bird is the most numerous and conspicuous wader of the region. It occurs in Argyll year-round, and numbers often rise noticeably during spring and autumn passage.

The Oystercatcher owes much of its success to its powerful bill and its skill in opening shellfish that many other waders cannot open, such as cockles and mussels. Its vital statistics are those of a long-lived seabird. Only 5.2% of juveniles and 1.4% of adults die in winter. Females do not breed until they are 3-6 years old and males until they are 5-8. One Oystercatcher was recovered alive 31 years after it had been ringed (BTO data, Migration Atlas).

Both Gray and B&R found Oystercatchers widespread and usually numerous on the shores of the mainland and islands of Argyll. B&R knew there was considerable immigration in autumn and that the large winter flocks contained birds of both British and continental origins. They recorded that Oystercatchers in east Scotland bred inland along rivers and streams much more than they did in the west, where breeding was mainly coastal and on rocky islets. While both breeding Atlases showed most squares in Scotland and every square in Argyll to be occupied, this striking difference was confirmed in the Second Atlas which showed much higher inland density in the east than in the west of Scotland. The spread inland to breed along rivers and by fresh water (which took place in Scotland in the late 19th century and in northern England in the 1940s) is believed to have occurred when Oystercatchers extended their diet to earthworms and began to feed on fields and moorland. In the 1980s Scotland held about 70% of the British breeding population of 33,000-43,000 pairs but only about a quarter of the winter population of 200,000 birds (Thom).

Return to breeding areas occurs early in the year. In Argyll pairs can be seen on territories as early as mid-February, even though eggs are not laid until May. Numbers of non-breeders at many coastal sites remain high throughout the breeding season. Pairs breed singly, spaced fairly regularly along the seashore or on islets, more rarely by fresh water. Nests are on shingle, rock or sand and most hold two to four eggs. Incubating adults depart silently and unobtrusively if disturbed, but those with large young fly close past one's head giving frantic alarm calls that literally make the ears ring. Families may stay near the breeding site for some weeks, and in 2001 at Otter Ferry, a brood of three noted on 20 July were still being fed by parents on Christmas Day 2001 and on 3 March 2002 (ABR)!

The species was recorded in 70% of 10-km squares in Argyll during work for the Second Atlas. However, few sites have been regularly counted. The island total on Coll was estimated at 100 pairs in 1987 (ABR) while Coll RSPB Reserve held 85 pairs in 1994, 82 in 1995, 65 in 1996, 57 in

1997, 34 in 2000, 39 in 2003, and 41 in 2004; Gunna held 12 pairs in 2004 (S. Wellock pers. comm.). Tiree was estimated to hold *c.*300 pairs in 1987 and 227 pairs were counted there in 1994 (when one area total had increased to 101 from 58 pairs in 1987-88); on the Reef, 57 pairs were counted in 1998 and 127 pairs in 2004 (ABR).

On Islay, 309 pairs were counted during the Rinns Survey in 1994 (86% of these were coastal, mainly on flatter rocky coasts; 9% by freshwater and 5% on farmland). Loch Gruinart RSPB held 16 pairs in 1986, 19 in 1991, 21+ in 1993, 12 in 1994, nine in 1995, 18 in 1996, 22 in 1997 and ten in 1999 (ABR). On Colonsay an incomplete count in late May 1986

The Oystercatcher is one of the most distinctive birds of the Argyll shoreline, as here at Loch Long. *Margaret Staley*

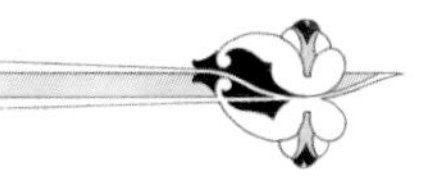

found 131 pairs + *c.*150 non-breeding birds, while in 1993 there was an estimated total of 70 pairs (ABR). In 2002 there were 55 pairs on Colonsay itself and 28 pairs on Oronsay while in 2004 there were 41+ pairs on Colonsay alone (D. Jardine pers. comm.).

On Sanda Islands between 20 and 30 pairs were counted annually during 1998-2001, while on the Treshnish Islands during 1998-2001 annual counts varied between seven and 23 pairs. On Taynish NNR 3-4 pairs were counted annually during 1999-2001, Moine Mhor held four pairs in 1991, while there were at least six pairs on Shuna in 1994. In the SAMS study area (Argyll) in 2000, 94 pairs were counted at 54 sites (mostly islets in sealochs); of 47 pairs with known outcome, 25 (53%) were successful and 22 pairs (47%) were unsuccessful; 19 of these 22 were at mink-predated seabird colonies (ABR).

Most British breeders move south for the winter, many remaining on British coasts but some, especially juveniles, wintering as far afield as France and Iberia. Oystercatchers wintering in the west of Scotland are mainly breeders from Scotland, the Faeroes & Iceland, while those on the east coast are mainly from Norway (Migration Atlas). An adult ringed in Iceland in June 1956 was found dead in Kintyre in January 1960 (1,337km); and one ringed in Jersey (Channel Islands) in March 1986 was found dead on Tiree in April 1994 (878km). Similarly, of 60 birds recovered in Argyll after being ringed outside the county when fully grown, 52 had been ringed, mostly in autumn-winter, between Cornwall, Devon and Co. Cork, and the Lancashire-Cumbria estuaries, while three had been ringed in March (presumably at or near their breeding grounds) in Fair Isle, Grampian and Tayside. These included individuals with minimum ages of 15 years (3 birds), 16 (3), 17 (1), 18 (2) and 24 (1). Chicks ringed in Argyll have been recovered in Northern Ireland (two), Co. Cork, near Carnoustie (Tayside) and Clwyd, but the furthest was a chick ringed on Coll in June 1977 and shot in September 1982 near Trebeurden, (on the Channel coast of France, directly south of Devon) (897km). Chicks ringed in the Western Isles (three), Orkney and near Inverness have been recovered in Argyll.

Southward passage peaks in August. Many were heard over Tobermory during a heavy passage of waders on the night of 31 August 1984, and a similar nocturnal passage was noted over Oban on 13-15 August 1991. At seawatching sites many are counted moving south in August. Some of the higher counts recorded at MSBO include 3,709 in 114h in August 1991; 1,239 in 159h in August 1993; 1,297 in 82h in August 1996 (max 180 in 5h on 8 August); 2,923 in August 1997 (max day-count 1,180 in 6h on 10 August); and 2,559 during 42 days between 5 July and 13 September 2001 (ABR).

Inland breeders tend to move to the coast in winter. Many 10-km squares on the Argyll coast were occupied in both winter and summer, but some inland squares, especially in Mid-Argyll, became empty in winter (Winter Atlas). The winter Shorebird Survey found that between 10,500 and 14,500 Oystercatchers wintered in the Inner Hebrides and along the mainland shore between Kintyre and north Sutherland (Thom). A winter shorebird count in 1984-85, covering 84% of the estimated 2,352km coast of Argyll, found 8,800 Oystercatchers, making it the most numerous shorebird. Next most abundant was Eurasian Curlew (6,030), and third was Ringed Plover (2,673) (Madders & Moser 1986). The NEWS survey (December 1997-January 1998) found 4,799 Oystercatchers on the coasts of Argyll, making it again the most numerous winter shorebird; next was the Common Eider 3,283 and third was Curlew 2,563; no other wader or wildfowl exceeded 2,000. Tidal mudflats, where regular counts are made, often hold their highest numbers in July and August, but numbers remain considerable throughout the winter. ABR records show that Loch Indaal, Holy Loch, Campbeltown Loch and Otter Ferry have maximum monthly counts in midwinter that are usually in the range 300-700; sites with typical maxima of 100-300 include Lochs Gruinart, Riddon and Gilp, while sites with up to 100 include Lochs Crinan, Long, Don, Ledaig Point, The Strand (Colonsay) and others. A total count on Colonsay during 18-25 January 1985 found 249 birds. 120 were counted on the coast of Coll in January 1985, and a complete coastal survey of Coll found 288 in December 1997; 176 were counted at Crossapol on 8 March 1998 (S. Wellock pers. comm.). Numbers at the main sites sometimes rise to sharp peaks during return passage in March-April, e.g. 833 on 23 March 1988 and 840 in March 1992, both at Loch Indaal. Nocturnal spring passage was heard on Mull on 18-19 April 1985 and in Oban on 10-11 March 1991 (ABR). The Oystercatcher was one of ten species recorded throughout the year at Ledaig Point by Jennings (1995).

Clive Craik

Avocet

Recurvirostra avosetta

Vagrant.

Although the Avocet is a regular breeder in England, it remains an exciting find in Scotland, especially away from the east coast. It is not recorded in Scotland every year, although small influxes occur from time to time, as in 1984. There are scattered records all down the western seaboard, from Lewis to Dumfries & Galloway, including at least four in Argyll (Table). With the exception of a multiple sighting during a seawatch in 2002, all the Argyll records refer to single birds.

Records of Avocets in Argyll to the end of 2006.

Date	Location	Comment	Reference
19 Sep 1936	Loch Seil		SN 1936:164, B&R
9 Jun 1977	Lochdonhead (Mull)	Feeding on tidal mud and in shallow water	SB 10:135
15 May 1986	Brunerican Bay (Kintyre)		SB 14:235, ABR 4:21
20 Aug 2002	Uisaed Point (Kintyre)	Three juveniles flying south with Oystercatchers	Argyll Database

B&R state that "two Avocets were noted in Argyll in spring 1947 and 1948." However, details were not published in the annual Scottish bird reports in SN, and it is not known where they were or, indeed, whether they were within the current Argyll recording area.

Tristan ap Rheinallt

Stone-curlew

Burhinus oedicnemus

Vagrant.

This southern species, which breeds in south-east England and is only a rare vagrant to Scotland, Wales and Ireland, has been recorded in Argyll only once. A bird was in open fields near Craigens, at the south-eastern end of Loch Gruinart, Islay, on 23 and 24 May 1997 (SBR 1997:30). It was surely no coincidence that a Stone-curlew was on the Calf of Man on 22 May 1997, only the second record for that island (Bagworth 2000). Interestingly, the eighth and ninth records for Norway were on 29 April and 14 May 1997, and the ninth Finnish record was on 2 June (Birding World 11: 25). There were 26 records of Stone-curlew in Scotland to the end of 2001.

Tristan ap Rheinallt

Little Ringed Plover

Charadrius dubius

Vagrant.

The only Argyll record of this species concerns an individual at the American Monument car park on the Mull of Oa, Islay, on 16 May 1983 (SBR 1983:20, ABR 1:39). Full details, with a photograph, were published by Shutes & ap Rheinallt (1995). Although Little Ringed Plovers breed sporadically in Scotland, records from western Scotland north of the Central Lowlands are extremely rare.

Tristan ap Rheinallt

Ringed Plover

Charadrius hiaticula

This is a widespread and fairly common breeding species that occurs here throughout the year, almost always by water and usually on sandy shores and muddy tidal flats.

H&B described the Ringed Plover as "numerous" on the sandy shores of Tiree, "abundant" about Loch Creran and "found far up the sealochs, where also they appear in winter in flocks". Gray described it breeding by "inland lakes, such as... Loch Awe" and commented that the birds he shot on spring migration were "so much smaller" than local breeders that "they must belong to a southern race". B&R stated that it was very common down the Atlantic side of Kintyre, "plentiful" on Islay in 1936, and "common in all the sandy bays on Jura in June 1939". They also reported breeding on Gigha, Colonsay, Tiree, Coll and Mull.

Ringed Plovers breeding in the British Isles are all *C. h. hiaticula*, a race that breeds from Greenland and Iceland to the Baltic region and winters as far south as west Africa. British birds of this race make shorter migrations than *hiaticula* from further north and west, some wintering in France and Spain, some going no further than south-west England and Ireland, and some apparently remaining close to their breeding sites. As part of the same general movement, *hiaticula* from the Netherlands to the Baltic Sea region may winter in the British Isles. Small dark birds of the eastern race *C. h. tundrae* are reported in Argyll in spring and autumn of most years, as they migrate between breeding in Arctic Russia and wintering in eastern and southern Africa (Migration Atlas, Winter Atlas).

Throughout the year, but especially from autumn to spring, flocks occur on sandy beaches and on muddy sand in estuaries and sealochs. This was one of ten species recorded throughout the year at Ledaig Point by Jennings (1995). Groups of non-breeders are present throughout the summer at many sites. Autumn passage is evident from mid-July and usually peaks in August or September. Probably the largest numbers at this season (counts of up to several hundred) are on Tiree, especially in its larger bays. Smaller numbers are found at Lochs Gruinart and Indaal, on Colonsay, and at Ledaig Point, Killinallan Point, Rhunahaorine Point, Otter Ferry, and on the intertidal flats of Lochs Caolisport, Don, Gilp and elsewhere. Midwinter numbers at some sites remain near the high levels of autumn. Large wintering populations occur on Tiree, Islay and Colonsay. In the winter shorebird survey of 1984-1985 covering 84% of the 2,352km coast of Argyll, this was the third most numerous species with 2,673 individuals, exceeded by Oystercatcher (8,800) and Eurasian Curlew (6,030) (Madders & Moser 1986). The NEWS count in December 1997-January 1998 found 1,115 Ringed Plovers in Argyll (43% on Tiree). Spring passage is evident in April and May, when numbers increase considerably above their midwinter values. This passage up the west coast of Britain is thought to consist of birds of both races, but mainly *hiaticula*.

Ringed Plover, an unobtrusive but widespread shorebird. *Philip Kirkham*

By April, most of the birds that breed in Argyll have returned onto territories. Pairs breed singly, preferring shores of sand or small pebbles to large stones or solid rock. Their penchant for sites that are also attractive to humans leads to a conflict that can be witnessed every year on sandy beaches all over western Scotland. The species tends to be absent from the huge lengths of unbroken rocky seashore found in Argyll, but it nests inland on suitable ground around reservoirs and large lochs, although not on higher ground. The remarkable broken-wing display of the parents is effective in distracting intruders away from the crouching young, which are among the best-camouflaged of all wader chicks. At the time of the Second Atlas, Ringed Plovers were found breeding in 55% of 10-km squares in Argyll. In the smaller 1-km squares of the BBS, it was found in one of 16 in 1998, one of 15 in 1999, and none of ten in 2000. Although it is known to breed in all the recording areas of Argyll, the only area with a long series of breeding counts is Colonsay. Here 46 pairs were counted in 1986, 23 in 1988, 22, 20, 21, 39, 36, 41, 42, 30 and 46 pairs in 1994-2002. On Tiree, an estimated 200 pairs bred in both 1987 and 1989, and 100 pairs in 1994 (1.1% of the British total); on the Reef, there were 69 pairs in 1994, 51 in 1998, at least 50 in 2000 and 57 in 2002. In 1984 119 pairs were counted on Tiree and 220 pairs on Islay (Thom). On Islay in 1994, 43 pairs were counted in the Rinns Survey, mostly near Bruichladdich. On Coll, an island total of 20-30 pairs was estimated in 1987, and on Coll RSPB Reserve there were 14, 12, 13 and six pairs in 1994-1997 and 22 pairs in 2000. Recently, 4-5 pairs have been recorded each year on the Treshnish Isles and 6-8 pairs on Sanda; and five pairs were counted on RSPB Loch Gruinart reserve in 1986 (ABR and Argyll Database).

Many were heard flying over Tobermory during a strong passage of waders in mist and heavy rain on the night of 29 August 1984. Along with large numbers of other waders, 230 were grounded by poor visibility at MSBO on 12 August 1999. Large numbers are recorded moving south past this seawatching site in some years, as shown by the counts in 1996: 122 in 81h in July; 728 in 82h in August; and 60 in 80h in September (ABR). There have only been two ringing recoveries involving Argyll. A chick ringed on Tiree in 1989 was found dead on the Isle of Sanday (Highland) in March 1991 and a chick ringed on Harris (Western Isles) in 1981 was found dead on Tiree early in 1990.

Clive Craik

Killdeer

Charadrius vociferus

Vagrant.

The first record of a Killdeer in Argyll concerns an individual on Colonsay on 7 and 8 January 1984, discovered during Winter Atlas survey work (BB 80:534). Winter occurrences of Killdeers, unlike many other North American wader species, are typical. The Colonsay bird was the fourth to be recorded in Scotland and several have been seen since. Curiously, the second Argyll Killdeer was found nearby, at the airstrip on the island of Oronsay, on 18 October 2006.

Tristan ap Rheinallt

Dotterel

Charadrius morinellus

Scarce migrant, mostly seen in late April and May. Breeding occurs on the northern hills in at least some years, and may have occurred on Islay in 1990.

The early authors had little or nothing to say about the Dotterel as a breeding species in Argyll. B&R did not include the county in their description of the species' main breeding range and, in the First Atlas, the only record that may have related to the current Argyll recording area was an instance of possible breeding on or close to its northern boundary in the Glen Etive area. Possible breeding at unnamed site(s) was also reported in 1976 (SB 10:93) and confirmed in both 1982 and 1983 (ABR 1:39). These appear to be the first confirmed breeding records for Argyll.

In the Second Atlas, birds were recorded in several squares – all shared with adjacent recording areas – in the Glen Fyne area and between the north end of Loch Etive and the Water of Tulla. However, no evidence of breeding was found. Two birds were seen on 2 May 1992 at a location where breeding had occurred in the past (ABR 9:29), and distraction display was exhibited by a pair at a past breeding site on 28 June 1997 (ABR 14:48). A juvenile was seen in the Beinn Dorian area

Breeding in small numbers and only on the highest hills, the Dotterel is one of Argyll's least known birds. *Margaret Staley*

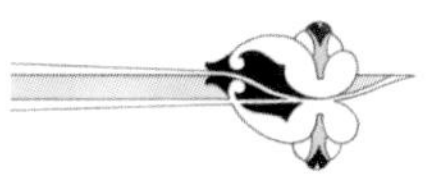

on 1 July 2001 (ABR 18:53).

The presence of Dotterel on the high tops in April or May does not necessarily imply breeding, since migrants can be found in the same habitats. Away from the Glen Etive area, there are recent spring records from Mull (Ben Buie and Beinn Talaidh), Cowal (Beinn Luibhean) and Islay (Beinn Bhàn). All these could well refer to migrants. However, the presence of a pair in suitable habitat on Islay on 2 June 1990, followed by a sighting of five or six birds in the same area on 28 July that year (ABR 7:28), is strongly suggestive of breeding. This would presumably have been an isolated occurrence, since birds have not been reported from the Islay hills since.

Migrants are also seen at low altitudes. The earliest report seems to be that of two birds shot at Ardimersay on Islay on 17 February 1843 (Elliott 1989), but the unusual date must cast doubt on this record. Even though Dotterel were much more abundant in Scotland on spring migration than now, the main arrival was in April (Gray, B&R). There is no evidence of how abundant Dotterels were on passage in Argyll itself (B&R), and only a handful of records, together with one or two general references, predate the 1970s.

Analysis of records from 1968-2003 (excluding those from the North Argyll hills and the 1990 Islay occurrence above) shows that migrants pass through Argyll during a fairly well-defined period in spring, the earliest and latest dates being 22 April and 30 May. Many fewer are seen in autumn, as in Scotland generally; most Scottish birds are believed to migrate to the wintering grounds in a single flight (Migration Atlas). The earliest autumn record involved a bird at the Mull of Kintyre on 2 August 1982 (ABR 1:39), and the latest involved two birds seen with Golden Plovers at Machrihanish on 10 October 1995 (ABR 12:42). The largest number seen together was 12 birds, also at Machrihanish, on 4 May 1975 (SB 9:198). Most of the 24 records in the Figure come from the islands, mainly Islay but also Mull, Tiree and Oronsay. With the exception of the Cowal record above, all mainland records come from south Kintyre. However, there is also a record of five birds photographed near Musdale, Mid-Argyll on an unspecified date in April 2003.

Tristan ap Rheinallt

American Golden Plover

Pluvialis dominica

Vagrant.

This species, which breeds mainly at high latitudes in North America, has been recorded in Argyll on five occasions. Single juveniles were at Sandaig on Tiree from 4 to 9 October 2001 (BB 95:491), and at Ardnave on Islay from 21 September to 2 November 2003 (BB 97:577). An adult, starting to moult out of summer plumage, was at Sandaig and Middleton on Tiree on 13-14 September 2004 (BB 98:650). A first summer bird was at Loch Beg, Mull on 3-4 September 2005, and one was present on Oronsay on 25-26 September 2005 (BB 100:36). In common with most other American waders recorded in Scotland as a whole, records of juveniles on the islands in autumn are typical. However, in view of the regular occurrence of species such as Buff-breasted Sandpiper and Pectoral Sandpiper, it is perhaps surprising that there have not been more records of American Golden Plover in Argyll. The clear increase in the number of British records since the early 1970s is attributed to growth in observer numbers and better identification skills (BB 97:577). This suggests that closer scrutiny of autumn Golden Plover flocks on the Argyll islands might result in more records.

[A record of a summer-plumaged adult at Traigh nam Barc on Colonsay from 3 to at least 5 October 1992 (Jardine & Jardine 1994), originally accepted as an American Golden Plover (BB 86:477), has recently been reassessed and is now considered indeterminate American or Pacific Golden Plover (BB 97:577-478).]

Tristan ap Rheinallt

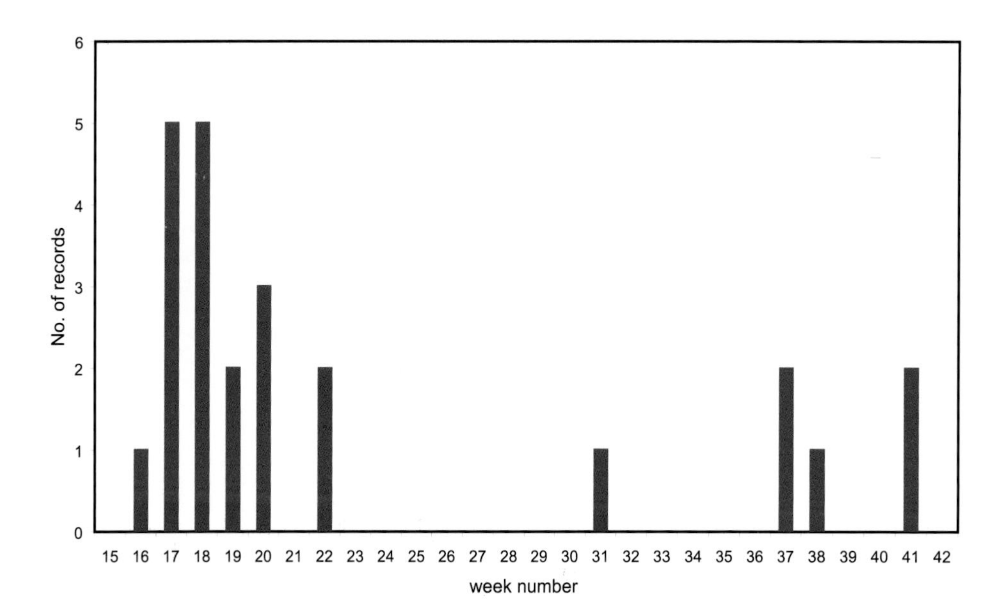

Seasonal occurrence of migrating Dotterels at low altitude in Argyll.

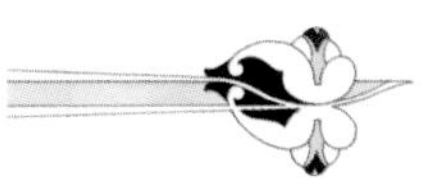

Pacific Golden Plover

Pluvialis fulva

Vagrant.

The Pacific Golden Plover breeds in Siberia and Alaska. Although it is only a rare visitor to the British Isles, records have become much more frequent in recent years, with around 15 birds seen in Scotland to the end of 2002. There are two records from Argyll. The first concerns an adult seen in a small group of Golden Plover at Vaul on Tiree on 12 October 2000 (BB 94:469). The second was thought to be a first summer bird, and was at Balevullin, Tiree, from 29 August to 2 September 2006.

Most Scottish records come from the Northern Isles. However, there was a series of records from South Uist (Outer Hebrides) in the period 2000 to 2003. It has been suggested that at least three different birds were involved, one of which overwintered in the North Boisdale area in 2001/2 and 2002/3. The arrival dates of this bird in the small Golden Plover flock at North Boisdale (14 October 2001, 13 October 2002) corresponded closely to the date of the Tiree sighting in 2000, leading to the suggestion that the same individual was involved (Stevenson 2004).

Tristan ap Rheinallt

European Golden Plover

Pluvialis apricaria

Moderate but probably decreasing numbers breed on moorland in several parts of Argyll. Large numbers are present at traditional sites by the coast in winter and during spring and autumn passage, especially on Tiree, Islay and Mull.

Gray described this species as "extremely abundant" over all the western counties of Scotland and as a "constant resident" on Mull, Islay, Jura and Colonsay. The "immense" flocks that formed in autumn were impossible to count as they covered "many acres". Similarly, we shall never know how many were in the flock seen on Tiree Reef on 9-10 March 1984; it "stretched for half-a-mile" and held "uncountable thousands" (ABR). Gray quotes how 18 of a flock of 70-80 were killed by a single shot; and that "108 were bagged on 22 January 1848 at one discharge". In a detailed description, H&B said that the species had "always been abundant on the moors of Mull" and that "large flights occurred on the moorlands of Benderloch and in Kintyre". They recognised that there were fewer suitable winter sites on the west Scottish coast than in the east, so that there were "many places where it is comparatively scarce, or even rare" but that large flocks formed in winter in favoured areas in the west. They quoted one account that "many thousands" wintered on Tiree and Coll, "arriving in the end of August and leaving in April". They considered it "more or less common" on "other larger islands such as Islay, Jura, Mull, etc." but said that it did not breed on Tiree.

B&R gave early breeding records from Islay (in 1926 and 1936), Jura (1939), Tiree (1865) and Coll (1899). They mention the arrival of large numbers of winter visitors of both races in September and October, and the great size of some winter flocks, especially on Tiree. They also describe remarkable cold-weather movements on Tiree in December 1906 and at south-west Scottish lighthouses in December 1914, and give examples of high mortalities during severe storms on Islay in January 1889 and elsewhere in spring 1947. B&R recorded the northern race on Islay and Tiree, quoting recoveries in western Scotland of birds of this race ringed in Iceland.

Within Britain, breeding Golden Plovers are confined mainly to the uplands of Scotland, northern England and central Wales. Numbers in Britain decreased from 29,400 pairs in 1968-72 to 22,600 pairs in 1988-91, mainly due to habitat loss (agricultural intensification and afforestation). The First Atlas showed the main breeding areas in Argyll to be Mull, Islay and Kintyre (with none on Coll, Tiree or Colonsay). The Second Atlas showed several new breeding squares in Mull, Islay, Jura and Colonsay, possibly due to better coverage rather than range extension. The species was found breeding in 28% of 10-km squares in the county. In 1-km square counts of the BBS, breeding was recorded in 4/16 squares in 1997, 2/16 in 1998, 2/15 in 1999, 3/12 in 2000 and 1/6 in 2001 (ABR); and in 1/14 squares in the Countryside 2000 survey (Wilson & Fuller 2001).

Compared with the numbers present here in winter and on passage, few are reported breeding each year and most reports are of territorial males or of pairs in suitable habitat. Only one report in ABR mentions young (an adult and juvenile on Mull in 1994), and there seem to have been no explicit accounts of nests or eggs. There are no recent breeding records from Coll and apparently none at all from Tiree. Presumed breeding is reported most regularly from Mull, Islay and Mid-Argyll and in some years from North Argyll, Colonsay, Kintyre and Jura. However, only small numbers of sites or territories are mentioned. The highest counts on record were 16 presumed pairs on Mull in 1985, ten territories there in 1989, and six sites in 1999; and an estimate of 10+ pairs on Islay in 1989. This paucity may reflect under-reporting but may also be a result of loss of moorland habitat in recent decades. Breeding birds are all of the southern form.

Some British breeders migrate to the west coasts of France, Iberia and Morocco for the winter, but ringing suggests that only a minority do so. Around 100,000 are shot annually in France but few British or Irish bred birds are reported there. Many British breeders remain within the British Isles and they are joined here by wintering migrants from Iceland, Scandinavia and further east. Many of these are of the northern form *altifrons*. The two forms are indistinguishable

A bird of remote moorlands in summer, European Golden Plovers are under-reported as a breeding species in Argyll. Our understanding of their status is therefore limited. *Philip Snow*

in winter but have distinct breeding plumage, the northern form being brighter and of more spangled appearance. The two are thought to be extremes of a north-south cline rather than separate subspecies. Many of those wintering in Ireland and west Scotland are from Iceland (Migration Atlas, Thom). Ringing recoveries involving Argyll show this range of migratory behaviour. A chick ringed on Mull in 1985 was shot near Santander (Spain) in February 1986 (1,456km). Another chick ringed on Rum in 1958 was found dead on Tiree in December 1959. Three birds ringed as chicks in Iceland in 1928, 1929 and 1935 were respectively shot or found dead on Tiree in April 1929 and on Islay in February 1936 and December 1935 (1,167, 1,342 and 1,319km). An adult ringed in the Netherlands in November 1956 was found dead on Tiree in April 1957 (877km).

In winter, most Golden Plovers feed and roost intertidally or close to the sea, often at traditional sites. The winter population has been estimated at over 300,000 birds in Britain and a similar number in Ireland (*cf.* only 23,000 pairs that breed in the British Isles) (Winter Atlas). In the midwinter 1977-78 survey, over 30,000 were counted in Scotland and all flocks numbering more than 2,000 were between the Ythan and Lothian on the east and between the Solway and the Clyde in the west. The Inner Hebrides held relatively few, hundreds rather than thousands (Thom). The Winter Atlas showed a striking change in distribution from that seen in summer. Birds were absent from the north-west mainland of Scotland and other uplands of the British Isles. Their main presence in Argyll was on Islay and Tiree; Jura and most of Mull and of the mainland were empty.

In the winter shorebird count of 1984-85 covering 84% of the coast of Argyll, this species was twelfth in abundance with only 155 individuals (Madders & Moser 1986). The NEWS count (December 1997-January 1998) found 892 in Argyll (783 on Tiree, 100 on Islay and nine on Coll) making the Golden Plover the sixth most numerous wader in Argyll in that count. Tiree has always been the stronghold of passage and wintering birds. The largest counts on Tiree appear to have been 4,500 on 26 April 2000, 3,447 on 10 November 2003, 5,150 on 19 April 2004 and 6,740 on 27 September 2005 (ABR, Argyll Database). Two or three thousand are not unusual there in autumn, winter or spring. Other important passage and wintering sites occur on Islay, especially at Loch Indaal (where maximum monthly counts usually attain 200-400 in winter, with 780 in December 1990, 1,024 in November 1991 and 1,000 in October-November 2003), Loch Gruinart (usually in range 100-700 with 1,500 in November 1997), Ardnave (passage counts up to 200-500 but 800 in March 1998) and Killinallan Dunes (several hundred). There are important sites on Mull at Fidden (100-500 in spring but fewer in autumn), Loch Don and Loch Beg, and on Colonsay (where maximum monthly counts in 2001-2004 were 25, 125, 163 and 152). On Coll, there is a strong spring passage in some years, with high April counts of 200 in 1992, 250 in 1994, 630 in 1995, 250 in 1996 and 500 in 2004. There were 1,050 on Coll in October 2005. At The Laggan, Kintyre, high counts have included 909 in October 2001, 580 in October 1998 and 530 in March 1995. Smaller flocks or single birds occur regularly during passage and winter at many other sites in the county (ABR). Jennings (1995) found this species to be less-than-annual at Ledaig Point, occurring only in February and in August-September.

Clive Craik

Grey Plover

Pluvialis squatarola

Uncommon passage migrant, recorded most frequently in Kintyre and the islands. Small wintering population, concentrated on Islay and Tiree.

In Britain, wintering Grey Plovers from the Russian High Arctic are most numerous along the south-east coast of England between the Wash and the Solent. The species is relatively scarce in Scotland and Ireland (Migration Atlas), though there are small wintering flocks in some muddy estuaries. Gray claimed that Grey Plovers wintered in the Firth of Clyde in limited numbers, but H&B described the species as a great rarity in the west of Scotland, though recorded on Tiree in the autumn. Anderson (1898, 1913) stated that the species was scarce but regular on Tiree in both spring and autumn. B&R also described the Grey Plover as mainly a passage migrant, occurring during both seasons on Islay and Tiree, with maximum counts of 20 and 17 respectively during the month of September. However, they believed the species to be rare on the Argyll mainland. As late as the 1970s, Grey Plovers were still recorded relatively infrequently in Argyll, though there were high counts of 29 on Islay on 4 October 1975 (Elliott 1989) and 27 at Machrihanish on 18 October 1976 (SB 10:92).

During the 1980s, however, sightings became more frequent. Partly this was no doubt due to the increased popularity of birdwatching, but at the same time numbers of wintering Grey Plovers in Scotland, as in the rest of Britain, have increased substantially in recent decades (Thom, Migration Atlas). This has been associated with a change in status within Argyll from passage migrant to passage migrant and winter visitor.

Numbers vary considerably from one year to the next. Most records come from the islands. On the mainland, birds have been recorded most frequently in south Kintyre and in the Connel area, with fewer records elsewhere on the west coast of the mainland. Loch na Cille (Danna) in Mid-Argyll, for example, has produced sightings in several years. A high proportion of the Kintyre records refer to birds flying south past Uisaed Point in autumn.

The first migrating adults appear in Britain in late July, though juveniles do not arrive until September (Migration Atlas). In Argyll, records prior to mid-August are very few and birds often do not appear until September. By far the highest autumn counts come from Islay, with peaks of 69 at Loch Gruinart on 20 September 1993 (ABR 10:43) and 50 at Loch Indaal on 27 October 1997 (ABR 14:48). Elsewhere, double-figure counts are almost unknown.

In winter, birds appear to be confined to a smaller number of favoured locations, as might be expected. Again, Loch Gruinart and Loch Indaal are among the main sites, with a peak count of 48 at the former loch on 16 February 1998 (ABR 15:52). Good numbers have also been recorded on Tiree, with 28 counted along the coast in late January 1987 (ABR 5:7) and 45 during a complete coastal count in mid-January 2000 (ABR 17:54). Elsewhere, as in autumn, numbers are much lower. A single bird at Dunoon on 22 February 1986 (ABR 4:21) appears to be the only Cowal record, although nearby Ardmore Point is a regular haunt.

Most spring records come from the islands and Kintyre in April and the first half of May. Rarely are more than five individuals involved, though 14 were at Loch Gruinart on 7 May 1991 (ABR 8:40). Birds occasionally occur on grassland at this season, rather than in the intertidal zone. There are a few late records of presumed migrants in the first week of June. Although there is a small summering population of non-breeding birds in Britain and Ireland (Migration Atlas), there appear to be only two records from Argyll in midsummer (mid-June to mid-July). Four birds were at Salum Bay on Tiree on 26 June 1994 (ABR 11:46), and one flew south past Uisaed Point on 28 June 1995 (ABR 12:43).

Numbers of Grey Plovers recorded in Argyll have increased since the 1980s. *Eddie Maguire*

Tristan ap Rheinallt

Northern Lapwing

Vanellus vanellus

Localised breeder and widespread wintering species, with numbers highest on Tiree and Islay.

Once a familiar bird of open countryside throughout Britain, the Lapwing has attracted attention in recent years because of the detrimental impact that changing agricultural practices are having on its range and abundance. Gray described the Lapwing as very abundant throughout the western counties of Scotland, including on islands such as Iona and Mull, where Graham stated the species to be "common enough at all times of year." H&B, whilst claiming that hundreds or even thousands of pairs bred on Tiree, warned that the collection of eggs for London tables was having an impact on numbers on some of the islands. B&R described the species as breeding commonly on Islay, Colonsay, Oronsay, Coll and Tiree, having increased on the last island following a decline in the early years of the century. Small numbers also nested on Gigha, Cara, Mull, Lismore and Jura, though numbers had apparently been much higher on Jura a century earlier. Little information was provided about breeding on the mainland.

The First Atlas showed that Lapwings bred throughout the mainland and islands of Argyll, except for the high ground in the north-east. It was suggested that numbers had increased in the north of Britain, perhaps as a result of climatic amelioration, in contrast to southern areas where changes in land-use and farming practice had led to a decline. Twenty years later, the distribution on the islands remained more or less unchanged but a considerable decline was apparent in mainland Argyll north of Kintyre, with Lapwings breeding only in scattered 10-km squares (Second Atlas). The range reduction observed in north-west Scotland, west Wales, south-west England and Ireland was attributed in the main to a decline in mixed farming, which had resulted in more and more grassland in these areas. However, an earlier study, which involved survey work in Argyll and elsewhere, had suggested that drainage and subsequent improvement of marginal farmland might be the most important factor reducing the abundance of some breeding wader species in Scotland (Galbraith *et al.* 1984). This was the suggested explanation for observed reductions in breeding Lapwing populations in Mid-Argyll and Kintyre in 1983 (ABR 1:41). Galbraith *et al.* (1984) further proposed that, although Lapwings apparently continued to breed at high densities on improved land, breeding success might be low and the continuation of these populations might depend on recruitment from marginal areas.

Since the Second Atlas, there have been further reductions in at least part of the Lapwing's range in Argyll. By 1993, Westport Marsh was one of the few remaining breeding sites in south Kintyre, with six pairs. In the same year, only one or two pairs were found breeding on the mainland along the coastal stretch between Castle Sween and Point of Knap (ABR 10:44). In 1994, Lapwings were reported to be absent from three regular breeding sites in the Connel area (ABR 11:47). Westport Marsh was drained in 1995 and the eight pairs nesting there failed (ABR 12:43), and although at least four pairs still bred in south Kintyre at The Laggan in 1999 and in 2002 (ABR 16:53, Argyll Database), this compared with a total of 68 pairs ten years earlier (ABR 6:3). Further north at Rhunahaorine Point, on the other hand, 30 pairs were estimated to breed in 1997 (ABR 14:49), compared to 18 in 1991 (ABR 8:40). Nevertheless, it seems that in parts of the mainland, the Lapwing is becoming a rare sight. For

Lapwings displaying at Fidden, Mull. *Philip Snow*

instance, a bird at Taynish NNR in April 2000 was the first reserve record since 1995 (ABR 17:54), while two at Otter Ferry on 20 July 2002 were the first seen there by the observer for many years (Argyll Database).

On its island strongholds, the Lapwing still breeds in good numbers. The Table gives recent counts of breeding pairs for some of these areas, with highest counts from the past where significantly different (data from ABRs). Overall, there is evidence of a decline on Islay, Colonsay and Coll, although in the case of Coll this may have been preceded by an increase. Some of these areas are reserves where harmful changes in land use are unlikely, so it seems that explanation for the decline must be sought elsewhere. Two factors that have been invoked to explain poor breeding productivity at these sites are poor weather in spring and predation by crows. The latter was thought to be the main cause of a 91 per cent failure of Lapwing nests at the egg stage on Coll in 1997 (ABR 14:49). Conversely, good breeding success on Colonsay in 1993 was thought to be associated with a cull of Hooded Crows (ABR 10:44). There is no evidence of a major decline on Tiree, where an intact crofting system continues to provide good habitat for perhaps 1,500-2,500 breeding pairs and numbers at The Reef reserve have increased from 230-250 pairs in 1993-1995 to 300-315 pairs in 2000-2002 (J. Bowler pers. comm.).

visitor. This was the case in the parish of Kilchoman on Islay, for example (NSA) and elsewhere in Scotland (B&R). By the late 19th century, however, Lapwings were present in Argyll in winter, though in varying numbers according to location and weather (H&B). Severe winters could lead to extensive mortality, as on Tiree in 1878 (H&B), and to presumed influxes, as in January 1929 (B&R).

As shown in the Winter Atlas, Lapwings are found in most low-lying areas of Argyll in winter, but the main centres of concentration are Tiree and Islay, which offer suitable areas of open lowland grassland or machair combined with largely frost-free winters. Counts in the range 1,000-1,500 birds are regularly reported from Islay and 2,000-3,000 birds from Tiree, the maximum being an estimate of 5,000-10,000 on Tiree in mid-winter 1984/85 (Thom). Several hundred are also sometimes recorded on Coll and Colonsay in the winter months but mainland flocks seldom hold more than 100, except in south Kintyre, where 1,000 were in lowland grassland on the Laggan on 4 November 1989 (ABR 6:30) and 2,050 in February 1994 (ABR 11:47). The open coast holds relatively few birds, with fewer than 1,200 Lapwings recorded in a survey of more than 80 per cent of the Argyll shoreline in winter 1984/85 (Madders & Moser 1986), and 865 in a similar survey in winter 1997/98 (ABR 15:53).

In some winters, large arrivals are recorded between November and February, presumably in response to colder weather on the mainland or further afield, though there are no ringing recoveries to confirm this. As a result, the Argyll population often appears to peak in late winter, although numbers vary from year to year. Notable influxes were reported from Loch Gruinart in February 1989 and February 1993, and from the Laggan in Kintyre in November 1989 and December 1993 (ABR 6:30 and 10:44). On the other hand, harsh weather may result in departure from favoured locations, as from Islay in early 1986 (Elliott 1989).

Area	Number of pairs	Year	Maximum number of pairs (year)
Loch Gruinart RSPB reserve (Islay)	207	2006	297 (1994)
Ardnave (Islay)	77	2006	
Rhinns of Islay (excluding above areas)	177-186	1994	
Tiree (whole island)	491	1994	3,000-3,500 (1988)
The Reef (Tiree)	315	2006	
Coll (whole island)	60-70	2003	500-1,000 (1988)
RSPB reserve (Coll)	43	2003	140 (1995)
Colonsay	26	2003	140 (1986)
Oronsay	52	2000	

Numbers of Lapwings breeding at their principal island sites, 1994-2006.

In Argyll as elsewhere, post-breeding flocks of Lapwing can be seen as early as mid-June, and numbers build up gradually through late summer and early autumn. Flocks of several hundred are sometimes reported in August and September, and several counts from Islay in August have approached or exceeded 1,000, whilst up to 3,000 are regularly present on Tiree at this time. Given the number of pairs breeding on these islands, these flocks could well consist exclusively of local birds. In the past, most or all of these birds would presumably have moved away with the onset of colder weather. Some still do so, and there are several recoveries of birds ringed in Argyll as chicks and recovered in Ireland during the winter months. Many Lapwings breeding in north-west Britain winter in Ireland (Migration Atlas). Nevertheless, there are still plenty in Argyll in the winter, although this was not always so. Indeed, the species was once regarded primarily as a summer

Lapwings in Argyll, as elsewhere in Scotland, return to their breeding grounds in February and March. Although passage migrants, presumably destined for Scandinavia, are seen in the Northern Isles in April and May (e.g. Thom), there is little or no evidence of passage through Argyll at this time.

Tristan ap Rheinallt

Red Knot

Calidris canutus

Uncommon passage migrant, mostly in autumn, with the largest numbers in Islay and south Kintyre. A few winter, mostly on Islay. Occasional birds occur in summer.

Knot wintering in Britain belong to the race *islandica* and originate from northern Greenland and high Arctic Canada. They stop off in western Iceland on their way south in autumn, and some do the same on the return journey in spring (Migration Atlas). Unlike many species that breed or stage in Iceland, Knot are scarcer in Argyll than in areas to the south and east. This is presumably because, in autumn, birds make a non-stop flight from Iceland to moulting areas in large estuaries such as the Wash, the Dee and the Ribble, and also in the Wadden Sea. In spring, the same happens in reverse, but birds leave wintering grounds that are more widely distributed than moult sites (Migration Atlas).

Gray was perhaps the first to remark on the scarcity of the Knot in western Scotland, believing Islay and North Uist to be the only Hebridean islands where the species had been recorded. H&B also regarded the Knot as a scarce bird, but they did not refer to a published record of hundreds at Loch Gilp in autumn 1887 (McWilliam). They stated that, in some years, small numbers occurred in Tiree in the winter months, while Anderson (1898, 1913) described the species as regular on the island, where it was found in small flocks in autumn and also occurred in spring. More than half a century later, B&R still categorised the Knot as rare on the west coast of Scotland north of Dumbarton, but again noted its occurrence on Tiree, primarily as an autumn migrant, and also on Islay. Similarly, Thom claimed that only low numbers occurred in the west of Scotland, the Knot being almost exclusively a passage migrant to the Hebrides. However, the Winter Atlas revealed the presence of birds on Islay, Colonsay, Coll and Tiree, as well as a few scattered mainland localities in Argyll, during November to February.

Loch Indaal, Islay, is one of the best places to find Knot in Argyll. *Eddie Maguire*

From more recent records, it is clear that there is considerable year-to-year variation in the numbers of Knot occurring in Argyll, both during main autumn passage and at other times. Generally, autumn migrants are first seen in mid- to late July, but the main concentrations occur in August, September and October with, as expected, juveniles becoming more frequent as the autumn wears on. There appear to be no inland records. A colour-ringed adult seen at Loch Gruinart on 4 August 2003 was reported from the Wadden Sea less than two months later (Argyll Database).

Islay is the main stronghold in Argyll, with more or less regular flocks at both Loch Gruinart and Loch Indaal. At the former site, a count of 300 on 12 October 1984 was exceptional, but flocks exceeding 100 have been recorded on several occasions. At Loch Indaal, 50 is a more typical maximum autumn count, but 300 were recorded on 28 October 1996. However, the highest-ever count in Argyll comes not from Islay but from Uisaed Point in Kintyre, where 741 were counted flying south in 5h on 29 August 1993. Regular seawatching at Uisaed Point has shown that birds pass through in good numbers in some years but not in others. On 12 August 1999, 145 were grounded there briefly in poor visibility.

Away from these main sites, numbers of Knot in autumn tend to be much lower, and double-figure counts are infrequent except on Tiree (maximum 41 at Gott Bay on 11 September 2000), at Ledaig Point (maximum 80 on 6 September 1984) and in the Loch Crinan area (maximum 61 on 30 August 2002). Other regular locations include Oronsay, Loch Don on Mull, and Loch Gilp. Records from Cowal are almost non-existent, though two were seen at Otter Ferry on 22 October 2000 and 20 on 22 August 2004.

Winter records are generally restricted to a few birds at widely scattered locations, except on Islay. There, flocks of 50 or more are recorded from Loch Indaal and Loch Gruinart in some winters, with a particularly high count of 140 at Loch Indaal on 1 February 1996. May sees a light northward passage that occasionally extends into the first few days of June. Numbers are generally small, though 75 were counted on Mull on 7 May 1981 following overnight arrival of low cloud and mist, and a flock of around 25 to 30 apparently lingered at Loch Indaal for more than a fortnight in May 2000.

Finally, there are a few late-June records, mostly from Islay, the highest count being eight at Loch Gruinart on 28 June 1994. First-summer birds, part of Britain and Ireland's small summering population, may account for most of these records. A notable exception is a flock of 40 adults in breeding plumage that stopped briefly at Hough Bay on Tiree on 16 June 2003 (Argyll Database).

Tristan ap Rheinallt

Sanderling

Calidris alba

Mainly a passage migrant, most numerous in Tiree, Islay and south Kintyre. Regular wintering is confined to Tiree, Islay and Coll. A few non-breeders occur on the islands in summer.

The Sanderling is associated with open sandy beaches, but in Argyll it also occurs within the sandier parts of estuaries. Although birds breeding in Greenland, Siberia and perhaps the Canadian Arctic are believed to occur in the British Isles, the origin of our passage and wintering populations is still the subject of debate (Migration Atlas). Nevertheless, it seems probable that many Sanderlings seen in Argyll during autumn have come from Greenland via Iceland, the same route being followed in reverse in spring.

Gray described the species as very common and, as long ago as 1892, H&B recognised Tiree as its main stronghold in Argyll. This island is now known to hold nationally significant numbers. Flocks are present from early autumn to late spring, with the first influx of adults normally in the second half of July. On 23 July 1998, for example, a count of the main sites on Tiree found 409 birds, while there were 430 at Gott Bay alone on 31 July 2002 (Argyll Database). Numbers peak in August or the first half of September, and the highest total on Tiree to date was an estimated 1,500 to 2,000 in mid-August 1995.

Numbers fall as autumn wears on, but Tiree still holds several hundred in midwinter. For example, 353 were found there on 25-26 January 1987, and 364 (55 per cent of the Argyll total) were counted during the NEWS count in December 1997-January 1998. A complete survey of the island's coast on 14 -20 January 2000 found 589 birds.

In April and especially May, migrants reappear during the pronounced northward passage of Sanderlings up the west coast of Britain (Thom). A count of 576 between Hynish and Gott Bay on 9 May 1999 was notable (ABR 16:54). In some years at least, migration continues through early June.

Islay and, in recent years, Coll are the only other places in Argyll where this species is regularly reported throughout the winter, though numbers are much smaller. As on Tiree, adults appear from mid-July, and at least 100 were seen at Laggan Bay on Islay on 23 July 1972. Numbers on Islay peak in mid-autumn, particularly at Loch Gruinart, where 364 were counted on 24 August 1990. Numbers wintering on Islay vary and in some years there are almost no records. Counts rarely exceed 50, but 150 were at Loch Gruinart on 19 January 2002, for example (Argyll Database). On Coll, there was a total of 176 in midwinter 1997/98. Return passage through these islands in late spring involves scattered flocks, sometimes numbering a few tens of individuals.

Elsewhere in Argyll, the Sanderling is almost exclusively a passage migrant, with no records shown in the Winter Atlas. The largest numbers in autumn occur in south Kintyre, where from July to September birds are regularly seen flying south past Uisaed Point. Daily counts there sometimes reach 80 birds, occasionally more, and the highest was 116 on 10 August 2001. Nearby at Machrihanish, 118 were counted on 26 July 1976 and no fewer than 180 on 6 September 1978. Other mainland sites where birds have appeared include Tayinloan, Skipness, Toward Point, Ardrishaig, Loch na Cille (Danna), Ledaig Point, and Loch Crinan and the Add

The shores of Tiree support nationally important numbers of Sanderling from autumn to spring. *Philip Kirkham*

Estuary, but they do not produce regular records. A count of 35 at Benderloch on 26 July 1988 was exceptional. On the islands, the Sanderling is regularly recorded in autumn on Oronsay, Mull and Iona. Flocks are usually no larger than 20 birds, but there are several records of up to 45 from Colonsay and Oronsay in August and September.

Midwinter records away from Tiree, Islay and Coll are rare and usually involve only singles or very small numbers. Northbound migrants appear in mid-May, sometimes earlier, and the first are often reported from the islands, especially Oronsay, Mull and Iona. Most flocks contain fewer than 20, but 43 were at Ardalanish Bay on Mull on 24 May 1998 and several higher counts have been made on Iona, where the most were 70 on 27 May 1997.

On the west coast of Kintyre, a substantial movement of northbound migrants was reported in the spring of both 1990 and 1991. In 1990, returning birds were first seen at Uisaed Point on 29 April but passage peaked rather later, the largest flock being 190 on 9 June. The following year, 60 were seen at Uisaed Point on 4 June and 45 at Rhunahaorine Point the next day. Spring migrants have not been reported on this scale in recent years, but the presence of ten birds at Tayinloan on 30 May 2001 indicated that Sanderlings still pass through on occasion. Nevertheless, there is an almost total absence of spring records from other parts of the mainland coast.

Only about four weeks separate the last spring Sanderlings from the first autumn ones. During this interval, small numbers of non-breeders, most presumably immatures, are sometimes reported from the islands. Singles and flocks of up to ten have been seen in recent years on Tiree, Islay, Colonsay, Oronsay and Iona, and summering birds may well be regular on these islands.

Although birds occasionally turn up on fresh water, notably a flock of 45 at Loch a' Phuill on Tiree on 29 May 1999, all Argyll records have been on or very close to the coast.

Tristan ap Rheinallt

Semipalmated Sandpiper

Calidris pusilla

Vagrant.

Between 6 and 11 September 1999, four individuals were recorded at two sites in Argyll (BB 93:530-531). At Gott Bay (Tiree), a juvenile was seen on 6 September and on 9-10 September and an adult on the 9th-10th. Meanwhile, at Loch Gruinart (Islay), a juvenile was recorded on 9-11 September and an adult on the 10th. Both Tiree birds were apparently present until at least 11 September (ABR 16:55). These records form part of an exceptional influx of this North American species, centred on western Scotland and associated with north-westerly gales (BB 93:531). Argyll, the Outer Hebrides and Dumfries & Galloway all had their first accepted records of Semipalmated Sandpiper during this period.

Tristan ap Rheinallt

Little Stint

Calidris minuta

Scarce but annual passage migrant, mainly in autumn.

Little Stints are primarily passage migrants in Britain, breeding in the high Arctic of Scandinavia, Russia and Siberia, and wintering in Africa. They are much commoner in the east and south of the country than in the west. Indeed, Gray made no mention of the Little Stint in Argyll, but H&B quoted records from Mull and Tiree. One was also said to have been shot on Loch Sween on an unspecified date in the late 19th century (ASNH 1897:45). Anderson (1898, 1913) reported that Little Stints were less than annual visitors to

Small numbers of Little Stints visit Argyll in autumn each year, *en route* to their African wintering sites. *Eddie Maguire*

Tiree, with flocks of up to 20, mainly in Gott Bay. "Large flocks" were said to have occurred on the island on 31 August 1892 (ASNH 1893:161, B&R). On nearby Coll, Little Stints were said to have been observed and specimens obtained in late February 1902, though there was some confusion over the dates, while "many" were present on Crossapol Sands in April the same year (ASNH 1902:251-2, 1903:50). Although B&R quoted these records (without specifying the time of year), they are incompatible with what is now known of the movements of the species and seem certain to have resulted from misidentification.

Nevertheless, it is possible that Little Stints were more numerous in Argyll in the past than today. B&R's own observation of a flock of 50 to 60 at Gruinart on 16 September 1937 has never been matched, despite the increased scrutiny now given to wader flocks. On the other hand, in 1986 Thom believed that there had been no significant change in status in Scotland over the previous 30 or 40 years.

The current status of the Little Stint in Argyll is that of an annual visitor in small numbers, mainly to Kintyre and the islands in autumn. In the 19-year period between 1985 and 2003, birds were seen every autumn but in only nine spring periods. Most recent records have involved single birds but there have been a few double-figure counts (Table).

The number of autumn records varies greatly from year to year. In 1990 and 1997, for example, only one bird was recorded, while in late September 1996 birds were reported from Tiree, Mull, Islay, Oronsay and south Kintyre. These records were associated with a major influx into western Europe. Indeed, most good autumns for this species in Argyll have been associated with higher than average numbers elsewhere in Scotland. Birds found in western areas are probably largely weather-displaced juveniles (BWP).

Counts of more than ten Little Stints in Argyll, 1973-2004.

Date	Location	Count	Reference
22 Sep 1973	Loch Indaal (Islay)	11	SB 8:243
5 Sep 1981	Gott Bay (Tiree)	42	ABR 1:42
25 Aug 1989	Loch Gruinart	10+	ABR 6:31
25 Sep 1996	Machrihanish	15 (max)	ABR 13:50
18 Sep 1998	Bridgend (Islay)	17 (max)	ABR 15:54
30 Sep 2000	Loch Gruinart	18 (max)	ABR 17:56
28 Sep 2001	Uisaed Point	12	ABR 18:56
20 May 2004	Vaul Bay (Tiree)	15	Argyll Database

Most records have occurred in the second half of September, the earliest and latest dates being 5 August and 25 October. Sometimes individuals and small flocks have apparently lingered for days or even weeks, and a few birds have been noted on southward migration past Uisaed Point in Kintyre. Spring records have been concentrated in a much shorter period, between 17 May and 12 June, with rarely more than one record a year. Outside these periods, two were seen at Bruichladdich on Islay on 8 July 1993 (ABR 10:45) and three at Liath Eilean, Danna, on 21 July 2003 (Argyll Database). The only mainland records away from Kintyre, other than those quoted above, come from Oban, where there was one bird on 30 September 1992 (ABR 9:30), and the Add estuary, where there were two on 8 September 1998 (ABR 15:54), one on 21 August 2001 (ABR 18:56) and one on 12 June 2006 (Argyll Database).

[A few winter and early spring records have been published in ABR but have failed to gain acceptance for publication in SBR. The Argyll Database also contains a record of one on Mull on 23 April 2003, an unusual time of year.]

Tristan ap Rheinallt

Temminck's Stint

Calidris temminckii

Vagrant.

Although there is a tiny breeding population in Highland Region, this species is mostly a scarce and irregular visitor to Scotland from its main breeding grounds in Scandinavia and northern Russia. Records away from the east coast and Northern Isles are few and far between. The first of four accepted Argyll records, all of which involved single birds, occurred on the rather unusual date of 9 July 1974 at Machrihanish (SB 8:435). A juvenile was then at Fidden on Mull on 17 September 1985 (SB 14:105, ABR 3:31), and a bird was at An Fhaodhail on Tiree on 23 August 1992 (SBR 1992:27, ABR 9:31). Finally, on Islay a moulting individual spent several hours in front of the hide at Loch Gruinart on 15 and 16 May 2000 (ABR 17:56).

Tristan ap Rheinallt

White-rumped Sandpiper

Calidris fuscicollis

Vagrant.

A moulting adult was seen with Dunlin at Loch Gruinart on 13 August 2000 (BB 94:470, ap Rheinallt 2001). This, the first Argyll record, occurred during an exceptionally good year for this North American species in Scotland and the UK as a whole. Six individuals were recorded in the Outer Hebrides, two in Orkney, two in north-east Scotland and one in Shetland in 2000. Although most were in September and October, the Orkney and Shetland birds occurred in July (BB 94:471). Like the Islay individual, they were adults; juveniles do not migrate until later in the autumn (Hayman *et al.* 1986).

The second Argyll record concerned a bird at Loch Gruinart, Islay, on 17 October 2005.

Tristan ap Rheinallt

There have been only four accepted records of Temminck's Stints in Argyll. *Jim Dickson*

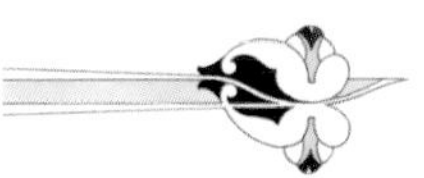

Baird's Sandpiper

Calidris bairdii

Vagrant.

An adult in breeding plumage was at Ronnachmore, near Bowmore on Islay, on 3 June 1979 (BB 73:507). Although this was the only date accepted by BBRC, the bird was said by Elliott (1989) to have been present since the end of May. Twenty years later, a juvenile was at Loch Gruinart from 5 to 21 September 1999 (BB 93:532). This occurrence was associated with the exceptional influx of North American waders that resulted in Argyll's first four Semipalmated Sandpipers.

In Scotland, there were 32 records to the end of 2002, all but one in autumn. The Outer Hebrides accounted for 11 of these records, but there were no other sightings in western Scotland away from Islay (Anon. 2003).

Tristan ap Rheinallt

Baird's Sandpiper, a very rare vagrant to Argyll from North America. *Jim Dickson*

Pectoral Sandpiper

Calidris melanotos

Rare autumn migrant, with a few spring records.

Although its nearest breeding grounds are in Canada's Hudson Bay, the Pectoral Sandpiper is a regular autumn visitor to the British Isles. This high frequency of occurrence is thought to be linked to the species' strong south-easterly movement across Canada in autumn, with consequent overshooting into the paths of Atlantic depressions or the jet stream, but it is also possible that Britain lies on the normal migration path of birds regularly wintering in Africa (Migration Atlas, Lees & Gilroy 2004). The Pectoral Sandpiper was first recorded in Scotland in 1928, and there have been records every year since 1973. In Argyll, the species was first recorded at Campbeltown on 17 October 1978 (SBR 1978:25). Since then, there have been 18 more accepted records (to the end of 2004). Twelve of these fell within the period 29 August to 29 October, with an early bird at Loch a' Phuill on Tiree on 3 August 2000 (ABR 17:56). The four spring records were between 29 April and 22 June.

Of these 19 records, nine came from Loch Gruinart, Islay, five from Tiree, three from Mull and two from Kintyre. Three juveniles were seen together at Loch Gruinart on 13 and 14 September 2000 and one remained to 1 October (ABR 17:56). Interestingly, while autumn 2003 produced the largest influx of Pectoral Sandpipers ever recorded in Britain and Ireland (Lees & Gilroy 2004), only two birds were seen in Argyll, both at Loch Gruinart (Argyll Database).

Tristan ap Rheinallt

Curlew Sandpiper

Calidris ferruginea

Scarce but annual passage migrant, with most records in autumn.

The Curlew Sandpiper breeds in the high Arctic and winters mainly in Africa. Since the nearest major staging area to Britain is the Wadden Sea, the species normally occurs in greatest numbers in the east and south of the country. It was recorded as a visitor to Argyll in the 19th century. Gray described it as occasional on Iona and Mull, and sparingly distributed along the shores of mainland Argyll, being especially notable in early autumn. According to Graham, individuals were occasionally shot among other sandpipers. B&R gave early dated records from Tiree (23 September 1898), Skerryvore (31 July 1902) and Loch Indaal (September 1937).

Throughout the first half of the 20th century, the Curlew Sandpiper was regarded as rare on the west coast of Scotland north of the Clyde (B&R). It was recorded less than annually in Argyll until the mid-1980s, and at no more than two locations in any one year. With the exception of ten on Loch Gruinart in August 1962 (Booth 1975), no count exceeded four birds. In autumn 1988, however, there were reports from four different locations, with a record count of 17 at Loch Gruinart (ABR 5:21). This was part of a major influx into the north and west of Britain (Migration Atlas).

Since then, Curlew Sandpipers have been recorded in every autumn except 1995 and 1996. As in earlier years, nearly all records have come from the islands (Coll, Colonsay, Islay, Mull and Tiree) or from Kintyre. Outwith Kintyre, there have only been five mainland sightings. All but two of these came from the Add Estuary and Loch Crinan area, where there were six on 30 August 1998 (ABR 15:55), one on 12 and 14 September 1999 (ABR 16:56) and two from 31 July to 5 August 2002 (Argyll Database). The other mainland records involved a single at Benderloch on 21 September 1985 (ABR 3:31) and five juveniles at Loch na Cille (Loch Sween) on 9 September 2005, two of which remained until 12 September (Argyll Database).

Some of the recent increase in records certainly reflects increased observer activity. Nevertheless, there is also a great deal of year-to-year variation. As with the Little Stint, it is known that weather conditions in some years can displace juvenile birds westwards from their usual overland migration route, producing influxes into Scotland and the rest of the UK, as in 1988 (Thom, Migration Atlas). Such influxes were responsible for at least some of the small number of double-figure counts in Argyll.

Most autumn migrants pass through Argyll between mid-August and mid-October, with numbers of juveniles tending to peak in September (Table). An adult in almost full breeding plumage was on Tiree on 8 July 2006, a notably early date. A few adults are sometimes seen in the county from late July, while occasional late-autumn records include a single at Westport on 7 November 1987 (ABR 5:7) and two birds with Golden Plovers at Heylipol on 13 November 2001 (ABR 18:56).

Because most birds wintering in West Africa return overland to Siberia, very few occur along Atlantic coasts in spring (BWP). Not surprisingly, therefore, spring records are few in Argyll, occurring in 12 of the 27 years from 1980 to 2006. Rarely has more than one bird been seen in Argyll at this time of year, but the spring of 1999 was exceptional, with records from three locations on Tiree and one on Islay. Up to three birds were seen together at Gott Bay and at Loch Gruinart (ABR 16:56). Dates of spring records have ranged from 16 April to 12 June.

Records of ten or more Curlew Sandpipers in Argyll to the end of 2006.

Year	Location	Date	Maximum count
1962	Loch Gruinart	August (date unknown)	10 (Booth 1975)
1988	Loch Gruinart	12 September	17 (ABR 5:21)
1996	Loch Gruinart	11 and 29 September	10 (ABR 13:50)
1998	Loch Gruinart	11 September	46 (ABR 15:55)
1999	Loch Gruinart	6 September	33 (ABR 16:56)
2000	Loch Gruinart	23 September	12 (ABR 17:56)
2001	Loch a' Phuill	30 September	15 (ABR 18:56)

Records in Britain outwith the period April to November are exceptional (Migration Atlas). Nevertheless, singles were on Islay on 5 February 1976 (SB 10:97) and Tiree on 14 January 2002 (Argyll Database).

Tristan ap Rheinallt

Purple Sandpiper

Calidris maritima

Widely distributed along rocky island coasts from September to May, with the highest numbers in Tiree. Scarcer on the mainland.

The Purple Sandpiper differs from other calidrids in that it winters primarily on exposed rocky shores, where it feeds mostly on winkles, mussels and shrimps. It is mainly a winter visitor to Britain and Ireland, and it is suggested that most of the British wintering population comes from arctic Canada, the remainder belonging to the shorter-billed Norwegian population. At least some of the former stop off to refuel in Iceland or Greenland (Migration Atlas).

Because of their preference for rocky shores rather than estuaries, Purple Sandpipers are widely dispersed along the coast and their distribution is difficult to assess. Gray described the species as occurring throughout the west of Scotland, and this was also the view of H&B for Argyll, though they pointed out "a distinct tendency to incline more to the insular portions than to the mainland." Graham reported the occasional presence of large flocks on Iona and Mull, though small parties of half a dozen or so were more typical. Tomison (1907) described the species as a regular winter resident on Skerryvore.

The islands still hold the majority of Argyll's Purple Sandpipers. The Winter Atlas shows them to be concentrated in Tiree, Coll, Islay and Mull, with more scattered records in Kintyre and a few other locations. The Winter Shorebird Count of 1984/85, which concentrated on non-estuarine coasts, produced an estimated total of 318 Purple Sandpipers in Argyll[1]. Of these, 226 (71%) were on the larger islands, with Tiree holding the most birds (119), followed by Mull (65) (Madders & Moser 1986). An incomplete repeat survey in winter 1997/98 produced a total of 369 birds, none of which were on mainland coasts[1]. Of these, 262 were on Tiree, which seems to be the only Argyll island to have produced three-figure counts of this species. The highest totals to date from Tiree have been 377 in February 1995 (J. Bowler pers. comm.), 288 in January 1987 and 368 during a complete coastal count in February 2006.

On the other islands, mainly Islay, Mull, Staffa, Coll, Colonsay and Oronsay, maximum counts of 20 to 30 birds are more typical, though 43 were reported from Portnahaven on Islay on 28 February 1990 and 55 from Coll in the winter 1997/98 survey. The only part of the mainland to produce comparable counts is south Kintyre, particularly the Machrihanish area. A total of 43 were recorded flying south past Uisaed Point on 25 October 1989, with 38 on 29 October 2001 and 40 on the shore at nearby Westport on 20 December 1989. Not far away, 44 were at Southend on 11 March 1973 (SB 8:242).

Other regular mainland sites include Ledaig Point, which regularly held small numbers during the 1980s at least, and

Dunoon, where up to 20 birds have been recorded in recent winters. Eilean Aoghainn in Loch Fyne and Skipness in Kintyre have also produced several records. Purple Sandpipers are known to show strong site-fidelity from one winter to the next, so sites such as these are likely to hold birds every year. An isolated record of a single bird at Otter Ferry on 22 October 2001, on the other hand, could refer to a passage migrant.

In many years, Purple Sandpipers are not seen in Argyll until the end of September or even sometimes the end of October. In some years, however, a few may be reported as early as the first few days of August. For example, two birds were on the Treshnish Isles on 4 August 1980, and one at Scallastle on Mull on the same date in 1987, while in the past, Purple Sandpipers were occasionally recorded on Skerryvore in late July. This unusual pattern may be related to the fact that the two wintering populations arrive in Britain at different times: Norwegian birds as early as July in order to moult, and Canadian birds in October, having moulted elsewhere (Migration Atlas). The main influx of Purple Sandpipers into Argyll is likely to involve the Canadian population, perhaps coming via Iceland, while the few earlier birds in some years may belong to the Norwegian population, although these are mostly found on the east coast of Britain. Recent observations on Tiree support the idea of two separate arrivals, with a small passage of birds recorded from early September to mid-October and then few or no records until December, when birds become more widespread around the rocky shores (J. Bowler pers. comm.). A colour-ringed bird present at Scarinish Pier, Tiree, on 5-10 February 2006 had been caught and identified as a female at Eardskagi, Reykjanes Peninsula, south-west Iceland on 8 May 2005.

The shores of Tiree support several hundred Purple Sandpipers each winter. *Philip Kirkham*

Numbers of Purple Sandpipers in Argyll can still be high in the first half of May, perhaps indicating that passage migrants stop off on their way north. For example, 155 were reported from Tiree during 10-14 May 1986 and 40 from Staffa on 8 May 1991. In some years, however, birds appear to be absent or nearly absent from favoured locations during this period, suggesting that the presence of spring migrants may be weather-dependent. There are few records from the second half of May, although 31 were at Hough Bay on Tiree on 16 May 1992. There is one June record, involving two birds seen on Tiree on 7 June 1989 (RSPB warden's report).

Although numbers of Purple Sandpipers wintering in the UK are thought to have fallen in recent years, there is no firm evidence of a decline in Argyll. While rocky shores and reefs constitute the preferred habitat, birds sometimes join other waders on sandy or muddy shores, especially where seaweed has been washed ashore. There are no Argyll records away from the coast.

[1]These surveys included Gare Loch and inner Loch Linnhe, both of which are outside the Argyll recording area covered in this book.

Tristan ap Rheinallt

Dunlin

Calidris alpina

This small wader breeds on wet moorland and marshy ground in several parts of Argyll, chiefly on Tiree. Passage flocks are widespread and, while most wintering birds are found on Islay and Tiree, smaller flocks may occur wherever there are tidal flats of mud and fine sand.

The year-round presence of Dunlins involves three races. All those that breed in the British Isles are *C. a. schinzii*, and the breeding range of this race extends from south-east Greenland through Iceland to Scandinavia. It occurs on British coasts on spring and autumn passage but winters from western Europe south to west Africa. *C. a. alpina* breeds from northern Scandinavia to west Siberia; it arrives in Scotland in large numbers from early August to November and the large winter and passage flocks on British estuaries are mainly of this race. *C. a. arctica* breeds in north-east Greenland and winters in west Africa, and small numbers occur briefly in west Scotland on spring and autumn passage (Migration Atlas). Gray realised that at least two races were found here; commenting that "larger birds from the east coast of Scotland are not bred on our moors but are migrants from other countries". The smaller, Scottish birds were "found breeding on almost every moorland and marshy tract where Snipe or Golden Plover" occurred. B&R also distinguished between the southern (*schinzii*) and northern (*alpina*) Dunlins. They recorded wintering birds on Tiree but considered them "not common" on Islay in winter. They recorded breeding on Islay in 1936 and on Jura in 1939, noting that "hundreds" bred all over Tiree in 1898 and 1899, many still in 1913, but few by 1950, while small numbers bred on Coll in 1899, 1937 and

1938.

British birds arrive back on their breeding grounds on moorland and machair in March-April, and most chicks hatch in May or June. Breeding was recorded in 20% of 10-km squares in the Second Atlas. Records suggest that Argyll held several hundred breeding pairs in the early 1990s but that numbers have since decreased. The Second Atlas shows highest densities on Tiree, Coll and Kintyre, with important but lower densities over much of Islay and Jura. Dunlins breed in most years in small numbers on Mull and Colonsay and in North and Mid-Argyll, but no records of breeding were traced from Cowal. Tiree, the breeding stronghold of the county, held an estimated 250-350 pairs in 1987 and *c.*300 in 1988 but, by 1994, numbers had decreased by about 60% to 143 pairs, although still 1.5% of the British total. Some 30-40 pairs bred on The Reef in 1998 and 46 pairs in 2002; and a minimum of 22 pairs were counted in one part of Tiree in 2000. A count of most of Tiree in 2004 found 190-200 pairs (J. Bowler pers. comm.). Numbers on Coll have decreased, from 20 pairs in 1987 to seven in 1995, three in 1997 and at least one in 2000; in 2004 a whole-island count found 11 pairs including only one on the RSPB Reserve. On Islay there were 14-15 pairs in a survey of the Rinns in 1994. RSPB's Loch Gruinart Reserve held around 4-6 pairs for most of the 1990s; a single pair was counted there in 2000 and there were five clutches in 2002. Four pairs bred at Ardnave in 2006. In 1996, four pairs are thought to have bred on mainland Colonsay and another 11 on Oronsay. Small numbers are reported breeding, regularly or occasionally, from North and Mid-Argyll, Mull, Kintyre and Jura.

This is one of several wader species in which the female departs when the chicks are still small, as early as mid-June, leaving the male to complete the rearing. The young fly at three weeks and, after forming small flocks, all have usually left the breeding ground by late July. Many birds of all three races are on the move from late July to October and, as in spring, passage is noted at many sites. "Unprecedented" numbers coincided with an algal bloom at Loch Gruinart in late summer 1996 (3,000 on 22 August); and unusually high numbers were on passage at MSBO in 1997; 587 in July (maximum of 233 on 24 July), 1,150 in August (maximum of 210 on 12 August) and 70 in September. During a heavy passage of waders in mist and rain, many Dunlins were heard at night over Tobermory from 2340 hrs on 29 August 1984; and *c.*1,000 moved south in fog at the Mull of Kintyre Lighthouse on 2 August 1982. This was one of ten species recorded throughout the year at Ledaig Point by Jennings (1995).

In winter, flocks of several hundred Dunlin can be seen on Islay and Tiree. *David Palmar*

From August to February, the largest flocks in Argyll are on Islay and Tiree, both holding several hundred birds. Counts at Lochs Gruinart and Indaal record maximum monthly totals in winter of around 400-600. On 9 January 2001, 499 were counted in the main bays of Tiree and a complete coastal survey of Tiree on 14-20 January 2000 found 609 birds. Other

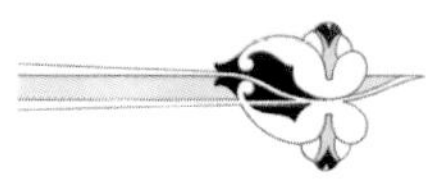

wintering flocks that often exceed 100 birds are on Colonsay and sometimes at Lochs Don, Gilp and Crinan, with smaller numbers at many other less extensive mudflats (ABR). In a winter shorebird survey covering most of the Argyll coast in 1984-85, this was the seventh most numerous species with 966 birds (Madders & Moser 1986). In the NEWS count of December 1997-January 1998, 896 were counted in Argyll, of which 39% were on Islay and 32% on Tiree.

Counts at sites on Islay, Colonsay, Tiree, Kintyre and Mull record large declines in March and April as *alpina* return to their breeding grounds in the tundras of northern Europe and Asia. In most years, this is followed in May by a sharp peak of birds in breeding plumage, mainly returning *schinzii*, possibly with some *arctica*. A bird definitely identified as *arctica* was recorded on passage with a small group of *schinzii* at Fidden on Mull on 12 May 1998 (Argyll Database). Their refuelling stopover is brief, as this 1981 ABR record from Mull shows - "400 summer-plumaged birds in Scallastle Bay on the morning of 7 May 1981 had departed north by the afternoon; and 1,500 in summer plumage at Loch Don on 7 May had decreased to 500 by 8 May and 60 by 10 May". A massive flock of 2,330 birds was counted at Gott Bay, Tiree, on 17 May 2006. Northward passage is also observed at this time at regular seawatching sites. There was a "heavy passage" over Tobermory on the night of 18-19 April 1985 (ABR). An adult ringed in Kintyre in September 1974 was shot near Coruña (Spain) in December of that year (1,364km) and an adult ringed near Boston (Lincs) in 1977 was found dead near Barcaldine in 1984. Ringed birds presumed to be *schinzii* (since they bred or were hatched in Britain) have been recovered as follows; an adult ringed on Walney Island (Cumbria) in 1987 was found dead in Kintyre in 1989, a chick ringed on Mull in June 1982 was recorded alive in Poole harbour (Dorset) in April 1985 (697km) and an adult ringed in Kent in December 1992 was seen with young on Coll in 1994, showing that at least one of our breeding birds wintered within the British Isles.

Clive Craik

Broad-billed Sandpiper

Limicola falcinellus

Vagrant.

Although the Broad-billed Sandpiper breeds no further away than southern Norway, it migrates overland in a southerly to south-easterly direction (BWP) and is a vagrant to the British Isles. There are two Argyll records. The first concerns a bird seen briefly at Balephetrish Bay on Tiree on 13 May 1994 (BB 88:514). This was only the third from the west coast of Scotland (SBR 1994:29). The second Argyll bird was also on Tiree: a well-marked individual (presumably adult) was watched and photographed at close range with Dunlin at Scarinish Pier on 31 May 2005. It was relocated in Gott Bay on 1 June (BB 100:41).

Tristan ap Rheinallt

Buff-breasted Sandpiper

Tryngites subruficollis

Rare autumn migrant, with three spring records.

Although it breeds largely in the Canadian High Arctic, the Buff-breasted Sandpiper is, like the Pectoral Sandpiper, regarded as a scarce migrant rather than a vagrant to the British Isles. Apparently a small proportion of the Canadian population makes the direct sea crossing from New England to South America (BWP), and some of these birds are displaced to the east by weather systems.

The Scottish records of this species have a wide geographical spread, with the west of the country well represented. The total for Argyll (to the end of 2006) is 15 records (Table).

As with most other transatlantic wader species, Kintyre and the islands have a monopoly of the records. In accordance

Records of Buff-breasted Sandpipers in Argyll to the end of 2006.

Date	Location	Comment	Reference
28 September 1971	Machir Bay (Islay)	Sixth Scottish record	BB 65:334
7 - 16 September 1974	Machrihanish		BB 68:318
31 May 1983	Arnabost (Coll)	Feeding on tideline	SBR 1983:22, ABR 1:44
21 - 24 September 1983	Fidden (Mull)		SBR 1983:22, ABR 1:44
20 June 1987	Killean (Kintyre)		SBR 1987:23, ABR 5:8
6 September 1989	Gott Bay (Tiree)		SBR 1989:20, ABR 6:32
6 and 13 September 1996	Hough (Tiree)	Two juveniles	SBR 1996:32, ABR 13:52
8 September 1996	Ardnave (Islay)	Three juveniles	SBR 1996:32, ABR 13:52
5 - 7 September 1999	Loch Gruinart (Islay)	Juvenile; with Dunlin flock in intertidal zone	SBR 1999:56, ABR 16:57
12 September 2001	Frenchman's Rocks (Islay)	Juvenile	SBR 2001:60, ABR 18:57
17 - 19 June 2004	The Reef (Tiree)	Adult	Argyll Database
15 - 16 September 2004	Loch a' Phuill (Tiree)	Juvenile with juvenile Pectoral Sandpiper	Argyll Database
3 - 8 September 2005	Tiree (various locations)	Three juveniles	Argyll Database
29 August 2006	Loch a' Phuill (Tiree)		Argyll Database
10 September 2006	Oronsay (Colonsay)	Juvenile	Argyll Database

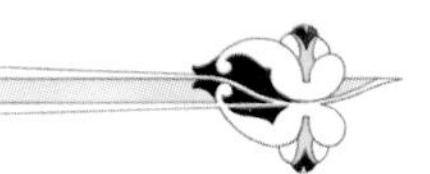

with the general pattern in Britain, most have been in autumn. There was also a single record in May and two in June. Multiple occurrences of this species in Britain, although an exciting sight for the observer, are not particularly unusual; the two 1996 Argyll records contributed to the highest total of birds seen in Britain since 1977. The records that year showed an unusual northerly bias, with Argyll, the Outer Hebrides and Lothian being the favoured counties (Fraser *et al.* 1999). The arrival of the 1999 bird was associated with the same weather conditions that brought Argyll's second Baird's Sandpiper and two of its first four Semipalmated Sandpipers to the same location. Although the number of British records declined steadily since the 1970s (Fraser & Rogers 2001), there is no sign of a similar trend in Argyll.

Tristan ap Rheinallt

Ruff

Philomachus pugnax

Uncommon migrant, with most records in autumn.

Early records of this species from Argyll are few. The first dated record appears to be of a bird on Coll around 16 September 1905 (ASNH 1906:201). Irby (1899) included the Ruff in his list of species from Tiree, and Anderson (1913) also reported that single birds were occasionally seen there in autumn. On Islay, one shot near Port Ellen on 11 September 1912 was said to be the first record for the island (B&R, Booth 1975).

From the 1950s onwards, Ruffs began to be recorded with increasing frequency, and from 1973 onwards records were more or less annual. A bird at Keills by Danna in Mid-Argyll on 7 June 1973 (SB 8:244) appears to represent the first spring record for Argyll. Two years later, on 18 May 1975 (SB 9:204), a pair was seen displaying at Machrihanish, and one was seen at Kilmartin on 21 August (Rainier 1975). The first indication that larger numbers might sometimes be present came in 1980, when numbers in the Bridgend area of Loch Indaal on Islay peaked at 16 on 19 September (unpublished record). Lekking was recorded on Tiree in 2004, 2005 and 2006 but breeding was not proved.

Since 1980, the frequency of records has continued to rise until, today, Ruffs can be described as uncommon but regular migrants to Islay, Tiree and Kintyre. Unlike many other waders, they are typically found in flooded fields rather than on intertidal sand and mudflats, though they certainly occur in the latter habitat as well. Some accompany Golden Plover flocks on short turf. Fewer are seen away from these favoured locations, but birds have been recorded from Mull, Colonsay, Oronsay, Jura and Iona in recent times. Records from mainland locations other than Kintyre are infrequent. Spring migration lasts from late March to early June, and autumn migration from late July to mid-November, with a very late bird at Loch Gruinart on Islay from 24 to 26 November 2001 (ABR 18:58). The peak autumn period is late August and September, when migrants have been seen flying south

Most records of Ruffs in Argyll come from Islay, Tiree and Kintyre. *Philip Kirkham*

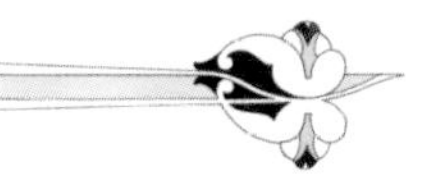

past Uisaed Point in Kintyre in small numbers. Outside these seasons, a bird was at Craignish on 10 and 11 February 1981 (ABR 1:44), and there have been a few records in late June and early July.

As elsewhere in Scotland, many more birds are seen in autumn than in spring, when most records concern single birds. Small groups are not infrequent in autumn, but few counts exceed ten birds. In addition to the above 1980 record from Loch Indaal, 14 were on Gruinart flats on 11 September 1988 (ABR 5:22) and 12 at Middleton on Tiree on 9 September 1998 (ABR 15:56). These counts were eclipsed by the flock at Loch Gruinart from 20 September to 1 October 2000, which peaked at 43 birds on 22 September (ABR 17:58). This is a significant number in a western Scottish context, although larger flocks, sometimes exceeding 100 birds, are not infrequently recorded from the north and east of Scotland, where Ruffs are generally commoner.

Tristan ap Rheinallt

Jack Snipe

Lymnocryptes minimus

Scarce autumn passage migrant and winter visitor, with Islay, Mid-Argyll and Tiree accounting for some 70 per cent of recent records.

The Jack Snipe is a passage migrant and winter visitor to the British Isles from its breeding grounds in Scandinavia and Russia. Owing to the decline in shooting interests, it is perhaps a less familiar bird in Argyll today than in the past. Older naturalists such as Gray and H&B described it as occurring in the same localities as Common Snipe, being not uncommon though certainly present in smaller numbers than its relative. According to H&B, it was common though locally distributed in Tiree, where it formed about 25 per cent of the combined bag of Common and Jack Snipe on the island. This compares with an estimate of 11 per cent for Britain as a whole in the early 1980s (Winter Atlas). Although there are several possible explanations for the difference between these two estimates, including decline in numbers as reported by Anderson (1913) for Tiree, it is important to note that Jack Snipe, when flushed, are easier to shoot than Common Snipe. Thus both percentages are likely to be too high, perhaps by as much as an order of magnitude (*cf.* Migration Atlas).

The Jack Snipe is notorious for its secretive behaviour,

The secretive Jack Snipe is even more reluctant to fly than the Common Snipe. *David Palmar*

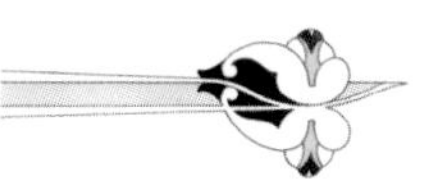

which explains why estimates of the British wintering population have varied widely. Over Britain as a whole, birds tend to be found singly or in small numbers in open wetland habitats, avoiding moorland and mountains (Winter Atlas, Migration Atlas). Gray described them as occurring in small groups in the marshes of Islay, Jura, Iona, Mull and the smaller islands, while B&R referred to considerable numbers sometimes in winter on Islay and Tiree, where the preferred habitat was mossy bogs rather than muddy places.

Observations on Islay over many years (C. R. McKay pers. comm.) indicate that, whilst Jack Snipe occupy a range of wetland habitats, they prefer the edges of small pools, creeks, flushes, wet runnels and ditches. Sites are characterised by tall vegetation of 30 to 50 cm height providing plenty of natural cover, which is not a critical requirement for Snipe. Although most sites on Islay are lowland in nature, birds are also seen in remoter moorland mires and bogs. Normally widely dispersed and elusive, they may become more obvious in freezing conditions as they concentrate around ice-free ditches, springs and small burns with suitable cover.

Jack Snipe are apparently more resistant to harsh weather than Common Snipe (Winter Atlas). Nevertheless, hard-weather movements do take place, and B&R described them in the Black Linn stream in the centre of Oban during severe frosty winters.

The only available distribution map is in the Winter Atlas. This suggests that the species is very thinly distributed in Argyll, with only 11 occupied 10-km squares, and only Islay and the west coast of mid-Argyll producing any suggestion of concentration. However, Argyll records for 1980 to 2003 indicate that, as might be expected, the species is present in most areas, although Islay and Mid-Argyll predominate. Tiree, though smaller, is next in importance judged by number of records (Table).

As on the Winter Atlas map, most mainland records are close to the coast. By far the largest number of records at a single site (26) come from Loch Gruinart on Islay, which also produced several undated records.

Geographic distribution of 169 records of Jack Snipe in Argyll, 1980-2003[1].

Area	% of records
MAINLAND (including minor islands)	
Mid-Argyll	18
North Argyll	6
Kintyre	3
Cowal	<1
ISLANDS	
Islay	39
Tiree	14
Mull	7
Coll	4
Colonsay	4
Oronsay	2
Gigha	<1
Sanda	<1
Treshnish Isles	<1

Approximately 90% of records concerned single birds. Of the remainder, nearly all involved just two or three individuals, but six birds were at Airds Bay, Loch Etive, on 17 January 1998 and four were at East Kames, Loch Fyne, on 7 March 1999. Six were reported to have been killed on Tiree by a visiting shooting party in mid-October 2003. There are also older records of six birds at Skerryvore on 22 October 1898 (ASNH 1899:156) and four at Bridgend on Islay on 13 March 1976 (SB 10:93).

The seasonal pattern of records during 1980-2003 shows that the main arrival occurs from mid-October onwards, a few birds sometimes arriving as early as mid-September (Figure). This agrees with the pattern in the British Isles generally, arrival being somewhat later in the west than in the east (e.g. Winter Atlas, Migration Atlas). According to Thom, early individuals sometimes arrive in Scotland in mid-August, but investigation of earlier published August records from Argyll (not included in the Figure) suggests that identification was

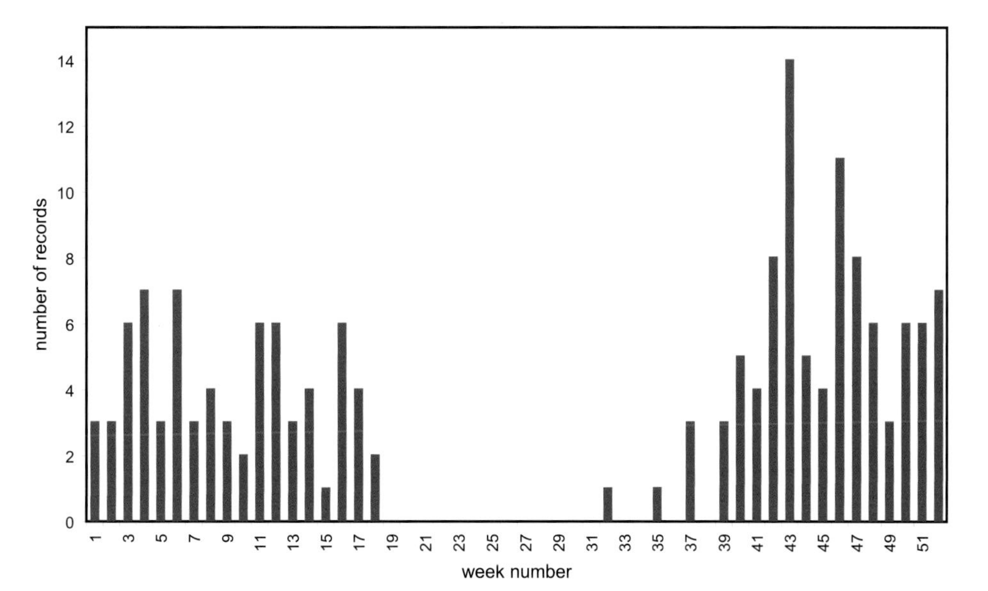

Weekly variation in Argyll records of Jack Snipe, 1980-2003[1].

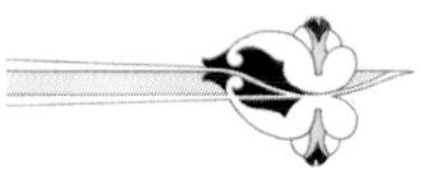

not established beyond doubt.

There is a clear peak of records in October and November (weeks 40-48), presumably reflecting the presence of passage migrants. Indeed, there is a suggestion that this is a double peak, and if so it corresponds to the situation at Paisley Moss in the Clyde area, where the later peak may represent birds that remain for the winter (Thom).

From December, there is little evidence of change in numbers in Argyll until the end of April, when records tail off abruptly. However, a return spring passage is thought to occur on Islay (C. R. McKay pers. comm.), and it could be that the small peak of sightings in the second half of April (weeks 16-17) reflects this. There are at least two well-documented reports of birds in the first few days of May, but occurrence in Argyll after mid-May is regarded as unconfirmed despite the existence of published records (e.g. SB 10:93, Elliott 1989).

[1]Sightings of more than one bird at the same location on the same date count as single records.

Tristan ap Rheinallt

Common Snipe

Gallinago gallinago

Snipe breed on suitable marshy ground in many parts of Argyll but the largest numbers are found on the outer islands. Higher numbers occur on passage and in winter, particularly on the islands. Freezing weather can cause many to move.

The metallic sound made by displaying male Snipe during their near-vertical aerial dives is one of the most remarkable sounds produced by any bird. Caused by the vibrating outer tail feathers, this "drumming" was likened by Graham to bleating, a similarity which earned the species its Gaelic name *gabhar-adheir* (aerial goat). For most of the year, however, Snipe are reluctant to fly until an intruder is within a few metres. Also, unlike most waders, they rarely form large flocks. Thus they are difficult to count except early in the breeding season when males are displaying.

Spring passage towards the north and east occurs in February-March and birds are in breeding areas in Argyll bogs and marshy fields by early May. Breeding requires damp soil all through the breeding season until late June, when young can leave the area; thus dry summers lead to poor productivity. Autumnal passage takes place in September-October. Most British Snipe are relatively sedentary but those from countries to the north and east (from Iceland to Russia) winter in south and west Europe (the Low Countries, France, Iberia, British Isles), some as far as south of the Sahara. Severe frost in Britain can mobilise large numbers to seek unfrozen ground.

Snipe in Argyll belong to two races, *G. g. gallinago* and *G. g. faroeensis*. The former breeds throughout the Palearctic region with the exception of Iceland, the Faeroes, Orkney and Shetland, which are occupied by the darker and more rufous-plumaged *faroeensis* (BWP). Proof that *faroeensis* occurs in Argyll comes from Tiree, where a Snipe ringed as a juvenile in Iceland on 16 July 1938 was recovered in November the same year. The only other recovery of a foreign-ringed Snipe in Argyll was on Islay on 30 November 1965, the bird in question being an individual of the race *gallinago* ringed in the Vestfold area of Norway about seven weeks earlier.

Overall, it is estimated that 750,000 to 1 million Snipe visit Britain and Ireland in winter from Iceland, northern Europe and central Europe. This dwarfs the local winter population of more than 70,000 birds (Migration Atlas). Geographical considerations make it likely that most of those visiting Argyll originate from Iceland. Elliott (1989) believed this to be the case for Islay, where many passage and wintering birds are strongly tinged with rufous.

Other recoveries in Argyll illustrate the shorter migrations of Scottish-bred birds. Four chicks ringed on Tiree in 1927 were shot there in October-December of 1928, 1929 (2) and 1931; and a chick ringed on Tiree in 1924 was shot in Co. Cork (Ireland) on 28 November 1928. A chick ringed at Almondbank (Tayside) in 1935 was shot in Kintyre on 7 October 1936; a chick ringed at Aberlady Bay (Lothian) in 1937 was shot in Kintyre on 9 September the same year; and a juvenile ringed on South Uist on 2 November 1988 was shot in Kintyre 12 days later.

Gray described this as "an abundant species all over the western counties". In some areas it had "multiplied" greatly as Merlins and Peregrines had been "so systematically killed" while, elsewhere, it had become less numerous after ground had been drained ("two or three pairs at most where formerly as many hundreds were reared").

H&B found it "common and generally distributed in most suitable haunts from north to south Argyll in varying numbers". Pride of place went to Coll and Tiree for "the number they yield in autumn and winter, whilst a considerable number also breed there". It was abundant on Mull and Iona, and present on Staffa and the Treshnish Isles. They noted that most of the Snipe on Tiree in autumn and winter came from "more northern breeding grounds". As an example of a good bag on Tiree, H&B relate that 69 birds were shot there by one gun in one day in 1880. They go on to say that Snipe were scarce on Tiree in the cold winters of 1878-9 and 1879-80, but "extraordinarily numerous" in the rainy November of 1890, when "no less than 641 were killed by two guns in seven days". Sixteen years later, it seems that the capacity for slaughter had grown with the efficiency of shotguns: on 29 October 1906, two guns on Tiree killed 249 Snipe in six hours, and the same two people killed 1,108 Snipe in eight days, shooting for less than six hours a day (Anderson 1913). During 11 days in November 1908, two guns killed 1,293 Snipe on Tiree (B&R). Thom recorded that the average number shot per gun-day on Tiree fell from 68 in 1911-1914 to six in 1971-1983.

In 2005, Snipe-shooting still takes place on Tiree, except on the RSPB Reserve. It is usually confined to one or two weeks in October-November when, typically, four guns may shoot for five days, and a good bag for a year would be 300-350 birds (Tiree Estate, pers. comm.). In Britain and Ireland, at least 85,000 are shot each winter, so the wintering population must be many hundreds of thousands, although seeming less because Snipe are not easily flushed (Winter Atlas).

By 1953, B&R found that the species had become scarcer almost everywhere, because of drainage rather than shooting. Snipe were still present where marshy ground remained, and some were breeding in heather and on dry hillsides. They describe how on 21 December 1909, severe weather drove numbers of Snipe into the town of Tobermory.

The First Atlas found evidence of breeding in almost all the 10-km squares of Argyll. It gave a total for Britain and Ireland of 80,000-110,000 pairs, and Thom considered that Scotland probably held a third to a half of these. The Second Atlas found a probable minimum of 30,000 pairs in Britain and 10,000 pairs in Ireland, the change map showing many losses caused mostly by drainage of marshy ground. However, the distribution map still showed Snipe to be present in most squares in Argyll with the highest densities on Islay, Coll & Tiree.

During work for the Second Atlas, Snipe were recorded breeding in 51% of 10-km squares in Argyll. In BBS surveys they were found in three of 16 1-km squares in 1998, four of 15 in 1999 and two of 12 in 2000, and in two of 14 Countryside 2000 squares.

Most counts of breeding numbers (as drumming males) have come from the islands. On Colonsay regular counts during 1991-2004 averaged 40 drumming males. On Coll RSPB Reserve, counts during 1994-2004 found an average of 75 with a maximum of 165 in 1995 and minimum of 22 in 2000. The RSPB's Loch Gruinart reserve reported numbers varying between ten in 1985 and 68 in 2001, and 51 pairs were counted in the Rinns survey on Islay in 1994 when the highest densities were found on agricultural land. In 1987, 200-400 pairs were estimated to be breeding on Coll and 500-1,000 pairs on Tiree. The Tiree total was put at 1,200-2,000 pairs in 1988 and 300 pairs in 1994; 87 pairs were counted on The Reef in June 1998; counts of drumming males on The Reef were 120 in June 2002, 75 in April 2003 and 134 in June 2004 (ABR, Argyll Database). Before it was drained, Westport Marsh in Kintyre held 40 birds in 1990 (ABR).

The Winter Atlas showed absence from a large part of the central and west Highlands. There was a higher proportion of occupied squares in Islay, Colonsay, Coll and Tiree than elsewhere in Argyll, and many empty squares in Kintyre,

Drumming males advertise their presence, but otherwise Snipe are difficult to flush or to count. *Margaret Staley*

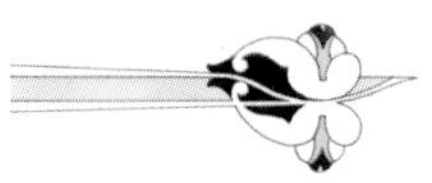

North Argyll and the east of Mull, perhaps reflected a move of Snipe to the coast in winter.

With the caveat that this species is particularly likely to be underestimated, 293 Snipe were found in Argyll during the NEWS count of winter 1997-1998 (190 on Tiree, 34 on Mull, 33 on Coll, 19 on Islay and smaller numbers elsewhere) making it the eleventh most numerous wader. In winter 1984-85, Madders & Moser (1986) found Snipe the tenth most abundant wader with a count of 215 in the county. During regular visits to Ledaig Point, Jennings (1995) recorded Snipe in only one year during 1982-1994. The largest numbers on passage and in winter are found on Tiree. In late September 2001, 500 were estimated to be on the island, and a complete coastal survey of Tiree on 14-20 January 2000 found 319 birds.

Passage of Snipe has been monitored at the usual sea-watching sites. In 1989, at Frenchman's Rocks 65 flew south on 20 August, while at MSBO/Uisaed Point 49 passed in 1.5h on 21 August and 14 flew in off the sea on 11 September.

Clive Craik

Great Snipe

Gallinago media

Vagrant; old records only.

The Great Snipe is one of only three rare waders to have been recorded more frequently in Britain before 1950 than after 1950, the other two being Cream-coloured Courser and Eskimo Curlew. Many of the earlier records refer to birds that were shot, and the fall in records over the past 70 years or so appears to be due to a combination of reduced hunting pressure and a genuine decline in some parts of the species' breeding range on the Continent (Evans 1994).

Old records of this species are difficult to evaluate. Two early records in Argyll concern specimens that were exhibited to the Glasgow Natural History Society and are therefore presumed to be genuine. One of these was shot at Ardrishaig in autumn 1864 (Gray, Proc. Nat. Hist. Soc. Glasgow 1: 101) and is presumed to be the same as the one said by Graham (p. 232) and by H&B to have been shot at Lochgilphead (McWilliam). The other was shot near Otter, Loch Fyne, in 1903 and exhibited on 22 December (ASNH 1904:215, McWilliam, Trans. Nat. Hist. Soc. Glasgow NS 7: 204).

[A sight record of one at the Rinns of Islay lighthouse on 27 November 1888 was not considered to be fully confirmed by H&B, who placed it in square brackets. Similarly, B&R singled out a record from Eigg as being "better authenticated" than other records from the Inner Hebrides. Thus, although the Islay record was published without qualification by Elliott (1989), it is best regarded as unconfirmed. The same applies to a record of one shot in Kintyre in 1887, but not published until more than 70 years later by Gibson & McWilliam (1959).]

Tristan ap Rheinallt

Wetlands on Tiree hold very high densities of breeding waders. *David Wood*

Long-billed Dowitcher

Limnodromus scolopaceus

Vagrant.

There is only one confirmed record of this vagrant North American wader in Argyll: a bird was on a small pool near Islay Airport from 18 to at least 19 June 1986 (BB 81:559). According to Elliott (1989), it was present from 3 to 23 June.

In addition, there are three records of unidentified dowitchers (this species or Short-billed *L. griseus*). One, the second dowitcher for Scotland, was shot at Dalnahassoch, near Crinan, on 2 September 1891, and exhibited to the Zoological Society (H&B). H&B wrongly claimed that there were two occurrences, but this was corrected soon afterwards (ASNH 1893:45).The other two records concern individuals at Loch a'Phuill on Tiree from 6 to 8 October 1969 (BB 63:276) and Loch Riddon on 5 April 1973 (BB 67:321).

Tristan ap Rheinallt

Woodcock

Scolopax rusticola

Widespread but probably under-recorded breeder. Numbers are augmented during the winter months by immigrants from Scandinavia and other parts of Scotland, while a small proportion of native birds leave for Ireland and possibly elsewhere.

The Woodcock is a widespread breeding species in woodland throughout Britain and Ireland. Because it is seldom active during the day, it is inconspicuous and may be overlooked. It is an important quarry for the sportsman, and most ringing recoveries involve birds that have been shot.

The Woodcock was widely reported from Argyll parishes in the two Statistical Accounts, but only as a migrant and winter visitor. In the past, the Woodcock was not a common breeder in the British Isles, but its range expanded considerably during the 19th century, probably as a consequence of climatic change (Second Atlas), though B&R considered protection during the nesting season to be the most important factor in Scotland. Elliott (1989) suggested that breeding may have commenced on Islay in the first half of the 19th century, while Graham reported an instance of breeding on the Ross of Mull around mid-century. H&B reported a large increase in breeding records from Argyll from about 1870 onwards.

In today's landscape, breeding Woodcock favour deciduous or mixed woodland with plenty of cover at the lower levels, but conifer plantations are also used. The First Atlas showed it widely distributed in Argyll, though absent from Coll and Tiree, and scarce in the south and west of Kintyre and in the western parts of Mull. By the time of the Second Atlas, there had apparently been a major decline, especially in northern parts of the mainland and on Islay, but with a westward range extension on Mull. In fact, decline was observed across most of Britain and Ireland. It was attributed to the maturing of conifer plantations (Second Atlas), although this was unlikely because most Woodcock in conifer forests breed in older, not younger stands of trees (S.J. Petty, pers. comm.). Under-recording may also have exaggerated the extent of its decline. Records since 1991 have added little to this picture, and estimates of the breeding population are available for only very few areas. Data from Colonsay suggest that the number of roding birds varies considerably from year to year. Such variation has also been noted in the past, with unusually high numbers breeding in some years, as on Mull in 1929, apparently following an influx of birds in late February (B&R).

Ringing recoveries show that most Woodcock that breed in the British Isles are sedentary, as H&B affirmed for birds on the west coast of Scotland. However, a small proportion of the population is migratory and may move considerable distances (Migration Atlas). Data from Argyll illustrate this. While several chicks ringed within Argyll have been recovered there in the winter months, only two have been recovered outside the county. One, ringed on Islay in May 1930 and recovered in Antrim (Ireland) in January 1931, chose a similar migration route to many other Scottish birds (Thom). The other, ringed on Islay in June 1936, was shot nearly 300km to the north-north-east at Brora (Highland Region) in January 1941.

In autumn, there is a widespread arrival in the British Isles of birds from Fennoscandia and Russia (Migration Atlas). The first usually arrive in mid-October, although they may not reach the west of Scotland and Ireland until later. This suggests that early migrants seen in September on Tiree, for example, may have a more local origin. The main influx into the Argyll islands occurs in November. For example, one or two birds were reported from eight places on Islay on 23 November 2001, presumably reflecting a recent arrival.

The influx into Britain continues until late December, with immigrants greatly outnumbering native breeders by midwinter. Most of those wintering in Scotland come from Norway, Sweden and Denmark (Migration Atlas). Thus a chick ringed in Sweden on 10 August 1938 was recovered at Glendaruel in Cowal on 3 January 1939. First-winter birds ringed in Fife on 21 October 1990 and Fair Isle on 4 November 1997, then shot on Islay on 4 November 1990 and 12 January 2000 respectively, may also have come from Scandinavia. On the other hand, the recovery of three chicks ringed in Tayside demonstrates that Argyll's wintering population includes birds from elsewhere in Scotland.

Some of the islands, particularly Islay, were famed in the past for winter Woodcock shooting. More than a thousand were shot on two Islay estates in the winter of 1846/47 (Gray, B&R), and a similar number in a fortnight at Islay House in

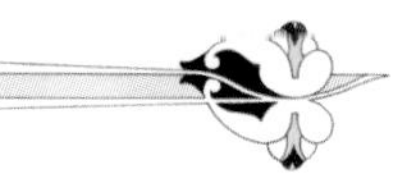

winter 1937/8 (B&R). Large bags were also obtained on Jura, Coll, Tiree and Colonsay (H&B, B&R, Jardine *et al.* 1986).

It was not until the early 1980s that a systematic attempt was made to map the distribution of wintering Woodcock in Argyll. The Winter Atlas shows good densities along the west mainland coast as well as in the south of Cowal and parts of Islay, Jura and Mull, but fewer records from Coll and Tiree, from coastal areas north of Seil in Mid-Argyll, or from inland areas of the mainland. Although Woodcock avoid high ground, they may be present at moderate altitudes. For example, two were encountered at about 350m on the slopes of Beinn Sgulaird in North Argyll on 12 December 1999.

It is well known that severe winter weather causes Woodcock to move west. Argyll, with its mild climate, may be expected to receive birds from further east in Scotland or even from the Continent in midwinter. Thus Pennant (1789, quoted in B&R) claimed that Woodcock did not reach the coasts of Lorn until December or January. More recently, observers have often reported unusually large numbers during cold spells, some entering gardens to feed during daylight. This occurred during the great storm of February and March 1947, when the gardens at Tobermory were said to be full of Woodcock (B&R). Large numbers were also reported in January 1982 and December 1995, though in 1995 this was ascribed to local birds being driven out of cover by severe frosts (SBR 95:33). Woodcock have been described as being most abundant on Coll and Tiree during severe winters (H&B, B&R), presumably seeking sanctuary on these mild islands.

Woodcock are most easily seen when 'roding' over their territories at dusk. *Margaret Staley*

Most continental migrants leave Britain during February and March, though some remain until mid-April, by which time resident females are incubating (Migration Atlas). As in Scotland as a whole (Thom), there is usually little evidence of return migration through Argyll in spring. However, in March 1884 Woodcock were unusually numerous on Islay as part of a more widespread movement across Scotland between the Clyde and the Forth (B&R).

Tristan ap Rheinallt

Black-tailed Godwit

Limosa limosa

A regular but local spring and autumn migrant, recorded most frequently from Islay, Tiree and south Kintyre. Numbers usually peak in late April and early August. Occasional individuals are seen in winter.

Black-tailed Godwits of two races, *limosa* and *islandica*, occur in Britain. All of those seen in Argyll probably belong to the latter race, which breeds principally in Iceland and occurs commonly in Britain and Ireland as a passage migrant and winter visitor. The small British breeding population of *limosa* winters further south.

At one time, this species was regarded as a rarity in the west of Scotland. Gray provided no records for Argyll, while H&B went to some lengths to justify their belief that it had occurred on Tiree. Anderson (1913) stated that a few were occasionally seen on the island in spring and autumn. More recently, B&R reported an increase in numbers in Scotland, both on passage and in winter, but still knew of only one record from mainland Argyll and few from the Inner Hebrides. The increase, which started in the early 20th century and has been attributed to climatic amelioration resulting in the growth of the Icelandic breeding population, has continued. Thus while fewer than ten Black-tailed Godwits in total were reported from Islay before 1975 (Booth 1975), several times that number now occur in most years.

The first migrants of the autumn arrive as early as the last week of June in some years but not until mid-July in others. At this time, tightly packed flocks of adults in full breeding plumage are sometimes seen on estuaries, at the margins of freshwater lochs, or flying south past certain headlands. Intensive wader-watching at Loch Gruinart on Islay over the past two to three years has demonstrated that although numbers at any one time do not usually exceed 10 or 20 birds, turnover in early autumn is high. It appears that adults only stop off briefly, perhaps as a result of bad weather, before continuing south.

Small groups continue to arrive through August and September, juveniles appearing later than adults and possibly staying longer. Most autumn records come from Islay, Tiree, Mull and south Kintyre. Numbers of adults generally peak in late July or early August, the highest count coming from Tiree, where there were 95 at Loch Riaghain and 74 at Loch an Eilein on 16 August 2004. A mid-September peak was observed in 2001, with 32 at Loch a' Phuill on Tiree on the 17th and 42 at Uisaed Point in Kintyre on the 21st, while in 2002 there was a record count of 101 at Uisaed Point in early September. Most of these were presumably juveniles.

The only regular site on the mainland appears to be Loch Crinan and the Add Estuary, where one to three birds are seen more or less every autumn. There are a few recent records from other locations in Mid-Argyll and from North Argyll, but none from Cowal. Birds are also occasionally reported from Colonsay, Coll and Gigha, but there seem to be no records from Jura.

The last birds of the autumn are usually seen in October, with a few sometimes lingering to mid-November. The Winter Atlas showed no records from the west or north of Scotland. More recently, occasional individuals have been recorded in Argyll during December, January and February, the first being a bird seen at Ruaig on Tiree on 10 January 1992. Their presence presumably reflects the growth in the British wintering population.

Birds wintering in Britain return to Iceland during April and May. In many years, they are not seen in Argyll until the beginning or middle of April, though there are a few March records, the earliest being eight at Ardnave on Islay on 3 March 1994. Numbers vary from year to year. In 1995, for example, spring migration through Argyll was almost non-existent, while 1997 produced higher totals than usual. As in autumn, adverse weather may lead to more sightings.

The Add Estuary is probably the best place to look for Black-tailed Godwits in mainland Argyll. *Philip Kirkham*

Islay, Tiree and south Kintyre account for an even higher proportion of records in spring than in autumn. On the mainland there appear to be only three spring records away from Kintyre, involving birds seen on the Add Estuary in 1999, 2001 and 2004. Peak numbers on Islay are comparable to those in autumn, but Tiree has produced some higher counts in recent springs, with 163 in the Loch Bhasapol area on 29 April 1994, 213 around Loch an Eilein and Loch Bhasapol on 24 April 1997, and 100 at the four main lochs on 27 April 2000. As in early autumn, spring flocks usually stay only for a few days at most.

Numbers in May are often much lower than in late April, though migration may continue until early June. This leaves only two to three weeks between the end of spring passage and the beginning of autumn passage. There are a few mid-June records in the county that could refer to summering non-breeders. Although Black-tailed Godwits have bred sporadically in different parts of Scotland, they have never

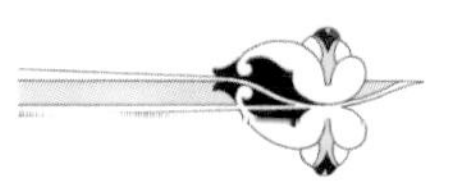

done so in Argyll.

More than half the Icelandic population is thought to winter in Ireland (Migration Atlas), and it might be expected that some of these would pass through Argyll. While there is no direct evidence for this, ringing has shown a link with the south of England. On Tiree, there has been a recovery of a bird ringed in Norfolk and sightings of other birds colour-ringed in Norfolk (three) and Hampshire (one).

Tristan ap Rheinallt

Bar-tailed Godwit

Limosa lapponica

Mainly an autumn migrant and winter visitor, with the largest numbers occurring on Islay. Birds are also regularly seen on Tiree and at a few other island and mainland sites. Immatures remain through the summer, especially on Islay.

Bar-tailed Godwits are mainly passage migrants and winter visitors to British and Irish coasts, congregating in large flocks on major estuaries such as the Wash. Wintering birds probably originate from northern European and west Siberian breeding populations, although birds from further east, that winter mainly in West Africa, also occur on migration. The wintering population is increasing, possibly as a consequence of reduced hunting pressure (Migration Atlas), and it is possible that numbers in Scotland were once much lower than now (B&R).

The number of Bar-tailed Godwits seen in Argyll varies considerably from year to year. *Eddie Maguire*

It has long been known that small flocks occur on migration in Argyll (Gray). Their distribution reflects their preference for sandy or muddy estuarine habitats. Today, by far the largest flocks are found at Loch Indaal and Loch Gruinart on Islay, although these are modest compared to numbers in other parts of Scotland, especially the east coast. Bar-tailed Godwits are also found regularly at several sites on Tiree as well as at Loch Don on Mull and The Strand on Colonsay. The importance of Tiree for passage and wintering Bar-tailed Godwits was recognised as long ago as 1892 by H&B, although they did not mention Islay. On the mainland, the most consistently used sites are Loch Crinan and Loch Gilp in Mid-Argyll.

The pattern of movement of this species in Argyll appears complex, with a great deal of variation in numbers from year to year. Some of this may be because Bar-tailed Godwits are highly mobile, often moving between as well as within wintering areas during a season (Thom).

Bar-tailed Godwits are found year-round at the two main Islay sites. The presence of a small number of summering non-breeders has been recognised since at least 1936 (B&R). Most of these are thought to be first-summer birds, lacking any sign of breeding plumage. However, it is known that some also stay on their wintering grounds in their second summer (Migration Atlas). Of late, the number of these summering non-breeders seems to have increased. Numbers were particularly high in 1992, when 230 were counted on Loch Indaal on 8 June, 143 on 21 June, and 51 on 29 June. Counts of less than 100 are more usual. Away from Islay, a few Bar-tailed Godwits appear to summer more or less regularly on Tiree, but otherwise there are few summer records, mostly from Colonsay/Oronsay and Mull.

Adult birds return to British estuaries from late July (Migration Atlas). However, like other waders coming from a north-easterly direction, Bar-tailed Godwits tend to arrive later in the west. Thus at Uisaed Point in Kintyre, where small groups of migrating Bar-tailed Godwits are seen flying south nearly every autumn, the first are not usually seen until mid-August.

Generally speaking, summer-plumaged adults occur only in small numbers in Argyll, stopping off briefly on their way to moult elsewhere. The main influx, consisting mostly of juveniles, occurs in September, when small numbers of birds are seen in widely scattered locations on the mainland and islands as well as at the regular sites. Numbers on Islay at this time vary widely, being very low in some years. High counts, indicative of a mid-September peak, include 500 at Loch Indaal on 15 September 1980, 323 at Loch Gruinart on 12 September 1988, and 292 at Loch Indaal in September 1991. Up to 40 have been counted on Tiree at this time, up to 25 at Loch Don, and lower numbers elsewhere. In September, birds may turn up on the coast anywhere in Argyll, usually singly, though there are no recent records from Jura.

Migration continues through October, but by November birds are mostly confined to a small number of regular wintering sites. Chief among these is Islay, where numbers often peak in January or February and the two main sites regularly hold a total of 200-400 birds. Numbers on Tiree are usually much lower, the highest total being 69 in January 2000. Loch Don appears to be the only other site consistently holding more than ten birds in winter, but Loch Crinan and Loch Gilp are also regular wintering sites.

At the end of the winter, birds move from British and Irish coasts to the Wadden Sea to undergo pre-migratory fattening prior to returning to their breeding grounds. The main movement starts in February and continues through March (Migration Atlas). On Islay numbers fall steeply from a late-winter peak in some years, but in others they remain at much the same level until April or May. In 1992, for example, 250 were at Loch Indaal on 20 April and 130 on 26 May. These could have included lingering winter visitors, northbound adults, or immatures destined to stay the summer. On the whole, spring passage through Argyll appears to be light, but singles and small groups have been seen in widely scattered locations from March through to early June.

[The counts for Oronsay in 2000 (ABR 17: 60, Table 26) were included there by mistake and should be ignored (P Daw, pers. comm.)]

Tristan ap Rheinallt

Whimbrel

Numenius phaeopus

A regular passage migrant in small numbers, mainly to the islands. More frequent in spring (April and May) than in autumn (July to October). Also recorded regularly in summer, and rarely in winter.

Although the Whimbrel has a small Scottish breeding population, this does not extend as far south as Argyll, where the species is mainly a passage migrant. Most birds seen in Argyll probably belong to the Icelandic population, though some may breed in the Faeroes or Fennoscandia as well as presumably in Scotland.

It is well known that Whimbrel migrating through the British Isles follow a more westerly path in spring than in autumn (B&R, Migration Atlas). The species' Gaelic name, *Eun-bealltain* (Beltane bird), illustrates its association with spring and, more specifically, with the end of April and the beginning of May.

Gray, quoting Graham, claimed that Whimbrel were found on Iona only during May, arriving in "very large flocks" at the beginning of the month. "Large flocks" were also reported from Tiree in the 19th century, and "immense flocks" from unspecified islands in 1865 (B&R). Although these terms are rather vague, they suggest that numbers of migrants visiting Argyll must once have been higher than they are today. Further evidence comes from the statement in Elliott (1989) that the largest counts on Islay, in both spring and autumn, occurred in the mid-1950s. Certainly, numbers observed in Argyll today are relatively small compared with the large concentrations that occur at a few regular sites further south in western Britain and Ireland.

There are several older records from Islay during March (Thom, Elliott 1989). For example, one was at Ardnave on 22 March 1972 (SB 7:350), and another was on the island on 17 March 1973 (SB 8:238). These days, birds are rarely seen before mid-April and passage does not usually begin in earnest until around 20 April, continuing until the middle or end of May, with sometimes a few stragglers into June. The highest numbers in recent years have occurred in Kintyre and on the islands, especially Islay, Coll and Tiree. On Islay, unusually high numbers were reported during northerly winds in mid-May 1988, when 117 were seen at Loch Gruinart and Loch Gorm on the 18th. In south Kintyre, several flocks were apparently grounded by calm, hazy weather on 3 May 1990, with a total count of 313 at six sites, the most being 100 at Machrihanish airfield. More than 100 were on Tiree on 11 May 1987, 101 on Coll on 8 May 1992, and 125 at four Islay sites on 9 May 2000 (with 100 at Craigfad, near Port Charlotte, six days earlier).

Most records of Whimbrel in Argyll come from Coll, Tiree, Islay and Kintyre. *Eddie Maguire*

Migrating Whimbrel are known to use both coastal and overland routes. However, H&B commented that they were commoner on the outlying islands of Argyll than the mainland. With the exception of Kintyre, this is still true today and, although there are recent spring records from all mainland areas, Whimbrel seem to be completely absent from some areas in some years. Also, numbers are usually small. The only flocks containing more than 20 in recent years were in Cowal: 44 at Ardyne Point on 2 May 1993 and

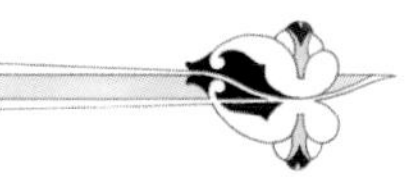

22 at Ardlamont Point seven days later. These are among the few records of this species from Cowal.

Whimbrel do not return to their breeding grounds until they are at least two or three years old. Many younger birds spend the northern summer in the African wintering areas. Midsummer records are not infrequent in Argyll and could refer to immatures, failed breeders, or perhaps wandering non-breeders. Mostly they involve single birds, a report of eight at Loch Indaal on Islay on 19 June 1997 being exceptional.

During autumn passage, most birds passing through Britain occur along the North Sea coast and in southern England (Migration Atlas). In Scotland, autumn migrants first appear in mid-July and passage is finished by the end of October (B&R). Although migration through Argyll at this season is similarly protracted, numbers are much smaller than in spring. Indeed, early ornithologists regarded the Whimbrel as scarce or rare in Argyll outside the months of April and May (Gray, H&B). This description could also apply to some recent years when there were no more than a handful of autumn records. In other years, however, larger flocks are reported. For example, 58 flew south past Frenchman's Rocks on Islay on 23 August 1989, while 46 were at Loch Gruinart on 3 September 1990 and 76 there on 14 August 1998. In August 2001, there was a widespread arrival, with 31 at Uisaed Point on 23rd, and 18 at Crossapol on 28th.

In some years, Whimbrel have left Argyll by mid-September. In others, they remain into October, with most records during this month involving single birds. There are a few recent records from November, the latest being of a bird with an injured leg at Claggain Bay on Islay on 25 November 1989.

Whimbrel normally winter in the southern hemisphere or the tropics of the northern hemisphere. However, occasional birds spend the winter in Britain and Ireland, mostly in the south. The Winter Atlas showed only one record for Scotland: a bird seen at Port Mòr on Colonsay on 12 January 1984 (Jardine *et al.* 1986). Also, B&R reported winter records from Tiree. These appear to date from 1901 and 1902, when single birds were seen in January and February (SN 1915:43).

[B&R quoted a claim of a Whimbrel nest found at Machrihanish by Dougal McIntyre, but there appears to be no evidence to support this unusual and isolated record. Gray stated on the authority of Elwes that Whimbrel occurred in flocks during winter on Islay, but this statement was ignored by H&B and later authors. An unusual record of 29 seen at Bowmore on Islay by Gordon Booth on 2 July 1973 (SB 8:239) was not mentioned by Booth (1975) and seems likely to be an error.]

Tristan ap Rheinallt

Eurasian Curlew

Numenius arquata

This is a fairly common breeding species in suitable moorland habitat. In winter and during spring and autumn passage, highest numbers are found where extensive tidal mudflats provide good feeding grounds.

The species has been known to breed in most areas of Argyll. H&B noted that it was about 1840 when Curlews "first made their appearance on the high lands north of Loch Awe". They observed that the species bred where moors were "extensive and not very steep", and that "they prefer the flatter mosses and moors of Kintyre, a limited area above Benderloch, Crinan and shores of Loch Awe to the more precipitous mountain slopes". B&R recorded breeding on Jura ("commonly" but no date), the Treshnish Isles (1892), Iona (1948), Coll (1929 and 1938), and Islay (1891, 1936, 1937, 1939 and 1948). They recorded that there was no nesting on Tiree in 1899 and that there had "still" been no breeding record from Tiree when they published in 1953; this is still true in 2004. Thom commented that numbers were declining on the Inner Hebrides, that the only island with a population of any size was Islay, and that Tiree and Coll no longer held any breeding pairs (but see below).

Curlews return to their breeding territories as early as February, although usually the four eggs are not laid until late April or May. Most breed on moorland, blanket bog and unimproved farmland, up to *c.*800m asl, preferring reasonably tall vegetation in which nests are concealed and chicks can hide. Both sexes incubate and tend the small young, but females are thought to depart in July, when young are still dependent, leaving the later rearing to the male.

The Second Atlas recorded breeding in 50% of 10-km squares visited in the county. In the much smaller 1-km squares of BBS surveys since then, one of 16 squares was occupied in 1998, one of 15 in 1999, none of 12 in 2000, and none of 14 in a Countryside 2000 survey (Wilson & Fuller 2001). In the RSPB's Loch Gruinart reserve breeding numbers varied between 12 and 42 pairs during 1985-2004. A complete count of the Rinns of Islay in 1994 found 99 pairs, mostly inland and 62% on uplands. In 1995, a complete count of Coll found 11 pairs, but only one pair was found there in 2004. There were no records of breeding on Colonsay during the twenty years to 2004 (D.C. Jardine pers. comm.). Moine Mhor NNR held six pairs in 1991, four in 1993, but "none in 1999 for the first time since regular monitoring began". There are occasional reports of adults with young from many parts of the county (ABR). Concern has often been expressed about declines of suitable breeding habitat for this and other species caused by two main factors – afforestation and agricultural improvement. These changes have been so extensive and widespread in Argyll that they must surely have

The call of the Curlew is one of the most evocative sounds of moorland in spring and summer. *David Wood*

led to decreases in breeding Curlews but, unfortunately, there seem to be no "before" and "after" counts to quantify this.

By September, birds have usually left the breeding areas and most have arrived on the wintering grounds. Ringing shows that many passage and wintering birds in Britain come from Norway, Sweden and Finland (Migration Atlas). Most British birds move south-west, those from Scotland wintering on the coasts of western Britain or Ireland. There have been several movements to or from Argyll that illustrate this general southwest-to-northeast shift in the centre of gravity of the population. A chick ringed in Finland in 1962 was found dead at Machrihanish in 1969, a chick ringed in Norway in 1991 was found dead on Islay in 1992, an adult ringed at Benderloch in January 1981 was shot in Finland in June 1982 and an adult female ringed in Finland in 1985 was seen alive at Loch Gilp in 1991. There is only one recovery of an Argyll-bred bird that reflects this movement. A chick ringed on Islay in 1963 was shot on the Aran Islands, Co. Galway (Ireland) in December 1964. Birds ringed as chicks in eastern Scotland (at Banff, Newtonmore and Almondbank) have been recovered in Argyll (BTO).

Numbers peak in Argyll at times of passage (August-September and March-April), but substantial numbers are present throughout the winter when birds are often seen feeding in fields as well as intertidally. At the regularly counted sites of Lochs Gruinart and Indaal, the combined total during autumn passage has often exceeded a thousand birds, and several hundred are usually present throughout the winter. Numbers there during spring passage are usually lower than in autumn, the total rarely exceeding 600. A coastal survey of Tiree during 14-20 January 2000 found 845 birds. Several hundred are regularly counted in autumn at the Holy Loch, at The Laggan and Machrihanish, and on Colonsay, while elsewhere flocks of up to 50 are not unusual (ABR). The NEWS count for Argyll (December 1997-January 1998) found 2,563 birds, of which 35% were on Tiree; this was the second most numerous wader in the county after Oystercatcher (4,799). Madders & Moser (1986) also placed it second with 6,030 birds. Jennings (1995) found it throughout the year at Ledaig Point.

Curlews can sometimes be heard calling as they migrate at night and occasionally the flocks are seen silhouetted against a moonlit sky or the moon itself. Even more dramatically, on 17 April 1989 an observer on Tiree saw an arriving flock of 107 "spiralling down from a great height", suggesting migration at altitude. Movement during spring passage can sometimes be sharply recognised. In 1988, again on Tiree, "5-15 Curlews were present daily in April, except for marked passage of 50-70 daily on 17-19 April". At the Mull of Kintyre, passage during 7-20 March 1983 included 240 flying north on 12 March and 700 on 14 March. Autumn passage was noted at MSBO during 19 August-23 September 1989 with a maximum day-count of 121 on 3 September (ABR).

Clive Craik

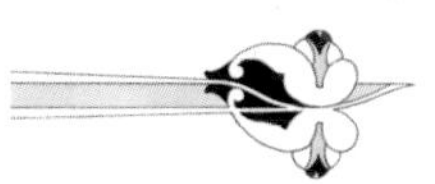

Spotted Redshank

Tringa erythropus

Scarce migrant, mostly in autumn.

Spotted Redshanks breed at high latitudes and winter from western Europe across to China and south-east Asia. In Britain, numbers are at their highest in autumn, with eastern England seeing the bulk of migrants. The species was not known to occur in Argyll by Gray, H&B or B&R. The last-named authors suggested that autumn migrants passed overland from the Forth to the Clyde to reach south-west Scotland, where records were regular. At the time, there had been only one record from the Outer Hebrides.

It was not until 6 December 1955 that the Spotted Redshank was first noted in Argyll, a bird at Loch Gruinart on this date being the first for the Inner Hebrides (SN 69:125, SB 1:31). Although Gibson & McWilliam (1959) stated that they knew of several autumn records from Campbeltown since 1952, the next record for which full details are available comes from Tiree, where a bird was at Baugh on 28 September and 3 October 1968 (SB 5:324). Following this, Spotted Redshanks were reported annually during 1970-1976 but there were then only three published records to the end of the 1980s. The species was then recorded in 10 of the 17 years between 1990 and 2006. The reason for these fluctuations is not known.

Islay (especially Loch Gruinart) and south Kintyre (particularly Uisaed Point) account for a high proportion of Argyll occurrences. Records at Uisaed Point generally involve birds flying south or stopping off briefly, but individuals sometimes stay up to several weeks on the flooded fields at Loch Gruinart. Elsewhere, there are three records from Tiree (September 1968, July 1973, May 1997), two from Mull (May 1986, July 1999), one from Coll (July 2004) and three from the mainland. All of the mainland records come from Cowal and involve single birds: at Loch Riddon on 28 September 1971 (unpublished) and 5 September 1975 (SB 9:202), and at Kames on 13 September 2004 (Argyll Database).

Although the first Argyll record was in December, all others have been in spring (7 April to 11 May) or autumn (10 July to 18 November). The Figure shows the weekly distribution of records during the period 1980-2001. Autumn records outnumber spring records by about three to one, reflecting the situation in Scotland as a whole. The data appear to show two autumn peaks, corresponding perhaps to adults and juveniles.

Most records concern single birds, but three were reported from an unspecified location or locations on Islay on 5 October 1970 (SB 6:370) and three were at Campbeltown from 12 to 18 September 1976 (SB 10:95).

Tristan ap Rheinallt

Common Redshank

Tringa totanus

This is a widespread but decreasing species that has vanished as a breeding bird from large parts of the county due to habitat loss, particularly on the mainland. It still breeds in good numbers on the outer islands, and it also occurs as a passage migrant and in winter.

Gray described the Redshank as "very abundant", stating that it bred plentifully in many inland districts of west Scotland, usually at considerable distance from the sea. H&B described it as common on the shores at Benderloch and common in winter on Tiree. Graham found it abundant along the shores of Mull and Iona but, like many others before

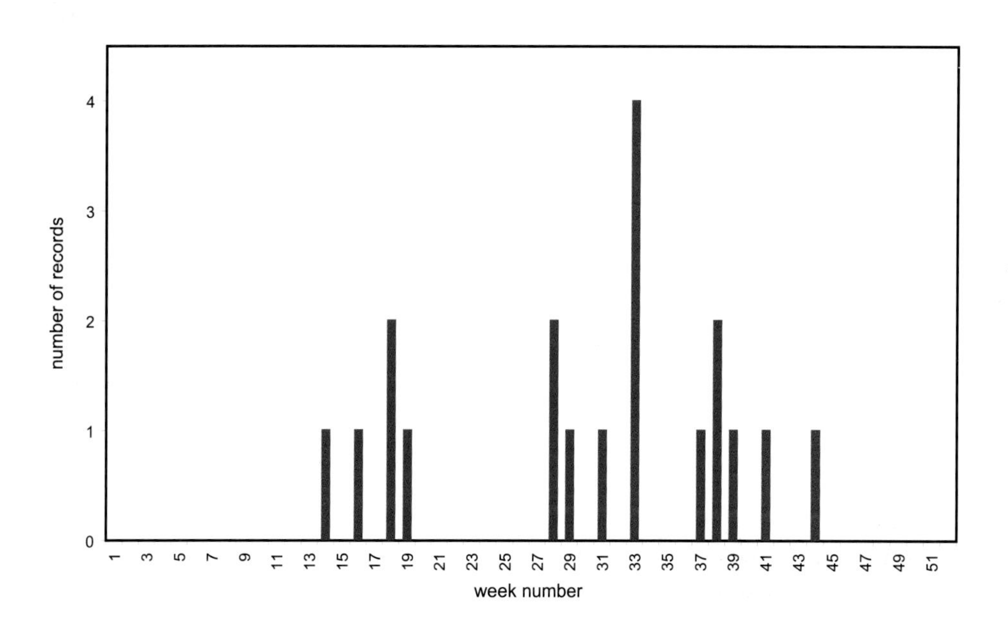

Weekly variation in Argyll records of Spotted Redshank, 1980-2001.

Spotted Redshanks nest on the Arctic tundra and taiga, and winter in Africa, Asia and around the Mediterranean. Very few are seen in Argyll. *Hugh Venables*

and since, he was exasperated when its alarm calls cleared the area of birds that he was trying to shoot.

B&R noted that Redshanks bred in every mainland county of Scotland and were common in the east but much rarer on the west coast to the north of Argyll. It was "very common in autumn and winter, from the Forth ... to Caithness, and as far north as Argyll on the west side". Thom recorded sharp declines, both in breeding numbers as wet agricultural land was drained or afforested, and, for reasons that were less clear, in wintering numbers on some estuaries, especially the Clyde.

The First Atlas showed Redshanks to be much less widespread in the north and west Highlands than elsewhere in Scotland and northern England; nevertheless, the species was present in most squares in Argyll except for an area around Oban. In the Second Atlas, Redshanks were recorded breeding in 40% of 10-km squares in the county and the highest densities were on Coll, Tiree, Islay and in part of Mid-Argyll. Several squares in Kintyre and Mid-Argyll had become empty, the two main causes being drainage and overgrazing of the damp pasturelands needed for nesting. In the 1-km squares of the BBS, breeding was recorded in 3/16 squares in 1998, 2/15 in 1999 and 2/12 in 2000, and in 1/14 of the Countryside 2000 squares (ABR).

The most regular counts of breeding numbers have come from Colonsay and from the RSPB Reserves. During 1995-2004 Colonsay (excluding Oronsay) held a mean of ten pairs, varying from 16 in 1999 to five in 2004, while counts on Oronsay during 1995-2002 gave a mean of eight pairs, varying from 14 in 2000 to three in 1996. During 1992-2001 Loch Gruinart held a mean of 90 pairs, varying from 114 in 1996 to 60 in 1999. Only 38 pairs were reported there in 2002, but by 2006 numbers had recovered to 106 pairs. Ardnave (Islay) held 30 pairs in 2001, while in 1993, 41 pairs were counted there in 384ha. In 1994 in the Rinns Survey (Islay), 46-48 pairs were concentrated at a few sites mostly around Loch Gorm. During 1994-2004, the RSPB's Coll reserve held an average of 39 pairs, varying from 15 pairs in 2001 to 56 pairs in 2004. The RSPB's Tiree reserve held similar numbers to their reserve on Coll (Argyll Database). In a whole-island survey of Tiree in 1994, 231 pairs were counted and this included an area also counted in 1987-88 where numbers had increased almost twofold, from 87 to 132 pairs. Small numbers have been reported breeding elsewhere in Argyll.

Most Redshanks that breed in the British Isles also winter here, although most move to the coast, particularly to the larger estuaries. Birds elsewhere in Europe are more migratory and the British Isles are by far their most important wintering area, holding 75% of the European total and *c.*15-20% of the world total (Winter Atlas). The Winter Atlas showed that Redshanks were present in winter in most coastal areas of Argyll, although at low density in many squares. Not surprisingly, the main flocks were found on the larger areas of intertidal mud.

In the NEWS count (December 1997-January 1998) 763 Redshanks were counted in Argyll (414 on Tiree, 98 on Mull, 94 on Coll, 22 on Islay and 135 along the mainland coast) making the Redshank the eighth most numerous wader. In winter 1984-85, Madders & Moser (1986) counted 1,365, placing it fifth. At Ledaig Point during 1982-1994, Jennings (1995) found Redshank present seasonally during April to September. Tiree usually holds the largest numbers both in winter and on spring and autumn passage. A coastal count of Tiree on 14-20 January 2000 found 415. An estimated 300-500 were present on Tiree in mid-August 1995, and an all-island wader count on that island in February 2006 found *c.*470. A complete coastal survey of Coll in December 1997 found 95, and 96 were counted on Coll in November 1991.

Elsewhere, the WeBS monthly counts of Redshanks in winter at the main estuarine sites (Lochs Gruinart, Indaal, Crinan, Caolisport, Holy Loch, Otter Ferry and elsewhere) have exceeded 100 rarely and are usually under 50. Peaks tend to occur in spring and autumn. Counts of Redshanks on passage are regularly made at seawatching sites.

Redshanks breeding in the British Isles belong to the race *T. t. totanus*, which occupies most of the species' European range. However, Icelandic and Faeroese birds are assigned to another race, *T. t. robusta*, on the basis of their larger size. Ringing shows that many of the latter winter in Britain and Ireland, where the earliest adults may arrive in late June (Migration Atlas). Southward passage is apparent in Argyll from the end of June to September and, although some of these may come from further north in Scotland, many are likely to have an Icelandic origin. This applies, for example, to birds passing offshore in association with Arctic wader species such as Sanderling and Knot.

Redshanks wintering in northern Scotland are almost exclusively Icelandic birds, with the proportion of this race decreasing southwards (Migration Atlas). The only foreign-ringed Redshank ever recovered in Argyll was ringed as a chick in Iceland on 14 June 1966 and recovered on Islay on 5 February 1967.

A small high-tide roost of Redshanks in Loch Gilp. *John McAvoy*

Other recoveries show where many of Argyll's breeding birds spend the winter. Four chicks ringed in the county were recovered in the southern part of the British Isles during October-March (Cornwall, Essex, Counties Cork and Dublin); and birds found in Argyll during March-August had been ringed outside the breeding season as fully-grown birds in Wales (6), Lancs/Merseyside (2) and Co Clare (Ireland) (1). Colour-ringed Redshanks seen breeding on Tiree in 1997 (3 birds) and 1999-2000 (one individual present in both summers) had been ringed in Cardiff Bay in winter.

Clive Craik

Greenshank

Tringa nebularia

Scarce breeding species, apparently confined to Mull and the northern mainland. Widespread migrant in autumn and to a lesser extent in spring, with regular wintering at a few sites.

The Greenshank has long been known as a breeding species in Argyll, although there is no indication that it has ever been common or widespread. Gray referred to pairs nesting near the Black Mount, on the northern boundary of the Argyll recording area, and breeding apparently occurred once on Tiree (H&B, Irby 1899, Anderson 1913). However, Graham described the Greenshank as "quite a rarity" on Iona and Mull. According to B&R, Greenshanks nested occasionally on Jura, although they quoted no specific records.

The First Atlas shows confirmed breeding in two 10-km squares south and east of Oban and another, shared with Highland Region, in the area of Loch Tulla. Probable breeding was recorded in another mainland square and on the Ross of Mull. In the Second Atlas, evidence of breeding was found only in the Loch Tulla square and the nearby Glen Kinglass area. Since 1980, in fact, breeding has been confirmed only on Mull and the mainland of North Argyll, birds typically returning to the same sites year after year. There have also been a few reports of birds in suitable habitat in Mid-Argyll.

No recent estimate of the breeding population in the Argyll area is available. Nethersole-Thompson & Nethersole-Thompson (1979) estimated the population in the 1970s to be 15-20 pairs, though the geographical area covered by this estimate would have included part of what is now the Highland area. In 1997, six pairs were reported from six localities (Ogilvie *et al.* 1999c). This is considerably higher than the average. No reports are received from breeding sites in some years, probably because of lack of observer coverage.

The interval between spring and autumn migration of Greenshanks through Scotland is more or less non-existent. In the Northern Isles, birds presumed to be on their way to breeding sites in Fenno-Scandia are still passing through in

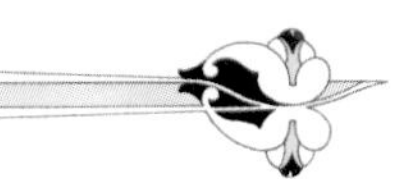

late May and early June, while females leave Scottish breeding sites as early as mid- to late June (Thom, Migration Atlas). Thus birds at coastal sites such as Loch Gruinart on Islay or The Strand on Colonsay in June may be late spring migrants, early autumn migrants or non-breeders. From the first few days of July, however, there is a clear increase in numbers and the area over which they occur. Southbound migrants are reported widely from the coasts of all parts of the mainland and the islands. Numbers are generally small, counts of more than 12 being infrequent. Recent high counts include 20 at Loch Beg on Mull on 21 to 24 September 1990 (ABR 7:32), 13 at The Strand on 25 October 1996 (ABR 13:56) and 17 September 1997 (ABR 14:55), 15 at Loch Don on 27 July 2000 (ABR 17:62), and 23 at Uisaed Point on 21 July 2003 (Argyll Database). None of these, however, matches the count of 26 at the head of Loch Indaal on 9 September 1973 (Elliott 1989). Interestingly, B&R stated that they had never seen as many Greenshanks together as they saw at this location in September 1937. Gray also singled out Loch Indaal for special

Argyll forms the south-west tip of the Greenshank's breeding distribution in Europe. *Philip Snow*

mention as a haunt of the Greenshank, proving more reliable in this instance than H&B, who insisted that the species was no more than a rare migrant on the west coast of Scotland, except possibly on Tiree.

Autumn migration through Argyll continues over a period of three to four months, with birds from breeding areas in north-east Europe possibly passing through later than their Scottish counterparts (Migration Atlas). From October onwards records tend to be fewer, although there are several regular wintering sites holding small numbers of birds. These include Loch Don and Loch Beg, Loch Gruinart and The Strand. Generally speaking, these are also the sites most favoured by migrants in autumn and again in spring. In addition, single birds have recently been reported in winter from several sites in Mid- and North Argyll. Returning migrants, presumably destined for breeding sites in Scotland, are seen in March and April at many different coastal locations, though numbers are smaller than in autumn. Fewer are seen in May, when most Scottish breeders have already been on territory for several weeks (Migration Atlas).

Tristan ap Rheinallt

Greater Yellowlegs

Tringa melanoleuca

Vagrant.

One was seen and photographed near Islay Airport on 25 October 1985 (BB 81:559). It constituted the fifth Scottish record of this North American wader, which is much rarer on this side of the Atlantic than its smaller congener, the Lesser Yellowlegs. Seventeen years later, on 11 May 2002, an individual was found on the floods at Loch Gruinart on Islay, where it stayed until 14th. It is possible that this was the same bird as one seen on St Kilda between late April and 9 May 2002 (BB 96:571).

Tristan ap Rheinallt

Lesser Yellowlegs

Tringa flavipes

Vagrant.

There are four Argyll records of this North American rarity, which is a less-than-annual visitor to Scotland. A bird was reported from the northern shore of Loch Creran on 3 March 1951 (BB 46:34), while a juvenile was at Ulva Lagoons, near Tayvallich, from 30 September to 11 October 2000 (BB 94:474). On Islay, a Lesser Yellowlegs was on the floods at Loch Gruinart from 25 to 27 May 2003 (BB 97:581), at exactly the same location where Argyll's second Greater Yellowlegs was recorded 12 months earlier. A first-winter bird was present at Loch Gruinart from 13 to 25 September 2004, and probably the same individual was on Oronsay on 25 September 2004 (BB 100:43).

Tristan ap Rheinallt

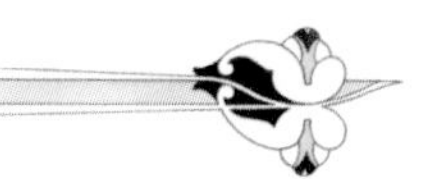

Green Sandpiper

Tringa ochropus

Scarce autumn migrant, occasionally recorded in spring.

Most Green Sandpipers are seen singly by fresh waters in autumn. *Roy Blewitt*

In Scotland, the Green Sandpiper is a regular autumn visitor in small numbers to freshwater habitats, the records being widely scattered (Thom). In Argyll, it is now known to occur more or less annually at this season, although it was regarded as rare in the past, with very few records prior to the 1970s. Neither Gray nor H&B made any mention of it, whilst B&R knew of no records from the Inner Hebrides, although they stated that it had occurred in mainland Argyll. Given that birds in flight are conspicuous and vocal, it is tempting to conclude that there has been a genuine increase in recent years.

After only nine published records during the 12-year period 1968-1979 (SBR), there were 56 in 24 years during 1980-2003. The seasonal distribution of the 55 dated post-1979 records shows a clear peak in early autumn, with most arrivals in the week 6-12 August (Figure). The earliest autumn migrant was one at Grasspoint on Mull on 1 July 1999 (ABR 16:63). Migration of this species is known to start very early, with adult females leaving the young in the care of the male (BWP).

It appears that birds almost invariably leave Argyll before the end of September, the latest recorded being one at Nerabus on Islay on 17 November 1991 (ABR 8:44). This could have been a wintering bird, as indeed could the one at Killinallan on Islay on 3 March 1989 (ABR 6:35). A few Green Sandpipers winter in Scotland in most years, usually in the south of the country (Thom).

Spring records are very few, their dates varying from 17 May to 4 June. The scarcity of birds in Argyll in spring reflects the situation in Britain and Ireland as a whole (Migration Atlas). Most records in Scotland at this season come from the east coast and the Northern Isles (Thom).

At least one Green Sandpiper was seen in Argyll every year during 1987-2003, except 1993. Islay accounted for 23 of the records analysed in the Figure, and Kintyre (including Sanda and Gigha) for another 11. Most of the others came from islands (Tiree, Mull, Coll and Colonsay) with just three

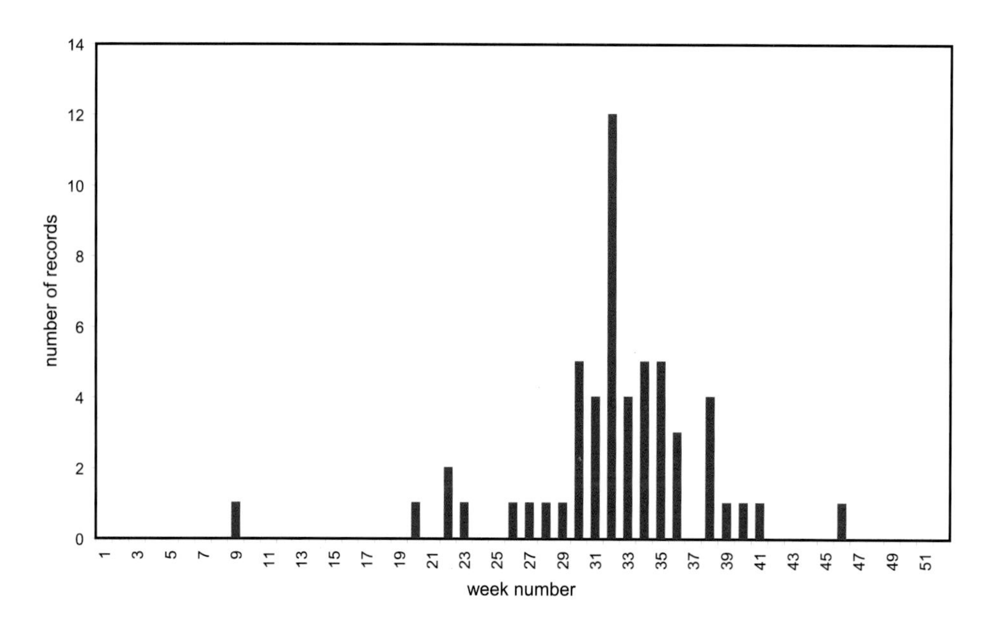

Weekly variation in Argyll records of Green Sandpiper, 1980-2003.

from the mainland outside Kintyre. These three all came from the Oban area, two autumn records from Benderloch and one from Loch Nell. In late July and early August 2004, an unprecedented influx on Tiree started with two on 28 July followed by single birds on 9, 10, 11 and 13 August and two on 12 August.

[The record of this species from a BBS square in 2000 (ABR 17: 63) is an error.]

Tristan ap Rheinallt

Wood Sandpiper

Tringa glareola

Scarce migrant, usually in late spring.

The Wood Sandpiper is mainly a spring passage migrant in Argyll. *Roy Blewitt*

Breeding widely in northern Europe, the Wood Sandpiper is mainly a scarce migrant to Scotland, although a few pairs nest in the Highlands each year (Chisholm 2007). In the late 1960s, breeding or probable breeding occurred for at least three consecutive years at probably the same site on Rannoch Moor, no more than a few kilometres outside the Argyll recording area.

The first Argyll record concerned a bird shot at Campbeltown on 6 August 1856 (H&B, B&R). For nearly a century, there were few if any additional records. B&R refer, without details, to a record from North Argyll, though this may not have been within the current Argyll recording area. A record of one at Vaul on Tiree in June 1950 (Boyd 1958) was not published at the time and is not referred to by B&R. Instead, a male at Loch Àiridh Dhaibhidh on Islay on 7 June 1954 was claimed to represent the first record for the Inner Hebrides (SN 66:129-145 and 68:5).

Records of migrants became more frequent from 1962 onwards, with four published records in the 1960s, five in the 1970s, five in the 1980s, 11 in the 1990s, and seven during 2000-03 (SBRs, ABRs, Elliott 1989). Of the 32 records, more than half (19) came from Islay, with other island records from Mull, Coll, Tiree, Oronsay and Luing. There have only been four mainland records: two in south Kintyre (Rhunahaorine Point, Westport Marsh) and two near Oban (Loch Feochan, Glen Lonan). Birds have stayed for up to 12 days at the same location. There have been several records of two birds together.

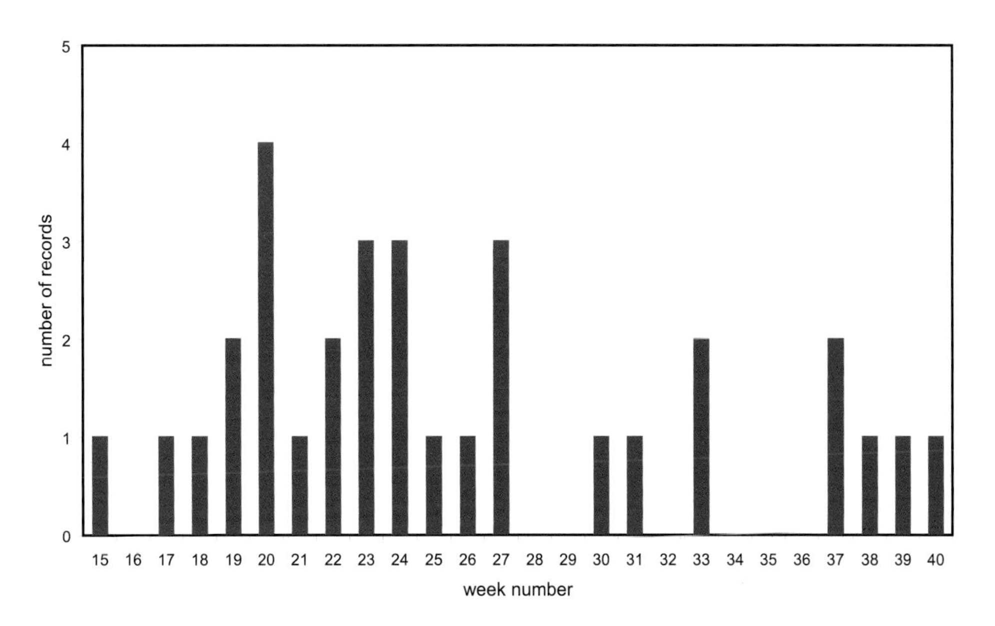

Weekly variation in Argyll records of Wood Sandpiper, 1962-2003.

The seasonal distribution of 32 recent records shows that most birds pass through in spring, particularly in May and early June (Figure). Autumn records are fewer and more scattered. Since adults are said to start leaving the European breeding grounds in late June (BWP), the early July records presumably refer to autumn migrants. The earliest spring migrant was a bird at Glen Lonan on 15 April 1992 (SBR 1992:32, ABR 9:33), and the latest autumn migrants were two birds on Islay on 6 October 1970 (SB 6:369). The 15 April date is unusually early in a Scottish context.

Tristan ap Rheinallt

Common Sandpiper

Actitis hypoleucos

This is a common summer migrant that breeds widely in Argyll, usually close to water. It occurs in spring and autumn passage in small numbers, mostly along the coast. There are occasional midwinter records.

Although Gray described this species as "everywhere common", H&B regarded it as "very common all through the mainland" but "rarer" on Colonsay, Oronsay, Jura, Coll and Tiree. A 1772 record from Gigha was given by B&R, who found it breeding commonly on shores there in 1949. They also found it on Iona and Eilean Annraidh in 1910, and they cited a report that it was well distributed on Jura in 1939.

Records in ABRs show that, during 1981-2002, there were four years when the first spring bird was reported in March, eleven years when it was during 1-15 April and seven years when it was during 16-30 April. The main arrival is in April but birds continue to arrive in May.

Pairs nest singly along shorelines and watercourses. Nests are well hidden in vegetation of medium height, sometimes in woodland, always close to the water, and usually along rock or shingle shores rather than sandy beaches, but also by freshwater lochs, reservoirs, streams, rivers and occasionally by the open sea. A territory length of 100-150m has been quoted (Second Atlas). The four eggs are laid in May and the chicks that hatch in early June are well-disguised and skilful at hiding. Parental alarms cause them to scatter and hide long before approaching intruders arrive, so smaller chicks are usually seen only when a family is taken by surprise. Birds depart southwards as soon as the young can fly and, by late July, the breeding grounds are empty.

In the Second Atlas, breeding was recorded in 68% of 10-km squares. In the 1-km squares of the BBS, it was found in two of 16 squares in 1998, two of 15 in 1999, and two of 12 BBS and one of 14 'Countryside 2000' squares in 2000. Breeding has been recorded in all areas of the county, including Gigha, the Treshnish Isles and Iona. Sixteen pairs were found in 26 km^2 of suitable habitat in the Eredine Forest area in 1996 (about one pair for every three hill lochs); 18 pairs were found on 41 hill lochs in that area in 1997 and 14 pairs in 1998. Regular counts on Colonsay found about 25 pairs in most years 1983-2005, varying between 44 in 1999 and 13 in 1995. On Coll, in 1989 at least 12 pairs bred inland and five pairs on the coast, and in 1997 there were two pairs on the RSPB reserve. On Islay, 26 pairs were counted in the Rinns Survey of 1994, of which 21 were coastal. On Mull, a WeBS count found 22 birds on the Inner Loch Scridain/Loch Beg area on 14 June 1998; and in 1999 a minimum ten pairs were on the shore of Loch Spelve (Croggan-Fellonmore; *c.*1.3 pairs/km) and five pairs on the shore of Loch na Keal (Scarisdale Point-Derryguaig; 1.4 pairs/km) (ABR).

In late July and August, passage birds are recorded singly or in small flocks along the coast. At Ledaig Point during 1982-1994, Jennings (1995) recorded this species seasonally, during April and again in August-September. At MSBO, 82 were logged flying south in 257h in July and August 1995, with a peak of 18 in seven hours on 19 July, and 15 passed on 22 August 2001, including one group of seven.

During 20 years with records (ABR for 1981-2002, and excluding the winter records below), there was one year when the last bird to be reported was on 30 July, five years when it was in August, three when it was during 1-15 September, eight when it was during 16-30 September, and three when it was in October. However, there have been several midwinter records. Two were at West Loch Tarbert on 16 January 1982 and there were singles at Croggan (Mull) on 26 November 1982, Crinan Ferry on 24 December 1985, Dunrostan on Loch Sween on 4 January 2000, Kilmun on 31 December 2001, Loch Feochan on 10 December 2002, Dunstaffnage Bay on 24 November 2006 and Loch Melfort on 15 December 2006. One was seen in the NEWS counts for Argyll in winter 1997-1998 (ABR).

Most birds from the British Isles are thought to winter in west Africa south of the Sahara (Migration Atlas). One of the earliest Argyll ringing recoveries of any species was of a chick ringed on Islay in June 1923 and recovered in the Loire-et-Cher region of France in April 1925 (a distance of 1,010km). A chick ringed on Colonsay on 17 June 1999 was caught and released near Campos del Puerto, Mallorca (Spain) on 14 April 2002 (1,970km). An adult ringed in Kintyre in May 1981 was found dead in Morocco in July of that year (2,921km).

Clive Craik

The noisy calls of displaying Common Sandpipers are a feature of coasts and freshwaters in spring. *Margaret Staley*

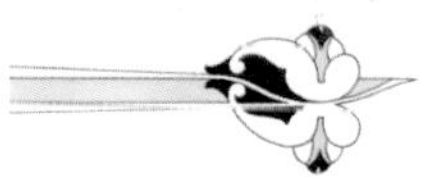

Spotted Sandpiper

Actitis macularius

Vagrant.

One was at Loch Indaal on Islay on 5 June 1984 (BB 78:551). This, the only Argyll record, was also the seventh Scottish record of this North American species, which attempted to breed on Skye in 1975.

Tristan ap Rheinallt

Turnstone

Arenaria interpres

A common and widespread migrant and winter visitor to Argyll coasts, with highest numbers on Tiree. Normally present from mid-July through to early June, with a few individuals remaining through the summer.

The Turnstone has long been recognised as a common species in Argyll (Gray, Graham, H&B). The first returning birds normally appear in July and the main influx is in August and September. At this time, birds are often noted in small numbers during seawatches, passing sites such as Uisaed Point in Kintyre in company with other waders that breed at high latitudes.

Most of the birds wintering in Britain and Ireland come from north-east Canada and northern Greenland, with many stopping over in Iceland on the way. A small minority come from Fennoscandia. Although birds from both populations also pass through Britain and Ireland on their way to wintering grounds further south (Migration Atlas), there is little evidence that numbers in Argyll are higher in autumn than in winter. At some sites, such as Loch Gruinart and Loch Indaal on Islay, counts tend to be higher at the end of the year. However, given that Turnstones disperse widely along rocky coasts, it is difficult to draw general conclusions from counts at a small number of sites.

Because of their habitat preferences, Turnstones are difficult to count accurately. It is clear that they are widely distributed in small numbers along the coasts of mainland Argyll in mid-winter, with higher densities on islands such as Tiree, Islay and Coll as well as parts of Cowal (Winter Atlas). The Winter Shorebird Count of 1984/85 (Madders & Moser 1986) gave an estimated total of 2,090 birds for the Argyll coast, with the main concentration (966 birds) on Tiree (Table). However, it is likely that this figure was an underestimate, especially in view of the fact that Turnstones are regular winter visitors to Skerryvore (Tomison 1907) and thus presumably to other skerries and rocky islets. This caveat also applies to the NEWS survey in 1997/98, which found that substantial lengths of mainland coast held almost no Turnstones.

Clearly, Tiree is the main wintering stronghold for this species in Argyll, the highest winter count there to date being 1,196 on 25-26 January 1987. A very similar number (1,191) were found during an all-island coastal survey on 5-10 February 2006. Other important wintering areas include stretches of the mainland coast as well as Mull and Coll, where 157 and 177 birds respectively were counted in the incomplete NEWS survey of winter 1997/98. Away from Tiree, counts of more than 100 birds at individual sites are exceptional at any season, being reported most frequently from Loch Gruinart and adjacent Ardnave Point, and also

Turnstones winter on rocky and pebbly shores across Argyll, especially where seaweed accumulates. *David Wood*

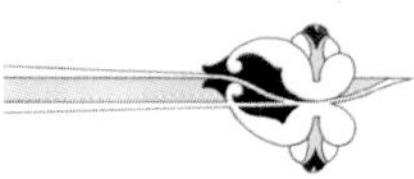

from Oronsay, Tayinloan, Ledaig Point and Otter Ferry. Other regular sites, holding 50 or more birds at times over the past 20 years, include Loch Indaal on Islay, Loch na Keal and Scallastle, both on Mull, and Campbeltown Loch and Holy Loch on the mainland.

As in autumn, evidence for a spring peak in numbers is rather weak. However, counts at Loch Gruinart suggest that numbers are often highest in February or March, suggesting arrival of birds that have wintered further south. This is consistent with the finding that Turnstones in Britain and Ireland may leave their wintering grounds as early as February (Migration Atlas). Similarly, departure from Argyll in spring seems to be early, with numbers greatly reduced by the end of April or even earlier. There is some evidence that Turnstones wintering in south-west Scotland leave their wintering sites earlier than those in south-east Scotland, perhaps then spending time in Iceland prior to moving to the western part of the population's breeding range (Migration Atlas).

However, there is evidence of intermittent passage on Tiree throughout May, with groups of up to 25 (or rarely 50) appearing briefly at coastal sites or occasionally inland (J. Bowler pers. comm.). Exceptionally, more may be involved, as in 1986, when 850 birds were counted during 10-14 May. Late migrants, which may be present on Tiree until the beginning of June (J. Bowler pers. comm.), probably fly directly to Greenland rather than stopping off in Iceland on their way (Migration Atlas). They leave behind them a few that remain through the summer. Some of these attain full breeding plumage and were thought in the past to nest locally (e.g. Gray), but H&B poured cold water on this hypothesis. Groups of up to 20 birds were widespread on Tiree in June and July 2001, though fewer were present the following year (J. Bowler pers. comm.) On other islands, especially Islay and Oronsay, scattered small groups are not infrequently recorded in summer, but counts rarely reach double figures. On the mainland, summer records are very few, but up to 12 were counted throughout June and July 2001 at Otter Ferry, where there is a regular flock.

Although Turnstones migrating through Scotland occasionally turn up well inland, they have never been recorded more than a few miles from the coast in Argyll.

Distribution of Turnstones in Argyll in mid-winter 1984/85.

Area	Count	Percentage of total
Tiree	966	46
Mull	280	13
North Clyde sealochs	237	11
Kintyre & Knapdale	236	11
Islay	129	6
North mainland	77	4
Colonsay	74	4
Jura	47	2
Coll	44	2
Total	2,090	

The survey included counts from Gare Loch and inner Loch Linnhe, both outside the Argyll recording area covered by this book.

They are normally associated with rocky or pebbly shores but can also be found in sandy and muddy areas, particularly if these have mussel beds or patches of seaweed. On occasion they abandon the seashore for adjacent fields. In Tiree, this habit is frequent throughout the winter, often becoming most noticeable in February or March (J. Bowler pers. comm.).

Tristan ap Rheinallt

Red-necked Phalarope

Phalaropus lobatus

A very rare but regular breeding species on Tiree until 1992 and in 1999-2000. Very rare occasional passage migrant elsewhere.

Although a common breeding species in Finland, Scandinavia, Iceland and around the Arctic Circle, Scottish Red-necked Phalaropes are now at the southern limit of their breeding range following the demise of the Irish population. This species was first recorded breeding in Britain in Orkney in the 19th century, reaching about 100 pairs in the 1920s but falling back to around 45 pairs in 1970 (Everett 1971). Numbers and range halved between the two breeding atlases with only 21 pairs in Britain and Ireland distributed in ten 10-km squares and the former Irish population reduced to 0-1 pair by 1988-91 (Second Atlas). The centre of the Scottish population remains in Shetland, but it has retained a toehold

Red-necked Phalaropes no longer breed regularly in Argyll. *David Wood*

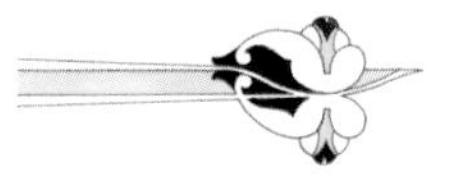

in the Outer Hebrides.

In Argyll, H&B knew the species occurred occasionally on Tiree. Two pairs were present and the first breeding record was documented when downy young were seen on 16 July 1901 (Laidlaw 1902). Laidlaw again found phalaropes on Tiree in June 1902 and 1903 (Laidlaw 1903, 1904) and Anderson (1913) described a few arriving regularly on Tiree between the last week of May and the first week of June and remaining to breed. The only breeding record away from Tiree was on Coll in 1912, when there may possibly have been another breeding pair (Bannerman 1961). There appear to be no further documented Argyll records until phalaropes were relocated on Tiree in 1955 when at least six birds were present and two nests were found (Boyd 1958). Thereafter, not more than two pairs were recorded in the ten years up to the 1968-70 survey (Everett 1971). Polyandry was suspected in 1968 when one female and two males were present and a nest was found but failed. In 1969-70 only a single adult was located. In 1979 there were four females and a male, but in 1983 when the site was next visited there were just two males. The site was checked in all but two years between 1984-92 with 1-3 present each year and successful breeding confirmed in 1989 and 1992. None were found during the next six years but, surprisingly, a pair reappeared in 1999 and again in 2000, although breeding was not suspected in either year. A male was present for one day in May 2004.

Tiree appears to have a choice of suitable breeding sites that could provide the close association of open water, emergent vegetation and both wet and dry marsh preferred by the species. More than one site has been used on Tiree although the site known to have held the largest colony, in 1953, has since become unsuitable following drainage. Phalaropes appear to be site-faithful but they can be inconspicuous and overlooked in breeding habitat.

Arrivals at breeding sites in Scotland from end of May-early June make the species one of the latest to arrive in spring. Information on phenology comes largely from detailed studies in Shetland. These have confirmed that females begin to moult before departing, sometimes as early as mid-June. Males follow in late July while juveniles can still be present into August (Second Atlas). The earliest date of spring arrivals on Tiree is 17 May and the latest record is 30 July.

Red-necked Phalaropes winter at sea but the general wintering area for Scottish birds and even the general direction of migration remain uncertain. Ringing recoveries from the nearest populations show that birds from Fennoscandia migrate, partly overland, to reach wintering quarters in areas of upwelling with abundant planktonic food in the Arabian Sea and the Gulf of Aden. There are no ringing recoveries of birds from the Icelandic population away from Iceland but Toms (in Migration Atlas) favoured the view that they migrate south *via* Greenland and Newfoundland.

There are no spring records in Argyll away from the breeding areas. The very few observations of autumn migrants all originate from MSBO (Kintyre) and include single juveniles on 13 August, 12 and 15 September 1992, 9 September 1995 and two just offshore on 6 August 2000. This paucity of records of migrants in Argyll reflects the situation elsewhere on the west coast of the UK, where it is markedly more scarce than on the east (Migration Atlas).

Roger Broad

Grey Phalarope

Phalaropus fulicarius

Almost annual passage migrant in small numbers, usually associated with autumn gales.

The Grey Phalarope is one of the few species susceptible to being "wrecked" along our shores during periods of severe weather in autumn. Birds migrating south from breeding

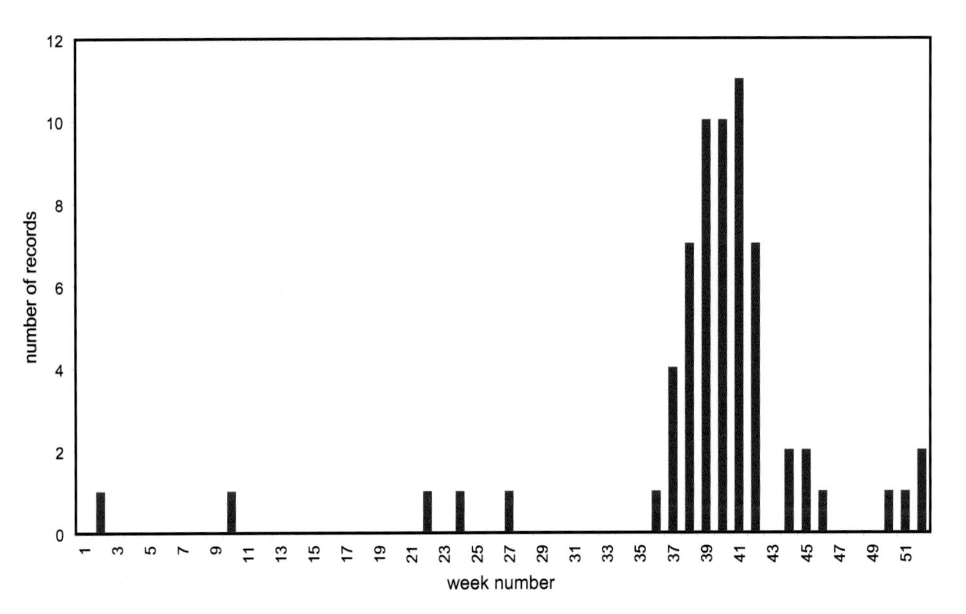

Weekly variation in Argyll records of Grey Phalarope, 1980-2003.

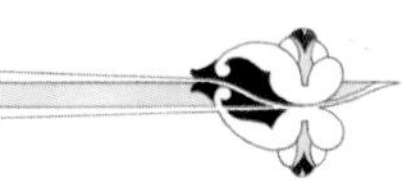

grounds in Iceland, Greenland and perhaps elsewhere (Migration Atlas) are driven inshore by westerly or north-westerly gales, where their apparent tameness may draw attention. In the past, this led some to an untimely end: Gray stated that he had seen specimens obtained from the Oban area, Loch Fyne and Loch Etive, while H&B reported two killed by a fisherman with an oar on Loch Fyne near Tarbert, and another killed by a boy with a stone at Ardfin on Jura. Both these events, together with a sighting of six birds on the northern shore of Loch Indaal on Islay (Scot-Skirving 1892, H&B) occurred in the autumn of 1891, when there was an influx of Grey Phalaropes along the coasts of Britain and Ireland. Birds were also killed at the lanterns of Skerryvore and Dubh Artach (B&R).

Sporadic records, mostly involving single birds, continued over the years. In September 1977 there was a small influx into Scotland, leading to several reports of definite or probable Grey Phalaropes from Islay, Colonsay and the Sound of Jura (SB 10:135). Only since 1989, largely as a result of increased interest in seawatching, have reports become more or less annual. The seasonal distribution of records during 1980-2003 shows a marked peak of sightings in the latter half of September and the first half of October. There have also been a few late autumn and winter records, but in line with the very sparse nature of spring passage through the British Isles (Migration Atlas), there have been none during April and May. Long-staying individuals in summer plumage were at Ballinaby on Islay from 11 to 20 June 1986 (ABR 4:25, Elliott 1989) and Pennygown on Mull from 3 to 12 July 1994 (ABR 11:55).

Most records during the period come from Kintyre and the islands, with Uisaed Point boasting the most as a result of consistent seawatching. The four mainland records outwith Kintyre come from Loch Feochan, Loch Sween, Dunoon and Oban Bay (one on 17 November 1990, previously unpublished). Most sightings involve single birds, the highest counts being six at Gartnatra on Islay on 24 September 1991 (ABR 7:45), seven flying south past Uisaed Point on 5 October 1995 (ABR 12:50), and six flying south past the same location on 15 September 2001 (ABR 18:64). At least 20 individuals were recorded in autumn 2004, most in September, and of 12 or more recorded in autumn and winter 2006, eight were in October.

Some claims of Red-necked Phalarope in Argyll, seen in circumstances more typical of Grey (e.g. SB 10:135, Jardine *et al.* 1986), seem almost certain to be referrable to this species, as are most records of unidentified phalaropes. Maguire (2001) provided a useful summary of the flight characteristics of the two species, based on field experience gained at Uisaed Point.

Tristan ap Rheinallt

Pomarine Skua

Stercorarius pomarinus

A regular autumn migrant in small numbers, with fewer records in spring and summer. Recorded in every month of the year.

Pomarine Skuas breed in the northern tundra and winter in tropical seas. On migration, they pass to the west and east of the British Isles, and large numbers are sometimes seen from the coast. Although Gray made no mention of this species in Argyll, H&B stated that the Pomarine Skua was "occasionally found on the coast, but less frequently than further west." This summary has stood the test of time. Of the early records from Argyll, the most notable are undoubtedly those associated with an unprecedented influx to the Firth of Clyde in autumn 1879 (H&B, B&R). This influx, which also brought thousands of birds to the east coasts of Scotland and England, has never been repeated on such a scale.

With the exception of the 1879 influx, published records from Argyll are rather few and far between until the 1980s, and mainly concern single birds. B&R referred to sightings of birds on passage off Colonsay and Tiree without giving details. Booth (1975) could only list two records for Islay, and Jardine *et al.* (1986) the same number for Colonsay and Oronsay.

Over the past two decades, singles have been seen almost every year in spring and autumn. Most records come from Kintyre and the islands or from ferry crossings. Two birds were seen north-east of the Garvellachs on 8 June 2001 (ABR 18:64). There seem to be no recent records from the mainland coast away from Kintyre.

Most spring records have been in May, although Pomarine Skuas have also been recorded in March and April. They mostly involve singles or small groups of up to eight birds. The spring of 1987 was, however, exceptional. Flocks totalling some 140 birds were seen between Tobermory and Coll on 12 May, and five flew north past Rubha Chraiginis on Tiree the following day (ABR 5:8). This occurrence coincided with the main period of northward movement past North Uist (SBR 1987:26). It seems likely that Pomarine Skuas following their normal spring migration route, which lies well to the west of Argyll waters, pass closer inshore in particular weather conditions. Multiple occurrences at Uisaed Point at this season have been associated with north-westerly gales.

Sightings of birds in June and July are not unusual. At least some of the former are likely to be late spring migrants, whilst the latter involve failed breeders on their way south from breeding grounds in the high Arctic (Migration Atlas). Land-based seawatching in recent years has shown that there is a trickle of birds moving south through Argyll in autumn. The numbers involved are small and the highest counts are associated with severe weather: 26 flew south past Uisaed Point on 17 October 1991 (ABR 8:45), and 18 past Frenchman's Rocks on 31 October 1999 (ABR 16:64). Most of the birds involved in these movements were juveniles, with adults typically passing through earlier. The southward movement of this species in autumn is some three to four weeks later than the movement of Arctic Skuas (Migration Atlas), and Pomarine Skuas are perhaps more likely to be seen in Argyll in November and December than are the two commoner species. There are isolated records in January and February.

Tristan ap Rheinallt

Arctic Skua

Stercorarius parasiticus

Small, but long-established, colonies on Coll and Jura, which declined to 15 and 6 pairs in 2000. Widespread off coasts during passage, especially in autumn.

Arctic Skuas in Argyll feed predominantly by chasing terns, small gulls and auks to steal fish. They breed on remote moorland that has few or no predatory mammals, close to colonies of their hosts and tend to avoid areas with much human activity. Birds on passage often aggregate in bays where there are flocks of terns and small gulls, but when migrating they tend to remain some distance from the shore, though often within sight from land. Although most Arctic Skuas that breed in Argyll are dark-phase birds, most migrants are pale-phase birds from high latitude breeding grounds.

Arctic Skuas arrive in Argyll in late April and May, with passage continuing northwards through June. Autumn migration starts in July, but is mostly during August and September. Few are seen after mid-October. Migrants from high latitudes greatly outnumber local birds during the passage periods. Spring migration is often not very evident in Argyll, whereas in autumn birds tend to linger and come closer to coasts. However, numbers passing through Argyll are relatively small compared to passage past the west of Ireland, the Hebrides or Aberdeenshire. On average, only about 1-2 per day are seen passing regular seawatching sites such as Frenchman's Rocks, Islay, or MSBO during August-September, and maximum numbers are usually less than ten per day. Higher counts have included 24 or more from the Oban-Tiree ferry on 1 August 1984, 21 from the Oban-Colonsay ferry on 10 September 1997 and 32 passing in four hours off Hogh Bay, Coll, on 18 May 2004.

Small numbers have bred on Argyll islands as far back as records go, the main colonies being on Coll and Jura. Pennant (1789) found Arctic Skuas nesting on Jura in 1772. H&B reported they were "common" on Jura in 1892, but also stated categorically that they must have left the island and subsequently recolonised since there were none there around 1867. Whether this is correct, or they had simply been overlooked is unclear. There are few recent counts for Jura, but these include 20 pairs in 1970 (Cramp *et al.* 1974), 42 pairs plus 27 individuals in 1987 (Lloyd *et al.* 1991), three birds in 1996 (SBR) and six pairs in 2000 (ABR). The first record of Arctic Skuas breeding on Coll was in 1898, and the first estimate of numbers there was 'about' 15 pairs in 1937-39 (Furness 1987). Numbers reported over the years (Table) have varied considerably. It is unclear how much of this variation is due to real changes in numbers, and how much is due to counting errors and incomplete coverage in some years.

Apart from the long-established colonies on Coll and Jura, Arctic Skuas have occasionally held territories, and sometimes nested, elsewhere in Argyll. There may have been a few pairs on Islay before 1850 as old editions of Encyclopedia Britannica record this, but B&R record that it did not breed there in 1852. In 1922 it did nest on Islay and this was reported as an addition to the Islay list in that year. There have not been any breeding records from Islay in recent years. One pair nested on Tiree in 1891 and probably in several years that decade (B&R). Lloyd *et al.* (1991) and Everett (1982) reported nesting on Colonsay in 1975. Although Arctic Skuas from Jura are often seen at Colonsay, they apparently do not normally breed there, and there are no breeding records for Colonsay since 1975. Pairs or individuals occasionally settle on sites that could be held as territories at various places, especially on the Treshnish Isles, Mull, Colonsay, Tiree and Islay.

The 21 pairs of Arctic Skuas breeding in Argyll in 2000 represented about 1% of the UK population, whereas in 1969 and 1985, the 25 and 99 pairs in Argyll represented 2.4% and 3% of the UK population in those periods. Why numbers have fallen from the peak reached in 1985 is unclear. As Argyll lies on the southern limit of breeding range of the species, fluctuations in numbers might be expected to be especially pronounced. Breeding numbers might have been

Numbers of pairs, or AOTs (apparently occupied territories) of Arctic Skuas on Coll in different years.

Year	Pairs or AOTs	Reference
1937-1939	c.15	Furness 1987
1945	12	Furness 1987
1949	4	Furness 1987
1955	30-40	Boyd 1958
1970	6	Cramp *et al.* 1974
1984	50	SBR
1987	49	Lloyd *et al.* 1991
1989	37	ABR
1991	39	SBR
1992	25	ABR
1994	33	ABR
1995	27	ABR
1997	21	ABR
1998	20	ABR
2000	15	ABR
2005	12	J. Bowler, pers. comm.

Most Arctic Skuas that breed in Argyll are dark-phase birds. *Bob Furness*

affected through habitat loss, while downturns in numbers further north, which have certainly occurred in recent years in Shetland and Orkney in particular, may have reduced the availability of immigrants. Ringing and other studies provide little indication of how much Argyll's Arctic Skuas mix with other breeding groups further north, or depend on immigration. Thus predicting the future trend in breeding numbers is impossible.

Bob Furness

Long-tailed Skua

Stercorarius longicaudus

Rare migrant, with most records in autumn.

H&B admitted this species to the Argyll list on the basis of two specimens (male and female) said to be in the collection of the Maclaine of Lochbuie (Mull), and a sighting of a bird on Jura by Henry Evans, who allegedly threw bread to it. Evans (in litt. to Harvie-Brown) wrote that "a splendid example" was in Loch Tarbert in about 1883 or 1884; this presumably refers to the same record. Elliott (1989) states that one was at Blackrock on Islay in June 1914.

In the absence of any details, it is difficult to be certain about the validity of these old records, although it is reasonable to suppose that they are all likely to refer to distinctive summer-plumaged adults. This is unlikely to be the case for the next Argyll record, which occurred on the unusually late date of 22 October 1967 at Coull on Islay (SB 5:47, Booth 1975, Elliott 1989) and seems open to some doubt. Nevertheless, records subsequently became more frequent, with one in 1968, two in the 1970s, four in the 1980s, 11 in the 1990s, and 15 during 2000-06. Of the 33 records between 1968 and 2006, 10 were in spring (May and June) and 22 in autumn (August to October) and one was on 21 July. The earliest and latest dates were 8 May and 17 October. A third of these records resulted from seawatching at one location (Uisaed Point in Kintyre), the remainder coming from Islay, Mull, Coll, Tiree and surrounding waters. Most records after mid-September involved juveniles. Four seen between Coll and Tiree on 24 May 2003 (Argyll Database) is the highest count, most records involving singles.

The large northward migration of Long-tailed Skuas off the Outer Hebrides in spring is well known. However, these birds must pass well to the west of Argyll's coasts, as do Pomarine Skuas at the same season. Similarly, all four skua species are much less numerous in Argyll in autumn than they are along the east coast of Scotland.

Tristan ap Rheinallt

Great Skua

Stercorarius skua

One or two pairs have bred in some recent years on the Treshnish Isles and on Coll. Otherwise this species is an uncommon passage migrant and summer visitor.

Great Skuas on passage tend to keep some distance offshore, so their presence may be overlooked by seawatchers based on the coast, except when weather conditions force birds unusually close to land. Breeding Great Skuas favour remote

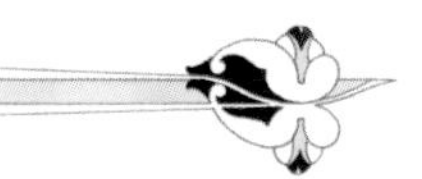

moorland close to colonies of cliff-nesting seabirds that they can kill or rob of fish. Since they do not breed until about 4-12 years old, they may hold territory as prospecting pre-breeders for several seasons before starting to nest. Once they have nested, they normally return each year to exactly the same location.

A small, but apparently increasing, number have been summering in Argyll in recent decades. The first proven breeding occurred in 1989 on Coll, after one or two pairs had held territory there for several successive summers (ABR). Since then, 1-5 pairs have summered on Coll, but breeding has not been proved in most years. The first successful breeding on Coll was in 1997, when one pair reared two chicks (ABR). Two pairs attempted to breed there in 2004, one of which fledged a single young (S. Wellock pers. comm.). Birds or pairs have also held territories in the Treshnish Isles in most summers since 1996 and possibly for several years earlier. The first proven breeding in the Treshnish Isles was in 1998, although a pair was diving at people in 1996, which implies that they had eggs or chicks in that year. Numbers holding territories in the Treshnish Isles are uncertain, but one or two pairs have been seen on Fladda, while six adults were on Lunga in 1999 (ABR). This suggests that there were about six pairs in Argyll in the late 1990s, though Seabird 2000 recorded only three pairs for Argyll. A territorial pair were on Tiree during May-June 2004. These are the southernmost breeding sites in Scotland, but represent less than 0.1% of the UK population which is mostly found in Shetland and Orkney.

Surprisingly, there are quite a number of records of Great Skuas in Argyll, especially Islay, from as early in the year as February (ABR). Probably these are exceptionally early spring migrants heading towards colonies further north, but even the identity of the species is open to some doubt given that South Polar Skuas *Stercorarius maccormicki* and Brown Skuas *S. antarctica* (southern hemisphere populations) may be present in the North Atlantic in small numbers as wandering immatures or non-breeders, and these are very difficult to distinguish from the Great Skua.

Most Great Skuas winter south of the English Channel and tend to return to breeding areas from late March onwards (Klomp & Furness 1992). Most records in Argyll are between May and early October, late migrants being seen into November in a few years (ABR). Numbers in Argyll peak in August-September with passage of birds from northern Scotland, and probably also from Iceland. However, the passage through Argyll is weak, with much lower numbers than seen off the west of Ireland, the Hebrides or Aberdeenshire. Most passage is seen from Frenchman's Rocks, Islay, or from MSBO. At these sites, Great Skuas are seen at a rate of about one every two days during the autumn passage period, with rarely more than four in any one day.

Great Skuas are conspicuous and noisy while displaying on their territories in spring. *Bob Furness*

The increase in numbers summering in Argyll reflects a large increase in numbers in Shetland and Orkney together with range expansion. In recent decades, range expansion, often involving birds ringed as chicks in Shetland, has

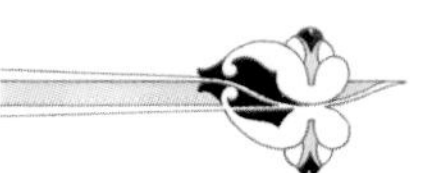

mostly been northwards to Spitzbergen, north Norway and north Russia (Furness 1987). Argyll may represent limits of tolerance of summer temperatures for this cold-adapted species. No studies of feeding or behaviour have been carried out in Argyll. Elsewhere in Scotland, Great Skuas in large colonies feed mainly on fish (including fishery discards); where the species nests in small numbers, they tend to feed predominantly by killing other seabirds such as small gulls and auks, so it is likely that the birds summering on Coll and Treshnish Isles do the same.

Bob Furness

Mediterranean Gull

Larus melanocephalus

Until recently a vagrant, but recorded much more frequently over the past few years.

Although considered an extreme rarity in the British Isles as recently as 1940, the Mediterranean Gull has since colonised England and now Northern Ireland as a breeding species. It has become a regular, though scarce, visitor to parts of Scotland. However, although there are now several records annually from Ayrshire, it has, until recently, been rare in Argyll. Eight of the fifteen accepted records come from Kintyre, six of them from a single site. Since autumn 2003 there has been a notable increase in reports and, in addition to those listed in the table below, there are records under consideration at the time of writing relating to six further individuals seen during 2006 (four in the Tarbert-Lochgilphead area, one on Islay and one at Loch Etive) (J. Dickson pers. comm.).

The increase in records from the late 1990s parallels a similar increase over Scotland as a whole, and the concentration of earlier sightings in south Kintyre suggests Northern Ireland as a source for these wandering birds. With the first successful breeding in Northern Ireland during 2002, it seems quite possible that this species may become established in Argyll in the not too distant future.

Tristan ap Rheinallt

Mediterranean Gull (centre) with Black-headed Gulls at Inverneil, Mid-Argyll, in January 2007. *Jim Dickson*

Records of Mediterranean Gulls in Argyll to 2006.

Date	Location	Comment	Reference
19 July to 5 September 1975	Campbeltown	Adult; fifth Scottish record	SB 9:211
29 October 1976	East Loch Tarbert (Kintyre)	Adult	SB 10:99
15 December 1992	Torrans (Mull)	Adult	SBR 1992:34
17 to 19 September 1995	Uisaed Point	First-winter	SBR 1997:41, ABR 14:57
7 November 1998	Campbeltown Loch (Kintyre)	Second-winter	SBR 1998:58, ABR 15:63
21 April 2000	Uisaed Point	First-summer	ABR 17:66
5 October 2000	Loch Bhasapol (Tiree)	First-winter with damaged leg	ABR 17:66
13 to 19 August 2003	Uisaed Point	Adult	Argyll Database
19 August 2003	Uisaed Point	Juvenile / first-winter	Argyll Database
17 October 2003	Uisaed Point	Adult	Argyll Database
1 and 14 July 2004	Loch an Eilein (Tiree)	First summer	Argyll Database
31 August to 5 October 2004	Uisaed Point	Juvenile / first-winter	Argyll Database
19 February 2005	Eilean Traighe, Loch Caolisport (Mid-Argyll)	Second-winter	Argyll Database
14 November 2005	Loch Gilp (Mid-Argyll)	Adult	Argyll Database
21 August 2006	Loch Gilp (Mid-Argyll)	Two juveniles	Argyll Database

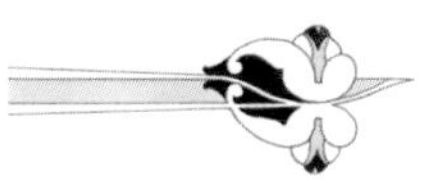

Laughing Gull

Larus atricilla

Vagrant.

The second Scottish record of this North American species concerned an adult in summer plumage near Loch Skerrols on Islay on 21 April 1974 (BB 68:320, Verrall 1977b). More recently, a first-winter bird was seen at Cliad on Coll on 28 November 1998 (BB 92:579), followed by a summer-plumaged adult at Loch Gruinart on Islay on 14 to 21 April 1999 (BB 93:536). In late 2005, in the wake of Hurricane Wilma, a remarkable influx of Laughing Gulls occurred in Britain involving at least 50 individuals. Two were found in Argyll, an adult in Crossapol Bay, Tiree, on 7 November and another adult found at Machir Bay, Islay, on 8 November and present there and at Loch Gorm until 16 November (BB 100:46-48). In 2006, two further adult birds were located. One stayed in Campbeltown from 10 January into April, and the other was seen off Gigha from the Islay ferry on 15 June.

Tristan ap Rheinallt

This adult Laughing Gull was at Campbeltown during January-April 2006. *Jim Dickson*

Little Gull

Larus minutus

Annual visitor, most frequently in autumn but may be encountered at any time of year. Some individuals stay for prolonged periods.

Little Gulls from breeding populations in the Baltic area and north-west Russia pass through Britain and Ireland on spring and autumn migration, the largest numbers being seen on the east coast. In addition, small numbers winter, most notably in the Irish Sea.

H&B do not include the Little Gull in their list of species from Argyll. The first record came in 1903, when a bird was seen at Skerryvore on 24 September (Tomison 1907, B&R).

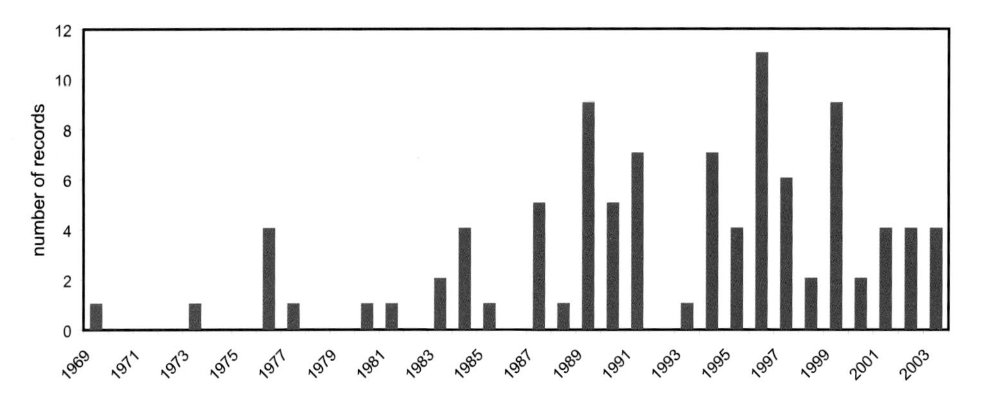

Figure 1. Records of Little Gulls in Argyll, 1969-2003.

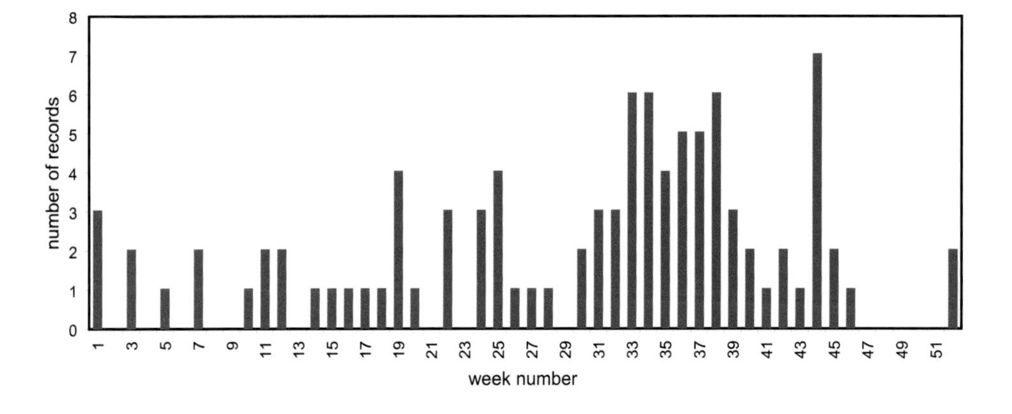

Figure 2. Weekly distribution of Little Gulls in Argyll, 1969-2003.

The second involved a moulting adult at Kilberry on 10 June 1952 (SN 68:117). The next record, in 1969, marked the beginning of a gradual increase through to the late 1980s, though with considerable year-to-year variation (Figure 1). This increase mirrors an increase in Scotland as a whole since the 1950s, matching a documented westwards expansion in the breeding range (Thom, Migration Atlas). Nevertheless, Little Gulls remain much scarcer in western Scotland than in the east, where counts of several hundred birds are not unusual. The seasonal distribution of the 97 Argyll records since 1969 shows that, while birds can turn up at any time of year, there is a pronounced autumn peak, extending from late July to the end of September, with perhaps a further small arrival at the end of October and beginning of November (Figure 2). Birds apparently reach Britain in two waves in autumn, the first possibly resulting from an initial post-breeding movement to sheltered sites for moult, and the second representing general dispersal to winter quarters (Migration Atlas).

Little Gulls are seen every year in Argyll. *Jim Dickson*

Many of the Little Gulls recorded in autumn in Argyll are seen with groups of Kittiwakes during sea-watches. In 1989 there was a widespread arrival in late August, with birds reported from Kintyre, Gigha, Islay, Colonsay, Tiree and Mull over a 15-day period. There is also a weak spring passage, and a concentration of records in mid-June, which appears to represent an arrival of first-summer birds (Figure 2). Some first-summer birds have lingered for prolonged periods in colonies of terns and Black-headed Gulls.

Both adult and immature birds have been recorded in every season, but juveniles and first-winters are more frequent than adults in autumn, whilst adults in summer plumage are decidedly infrequent. Of the 97 recent records, more than half come from the islands: Islay (23), Mull (14), Tiree (11), Gigha (2), Colonsay (1) and Oronsay (1). Most of the mainland records (30) come from south Kintyre, with one site (Uisaed Point) accounting for no fewer than 24 of these records. Birds have also been seen along the west coast of the mainland as far north as Ledaig Point, and in Loch Fyne at Inverneill and Dunderave Point, east of Inveraray. Although most records concern single birds, as many as five have been seen flying south past Uisaed Point in a day.

The record numbers in autumn 2004 (at least 18 individuals, 10 at Uisaed Point) are not included in the above figures.

Tristan ap Rheinallt

Sabine's Gull

Larus sabini

Scarce autumn migrant, with occasional records at other times of year.

As recently as 1986, Thom described the Sabine's Gull as a vagrant to Scotland, albeit annual since 1972. It has since become clear that this Arctic breeder is in fact a scarce but regular migrant during the autumn, when it is reported widely from coastal areas.

The first record of Sabine's Gull in Argyll concerned an adult shot at Loch Spelve on Mull on 7 or 8 September 1883 (H&B, B&R). This was only the second Scottish record. In August 1894, one was reported from Kilbrannan Sound outside Campbeltown Harbour (ASNH 1897:46, B&R), and in late October 1903 one was collected at Belnahua, Easdale (ASNH 1904:57,143,217, B&R). Rather more unusual, in terms of the date, were birds seen at Skerryvore in January or February 1905 (ASNH 1906:202, Tomison 1907) and on 30 November 1907 (ASNH 1907 report: 205, B&R). Following these five early records, there was a gap of 70 years until records from Islay (two), Oban and Machrihanish between 1977 and 1983, but none during the remainder of the 1980s.

Records were then annual between 1990 and 2003, except for two blank years (1998 and 2002). Recent interest in seawatching explains much of this steep rise in sightings. Indeed, of 31 records during the twelve-year period 1990-2003, no fewer than 19 came from two seawatching sites:

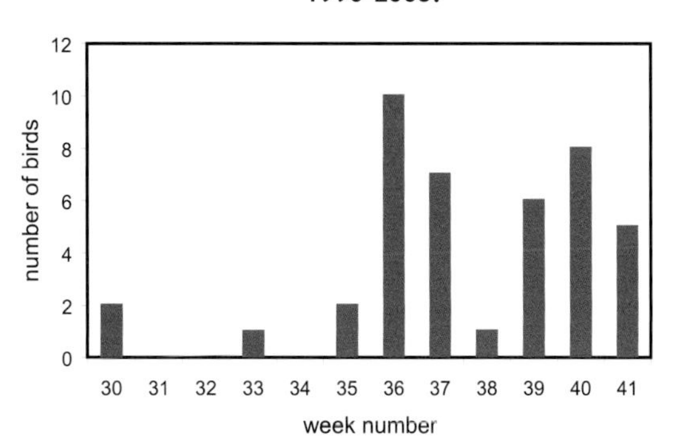

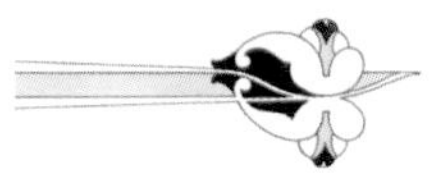

Frenchman's Rocks on Islay and Uisaed Point in Kintyre. The others came from Islay (four), Tiree (four), Kintyre (three) and Colonsay. All but one occurred between 27 July and 13 October, reflecting the species' status as an autumn migrant. The exception was a first-winter bird seen at Port Wemyss on Islay on 4 January 1991 (SBR 1991:41, with location given incorrectly as West Wemyss, ABR 8:46, ABR 9:9). Although most records involve single birds, there are some multiple occurrences. For example, four juveniles were seen at Frenchman's Rocks on 11 September 1994, and five at Uisaed Point on 13 October 1997. These records and many others were associated with strong westerly or north-westerly winds. It is assumed that, in calmer conditions, the birds would have been migrating well offshore.

The Figure illustrates the number of birds (rather than the number of records) in each week during the autumn, 1990-2003. After a few scattered sightings in late July and August, the main occurrence is in September and the first half of October. The week with the most records is Week 36 (3 to 9 September); this corresponds well to the situation in Britain as a whole, where the peak is usually in the first ten days of September (Fraser & Rogers 2001). Adults tend to migrate earlier than juveniles, almost all the birds recorded in Argyll during Weeks 39-41 being juveniles. The record numbers in autumn 2004 are not included in the above figures. There were accepted records of 34 individuals (18 on Islay, 13 at Uisaed Point and three on Tiree). Unfortunately, no descriptions were provided for claimed sightings of at least 20 further individuals.

Tristan ap Rheinallt

Bonaparte's Gull

Larus philadelphia

Vagrant.

Single adults were at Bridgend on Islay on 26 and 27 June 1975 and 12 September 1975 (BB 69:340). These were the fifth and sixth Scottish records of this North American species, although Elliott (1989) and Evans (1994) considered both to refer to the same bird.

Tristan ap Rheinallt

Black-headed Gull

Larus ridibundus

Resident with scattered breeding and winter distributions. Breeding numbers in Argyll & Bute decreased by 39% between 1987 and 2000, when only 679 pairs were recorded.

On the mainland, Black-headed Gulls are found with other gulls throughout the year at places with reliable sources of food, such as estuaries, harbours, fishing quays, car parks and lay-bys. On outer islands such as Colonsay and Islay, however, they are scarce or absent in winter and increasingly so in summer (see below). Flocks form near breeding sites in March before the birds return to colonies in April and May. These usually hold less than 100 pairs and are often on islets and skerries in sheltered waters such as sealochs. No inland

Small flocks of foraging Black-headed Gulls are a common sight around Argyll's coasts in winter. *Philip Kirkham*

breeding sites were found on the mainland in 2000. Unlike other gull species of this habitat, whole colonies often move sites unpredictably from year to year.

B&R mentioned breeding on Islay, Coll and Tiree but recorded an absence on Mull. Gibson (1958) found that the species bred much less commonly in south Argyll than in the rest of the Clyde area. The 679 pairs found in Argyll & Bute in Seabird 2000 represented only 1.6% of the Scottish total and 0.5% of the British Isles total. Only 428 pairs were found in 1969, when coverage was possibly less complete (Cramp *et al.* 1975). Colonies in Argyll are small compared with elsewhere. The largest concentration found in Seabird 2000 was 187 pairs at Loch Bhasapol (Tiree), but Eilean Inshaig (Loch Craignish) held 311 pairs in 1992, and the islet at Whitehouse Bay (Inverneill, Loch Fyne) held 161 pairs in 1993. Following predation by American Mink that caused whole-colony breeding failure at Inshaig in 1992, 1993 and 1994 and at Whitehouse Bay in 1993, both sites became empty. By 2002 Inshaig had been restored almost to its former species variety and abundance after mink control in 1997-2001, but Whitehouse Bay (where there was no systematic control of mink) remained empty. Several smaller colonies also disappeared due to mink, such as the colony of 40-50 pairs on the islet in Tayvallich harbour (Anon 1995).

Between 1989 and 1996, widespread annual breeding failures caused by mink accompanied a 52% decrease in breeding numbers in a study area on the mainland coast of Argyll and Lochaber (Craik 1997). Thereafter numbers continued to decline, and by 2001 they had decreased by 72% overall. Most of the remaining birds, 84% of 178 pairs, were then breeding at a single site, Eilean Inshaig, where mink were controlled each year (Craik 1998 and unpublished results). Some of this decline of Black-headed Gulls along the mainland coast can be explained quantitatively by known mink-related breeding failures. However, mink are unlikely to have been the only cause as there were similar or larger decreases on outer islands where mink were either absent (Colonsay, Tiree) or locally present but not identified as

Distribution and abundance of breeding Black-headed Gulls (apparently occupied nests) in Argyll during Seabird 2000.

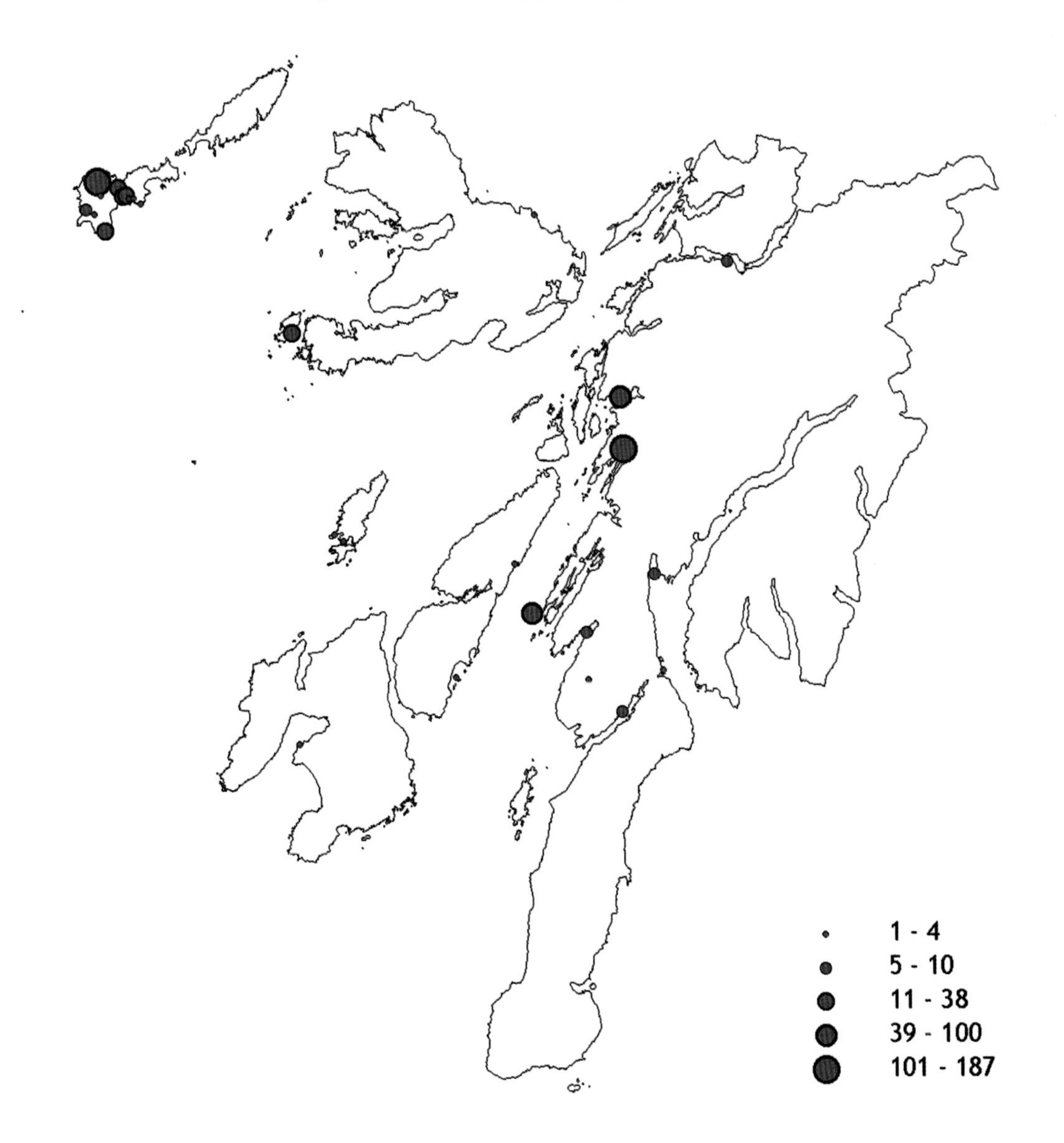

a cause of breeding failure (Islay). At the RSPB's Loch Gruinart reserve (Islay) breeding numbers decreased from about 90 pairs in 1990-92 to less than ten in 1996 and 1997, with none recorded in 1998 and 1999 (ABR); and only one pair was recorded on Islay in Seabird 2000. On Colonsay-Oronsay, there were 40 pairs in 1969, 36 in 1985, 71 in 1986 but only five in 2000 (Jardine *et al.* 2002). Tiree, where a single pair was first recorded breeding in 1889 (H&B), is now the stronghold of this species in Argyll. 506 pairs were counted at 11 sites in 1986, 685 pairs in 1987 (J. Bowler pers. comm.), 432 pairs at 15 sites in 1989, and 294 pairs in 1994 (ABR). During Seabird 2000, 308 pairs were counted on Tiree, when most of the rest were in Mid-Argyll (242 pairs). In 2004, however, numbers on Tiree had increased again to 520 nests at eight sites (J. Bowler pers. comm.).

Most British Black-headed Gulls do not migrate, but British-ringed birds have been recovered in Europe (from Norway to Spain) and, in smaller numbers, from North Africa. Numbers in Britain are augmented in winter by the arrival, mostly in the east, of large numbers of continental birds (Winter Atlas, Migration Atlas). Records in Argyll of birds ringed as chicks in Germany, Norway and Iceland (one each) show where some of our wintering Black-headed Gulls originate. Regular monthly counts at Lochs Gruinart, Indaal and Crinan have shown maxima in late summer and autumn, suggesting the presence of passage birds at that time of year. Spring and autumn counts at Lochs Gruinart and Indaal often exceeded 100 birds before 1996 but high counts have been fewer since then. Elsewhere, flocks of up to 600 have been recorded at several sites, but the only records of over 600 have been at Loch Caolisport (670 in October 2000 and 740 on 14 January 2001) and at Machrihanish (*c.* 1,200 on 9 February 1987) (ABR).

High counts made at seawatching sites have included 680 flying north at Tayinloan on 25 March 1989. At MSBO, 350 were recorded going north on 29 March 1989, 900+ passing on 19 September 1989, 180 moving south in three hours on 13 October 1989, 168 moving south on 11 September 1993, and 97 passing in four hours on 6 August 1996. At Frenchman's Rocks, Islay, 141 were counted in 12.5 hours in late October 1996, and 98 in three hours on 27 October 1996 (ABR).

Clive Craik

Increasing numbers of Ring-billed Gulls are being seen in Argyll. *Jim Dickson*

Ring-billed Gull

Larus delawarensis

The Ring-billed Gull is a scarce visitor to Argyll, mainly in spring.

Following the first British record in 1973, numbers of this transatlantic visitor increased steeply at the beginning of the 1980s, and more than 50 new birds have been reported nearly every year since 1982 (Fraser & Rogers 2006a). A more gradual increase has occurred in Scotland over the same period. Between January 1983 and the end of 2006 there were 38 accepted records in Argyll, involving about 31 birds (Table).

The large increase in 2005-2006 may be due to a real increase in numbers, or greater attention by observers, or both. A high proportion of these records occurred during February to May, suggesting northbound migrants. This reflects the situation in Britain as a whole, where Ring-billed Gulls that have wintered in south-west Europe may be caught up with the early passage of gulls returning to their breeding sites (Fraser & Rogers 2006a).

Tristan ap Rheinallt

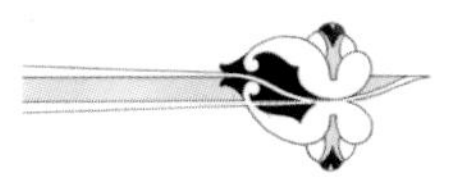

Records of Ring-billed Gulls in Argyll to 2006.

Date	Location	Comment	Reference
27 January 1983	Gott Bay (Tiree)	Adult	BB 77:530
26 March 1984	Lochgilphead	Adult	BB 78:555
21 April 1987	Ardnave Loch (Islay)	First-winter	BB 81:564
24 February 1988	Lussa Bay (Jura)	Three adults	SBR 1988:29, ABR 5:30
2 February 1989	Holy Loch	Adult	SBR 1989:27, ABR 6:37
4 -12 May 1989	Machir Bay (Islay)	Second-winter	SBR 1989:27, ABR 6:37
14 December 1989 13 June-30 Aug 1990 17 April-3 Sept 1991 14 March-5 Sept 1994 22 Feb-16 March 1995 17 Feb-16 March 1996	Port Charlotte and Loch Indaal (Islay)	Second winter, later adult (presumed returning bird)	SBR 1989:27, 1990:37, 1994:35, 1995:38 and 1997:42, ABR 6:37, 7:34, 8:46, 11:57, 12:52 and 14:58
23 August 1990	Oban Bay	Second-summer	SBR 1990:37, ABR 7:34 and 9:9
14 Jan-15 April 1991	Oban	Second-winter	SBR 1991:42, ABR 8:46
25 May-4 June 1991	Uisaed Point (Kintyre)	First-summer	ABR 8:46
7 November 1992	Proaig (Islay)	Adult	SBR 1992:35, ABR 9:35
24 December 1992	Tarbert (Kintyre)	Second-winter	SBR 1992:35, ABR 9:35
5 July 1994	North Ledaig	First-summer /second-winter	SBR 1995:38, ABR 12:52
3 April 1997	Port Askaig (Islay)	First-summer	SBR 1997:42, ABR 14:58
15 May & 19 July 1999	Sorobaidh Bay and Heylipol Farm (Tiree)	Third-winter, later adult	SBR 1999:68
12-26 March 2000	Machir Bay (Islay)	Adult	SBR 2000:67, ABR 17:67
4 April 2000	Lochan Luing, Rhunahaorine (Kintyre)	First-summer	SBR 2000:67, ABR 17:67
23 June-24 July 2001	Crossapol Farm (Tiree)	Adult with damaged wing; killed by a car on or before 24 July	SBR 2001:72, ABR 18:67
30 Dec 2001-2 Jan 2002	Bowmore (Islay)	First-winter	SBR 2001:72, ABR 18:67
11 February 2003 21 February 2004 29 March 2005 8 November 2005	Machir Bay (Islay)	Adult (possibly the bird seen here in 2000)	Argyll Database
19-20 March 2004	Balephetrish Bay (Tiree)	Two adults (one on 20 March)	Argyll Database
4 April-10 May 2005 12 Sep 2005 -5 Mar 2006 16 Nov 2006 (into 2007)	Oban Bay	First-winter in Apr 2005; second-winter in late 2005; third-winter/adult late 2006; presumed same bird	Argyll Database
28 Feb - 5 Mar 2006	Oban Bay	Another second-winter	Argyll Database
4-5 April 2005	Bowmore (Islay)	First-winter	Argyll Database
5 April 2005	Loch a' Phuill (Tiree)	First-winter	Argyll Database
14 Jan - 19 April 2006	Oban Bay	Adult (additional bird to the long-staying second-winter also present - see above)	Argyll Database
2-6 February 2006	Sorobaidh Bay (Tiree)	Adult	Argyll Database
22 February 2006	Bowmore (Islay)	Second-winter	Argyll Database

Common Gull

Larus canus

The Common Gull is widespread and numerous in Argyll throughout the year. 2,683 breeding pairs were found in Argyll & Bute in 2000.

Common Gulls are found throughout the British Isles in winter, but breeding is largely confined to Scotland and north-west Ireland (Winter Atlas, Second Atlas). Adults return to colonies in late March or early April. Most in Argyll now breed coastally. Nests are usually close to suitably tall and dense vegetation, such as rushes, Scots Lovage or coarse grasses, in which the chicks can hide. Eggs are laid in early to mid-May and hatch in early June. Most young fly in early July, slightly later than Black-headed Gulls but about two weeks earlier than the large gull species.

H&B recorded the species as abundant around Iona and Mull, present on Tiree and Jura, and breeding commonly on mainland sealochs. B&R gave breeding records from most parts of Argyll including all the larger islands. Gibson (1958) mentioned "small isolated colonies on many moors and beside hill lochs throughout entire Clyde area" and said it was "at one time the commonest nesting gull but now overtaken by the Herring Gull". In Seabird 2000, 2,683 pairs were counted breeding in Argyll & Bute, an increase of 22% since 1987 but close to the number found in Operation Seafarer in 1969. In 2000 Argyll held about 13% of the Scottish population.

Counts from many individual sites throughout the county are given in the ABR each year. The following summaries of breeding numbers are taken from ABR, or from Seabird 2000, unless otherwise stated. In a survey of freshwater lochs in Argyll in May and June 1985 (excluding Mull, Colonsay, Coll and Tiree), 493 freshwater bodies were visited and 675 pairs of Common Gulls were found in 29 10-km squares; the most populated 10-km square held 190 pairs (Broad *et al.* 1986). Results from Seabird 2000 suggest that many inland colonies occupied in 1985 and 1969, mostly by upland lochans, have disappeared. In the SAMS study area (Argyll) (mostly islets along mainland coast) during 1992-2001, about 800-1000 pairs were recorded each year at 20-40 colonies. The largest colony in Argyll, in Loch Etive, held about 300 pairs each

Distribution and abundance of breeding Common Gulls (apparently occupied nests) in Argyll during Seabird 2000.

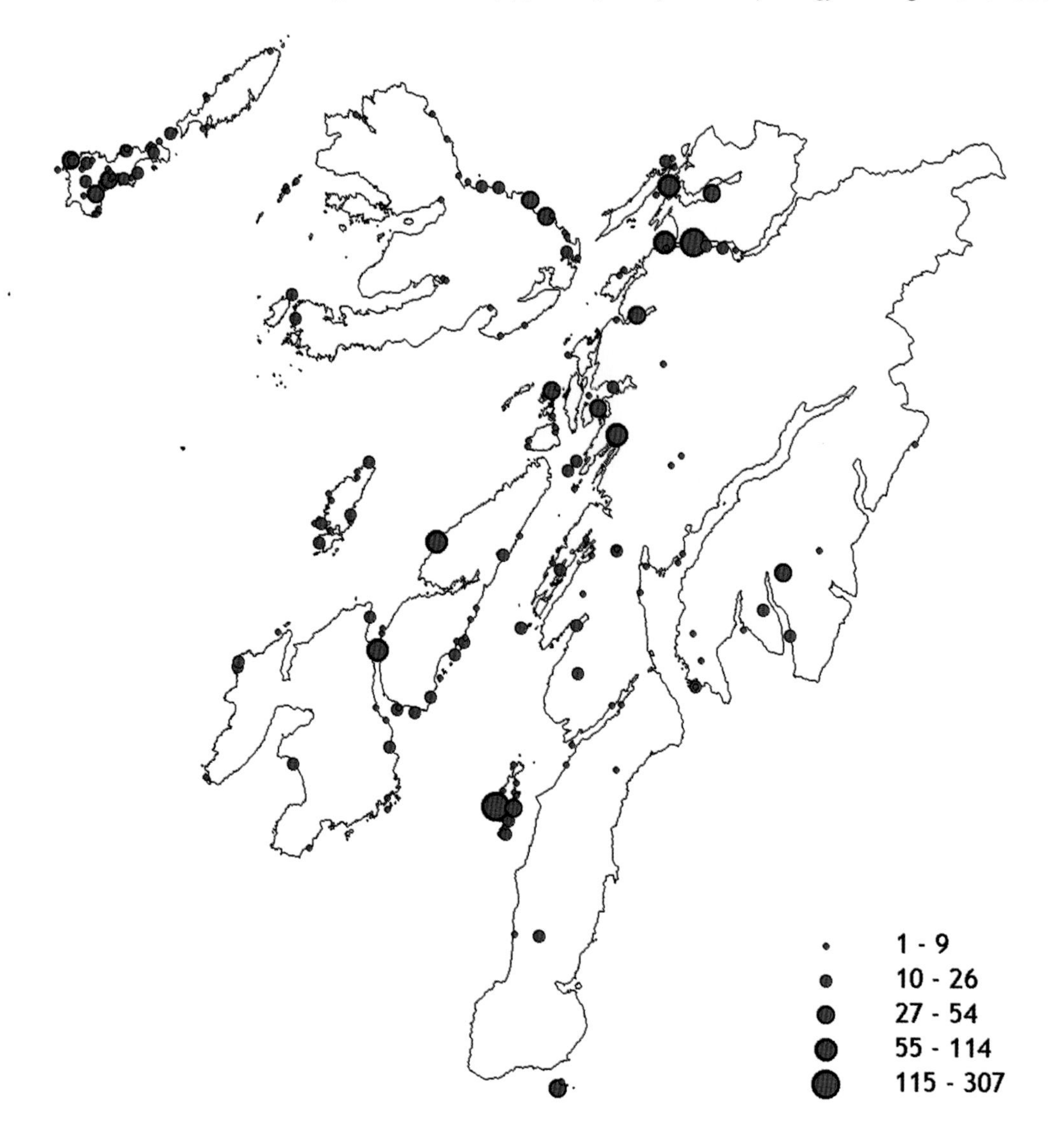

Although Common Gulls are still common in Argyll, their colonies are highly sensitive to mink predation. *David Palmar*

year, but most Argyll colonies are much smaller. For example, in 2000, of the other colonies in that study area, six held 51-90 pairs each, 23 held 11-50 pairs, 22 held 2-10 pairs, and ten sites held single pairs (J.C.A. Craik, unpubl. data).

Coll held 45 pairs in 1995 and 17 pairs in 2000. Tiree held 330-350 pairs at 19 colonies in a complete survey in 1989, 98 pairs in a partial survey in 1994, and 342 pairs in 2000 (including Gunna). Colonsay-Oronsay held 28 pairs in 1969, 46 in 1985, 98 in 1986, and 81 in 2000 (Jardine *et al.* 2002). RSPB Loch Gruinart (Islay) held 23-50 pairs during 1989-1992 and 11-28 pairs during 1995-1997. There were 411 birds at 14 small colonies (largest colony 85 birds) in a complete survey of the Rinns area in 1994, and 71 pairs in a boat survey of the whole Islay coast in 2000. In 1985, Common Gulls were "breeding in small numbers at many coastal sites and at some inland lochs" on Jura, and 237 pairs were counted in a boat survey of the whole Jura coast in 2000. On Scarba, 52 birds were recorded at colonies in a whole-island count in 1996, but only 15 pairs were found in a whole-coast survey in 1999-2000. On Mull, 78 nests were counted in 1986, including 22 at Loch Don; there were 58 nests at Garmony in 1997; and 213 pairs were counted in a whole-coast boat survey in 2000. On the Treshnish Isles, ten pairs were counted in 1998 and 17 pairs in 2004 (TIARG Reports). On the Sanda Isles, there were 38 pairs in 1969, 25 in 1989, and numbers during 1991-2001 varied between 14 pairs in 1986 and 56 in 1996 (R. Morton pers. comm.)

Exposed chicks sometimes die in heavy rain, but starvation is rarely a cause of breeding failures, probably because Common Gulls exploit a wide range of marine and terrestrial food, both animal and plant. Colonies and pairs unaffected by predators almost always succeed in raising young, but Common Gulls are severely affected by the many predators found in Argyll. American Mink and Herring Gulls in particular, and Peregrine Falcons and Buzzards to a lesser extent all affect breeding success. In the 1990s, 23 colonies apparently free of these predators produced an average of 0.7-0.9 fledged young per pair; 18 colonies affected by native predators produced an average of 0.4 and rarely failed completely; and 36 colonies affected by mink averaged 0.04-0.06 and usually failed completely (Craik 1999, 2000). Most colonies of Common Gulls are on small islets. The spread in the 1980s of mink greatly reduced the safety of these havens, and an overall 39% decrease between 1989 and 1998 in a study area was preceded and explained quantitatively by annual whole-colony breeding failures caused by mink. The decrease was accompanied by the disappearance of Common Gulls from at least 20 former colonies of 10-100 pairs (listed in Craik 1998). Several smaller sealochs lost all their breeding Common Gulls after repeated, well-documented mink-caused breeding failures on small islands. One of these sealochs was Loch Creran where, during 1996-2002, the only breeding Common Gulls that remained were those that nested on a factory roof. To conserve this species, mink are now removed annually near affected colonies. This has greatly improved gull breeding success and has conserved the colonies in some sealochs and restored them to others (Craik 1998).

Gray was the first to report that this gull makes a conspicuous migration across Scotland and, more recently, two detailed accounts of this movement have been given (Radford 1960, Vernon 1969). Birds from Scandinavia winter in east and central Scotland and, as part of the same general

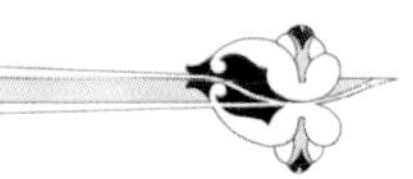

movement, many birds from west Scotland move south and south-west in autumn (Migration Atlas). Chicks ringed in Argyll and recovered more than 100km away have been found in central and southern Scotland (eight), northern England (five) and Ireland (14, ranging from the far north to the far south-west). The only recovery of an Argyll bird outside the British Isles was of a chick ringed near Tighnabruaich (Cowal) in 1964 that was shot near Golega, Portugal, in December of that year (1,851km). Birds ringed more than 100km away and recovered within the county came from near Perth (three), near Inverness (two) and Ardnamurchan (one).

The presence in Argyll of passage or wintering birds from further north explains the fact that counts outside the breeding season often greatly exceed local breeding numbers. Many counts of feeding or roosting flocks have been recorded in ABR. The highest were 1,400 on 24 September 1990, and up to 1,000 in September and October 1991, both at the Laggan (Kintyre). Other sites with regular or occasional counts of 500-1,000 birds were Lochs Gilp, Indaal and Gruinart and the Holy Loch, and Lismore, Oban Bay, Machrihanish Bay and Breachacha Bay. This movement is also reflected in seawatching records. There was heavy passage off Sanda in 1980 (600 birds passed on 15 September, 700 on 17 and 550 on 28 September). At MSBO, passage was regular from 7 August to 31 October 1989 with a peak of 1,500 on 27 August. During passage in September and October 1991, a peak of 170 moved south in six hours on 22 September; and 560 passed southwards on 3 December 1993.

Clive Craik

Lesser Black-backed Gull

Larus fuscus

This gull is a common summer visitor that breeds widely along the coast, usually on small islands, sometimes singly but more usually in colonies of up to 500 pairs or more. Seabird 2000 found 3,235 pairs in Argyll & Bute.

The Seabird 2000 total of 3,235 pairs in Argyll & Bute was a one percent increase since 1987, but a 23% decrease since 1969. It represented 13% of the Scottish total but only about 3% of the British Isles total.

A few Lesser Black-backs are recorded in Argyll in the midwinter months of most years, suggesting that a small number spend the winter here. The main arrival is usually in mid-March and most have left by late October. While there are many Herring Gull colonies in the county with few or no Lesser Black-backs, the reverse is not true. Almost all the Lesser Black-backs breed in colonies of 50-500 pairs alongside or surrounded by larger numbers of Herring Gulls. Lesser Black-backs seem to be less attached than Herring Gulls to particular breeding sites and consequently their colonies may vary more in size from year to year.

Gray, H&B, and B&R give early records but no numbers. Gibson (1985) gives numbers breeding at the Burnt Islands (Kyles of Bute) and at several sites in Kintyre and Loch Fyne for some of the years 1940-1980, including years of first breeding at some sites. Changes involving sites with 100

The largest colony of Lesser Black-backed Gulls in Argyll is on an island in the Sound of Jura. *David Palmar*

or more pairs reported by him are supplemented below by more recent counts including those of Seabird 2000. In the 1950s to 1970s Gibson found 100-200 pairs breeding in large mixed colonies, both on hill slopes north of Mull of Kintyre and in the Loch an Eilein area, Kintyre; at both of these sites all the gulls had disappeared by 1999 for unknown reasons. In Loch Fyne, Gibson recorded an increase on Glas Eilean from one pair in 1954 to 100 pairs in 1985, and there were still about 40 pairs here in 1997 and 2000. However, at Sgat Mor where Gibson recorded an increase from "a few" pairs in 1924 to about 125 nests in 1956, there were none in 1979 or 1999-2001, although both Herring and Great Black-backed Gulls were present in strength. On Sanda Isles Lesser Black-backed Gulls first bred in the late 1920s and numbers of pairs increased to about 30 in the early 1940s, 110 in 1964, 290 in 1969, but then fell to 106 in 1980 and 111 in 1985 (Gibson 1985); and during 1991-2001 counts of pairs varied irregularly between 59 and 160 (R. Morton pers. comm.)

Other recent counts at breeding sites have been as follows; all are from the ABR or Seabird 2000 unless otherwise stated. Each year during 1994-2001, the total recorded in the Argyll part of SAMS study area (islands along the mainland coast) was about 800-1100 pairs at 10-20 sites; during this time the largest colony, with about 300-500 pairs, was Reisa mhic Phaidean in the Sound of Jura. On Coll there were over 100 pairs in 1985, 129-152 in 1987, at least 128 in 1989, 179 at six colonies (in partial count of island) in 1995 and 102 in a whole-island survey in 2000. On Tiree there were about 292 pairs at eight sites in 1986, at least 129 in 1987, 246 in 1989, two "large" colonies on Soa, and 50 pairs at Loch na Gile in 1993, 122 in 1994, and 597 pairs in a whole-island survey in 2000. On Colonsay-Oronsay there were three pairs in 1969, 31 in 1985, 41 in 1986, and a notable increase to 226 pairs in Seabird 2000 (Jardine *et al.* 2002). On Islay there were 60 adults at a colony on Duich Moss in 1990, and 267 pairs in a whole-coast boat survey in 2000. On Jura, there were an estimated 520-780 adults at a large mixed gull colony at Shian Bay in 1985 but only 52 pairs in a whole-coast boat survey in 2000. On Scarba 200-225 pairs were found in a whole-island count in 1996 but only 44 in a whole-coast boat survey

Distribution and abundance of breeding Lesser Black-backed Gulls (apparently occupied nests) in Argyll during Seabird 2000.

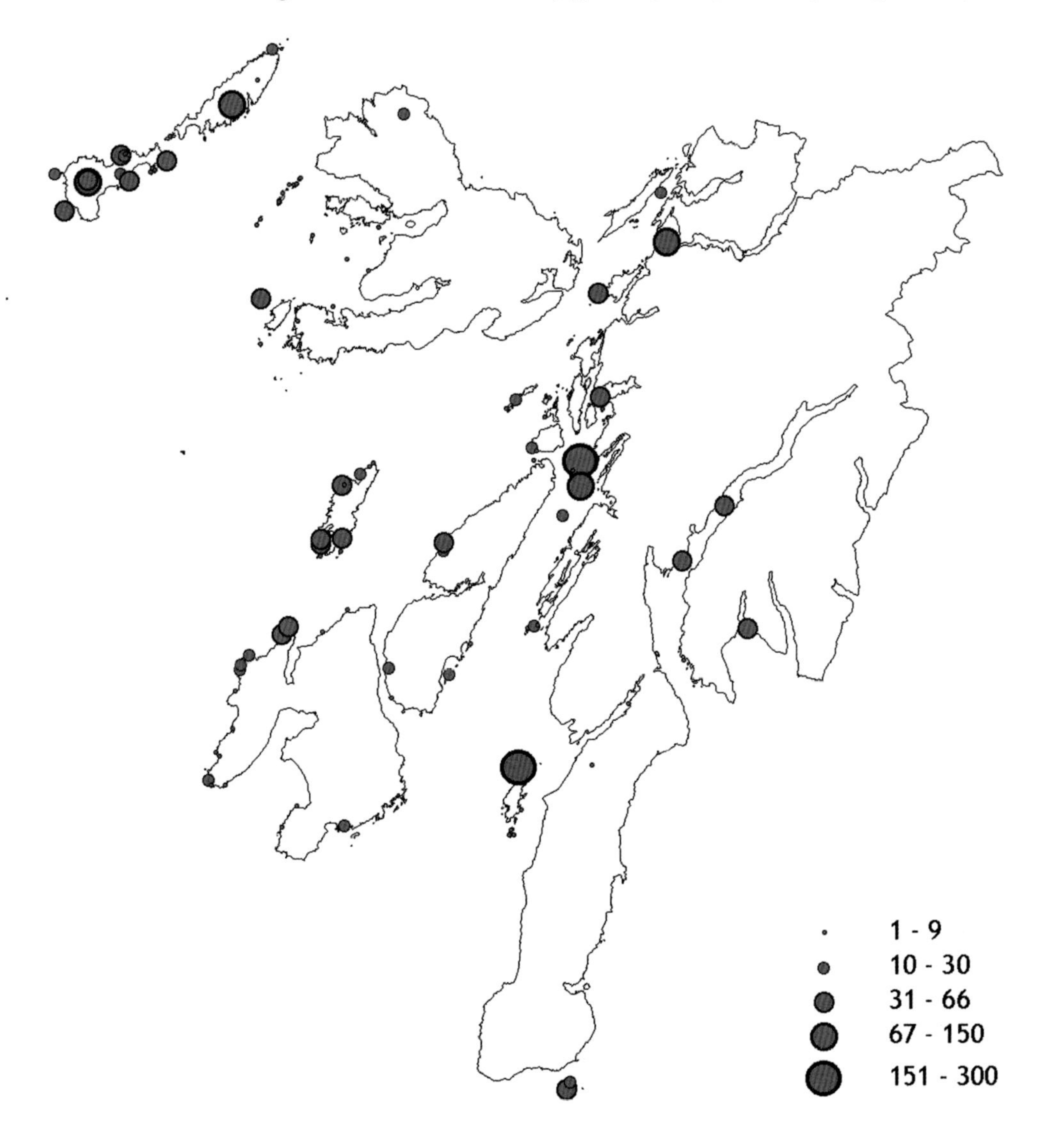

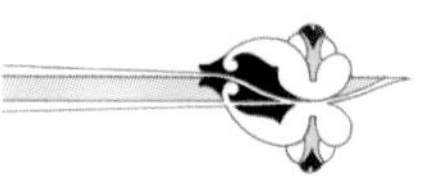

in 1999-2000. At Na h-Urrachann, a mixed gull colony in south-west Scarba discovered in 1985 but not mentioned in the records of Operation Seafarer (1969) there were about 50, 29 and 24 pairs in 1985, 1987 and 1999. Estimates on the Treshnish Islands were 15-24 pairs in 1986 and 40 in 1999. There were about 30 pairs on the Dutchman's Cap in 1996.

Away from the breeding sites, there have been counts of 400 or more birds as follows (from ABR for years 1980-2001); 750 during silage operations at Laggan (Kintyre) on 16 May 1989, 400 at Chiscan Farm (Kintyre) on 28 April 1991, 700 at Kiloran Bay (Colonsay) on 3 August 1994 and 537 at Loch Bhirceapol (Tiree) on 12 May 1999. Significant numbers passing seawatching sites in Argyll are given in ABR for each of the years 1990-91 and 1993-2000. These included 101 moving south in two hours at Mull of Kintyre on 19 August 1990 and at MSBO, 239 in March-April 1994, 1,074 moving south in 296 hours in August-September 1995 with a maximum day count of 186 in 6 hours on 10 August; 332 in August 1997 and 738 in September-October 1998. At Frenchman's Rocks (Islay) maximum day-counts were 180 moving south in nine hours on 28 August 1994, 155 in 6.5 hours on 25 August 1995, and 110 in three hours on 8 September 2000.

Most of the British population are migratory and spend the winter on the shores of west Mediterranean countries, mostly Spain, Portugal and Morocco. Birds ringed in Argyll, mostly as chicks, have been recovered in Worcestershire (one), Ireland (nine), Portugal (four), Spain (three) Morocco (two) and the most distant in The Gambia (4,749km). One of the Portuguese recoveries is of historical interest. A chick ringed in July 1910 on Eilean Dubh in the Lynn of Lorn (where the species still bred in 2003) was shot near Aveiro in the Algarve in December 1910. Some of the Lesser Black-backs present in the British Isles in autumn and winter are from Iceland, the Faeroes and north-western Europe (Migration Atlas). Birds ringed elsewhere and recovered in Argyll have come from Orkney, Walney Island (Cumbria) (two), Derbyshire, Worcestershire, Gloucestershire (two) and Avon; the furthest was from Iceland (1,247km). Two birds recovered in Argyll were notable for longevity; one was 18 years and one was at least 19 years old.

Of five subspecies that breed in Eurasia, and three in Europe, only *L. f. graellsii* breeds in the British Isles. *L. f. fuscus* (north Scandinavia) and *L. f. intermedius* (south Scandinavia) both have darker wings and mantle. Birds resembling *intermedius* are occasionally seen in Argyll; *e.g.* two birds seen from the Oban-Craignure ferry on 7 May 1993 and one at Frenchman's Rocks (Islay) on 14 October 1993 (ABR).

Clive Craik

Yellow-legged Gull

Larus michahellis

Vagrant.

Since October 2005 the BOU has treated this former subspecies of Herring Gull as a separate species. The status of the 'Caspian' or 'Steppe' Gull *Larus michahellis cachinnans* is, at the time of writing, still under review.

Although there have been several claimed sightings of Yellow-legged Gulls in Argyll in the past, there are currently only two accepted records. The first was found roosting with Herring Gulls at Soa Point, Tiree on 23 February 1998 and was identified as belonging to the Mediterranean form 'michahellis'. The second was seen on 1 and 7 September 2002 at Craigens, Gruinart, Islay and was accepted by SBRC with the proviso that the race/species *atlantis* was not ruled out.

Paul Daw

Herring Gull

Larus argentatus

This is the most abundant gull in Argyll throughout the year, breeding on numerous islets along the coast, and forming flocks outside the breeding season of up to several thousand birds. Recently, several large colonies have disappeared, and very few now breed inland.

Most Herring Gulls in Argyll breed on small to medium-sized islets, often in association with smaller numbers of Lesser Black-backs and much smaller numbers of Great Black-backs. In mixed colonies each species occupies a particular habitat, leading to rough demarcation of breeding areas.

Gray described the Herring Gull's habit of dropping shelled molluscs onto hard surfaces to open them before eating. More than 135 years later, this is still a common sight in Argyll. No other gull seems to have acquired the technique, crows being the only other birds that regularly use it. Immature Herring Gulls sometimes amuse onlookers by dropping whelks onto the sea, then diligently searching the surface.

Graham considered this species much commoner than Lesser Black-backs on Iona and Mull. He described how the two species bred on the same small islands and gave amusing accounts of collecting hampers full of their eggs. H&B described breeding sites on the Treshnish Isles (Lunga and Dutchman's Cap) and on Tiree. B&R considered that Herring Gulls had "undoubtedly increased enormously as a breeding species since the beginning of the (twentieth) century".

More recently, considerable changes in breeding numbers have been recorded in some areas. Gibson (1985) gives histories of numerous colonies in the Clyde area, particularly

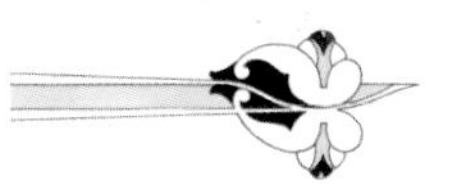

during 1940-1985. He traced the increase on the three Sanda islands from 1898, when the colony of nearly 50 pairs on Glunimore was "the largest colony in the Clyde area" to a total of 1,900 nests in 1980. The three islands held 1,500-1,800 pairs in 1989, 980 in 1997, 710 in 1998, 821 in 1999, and about 700 in each of the years 2000 and 2001 (R. Morton pers. comm.). Gibson also described increases at six inland colonies. During the mid-twentieth century all these reached maxima in 1979, when they held the following numbers of pairs; Mull of Kintyre cliffs (*c.*250), hill slopes north of there (over 350), Dun Ban (west Kintyre) (minimum 100), Loch an Eilein area (minimum 100), Loch Romain area (75), Knapdale moors and lochs (100). However, in 1999 five of these six were empty of large gulls (Seabird 2000, when Dun Ban seems not to have been visited). By way of contrast, Gibson gave changes in numbers up to 1979 over the same period on seven islands in Loch Fyne and two in the Kyles of Bute. During Seabird 2000, numbers on all but one of these were found to have increased considerably since 1979.

Coll held 1,026-1,143 pairs in 1987 and 451 pairs in 2000, while Tiree had 1,482-1,513 pairs in 1986 and 902 pairs in 2000. In 1969, 344 pairs were counted on Colonsay-Oronsay, 1100 in 1985, 1160 in 1986, and 1121 in 2000 (Jardine *et al.* 2002). Scarba held 170 nests in 1987 and 291 pairs in 1999-2000. The coast of Mull held 109-280 nests in 1986 and 959 pairs in 2000 (excluding Treshnish, but including 60 pairs on Staffa). Treshnish held 302-389 pairs in 1986, and about 225 pairs in 1999 (largest colony 54 pairs) (ABR, Seabird 2000).

In Seabird 2000, 15,370 pairs of Herring Gulls were counted breeding in Argyll and Bute, compared with 14,946 in the 1987 seabird census and 11,004 in Operation Seafarer in 1969, when coverage is known to have been less complete. In Argyll alone, 13,103 pairs were found in Seabird 2000.

The largest colonies ever reported in Argyll were an estimated 1,820-2,730 breeding Herring Gulls at Shian Bay (Jura) in 1985, and 810 clutches counted at Bach Island (Kerrera) in May 1999. However, large colonies are difficult to count accurately and several islands in Argyll may hold larger numbers.

During the 1990s, many Herring Gull colonies on islands along the mainland coast and off Mull fledged no or very few young each year because of predation by American Mink. Several large colonies affected in successive years eventually became empty, notably the Creag archipelago off Lismore, the Eilean nan Coinean-Eilean Fraoich group south of Carsaig in the Sound of Jura, all the islets in Loch Caolisport, especially Liath Eilein, and Eilean Loch Oscair off Lismore (see Daw 2000 for other examples). In the SAMS study area a 37% decrease in numbers of breeding Herring Gulls was found between 1989 and 1998, from 10,143 pairs at 73 sites to 6388 pairs at 44 sites; most of these sites were in Argyll. Comparison of productivities between sites at which mink had and had not been removed suggested that most of this decrease could be explained by annual mink-caused breeding failures (Craik 1998).

Throughout the year, large flocks of immature and adult Herring Gulls are found at rubbish dumps, estuarine sealochs, fish-farms and flooded fields, and many often roost within a few km of such feeding areas. Some of the largest flocks occur in autumn when flocks over 500 birds are frequent, and several counts exceeding 2,500 have been recorded (ABR).

The Herring Gull is the commonest and most sedentary gull in Argyll. *Louise Wood*

Distribution and abundance of breeding Herring Gulls (apparently occupied nests) in Argyll during Seabird 2000.

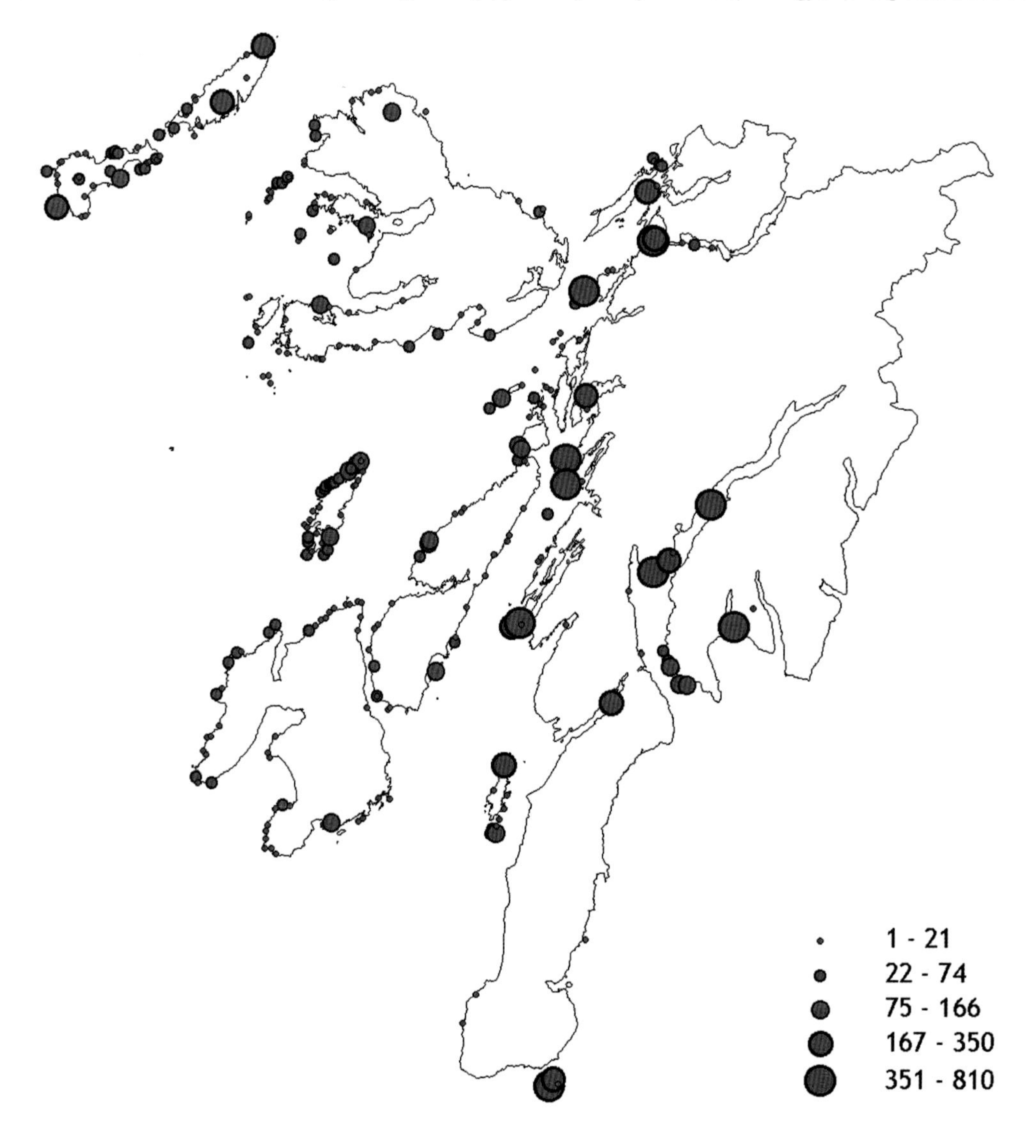

Counts of hundreds of Herring Gulls passing MSBO per day have been recorded in spring and autumn (ABR).

Herring Gulls breeding in the British Isles disperse widely outside the breeding season, but most remain within the British Isles and most move in a southerly direction (Migration Atlas). This pattern is reflected in recoveries of birds ringed as chicks in Argyll. Most of the more distant recoveries (>100km) have come from Ireland, south-east Scotland including the Firth of Forth, Cumbria and the Solway Firth, Lancashire, Merseyside and North Wales. The most distant were from Plymouth, St Austell and Scilly. The same pattern is seen in chicks ringed outside the county and found in Argyll. Most of these were from Canna, the Outer Hebrides and the north and east coasts of Scotland; the two furthest came from Fair Isle and Shetland.

Many Herring Gulls were colour-ringed during 1980-1990 at refuse tips in south and west Scotland, including those at Oban, Lochgilphead and Bowmore in Argyll. Birds ringed at Bowmore tip have been recovered from St Kilda and Amsterdam (one each). At the time of writing (2002), the Amsterdam bird was the only foreign recovery of Herring Gulls to or from Argyll and, at 818km, the most distant. Ringing in Argyll has emphasised that, perhaps more than any other gull, Herring Gulls seem reluctant to make lengthy sea crossings.

Clive Craik

Iceland Gull

Larus glaucoides

Scarce visitor during the winter months, with the majority of records in January and February. Some long-stayers linger into May and there are a few summer records. Numbers vary a great deal from year to year.

Iceland Gulls, like Glaucous Gulls, are regular winter visitors in small numbers to Britain and Ireland. Because of potential confusion between the two species, the reliability of some older records is open to question. Thus Gray reported that only the Iceland Gull had occurred in Argyll, while H&B claimed the opposite.

It is thought that most wintering birds in the British Isles belong to the population that breeds in east Greenland. These disperse from September through to November but numbers in Scotland peak later in the winter, with birds often appearing in the wake of northerly gales (Migration Atlas). This is certainly the case in Argyll, where a few scattered individuals sometimes appear during the last three months of the year, but most records are in January and February. Kintyre and the Oban area on the mainland, and Mull and Islay among the islands, seem to be the most favoured locations. Records from Cowal are few and there appear to be none from Jura or Gigha.

Although very few birds are reported in some years – only one in 1985, for example – there are clear influxes in others. The most notable of these occured in late 2004 and early 2005 as part of a major influx of both Iceland and Glaucous Gulls into Scotland. At least 33 individual Iceland Gulls were recorded in Argyll between December 2004 and April 2005, approximately 50% more than the previous high totals that occurred in early 1983 and in 1992/93 (Dickson & Daw 2005). Oban is the favoured location for this species in Argyll, reflecting the fact that in Scotland as elsewhere, white-winged gulls have a habit of following boats into port, with notable concentrations reported from Stornoway and Ullapool in particular.

Good numbers were also reported from Argyll in the early part of 1984, 1991, 1993, 1998, 2000, 2002 and 2007. The 1983 and 1984 influxes were part of a broader pattern of movement affecting not just the British Isles but other parts of Europe (Thom, Migration Atlas).

It is not unusual for birds arriving in January or February to stay in the same location for two or three months. Most have normally left by mid-April, the breeding colonies being reoccupied during late April and early May (Migration Atlas).

This first-winter Iceland Gull was at Campbeltown in February 2007. *Jim Dickson*

However, some immatures remain into May or even June. July and August records, on the other hand, are very rare, the only reports from these months during 1980-2007 involving single first-summer birds at Uisaed Point in Kintyre on 27 August 1995 and 11 July 1996 and at Loch a' Phuill, Tiree, during 7-11 July 2007. Thus there are no recent records of over-summering, but one that spent the winter of 1921/22 in Oban Harbour remained until August 1922, when it was found with a broken wing (B&R).

Although the vast majority of Scottish records of the Iceland Gull refer to the race *glaucoides*, a few are assigned to *kumlieni*, which breeds in Canada. To date, there are no accepted records of this form from Argyll. However, it seems likely that closer scrutiny of Iceland Gulls would reveal the occasional Kumlien's.

Tristan ap Rheinallt

Glaucous Gull

Larus hyperboreus

Scarce visitor, mostly during winter. Pattern of occurrence as Iceland Gull. More numerous than Iceland Gull in most winters.

The Glaucous Gull, like the Iceland Gull, is an uncommon winter visitor to the mainland coasts and islands of Argyll. Although B&R could find few records from the Inner Hebrides, there is no reason to suppose that it has become more numerous in recent years. The pattern of occurrence is similar to that of the Iceland Gull, with a few scattered individuals appearing from October or sometimes September onwards, followed by a more or less pronounced peak in January and February. Although numbers of Glaucous Gulls in Scotland are said to peak earlier in the winter than Iceland Gulls (Thom, Migration Atlas), there is no evidence that this is the case in Argyll.

The origin of Glaucous Gulls wintering in the British Isles is unclear, but may include Iceland as well as Greenland, Norway and Svalbard (Migration Atlas). As with Iceland Gulls, their appearance is often preceded by northerly gales, and most of the birds seen are immatures. Numbers recorded in Argyll vary considerably from year to year, but this variation is less pronounced than that of Iceland Gulls. During 1980-2003, at least five individuals were recorded each year.

Winters with good numbers of Iceland Gulls in Argyll also tend to have good numbers of Glaucous Gulls, as in Scotland generally (Thom). Thus there were small influxes of Glaucous Gulls into Argyll in early 1984, 1991, 1998, 2000 and 2007. A major influx of Iceland and Glaucous Gulls into Scotland that occurred in late 2004 and early 2005 produced exceptional numbers of both species in Argyll. At least 30

Glaucous Gulls often occur at fishing harbours. This one was at Tarbert in February 2007. *Jim Dickson*

individual Glaucous Gulls were recorded in Argyll between October 2004 and April 2005, nearly double the previous highest winter total of 16 in 1997/98 (Dickson & Daw 2005).

However, the highest number of birds seen together at one place appears to be seven at Campbeltown on 30 January 1981. Kintyre, Islay and Mull seem to be among the favoured locations, as with the Iceland Gull. However, Tiree has more records of this species than of Iceland Gull, while the opposite is the case for the Oban area. There are few records from Cowal, and apparently none from Jura.

Birds that turn up in the early part of the year may remain in the same location for several months, not leaving until April, May or even June. It is likely that some birds return to the same place in successive winters, as has been observed elsewhere in the British Isles. A few immatures remain in Argyll over the summer or even, occasionally, for years. These include a bird that was first seen at Tobermory on 13 June 1979, when it was in its second calendar year, and remained until April 1984. Another remained for several years at Loch Indaal on Islay in the late 1980s. However, new arrivals in June, July and August are unusual and may result from purely local movements. Birds do not normally leave their breeding colonies until September or October, but there is evidence from several European countries that immatures from migratory populations summer to the south of their natal area (Migration Atlas).

As with the Iceland Gull, nearly all records are close to the coast. However, one seen in February 1983 at Portsonachan on Loch Awe was more than 20km from the open sea. A bird at Craignure on Mull on 18 June 1993 was believed by the observer to be a Glaucous x Herring Gull hybrid.

Tristan ap Rheinallt

Great Black-backed Gull

Larus marinus

Common resident, breeding on small islands along the coast.

Some larger colonies of Great Black-backed Gulls in Argyll are monospecific or nearly so, although Herring Gulls may breed in separate areas on the same island, sometimes adjoining or

The Great Black-back, Britain's largest gull, is a very widely distributed breeding species around our coast. *David Palmar*

surrounding, sometimes well apart from the larger gull. Great Black-backed Gulls often occupy the central, higher part of an islet, while Herring Gulls nest along the shore. Alternatively, larger Herring Gull colonies often contain scattered single pairs of Great Black-backs; equally, however, single pairs of Great-Black-backed Gulls often nest alone on skerries or clifftops, with no other gull species nearby.

Great Black-backed Gulls were evidently much scarcer in Argyll at the end of the 19th century than they are now. H&B failed to find them on Treshnish or Tiree, although they recorded large numbers of Herring Gulls on both. B&R mention breeding on the Sgat Islands (Loch Fyne), Stacks of Oa (Islay) (in 1913), Cara (Gigha) (in 1949), Colonsay & Oronsay, Gunna (Tiree) and Treshnish (in 1925). Numbers on the Sanda Islands increased from a single pair in 1898 and 1900 to 35 pairs in 1989, 54 in 1999 (highest on record) and then declined to 33 in 2001 (Gibson 1970, 1990, Clyde Ringing Group). Numbers on small islands in Loch Fyne have also increased. On Sgat Mor, where a single pair was recorded in 1924, between 55 and 72 pairs bred in each of the years 1998-2002; on Eilean Buidhe (Portavadie), *c.*20 pairs in 1947 had increased to 55 pairs in 2000; and on Glas Eilean single pairs in 1960, 1964 and 1969 had increased to *c.*20 pairs in 2000-2002 (Gibson 1970, 1990, J.C.A. Craik unpubl. data).

Records from Gibson (1970, 1990) show how the species increased at a mainland site in Kintyre. "Kintyre North Moors" (Loch an Eilein and Loch Romain) held 11 pairs in 1949/1958, 21 in 1969, over 50 in 1976, and over 60 in 1987, making this the largest, albeit scattered, colony of this species ever to have been recorded on mainland Argyll. In 1999 no large gulls were found breeding at any of Gibson's mainland sites in Kintyre and Knapdale (Seabird 2000).

The 1,736 pairs found in Argyll & Bute (1,729 in Argyll) in Seabird 2000 showed a 76% increase since 1987, and an increase of 196% since Operation Seafarer in 1969. In Seabird 2000, Argyll & Bute held about 12% of the 14,773 pairs in Scotland and 9% of the 19,691 pairs in the British Isles. The largest single colony ever recorded in Argyll seems to have been at Shian Bay (Jura). Although estimated by proportion

Distribution and abundance of breeding Great Black-backed Gulls (apparently occupied nests) in Argyll during Seabird 2000.

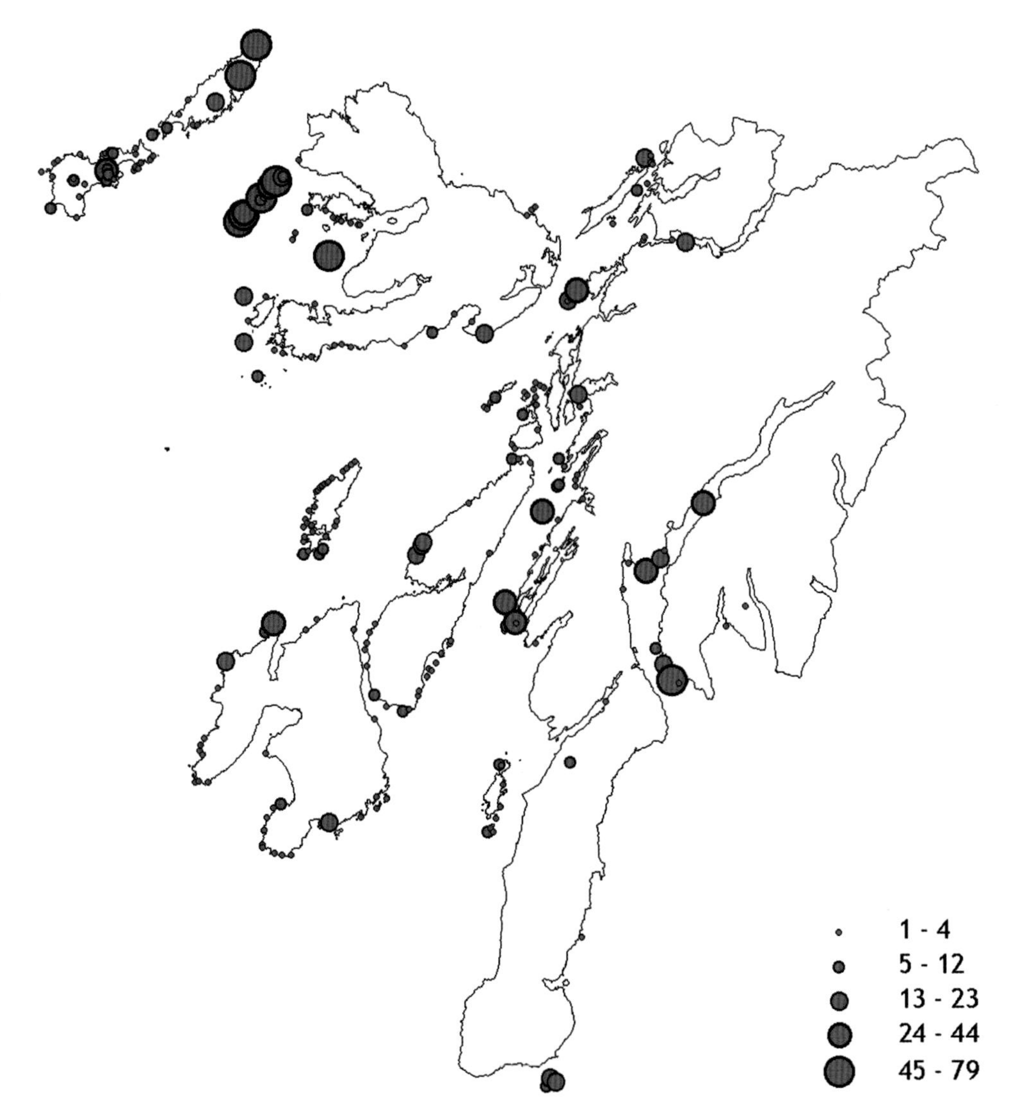

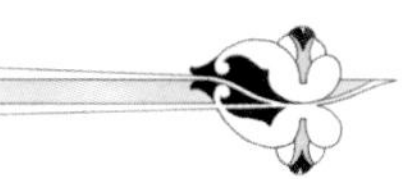

based on a single sample count, this site was reckoned to hold 260-390 adult Great Black-backs in early June 1985 (ABR). The Treshnish Islands held 342 pairs in 1999, the highest concentration of the species in Argyll, perhaps related to the large numbers of Puffins available as prey. Seabird 2000 found 177 pairs on Coll, 142 on Tiree, and 77 on Jura; and the 76 pairs on Colonsay-Oronsay were a notable increase from 17 in 1969 (Jardine *et al.* 2002). Islands along mainland coast (SAMS Argyll) held 562 pairs at 57 sites (1-65 pairs in size) in 2000.

Throughout the year, flocks occur at feeding sites such as tidal mudflats, fishfarms and rubbish tips, and at roosting sites such as the heads of some sealochs. Large flocks appear in all of the non-summer months, but the largest seem to be in March and from September to November. Flocks exceeding 100 are frequent, and the largest reported have been 505 at Loch Feochan in March 2000, 430 at Loch a'Phuill in October 1989, 385 there in November 1998, and 340 at the Add Estuary in September 2000 (ABR).

Seawatching from MSBO revealed light southward passage in September-October 1991, with a peak of 90 in six hours on 22 September, 313 in March-April 1994, and 302 during 18 September-12 November 1998 (ABR). Like Herring Gulls, Great Black-backs native to western Scotland make a short but detectable southward dispersal in winter (Winter Atlas, Migration Atlas). All fourteen ringed in Argyll as chicks and recovered at more than 100km had moved in a southerly direction (between 112 and 230 degrees); they were recovered from Ayrshire, Cumbria, Lancashire, Merseyside, and over much of Ireland from the far north (Co. Donegal) to the south (Cork). Likewise, all twelve recovered in Argyll and ringed over 100km away all came from the north, on bearings of 147 to 223 degrees, from the Moray Firth, Canna, and one each from Tongue, the Flannan Islands, North Rona, St Kilda, Orkney and Bear Island (between Norway and Spitsbergen); the last movement of 2,354km was the only international recovery of this species involving Argyll.

Clive Craik

This Ross's Gull at Ormsary was first seen on 14 December 2006 and stayed for four weeks. *Bob Furness*

Ross's Gull

Rhodostethia rosea

Vagrant.

Up to the end of 2005 this sought-after Arctic species had been recorded in Argyll on just one occasion: an immature was at Frenchman's Rocks on Islay on 15 August 1976 (BB 70:425). This was only the seventh Scottish record, although there have been many records since, especially in Shetland. Almost exactly 30 years later, an adult was seen at Aird, Tiree, on 9 August 2006. Then, on 14 December of the same year, a first-winter bird was found at Ormsary, Mid-Argyll. It stayed for four weeks and was seen and photographed by many observers. Probably the same bird was then present at Portavadie, Cowal, from 11 February to at least 25 February 2007.

Tristan ap Rheinallt

Kittiwake

Rissa tridactyla

The Kittiwake is the second most abundant breeding gull in Argyll with just under 9,000 pairs. It has a restricted breeding range, being confined to western Colonsay (where three quarters of the population breeds) and a handful of other localities.

The Kittiwake was well known to the Victorian naturalists and was thought to be the commonest gull in Argyllshire waters (H&B). They reported it breeding at a number of locations where it no longer nests (e.g. Staffa, Gribun on Mull and Eilean Dubh near Ledaig) but they provided no population estimates other than 'hundreds breed on Tiree'.

The population of Kittiwakes breeding in Argyll increased

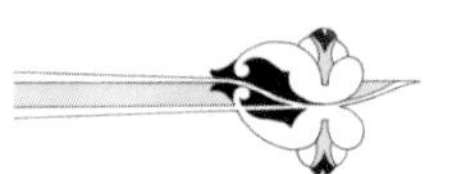

Distribution and abundance of breeding Kittiwakes (apparently occupied nests) in Argyll during Seabird 2000.

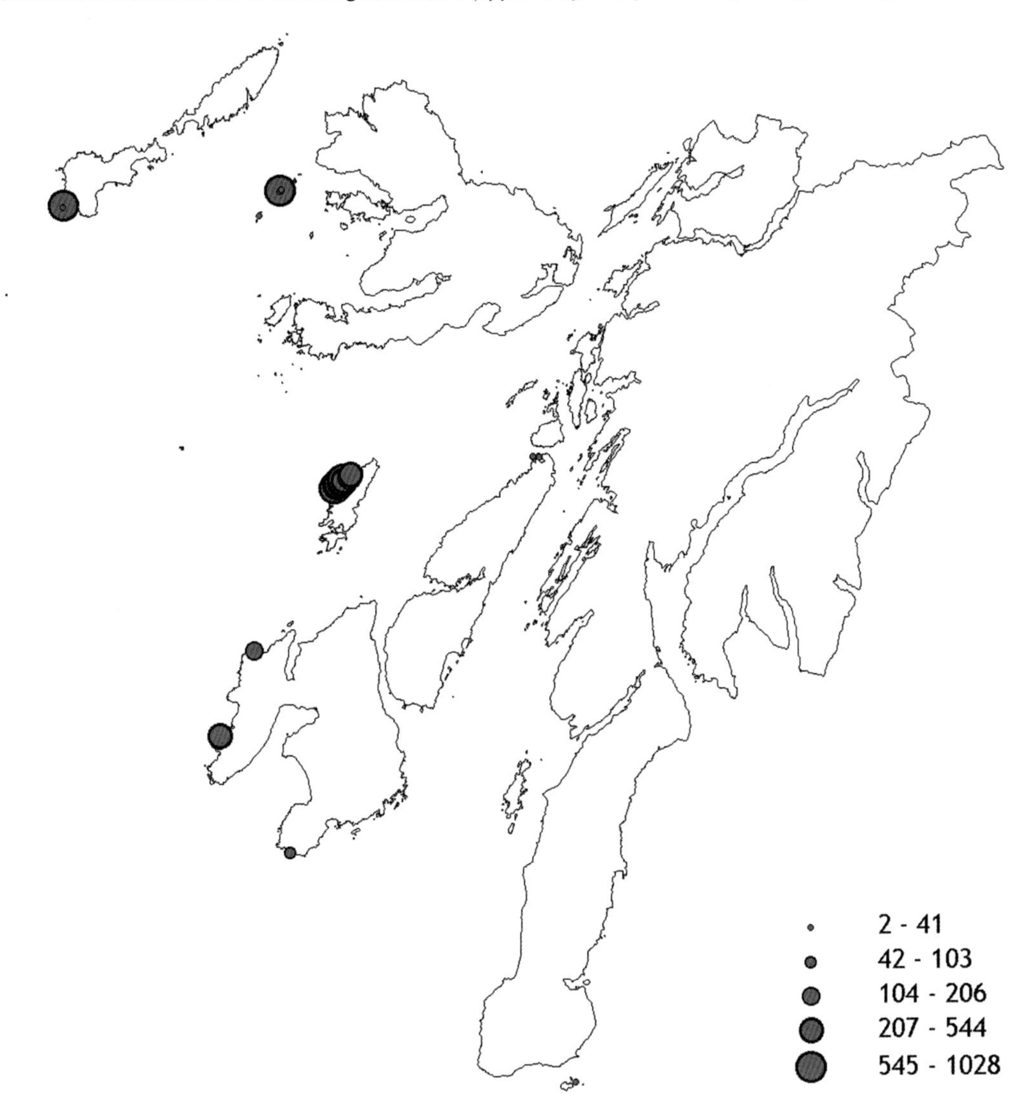

The largest colony of Kittiwakes in Argyll is on Colonsay, with around 9,000 apparently occupied nests. *David Wood*

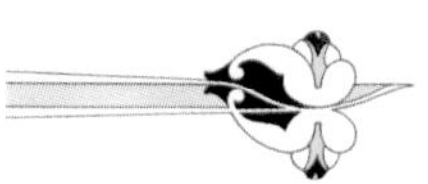

significantly (+143%) between Operation Seafarer in 1968-70 (3,983 pairs) and the next survey in 1985-87 (9,690 pairs plus 36 birds) (Lloyd *et al.* 1991). The reasons for this large increase are not known; a significant proportion of this increase (4,076 pairs) was at the largest colony on Colonsay, suggesting that the count made there in 1969 may not have been complete. There has been only a modest change since 1985-87 with a slight decline in the total population to 8,976 apparently occupied nests (AON) in Seabird 2000. On Colonsay the population, which is found entirely between Port Mor and Kiloran Bay, had increased by 4% to 6,485 AON.

Elsewhere breeding was found on Tiree at Ceann a' Mhara (859 AON). Counts at this colony show that it can vary between years with 1,213 AON reported in 1987 and 901 AON in 1989. On the Treshnish Isles 786 AON were found during Seabird 2000, a significant increase on the 305 AON found in 1986. On Islay 775 AON were located during Seabird 2000, mainly between Lossit and Tormisdale, to the north-west of Sanaigmore and on the Mull of Oa. There is a small colony at Eilean Mor and Eilean Beag, the islets off northern Jura, where 28 AON were found during Seabird 2000. Kittiwakes became re-established as breeders on Glunimore (near Sanda) in 1998, having stopped breeding there in 1995; nine AON were found in Seabird 2000.

Verrall & Bourne (1982) reported that the main period of migration of the Kittiwake off Islay was later in the autumn than some other seabirds, with the peak occurring in October. More recent observations at the same site (Frenchman's Rocks) also found large movements in August and September. The first juveniles are normally noted during the first week in August and from then a large proportion of the birds can be in immature plumages *e.g.* on 16 October 1976, when 3,650 passed in one hour (the highest rate recorded), 60% were immature. It is likely that many of these birds are from more northerly colonies. Kittiwakes are seen offshore in any month of year. In 1994 the second highest hourly average movements were noted during January.

There are only a few recoveries of birds ringed in Argyll. An adult ringed on Colonsay in 1990 was shot in Greenland in September 1993, and an adult ringed on Treshnish in 1994 was seen alive in the Netherlands in July 1996. Birds recovered in Argyll had been ringed in Iceland (two), Faeroes, Ireland (three), Isle of Man, Northumberland (two) and East Lothian. In June 2000, three colour-ringed Kittiwakes, all of which had been ringed as chicks in 1999 at colonies in Brittany, were seen at Machrihanish (Maguire 2005).

David Jardine

Ivory Gull

Pagophila eburnea

Vagrant.

Older records of this beautiful Arctic gull are extremely difficult to assess. In the words of Evans (1994): "... so many of the old records, once scrutinised, clearly related to either Iceland or Glaucous Gulls, or even Mediterranean Gulls. In fact, the descriptions of many did not eliminate albinistic gulls (of which many occur) and were, in the main, of very poor quality." These difficulties perhaps explain why some authors, including B&R and Thom, have tended to be rather vague about older Scottish records.

The following old records of Ivory Gull in Argyll have the best credentials:

(1) In January or February 1867, one was found dead on a loch on Islay after a heavy storm (H&B). This was possibly the individual said by Gray to have been "killed on Islay" at around the same time as the Campbeltown bird below. The specimen was apparently retained by the finder, Mr Crawshay of Gateshead, and its existence was corroborated by others.

(2) In February 1867, one was shot at Campbeltown and the specimen exhibited to the Glasgow Natural History Society (Gray, Proc. Nat. Hist. Soc. Glasgow 1: 168).

(3) On 21 January 1873, one was shot at Campbeltown and subsequently exhibited to the Natural History Society of Glasgow (McWilliam, Proc. Nat. Hist. Soc. Glasgow 2: 209).

In recent years, there have been two additional sightings, both well documented. On 30 November 1969, a bird described as "second-winter" was seen from a scallop boat between Coll and Ardnamurchan Point (SB 6:94; see 1969 BBRR). It is uncertain whether this was in the Argyll or Highland recording areas. On 23 January 2000, a first-winter bird was photographed at Ardnave Point on Islay; it stayed until the next day, when it was seen by several observers. It is possible that this was the same individual as one seen earlier in the month on the Isle of Lewis (BB 94:478).

[Records considered unacceptable are:

(4) According to Gray, one or two Ivory Gulls were seen on Islay prior to the 1867 record, but no details are given.

(5) In 1863, one was procured and others seen near Minard (Gray). This claim of multiple sightings is highly unlikely.

(6) In 1867, one was found exhausted at Ardchattan and retained by Mr McCalman of Ardchattan (Gray, H&B). However, there is no evidence that the specimen was ever seen by a knowledgeable ornithologist.

(7) Prior to 1887, one was seen for several weeks at Loch Etive during a severe winter (H&B). Although this record is listed by Naylor (1996), there seems to be little or no supporting evidence. The record was communicated to Harvie-Brown in 1887 by W. Anderson Smith, but originally reported by the Rev. I. Sutherland, minister at Ardchattan. It seems possible that it could have been the same as the 1867 record.]

Tristan ap Rheinallt

Bridled Tern

Onychoprion anaethetus

Vagrant.

A Bridled Tern was on Tiree from 30 June to 9 July 1994 (G. Evans *et al.*); it may have been the same individual as the one seen in Cumbria at the beginning of June that year (BB 89:507). The Tiree occurrence represented the fourth Scottish record of this strikingly plumaged tern species, which is an inhabitant of warmer latitudes with breeding colonies in West Africa, the Red Sea and further afield.

Summer records are typical of Bridled Terns, the previous Scottish records being in late July and early August. More recently, one at Arbroath (Angus) on 19 July 2003 (BB 98:661) was the first to be recorded in Scotland (and the UK) since the Tiree bird.

Tristan ap Rheinallt

Little Tern

Sterna albifrons

Scarce summer visitor with about 120 pairs in 2000, with regular breeding sites restricted to Coll, Tiree and Islay. Scarce migrant elsewhere on the coast.

H&B saw Little Terns on Tiree in June 1889 but failed to find evidence of nesting. Subsequently, eggs sent from the island confirmed breeding, and in 1891 nesting was recorded at four locations (two colonies and elsewhere in scattered pairs). Anderson (1898, 1913) recorded breeding in several small colonies on Tiree. Boyd (1958) documented breeding at Balephuil Bay in 1942 and 1952 with 12 and 30 pairs respectively and an island population in 1955 of 65 pairs. Breeding was recorded at 13 other localities on Tiree during 1969-88 (Broad & Cadbury 1989) and more than 20 localities by 2004. Irby (1898) did not record Little Terns on Coll. McDougall (1938) observed them on Coll in 1937-38 but did not record breeding. Boyd (1958) thought that they probably bred at the west end of Coll and noted sightings from Gunna in June 1949 and May 1954. Eighteen breeding pairs were located on Coll in three colonies in 1970 (Blatchford 1971). The results of more regular monitoring and extensive surveys on Coll, Gunna and Tiree, principally by RSPB staff since the early 1980s, have shown that these three islands together regularly hold an average of about 80 pairs (Table 1).

Islay also has a regular history of breeding Little Terns. Booth (1975) reviewed the earlier records and refers to colonies of up to four nests at several sites during 1970-79. More recent information (Table 1) gives an average island population of a little more than 20 pairs, concentrated at 3-4 sites since 1987.

A literature review by Jardine *et al.* (1986) refers to breeding on Colonsay in 1935 and 1947 and mentions 6-8 birds at The Strand as well as 15-20 on Oronsay in 1947. Thereafter, records are intermittent with a possible breeding record in one 10-km square (First Atlas), three on The Strand in May 1982 and one on Oronsay in late May 1984. Two separate pairs were again confirmed breeding on Colonsay in 2000 but none have been relocated since.

On the mainland, breeding occurred regularly at a site in Kintyre where there were two pairs in 1969-1970 (Cramp *et al.* 1974). Single birds were present in June 1983 and May 1991, but nesting did not occur again until 2006 when up to 28 adults were at the colony and at least two young fledged. No other documented mainland Argyll breeding records have been found although the First Atlas includes a possible breeding record at Machrihanish.

Counts at Little Tern colonies show considerable year-to-year fluctuation. Birds readily switch between colonies and the proportion of adults nesting in any one year can vary (Mitchell *et al.* 2004). Ideally, a snapshot of the population is best achieved by co-ordinated surveys at all suitable sites in the same year and within the period mid May to late June. Full or near-full coverage was achieved in Argyll in 1987, 1996 and 2000 (Table 1). Previously published totals for Argyll are slightly different: Lloyd *et al.* (1991) give 96 pairs for the period 1985-1988, and Mitchell *et al.* (2004) give 126 Apparently Occupied Nests (AON) for counts conducted in 1999 and 2000. The reason for the first discrepancy is unclear, but the second may have been caused by a colony shift on Coll between 1999 and 2000 resulting in double counting of birds.

The Argyll population appears to have been remarkably stable during 1987-2000 with little variation in numbers between surveys. Figures for 2000 represented about 35% of the Scottish and 5% of the population in Britain and Ireland.

Table 1. Co-ordinated counts of Little Terns (apparently occupied nests) in Argyll, 1986-2000.

Year	Coll & Gunna	Tiree	Islay	Colonsay	Total
1987	12	75	21	-	108
1996*	6**	66	30	-	102
2000	32	62	19	2	115

* RSPB Unpublished data. ** No survey on Gunna.

This apparent stability contrasts with the situation elsewhere. A long-term decline, that saw an 18.5% decrease across Britain and Ireland between the atlases, saw the population reach an all time low in 1998 with 1,700 AON (Ratcliffe *et al.* 2000). While the largest decline was in south-east England, there has been a considerable shift in centres of population nearer to Argyll. Little Terns no longer breed in Northern Ireland and the all-Ireland population has fallen by 25% since 1984. In

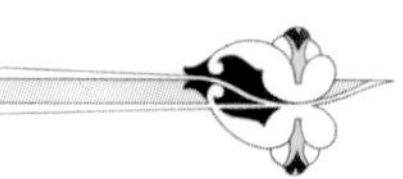

Around 100-200 pairs of Little Terns nest in Argyll each year. In 2006, they re-colonised a mainland site where they last bred over 30 years previously. *Jim Dickson*

Scotland numbers have halved on the east coast since 1985-88 while numbers in the Western Isles doubled in the same period. Currently, the Western Isles and Argyll support the majority of Scottish Little Terns (Ratcliffe *et al.* 2000).

Colonies in Argyll have ranged from scattered single pairs to the largest which held 38 pairs in 1998. Most are towards the lower end of this range (Table 2) and the average size, at six pairs during the recent three full surveys, is considerably lower than the figure of 30 pairs which the Second Atlas calculated for Britain and Ireland.

Throughout most of the range in Britain and Ireland, the majority nest at the coast immediately adjacent to shallow sea water areas where they feed close to the shore. There is a strong preference for nesting on bare or lightly vegetated sand and shingle near the high tide mark where they are vulnerable to flooding, being buried by blown sand, and human disturbance. Some typical coastal breeding sites in Argyll have been threatened by gravel extraction, but inadvertent recreational disturbance is potentially a more serious threat. This has been a particular recent concern on Tiree where windsurfing has increased recreational usage of many previously secluded beaches.

Table 2. Number and size of Little Tern colonies in Argyll in 1987, 1996 and 2000.

Colony size (pairs)	1987	1996	2000
1-5	11	8	14
6-10	5	3	2
11-15	2	2	3
16-20	0	0	0
21-25	0	0	1
26-30	1	1	0

Unusually, some Little Terns on Tiree regularly breed 450-1500m inland, on the crumbling bases of wartime hangers at the disused airfield. These sites will first have become available to Little Terns around 1947. It is not documented when they were first colonised, but they have been in use since at least 1955 when they held a total of 50 pairs and have remained attractive to Little Terns to the present day. In recent years 1-2 pairs have nested occasionally on the margin of a fresh water loch shore. The proportion of pairs nesting inland on Tiree is highly variable with 22-95% breeding inland in the three co-ordinated surveys. Pairs settle at inland colonies earlier than those on the coast (J. Bowler pers. comm.).

There is little information on breeding success at Argyll colonies. Widespread breeding failure in some years seems most likely to be related to failure in food supply or extended inclement weather. During cool wet spells, foraging may be more difficult and eggs and small chicks left unattended for longer periods are vulnerable to chilling. On Tiree such losses can affect both coastal and inland colonies. Here, annual monitoring in 2002-04 gave figures of 0.16-0.63 chicks per AON for a population of 59-67 AON. This is similar to figures given for Britain and Ireland, which were considered insufficient to maintain the population by recruitment alone and likely to have contributed to the population decline (Ratcliffe *et al.* 2000).

Unlike mainland colonies, the Argyll island population does not have to contend with Fox predation and has, so far, remained mink-free. Ferrets are a threat on Islay and also on Coll. Introduced Hedgehogs are a serious predator of waders and other ground-nesting species on the machairs of the Western Isles. They have been introduced to Tiree, but they do not seem to be present in numbers that represent a serious threat to terns or other ground-nesting species. Little Terns may loosely share their inland sites with small numbers of Common and Black-headed Gulls, Lapwings, Dunlins, Oystercatchers and Ringed Plovers. Some measure of defence from predation may be gained from nesting with the smaller gulls that join with the terns to mob larger gulls and corvids flying overhead. While Common Gulls are regular predators of wader chicks, there is no evidence of predation on Little Terns (J. Bowler pers. comm.).

The Little Tern is a scarce migrant elsewhere in Argyll, and most records are the result of systematic sea-watching since the establishment of MSBO. Spring seawatching from MSBO in 1989-92 produced occasional records in May, and in total 12 were flying north and six were heading south. The first spring arrivals are often seen at breeding localities where the earliest date is 6 April but, in most years, the first birds usually arrive in the second half of the month with the majority arriving in early May. On Tiree, colonies established early are often vacated by first week of July and only the occasional birds remain by early August.

In autumn Gray recorded "stray specimens occasionally being obtained at a distance of one or two miles from the sea in some parts of Argyleshire and Ayrshire". Recent autumn records are strictly coastal. Seawatching from MSBO has produced occasional records, rarely more than 1-3 on any day and most moving south. One off Frenchman's Rocks, Islay, on 24 September 1996 in four years of seawatching indicates the scarcity elsewhere on passage. Seasonally, the latest record traced was on 24 October 1953 (Boyd 1958).

There has been little ringing and no recoveries involving Argyll colonies and movements of Argyll birds remains a matter of conjecture. British Little Terns winter in inshore waters off West Africa and it is presumed that first-year birds stay in winter quarters during their first summer, although at least some return and breed at two years old (Cramp *et al.* 1985).

Roger Broad

Caspian Tern

Hydroprogne caspia

Vagrant.

The only Caspian Tern to have been recorded in Argyll was an adult seen from the Islay ferry between Ardpatrick Point and Gigha on 6 June 1981 (D. L. & Mrs R. Z. Clugston) (BB 75:510). This was the eleventh Scottish record of this rare visitor, whose nearest breeding colonies are in the Baltic.

Tristan ap Rheinallt

Black Tern

Chlidonias niger

Rare migrant, usually in September.

The Black Tern, which breeds widely on the Continent, is an annual passage visitor to Scotland, occurring in greatest numbers on the east coast. According to Gray, small flocks were occasional in Loch Fyne; for example, five were seen at Minard in September 1860 (Proc. Nat. Hist. Soc. Glasgow 2: 63). The species was not listed by H&B, whose definition of Argyll excluded Loch Fyne, however. B&R stated that Black Terns had been recorded in mainland Argyll, but not in the Inner Hebrides.

The first recent Argyll record was on 27 May 1974, when two were seen at Loch Gruinart on Islay (SB 8:441). With the exception of one at Dervaig on Mull on 15 September 1981, there were no further records until 1985, since when the species has been recorded with increasing frequency, although it was not until 2000 that there was more than one record in a year. Of the 15 accepted records between 1974 and 2006, 11 involved single birds and three involved two birds. The remaining record was of a group of six flying south past Uisaed Point in Kintyre on 12 September 1992 (SBR 1993:37 {where record was dated incorrectly as 1993}, ABR 10:57). This record was associated with a large influx into Scotland, which produced Arran's first occurrence of this species as well as 19 birds flying south past Turnberry Point (Ayrshire), both also on 12 September 1992 (SBR 1992:39).

All but one of the 15 recent records came from Kintyre and the islands, with five from Islay, four from Tiree, three from Kintyre, one from Mull and one from Colonsay. The sole mainland record concerns a bird seen on lower Loch Fyne on 6 September 1989 (SBR 1989:29, ABR 6:40). Ten of the records were in September, two each in May and July, and one in early October.

Tristan ap Rheinallt

White-winged Black Tern

Chlidonias leucopterus

Vagrant.

Although there were nearly 750 records of this continental species in Britain and Ireland between 1950 and 2003, relatively few individuals penetrate as far north as Scotland. The first and only Argyll record concerns an adult seen at Balephetrish on Tiree on 2 and 3 September 1999 (BB 93:538).

Tristan ap Rheinallt

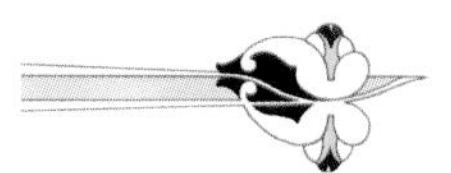

Sandwich Tern

Sterna sandvicensis

This is a regular passage migrant and an occasional breeder; single pairs are known to have hatched or raised young in 1986, 1994 and 1996. Small numbers are regularly seen in spring and summer, particularly in the south of the county, but most records are in autumn.

Pairs of Sandwich Terns are sometimes seen at colonies of Common and Arctic Terns; however, breeding can be difficult to detect among much larger numbers of other terns and may have occurred more often than the records show. Gray recorded serious declines of breeding numbers on both east and west Scottish coasts, some of its best known haunts, including islands on the Firth of Clyde, having become deserted. Gibson (1969) knew of no breeding sites in the Clyde part of Argyll but thought it likely that one of Gray's sites had been a tern colony at Carradale in Kintyre. Graham made no mention of the species on Iona, but H&B recorded the shooting of a Sandwich Tern at Gott Point on Tiree, and they recognised the species as a regular autumn migrant.

None were recorded definitely breeding in Argyll in Seabird 2000. The few that do occasionally breed in the county are an insignificant proportion of the 1,068 pairs in Scotland in that survey (when most were on the east coast). Breeding in Argyll was confirmed or strongly suspected in only four years between 1980 and 2001. In 1986, a pair bred and a half-grown chick was ringed at a mixed tern colony on Sgeir an Eitich, Ganavan, near Oban, and in 2001 a pair were present and may have laid among Arctic Terns on Fladda in the Sound of Luing, but the whole colony deserted early after predation by mink. Recently, the breeding site most favoured by Sandwich Terns in Argyll has been the mixed tern colony on Machrihanish Island. In 1994 two pairs summered there and a pair were seen feeding two unfledged young; in 1996 two pairs raised at least one young; in 2000 a pair summered but with no sign of breeding; and in 2001 at least five birds summered, coitus was noted on several occasions, and a recently fledged young photographed there on 17 July may well have been raised at the colony.

The earliest arrivals recorded in ABR during the years 1980-2007 was a single at MSBO on 15 March 2007, but in most years the first are seen in early to mid-April, usually single birds in Kintyre or Islay. Singles or groups of up to twenty are regularly reported in April-May, almost always from Cowal, Kintyre, Islay and Tiree. Autumn records also come mainly from the south of the county, but flocks are larger, up to 30 or 40, and juveniles are not uncommon (ABR).

In recent years considerable numbers have been counted at MSBO between July and September (for example, 88 in 1997, 73 in 2000 and 152 in 2001) but counts at Frenchman's Rocks on Islay are usually much lower. The latest dates on which birds were seen in the county during 1991-2001 ranged from 4 September to 7 November, almost always in Kintyre, Cowal or Islay (ABR).

There have been two midwinter records. On 9-10 January 2003, one was with a Forster's Tern in Oban Bay; and, on 6-9 December 2005, one was at Shuna Sound, near Luing (Argyll

The occasional nesting attempts by Sandwich Terns in Argyll occur at colonies of other tern species. *Photo: Philip Kirkham*

Database).

Ringing has shown that most Sandwich Terns from Britain winter along the west coast of Africa, mainly in Ghana, Senegal, Ivory Coast, Sierra Leone and Liberia (Migration Atlas). However, ringing has not yet given any information about those seen in Argyll.

Clive Craik

Forster's Tern

Sterna forsteri

Vagrant.

Unknown in Britain prior to 1980, Forster's Tern had accumulated a total of 20 records by the end of 2003. In Argyll, the occurrence of a well-photographed individual at Loch Feochan and later at Oban from 8 to 11 January 2003 (BB 97:585) represented only the fourth Scottish record of this transatlantic visitor. The winter date is typical. Interestingly, it was accompanied on 9-10 January by a Sandwich Tern, not previously recorded in Argyll in winter. For a full description of this occurrence, accompanied by photographs, see Jackson (2003).

Tristan ap Rheinallt

Common Tern

Sterna hirundo

A widespread but declining summer visitor, mostly breeding on small islets close to the mainland. 1,362 pairs were counted in Argyll & Bute in Seabird 2000, when Argyll held the second largest colony of Common Terns in the British Isles and the largest in Scotland.

The Common Tern breeds on the smaller islets and skerries in several of the sealochs and sounds of Argyll, but it is absent from long stretches of coast. It is the most numerous tern along the mainland coast, where the Common:Arctic ratio is more than 4:1, but this ratio is reversed on the outer islands. In 2000 on Tiree, for example, it was about 1:12 and on Colonsay about 1:6. Most colonies hold under 100 pairs and few, if any, now breed inland or by fresh water.

The first Common Terns in Argyll are usually seen early in May, but during 1983-2000 there were five years when they appeared in April, usually in the last few days; the earliest was at Tobermory on 6 April 2000. After settling at colonies in late May and early June, most lay from early to mid-June and peak fledging is in the second half of July. Southward passage along the coast occurs between July and September. During 1983-2000 the last recorded date was usually in September, but there were two years when it was in late August, two years when it was in October, and two years when it was in early November, including the latest, one at Loch Indaal on 14 November 1991 (ABR).

The earliest counts in Argyll were made on a cruise in Loch Fyne in 1899. These show vividly how much more numerous terns were in the past (Paterson & Renwick 1900). They found about 70 pairs on Eilean Buidhe (Portavadie), at least 100 pairs of Common/Arctic Terns on Glas Eilean, 50-60 pairs on Eilean Aoghainn, and small numbers at three other sites; thus most of the islands in Loch Fyne held breeding terns. A century later, all six sites held colonies of large gulls, most having 200-400 pairs of Herring and Great Black-backed Gulls. One or two pairs of Common Terns are recorded at Glas Eilean in some years, but otherwise terns are absent from all these sites. Their last stronghold in Loch Fyne (the unnamed islet at Whitehouse Bay, which held 109 pairs of Common Terns and smaller numbers of Arctic Terns in 1987) was extinguished by depredations of American Mink in the 1990s. B&R mention early records from all the outer islands. They give the earliest report of a large colony in Argyll, on "an islet near Texa" (Islay) with 400-500 nests in 1906 and 1907 but which was greatly reduced by 1917. Gibson (1976) recorded all known breeding sites that had been used in south Argyll up to 1969 (20 sites in Kintyre, eight in Knapdale, three in Cowal, and about 50 pairs by hill lochs between Loch Fyne and Loch Awe); most of these held small numbers of birds. Later, Gibson (1979) reported that almost all of these sites had become empty, but in 1989 he recorded a modest increase to 48 pairs at six sites in Kintyre (Gibson 1990); and 17 pairs were found in Kintyre in Seabird 2000.

In 2000, 1,362 pairs of Common Terns were counted in Argyll & Bute, 28% of the Scottish and 9% of the British Isles totals. A single colony off Mull with 768 pairs was the largest in Scotland and was exceeded in the British Isles only by Coquet Island in Northumberland (Seabird 2000). The total was a 36% decrease since 1987 when Argyll & Bute held 2,137 pairs and the 728-pair Mull colony was the largest in the British Isles. In Operation Seafarer in 1969, 788 pairs were recorded in Argyll & Bute; the apparent increase by 1987 was attributed to better coverage, although the appearance of the large Mull colony probably contributed.

Between 1987 and 2001 the SAMS (Argyll) area, mainly small islands along the mainland coast, held around 1,000 pairs each year (maximum 1,530 pairs at 16 sites in 1987; minimum 826 pairs at nine sites in 1998). This decrease of 46% between those two years accompanied widespread annual breeding failures caused by mink predation (Craik 1997, 1998). Systematic control of mink near colonies began in 1995; in most years this measure increased Common Tern productivity compared with colonies where mink were not removed, and numbers had partly recovered to 1,181 pairs by 2000. In the SAMS study during 1981-2000 there was only one year (1985) when severe food shortage led to widespread tern chick starvation, aggravated by exceptionally heavy rainfall in July. However, in every year productivity was seriously reduced by predators, notably American Mink, Otters and Peregrine Falcons (Craik 1992, 1998).

Smaller numbers of Common Terns breed on the outer islands. High counts (mostly from ABR) in recent years have included 50 nests on Treshnish in 1995, 47 adults on Islay in 1996, 60 adults (and 27 young ringed) on Jura in 1992, 200 Common/Arctic Terns at a Scarba islet in 1992, and 31 pairs on Colonsay-Oronsay in 2000 (Jardine *et al.* 2002). Over 200 pairs were counted on Coll in 1995 and 41 pairs on Tiree in 2000.

At MSBO a few tens or hundreds are reported in most autumns, but impressive totals were seen in 1993 (1,040 in 159 hours in August) and in 1994 (1,897 in 32 hours in late July). Spring passage is less impressive, for example 145 in 82 hours in May 1995 (ABR). Fewer are recorded at Frenchman's Rocks, Islay. Common Terns from the British Isles winter on the coast of west Africa, particularly from Senegal to Ghana, an area where there is a culture of catching and killing terns. Many recoveries of chicks ringed in Argyll come from birds caught on ships at sea off west Africa or from necklaces made of bird-rings by children in Senegal. The countries of recovery of Common Terns ringed in Argyll clearly reflect their migration route and wintering area: France (2), Portugal (1), Spain (4), Morocco (6), Mauretania (3), Western Sahara (1), The Gambia (1), Sierra Leone (2), Senegal (26), Togo (2), Ghana (6), Guinea Republic (5), Guinea Bissau (7) and South Africa (1).

[The record in ABR 3:38 of "*c.* 200 pairs" at Port Olmsa, Colonsay, on 18 June 1985 is a misprint and should be "about 20 pairs" (D. C. Jardine, pers. comm. 2002).]

Clive Craik

Distribution and abundance of breeding Common Terns (apparently occupied nests) in Argyll during Seabird 2000.

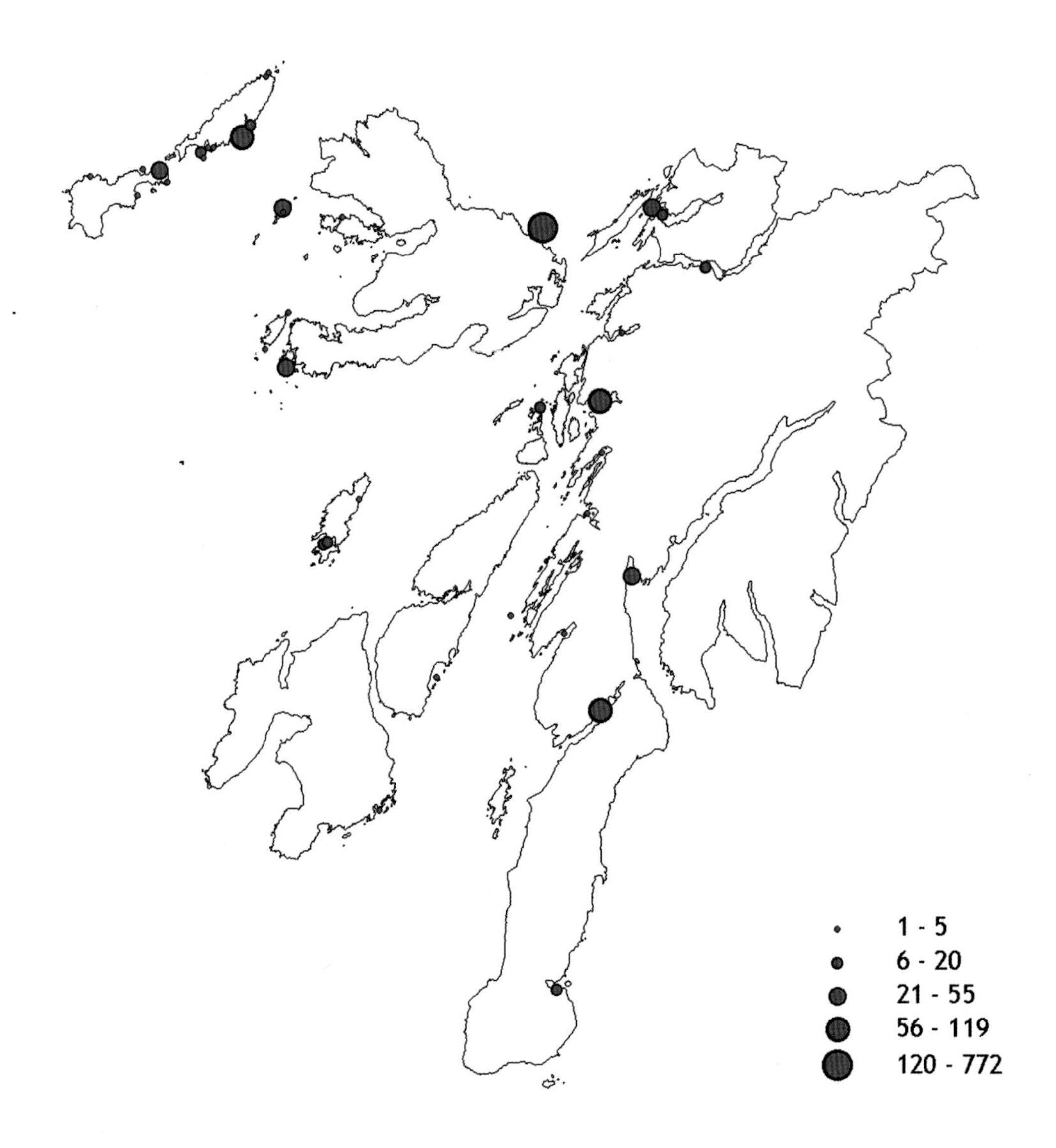

The spectacle of foraging Common Terns (bottom left) and Arctic Terns has become rarer in Argyll due to predation of their colonies by mink.

All photos: Bob Furness

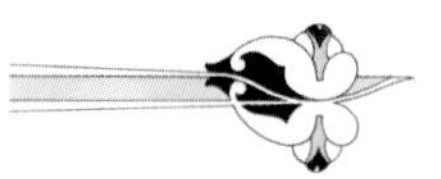

Arctic Tern

Sterna paradisaea

This summer visitor breeds in small colonies, particularly on Islay, Jura, Colonsay, Coll, Tiree and Mull, and elsewhere mostly on small islets in sealochs and sounds. In Seabird 2000, 1,823 pairs of Arctic Terns were counted in Argyll & Bute.

At the end of their epic migration from Antarctica, Arctic Terns are usually first recorded in the county in early May. There were five years during 1980-2000 when the first were in late April, the earliest having been one on Colonsay on 22 April 2000 (ABR). Adults settle at colonies in late May, the first chicks appear in mid-June and peak fledging is in mid-July. Most leave the colonies in late July and August and, unlike Common Terns, they are rarely if ever found breeding at the end of August or early in September. During 1980-2000 there were six years when the last Arctic Tern was reported during October, and the latest was on 4 November 1999 at Ardnave (ABR).

Along the mainland coast, Arctic Terns breed on rocky skerries and (in much smaller numbers) on sandy beaches. Some colonies are "pure", others are mixed with Common Terns. Whether in pure or mixed colonies, there is a noticeable difference in breeding habitat between the species, with Arctic nesting peripherally, often on almost bare rock, and Common Terns nesting further from the sea among short grass or other vegetation. Rather than hiding in vegetation like Common Tern, Arctic Tern chicks respond to danger by scattering widely over intertidal rock and "freezing", relying on their plumage for camouflage. The notorious ferocity of Arctic Terns breeding on the mainland is almost absent on skerries rarely visited by humans or other large animals.

Gray regarded Arctic Terns as "much commoner" than Common Terns in west Scotland, and described them as "frequenting rocky islets in almost all west coast lochs". One such loch he mentioned was Loch Etive (where very few or none bred each year during 1990-2007). Graham gave the Arctic:Common Tern ratio on Iona as about ten to one; he

Distribution and abundance of breeding Arctic Terns (apparently occupied nests) in Argyll during Seabird 2000.

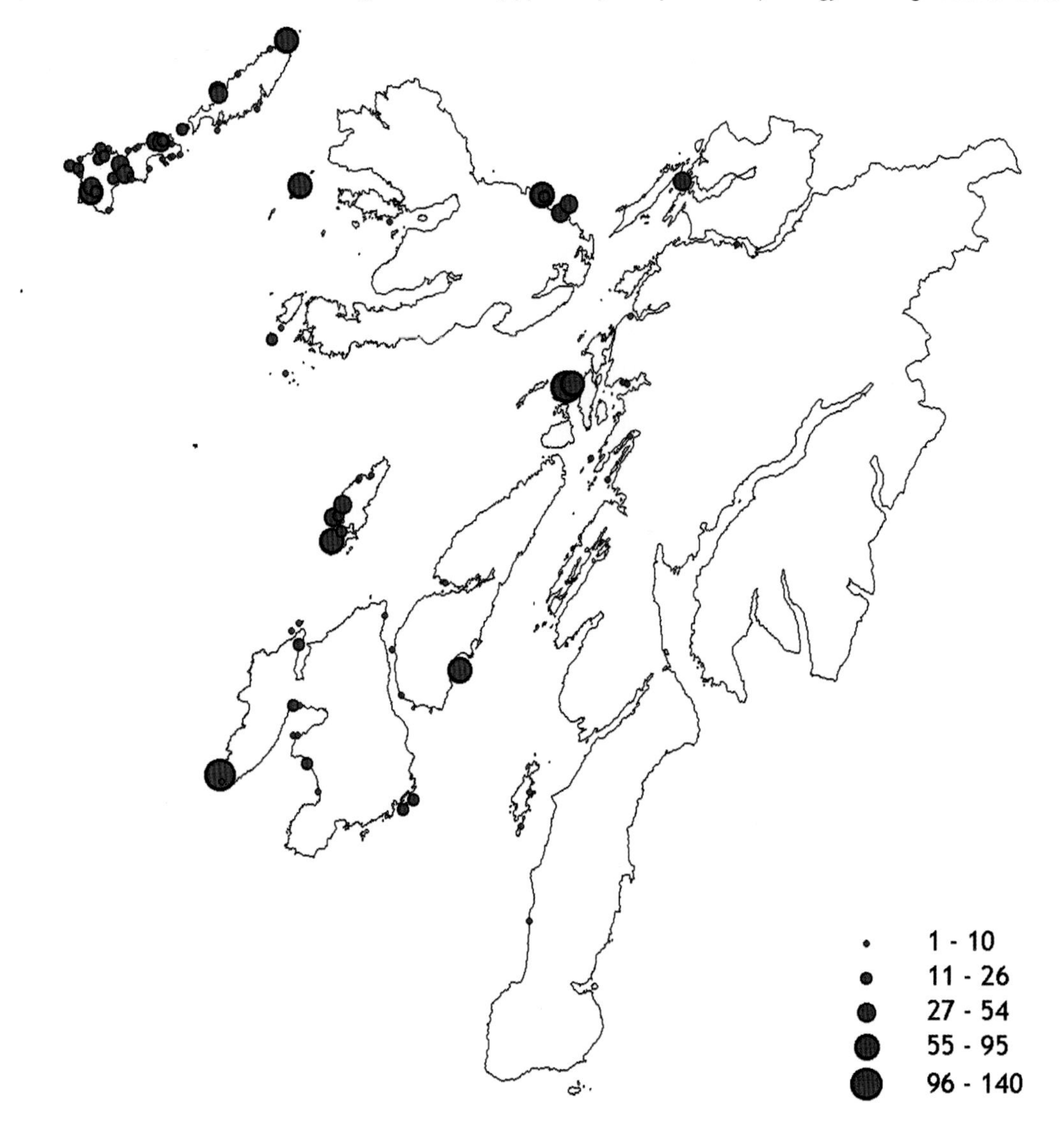

considered that Arctic Terns arrived at Iona unfailingly on 12 May every year. H&B recorded Arctic Terns on Tiree (on an island in Loch an Eilein, and on the Reef, both areas where they still breed) and on Islay (mainly on "freshwater lochs, having deserted the shoreline, greatly owing to persecution..."). They found them on Jura in 1879 (noting that they bred in different habitat from Common Terns) and at Tarbert, Loch Fyne, in 1871. However, they were unable to say which species, Common or Arctic, inhabited the "sandy portions of Kintyre", or to "personally inspect innumerable other colonies occupying almost every isolated rock, or skerry, or the islets of the long sealochs". They believed that Arctic Terns increased relative to Common further out from the mainland, a finding that is certainly true over a century later. B&R recorded breeding on Treshnish in 1865, Coll in 1899, Jura in 1917, the Burnt Islands in about 1930, Colonsay in 1942, and Iona in 1910; and they found that numbers on Tiree in 1913 had decreased in comparison with earlier years. Gibson (1976) gave brief histories of 14 former breeding sites in the Clyde part of Argyll (four on mainland Kintyre: Sanda and Sheep Islands; Tayvallich islet; west Knapdale islets; and six islands in Loch Fyne). In an update, Gibson (1990) reported 83 pairs at six sites in Kintyre in 1989 and 15 pairs at Tayvallich islet in 1988.

The 1,823 pairs in Argyll & Bute in Seabird 2000 were a decrease of 30% from the 1987 census, but 18% higher than in Operation Seafarer in 1969. They amounted only to about 4% of the Scottish total and 3% of the British Isles total. The stronghold in Argyll is Tiree where 491 pairs were counted in Seabird 2000, or 27% of the Argyll & Bute total. In the Argyll part of the SAMS study area, consisting mainly of islets along the mainland coast, the largest total during 1984-2003 was in 2002 (471 pairs at 12 sites), caused mainly by an unusually large colony that year of *c.*350 pairs on Fladda. In Seabird 2000, 109 pairs were counted on Coll, 96 pairs on Colonsay and 105 on Oronsay, and another 150 non-breeders were present on Colonsay; *c.*176–215 pairs were counted on Islay and *c.*101 pairs on Jura; 153 individuals (perhaps 77 pairs) were counted on Treshnish, while the rest of Mull held 168 pairs.

Late-summer records of flocks of more than 100 birds recorded in ABR for 1980-2001 were as follows (some of these included juveniles, and some were at colonies where numbers had increased after breeding, sometimes hugely, by arrivals of birds from elsewhere): 1,000 Common + Arctic at Reisa mhic Phaidean, Sound of Jura, on 19 August 1990; 340 on rocks off Hynish on 22 July 1998; 417 at Loch an Eilein and Loch a'Phuill on 12 July 1999; 250 at Loch a'Phuill on 17 July 2000; 260 at Milton on 24 July 2001; and *c.*300 at Gunna Island on 26 July 2001.

Most Arctic Terns depart south from late July to September, although some stay longer in years such as 1995, when many more than usual were seen in Kintyre and Islay in October. Considerable but variable numbers pass MSBO each autumn, including notable totals of 1,153 in 1994 and 1,533 in 2001; smaller numbers are recorded at Frenchman's Rocks, but at both sites Arctic Terns pass somewhat later in the autumn than Common Terns (T. ap Rheinallt pers. comm.).

Chicks ringed in Argyll have been recovered (one each) in South Africa, Angola, Ireland and Tayside, while birds recovered in Argyll had been ringed as chicks (one each) in Orkney, the Farne Islands and Anglesey.

Clive Craik

Roseate Tern

Sterna dougallii

Rare migrant. Has bred.

The UK breeding population of this Red-listed species has suffered a major decline over the last quarter-century, falling from 601 pairs in 1975 to 53 pairs in 2000 (Gregory *et al.* 2002). Although this decline has to some extent been compensated for by an increase in the Irish population, with the result that total numbers in the British Isles have recovered a little in recent years (Migration Atlas), there is no doubt that the Roseate Tern is still very much at risk. Currently there are no breeding colonies in the west of Scotland, but this was not always the case. In the latter half of the 19th century, the species apparently bred in considerable numbers on the islets off Carradale in Kintyre (Gray, B&R), where Gray collected a "basketful of eggs" of this species and Common Tern within the space of a few minutes on one occasion in the late 1860s.

Gibson & McWilliam (1959) also claimed that Roseate

Records of Roseate Terns in Argyll (excluding Kintyre), 1955-2007.

Date	Location	No. of birds	Comment	Reference
June 1955	Tiree	1	First for the Inner Hebrides	SB 1:118, Boyd 1958
25 May 1975	Frenchman's Rocks (Islay)	2		SB 9:213, Verrall & Bourne 1982
2 June 1975	Near Portnahaven (Islay)	5		SB 9:213, Elliott 1989
17 June 1975	Kiloran Bay (Colonsay)	1		SB 9:213, Jardine et al. 1986
28 September 1976	Loch Indaal (Islay)	1		SB 10:100, Elliott 1989
21 June 1985	Grass Point (Mull)	1		SB 14:110, ABR 3:37
18 May 1987	Off Coll	2		SBR 1987:29, ABR 5:30

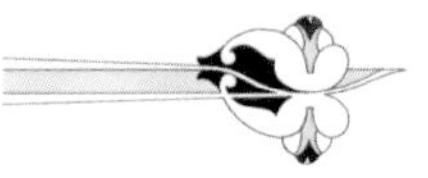

Terns bred on islets at West Loch Tarbert until the mid-1920s. However, this statement is at variance with the account of B&R, who believed that it had ceased to breed in Scotland towards the end of the 19th century, only returning in the second quarter of the 20th century.

Most of the more recent records of this species in Argyll also come from Kintyre. In 1952 and 1953, birds were present at an undisclosed site, with two pairs rearing three young in the latter year (SN 67:105). During the period of the First Atlas (1968-1972), possible breeding was reported from west Kintyre, with birds being seen in three 10-km squares. Then, up to seven birds were reported in an Arctic Tern colony at Tayinloan in the summers of 1975 and 1976 (SB 9:213 and 10:100). After a long interval, single birds were seen in the tern colony at Machrihanish on 27 July 1994 and 22 July 1995 (SBR 1996:42, ABR 14:62), and three were there from 17 to 19 August 2001 (ABR 18:71).

Elsewhere in Argyll, Stewart (1938) claimed to have seen birds in upper Loch Fyne in 1919 and 1920. Since then, there have only been seven accepted records, the most recent being in 1987 (Table).

Taken together, the Kintyre, Islay and Colonsay records suggest a range expansion in the early to mid-1970s, followed by an abrupt contraction. It remains to be seen whether the recent sequence of records from Machrihanish heralds a possible return of this species as a breeder to Argyll.

Tristan ap Rheinallt

Common Guillemot

Uria aalge

The Common Guillemot is the most abundant seabird breeding in Argyll, with over 42,000 birds. It is commonly found around the island coasts, but breeding is restricted to five areas on the islands and two in Kintyre.

Guillemot remains were found by Victorian archaeologists during excavations of the shell middens that were occupied 6,000 years ago on Oronsay (Anderson 1898, Bishop 1913), suggesting that this common seabird has a long association with the Argyll islands. The Victorian naturalists also recorded its presence as a breeding species on the south cliffs of Mull, and at Ceann a' Mhara on Tiree where they reported around 400 pairs (H&B). Guillemots still breed at this latter site and 1,974 birds were counted ashore during Seabird 2000. McNeill (1910) was the first to note the Guillemots breeding on the cliffs of western Colonsay; this is now the largest colony with over 60% of the Argyll total. The count for this island in 2000 was 26,469 and this represents a significant increase in numbers since previous counts in 1969 (1,595) and 1985 (13,617) (Jardine *et al.* 2002). This substantial increase led to an increase in the total breeding population in Argyll from 1,643 apparently occupied sites and 1,604 birds in 1968-70 (estimated total of *c.*5000 birds), to 36,848 birds in 1985-87

Huge breeding assemblages of Guillemots and other seabirds are one of the ornithological spectacles of Argyll. *Louise Wood*

(Lloyd *et al.* 1991) to 42,697 individuals in Seabird 2000. Harris *et al.* (2000) showed that annual adult survival of Guillemots at Scottish colonies, including Colonsay, was very high (over 95%). Other breeding colonies are found on the Treshnish Isles (9,566 birds – 20% of Argyll population), on Islay (1,176 birds) and on Sanda, its adjoining isles and the Mull of Kintyre (3,543 birds). Former breeding stations from which no records were received in 2000 include Cara, Staffa, the islets west of Iona and near Ulva.

With such large breeding colonies it is not surprising that this species is seen very regularly during sea watches from western headlands, although on many occasions it is not possible to differentiate distant birds from Razorbills. Peak numbers are usually recorded in June and again in October during the post-moult dispersal. While some Guillemots from Argyll have been found to disperse to the English Channel and the Bay of Biscay, others are to be found in the coastal waters during winter. In January to March 1994 a huge number of Guillemots and Razorbills were regularly watched moving south past the west end of Orsay at Portnahaven, at rates of 100-1,000 per minute for 1-3 hours around low water. These birds appeared to be feeding in the strong tidal stream which flows north-west past Islay; the movement involved many thousands of birds, but precise numbers were difficult to provide because some individuals were probably counted more than once as they flew back to where the tidal stream begins.

In 1969, a massive seabird wreck occurred in the Irish Sea, extending into Argyll, when *c.*15,000-20,000 birds were estimated to have perished in south-west Scotland, of which *c.*90% were Common Guillemots (Stewart 1970). Such wrecks tend to occur in late summer or autumn, and often involve mostly young birds. In many instances these birds seem to fail to find food and move towards the heads of sea lochs as they starve. Numbers of Guillemots starving in wrecks vary from year to year, but such mortality may occur to some extent in most years. The head of Loch Fyne often holds a particularly large number of Guillemot corpses in early autumn. In 2006, especially large numbers of Guillemots were wrecked in Argyll, with over 100 dead birds

Distribution and abundance of breeding Common Guillemots (individual adults) in Argyll during Seabird 2000.

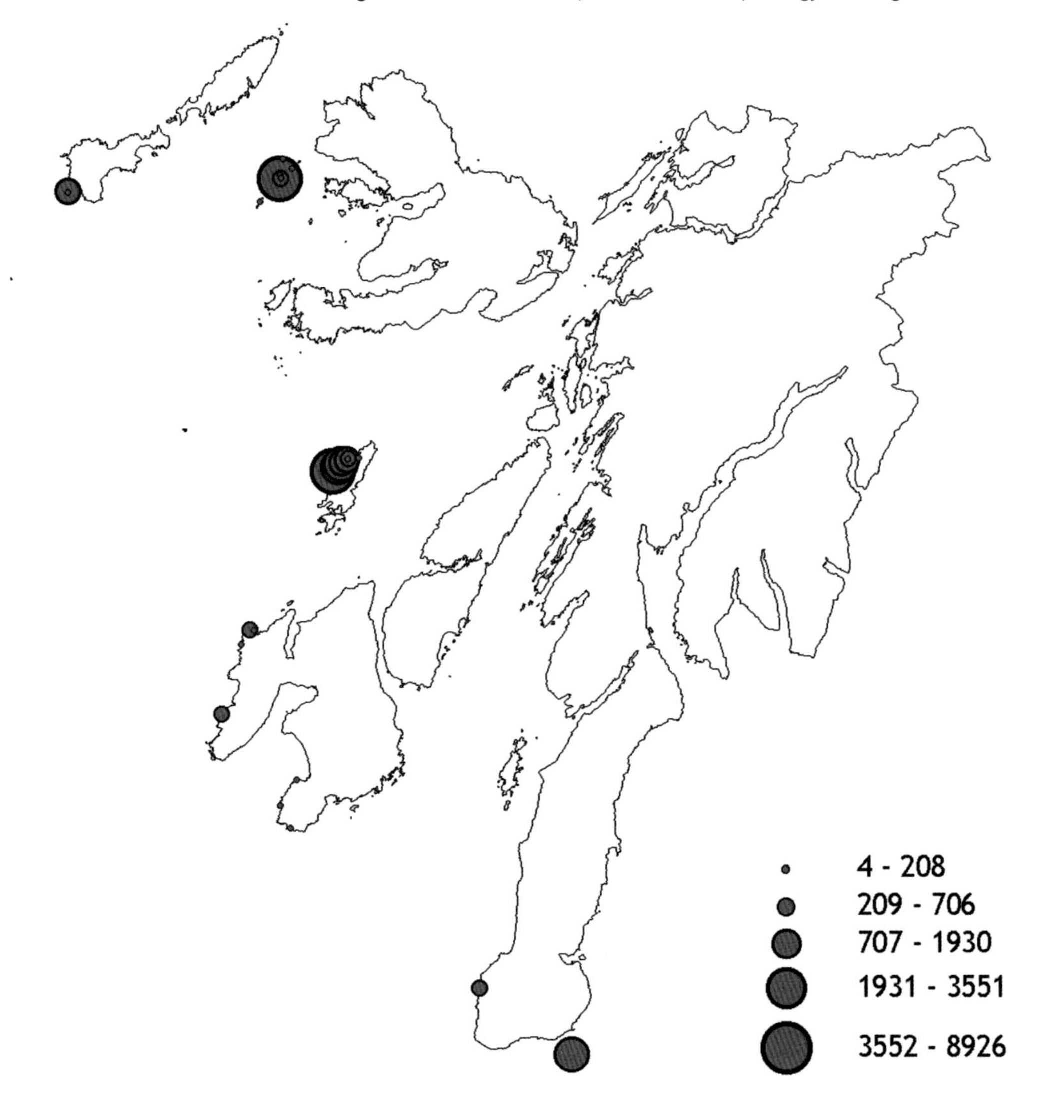

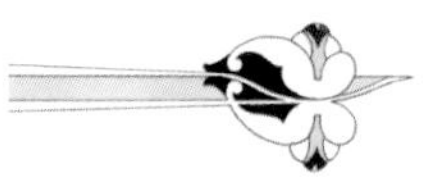

found on 500m of shoreline at the head of Loch Fyne, and several starving birds killed by traffic on the adjacent main road (McAvoy 2006: *Eider* (December 2006):4-7). These wrecks may reflect the fact that Guillemot numbers are at a particularly high level at present, rather than necessarily indicating any sinister changes in fish stocks or environmental conditions.

Birds ringed in Argyll have been recovered off Portugal (1), Spain (10), France (68 – many of these following the *Erica* oilspill), Netherlands (3), Germany (1), Denmark (1), Sweden (2), Norway (4), Faeroe Isles (1), Ireland (33), Wales (21) and England (28). Birds recovered in Argyll had been ringed in Ireland (15), Wales (5) and elsewhere in Scotland (53).

The variation in plumage between the northern nominate race *U.a.aalge* and the browner southern race *U.a.albionis* is clinal and authorities indicate that separation is not straightforward (BWP). Some birds in Argyll are certainly light chocolate brown in colour and indeed may be of the southern race, not normally recognized as breeding in Scotland; this could be a useful area for future study. Counts at breeding colonies in Argyll normally show 5-12% bridled birds.

David Jardine

Brünnich's Guillemot

Uria lomvia

Vagrant.

One was found dead at Loch Caolisport on 11 October 1969 (BB 63:281). This was only the third Scottish record of this rare visitor from higher latitudes. Not until 1980 was one seen alive in British waters.

Tristan ap Rheinallt

Razorbill

Alca torda

Razorbills are not as numerous as Common Guillemots in Argyll, with around 9,000 birds counted at breeding colonies. Most migrate, but small numbers are regularly found in sea lochs in winter.

Victorian archaeologists found the remains of Razorbills in their excavations of the shell middens that were occupied 6,000 years ago on Oronsay (Anderson 1898, Bishop 1913), suggesting that this common seabird has a long association with the Argyll islands. Thompson (1851) reported the

Over a thousand Razorbills nest on the Treshnish Isles. *Louise Wood*

earliest recorded Razorbills breeding on the Mull of Oa on Islay. Other early writers noted them breeding on the Treshnish Isles, the south of Mull (H&B) and Colonsay (McNeill 1910). While they reported it in good numbers, they noted it was less common than the Puffin (Gray).

There has been a steady increase in the number of breeding birds reported in the three late 20th century seabird censuses conducted in Argyll. In 1969-72 during Operation Seafarer some 1,562 apparently occupied sites and 406 birds were recorded; they had increased to 6,230 during the 1985-87 census (Lloyd *et al.* 1991). The population continued to increase (by 48%) to 9,056 individuals counted during Seabird 2000. The breeding population of Razorbills, restricted to seven different major stations, is more uniformly distributed than the Guillemot; around 33% are found on Sanda and the adjoining isles and the Mull of Kintyre (3,091 birds), 30% are found on Colonsay (2,739 birds), 19% on Islay (1,753 birds) and 10% on the Treshnish Isles (1,232 birds). There are small colonies on Tiree at Ceann a' Mhara (374 birds), on Eileach an Naoimh in the Garvellachs (eight birds), Eilean Mor (eight birds) and Eilean Beag (seven birds) off northern Jura.

In winter relatively small numbers are recorded feeding offshore and it is not until early spring that birds are recorded back on the breeding cliffs. Like the Common Guillemot, Razorbills are regularly noted during sea watches from western headlands; often it is impossible to distinguish the two species, or the proportions of each, when birds are passing at long distance.

Razorbills are more migratory than Guillemots with birds ringed in Argyll having been recovered off Morocco (4), Algeria (1), Portugal (5), Spain (10), France (23), Belgium (1), Netherlands (5), Germany (3), Denmark (1), Norway (3), Ireland (17), Wales (7) and England (16). Birds recovered in Argyll had been ringed in Isle of Man (1), Wales (6) and elsewhere in Scotland (19).

David Jardine

Distribution and abundance of breeding Razorbills (individual adults) in Argyll during Seabird 2000.

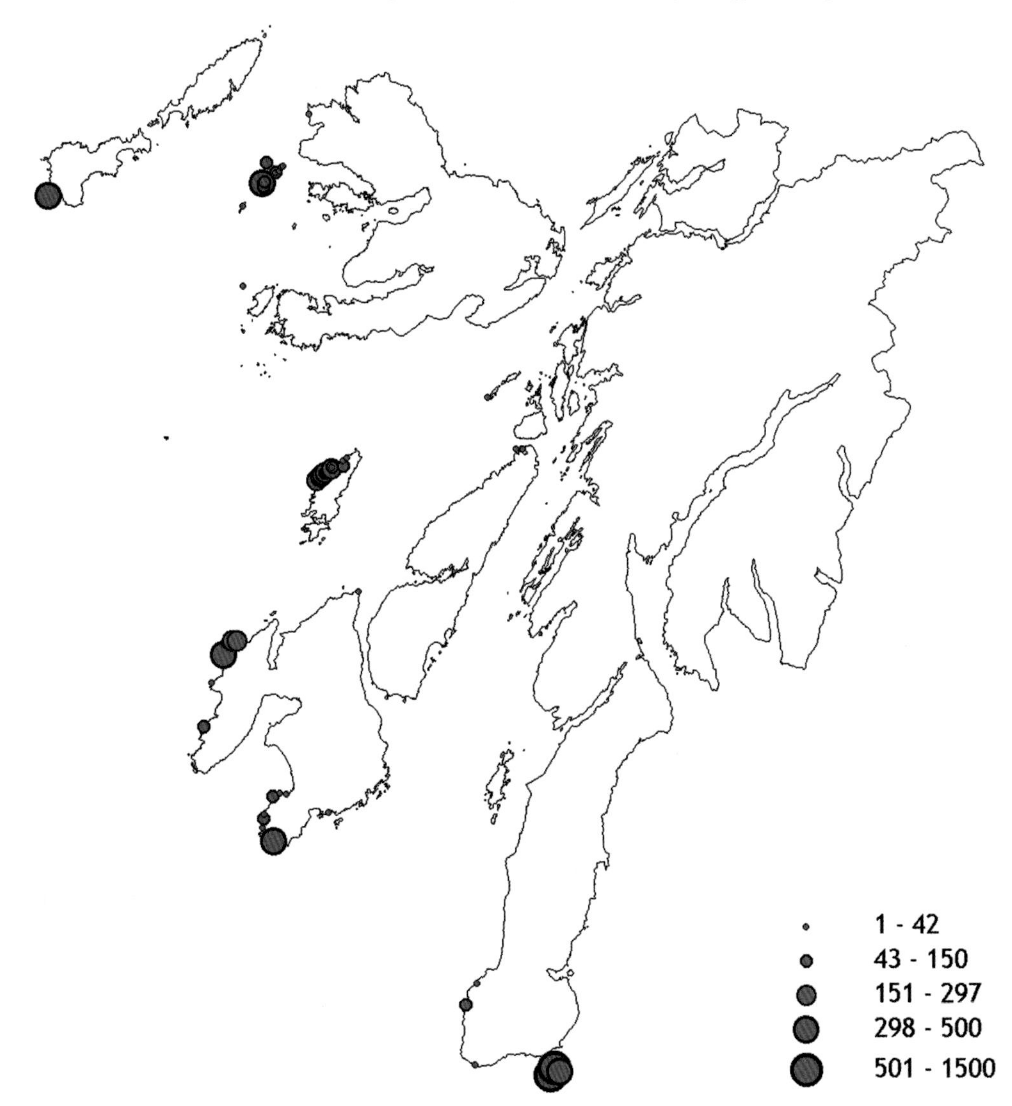

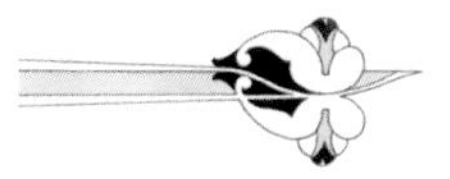

Great Auk

Pinguinus impennis

Extinct

Once very numerous in the North Atlantic, this flightless sea bird was widely harvested for food, down and eggs for hundreds of years. By the late eighteenth century, over-exploitation had restricted its breeding distribution to just a few colonies off the coast of Iceland. The last known Scottish bird was killed on St. Kilda in about 1840 (Thom) and the story of the killing of, supposedly, the 'last two' birds on the island of Eldey, Iceland, in June 1844 is well known. That they once occurred in Argyll waters is attested by the finding of Great Auk bones in Mesolithic shell middens on Oronsay (Grieve 1923).

Paul Daw

Black Guillemot

Cepphus grylle

The Black Guillemot is much less numerous in Argyll than the Common Guillemot or Razorbill, but may be more familiar because it is the most widespread breeder and occurs close to shore throughout the year, and is often to be seen in sea lochs.

During the Winter Atlas the Black Guillemot was found, in its white winter garb, scattered in singles or small groups (usually fewer than ten birds) around the entire coast of Argyll, including in the sea lochs. During late March and into April, Black Guillemots gather in the early morning into pre-breeding flocks where they display and pair up. This is normally the best occasion to estimate population levels as nests are hidden in deep crevices and the breeding population is widely dispersed. The largest groups are often to be seen in these spring gatherings, e.g. 240 off Craro, Gigha, on 2 April 1987.

The SAMS seabird study on the small offshore islets of Argyll during the 1980s and 1990s has provided some information on the breeding performance of Black Guillemots. This suggested that in the absence of ground predators the number of chicks reared per pair varied between 0.67 and 1.5

Black Guillemots breed around most of the rocky coastlines of Argyll. *David Palmar*

Distribution and abundance of breeding Black Guillemots (individuals in spring) in Argyll during Seabird 2000.

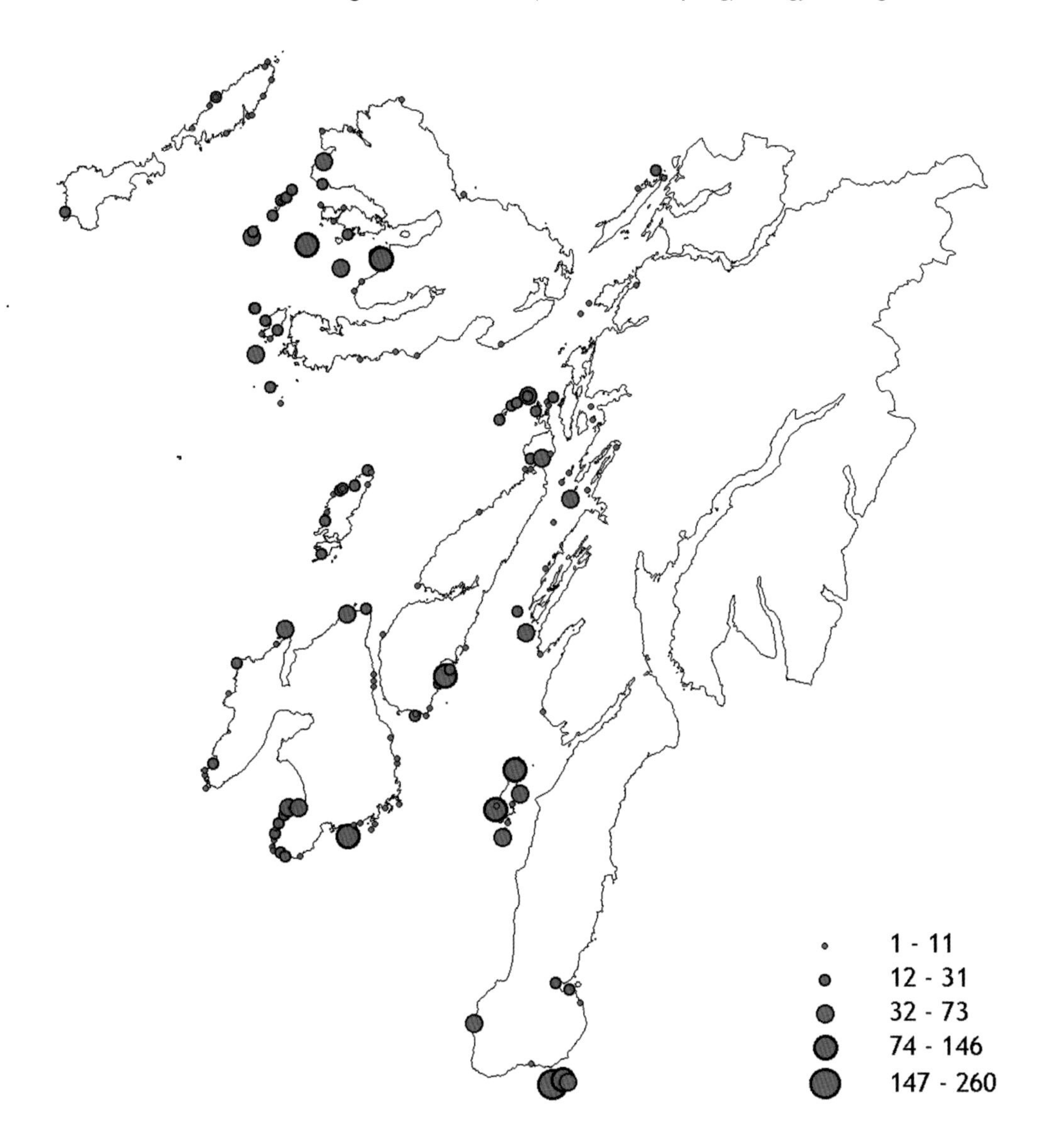

young per nest (although sample sizes were small). This study also found that American Mink and Otters killed breeding adults; it also noted the disappearance of Black Guillemot as a breeding species from over ten of these small colonies (Craik 1997). The population on Sanda and the adjoining isles, where mink were reported during the 1990s fell from 260 birds in 1993 to 155 in 1997. Following control of mink the population rose again to 268 birds in 1999.

The Victorian naturalists found Black Guillemots around much of the Argyll coast, except the Sound of Mull, where they preferred islands to the shore of the mainland (H&B). This describes well the distribution found in Operation Seafarer (1969-73) when 230 pairs and 695 birds were reported, although the survey was not based on early spring counts. Therefore, it was not surprising that the total reported in 1985 increased to 269 pairs and 2,605 birds (Lloyd *et al.* 1991). In Seabird 2000 a total of 3,046 birds was counted, probably with better coverage than in the previous census, thus trends in numbers are unclear. There is concern that in some areas depredations of mink may be reducing Black Guillemot numbers at least locally.

Following breeding, moult gatherings of Black Guillemots are a common feature, and at times these can lead to significant congregations such as the 144 in the Sound of Gigha on 27 October 1997. British populations of Black Guillemot are usually sedentary, with relatively local dispersal normally being reported from ringed birds. Chicks ringed on Sanda, off Kintyre, also reflect this with three recovered locally five, nine and twelve years later. Other recoveries include a chick ringed on Sanda in June 1994 found on Rathlin Island (Co. Antrim, Ireland) (42km) in August 1994 and an adult ringed on Sanda in June 1981 found on the Isle of Man (130km) in December 1992. A chick ringed at Copeland Bird Observatory (Co. Down) in 1994 was breeding on Sanda in 1998. This relatively sedentary pattern is reflected also in the results of sea-watching studies. Only on a few occasions have more than 100 birds been noted moving on a single day, 218 flying south in three hours on 22 September 2000 at Uisaed Point, Kintyre, being the largest reported.

David Jardine

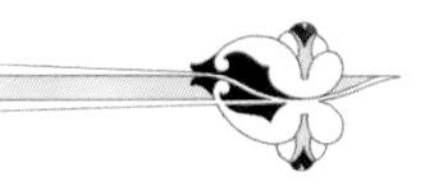

Little Auk

Alle alle

This is a rare winter visitor, usually occurring in small numbers. The impressive migration movements noted on the north and east coasts of Scotland have not been observed in Argyll.

There were few records of Little Auks in Argyll in the 19th century, with Graham, who had many years experience, never coming across a specimen. Gray records a few being captured near Oban in the winters of 1866-67 and 1868. H&B also record an individual from Oban, along with records from Mull, Tiree and Jura. Little Auks are vulnerable to adverse weather conditions and records are most frequent following winter gales. B&R record a major wreck in 1894-95 when birds were found in Campbeltown, Oban, Mull, and Islay. They also record small flocks being seen periodically in winter off Skerryvore. Unfortunately most records of this delightful auk are of dead or moribund birds, e.g. 100 were found dead in late February 1988, mainly on Islay (ABR). Others have been found ashore as victims of oil spills.

There has been an increase in sightings of Little Auks in Argyll in the latter part of the 20th century, probably due to the increase in observers. There have also been more sightings from southern Argyll, with most recent records now coming from popular seawatching locations such as Frenchman's Rocks on Islay and Uisaed Point in Kintyre. Most sightings are of individual birds, or of small groups, few records reaching double figures. At Frenchman's Rocks, 11 were recorded on 6 November 1996, 41 were seen on 12 December 1993 and 20 flew south past the nearby Portnahaven on 30 December 1990. The largest group, however, were 110 seen flying past East Loch Tarbert, Loch Fyne, on 14 December 1997.

'Wrecks' of more than 100 Little Auks can follow spells of adverse weather. *David Wood*

Most Little Auks are recorded between late October and early March. One bird has been seen as early as 7 September at Uisaed Point and there are records on 20 and 23 September. Corpses from winter casualties are regularly found into April, although there are a couple of records of living birds in early April and one was seen in summer plumage from the Oban–Colonsay ferry on 15 April 1994. Remains of a dead bird found on Kiloran Bay, Colonsay, in 1993 were confirmed as the nominate race *Alle alle alle*. The larger, high Arctic race *A. a. polaris*, which has been recorded elsewhere in Scotland (Thom), has not yet been recorded in Argyll.

David Jardine

Puffin

Fratercula arctica

This attractive 'sea parrot' with its colourful beak and orange legs is an uncommon breeder in Argyll, restricted to a few small offshore islands.

In the late 19th century the Puffin was considered the most abundant of the seafowl in the west of Scotland (Gray). This may now seem surprising, but is perhaps less so given the relatively recent substantial increases in the populations of Common Guillemots and Razorbills. Like today, its stronghold was in the northern isles of Argyll. Graham records it on Staffa and H&B note that it was increasing rapidly, with the numbers doubling on Eriskay, off Mull, from one year to the next. These authors noted it was common on the Treshnish Isles and that it was frequently seen in the waters around Tiree. Also around this time there was an important station on the Mull of Oa, Islay (Gray). This was still present in 1914 and B&R report that Puffins were still there in 1939, but it is now no longer occupied.

Harris (1984), in his monograph on the Puffin, gives the most comprehensive account of its breeding distribution and numbers in Argyll. He records a total of 14 breeding colonies, more than double the number shown in Cramp *et al.* (1974) or in Lloyd *et al.* (1991). He records five colonies of between 100 and 1000 pairs and nine sites with fewer than 100 pairs. Not all of these sites are now occupied, as Puffins were not recorded during the Seabird 2000 count at the following former small colonies – Mull of Kintyre, Corr Eilean and Eilean Mor (McCormaig Isles) in the Sound of Jura, Sanaig Cliffs (Islay), Eilean Mor (North Jura), or Coll.

The Treshnish Isles, Staffa and Stac mhic Mhurchaidh (west of Iona) remain the centres of the Argyll population. This population has been increasing in recent years, for in 1971 the Treshnish Isles Ringing Group only recorded 774

Puffins sweep their bills from side to side as they feed, so their catch is often arranged head, tail, head, tail. *Louise Wood*

apparently occupied burrows (AOB) and this increased to 1,631 AOB in 1995. Seabird 2000 recorded 1,788 AOB on the Treshnish Isles and 328 birds were seen on Staffa. These birds are part of an important supporting cast to the ecotourism industry which has developed in recent years watching cetaceans to the west of Mull.

Puffins have never favoured Colonsay, despite its large colonies of auks, and only one bird was recorded ashore during Seabird 2000. Breeding has never been demonstrated here; this is believed to be a consequence of the many rats that are known to depredate Puffin populations. Harris (1984) relates how Glunimore (near Sanda, Kintyre) was colonized around 1920. This population grew to around 200 pairs in 1955, but was destroyed by a rockfall in the 1960s. Around this time Puffins colonized Sheep Island nearby and this population grew to around 250 pairs in 1971. There were two pairs on Sanda itself, a colony that increased to around 250 pairs in 1978. There had been a decline in this population by the time of Seabird 2000 when only 290 birds were counted on all three of these islands.

Despite the reduction in the number of breeding colonies reported since Harris (1984), the number of birds reported during the seabird censuses has increased (Table).

Many thousands were noted in Loch Fyne each year in early May during the 19th century (Graham), an influx which is no longer recorded, no doubt due to a reduction in available food (small pelagic fish) brought about by changes in fishing practice. With the northerly breeding distribution

Years of census	Number of pairs or occupied burrows	Number of birds	Estimate of total number of birds
1969-70	1,200 pairs	39 birds	2,439
1985-87	75 pairs	3,091 birds	3,241
1999-2001	1,788 apparently occupied burrows	719 birds	4,295

Estimated number of breeding Puffins in Argyll.

Distribution and abundance of breeding Puffins (apparently occupied burrows) in Argyll during Seabird 2000.

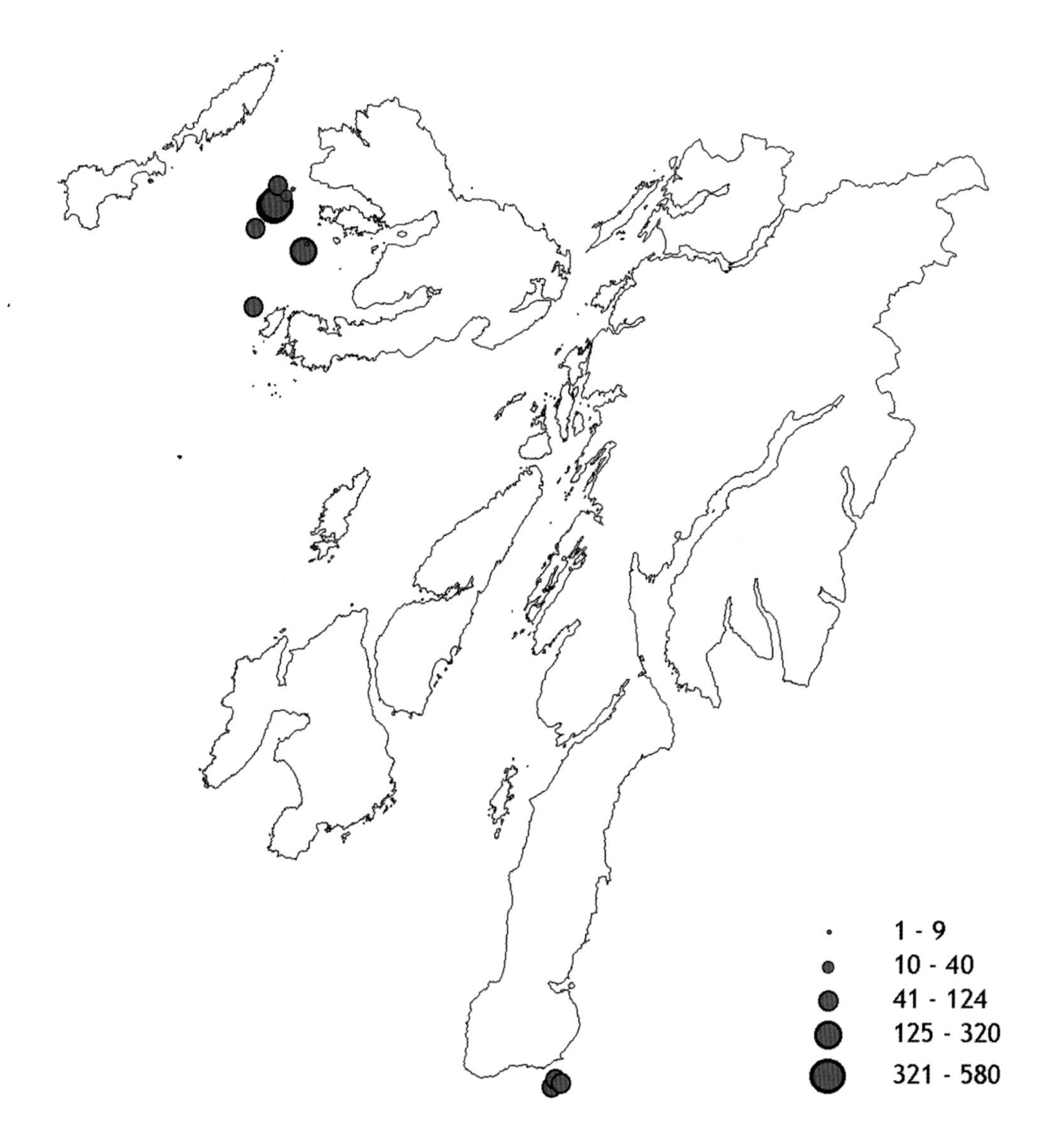

of the Puffin, and much of the sea-watching done in the south at the Frenchman's Rocks (Islay) and at Uisaed Point (Kintyre), it is not surprising that this bird is only reported in small numbers. Peak numbers reported at these sites are in late June to early August, with usually fewer than ten birds recorded per hour at the former site. Puffins ringed in Argyll have been recovered in Portugal (1), Iceland (1) and Ireland (2). Birds recovered in Argyll had been ringed in Norway (1), Wales (1) and elsewhere in Scotland (13).

David Jardine

Pallas's Sandgrouse

Syrrhaptes paradoxus

Extremely rare. Last invasion in 1888.

The Pallas's Sandgrouse is (or was) well known for making occasional eruptive movements from its breeding grounds on the steppes of Asia. One such eruption, in May 1888, produced a notable invasion of Scotland. Some 2,000 birds were thought to have reached the country, and breeding took place that summer and in 1889 (B&R, Thom). As part of this invasion, there were records from various parts of Argyll. These were analysed in detail by H&B (Table).

Since this species has now become an extremely rare visitor to Britain, the chances of there being any further Argyll records seem minimal.

[The species was also apparently recorded from Kintyre, but no details of date or location are available (Gibson & McWilliam 1959).]

Tristan ap Rheinallt

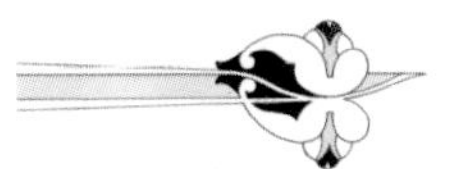

Records of Pallas's Sandgrouse in Argyll during the invasion of 1888.

Date	Location	No. of birds	Comment
28 May - 5 Oct	Tiree	*c.*85	Fed on *Chenopodium* seeds at top of sandy shores.
17 Jun	Appin	1	Sent to an Oban taxidermist on that date.
17 Jun	Loch Awe	1	As Appin.
19 Jun	Colonsay & Oronsay	11	"The first and only ones observed."
16 Sep	Kilberry	9	Flying south; one also recorded on another date.
Unknown	North-west Mull	2	Seen.
Unknown	South-west Mull	>1	Observed, "probably part of the Tiree flocks".

Rock Dove

Columba livia

Resident, concentrated in the islands and Kintyre. Populations inhabiting islands and some mainland coastal areas consist mainly or entirely of birds showing wild-type plumage. However, Feral Pigeons also occur, mainly in mainland towns.

The ancestral Rock Dove is a bird of coastal cliff habitats that uses fissures and caves for nesting and roosting. Abandoned buildings may also be occupied, as on Islay and Tiree. Most foraging takes place on open land not far from the nesting and roosting sites, with stubble fields, re-seeded areas, and machair being favoured feeding habitats. Rock Doves are well known for having an extended breeding season. Graham (in Gray) found hatched young in the Mull area as early as 2 April, and unhatched eggs as late as September. More recently, an incubating bird was reported from Islay on 30 January 1992.

Although the OSA and NSA largely fail to distinguish between the different species of pigeon, the writings of early naturalists such as Gray, Graham and H&B demonstrate that Rock Doves were then common on most if not all of the Argyll islands as well as on stretches of the mainland coast, and numerous in some locations. In the early part of the 20th century they bred, sometimes in large numbers, on Gigha, Islay, Jura, Colonsay, Tiree, Coll, the Treshnish Isles, Mull and Iona, and were considered common on the west coast of the mainland (B&R).

However, B&R also stated that the Rock Dove was a "much commoner bird in the past than it is to-day." In Argyll, evidence for a decline came from Appin, where Rock Doves were said to have ceased to breed in some caves, and the Ross of Mull, where caves occupied by large numbers of Rock Doves in 1901 held only Starlings in 1921. B&R believed that competition from Starlings was responsible for the reduction but did not discuss changes in agricultural practices or patterns of human occupation.

No attempt was made to map the distribution of Rock Doves in Argyll until the First Atlas, which showed birds to breed throughout the major islands and Kintyre as well as along most of the remainder of the west coast. However, they were largely absent from inland areas and Cowal, their avoidance of high ground reflecting the picture across Scotland. The Second Atlas showed loss from some parts of the mainland coast, compensated by expansion in Islay and especially Mull. This may or may not represent real change. However, there has recently been a genuine increase in Colonsay, possibly linked to an increase in arable (or brown re-seeding) land (D. C. Jardine pers. comm.). On the other hand, the number of pairs nesting on Sanda has fallen from around ten to fewer than five in recent years.

According to the First Atlas, the whole of Argyll except for Cowal fell within the area occupied by wild Rock Doves as opposed to Feral Pigeons. This is an over-simplification. As early as the 19th century, Gray commented that some of the birds along the mainland coast of Argyll were "of mixed appearance", and much the same was said for Jura (H&B). Feral Pigeons, whose ancestors are believed to be a mixture of Rock Doves and domesticated pigeons reared originally for food, presumably have a long history of interbreeding with Rock Doves in Argyll as elsewhere. More recently, stray racing pigeons rather than Feral Pigeons are probably the main genetic influence on Rock Doves on the islands. However, it is interesting that, in parts of Argyll still occupied almost entirely by birds with wild-type plumage, interlopers tend to keep to themselves (pers. obs., J. Bowler pers. comm.). Thus displacement of Rock Doves by Feral Pigeons could happen mainly through competition rather than interbreeding.

Given that the Scottish islands are among the few places in the world where intact gene pools of the wild Rock Dove might still exist, the fate of these populations is clearly of concern. Normally, the proportion of birds with wild-type plumage is used to estimate influence by feral or domestic birds. It may not be a particularly accurate indicator, but in the absence of genetic studies it is the best available. Unfortunately, accurate estimates of the proportions of different plumage types in different areas of Argyll are not to hand. However, the few counts suggest that more than 95 per cent of birds on Islay, Tiree and Colonsay still resemble wild Rock Doves. The same probably applies to other islands such as Jura, Coll, Mull, Iona, the Treshnish Isles and Gigha.

On the mainland, the situation is more complex. Numbers of this species seem highest in Kintyre, where the majority resemble wild-type Rock Doves. The same is probably true of the few birds that breed in traditional cliff habitats further north along the west coast. However, Feral Pigeons are also regularly reported, mainly from towns such as Dunoon, Campbeltown, Inveraray, Oban and Connel. Counts reported

Flocks of birds showing predominantly 'pure' Rock Dove plumage occur on several Argyll islands, including, as here, on Sanda. *Margaret Staley*

from these towns do not exceed 20 or 30 birds, and it may be that some are domestic, being kept in pigeon lofts, rather than feral. Published records suggest that their numbers may have increased in recent years, but given that birdwatchers rarely bothered to report Feral Pigeons in the past, it is difficult to be sure. Similarly, there is little direct evidence that the proportion of non-wild-type plumages is increasing in any cliff-dwelling population although, on Sanda, the first occurrence of a feral bird in the breeding population of native Rock Doves was said to have been in 1997.

Although domesticated Rock Doves are renowned for their homing ability, free-living populations are largely sedentary (Migration Atlas). Nevertheless, they may cover considerable distances in search of food. Indeed, Graham (p. 81) reported: "They seem to be migratory, to a certain extent in quest of food, at seedtime and harvest, if, as is often the case, the island crops are a little earlier than those on the mainland. Then our fields are covered with those petty plunderers, and at night the caves are filled with roosting birds, which remain about the island as long as food is very plentiful, and then decamp".

The habit of gathering in flocks to feed, especially on stubble fields during the autumn and winter, is well known. Nevertheless, Kintyre is the only part of the Argyll mainland from which such flocks have been reported in recent years, the largest count being 119 at Carskiey, near Southend, on 30 November 1990. On Islay, on the other hand, feeding flocks numbering more than a hundred birds are regular, the largest being 400 on 26 November 1977. Populations on other islands appear to be somewhat smaller, with maximum flock counts of 200+ birds on Tiree, Iona and Coll, and 100+ on Mull, Colonsay and Oronsay.

Tristan ap Rheinallt

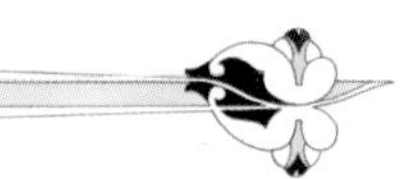

Stock Dove

Columba oenas

Rare resident, with small breeding populations in the Kilmartin area and south Cowal, and possibly also in south Kintyre. Occasional lone migrants turn up on some of the islands in spring and autumn.

The Stock Dove was once regarded as very rare in Scotland. Gray, for example, knew of only two records from the whole country. However, a rapid northward and westward expansion took place from the late 19th century onwards, apparently linked to the spread of arable farming (Thom). After moving into northern England, the species colonised Scotland around 1866 and in time reached almost every mainland county, although Argyll represented its northern limit on the west coast (B&R).

It seems that Stock Doves never became common in Argyll. The earliest records date from the 1920s, with nesting at the Mull of Kintyre in 1928 and birds recorded at Carradale and Dalmally in 1928-29. Stock Doves occurred in Knapdale in 1936 and Dunstaffnage in 1943 (B&R). The First Atlas indicated that Stock Doves were present only in a few widely scattered 10-km squares in mainland Argyll, with breeding confirmed in Appin and Ardyne. Although the Winter Atlas produced records from only two squares, comparison of the First and Second Atlases suggests little change in the intervening period, the number of occupied 10-km squares in Argyll remaining more or less the same. Nevertheless, there is evidence for a more general range contraction in Scotland in the second half of the 20th century (Thom, Second Atlas), with Bute and Arran for example losing most or all of their breeding birds by the 1980s (Thom). This suggests that the Argyll population could have been higher around the middle of the century, but there is no evidence to confirm this.

The area north of Lochgilphead, centred on Kilmartin, has accounted for the majority of records in recent decades. Confirmation of breeding did not come until 1993, when a pair bred in a nest box near Ford. Presumably the population is very small, as no count from the area has exceeded four birds, but it appears to have persisted from the time of the First Atlas to the present.

There is also a distinct cluster of records in the south of Kintyre between Campbeltown and Southend, with scattered sightings of one to three birds between 1989 and 2000. Again it seems likely that there is a small breeding population, although nesting has never been confirmed. The same applies to the south of Cowal, where there have been fewer reports but where confirmed breeding in 1971 was followed by suspected breeding near Tighnabruaich in 1989, and confirmed breeding on the Knockdow Estate in 2006. Stock Doves occur in some numbers in the Clyde area, not far from the eastern limits of Cowal.

The situation in North Argyll is less clear. Since the First Atlas, there have only been two records, involving three birds seen at Ardchattan Priory on 23 November 1985, and a single bird photographed in a garden at Rhugarbh Croft, Appin, on 11 July 2007. Thus it is likely that any former breeding population has now disappeared. Elsewhere on the mainland, there have only been a few scattered records that could refer to migrants or dispersing birds. Single migrants have also been seen on several islands, almost always in spring (April to June) or autumn (September to October) (Table).

Although British Stock Doves are known to be highly sedentary, ringing recoveries show that a few move considerable distances, though there is no evidence of a directional component at any time of year (Migration Atlas). While native birds must account for the majority of the above island records, it is possible that Fennoscandian birds, which are highly migratory, may occur occasionally. However, the fact that the species is very rare in the Outer Hebrides argues against a northern origin.

[Two additional records from Islay, involving 20 birds seen on 27 November 1973 (Elliott 1989) and eight on 19 October 1979 (SBR 1979:34, Elliott 1989), are highly anomalous and are not considered acceptable in the absence of supporting details.]

Tristan ap Rheinallt

The Stock Dove is rare in Argyll. *Philip Kirkham*

Stock Dove records from the Argyll Islands, 1976 - 2006.

Island	Month and year
Colonsay	May 1986 April 1995 June 2000
Gigha	April 1988
Islay	June 1977 February 1981 October 2002 October 2003
Mull	March 1976
Sanda	May 1989
Tiree	September 1997 April 1999

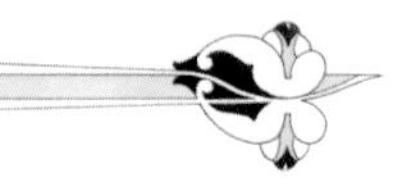

Wood Pigeon

Columba palumbus

This is a fairly common resident near woodland on low ground on the mainland, but it is less numerous on Mull, scarce on Coll and rare on Tiree. Flocks of several hundreds may form on the mainland in autumn and winter, especially in years with good crops of acorns or beechmast.

Around the year 1800 Woodpigeons were almost unknown in west Scotland. Gray describes how one feeding in a garden in a snowstorm in 1791 was unusual enough to attract spectators while, about the same time, discovery of a nest was "a great feat". Then, like Collared Doves a century and a half later, Woodpigeons rapidly multiplied and extended their range. New agricultural crops such as clover and turnips (and much more recently in the lowlands, oilseed rape), together with the destruction of raptors, a breeding season that lasts most of the year and secure breeding sites in new conifer plantations, are all thought to have assisted this expansion. The species had become a severe pest to farmers by 1870 when Gray described it as numerous through the west counties of Scotland, present on Mull and "introduced" on Islay. Graham described it as "unknown upon our rocky and woodless shores (of Iona)" but he found it "abundant" during his time at Ardrishaig (*c.*1858-1866). H&B described it as common in Argyll, increasing on the mainland and abundant on Mull, Islay and Jura. B&R give records from many parts of the county, including the Oban area, Islay, Jura, Gigha, Colonsay and Mull.

This species breeds primarily in woodland, but also nests in shrubs, on buildings and, where trees or shrubs are absent, among vegetation on the ground. The usual clutch is two, varying from one to three. Most young fledge in late summer but in lowland agricultural habitats eggs have been recorded in every month. Work for the Second Atlas (1988-91) found breeding in 48% of 10-km squares in the county and showed that, in Argyll and the West Highlands generally, breeding was at a much lower density than in eastern Scotland or in most of the British Isles.

Wood Pigeons were found in 12 of 29 broadleaved woods in Mid- and North Argyll during the Second Woodland Bird Survey 2003/4 (*cf.* 27 of 38 in 1985) and numbers had decreased by 67.9% since the 1985 survey (Amar *et al.* 2006, RSPB unpubl. data). During 1995-2001 it was recorded in 4/17, 5/21, 4/16, 7/16, 3/15, 4/12 and 1/6 BBS squares; and in 4/14 Countryside 2000 squares (ABR). Twenty birds were recorded in a single 1-km square in Cowal in summer 2000, probably an unusually high density. In contrast, Patterson *et al.* (1995) recorded it in less than 8% of census plots during spring in Sitka Spruce forest in Cowal. It breeds on Islay (e.g. four pairs at the RSPB's Loch Gruinart Reserve in 1986), on Colonsay (*c.*3 pairs bred June 1986) and on Coll (breeding was first suspected at the Lodge Plantation in 1989 and 1-2 pairs have since summered annually with breeding proven in some years). There are few records from Jura and it is not definitely known to have bred on Tiree, where it occurs as

Wood Pigeon numbers in winter tend to correlate with beech mast and acorn abundance. *Philip Kirkham*

a rare migrant with near-annual records of single birds in spring, mostly in May (ABR, Argyll Database).

The Winter Atlas showed fewer occupied squares than in summer, notably on Mull. In those squares that were occupied, the density was again much lower than in eastern Scotland or most of England. Nevertheless, flocks of up to a hundred are not uncommon in winter on the mainland of Argyll. During the severe winter of 1890-91, H&B described "vast flights" of woodpigeons feeding on beechmast near the castle at Inveraray, and they reported large numbers elsewhere on the same food, for example at Barcaldine. Bumper crops of acorns also attract large numbers that may remain for several weeks until the food is exhausted, as in 1990 and 2000. Such years contrast with those of poor acorn crops when the few flocks recorded are small, as in 1999. "Hundreds" flew down Loch Awe early in November 2001, and there are 14 records of gatherings of 100 or more during 1980-2001. The largest during 1980-2003 were *c.*500 at Benderloch on 23 January 1984, 300+ in oakwoods at Blarghour, Loch Awe on 26 November 2000, *c.*250 at Ledaig Point (unusual habitat!) on 15 December 1990 and *c.*250 at Inveraray on 10 December 1984 (ABR).

Winter flocks of up to 100 are not unusual on Islay. Smaller flocks have been recorded on Colonsay and Mull (rarely up to 100, usually a maximum 50 each year). Where there is little woodland, such flocks feed on farmland or on grain put out for other birds. An unusual midwinter record is of two killed at Skerryvore Lighthouse on 21 December 1897 (B&R). One bird wintered on Tiree in 2005/06 and odd birds sometimes remain to winter on Coll, although numbers there are bolstered by birds returning in spring.

Most Woodpigeons are highly sedentary and most ring recoveries are near the ringing site (median distance 5km). However, there is debate on the extent to which continental birds come to Britain for the winter. The very small number of international ring recoveries conflicts with the numbers of apparently migratory flocks seen along coasts. Gray described an amazing flock of twenty to thirty thousand apparently arriving on the east coast of Scotland (no date was given) and the Migration Atlas gives other records.

More locally, there are records of return passage in spring: for example, on 6-7 March 1938, B&R saw "extraordinary flocks at Largie, Argyll, evidently on migration". However, very few are ringed in Argyll and there is no evidence from ringing concerning the origins of birds in the area. The recovery map in the Migration Atlas shows a complete absence of records for the whole of north-west Scotland.

Clive Craik

Collared Dove

Streptopelia decaocto

Widespread but sparsely distributed throughout Argyll, associating with human settlement and avoiding higher ground. Resident at many locations, but mainly a late-spring migrant or summer visitor to some islands.

Most birdwatchers will be familiar with the Collared Dove's rapid colonisation of Europe around the middle of the 20th century. The first birds bred in England in 1955 and in Scotland two years later (Thom). By the time of the First Atlas, they were widely distributed as far north as Shetland, though rather sparse in the north and west. Although the reason for the sudden expansion of range remains unknown, the long breeding season is thought to have facilitated speedy colonisation (Thom).

Collared Doves in Argyll, as elsewhere, tend to associate with human habitation, avoiding open expanses of countryside, mountains and moorland. In winter, they take advantage of locations such as gardens, farms and distilleries, where there is a ready supply of food such as grain or seeds. Small flocks may congregate at food sources and the species is sometimes viewed as a pest. Shooting has occurred in Argyll, for example on Islay (Booth 1975, Elliott 1989).

Collared Doves may have arrived in the county as early as 1960, possibly on Mull (Thom). They were first noted on Islay in 1961 at Aoradh Farm (Gruinart) and then in 1962 at Port Ellen (Elliott 1989), although MacMillan (1965) stated that breeding did not occur at Gruinart until 1963. Two birds were seen on Iona in August and September 1963

Collared Doves first colonised Argyll in the 1960s. *Philip Kirkham*

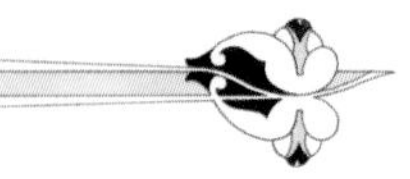

and again the following spring, and numbers built to 13 by August. The first mainland records were apparently in 1964, when birds were recorded in south Kintyre at Macharioch and Glenramskill House near Campbeltown. A pair nested at the latter location, though the chicks died (MacMillan 1965). Breeding occurred near Lochgilphead in 1967 and 1968 (SBR), and the species was first recorded on Coll and Tiree in 1969 (Thom) and on Colonsay in 1972 (Jardine *et al.* 1986). By this time it was widespread on the mainland, though with gaps in its range especially in the north and west of Cowal, in North Argyll away from the coast, and in parts of Mid-Argyll. It was also widely distributed on Islay and Mull, but unrecorded from Jura (First Atlas) although recorded there in 1985 (ABR 3:40).

By the mid-1970s populations were levelling off in many parts of Scotland, with decreases in some areas (Thom). In Argyll, numbers may have peaked in the 1970s and then declined. Thus on Islay, flocks of more than 50 were said to occur "in a number of places" (Booth 1975), with as many as 80 at Bowmore on 5 November 1977 (Elliott 1989). However, numbers were very low by the early 1980s, although a small recovery occurred later. Elliott (1989) attributed the decline to a reduction in production by the distilleries, with less grain being spilt on the roads. However, a decline was also witnessed on Colonsay (Jardine *et al.* 1986), where there are no distilleries, while a sudden population crash was reported from Tobermory in 1978 (ABR 1:56). Certainly, the 1981-84 Winter Atlas survey suggested that there had been no further expansion in Argyll since 1968-72. Records were very thinly scattered, with none at all from Tiree or Colonsay.

Differences between the summer distribution in 1968-72 and the winter distribution in 1981-4 may be explained by the fact that the Argyll population was partly migratory (see also below). On Colonsay, for example, Collared Doves were resident at the beginning of the 1970s but later became summer visitors (Jardine *et al.* 1986). Nevertheless, by the time of the Second Atlas in 1988-91 there had been a clear contraction in range in Mid- and North Argyll even during the summer months, the north-eastern corner of Argyll now being unoccupied. A range contraction was also apparent in some other parts of Scotland north of the Central Lowlands, although it was not discussed in the Second Atlas.

This general decline may have continued on the mainland, although colonisation of new locations continues to take place. Although still apparently widespread in Mid-Argyll and perhaps also in southern Cowal, birds are nowadays rarely reported from North Argyll, where since 1997 records have come only from Benderloch and Rhugarbh. In Kintyre, there are very few recent records away from the two regular sites of Skipness and Tayinloan, though a very high count of 58 birds was obtained at Machrihanish on 21 October 1993 (ABR 10:60). No Collared Doves were recorded in any of the 12 BBS squares or 14 Countryside 2000 squares surveyed in 2000.

On the islands the situation appears more complex. Before describing it in detail, it is worth looking at what is known about patterns of migration in this species. Ringing recoveries show that, during the colonisation of the British Isles, Collared Doves sometimes moved considerable distances, usually in a westerly or north-westerly direction. Since the mid-1970s, however, dispersal distances have decreased. While ringing points to August as the main month of dispersal, there is observational evidence for migration in late spring and early summer at sites as far apart as Heligoland (Germany) and the Hebrides (Migration Atlas). Migrants, either single or in small flocks, are regularly witnessed on several Argyll islands, the first sometimes arriving in early April and the last in mid-June. There are a few records from smaller islands such as Sanda and Lunga (Treshnish). Many birds move on quickly but others may remain on the larger islands for weeks or months, though there is rarely any firm evidence of breeding. Some observations suggest that spring immigration also occurs on the mainland, though the possibility that purely local movements are involved cannot be excluded. At Blairmore, for example, spring records are typical but the birds do not stay long, although there is an established resident population at nearby Dunoon. There is much less evidence for autumn migration, although birds thought to be on passage are occasionally reported from the islands.

The only island with a substantial resident population of Collared Doves appears to be Islay, where counts of 40 or more are not unusual, for example at Bruichladdich. However, a spring arrival has been witnessed in Portnahaven on several occasions, with birds gone by mid-May in some years and lingering through the summer in others. On Mull, records are widespread in spring and summer though they usually involve only small numbers, but winter records are much scarcer, suggesting that only a small proportion of the population is resident. The same applies to Tiree, although it seems that wintering there only began around 1996-97, two or three years after birds began to remain through the summer rather than being present only for a brief period in spring. An unusually large flock of 30 was seen on 9 June 2002 at Ruaig, while recently fledged young were seen on the island in 2003, 2004 and 2005 (J. Bowler pers. comm.). On Colonsay, there is a regular summering population but no recent winter records at all, suggesting that the change in status during the 1970s persists. On Coll, where breeding was recorded in 1988-91, Collared Doves were apparently absent or almost absent throughout the latter half of the 1990s but have recently become re-established, with some birds staying the winter. Finally, there are only a few records from Jura, although the species may well be resident in Craighouse.

It is likely that this species is generally under-reported, especially on the mainland. Many observers pay little attention to their local Collared Doves. This is unfortunate because there is much to be learned about its changing status and movements in Argyll.

Tristan ap Rheinallt

Turtle Dove

Streptopelia turtur

Scarce passage migrant, recorded most frequently in May and June.

Although breeding has been occasionally recorded in Scotland, the Turtle Dove is primarily a passage migrant through the country, arriving in some numbers in both spring and autumn. In Argyll, it is the most numerous of those terrestrial species that occur purely as migrants. Although Gray stated that a bird or birds had been shot on Islay, H&B could find no confirmed Argyll records. By the time of B&R, however, Turtle Doves had occurred in mainland Argyll as well as on Islay, Coll, Mull and Dubh Artach. One was also seen on Tiree in September 1951 (Boyd 1958).

Most Argyll records of Turtle Doves have come from the islands. *Philip Kirkham*

By the 1970s Turtle Doves were being recorded with increasing regularity in Argyll, and in the 27-year period from 1980 to 2006 there were records in every year except three (1981, 1984, 2000), the most records in a year being eight in 1991. Most involved single birds but there were a few of two together. It was not unusual for birds to stay for several days, and in 1999 one was apparently present at Whitehouse on Tiree for three weeks during September, a second bird accompanying it for two of those weeks (ABR 16:76). Similarly, a series of sightings of a juvenile/first-winter in the Bruichladdich area of Islay between 9 September and 21 October 2002 (Argyll Database) may well refer to the same individual.

Of 89 published records for 1980-2003 (ABR), 72 came from the islands and only 17 from the mainland (Table).

The seasonal distribution of the 74 records with known arrival dates shows a clear maximum in the second half of May and the first half of June, tailing off in late June and July. Multiple arrivals are not infrequent: for example, birds were recorded at four locations on Islay, one on Jura and one on Colonsay between 23 and 25 May 1991 (ABR 8:50). There is a scattering of autumn records in September and early October. The earliest spring migrant was a bird at Ugadale in Kintyre on 16 April 1982 (ABR 1:56-57), and the latest was a bird at West Parkfergus in Kintyre on 6 November 2002 (Argyll Database). However, there is also a single winter record, involving a bird found freshly dead at Kilmichael Glassary during January 1983 (ABR 1:57).

[A record of a flock of 15 at Kilberry on 27 September 1951 (SN 63:194) is highly atypical and not considered acceptable.]

Tristan ap Rheinallt

Geographic distribution of Turtle Dove records, 1980-2003.

Location	No. of records
Islands	
Islay	24
Tiree	17
Mull	17
Colonsay	7
Jura	3
Coll	3
Iona	1
Mainland	
Kintyre	10
Elsewhere	7

Common Cuckoo

Cuculus canorus

The Cuckoo is a familiar summer visitor, frequent and widespread on much of the mainland but less numerous on the outer islands.

The parasitic life cycle of the Cuckoo is bizarre enough to be science fiction, so it is not surprising that some early naturalists found the facts difficult to accept. As recently as 1957 a noted American ornithologist, Captain Acworth, was still sceptical, insisting that all Cuckoos were hybrids between a female of the host species and a male Cuckoo (Allen 1957).

Early Scottish authors described the Cuckoo as a common bird in the west Highlands, although H&B quote the report in the OSA that it occurred only rarely on Tiree and Coll. However, B&R described it as particularly common in parts of Argyll, adding that it was very common on Coll in 1899 "where hairy caterpillars were abundant" and reporting an estimated seven breeding females on Coll in 1938.

While Thom gives the earliest date on which a Cuckoo was recorded in Scotland "since 1970" as 2 April, the earliest

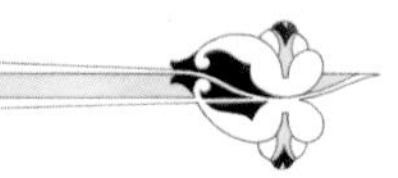

record for Argyll during the years 1980-2003 was one on Coll on 23 March 2003. There was no record for 1982 but, during the other 23 years, the first Cuckoo in Argyll was recorded during late March in two years, during 1-10 April in one year, during 11-20 April in 14 years, during 21-30 April in 5 years and on 1 May in 1980 (ABR). B&R describe the arrival of a flock of 25-30 Cuckoos near Lochgilphead on 27 April 1930.

The main influx normally occurs during the ten days after the first arrivals and usually most birds have arrived

In Argyll, the Cuckoo's main host is the Meadow Pipit. *Gordon Yates*

by early May, although arrival dates and numbers may vary considerably from year to year. Cuckoos are heard more often than seen and most records are of calling males, the bubbling call of the female being heard much less. In April and May birds are widespread and numerous in mainland Argyll and Mull, and regular but less widespread on the other large islands, although the far-carrying and persistent call may make them seem more abundant than they really are.

Cuckoos are often attracted to areas where there are concentrations of hairy caterpillars, particularly those of the Drinker Moth but also Fox Moth, Oak Eggar and Northern Eggar. Although such larvae cause irritating rashes on the hand and are shunned by other birds, they form an important part of the Cuckoo's diet.

Telegraph wires and lines of posts crossing rough pasture and moorland are often used by laying females to watch for potential hosts and to track them back to their nests. The task is made easier by the passerines' habit of mobbing Cuckoos, probably because their plumage, size and shape bear striking resemblance to those of the Sparrowhawk (Wyllie 1981, see especially Plate 6). During the host's brief absence from the nest, the Cuckoo pays a visit lasting only a few seconds, during which the single egg is laid. Each female usually lays about nine eggs but up to 25 have been recorded, usually in the late afternoon or evening and at intervals of two days (BWP). The newly hatched Cuckoo systematically heaves other eggs or chicks out of the nest to certain death, then dupes their parents into feeding and rearing it – the stuff of a thousand wildlife films but none the less miraculous for that.

In Argyll, the main host is thought to be the Meadow Pipit, and this fact perhaps dictates where many Cuckoos are reported – on or at the edge of moorland. Wooded glens surrounded by hill pasture, particularly those with old deciduous woods, seem especially favoured. No systematic investigation of other host species has been made locally, but it seems likely that they include Dunnock and Robin, and a Blackbird nest with a Cuckoo egg was found at Cornaigmore on Tiree in June 2000 but was deserted. A Ring Ouzel was seen feeding a young Cuckoo near Loch Melfort at about 150m asl (B&R).

Both Breeding Atlases showed Cuckoos in most of Argyll's 10-km squares, the few empty squares being in southern Kintyre and little-visited areas such as Jura. The species was recorded in 35 of 38 broadleaf woods surveyed in Mid- and North Argyll in summer 1985, when 73 Cuckoos were counted (Averis & Martin 1985). It was found in 7/17 BBS squares in 1995, 9/21 in 1996, 5/16 in 1997, 12/16 in 1998, 9/15 in 1999, 7/12 in 2000 and 1/6 in 2001. It was found in 10/14 Countryside 2000 squares (ABR). In the Taynish CBC, there were three territories in 1996, 1997, and 1998, two in 1999, and a record four in 2000 (*cf.* 1990-2000 average of two). A total of only seven calling males was counted in the Rinns Survey on Islay in 1994, compared with nine at the RSPB's Loch Gruinart Reserve on 15 June 1997. During work for the Second Atlas, the species was not recorded on Tiree and, although up to three calling males occur there each year and large independent juveniles were seen in 1954, 1988, 1993, 1999 and 2004, these possibly fledged elsewhere and, at the time of writing (2006), there have been no confirmed records of successful breeding on Tiree. The species is much commoner on Coll where juveniles are frequently seen being fed by Meadow Pipits and, for example, some twenty calling males were counted in 2005 (J. Bowler pers. comm.).

Few adults are seen or heard after June and most have left on southward migration by late July, so most of the Cuckoos seen here in late summer are juveniles. During the two weeks after leaving the nest the young are fed in the open by their diminutive foster-parents, an unforgettable sight. Sometimes the irresistible super-stimuli of the huge gape and the unusually loud begging calls compel other small birds in the area to help with the feeding! Almost all these young Cuckoos have left by mid-August and, according to B&R, they appear on passage at lighthouses in late August and the first half of September.

In view of this life cycle, it is not surprising that most records occur in April and May when males are calling. Even so, the sharp drop in records after this short season of courtship and egg laying is striking. During 1997-2003, the Argyll Database held grand totals of Cuckoos reported as follows; one in March, 121 in April, 221 in May, 99 in June, 12 in July, 11 in August and one in September. These 466 birds were divided by area as follows: Mid-Argyll 160, Mull 97, Islay 82, Tiree 34, Cowal 26, Colonsay 25, Kintyre 21, North Argyll 14, Coll four and Jura three. However, these figures may reflect reporting frequency rather than true abundance.

Probably because birds become less conspicuous in late summer, dates of last Cuckoos each year are much more scattered than those of first Cuckoos. During 20 years (1983-2003 with no record in 1993), the last Cuckoo of the year was reported in the last half of June in two years, the first half of July in one year, the last half of July in two years, the first half of August in four years, the last half of August in seven years, and the first half of September in four years. The latest of these was one at Dalmally on 15 September 1983. (ABR, Argyll Database). However, there is an earlier record of a Cuckoo "in Argyll" on 7 November 1935 (B&R).

Very few Cuckoos are ringed in north-west Scotland and there are no ringing recoveries involving Argyll. Further afield, much remains unknown about the migration route and wintering area. The few ringing recoveries show that almost all have left Britain by mid-September and suggest a south-easterly route through Italy. There have been no recoveries of British-ringed birds in Iberia or North Africa and only two recoveries altogether in Africa, both in January. A British-ringed chick was recovered in Cameroon, and a Dutch-ringed bird was found in Togo. Cuckoo numbers in the British Isles are in long-term decline for unknown reasons (Migration Atlas).

Clive Craik

Black-billed Cuckoo

Coccyzus erythrophthalmus

Vagrant.

A first-winter bird was found dead by a shepherd near Southend in Kintyre on 8 November 1950 (B&R, SN 63:131). According to the finder, the bird was one of a flock seen on 6 and 7 November! After confirmation of the identification by the British Museum, the skin was preserved at the Kelvingrove Museum. This was the first Scottish and second British record of this Nearctic rarity. There have since been two more records in Scotland, in Shetland in 1953 and sea area Forties in 1989.

Tristan ap Rheinallt

Yellow-billed Cuckoo

Coccyzus americanus

Vagrant.

Although the Yellow-billed Cuckoo has been recorded in Britain and Ireland on many more occasions than its congener the Black-billed Cuckoo, it shares with it the dubious distinction that most records refer to dead or dying birds. Thus, in Argyll, one was found freshly dead near the centre of Colonsay on 6 November 1904 and was sent to the Natural History Museum to be identified (ASNH 1910:184, B&R, Jardine *et al.* 1986). This was the first Scottish record. More than half a century later, the eighth of ten Scottish records to date concerned an individual found dying at Barcaldine in the last week of September 1969 (BB 65:349, SB 7:162).

Tristan ap Rheinallt

Barn Owl

Tyto alba

Scarce breeding species, but probably under-recorded. Occurs on the mainland and some islands, avoiding more mountainous areas. Occasional strays are recorded on islands that hold no breeding birds.

The decline of the Barn Owl as a breeding species in Britain and elsewhere in Europe, especially during the second half of the 20th century, has been well publicised. In Britain, intensification of agriculture has been blamed for a reduction in the rough grassland habitat used for hunting, while organochlorine pesticide poisoning may also have played a part (Second Atlas). The severe winter of 1962/63 has also been blamed for a decline in numbers (Thom).

Early authors had little to say about the status of the Barn Owl in Argyll. It is not mentioned at all in the OSA, while in the NSA it is listed only for the parishes of Ardchattan, Inveraray, and Saddell and Skipness. This suggests that it may not have been widely distributed prior to the middle of the 18th century. Gray knew it from only Islay and Mull, while Graham referred to the occasional "stray specimen" on the latter island. H&B provided little information other than to state that it was common in parts of Argyll, mentioning a

Roy Blewitt

John McAvoy

Barn Owls exploit natural nest sites in hollow trees (left) as readily as they do man-made ones in derelict buildings (right).

specimen collected on Tiree.

B&R alluded to a major decrease in numbers in Scotland between around 1850 and 1910, followed by a considerable increase. However, they implied that numbers in northern and western Scotland, where birds had always been uncommon and local, remained unchanged. Nevertheless, there had been a possible increase on Islay, and perhaps also on Mull, in the early years of the 20th century. Unfortunately, most of their evidence consisted of comments from individuals and may not be representative. In addition, large natural short-term fluctuations render casual estimates of the abundance of this species unreliable (Thom).

As with most species, the First Atlas represented the first attempt to map the distribution of Barn Owls in Argyll. Birds were found to be thinly distributed, with few occupied squares in Cowal and the northern part of the mainland. This reflected the species' general scarcity in the more mountainous areas of Britain, ascribed to severe winter conditions and lack of nest sites. Since Barn Owls may nest in cavities on crags, the former is presumably the more important. Although milder maritime zones were considered favourable, the First Atlas found Barn Owls absent from Tiree, Coll and Colonsay as well as the Outer Hebrides.

As expected for a largely sedentary resident, the Winter Atlas suggested little change between summer and winter, except in south Kintyre where no birds were recorded during the winter surveys. However, the Second Atlas showed a decline within Argyll, with losses from Mull, Jura and parts of the mainland, leaving Kintyre and Islay as the strongholds. While there is no evidence to link this decline with changing agricultural practices, there is an indication that collision with vehicles may be a major cause of death (ABR, Ogilvie

Barn Owl productivity in Argyll, 1993-2003.

Area	Years	Max. no. of pairs in any one year	Max. no. of fledged young in any one year (no. of broods)	Annual mean no. of fledged young per successful nest (range)
Islay	1993-2000	17	49 (16)	2.2-3.2
Cowal	1993-2003	17	36 (10)	1.7-4.2
Kintyre & Knapdale (FE)	1993-2003	21	45 (15)	2.0-3.0
Kintyre (non-FE)	1998-2002	22	41 (14)	2.4-3.7
Argyll	1999-2003	59	127 (48)	2.3-3.1

All data: ABR.

Barn Owls occur at low densities over much of Argyll, but more are probably seen dead on the road than alive on the wing. *Margaret Staley*

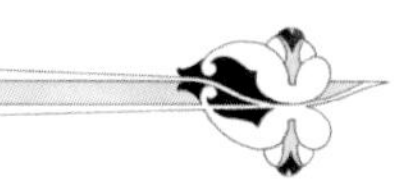

1992b) in Argyll as in Britain generally.

The Second Atlas probably painted an unduly pessimistic picture of the status of the Barn Owl in Argyll. Monitoring in more recent years, linked partly to provision of nest boxes, suggests that breeding was under-recorded, at least in Cowal and Mid-Argyll. Barn Owls also seem to be widespread on Mull, where some 20 pairs were thought to be present in 2002, although the Second Atlas shows only one occupied 10-km square. Birds have also been recorded recently from Jura, and Barn Owls are known to have bred on Gigha.

Survey work on Islay began in 1987, and the results of the first five years were presented by Ogilvie (1992b), who recorded 18 different breeding sites, all in derelict buildings. Complete coverage of the island was not achieved, and no attempt was made to search for nests other than in buildings, although the importance of cliffs and sea caves as breeding habitats has long been recognised (e.g. B&R). Most of the nesting sites identified in Cowal during 1996-98 were in natural rock crevices, perhaps formerly overlooked. Holmes (1986) found that the majority of nest sites discovered on mainland Argyll during 1983-85 were in old, disused farm buildings, steadings and hollows in trees. Similarly, some 75% of nests found on non-forestry land in Kintyre during 1995-98 were in buildings.

In fact, the list of sites recorded in Argyll includes sea caves, sea and inland cliffs, hollows in trees, holes and crevices among rocks, hollows under tree roots, and even the underside of the bridge linking the island of Seil to the mainland (B&R, Elliott 1989, Holmes 1986). In recent years, birds have made extensive use of nest boxes and barrels, particularly in forestry plantations, which represent valuable new habitat for Scottish Barn Owls.

During 1983-85, farmland interspersed with broad-leaved woodland was identified as the main Barn Owl habitat in mainland Argyll (Holmes 1986). On Islay, all but one of the breeding sites were within or on the edge of farmland, mostly rough pasture, and six were within or less than one km from young forestry plantations. The proportion of sites occupied by breeding pairs varied between 38 and 60% in different years. The number of fledged young per successful pair varied less, between 3.0 and 3.7. Some nests failed and the minimum number of fledged young in any one year varied between 13 and 33 (Ogilvie 1992b), showing the short-term fluctuations in productivity typical of this species.

More recently, monitoring has been carried out on Islay and in Cowal, Kintyre and Knapdale, some of it as part of a Forest Enterprise (FE) nest box scheme, as well as on non-FE land in Kintyre, where most nests are in buildings as on Islay. Comparisons among years and sites are difficult because of differences in methods; nevertheless, the picture is one of considerable year-to-year variation, as found by Ogilvie.

The usual measure of breeding success in these schemes, the mean number of fledged young per successful nest, varied between 2.3 and 3.1 during 1999-2003 (Table). Factors invoked to explain poor breeding success in some years include low vole numbers and poor weather during the breeding season.

Adult Barn Owls are largely sedentary, but young birds disperse within the first few months of life, though there is no directional pattern to this dispersal in Britain (Migration Atlas). Most recoveries involving Argyll are within 85 km of the ringing site, but chicks ringed in Cowal, Kintyre and Islay have been recovered in Dumfries & Galloway, Fife and Lothian respectively, involving displacements of 171 to 216 km. Within Argyll, wandering birds have occurred in recent years on Colonsay in 1988 (ABR 5:24) and on Sanda in 1989 (ABR 6:42). These were the first records for the islands concerned. More recently, Coll recorded its first Barn Owl in 2002 (ABR 19:94), with subsequent sightings of one or possibly two birds in the winters of 2003/04 and 2004/05 (J. Bowler pers. comm.). On Tiree, the first bird since 1892 was seen in October and November 2004 (J. Bowler pers. comm.).

Tristan ap Rheinallt

Eurasian Scops Owl

Otus scops

Vagrant.

One was found dead on a doorstep in Scarinish on Tiree on 6 April 1997, having apparently been killed by a cat. The specimen is preserved in the National Museum of Scotland (BB 91:496, ABR 14:67). This is the only record of this Continental species in Argyll. Most Scottish records come from the Northern Isles, but a bird was found long dead on Barra in June 1980 and others have occurred in western Scotland in Dumfries & Galloway and the Clyde region.

Tristan ap Rheinallt

Snowy Owl

Bubo scandiacus

Vagrant; mostly old records.

In the 19th century, this northern breeder seems to have been a reasonably regular winter visitor to Scotland (B&R). It subsequently became much rarer, but then bred on Fetlar between 1967 and 1975. Currently there are multiple records annually, although the number of individual birds involved is likely to be small.

Despite several recent records from the Outer Hebrides, the Snowy Owl was not reliably recorded in Argyll between 1900 and 2004. Some of the old records are vague and

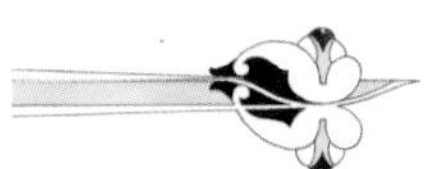

Tawny Owls are mainly nocturnal hunters, but will hunt during the day when they have large chicks. *Rob Jordan*

undated, but four are considered acceptable:

(1) One was trapped "on the top of Sanaig rocks" on Islay in April 1870 by James Brown, gamekeeper to E. Crawshay of Newcastle-upon-Tyne, into whose collection it appears to have passed (H&B). There is confusion over the date, since Booth (1975) quotes "W.R.P." (full name not given) in The Field of 1 June 1872 as giving a date of 15 April 1872.

(2) A young male was obtained on Tiree in November 1873 and the specimen seen by Harvie-Brown. A brief description is given by H&B.

(3) One was seen for two or three days at Inveraray in September 1891 by the Duke of Argyll and others, and described as being "as big as a white heron" (H&B, ASNH 1892:71).

(4) One was seen on Coll during the winter of 1891-92 (Irby 1899, p. 210, Boyd 1958).

In 2005, a large and quite heavily marked individual, thought to be an immature female, spent much of 29 January on the grass strip at Tiree Airport. It was not seen subsequently (BB100: 56).

[Records that cannot be dated even approximately and are therefore not considered acceptable include: unspecified record(s) from Mull (Gray, B&R); one or more birds on Iona prior to 1867 (Gray, Graham, H&B), one seen many years before 1891 in Glen Aray (H&B), and one in Kintyre some time before the First World War (Gibson & McWilliam 1959).]

Tristan ap Rheinallt

Tawny Owl

Strix aluco

A widespread resident of woodlands on the mainland and most islands.

This is the most abundant owl in Argyll, and although rarely seen, its territorial hooting in spring and autumn will be familiar to most people. The Tawny Owl is predominantly a woodland bird, but also occurs in a range of semi-open habitats, sometimes with few trees. It is a sedentary, nocturnal predator with a life history shaped by annual variations in the abundance of its rodent prey.

Tawny Owls probably reached their lowest numbers in Argyll in the first half of the 19th century as a result of deforestation, which started many centuries before. They will have benefited from the establishment of plantations on some large estates from the early-mid 19th century, but at the same time will have suffered from the Victorian's relish of removing anything with a hooked beak! The 20th century saw a general increase in numbers and range, mainly due to extensive afforestation since the 1920s, albeit mainly with coniferous species. The recovery was aided by a reduction in persecution as gamekeeper numbers declined, and by legislation that gave them full protection.

Gray noted it was scarce in Scotland around 1840, but had increased by 1870. He provided the first reliable information about its occurrence in Argyll having met with it frequently on the mainland, and also on Mull and Islay. H&B noted it was not rare on Mull and that it occurred on Jura. They said it was "common in all suitable places of the mainland from north to south" and that it frequented "portions of wooded nooks, wood-clad ravines, or old forest patches in the long sea-lochs and their shores and islands".

B&R made no specific mention of its presence on mainland Argyll, but noted there was evidence of an increase in Scotland during the last fifty years. They also mentioned a lack of breeding records for Islay, although they heard it calling at Bridgend in September 1937. But, it is likely to have bred on Islay before this date (Gray). B&R said it was common in the woods on Mull in 1929 and 1948, in agreement with earlier statements in H&B. Thom added little about its distribution in Argyll, but mentioned that it bred in a least three 10-km squares on Islay.

Recent information shows that Tawny Owls are widely distributed on mainland Argyll (First & Second Atlases, ABRs, Argyll Database). They are absent from the eastern mountains of North Argyll, Mid-Argyll and Cowal, but even here they occur in the lower glens, sometimes with few trees. They are most abundant in the forests of western Cowal, Mid-Argyll and Kintyre, reaching their highest density in mature woodland on the richest soils. Mull is the only island where they are widespread in suitable habitat (Second Atlas). On Islay, up to 20 pairs are present in larger woodlands, which were established around various 'big houses' from the 1850s onwards (M.A. Ogilvie & G. Yates pers. comm.). They breed in mature woodlands along the east coast of Jura (Second Atlas) and also on some of the smaller inshore islands such as Scarba and Gigha. They are absent from Tiree, Coll and Colonsay, probably due to the distance to existing populations, a shortage of nest sites and a lack of food. Two of the most important prey species (Bank Vole and Field Vole) are absent from all three islands (Corbet & Harris 1991).

When suitable habitat is available, food-supply is the main factor regulating the distribution and abundance of Tawny Owls, which are highly specialised predators of small rodents (Southern 1970, Petty 1992). Wood Mice and Bank Voles are often their main prey in woodland (Southern & Lowe 1982), but when grassland patches occur within territories, Field Voles often become more important (Petty 1999). The abundance of these three rodent species is crucial for Tawny Owls during autumn, winter and early spring, when ground vegetation is at its shortest and other prey are scarce. All three exhibit large annual variations in abundance and this affects the owls' breeding performance. Few pairs even produce eggs when rodents are scarce (Southern 1970, Petty 1992). In years when prey are plentiful, most pairs lay and many young are reared. Later in spring and throughout the summer, a wider range of alternative prey is taken, including fledgling birds, the young of larger mammals (particularly Rabbits), Common Frogs and even earthworms and other invertebrates (Galeotti 2001, Petty 1992, 1999).

A lack of nest sites is unlikely to be a significant factor limiting numbers and distribution of Tawny Owls (Petty *et al.* 1994). Although large dry tree cavities are preferred, a wide variety of alternative nest sites is used, including disused stick nests of other species and cavities in buildings. They even nest on the ground, particularly in conifer forests, but also in other habitats that lack suitable cavities (Yates 2005). In the more rugged parts of Argyll, cavities in crags and well-vegetated crag ledges are likely to provide one of the main alternative nest sites.

The only detailed study in Argyll was undertaken in the conifer forests of Cowal (Petty 1992). Nest boxes were used to monitor the population dynamics of 20-50 pairs annually,

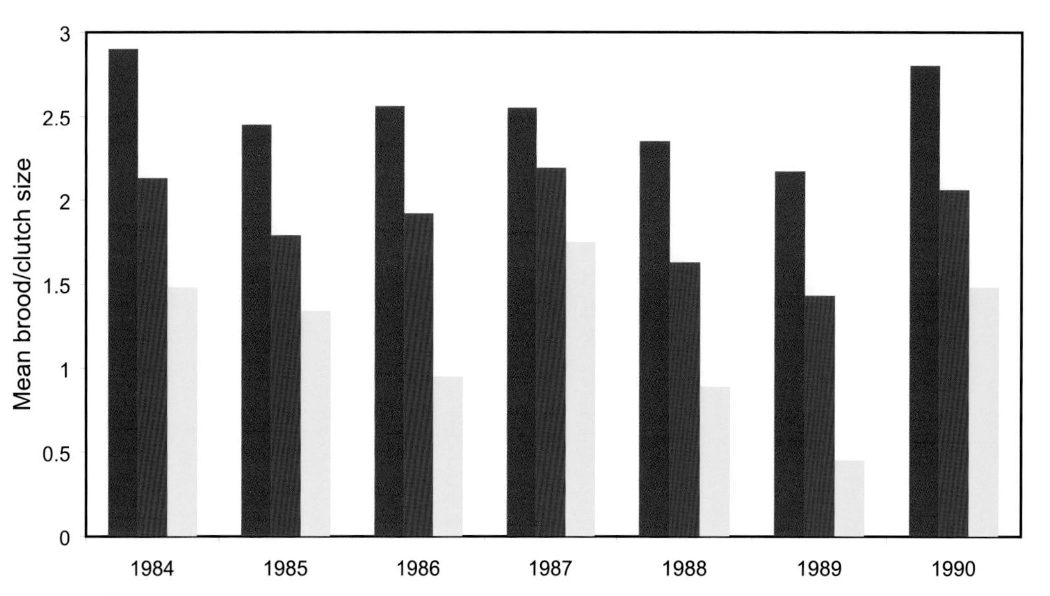

Annual variation in breeding performance of Tawny Owls in Cowal.

which were compared with a population in a similar habitat in Northumberland. Overall, breeding performance among years was less variable in Cowal than Northumberland, probably because Field Vole numbers varied less, and more Bank Voles and Wood Mice were available in Cowal. Even so, breeding performance still varied among years in Cowal, with a four-fold variation in the number of chicks produced per occupied territory (Petty & Lambin 2004) (Figure).

Currently, there is no estimate of the breeding population in Argyll. This would be possible to estimate if density figures were available for the range of habitats occupied by Tawny Owls. In the Cowal study, mean territory size was estimated at 69.8 ha (n=58), but this was the only area with such data available (Petty 1992).

A comparison between the First and Second Atlases suggests that Tawny Owls have slightly declined in the intervening years in Scotland, but probably not in Argyll. However, they are not easily recorded during normal atlas fieldwork because of their nocturnal habits. Thus any inference about population trends from atlas data is likely to be unreliable. Nevertheless, the range of Tawny Owls in Argyll has undoubtedly increased due to the establishment of new forest during the 20th century, and this will continue as existing forests mature. Conifer forests are usually colonised once they become fragmented by clear cutting, because these open patches within the forest are the richest habitats for small mammals, particularly Field Voles (Petty & Thomas 2003). The recent policy of encouraging the establishment of new, and conservation of existing, native woodlands will also be of long-term benefit to Tawny Owls.

A potential threat to Tawny Owls comes from the impoverishment of small mammal habitats that occurs once domestic animals and deer exceed certain densities (Flowerdew & Ellwood 2001, BS3). The main rodent prey species of Tawny Owls are dependent on the quality of ground vegetation in both woodland and open areas. Thus moves towards increasing the density of domestic stock, both on hill ground and in woodlands, together with rising numbers of Roe Deer, Red Deer and Sika Deer in Argyll must be viewed with concern. Northern Goshawks pose another potential hazard, as they are known to kill Tawny Owls (Petty *et al.* 2003). Goshawks are currently expanding their range in Scotland, but have not yet bred in Argyll (Petty 2007).

Tawny Owls are highly sedentary, and once established on a territory, often remain there for life (Petty 1992). Tawny Owls can breed as yearlings, but most breed for the first time at 2-4 years of age (Petty 1992). Few ringed birds have been recovered in Argyll (n=16). Only one (6%) was recovered more than 100km from the ringing location. However, these data should be treated with caution because many recoveries are of birds killed on roads or railway lines, and these individuals can be carried a considerable distance by whatever vehicle kills them (S.J Petty, unpubl. data). This appears to be a problem with Argyll recoveries too, as the mean distance between ringing and recovery point for eight birds found dead on roads and railway lines was 41km, in contrast to just 14km for eight birds dying from other causes.

Tawny Owls are sometimes recorded on islands where they do not breed, but such examples are rare. During 1988-91, there were reports of a bird on Colonsay. It is unclear whether this involved more than one individual, but there have been no subsequent records (D.C. Jardine pers. comm.). More recently, one bird was calling on Carnan Mor, Tiree, during 18-22 July 2004 (J. Bowler pers. comm.). Moreover, no birds ringed on the mainland have been recovered on any Argyll island. Such information helps to emphasise the Tawny Owl's sedentary nature.

Some Tawny Owls can live to a considerable age. In the Glenbranter study, the oldest recorded bird was 18 years old. This had been ringed as a nestling near Glenbranter village in 1984 and was found dead in Glendaruel (Cowal) in December 2002.

Steve J. Petty

Long-eared Owl

Asio otus

Scarce, little-known breeding species; numbers appear to fluctuate from year to year.

The status of the Long-eared Owl is poorly known, probably more so than any other bird in Argyll, due largely to its nocturnal habits. It hunts at night over open habitats for rodents, particularly Field Voles (Village 1981). It breeds in the disused nests of other species, usually in shelter belts or along the edge of more extensive forests, and occasionally on the ground.

Historic records of the Long-eared Owl in Argyll suggest it may have been more common in the past, but it is not clear whether the apparent decline reflects a reduction in the reporting rate of this secretive bird. H&B noted that, on the larger islands, the Long-eared Owl was common wherever there was sufficient woodland for nesting (e.g. on Jura). Gray noted that it bred in limited numbers on Mull, and was also well known in mainland woods.

The apparent decline since the 19th century may be real because the increase in woodland area in Argyll has led to loss of extensive open foraging habitats, which are essential for Long-eared Owls; whereas the Tawny Owl has benefited from reforestation. However, there is little evidence to suggest that the decline in Long-eared Owls is due to direct competition from Tawny Owls, although this is often suggested in the literature.

In recent times, breeding was reported from one 10-km square, probable breeding from another square and possible breeding from five squares during the First Atlas (1968-72). A little later in Mid-Argyll, Rainier (1983) reported breeding

Long-eared Owls can forage successfully over newly-planted coniferous woods and may, as here, use recently felled areas for nesting (nest in stump to left in main photo). *All photos: Steve Petty*

at West Loch Tarbert Woods in 1975, 1976 and possibly later, and probably breeding at Stonefield in 1977 and Achnamara in 1976 and 1982. There was an apparent increase by the time of the Second Atlas (1988-91) when breeding was recorded in eight 10-km squares and it was present in a further seven. It is not known whether this increase was real or a consequence of change in observer effort. However, the 1970s and 1980s saw much land reforested, and during the first few years after tree planting, rodents abound. Elsewhere in Scotland, Long-eared Owls have settled in these ephemeral habitats (Village 1981, 1992) and they have probably done so in Argyll. Petty (1985) found a newly fledged brood in a recently afforested area of Kintyre during 23-26 May 1983, indicating that eggs had been laid in mid-March.

During the period of the ABR (1980-2003) it was reported breeding in ten different locations (on Mull, Colonsay, Gigha, Danna and at Killellan Lodge, Otter Ferry, Black Mount Estate and Kilmichael Glen) and was reported from a further 27 sites. It may be that the Long-eared Owl is more common in Argyll than the available data suggest.

The discovery of breeding Long-eared Owls on Colonsay in 1984 led to further research. During the next 19 years, birds were present in at least 14 years; successful breeding was proven in 12 years and suspected breeding in one year. Broods

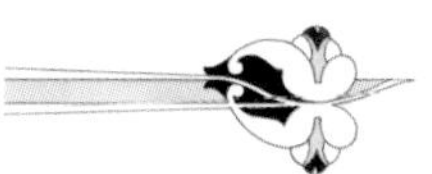

have been found by listening for the distinctive begging calls of fledglings during late evenings in June. In three years, two broods were found each year. The mean minimum fledged brood size for ten broods, where the number of young could be counted, was 2.5.

On Colonsay, a full survey has not been conducted but broods have been found in five different locations. Some of the more remote woodlands have not been checked, but moulted feathers have been found there, suggesting that breeding may be more widespread. Consistent fieldwork over the years suggests there may be 5-6 pairs breeding on the island. While it is not possible to extrapolate from this study, it again indicates that Long-eared Owls may be more common in Argyll as a whole than current information suggests.

Collection of pellets from around nest sites on Colonsay indicated they were feeding on Wood Mice (voles are absent from Colonsay), young Common Rats, birds (possible Wheatears and Willow Warblers) and insects (D.C. Jardine unpubl. data). On the mainland, Field Voles are likely to be the most important food.

Winter roosts on Coll (early spring 1989) and regularly at Aros Moss, Kintyre, suggest there may be immigration of Long-eared Owls into Argyll in autumn and winter from Scandinavia, as found in other parts of Scotland, but there are no ringing recoveries to support this (Migration Atlas).

In view of the lack of information about Long-eared Owls in Argyll, further work should be considered a priority.

David Jardine

Short-eared Owl

Asio flammeus

Widespread breeder, with numbers fluctuating widely from year to year. Also seen on migration and in winter.

The Short-eared Owl has apparently been widespread in Argyll since at least the late 19th century. Although it earns few mentions in the Statistical Accounts, both Gray and H&B described Short-eared Owls as occurring on Mull and Islay as well as generally on the mainland. Gray regarded the species as resident, but on Tiree it was apparently only a transient visitor (H&B). It does not seem to have been common everywhere, since Jardine *et al.* (1986) could only find a single record for Colonsay. Indeed, B&R were sceptical about some of the earlier claims, pointing out how few were the breeding records from the Inner Hebrides. They described the species as nesting sparingly and often sporadically on the Scottish mainland, with Argyll among the most favoured counties.

Some of the discrepancies among these authors' views may be due to the fact that the Short-eared Owl's main prey, the Field Vole, fluctuates widely in abundance from year to year. As a result, a particular area may have good numbers of breeding owls one year and none the next. Peaks in the vole population can be accompanied by high breeding densities and high success rates of Short-eared Owls, as in Argyll in 1936 (B&R).

Short-eared Owls hunt by day over moors, rough grassland and young forestry plantations. *Philip Kirkham*

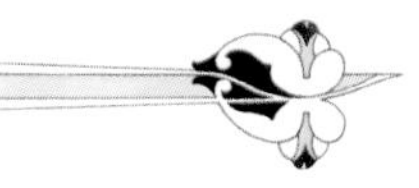

Work for the First Atlas showed that the species occurred more or less throughout Argyll, but with large gaps in distribution in parts of the mainland and no records from Colonsay or Tiree. In the Second Atlas the picture was rather different, with Mull, Islay and the southern mainland having birds in almost every 10-km square, whilst much of the northern mainland was unoccupied. Successful breeding was recorded on Tiree for the first time in 1989 (ABR 6:43), and birds were recorded on Coll in both Atlases, but there were again no records from Colonsay. Vole populations were apparently high in some parts of Argyll in both 1988 and 1989, with correspondingly high densities of breeding Short-eared Owls. On Mull in 1988, there were at least 13 territories and another 12 records of hunting birds during the breeding season; and on Islay, at least seven fledged broods were seen in a 10 km^2 area of young forestry (ABR 5:25). In 1989, about 20 pairs were present on the Rinns of Islay, though numbers breeding on Mull were low (ABR 6:43). Although these two years may have been unrepresentative, at least some of the change between the two Atlas periods is likely to be related to new forestry plantations, which encouraged the spread of this species in areas such as Mull (ABR 3:42) and the Rinns of Islay. Nevertheless, the latter location may hold only two or three breeding pairs in a poor year. Fluctuating densities have also been recorded recently in Cowal, where six breeding pairs were located in 1998, none in 1999, seven or eight in 2000, and five in 2001 (ABR). In June 2006 a pair with nest and three young were found on Colonsay, the first known breeding on the island (Argyll Database).

B&R regarded the Short-eared Owl as a passage migrant and winter visitor to every part of Scotland, its numbers fluctuating from year to year as in the breeding season. They singled out Islay and Tiree as two islands where the species was plentiful outside the nesting period. In the early years of the 20th century, birds apparently arrived on Islay in considerable numbers in late October (Elliott 1989). Nowadays, Mull seems to be the main stronghold of this species in Argyll in the winter months, with emigration from the island in spring prior to some breeding seasons such as 1986 (ABR 4:30) and 1989 (ABR 6:43). About 20 birds were flushed from a roost near Ardnacross on Mull on 11 January 1981 (ABR 1:57), and several other winter roosts were discovered in the early 1980s (ABR 3:42). In Kintyre, a regular winter roost at Aros Moss held up to eight birds in early 1989 (ABR 6:43). Nearby, migrants are not infrequently recorded during August to October at Campbeltown Airport, where up to ten were present in autumn 1996 (ABR 13:68) and 12 in 1997 (ABR 14:68).

Elsewhere, migrants and winter visitors do not seem numerous, and most sightings concern single birds at scattered locations on the mainland or islands, although nine were recorded at the north end of Jura on 29 February 1992 (ABR 9:40). On the mainland, there seems to be a concentration of records along the western fringes (Winter Atlas). Overall, there seems to have been a decline during the 20th century, although it is difficult to explain this since the origin of birds migrating through or wintering in Argyll is unknown.

Tristan ap Rheinallt

European Nightjar

Caprimulgus europaeus

Once widespread, but breeding confined to Kintyre and Cowal in recent years. Now possibly extinct. Passage migrants have been recorded on occasion.

The decline of the Nightjar, one of Scotland's most charismatic breeding birds, is well documented. Gray described it as a common bird in almost every mainland Scottish county, occurring also in the Inner Hebrides. B&R described it as common where there was much suitable habitat, although local overall but apparently still breeding in almost every mainland county. By 1968-72, however, there had been a major range contraction, and the situation was even worse in 1988-91, with very few birds outside Dumfries & Galloway (First and Second Atlases). In 1999, only six potentially breeding males were recorded in the whole of Scotland (SBR 1999:82). The main cause was thought to be climatic change, habitat loss not being as important in Scotland as elsewhere in Britain (Gribble 1983).

The situation in Argyll mirrors this overall decline. Perhaps surprisingly, there was no mention of the Nightjar in OSA, and the only mention in NSA referred to its occurrence in Ardchattan and in Kintyre, where it was abundant in the east but apparently absent from the west. Nevertheless, Gray described it as not uncommon in Islay, Iona and Mull as well as on the mainland. H&B, whilst implicitly disputing this statement as far as Iona was concerned, described the Nightjar as plentiful on the mainland, singling out Ledaig for special mention. They also stated that it occurred on Mull, where Graham described it as an uncommon breeder, and on "wooded isles" such as Jura. At one time, therefore, the Nightjar was clearly widespread in Argyll, perhaps absent only from Tiree and Coll, though recorded as a straggler on the latter island (Irby 1899). It bred on Colonsay until at least 1947 (Jardine *et al.* 1986).

Sadly, the situation is now very different. The First Atlas showed confirmed breeding only in two 10-km squares adjacent to West Loch Tarbert, with possible or probable breeding in a few other squares on the mainland in Kintyre and to the north of Lochgilphead, as well as on Mull and Jura. In a national survey in 1981, birds were found at only two sites, both in the south of the area, though ABR quotes records from three sites that year: Achnamara, Lochgilphead and Furnace (ABR 1:58). The Second Atlas produced a similar picture, with Nightjars in one 10-km square in Cowal – where breeding was confirmed – and two near West Loch

Tarbert. Within the Second Atlas period, five churring males were recorded at four sites in 1989 (SBR 1989:31), and birds were recorded from four sites in 1990 (SBR 1990:43). During the mid-1970s, birds were also heard in the Machrihanish area, where they had not been recorded in the 1968-1972 Atlas (SB 9:215 and 10:102). On Colonsay, birds were heard churring into the early 1980s (Jardine *et al.* 1986). On Islay, one was found dead in May 1970, and single males were heard in July 1973 and June 1974 (Elliott 1989). Finally, one was near Croig on Mull on 16 May 1985 (ABR 3:42, SB 14:113). It seems likely that at least some of these, e.g. the bird on Mull, were migrants on their way to breed elsewhere.

The Second Atlas was immediately followed by a Nightjar survey in 1992. Of 22 sites checked in Argyll, only four were occupied (SBR 1992:42). In 1993, four birds were recorded at two sites in Cowal (SBR 1993:40). There were no further records until 2000, when a bird was heard and seen near Tarbert in Kintyre on 2 May. One was reported from the same area the following year, and also from a site on Mull in 2001 and 2002. All these occurred in early or mid-May but there was no evidence of presence later in the season, suggesting that the birds may have been on migration. Birds were churring at two sites in the Dalmally area on the evening of 1 June 2005, and one was heard on the evenings of 22 and 23 May 2006 at a site on the Ross of Mull. One was heard on 25 May and heard and seen on 26 May 2006 at a site in the east of Mull.

Autumn migrants are now very unusual in Scotland. The only Argyll record involves a bird seen at Dervaig on Mull on 13 September 1988 (ABR 5:25).

[No details are available to support the record of a Nightjar at Loch na Keal on Mull on 15 January 1974, seen by A. E. Sutcliffe (SB 8:445). It was not known to the local recorder at the time (M. Gregory, pers. comm.). Although Thom stated that this sighting constituted the first acceptable British winter record of this species, it seems best to regard it as unconfirmed.]

Tristan ap Rheinallt

Across Scotland, the Nightjar declined dramatically as a breeding bird during the second half of the 20th century. *Philip Snow*

Alpine Swift

Apus melba

Vagrant.

One was observed for 20 minutes at Largybaan in south-west Kintyre on 15 April 1993 (BB 87:539) (not 14 April as reported in ABR 10:62 and SBR 1993:40). The following year, one was seen on Lunga in the Treshnish Isles on 11 July (BB 88:526). This southern European species has been recorded at scattered locations all over Scotland, where it is a less-than-annual visitor.

Tristan ap Rheinallt

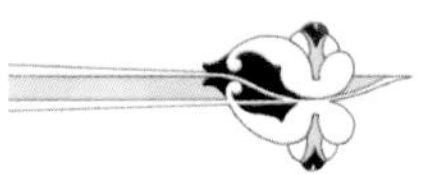

Common Swift

Apus apus

A summer visitor, breeding locally on the mainland. Wandering birds and passage migrants may occur anywhere.

According to old authorities, Swifts have never been common in Argyll. In the late 19th century H&B described it as "not very abundant nor generally spread over our area". The only breeding record mentioned by H&B was in Barcaldine Church tower and the old castle. They also quote Graham as saying a pair bred in the ruined tower of Iona Cathedral in 1867.

In the mid-20th century B&R described the species as "not very abundant in Argyll". One of their correspondents reported it being very abundant in Oban, while another once found a nest on Islay. Eight nests were found at Lochgoilhead

Colonies of Swifts can be found in a few towns in Argyll, as here in Dunoon. *Margaret Staley*

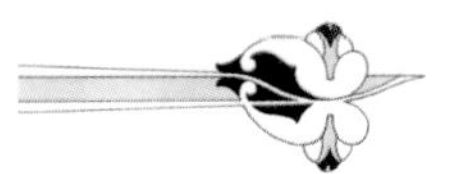

in 1922 (SN 1923:65-84, 101-122).

By the time of the First Atlas, Swifts were recorded as probably or definitely breeding in the 10-km squares covering Campbeltown, Dunoon, Inveraray, Kilmichael Glassary, Oban and Lochawe Village. During the 1980s they were noted breeding at all these localities as well as at Connel and an unspecified site in North Argyll, but surprisingly, not in Dunoon (ABR). Populations were small and in the range 8–10 pairs. There was also an interesting record of six pairs breeding on the sea cliffs at the Mull of Kintyre in 1981 (ABR). Evidence of possible breeding elsewhere on the mainland and islands almost certainly relates to the usual wandering birds in summer.

The breeding range in the Second Atlas indicated some contraction since the First Atlas. Breeding was confirmed in the Connel area, but there were no records for Kilmichael Glassary, and they were only recorded as 'seen' in the squares covering Dunoon, Lochawe and Oban. Elsewhere, there was a wide scattering of sightings with no evidence of breeding. During 1992–2006 there have been regular reports of probable breeding in small numbers at Campbeltown, Lochgilphead, Oban and in the Dunoon area. A pair was present at Inveraray during the breeding season of 2000, at least two pairs bred at Glassary primary school, Kilmichael Glassary in 2006, and there have been reports of odd pairs breeding at Taynuilt and Achnacloich (ABR, Argyll Database).

The historical evidence implies that the Swift has always been a relatively scarce breeding species in Argyll. The population is probably limited by the cool, wet climate which reduces the time that can be spent foraging and the availability of insect prey on which Swifts are totally dependent (Second Atlas). A lack of suitable nest sites may also be a factor. Most of the recent known breeding colonies have been in church towers.

During summer, and away from breeding colonies, there are regular reports of individuals or small groups from all areas of Argyll, including the remotest island groups. Occasionally much larger flocks have been noted, including 73 at Port Wemyss on 9 July 1995 and 157 at Machrihanish on 26 June 2001, prior to a thunderstorm. An unprecedented influx took place on 12 August 2004 when counts included at least 521 at various localities on Tiree, 441 flying north-north-east in 5h at Machrihanish and a minimum of 130 at Loch Gruinart, Islay. Smaller numbers were reported at Otter Ferry, Cowal and on Oronsay (Argyll Database). These flocks were too large to be local breeders and must have involved birds which had travelled a considerable distance. Swifts are known to travel perhaps as far as 2,000km in search of airborne insects during bad weather (Migration Atlas).

In the past 20 years, most first arrivals have been during 5–12 May. However, in three years birds were recorded during April and, in 1995, five were found on Islay on the exceptionally early date of 10 April. Most birds have departed by mid-August, but presumed migrants are regularly recorded during September, with a few stragglers into October. The latest dates recently recorded were of a single bird at The Mull of Oa on 23 October 2001 and one watched for half an hour at Colintraive, Cowal, on 3 November 2005. There is also an old record of one at Skerryvore on 17 November 1893 (Anderson 1894).

Paul Daw

Common Kingfisher

Alcedo atthis

Regularly recorded, mostly from a few mainland locations. Breeding has been proven only in Kintyre but is likely to occur elsewhere.

Although this species was recorded in the Statistical Accounts as occurring in Inveraray and Kilfinan, Harvie-Brown had reservations about some of the older records because the name "king's fisher" was also applied to the Dipper (Harvie-Brown papers, NMS). This confusion could be responsible for the statement in Gray that the Kingfisher was found in "almost every stream" throughout western Scotland south of Sutherland. Nevertheless, H&B reported occurrences in Benderloch, Inveraray and Jura. The only dated record involved two birds seen in the grounds of Inveraray Castle in September 1890. Shortly after publication of H&B, there were sightings of single birds on Skervuile Lighthouse, off the east coast of Jura, on 1 May 1892 (ASNH 1893:157), and on Mull in November 1893 (ASNH 1894:54) and September 1894 (ASNH 1894:257). In 1903, there were regular sightings from Carradale and one was seen in West Loch Tarbert (ASNH 1904:126). One was shot on Coll on 22 July 1903 (ASNH 1903:244, Boyd 1958).

The unmistakable Kingfisher can be seen at a very few locations in Argyll. *Roy Blewitt*

According to B&R, Islay was the only place in Argyll

Date	Location	Comment	Reference
3 Jun 1981	Knocklearoch (Islay)	Two birds	BB 75:513
Late Jun/Jul 1986	Lochgoilhead		BB 80:549
2 Jul 1993	Near Lochdon (Mull)		SBR 1993:40, ABR 11:69
15 May 1995	Fidden (Mull)		SBR 1995:46
9 to 11 Jun 1998	Glengorm (Mull)		SBR 1999:83, ABR 16:79
11 Jun 1998	Tynacoille (Islay)	Possibly the same as the Mull bird	SBR 1998:72, ABR 15:74

Records of European Bee-eaters in Argyll from 1980 to the end of 2006.

where the Kingfisher bred. Meiklejohn & Stanford (1954) found no evidence of recent breeding, but quoted recent Islay records from the Laggan, the Sorn and Ballygrant Loch. However, the First Atlas featured no records from Islay, or indeed anywhere else in Argyll. Nevertheless, Booth (1975) stated that there were records of single Kingfishers on Islay "in most months from 1969 to November 1972". Analysing 24 records from the 20th century, Elliott (1989) found no firm evidence that breeding had ever occurred on Islay. Instead, he attributed the records, which were distributed fairly evenly throughout the year, to "occasional exploration by birds dispersing from points south". However, it seems equally if not more likely that the species was once a resident, as Thom concluded.

B&R commented that many records from the north and west of Scotland appeared to be associated with post-breeding dispersal and they cited records from Coll and Mull as well as mainland Argyll. Then, as now, most Kingfishers seen in Argyll were in autumn and winter. Since the First Atlas, however, there has been a large increase in records at all times of year. The Second Atlas produced records from no fewer than six mainland locations, although breeding was not proven, and this reflected a general consolidation and northward extension of range in Scotland. Not until 1993, however, was breeding in Argyll finally proven, when a pair reared young at Carradale in Kintyre; this success was repeated the following year (ABR 11:69).

Kingfishers are now regularly recorded in several other areas of mainland Argyll, most notably Loch Etive, Holy Loch, south Kintyre and the area around Loch Crinan and the head of Loch Sween. Interestingly, some of these locations have been frequented intermittently for decades (e.g. SB 1:339). In the latter half of 2003, there was a flurry of records from various parts of the mainland, including Airds Bay, Loch Awe, Lochgilphead (where two, possibly three, birds were present in late September), Inveraray and Holy Loch (Argyll Database).

On the islands, Kingfishers continue to be reported from Islay, though rather sporadically. There have been several records from Mull, most recently in 2005-2006. It is possible that birds breed at or near some of these locations, although both adults and juveniles are known to move long distances on occasion (Migration Atlas).

Tristan ap Rheinallt

European Bee-eater

Merops apiaster

Vagrant.

Like several other species breeding in southern Europe, the Bee-eater occurs occasionally in Britain in late spring and summer, with rather fewer autumn records. Nesting is known to have occurred on a few occasions. Despite the species' southern distribution, most Scottish records come from Orkney and Shetland. Elsewhere in the country, it is very rare, with only 19 records in the 22-year period 1980 to 2001 (although one of these records involved seven birds). Almost one-third of these records come from Argyll (Table).

The spread of dates, from mid-May to early July, is typical. This is one rarity that is likely to turn up during the "lull" between the spring and autumn migration periods.

[A record of one at Portnahaven on Islay on 3 July 1985 (ABR 3:42, Elliott 1989, Ogilvie 1992c) was not submitted to BBRC at the time, and the details that could be gathered ten years later were insufficient to ensure acceptance (ABR 12:78).]

Tristan ap Rheinallt

European Roller

Coracias garrulus

Vagrant.

This declining breeder of southern and eastern Europe was seen more often in Britain in the past than today. B&R provided a long list of Scottish counties in which it had been recorded, mostly in June, September and October. Amongst the records they quoted was one of a bird that spent more than a week at Inveraray in February 1888. Although this date matches the one given by H&B, it is incorrect.

A letter sent to Harvie-Brown by the Duke of Argyll, dated 2 March 1888, begins: "The Roller was first seen by me here on Oct. 3 /87 in the wild ground of the Deer Park." The remainder of the letter, minus this first sentence, is quoted almost in its entirety by H&B. A postscript to another letter (date uncertain) reads: "I think I sent a notice to the Scottish

Date	Locality	Comment	Reference
10 Sep 1927	Achaforse High Wood (Mull)	Shot and presented to the Royal Scottish Museum	SN 1930:92, B&R
29 Sep 1968	Near Portnahaven (Islay)	Immature	BB 62:475, SB 5:391
15 Oct 1973	Loch Eck	Immature	BB 67:330
29 Sep - 12 Oct 1983	Sanaig and Loch Gorm (Islay)	Adult; first date 25 Sep according to Elliott (1989)	BB 77:540
20 May 1992	Gott Bay (Tiree)	Apparently present for an extended period	BB 86:500, ABR 10:62

Records of Rollers in Argyll from 1927 to the end of 2006.

Naturalist, of the occurrence of a Roller here in Oct 1887... I hear that another example of the same species occurred in 1888 – and was shot by Maclaine of Lochbuie, in the Isle of Mull." Given the changed date, it seems best to ignore H&B's assertion that the Mull bird was probably the same as the one seen at Inveraray.

Following these first two records, there have been a further five, all but one in September or October and all but one on the islands (Table). Tait (1969) briefly described the 1968 Islay occurrence, which was the first for the Inner Hebrides:

"On 29 September 1968 my eldest son and I saw a Roller at Cladville Farm, Portnahaven, where the bird had been seen earlier by Mr and Mrs Glover and J. Bain. We were able to get within 20 yards of the bird as it sat on a fence post, but unfortunately it was then frightened away by the arrival of the farmer's dog. It was not seen in the area again.

It resembled a small crow, especially about the head, and we noted a black bill, a brown line running through the eye, a light brown back and yellow legs. On being disturbed it flew rather like a pigeon before gliding into the next field. The brilliant blue underparts and wings, the latter with dark tips, were not obvious until the bird was seen in flight."

Tristan ap Rheinallt

Hoopoe

Upupa epops

Scarce migrant, with most records in spring.

The Hoopoe is a scarce visitor to Scotland from the Continent, with several records annually. These records come from all over the country, although in some years there is a tendency for autumn sightings to be concentrated in the Northern Isles. The species is one of the few rarities whose identification poses no problems, even for the most casual of birdwatchers. It is perhaps surprising, therefore, that there are so few early records from Argyll. The first concerned a bird procured in Campbeltown in 1887, and exhibited to the Glasgow Natural History Society on 29 November (McWilliam). Prior to 1970, there were only four further records: from Oban in 1930 (SN 1931:28), Skipness in 1950 (SN 63:188), Hunter's Quay in 1952 (Glasgow and West Scotland Bird Bulletin 1:15), and Taynuilt in 1968 (SB 5:337).

Records then became much more frequent, with six in the 1970s, 13 in the 1980s, nine in the 1990s, and six in 2000-2006. The best year was 1989, with five records.

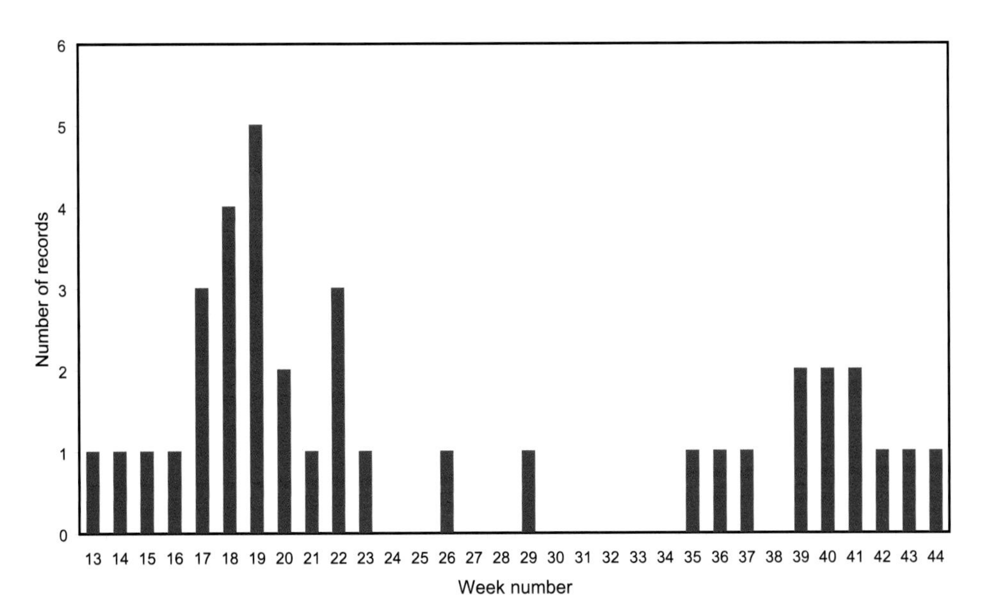

Weekly variation in Argyll records of Hoopoes, 1970-2006.

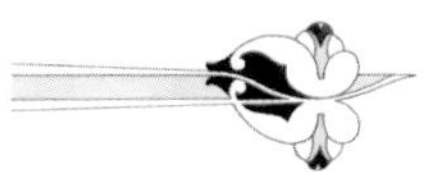

To date, all occurrences in Argyll have involved single birds. Unusually for a rarity, there have been more records on the mainland (23) than on the islands (16). Most of the mainland records come from Kintyre, Cowal, Oban and Loch Etive, with the remainder from the area between Oban and Lochgilphead, except for a single record from Glen Fyne. Of the island birds, eight were on Islay, four on Mull, two on Tiree, one on Coll and one on Iona.

The Hoopoe is recorded more frequently in spring than in autumn, with a peak in the second week of May (Figure). Earliest and latest spring dates are 29 March and 8 June, corresponding dates for autumn being 28 August and 2 November. There has been one summer record, involving a bird that stayed at Campbeltown from 29 June to mid-July 1970 (SB 6:383).

Tristan ap Rheinallt

Wryneck

Jynx torquilla

Rare spring and autumn migrant. May have bred.

The Wryneck appears in the list of birds given in the NSA for Inveraray (Vol. 7, 1845), but as no details are given its occurrence must be regarded as hypothetical. Gray gave no records from Argyll. Similarly, H&B questioned the validity of a breeding record from the north of Argyll, in a location (Nether Lochaber) outside the area covered by this book. B&R, whilst stating that the species had been noted in mainland Argyll and the Inner Hebrides, gave no details of any records.

Against this rather vague background, the first dated records concern individuals seen in the grounds of Kildalton House on Islay in 1913 and 1927, though the month of occurrence is unknown (Ross 1913, Booth 1975, Elliott 1989). The next record was not until 1969, when two were heard calling at Loch Tulla at the end of May and beginning of June (SB 6:106). Their arrival followed an unusually large influx of Wrynecks, presumably of Scandinavian origin, to the east coast and Northern Isles in early May. This influx preceded the first confirmed breeding for Scotland, three nests being found on Speyside in 1969, and records coming from suitable habitat in several other Scottish counties (Burton *et al.* 1970, Thom). The Loch Tulla records were mapped as "probable breeding" in the First Atlas.

Over the years since then, Wrynecks have continued to breed sporadically in the Highlands, and there have been four additional late spring records in Argyll. Since spring passage of this species peaks in early May (Migration Atlas), the June records in particular could represent breeding or attempted breeding. There have been a further five records in autumn, when birds are typically seen in more open habitats. Full details of all recent records are given in the Table.

Tristan ap Rheinallt

Records of Wrynecks in Argyll from 1969 to the end of 2006.

Date	Location	Comment	Reference
28 August 1969	Loch Awe		SB 6:106
17 September 1969	Druimdrishaig, Loch Caolisport	Ringed	SB 8:279 with incorrect location
21 May 1978	Loch Riddon	Two seen and heard	SBR 1978:34
13 October 1984	Bousd (Coll)		SBR 1984:36, ABR 2:37
6 October 1987	Sanda		SBR 1987:32, ABR 5:10
9 to 10 June 1991	Torlochan (Mull)		SBR 1991:50, ABR 8:52
11 September 1997	Cairnbaan		ABR 15:75
4 to 6 June 1998	Kilmartin Burn, near Slockavullin		SBR 1998:73, ABR 15:74-75
14 May 2001	Croig (Mull)		ABR 18:78 with month wrongly given as June

Green Woodpecker

Picus viridis

Rare but recorded regularly in Mull, North Argyll, and especially Cowal in recent years, with scattered records from elsewhere, suggesting a widespread distribution. Breeding may have occurred in Kintyre in 1998.

In the past, the Green Woodpecker was regarded as a rare bird in Scotland, and none of the early authors mention any Argyll records. Following a thin scattering of records from many parts of the country in the first half of the 20th century, breeding was finally confirmed in the Scottish Borders in 1951 (B&R). This was followed by a steady northward expansion, with breeding proven in many counties by the mid-1970s (Thom), although this was followed by an apparent contraction of the range in the south (Second Atlas).

The Green Woodpecker may have first occurred in Argyll as long ago as 1958, when one was seen at Tayvallich on 2 January (Rainier 1975). Two birds were then seen at Kilberry in Mid-Argyll in June 1969. Although published at the time (SB), this apparently isolated record was omitted from the

First Atlas, which featured no records from Scotland north of the Clyde and west of Loch Long. Nevertheless, there was an established population just east of the Argyll recording area, with breeding proven near Loch Lomond. This population seems to have been the source of the presumed colonisation of Cowal, where birds were seen near Lochgoilhead on 24 August 1972 (unpublished), at Strachur in 1976 (unpublished), and in the Loch Riddon area throughout 1977 (SBR) and in early

Green Woodpeckers may be extending their range in Argyll. Their distinctive call is worth listening for. *Roy Blewitt*

1978 (unpublished). In addition, the 1981-84 Winter Atlas featured a multiple record (two birds seen in a day) in grid square NS18, which includes the southern half of Loch Eck.

Although nothing is known about the origin of the Kilberry birds, further sightings in the western part of the mainland occurred in 1974, when one was reported from Lochgilphead (Rainier 1975), and in 1976, when a bird was seen at Saddell on 25 May (SB 10:102) and there were also reports from Taynuilt (unpublished). In 1979, one was heard calling at Kilmelford during March (unpublished).

At the same time, Green Woodpeckers began to turn up on the islands. On Islay, singles were seen or heard in May 1978 at Kilchoman (SBR), in January 1979 at Laggan Bridge (Elliott 1989), and in July 1979 at Ballygrant (Elliott 1989). Birds were present at two sites in the north of Mull in summer 1980, having apparently arrived at one of these sites two or three years previously (ABR 1:59). Although Elliott (1989) claimed that two or three pairs bred on Mull in 1981, no supporting evidence is available. In 1982, a bird at Arinagour on 7 June was the first for Coll. Lengthy movements in this species are unusual but may occur in severe weather, and presumably such movements account for the species' occurrence on the islands and the western fringes of the mainland.

The above sequence of sightings suggests that a fairly rapid colonisation of many parts of Argyll took place as part of the general northward expansion of this species. Thom considered that the Green Woodpecker probably bred on Islay and (fewer than five pairs) in mainland Argyll. However, the evidence for Islay appears to rest solely on the three records from 1978 and 1979, which might relate to just one bird. Similarly, there was no confirmation of breeding on the mainland. Although birds continued to be reported occasionally from the mainland and Mull during the 1980s, none were found in a survey of 38 deciduous woodlands in Mid- and North Argyll in 1985 (ABR 3:43). The Second Atlas showed only a single Argyll record, without breeding evidence, from near Tarbert at the north end of Kintyre. It may be that the severe winter of 1981/2 caused a decline in numbers over several years, as reported elsewhere in Britain (Second Atlas).

The 1990s saw an apparent expansion in Cowal, which might be linked to mild winters in the late 1980s (Second Atlas). Reports were more or less annual during 1992 to 2006, with several records in some years. Most reports came from the Loch Eck area but birds were also recorded at several other locations in Cowal, suggesting that the Green Woodpecker was widely distributed in this part of Argyll. Similarly, there were several records from the Benderloch area of North Argyll from 1997 to 2001, including a sighting of a territorial pair at Blarcreen in May 1997. Other records came from Mull, indicating a continued presence on the island, with a few scattered records from Mid-Argyll.

Breeding was thought to have occurred at Escart, near Skipness in 1998, where birds had been recorded previously. On this occasion, young were heard calling for food, but none were sighted. Despite the large number of records, there has been no firm evidence of breeding at any other location. However, drumming in this species is rare and proof of breeding hard to obtain (First Atlas). It is therefore possible that the Green Woodpecker breeds sporadically in Argyll. On the other hand, its disappearance from certain locations where it had been reported over several years suggests that colonisation is often unsuccessful.

Tristan ap Rheinallt

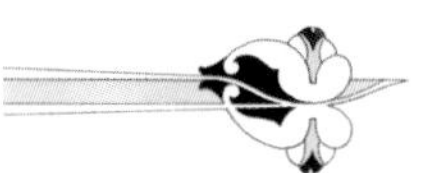

Great Spotted Woodpecker

Dendrocopos major

It is a widespread resident on the mainland and on Mull, and is recorded occasionally on Islay.

Although this species was described as widespread in Scotland in the 18th century (Thom), most old records refer to the east of the country and do not specifically mention Argyll (B&R). By the mid-19th century it was apparently no longer breeding in Scotland (Harvie-Brown 1892). At this time, it occurred sporadically as a winter visitor, with mention of birds being shot at Inveraray and on Islay (H&B, Gray). These were likely to have been birds of the northern race *major*.

From the 1890s onwards a remarkably rapid recolonisation of Scotland occurred (Harvie-Brown 1908). The first recorded breeding in Argyll was at St Catherines, Cowal, in 1919 (B&R). In 1921-22 they were found breeding in Cowal, at Glen Finart, Ardentinny, Strachur and Loch Striven, and by 1936 they were reported at several sites in Knapdale (B&R). This range expansion continued steadily, so that by 1946 they were present at Aros House and Gruline on Mull (B&R).

Great Spotted Woodpeckers are most abundant in oak woodlands. *Margaret Staley*

The First Atlas showed Great Spotted Woodpeckers breeding on most of mainland Argyll, apart from southern Kintyre and the north and east of Mull. There was a confirmed breeding record for Jura, but no records for Colonsay, Islay, Coll or Tiree. A single bird was seen on Colonsay in January 1973 and fresh borings were reported from the policy woodlands in July 1977 (Jardine *et al.* 1986).

Although essentially birds of deciduous, coniferous and mixed woodland, they readily visit gardens and bird feeders. They usually avoid isolated trees and small copses, and in Argyll appear to be more widespread in old deciduous and mixed woodland. Great Spotted Woodpeckers were found in all but four of 38 broadleaved woods surveyed in Mid- and North Argyll in 1985 (Averis & Martin 1985), and in all but three of 16 similar woods visited during 2003 (Amar *et al.* 2006, P. Daw unpubl. data). By contrast, during a study of spruce plantations in Cowal, only three were located in the spring of 1991 while none were found in 1992 (Patterson *et al.* 1995). They were recorded in only one of seven chiefly coniferous 1-km squares surveyed in 2000 (Wilson & Fuller 2001, P. Daw unpubl. data).

The Second Atlas showed breeding in 31% of 10-km squares in Argyll, with highest densities in parts of Cowal and Mid-Argyll. Breeding was also confirmed in North Argyll, the northern half of Kintyre and much of Mull, but there were no records of any kind for the remaining islands.

During 1993–2002, Great Spotted Woodpeckers were reported regularly from Cowal, Mid-Argyll (widespread in both areas), Mull and North Argyll. There have also been several records from Kintyre, including birds during the breeding season in the south of the peninsula.

Great Spotted Woodpeckers are occasional visitors to Islay. At least ten were recorded there in eight years during 1954–1985 (Elliott 1989) and single birds were found in six years during 1996–2004. There have been no recent records from Colonsay and none from Jura since one was heard at Inverlussa in June 1985 (ABR, Argyll Database).

A male seen in flight near Ballard on 24 February 2004 was the first recent record for Coll or Tiree (S. Wellock pers. comm.), although one was caught at Skerryvore on 28 October 1899 (Laidlaw 1900).

British birds belong to the race *anglicus*, which is highly sedentary (Migration Atlas). The race *major* from northern Europe is larger and prone to irruptive movements (BWP). According to B&R, individuals of the latter race were found on Islay and Mull. More recently, one at Bruichladdich on 22 October 1962 and one at Portnahaven two days later were thought to be part of a large irruption (SB 2:31, Migration Atlas). There have been no confirmed records of *major* in recent years.

Paul Daw

Sky Lark

Alauda arvensis

This is a common breeding species in open habitats throughout Argyll, occurring on moorland, coastal areas and farmland. Many emigrate for the winter, with remaining birds restricted mainly to coastal and low lying areas.

Although Argyll was not specifically noted, the Sky Lark was mentioned as being found in many parts of Scotland in the OSA and NSA and was presumably widespread and common during the 18th century. It would have benefited from extensive forest clearances over many centuries. Certainly by the latter part of the 19th century it was described as "very abundant in Mull and Iona on all cultivated areas, grass-lands, and coastal pastures" and "found abundantly on the mainland, where, however it can hardly be described as universal in distribution" (Graham). It was also said to be very common on Tiree and Jura (H&B). From the mid-20th century, there would have been some range contraction resulting from large-scale reforestation, as Sky Larks are one of the first birds to abandon such habitats (Moss 1979).

By the time of the First Atlas, Sky Larks were still recorded as probably or definitely breeding in every 10-km square in Argyll, apart from one in central Cowal and the square covering Staffa and Little Colonsay. However, this scale of mapping does not reveal detailed local distribution.

The Second Atlas showed some contraction in breeding range (mainly in Mid- and North Argyll) with records in only 79% of 10-km squares in the county. The abundance map showed considerable variation in numbers, the highest densities occurring in parts of Kintyre and on the islands (except Mull). Lowest densities were found in Cowal, Mid- and North Argyll, while there were moderate concentrations on Mull. To some extent, these changes reflected the establishment of coniferous forests. However, habitat preferences of Sky Larks are probably more complex than this (Donald 2004).

A survey of the Rinns of Islay in 1994 found *c.*2,020 territories, with highest densities on moorland, particularly north of Loch Gorm (ABR 11:70). Data from BBS squares in Argyll suggest they are more numerous on low-lying grassland near the sea and on upland habitats with a mixture of heather and rough grasses, rather than grass alone. Recent records show breeding in good numbers on smaller and more remote islands such as Cara (south of Gigha), Sanda and the Treshnish Isles. Recent censuses have produced the following results: 190 individuals present on Oronsay on 1 May 1998, 164 singing males over 440ha at The Reef in April 2000, and 93 territories in 279ha at the RSPB's Loch Gruinart Reserve in May 2000 (ABR).

As in most of Scotland, Sky Larks are essentially summer visitors, especially on higher ground. In the absence of ringing evidence, it is impossible to say whether these moorland birds migrate or just move short distances to lower ground in winter (Thom). From at least as far back as the 19th century, there are accounts of large flocks of Sky Larks arriving in Argyll in autumn and winter, especially during or following severe weather (Gray).

Recent records (since 1980) demonstrate that from September onwards flocks of 100-350 birds are present, especially on Islay, Tiree and Oronsay. Such flocks remain until late March or early April and may be composed of local

Changes in agricultural practices caused large declines in Skylark populations across Britain in the 1970s and 1980s. *Philip Kirkham*

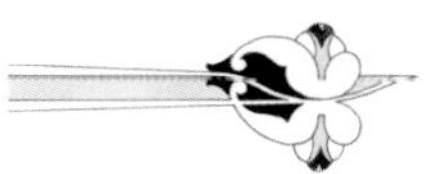

birds. The Winter Atlas shows high numbers along the west coast of Kintyre.

Much larger flocks of 700-1,000 or even more have been seen in southern Kintyre in September, but not during the winter (ABR). Sky Larks breeding north of the Baltic vacate their breeding grounds entirely and move as far south as the Mediterranean (BWP). Thus, these large autumn flocks may be composed of true migrants. Smaller flocks of up to 100 birds are reported from other coastal areas of Argyll during the winter. In late February-early March 2005, a large influx of Sky Larks was noted on Islay, Coll and Tiree. The origin of these birds was unknown. There was snow on the mainland at the time, but they could also have come from Ireland (C. McKay, pers. comm.).

Not all visiting Sky Larks travel entirely under their own steam. On 18 October 2003, three landed on the Oban-Tiree ferry, half way out from Mull to Coll, and two of these stayed to fly on to Tiree as the ferry neared the island (J. Bowler, pers. comm.). There are no returns of Sky Larks ringed or recovered in Argyll.

Paul Daw

A Sand Martin colony at a quarry near Blairmore, Cowal. Colonies at quarries can be much larger than those at natural sites, such as river banks. *Margaret Staley*

Shore Lark

Eremophila alpestris

Vagrant.

Shore Larks breeding in Arctic Eurasia winter in small numbers in Britain. Although recorded regularly from the east coast of Scotland, they are very rare in the west. Indeed, there is only one accepted Argyll record, of three birds at Bowmore and nearby Ardlarach on Islay on 18 and 19 October 1976 (SB 10:103, Elliott 1989). This record was associated with an exceptionally strong autumn passage of the species in Scotland (SB 10:193).

[The few other published Argyll records (Glasgow and West of Scotland Bird Bulletin 7:120, Jardine *et al.* 1986) are not considered acceptable, the dates of the sightings being extremely unlikely or completely unknown.]

Tristan ap Rheinallt

Sand Martin

Riparia riparia

A summer visitor, localised breeding species, and passage migrant.

Although widely distributed in Scotland, Sand Martins are restricted by the availability of suitable nesting sites (Thom). River banks and sand and gravel pits are ephemeral by their very nature and birds may have to relocate colony sites from year to year. Many smaller colonies are at remote or seldom visited locations, making it difficult to accurately assess population trends.

Evidence from older sources implies that overall distribution in Argyll has changed relatively little over the last 200 years, apart from gaps in occupation for some of the islands. In the latter part of the 19th century, Sand Martins were widely distributed as single pairs or large colonies in almost every parish on the mainland and on all remoter islands (Gray). The OSA in 1794 mentions 'mouse coloured swallows' inhabiting the sand banks of Tiree. They continued to breed there until at least 1886, but eventually the wind eroded the nesting site and by the end of the 19th century they were rare visitors to the island (H&B). H&B quoted Graham as saying that they occurred on Iona and Mull, but noted that they were not recorded on Jura.

The first mention of nesting on Islay was in 1913, when there were three known sites (B&R). Possible breeding was reported on Jura in 1939 and B&R found Sand Martins on Mull in 1948, but not on Iona. Boyd (1958) noted five pairs breeding successfully at Crossapol in 1955.

The First Atlas reflected this pattern. Apart from Cowal, where there were confirmed breeding records from most 10-km squares, distribution on the mainland was patchy with

significant gaps in south Kintyre and Knapdale. Breeding was confirmed for much of western Mull, parts of Islay and for two squares on Jura. There were no records for Colonsay, Coll, Tiree or any of the smaller islands.

As in much of Britain, a noticeable contraction of range was evident by the time of the Second Atlas. To some extent this was a result of the dramatic nationwide crash in numbers in 1983 (Mead 1985), although there was some evidence of a partial recovery after 1985. On the mainland, losses occurred in north Kintyre, around Loch Awe and Loch Fyne and in North Argyll. There were fewer confirmed breeding records for Islay and Mull, and none at all for Jura. There were breeding records for only 24% of 10-km squares in Argyll. The abundance map showed 'hot-spots' of moderately high density around Campbeltown, Lochgilphead and Dalmally.

Since the Second Atlas, there have been regular records of active breeding colonies in Cowal, Islay, Kintyre, Mid-Argyll, Mull and North Argyll (Table). Several colonies have been discovered during survey work on other species. Other small colonies doubtless exist undetected along secluded watercourses. The largest colony recorded in the county was at North Ledaig sandpit near Benderloch.

On Tiree, pairs were thought to be making breeding attempts in dunes near Loch an Eilein in 2001 and 2002. Then breeding was confirmed at Loch a' Phuill in 2002, with a pair fledging four young, the first breeding record for Tiree in nearly 50 years. By July 2005 there were 15 nest holes at this site (J. Bowler pers. comm.). On Jura, about eight Sand Martins were seen flying around the mouth of the Corran River in July 2006 and two recently excavated nest holes were found in the river bank (N. Tait pers. comm.). This was the first confirmed breeding record for Jura since the First Atlas.

Sand Martins are one of the first spring migrants to arrive. In most years birds are present by the first week in April. March arrivals are not unusual and the earliest recorded date was 16 March at Loch Skerrols, Islay, in 1993. Most have departed by the end of September, but there are occasional stragglers during October. One very late bird was at Ardilistry Bay, Islay, on 4 November 2001.

Although large gatherings of Sand Martins can occur in spring and autumn, there have been no reports of flocks of more than 100 or so in Argyll in recent years (ABR).

Ringing recoveries indicate that many of our breeding birds appear to take the same route through southern England on migration. Nine birds have either been ringed at breeding sites in Argyll and recovered at Icklesham, East Sussex, in autumn or ringed there (in autumn) and subsequently recovered in Argyll. The direction they take subsequently is suggested by six birds recorded passing through Belgium and central France and one ringed in Argyll and recovered in Malta. That some winter in West Africa is demonstrated by the three juveniles ringed at the North Connel colony in 1989-90 and all subsequently recovered at the Parc National du Djoudj, Fleuve, Senegal.

Paul Daw

Location and size of known Sand Martin colonies in Argyll.

Colony category	Location	Number of nest holes
Large colonies (more than 20 holes)	North Ledaig sandpit near Benderloch, North Argyll	Increased from 170 occupied holes in 1996 to 340 apparently active holes (out of 392 holes) in 1999. Since then numbers have fallen to less than 200 active holes.
	Barcaldine gravel quarry, North Argyll	107 holes in 2001.
	Kilmichael Glen wood yard, Mid-Argyll	Peaked at 110 active holes in 1998, but declined to 30 in 2002.
	Kilmartin Quarry, Mid-Argyll	100 occupied holes in 1996. No recent counts.
	Gorten, Mull	45 active nest holes in June 2002.
	River Breackerie, Amod, Kintyre	56 fresh holes in July 2001 and at least 23 active nests.
	Ballure, Kintyre	100 nest holes in groups of 40 and 60 in coastal sandbank. Only 10-20 occupied in 2000.
	Langa Quarry, Aros Moss, Kintyre	c.50 pairs breeding in approx. 500 holes in 2005
	Kilchiaran, Islay	25 occupied holes in 1996, 19 in 2002.
	Stronchullin, Cowal	At least 29 occupied holes (from a total of *c*.150) in 1999.
Small colonies, 1997-2005 (20 holes or fewer)	Cowal: Bealachandrain Farm, Blairmore, Gairletter, Little Eachaig River, River Massan, River Ruel and near Kilbride Farm.	
	Islay: Ardnave, Coull Farm, Laggan Bridge, Machrie River, Saligo, Tormisdale.	
	Kintyre: Bellochantuy (sandy cliff 3km to the N), Carskey Bay, Clachan Burn (near shore), Drumgarve (Glen Lussa), Keil (Southend), Lussa Loch (river bank north end), and Strone Glen, (I. Teasdale pers. comm.).	
	Mid-Argyll: Ashfield, Kerrara Drove Road (Oban), Leac a' Chaoruinn (Eredine), Lusragan Burn at Ardchonnel, River Add at Moine Mhor (several small colonies) and Tervine (Loch Awe).	
	Mull: Calgary, Loch Ba head, Loch Frisa, Scoor beach, Tenga/Crannich (two small colonies) and Torosay sand pit.	
	North Argyll: River Dearg at Barcaldine, Allt Mhoille (near Ben Cruachan).	

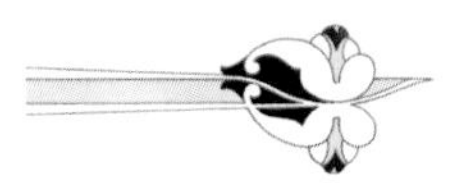

Barn Swallow

Hirundo rustica

This is a widespread and common summer visitor, often breeding in close association with man, and a passage migrant.

The Swallow may be seen almost anywhere in Scotland, either as a summer visitor or passage migrant, although it is scarce in mountainous parts of the far north-west and on the outer islands. As a breeding bird it is most numerous around farms and other rural habitations and may be found using unoccupied buildings in remoter areas. It usually avoids dense woodland, open moorland and heavily populated areas. It breeds along most glens and has been reported nesting at over 500m asl (B&R).

Since earliest times, the Swallow has been known as a widespread summer visitor. It was often mentioned in the OSA, including records from Mull and Gigha. In the mid-19th century, Gray described it as well known over the whole of western Scotland "from the sea margin to the highest moorlands" and says it was common in Mull, Iona, Tiree, Coll and probably all the smaller islands. He even quotes a report from a Mr Struthers who saw several soaring high above Ben Cruachan. By contrast, H&B, describing its status in Argyll and the Inner Hebrides towards the end of the 19th century, said that although numbers had recently increased, the Swallow "cannot be considered yet as very generally distributed".

In the mid-20th century, the Swallow was described as common on the mainland and found to be pretty common on Islay, nesting at farms and in some small townships. It also bred in villages and houses on Jura. 'Three or four' pairs were found on Gigha in 1949, but it was not found on Cara, where it had been reported a few years earlier. On Mull, Swallows were said to be fairly well distributed, and they were nesting on Lismore in 1942 (B&R).

According to the First Atlas, Swallows were generally distributed on the mainland and Islay. Breeding was also widespread on Mull, apart from the Ross of Mull where distribution was patchy. There were gaps on western Jura and eastern Tiree. Breeding was confirmed on Colonsay, but not on Coll or on the smaller and remoter islands, such as Scarba and the Treshnish Isles where Swallows are only occasional visitors (TIARG Reports).

The Second Atlas recorded them breeding in 76% of Argyll's 10-km squares. There had been few changes from the First Atlas apart from on Coll, where breeding was confirmed, and on Tiree where birds bred in all three 10-km squares. The abundance map showed high densities breeding in Kintyre, with moderate numbers elsewhere apart from northern Cowal and much of North Argyll, where Swallows appeared to be scarce.

There is evidence of recent increases on Coll and Tiree, although Thom had indicated that the status of Swallows

The number of Swallows returning to Britain in spring is mainly determined by their survival rate in the African wintering areas. *Philip Kirkham*

on Coll was uncertain. A pair at Breachacha Farm in 1985 appeared to be the first confirmed breeding for the island (Stroud 1989) despite Gray's comments (above). By 1992, 8-10 pairs were reported breeding there (compared to "2-3 pairs in most years") and in 2004 six pairs nested at Totronald alone, with many others elsewhere. Similarly on Tiree, 5-10 breeding pairs were reported in 1986, 20-30 pairs were estimated in 1987 (Shepherd *et al.* 1988) and by 2000 Swallows were reported as widespread, with breeding in most suitable buildings. A pair or two breed on Sanda Island every year and up to six pairs breed on Oronsay (ABR).

The majority of our Swallows arrive during the second or third week of April. This pattern does not appear to have changed greatly during the past 20 years. However, odd birds do arrive earlier in April and occasionally in the last week in March. The earliest dates in recent years are 17 March 2007 for a bird at Kilmore (near Oban), and 24 March, for single birds in 1982 (Mull of Kintyre Lighthouse) and in 1995 (at two locations).

Pre-migration gatherings can start as early as late July. An estimated 2,000 were at a reed-bed roost at Machrihanish Water on 31 July 2000. Usually most birds have departed by the end of September, but a few continue to pass through during October. In many years there is the odd record during the first week of November. These late records may involve

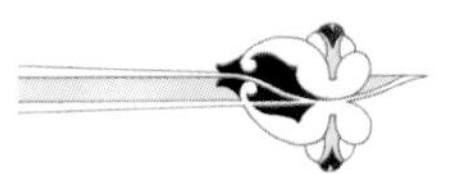

birds on passage from northern Europe (Second Atlas). Until recently, one at Port Ellen, Islay, on 24 November 1989 was the latest record (ABR). However, in 2002 a remarkable group of three birds (presumably a late brood) roosted in a heated coach used as a greenhouse at Vaul on Tiree throughout November, emerging to feast on insects on warm days around croft buildings. They were last seen on 17 December (J. Bowler pers. comm.).

Most Argyll ringing returns have been of birds ringed either as nestlings in the county and subsequently recovered at roost sites in autumn, or ringed as first-year birds at roost sites in autumn and subsequently recovered breeding in Argyll. The latter group includes two ringed at Fairburn Ings in Yorkshire in 1960 and 1961 and found breeding at different localities in Argyll in 1962. These returns indicate that many of our birds migrate through central England on their way to and from their wintering grounds in southern Africa. A nestling ringed in Kintyre in 1967 was found dead in northern Holland the following July, suggesting that not all Swallows return to their natal area to breed.

There are occasional records of albino birds, including an all-white bird at Grasspoint on 1 July 1989 and an entirely silver-grey juvenile near Tighnabruaich in early July 1996 (ABR).

Paul Daw

House Martin

Delichon urbicum

This is a common summer visitor on the mainland. It is less numerous on the islands and has not been recorded breeding on Tiree.

In Scotland, House Martins are most numerous and widespread in the south and east. In the north and west the climate and soil types are less productive for flying insects, their only food. These areas are also more sparsely populated and thus provide fewer suitable buildings for nesting (Second Atlas). Although they sometimes nest on cliffs, this is apparently more frequent in the east of Scotland (B&R). This habit seems to have become less common in Scotland recently (Thom).

The past status of House Martins in Argyll is clouded by confusion over names. In some cases they may have been included with Swallows (B&R). In the mid-19th century they were said to be much commoner on Iona and Mull than Swallows and cliff-nesting was noted near Oban (Gray). H&B said they occurred rarely on Jura, perhaps breeding on only one occasion, and rarely on Tiree. Breeding was recorded on Coll, at Arinagour in 1898, but not subsequently.

During the first half of the 20th century, House Martins

House Martins gather mud to build nests on buildings, and occasionally on cliffs. *John McAvoy*

were said to be scarce summer visitors to Islay, breeding in only two or three places. They were fairly well distributed on Mull and were seen on Lismore, but there were no records for Jura. By mid-century a decrease in numbers breeding in towns and villages in Scotland (as opposed to farms and along the coast) had been noticed (B&R).

According to the First Atlas, House Martins bred over most of mainland Argyll, apart from the Connel and Appin areas. Islay had records for 10-km squares covering Bridgend and the south of the island (the same locations as those cited in 1913 by B&R), while confirmed breeding was also shown for north and east Mull. There were also records for two 10-km squares, parts of which included Jura. Tiree had a sight record only and there were no records for Coll and Colonsay.

Only 48% of 10-km squares in Argyll had breeding House Martins according to the Second Atlas, indicating a slight overall contraction of range since the First Atlas. The main losses were on Mull, with birds breeding only in the far north and south-east of the island, and in North Argyll. Breeding was confirmed for two additional 10-km squares on Islay. Moderate densities were shown in the abundance map for south Cowal, parts of Kintyre, Mid-Argyll and the south of Islay. Elsewhere House Martins were thinly spread.

Recently there have been indications of range expansion. In June 2002, a pair nesting on the Backpacker's Lodge, Colonsay, was the first confirmed breeding for the island. Two pairs at Stronvar (near Uig) in 2004 constituted the first breeding for Coll in over 100 years. In 2002, three pairs nested at Lochdon, Mull, where there have been no recent breeding records.

In July 2002, one or more pairs apparently nested on cliffs at Singing Sands, near Port Ellen, the first cliff-nesting in Argyll in recent years (ABR).

House Martins arrive later than the other two hirundines, with the first arrivals often not seen in Argyll until late April or even early May. However, in some years a few appear in early April, the earliest recently being at Kilchurn Castle on 1 April 2001, at Southend, Kintyre, on 4 April 1999 and on Colonsay on 7 April 1995 (ABR).

Departure begins in August, and by the end of September most have gone (B&R). However, as House Martins start to breed later than many species, there may be broods still in the nest late in the season. Young were being fed at a nest in Barcaldine on 13 September 2001. Therefore, October records are not infrequent and a few linger well into November. The latest have been two juveniles on Islay on 13 November 1990, five at Connel on 17 November 1987 (ABR) and one at Machrihanish on 19 November 1974 (SBR 1974:447).

Migrants are seen on Tiree, the Treshnish Isles and other places outwith the normal breeding range, most frequently in spring. The few House Martins ringed or recovered in Argyll add little to our knowledge of movements of this species, but birds ringed and recovered elsewhere in Scotland indicate that they are very faithful to their natal area (Thom).

Paul Daw

Richard's Pipit

Anthus richardi

Vagrant.

Although this Siberian breeder is a regular autumn migrant in the Northern Isles, records from the west coast of Scotland are few and far between. It has been recorded on only two occasions in Argyll. On Islay, one was at Kilchoman on 28 September 1971 (SB 7:155) and another at The Oa on 10 September 1973 (SB 9:235).

Tristan ap Rheinallt

Tree Pipit

Anthus trivialis

A summer visitor that is common on the mainland in open woodlands, young forests and along woodland edges. Widespread on Jura and Mull, but scarce on Islay.

Although Tree Pipits occur over most of mainland Scotland, they are most numerous in the north and west, in mature oak and birch woods with canopy gaps. In addition, they occur in young or recently cleared conifer plantations, particularly along edges with taller trees. They are also be found among scattered birches well up the glens. Tree Pipits are much less frequent on the islands, and absent as a breeding species from the Outer Hebrides and Northern Isles (Thom).

There seems to be no mention of this species in Scotland until the middle of the 19th century. At that time it was said to be especially numerous in the area around Glasgow and well distributed, although by no means plentiful, in other parts of western Scotland, although there was no comment on its status in Argyll (Gray). By the first half of the 20th century, the Tree Pipit was widespread over most of Scotland and was by no means uncommon in suitable localities in Argyll. It was described as sparsely distributed in the woods of Mull (B&R).

The First Atlas showed Tree Pipits to be well distributed on mainland Argyll, apart from southern Kintyre and much of Cowal. There were confirmed breeding records for north and east Islay and Mull and probable breeding records for at least two 10-km squares on Jura. One was seen on Colonsay, but there were no records for the remaining islands.

In 1985, Tree Pipits were reported as plentiful in deciduous woods on Jura in early June (ABR 3:44). Also in 1985, a survey of broadleaf woodlands found them in all 38 sites visited, with an average of 12.6 birds per wood (Averis & Martin 1985).

The Second Atlas recorded Tree Pipits breeding in 54%

Tree Pipits continue to do well in Argyll, in contrast with their substantial decline in England. *Philip Snow*

of 10-km squares in Argyll. In general, the picture was of a significant range extension since the First Atlas, in striking contrast to the notable range contraction in southern and central England at this time. In particular, they now bred in most of Cowal, Kintyre and Mull and in two additional 10-km squares on Jura. Breeding was also confirmed on Scarba, but there were no records for Colonsay, Coll or Tiree. High breeding densities were shown for Mid-Argyll, Cowal and parts of Kintyre, Mull and North Argyll, most probably linked to the increasing availability of suitable habitat, not only in native woodland, but also in conifers. In Cowal, they were the eighth most abundant species in Sitka Spruce forests in late spring 1991 and the tenth during the same period in 1992 (Patterson *et al.* 1995).

In the Taynish CBC, an average 12 territories were found during the 14 years since the census started in 1990 and, despite annual fluctuations, the population remained fairly stable during this time.

In recent years, Tree Pipits have been found during the breeding season at a few sites on Islay. Also, singing birds have been reported from one or two sites on Jura but, bearing in mind the general paucity of records for the island, the species may well be more widespread (ABR). Otherwise the BBS and other records have indicated no obvious changes in distribution. Many of the Countryside Survey sites contained no suitable habitat in 2000, but 15 were counted in a single 1-km square where conifers had recently been felled (Wilson & Fuller 2001, P. Daw unpubl. data). They were found in all 16 broadleaved woods re-surveyed in 2003 in Mid- and North Argyll (Amar *et al.* 2006, RSPB unpubl. data), but they were fewer in number than in 1985 (Averis & Martin 1985), a pattern also noted in similar surveys in Wales (Amar *et al.* 2006).

The main arrival in Argyll is usually during the second or third week of April, but early individuals sometimes appear during the first week, and there is a record of an exhausted bird at Croggan on Mull on 25 March 1985. Autumn migration begins in August and most have left by mid-September. There are few October records, the latest in recent years being one at The Reef, Tiree, on 21 October 1998. Although there are 1980s records of considerable numbers passing through Argyll during August (ABR), this species is rarely reported as a passage migrant from the islands outwith its breeding range. During the ten years 1996-2005, there were only four records from Tiree, one from Colonsay and one from Coll (ABR, Argyll Database).

Paul Daw

Meadow Pipit

Anthus pratensis

An abundant breeding species on heather and grass moors with most leaving higher ground in winter. Those remaining occur mainly in coastal and low-lying localities. Large flocks occur on passage.

The Meadow Pipit is widespread and abundant on open ground throughout Scotland. Although fairly catholic in its choice of habitat, it is most numerous on grass and heather moors, where it is the most frequent host of the Cuckoo. Distribution is thinner in the more intensely farmed south and east of the country. Most breeding areas are deserted before winter, especially in the hills. Large numbers occur on

The Meadow Pipit is typically the most abundant bird in Argyll's open upland habitats. *Philip Kirkham*

passage (Thom).

Under its old name of 'Moss Cheeper', it is mentioned in the NSA in many places, although not specifically in Argyll. In the mid-19th century Gray refers to it as "everywhere common, often appearing in places where bird life is scarcely looked for". At the end of that century, it was said to be common everywhere on the mainland and on some smaller as well as larger islands. It was noted as scarce on moorland in winter (H&B). In the mid-20th century, B&R described it as common throughout Scotland and mentioned it breeding on smaller islands, such as Lismore. There were indications of periodic fluctuations in numbers.

In the First Atlas, Meadow Pipits were shown as breeding in almost every 10-km square in Argyll, from sea level to altitudes of over 1,000m, with the exception of squares covering the Treshnish Isles.

There was a sudden decline in England and Wales in the mid 1980s, from which there has been a slow recovery (Second Atlas). However, there was little evidence of a similar decline in Scotland, with few changes in distribution between the First and Second Atlases. The Second Atlas showed it to be ubiquitous in Argyll, being found in 94% of 10-km squares, including breeding records for the Treshnish Isles. The abundance map showed it to be common everywhere, but particularly numerous on the islands and in Kintyre.

Moss (1979) found that numbers increased following conifer planting, but then decreased once trees were more than five years old. Thus, reforestation is likely to have reduced the range of Meadow Pipits in Argyll, although they were reported in Sitka Spruce forests in Cowal, but at a slightly lower frequency than Tree Pipits (Patterson *et al.* 1995).

Although many of the 1-km squares surveyed in Argyll for the BBS have not been continuously covered, those that have show some evidence of a decline in numbers since 1994. Nevertheless, this is still by far the most numerous species present in summer in many areas. A survey of the Rinns of Islay in 1994 located *c.*1,416 territories, with the highest densities on moorland (ABR 11:71) and a sample count of 279ha at Loch Gruinart in June 2000 found 105 territories (0.38 pairs ha^{-1}).

In 2000, five of the Countryside Survey 1-km squares in Argyll with suitable habitat each held over 40 individuals and 100 were found in one square on Tiree (Wilson & Fuller 2001, P. Daw unpubl. data). The Meadow Pipit was by far the most numerous passerine in the survey. It is a widespread breeding species on the Treshnish Isles (TIARG Reports) and occurs on most of the smaller islands that have been visited in recent years (Argyll Database).

The Winter Atlas demonstrated clearly the extent to which Meadow Pipits desert higher ground in winter, with the main concentrations occurring along the mainland coasts, on Islay and the western half of Mull. Ringing recoveries suggest many Scottish birds winter in Iberia (Migration Atlas), but there is no ringing evidence of passage visitors from the northern continental range. On the other hand, there have been recoveries of birds ringed in Iceland and vice versa. Two birds ringed in Argyll have been recovered in France and one each in Spain and Portugal.

In spring, small groups of up to 50 or more are often seen returning to breeding areas, but passage is heaviest in autumn. In some years large flocks may be seen moving south from August onwards. Several thousand were thought to be present on Tiree in August 2000, hundreds were at Loch Crinan on 2 August 2002 and an estimated 2,000 passed through Sanda Island on 17 September 2002, with another 1,000 the following day (ABR, Argyll Database).

Meadow Pipits in Argyll presumably belong to the race *whistleri* of Ireland and northern and western Scotland, rather than nominate *pratensis* found in the rest of the range. Compared to the nominate race, *whistleri* is deeper and redder olive-brown above, with slightly heavier black streaks, while the ground colour of chest, sides of breast and flanks is a markedly deeper, cinnamon buff (BWP). However the validity of *whistleri* is uncertain as it may be only a clinal variant of *pratensis* (del Hoyo *et al.* 2004).

Paul Daw

Red-throated Pipit

Anthus cervinus

Vagrant.

The only Argyll record of this northern European species concerns an individual seen at Tobermory on 7 May 1975 (BB 69:352, SB 9:228). The vast majority of Scottish records come from Shetland and Fair Isle. On the west coast, Red-throated Pipits have been reported only from Mull, St Kilda, North Rona and Dumfries & Galloway.

Tristan ap Rheinallt

Rock Pipit

Anthus petrosus

This is a common resident, mainly along the coast, with some emigration and passage in autumn. It is a scarce passage and winter visitor elsewhere.

In Scotland, Rock Pipits occurs almost exclusively on rocky coasts, wherever the intertidal zone is extensive enough to provide adequate feeding. Thus, they are most abundant in the north and west but less common along the east coast and in parts of the south-west. Small numbers occur on passage and as winter visitors, when they may occasionally be seen inland (Thom).

In the early 19th century, the NSA mentioned the species in Kintyre, at Kilchenzie, and Gray said it was common along the shore at all seasons, preferring areas with rocks and sea weed. At the end of the 19th century, H&B said it occurred on Mull and all islands, large and small, but that it appeared rarer or more local in winter. Its status was largely unchanged by the mid-20th century, although small numbers were then known to occur on passage, in both spring and autumn (B&R).

The First Atlas showed Rock Pipits breeding along most of the coastline of Argyll, as well as on most of the islands, including smaller ones. On the mainland there were records up to the head of Loch Fyne, but gaps in Knapdale and Cowal. There was also a curious gap for the 10km square covering most of Colonsay.

At the time of the Second Atlas, distribution was little changed, although the gap on Colonsay was now filled and there were breeding records for the southern Treshnish Isles. There were some losses on Coll and Tiree and gaps at the southern tip of Kintyre. It was found in 67% of 10-km squares in Argyll. The abundance map showed high density in parts of Colonsay, Islay, Jura, the Ross of Mull and on the mainland around Loch Melfort. Numbers were much lower along the east coast of Kintyre where there are long stretches

The Rock Pipit is one of most characteristic birds of rocky shores in Argyll. *Philip Kirkham*

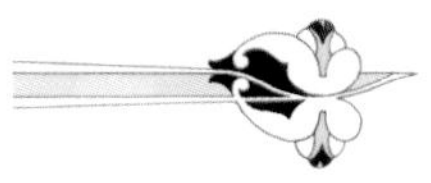

of sandy beach.

Rock Pipits can be very numerous in suitable areas. A survey of the Rinns of Islay in 1994 found *c.*115 territories, which was considered to be an underestimate. As expected, most were breeding along the rockier coasts, but pairs were found a short distance inland at Kilchiaran and Coull (ABR 11:71). A census on Sanda in 2001 found 39 breeding pairs (Argyll Database).

Away from the shore, Rock Pipits have been found during the breeding season at over 450m asl on Mull, in habitat more typical of Water Pipits. In June 1982, a pair was feeding young at Coire Allt Achadh Luirginn at *c.*457m asl (R.A. Broad pers. comm.) and in mid-April 2002 a territorial pair was present *c.*3km away, near the summit of Beinn Chreagach Mhor (*c.*550m asl) (Argyll Database). The species has also been recorded at high altitude in the Grampians and at 300m asl on Skye (Thom). That they can occur on even the smallest islets was demonstrated by at least two at Skerryvore Lighthouse on 10 September 2004.

The distribution in the Winter Atlas was similar to both the Breeding Atlases, except there were few records for Loch Fyne and parts of Kintyre. However, outside the breeding season birds can occur, sometimes in considerable numbers, on stretches of coast which are not suitable for breeding: 70 at Proaig on 3 November 1993, 67 along 760m of shore at Carskiey in late July 2001, and numbers built up to 70 at Machrihanish in December 2001. Smaller groups, apparently on passage, occur at many places along the coast in spring and autumn. There are relatively few Scottish ringing returns, so it is impossible to say where these birds come from. The only recovery for Argyll concerns a bird ringed on Sanda in 1986 and found dead in Co. Down (Ireland) in 1988, showing that some local birds move south in winter. Apart from records of gale blown birds a kilometre or two inland at the Laggan, Kintyre, in 1998 and 1999, there appear to be no recent inland records (ABR, Argyll Database).

Our breeding birds belong to the nominate race *petrosus*, which occurs along coasts of Ireland, Britain (except the south-east), Channel Islands and north and north-west France. A few individuals showing characteristics of the Scandinavian race *littoralis* are recorded in Scotland in most winters, including one (in Fife) ringed in Norway (Winter Atlas). The location of the only claimed Argyll record, at Cuil Bay on 27 March 1989, is now in the Highland recording area. This race is very similar to *petrosus* in winter plumage. Various local races have been described on Scottish islands, but these are currently viewed as clines of *petrosus* (BOURC).

The Water Pipit was formerly considered as a race of Rock Pipit (then named *A. spinoletta petrosus*), but has since been recognised as a separate species *Anthus spinoletta*. In 1996, a review of the two Argyll records (in 1982 and 1984 when it was still considered a race of Rock Pipit) found that neither was satisfactory and it was deleted from the Argyll list (ABR 13:71).

Paul Daw

Yellow Wagtail

Motacilla flava

Scarce but annual passage migrant. Both *M. f. flavissima* (Yellow Wagtail) and *M. f. flava* (Blue-headed Wagtail) are regularly recorded.

In the past there was possibly some confusion between this species and the Grey Wagtail. Although the NSAs list it for the parishes of Killean and Kilchenzie (Kintyre) and Inveraray, Gray did not include any Argyll records, while H&B did not regard its occurrence in Argyll as confirmed. Nevertheless, Anderson (1913) claimed the Yellow Wagtail

Almost all records of Yellow Wagtails in Argyll have come from Kintyre and the islands. *Kelvin Pearce*

to be a more or less annual visitor to Tiree, more frequent in autumn than in spring. This was at a time when large arrivals were witnessed every spring in the Glasgow area (B&R).

Yellow Wagtails were said to have bred in Islay in 1922 (SN 1923:73, B&R), but this remains an isolated occurrence, although the species was formerly a widespread breeder in the Clyde (First Atlas). There was a decline in Argyll records towards the middle of the 20th century, with one on Tiree on 5 June 1968 said to be the first on the island for many years (SB 5:350). From around 1980 onwards records became more frequent, and a few individuals are now recorded almost annually in Argyll on migration. A few of the records involve two birds seen together, but larger groups have not been recorded.

Of 45 records in the 25-year period 1981-2005, nine were said to involve Blue-headed Wagtails. Many other published spring records do not give sex or race, making it difficult to evaluate proportions of *M. f. flavissima* and *M. f. flava*. There have been two records of the Grey-headed Wagtail *M. f. thunbergi*. One was at Ulva Ferry on Mull on 16 May 1985 (SB 14:114, ABR 3:44), and three striking male birds were seen together near the Ringing Stone, Tiree, during misty conditions on 20 May 2005 (Argyll Database).

Of the 1981-2005 records, all but two came from Kintyre and the islands. The exceptions were single birds at Loch Tulla on 20 June 1988 (ABR 5:25) and Kilmartin on 29 August 1998 (ABR 15:77). Most of the island records came from Islay (14) and Mull (7), with two records from Colonsay and one each from Tiree and Sanda. All but one of the 15 records from mainland Kintyre came from the Machrihanish area, where in 2003 there were four records at Uisaed Point, involving five birds. The seasonal distribution of 44 dated records in this period showed that slightly more occurred in spring (24) than in autumn (19), with one midsummer record (9 July). Spring records peaked in late May and autumn records in late August, earliest and latest dates being 26 April and 27 October.

Tristan ap Rheinallt

Grey Wagtail

Motacilla cinerea

This is a widespread breeding species in riparian habitats on the mainland and larger islands, but it is absent from most hill areas in winter.

The Grey Wagtail breeds near fast-flowing water throughout mainland Scotland and on the larger Inner Hebridean islands. It is scarce or absent in Shetland, Orkney, the Outer Hebrides and many of the smaller islands. The area to the north of the Clyde and Forth is largely deserted in winter (Thom).

In the mid-19th century, the Grey Wagtail was said to be a permanent resident in the west of Scotland, a not infrequent summer visitor to Iona and Mull and a not uncommon winter visitor to Islay (Graham, Gray). It was mentioned from the parish of Killean (west Kintyre) in the NSA. H&B said it was generally much rarer than the Pied Wagtail and mentioned records from Jura and one from Tiree. By the mid-20th century it was described as widely distributed, but not very numerous, on the mainland and as breeding on Islay, Jura, Mull and Iona. It was said to desert much of its range in winter and many were thought to leave the country, although at this time it could be fairly common around the coasts. Its susceptibility to hard winters was also remarked on (B&R).

The First Atlas confirmed breeding for most of mainland Argyll, apart from an area south of Oban and a few squares in Cowal and Kintyre. Breeding was also recorded over most of Mull, parts of Islay and the south of Jura, but there were no records for Colonsay, Coll, Tiree or any of the smaller islands.

Pairs may often be found in woodland when suitable watercourses are present. For example, they were found in five of 38 broadleaved woods surveyed in 1985 (Averis &

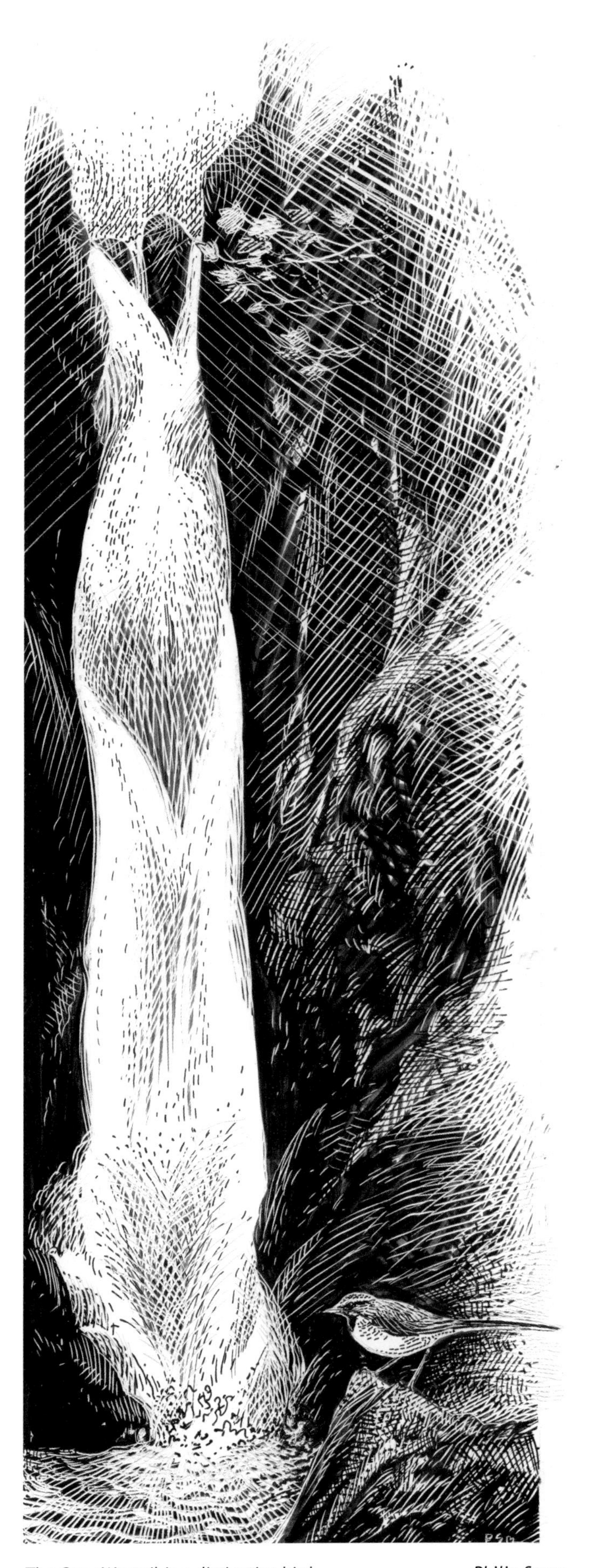

The Grey Wagtail is a distinctive bird of fast-flowing burns. *Philip Snow*

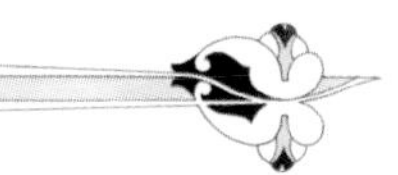

Martin 1985).

Although declines were reported following the severe winter of 1981/82, especially on Mull, there appears to have been a rapid recovery. The main changes shown in the Second Atlas included confirmed breeding on Islay, except the far north, and records for the Seil Island area and north Cowal. Grey Wagtails were found breeding in 61% of 10-km squares in Argyll. The abundance map showed high densities in central Kintyre, north Knapdale, north Cowal, eastern Mull and the Glen Orchy/Glen Lochy area.

On Colonsay, breeding was reported in 1991 (two pairs) and 1993, but otherwise the Grey Wagtail is only a scarce autumn migrant there. Elsewhere, available records suggest that the present breeding distribution differs little from that shown in the Second Atlas.

There is a single 19th century record for Tiree, and one at Gallanach on 14 October 1984 appears to be the first record for Coll (ABR). Since 2000 there have been almost annual records of migrants on both Coll and Tiree, mostly in autumn (Argyll Database). An immature was seen on Scarba in July 2004 (*Eider* September 2004).

The almost total desertion of higher ground in autumn is well illustrated in the Winter Atlas. Small numbers were found in Knapdale and in parts of Kintyre, but elsewhere only isolated birds were recorded. Ringing recoveries have shown that many Grey Wagtails from northern Britain move south and south-west to England, Ireland and France. The single Argyll recovery, of a bird ringed at Southend, Kintyre, in May 1975 and seen alive on the Isle of Man in August 1975, fits this pattern.

Grey Wagtails may return as early as mid-February, but the main passage periods are March and August-September. Passage is most noticeable on the coast; for example 13 were at Tayinloan on 19 August 2000. During 1994-2003, birds were found in winter in Cowal, Kintyre, Mid-Argyll and on Islay, mostly at coastal locations (Argyll Database).

Our birds belong to the race *cinerea*, which is found over most of the western Palaearctic.

Paul Daw

Pied Wagtail

Motacilla alba

Widespread and common breeding species, but absent from many areas in winter.

In summer, the Pied Wagtail is one of Scotland's most characteristic birds. It is found in a wide variety of habitats throughout the mainland and on most islands, frequently around farms and other rural habitations and along roadsides. Small numbers of the race *alba* (White Wagtail) breed on Shetland, but even here *yarrellii* is more abundant (Pennington *et al.* 2004). Many Scottish birds move south for the winter.

At the end of the 18th century, this species was mentioned in the OSA as appearing in the parish of Lismore and Appin 'at the stated seasons'. In the NSA, it was recorded in several Argyll parishes in the mid-19th century. Gray said it was very common in most districts, but that 'many hundreds' appeared to migrate southwards in autumn. According to Graham, it was found in all inhabited islands around Mull. H&B described it as scattered in pairs in suitable haunts on the mainland in summer. Strangely, they noted it was commoner in most places in winter than in summer. In the mid-20th century it was said to be common all over Scotland, mostly as a summer visitor. It nested commonly on Islay and more locally on Jura, Gigha, Colonsay and Mull. It was also present on Lismore, and three pairs were found nesting on Iona in 1948 (B&R).

Despite the steep drop in numbers in Britain following the severe winter of 1962/63 (CBC), breeding was recorded almost throughout Argyll in the First Atlas. The only confirmed record for Coll was at its north end, and there was a record for Oronsay, but not Colonsay.

Although Pied Wagtails are usually absent in coniferous

Many of Argyll's Pied Wagtails migrate south for the winter. *Philip Kirkham*

woodland, they were found in 16 of the 38 broadleaved woods surveyed in 1985 (Averis & Martin 1985).

Following the severe winter of 1981/82, recovery from any decline must have been rapid, as distribution in Argyll in the Second Atlas was almost identical to the First Atlas. Pied Wagtails were found breeding in 87% of 10-km squares in Argyll. The only changes were new breeding records for Colonsay. The abundance map showed high concentrations in central Kintyre, parts of Islay and North Argyll.

A survey of the Rinns of Islay in 1994 found 102 pairs, mainly on agricultural land, with concentrations in the north (ABR 11:72). A pair bred on Lunga in 2002, but breeding on the Treshnish Isles has been sporadic. In the same year, seven pairs bred on Oronsay and at least 40 pairs were estimated to be breeding on Tiree (ABR).

The Winter Atlas showed a move away from higher ground in autumn, but also demonstrated that a substantial population remained in south Argyll. In particular, there were significant numbers in Knapdale, Cowal, part of Kintyre and on Islay. Records since 2000 confirm this pattern. Twenty-three birds were seen at Tayinloan on 30 December 2001. The 84 birds counted in Machrihanish Bay on 6 November 2001 may have been late passage birds. There were regular winter sightings of small numbers on Oronsay and Tiree. Because most of our birds move south in autumn, winter roosts are seldom noted, but 25 were roosting at Oban Harbour on 24 February 1998 (Argyll Database).

Considerable gatherings may occur during passage from July to October and to a lesser extent during March and April. Recent counts have included 70 on Tiree on 22 March 2000, 70 along the road from Peninver to Campbeltown on 30 July 1999, 51 feeding in grass on Oronsay on 3 September 1999, 62 at Balemartine on 7 October 2001 and 89 flying over Otter Ferry in five minutes on 21 September 2002. A roost in a reed-bed at West Machrihanish between July and October 2001 held over 300 birds at its peak (Argyll Database). The origins and destinations of at least some of these birds were indicated by two adult males, one ringed in northern France in January 1995 and killed by a cat at North Connel in March 1995, and the other ringed on Coll in August 1983 and seen alive at Oldbury (Avon) in February 1985.

The race *alba* (White Wagtail) has been known as a passage migrant in Argyll since at least the late 19th century. H&B said that, since one had been obtained on Tiree in 1889, it had been recognised as a regular visitor "to and from Iceland" in spring and autumn in flocks of up to 50 birds. Currently, birds usually appear in spring from the end of March onwards, especially on the islands and in coastal areas, and passage continues until mid-May. At this time of year *alba* is clearly distinguishable from *yarrellii*. Recent counts have included 26 *alba* on Oronsay on 5 May 1997, 47 at Loch a' Phuill, Tiree, on 2 May 1998, 30 at Loch Gruinart on 24 April 2000 and 41 at Machrihanish on 11 May 2000. Considerable care is needed to separate *alba* in autumn, but large numbers have been reported between mid-August and mid-October, including 30 in the Machrihanish area on 30 September 2000 and 80 on Sanda Island on 18 September 2002. A few have been reported as late as 30 October, when six were seen on the shore at Balnabraid Glen, Kintyre, in 2000, and 4 November, when one was at Trudernish, Islay, in 2001 (Argyll Database). The only ringing recovery was of an *alba* juvenile ringed in Iceland in July 1985 and found dead at Skerryvore Lighthouse in September 1985.

Birds breeding in Argyll are normally of the race *yarrellii*. However, in June 2000 a territorial male *alba* associated with a female *yarrellii* near Cairnbaan. On 1 July 2003, an apparent family group (male and female *alba* accompanied by three juveniles) was seen at Islandadd Bridge on the Crinan Canal (Argyll Database).

Paul Daw

Waxwing

Bombycilla garrulus

This is an irruptive winter visitor that eats berries; it is not seen every year in Argyll.

Waxwings are annual winter visitors to Scotland in extremely variable numbers. In some years fewer than 50 are recorded, mostly near the east coast, while in other years major influxes involve thousands of birds, some of which reach the far west. Numbers appear to depend partly on the success of the breeding season in northern Fennoscandia and Russia and partly on the berry crop in southern Scandinavia (Svärdson 1957). Because of their liking for berries of ornamental shrubs they are often seen in parks and gardens, where they are very approachable.

Waxwings have been reported from Argyll since at least the end of the 18th century. There is a record of a 'Bohemian Chatterer' (as they were then named) being 'taken' in the parish of Glenorchy and Inishail in 1792 (OSA). They were mentioned in the NSA as having occurred at Inveraray. During major irruptions in the first half of the 20th century, Waxwings reached the Western Isles (and so presumably Argyll) in 1921, spring 1937 and winter 1946 (B&R). Between then and 1970, there were eight irruptions into Scotland (Table 1). Waxwings were recorded in Argyll in all but the 1957 irruption, often during late October-November.

During 1973–2004, there were records of Waxwings in Argyll in all but six years (1976, 1978, 1986, 1989, 1995 and 1998). In most years there were no more than two or three records, often involving single birds. Most records were during October-December, but there were a few during January-March (ABR, SBR). The exceptions to this general pattern occurred during irruptions (Table 2).

A curious feature of these records (Tables 1 & 2) is that there were areas where birds occurred more frequently and

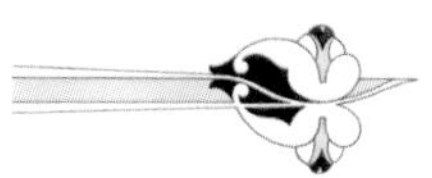

Table 1. Irruptions of Waxwings into Scotland, 1950-1972.

Year	Comments	Source
1957	Mainly restricted to the east coast of Scotland during February-March. No records for Argyll	Macmillan 1959
Winter 1958/59	More widespread than in 1957. A single bird was seen on Tiree on 1 January and 45 were reported in Argyll (no location or date).	Macmillan 1959
October-November 1959	Widespread in Scotland. Argyll records include 7 birds at Ardrishaig on 11 November, 15 at Kilmelford on 17 November, 1 at Benmore on 19 November and 6 at Barcaldine on 25 November.	Macmillan 1960
November 1961	Relatively small numbers involved compared to previous irruptions into Scotland. Only one record for Argyll, of "a 'bevy' at Barcaldine" on 29 October – the earliest report in Scotland.	Macmillan 1962
October-November 1963	Widespread in Scotland, involving substantial numbers. All Argyll records were in the latter half of November: 2 along the Blairmore/Ardentinny road on 17 November, 5 at Port Askaig during 21-23 November and 15 in Oban for two days during the last week of November.	Macmillan 1964
Winter 1965/66	A large number of birds involved (*c*.10,000 in Scotland). There were 117 records of 1,235 birds in the Argyll/Inner Hebrides faunal area. Unusually, some of the first birds to arrive were in Argyll, with four in Lochgilphead on 10 October (and at least 14 the following day). Other locations included Eredine, Dalmally, Kilmelford, and by 15 October well over 100 birds were scattered across Argyll. In November birds were recorded on Mull and Islay, and 100+ birds were at Crarae Gardens in late October-early November. There were no records after the end of November.	Everett 1967
Winter 1966/67	Numbers were much smaller in Scotland than during the previous winter. All records in Argyll were in October-November, including 12 birds at Benderloch on 20 October and *c*.40 at Inveraray on 30 October, which stayed until at least 11 November. The scattered groups in Argyll comprised about 135 birds.	Everett 1967
Winter 1970/71	All Argyll records were during October-November (33 reports in each month), including at 6 at Oban on 6 November; at the end of the month, there were 20 at Loch Awe, *c*.6 at Lochgilphead and 2 at Strachur.	Lyster 1971

Table 2. Major irruptions of Waxwings into Argyll, 1974-2004 (Argyll Database).

Year	Comments
1974	A large arrival in Scotland produced a series of records in Argyll during 27 October-18 November, including a maximum of eight birds in Lochgilphead during 6-15 November.
1988	The best autumn influx for many years led to record numbers in Argyll. After the first at Port Charlotte on 1 November, numbers built up rapidly with records from all mainland areas except Cowal, and from Islay and Mull. The largest flock was 42 birds at Taynuilt on 6 November. It was calculated that at least 90 were present in Mid-Argyll during 6-8 November. The last (single) was at Connel on 14 December.
1990	A small influx from 30 October to 9 December led to widespread reports of small numbers, with a maximum of five at Connel on 3 November.
1991	A slightly larger, but briefer influx than in 1990 produced widespread reports from 13 November to 6 December, with a maximum of 13 at Taynuilt on 24 November.
1996	Unusually, there were two separate influxes in the same year. The first was a large arrival in mid-January. After three were seen at Kilmartin on 17 January, there were reports from several localities in Cowal, Islay, Kintyre, Mid-Argyll and Mull with flocks of 20 in Dunoon and Oban. The last was at Connel on 31 March. The second influx of 1996 was in November and was concentrated within a three-week period, with only three records after the end of the month. Once again, most records were from Islay, Mid-Argyll and Mull, the largest flock being 45 at Dunstaffnage from 9-18 November. There were 24 at Ardrishaig from 20-26 November. The last (single) was at Loch Gruinart on 28 December.
2000/2001	The best winter for Waxwings since 1996, with birds arriving on the east coast of Scotland during the third week of December 2000. In Argyll, the first bird was seen on Islay on 28 December and up to five were recorded widely by the end of the year. A group of 24 seen briefly at Loch Skerrols on 29 December was the largest flock ever recorded on Islay. Early in 2001, birds were widely reported on the mainland, including flocks of 30 or more in Campbeltown on 1 January, 21 at Barcaldine on 5 January and 18 at Connel on 9 January. Apart from two records from Mull and a single at Craighouse (possibly a first for Jura), there were no records from the islands at this time. Most had gone by the end of January but a single was near Minard on 6 February and three late birds were in Oban on 24 March.
2003	There were small influxes during both January-February and October-November, with more records than usual from Cowal and a maximum count of ten near Inverinan (Loch Awe) on 19 February.
2004	An influx of unprecedented proportions occurred during late October with flocks of over 1,000 birds reported in the east of Scotland. This gave rise to record-breaking flocks in Argyll in early November, including over 100 birds in the Lochgilphead area and, unusually, several records from Coll and Tiree. The first reports came from the islands with two at Port Askaig on 21 October, followed by seven at The Lodge, Coll, on 23 October, 25 at Port Charlotte, Islay, on 25 October and one at Kenovay, Tiree, on 26 October. The first mainland birds were 50+ at Slockavullin, Mid-Argyll, on 25 October followed by 30+ on Seil Island on 30 October, increasing to 85 by 1 November. Mull had nine at Lochdon on 2 November, when 60 were also ranging around Oban. Further large flocks were reported in the following days, including 20 in Inveraray on 5 November, 75 near the Co-op in Lochgilphead on 6 November and 61 in North Connel on 7 November. The peak count was over 100 at Kilmory, Lochgilphead, on 9 November and 43 were in Campbeltown at about this time, but after 82 were seen at Connel on 14 November, the birds disappeared as suddenly as they had arrived.

Rowan and hawthorn berries are favourite foods of Waxwings in winter. *Philip Snow*

in larger numbers than elsewhere. In particular, Connel (both north and south of Loch Etive) and Lochgilphead regularly held birds in both invasion and non-invasion years. Although this might be observer-biased, it could also be due to better food availability. In the Lochgilphead area, birds were often seen feeding on the fruit of the Siberian Crab *Malus baccata* that has been widely planted by the Forestry Commission. Elsewhere, berries of *Sorbus* spp., *Cotoneaster* spp. and *Crataegus* spp. were avidly eaten. Waxwings have been reported from all recording areas of Argyll.

Paul Daw

Dipper

Cinclus cinclus

Widespread resident in riparian habitats, but scarce on Islay and absent from Colonsay, Tiree and Coll.

The Dipper is a bird of swiftly flowing burns and rivers in upland areas of mainland Scotland. It is largely absent as a breeding species from the Northern Isles and from many of the smaller islands in the west. It often nests and roosts under bridges or on other man-made structures over water.

Confusingly referred to as the 'Kingfisher' or 'Kingsfisher' in the older literature, Dippers were recorded as early as 1792 in Kilfinan (Cowal) parish (OSA) and in 1843 in lists for Inveraray and Killean (Kintyre) (NSA). Gray said they were common on Mull and Islay. Later in the 19th century, H&B stated that, although common on Mull, Dippers were not equally common in all districts of Argyll and the Isles. For example, they were quite abundant in Benderloch and nearby mountains and were found on Jura, but not on Tiree. H&B noted that the Duke of Argyll protected them on the River Aray, at a time when they were still considered a threat to angling by some keepers. B&R mentioned that Dippers have a considerable altitudinal range, being found nesting above 600m asl as well as near the coast. In severe weather they tended to move downhill and could be seen feeding in salt-water pools. They could also be found by the sea at other times of the year.

In the First Atlas, Dippers were widespread in Argyll, but by no mean ubiquitous. They were not found breeding along the western coastal areas of the mainland, nor in parts of Kintyre. Breeding occurred locally on Mull and Islay, but there were only sight records for Jura and Colonsay and no records at all for Coll or Tiree. Dippers were found in two of the 38 broadleaved woods surveyed in 1985 (Averis & Martin 1985). There were records from at least three lochs on Jura in June 1985, although breeding was not confirmed (ABR).

The Second Atlas showed the Dipper to be a widespread breeding species with a balance of gains (Jura, south Kintyre and parts of Mull) and losses (parts of Islay and Mid-Argyll) since the First Atlas. However, the timed tetrad counts indicated that in most places, even where breeding was confirmed, the Dipper occurred only at low densities and this was reflected in the abundance map. The only exceptions were in north Cowal and the area to the north of Loch Fyne, where it was rather more numerous.

During 1997-2003, breeding was confirmed at five sites on Mull, six in Mid-Argyll, one on Islay, one in North Argyll and two in Cowal. A roost of up to seven birds occurred at Knockstapplebeg on Conie Glen Water, Kintyre, in December 1998 (ABR).

There were occasional records from Colonsay in the first half of the 20th century, but since 1950 only four have been reported, the most recent in April 1986 (Jardine *et al.* 1986). There have been no records for Coll and just a single record for Tiree, on 4 November 1986 (ABR).

Apart from altitudinal changes during winter, some medium-distance dispersal also occurs, at least occasionally, as shown by an adult found dead at the River Garnock, Dalry, Strathclyde in February 1979. This bird had been ringed in May 1976 as a juvenile at Killean, Kintyre, 60km to the south-west.

Most British Dippers belong to the race *gularis*. However, the situation is complex and doubt has been cast on how reliably the races can be identified. Birds from Kintyre and possibly other parts of Argyll (e.g. Islay and Jura) have been ascribed to the Irish race *hibernicus*, which has decidedly

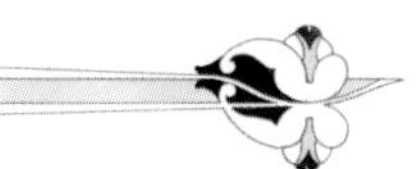

The Dipper is a specialist of clean, running fresh water. Populations across Britain appear to be relatively healthy. *John McAvoy*

darker upperparts and less rufous on the belly than *gularis*. The nominate race *cinclus* from northern Europe (often known as the Black-bellied Dipper) occurs almost annually in Shetland and Fair Isle, and occasionally elsewhere on the east coast, but has never been reliably reported in Argyll.

Paul Daw

Wren

Troglodytes troglodytes

A common resident in habitats with sufficient ground vegetation, although its numbers often decline after severe winters.

The Wren is a common resident found breeding throughout Scotland in a wide variety of habitats, often up to a considerable altitude. It is notably sedentary and several distinguishable races have evolved on isolated islands. Populations are prone to marked declines following severe winters, but numbers usually recover quickly.

H&B noted that, as far back as records go, the Wren was always plentiful in the gardens of Iona and Mull, and it was mentioned in several Argyll parishes in the NSA. The adaptability of the species has been commented on, at least since the 19th century, when it was said to occur "even in winter, in the bleakest hill districts" and to be at home on the larger islands, although less common or absent from the smaller ones and apparently only a winter visitor to Tiree (H&B). In the middle of the 20th century, B&R said that numbers had still not recovered from the severe winters of 1940/41 and 1941/42. Nevertheless, the Wren was then thought to be common on Islay and Jura and to be the most abundant small bird on Gigha and Colonsay. It also nested on Coll, Lismore and the Treshnish Isles, but B&R had no breeding record for Tiree.

The first breeding record on Tiree was in 1952, when two singing males were heard at Ceann a' Mhara in June and newly fledged young were being fed by an adult at Hynish in July (Boyd 1958). However, apparently Wrens did not become established on Tiree as the First Atlas showed suspected or confirmed breeding virtually everywhere in Argyll, except on Tiree. It is possible that the population was eliminated by the severe winter of 1962/63. In the mid 1980s, Thom said that Wrens bred rarely on Tiree, but only a short time later (1989) they were reported to be breeding in small numbers in suitable habitat on Coll and Tiree (Stroud 1989). They were present during the breeding season on the Garvellachs and

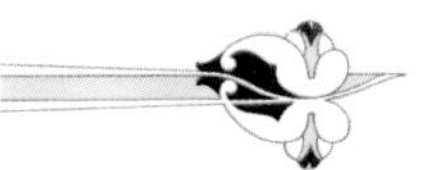

Lunga (near Scarba) when these islands were visited in 1975 and 1976 respectively (T.D.H. Merrie pers. comm.).

The Winter Atlas recorded Wrens in all but a handful of 10-km squares in Argyll and confirmed their sedentary nature. In some upland areas they were one of the few species to be found during winter.

Wrens were found in all 38 broadleaved woods surveyed in 1985, but were only the tenth most numerous species, possibly because numbers had not fully recovered from the severe winter of 1981/82 (Averis & Martin 1985). However, in a study of spruce plantations in Cowal they were the most numerous species in the spring of 1991, but had slipped to third place in 1992. Although numbers were lower in winter, they were the second most numerous species in 1990/1991 and fifth in 1991/1992 (Patterson *et al.* 1995).

Wren distribution in the Second Atlas was broadly similar to the First, except that there were now breeding records in all three 10-km squares on Tiree and in additional coastal squares in Kintyre and on Islay. There were confirmed breeding records from 84% of the Argyll 10-km squares. The abundance map showed areas of very high density in Cowal, Kintyre and Mid-Argyll. A survey of the Rinns of Islay in 1994 found 198 pairs, although this excluded forested areas which would have held substantial numbers (ABR).

Recent survey work has confirmed that Wrens are one of the most numerous species in both broadleaved and coniferous woodlands in Argyll. In 14 randomly selected 1-km squares (containing mainly coniferous woodland) they were found in all but one square (NM0244 on Tiree) (Wilson & Fuller 2001, P. Daw unpubl. data). Overall, they were the fifth most numerous species (average 9.35 birds per square). In one 1-km square containing mainly recently felled coniferous woodland, 26 individuals were recorded during one visit. In 29 broadleaved woods surveyed for the Second Woodland Bird Survey 2003/4 in Mid- and North Argyll, Wrens were found in much higher numbers (93.4% increase) than during the 1985 survey, thanks no doubt to the intervening mild winters (Amar *et al.* 2006, RSPB unpubl. data).

The 1-km squares regularly surveyed in Argyll for the BBS have shown little annual variation in numbers since 1994, although in one square in Kintyre a high total of 33 Wrens was recorded during a single visit in 1998. Wrens were found in 80% of BBS squares surveyed in 2003. Results from the Taynish CBC showed a gradual, but fluctuating increase over 17 years (Figure), possibly due to the recent run of mild winters. There was a significant relationship between Wren

The Wren is one of the commonest birds of gardens and woodlands. *John McAvoy*

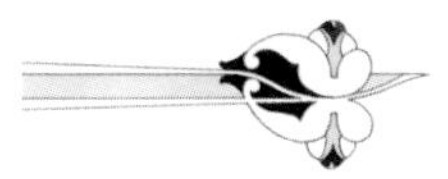

and Robin number over the same period. In 2002, the Wren was the most numerous breeding species at Taynish with 85 territories.

Records since the Second Atlas have indicated good breeding populations on some of the islands. In 1994, a survey of the Rinns of Islay, excluding forested areas that hold substantial numbers, located *c.* 198 pairs, and in 1997 49 territories were found at the RSPB's Loch Gruinart Reserve. A minimum of 20 pairs held territories on Tiree in 1999 and 26 pairs were found on Sanda Island in 2002. In 2003 on the Treshnish Isles, at least 14 singing males were recorded on Lunga and birds were present on Fladda (ABR).

Most Scottish Wrens, including those in Argyll, are considered to be of the race *indigenus*, which is found in Ireland and northern England and is slightly darker and less rufous than nominate *troglodytes* from southern and central England and continental Europe. There are also several island races in Scotland, most of which are thought to be largely sedentary (McGowan *et al.* 2003). Nevertheless, birds showing characteristics of *hebridensis*, the form found in the Outer Hebrides and probably Skye, have recently been seen on Tiree in winter together with *indigenus* type birds. However, an individual killed by a cat on Tiree in January 2003 and sent to the National Museums of Scotland was identified as being of the typical mainland form *indigenus* (J. Bowler pers. comm.). Apart from additional birds on Tiree in autumn, there is little evidence for the presence of migrants and there are no records of ringed Wrens being recovered in Argyll.

Paul Daw

Dunnock

Prunella modularis

This is a widespread resident, but nowhere numerous. It is scarce on Coll and Jura and only a winter visitor to Tiree.

The Dunnock is a common resident throughout mainland Scotland, but it is scarce or local in Orkney, the Outer Hebrides and some of the Inner Hebrides and it is absent from Shetland. Dunnocks are catholic in their choice of habitat as long as there is thick low growth of some kind for nesting, but they are particularly associated with gardens, farmland with hedgerows, scrub and young plantations. Dunnocks also occur as passage migrants and as winter visitors in small numbers (Thom).

In the mid-19th century the Dunnock was described as abundant "wherever man has settled even in the smaller isles" (Graham), although it was mentioned in only two Argyll parishes in the NSA. H&B said it was "common everywhere, but less abundant in the less populous and barer districts" and that it was mentioned "in all lists from the mainland and most of the Isles". However, they had only one record for Tiree, in September 1887.

B&R said that in the 1930s and 1940s the race *hebridium* was resident on Islay, locally common on Jura and that a few bred on Gigha and Colonsay. They considered that the birds breeding on Mull, where there were said to be large numbers on the Ross of Mull, were probably of this race. They make no mention of its status on Coll or Tiree. However, Boyd (1958) records one on Tiree in September 1956 and a few on Coll in spring and summer from 1945 to 1955.

Although the First Atlas showed suspected or confirmed breeding in most of Argyll, there were a few 10-km squares in Cowal and Mid-Argyll where presence only was recorded and

Population trends of Wren and Robin at Taynish NNR, 1990-2006.

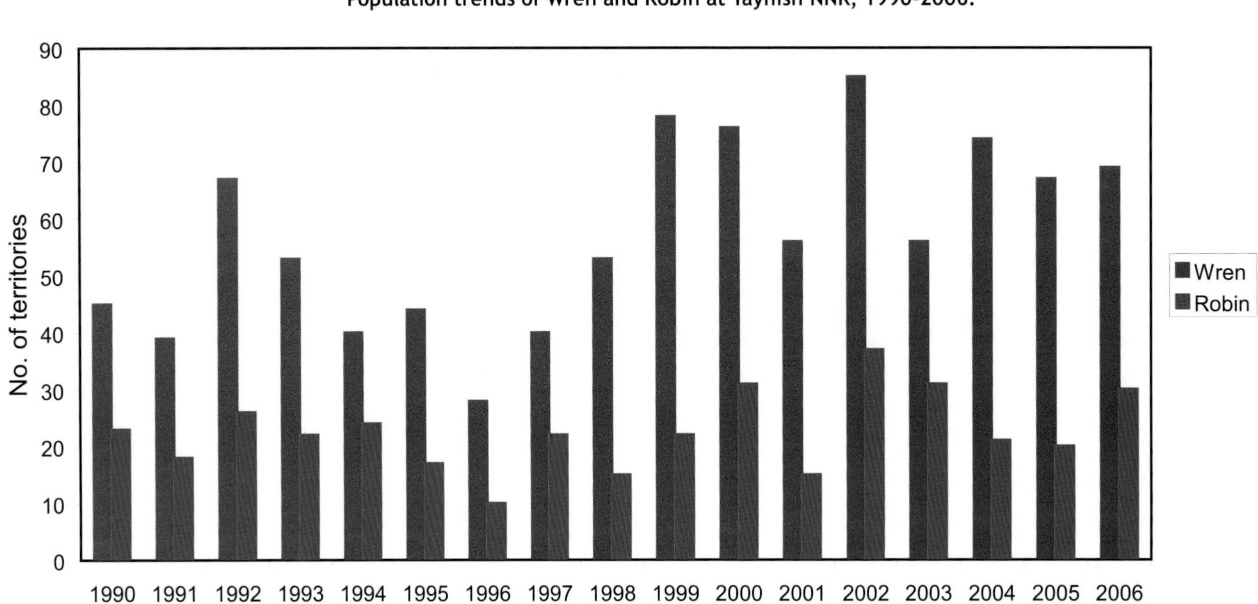

a curious (in view of comments in B&R) lack of records for most of the Ross of Mull. However, breeding was indicated on most islands including a probable record for Tiree and confirmed breeding on Coll. Dunnocks were found during the breeding season on the Garvellachs and Lunga (near Scarba) when these islands were visited in 1975 and 1976 respectively (T.D.H. Merrie pers. comm.).

The Winter Atlas showed Dunnocks in most of Argyll's 10-km squares, but mainly in small numbers. However, there were some gaps in Kintyre and on Mull and no winter records for Tiree.

A survey in 1985 found Dunnocks in only six of 38 broadleaf woods (Averis & Martin 1985), which agrees with an earlier findings that they were absent or scarce in grazed birch woods and many oak woods (Williamson 1974). However, during a study in Sitka Spruce forests in Cowal, they were found to be the fourth most widespread species in the spring of 1991 although they had dropped to seventh in 1992. Distribution was dramatically reduced in winter, when there were only a handful of records (Patterson *et al.* 1995).

In the Second Atlas, there were confirmed breeding records from only 55% of the 10-km squares in Argyll and, according to the abundance map, they were nowhere numerous. There was evidence of some contraction in breeding range, mostly from the higher ground of North Argyll and parts of north Kintyre. There were fewer confirmed breeding records on Mull and none on Tiree, although breeding was confirmed for all three 10-km squares covering Coll. However, they were probably breeding around The Manse on Tiree in 1988 (Stroud 1989). A pair bred on Eileach an Naoimh, in the Garvellachs, in 1991 (Argyll Database).

In 14 randomly selected 1-km squares (containing mainly coniferous woodland) Dunnocks were found in 50% of the squares, although mostly in small numbers (Wilson & Fuller 2001, P. Daw unpubl. data). In 2003/4 they were found in only two of 29 broadleaved woods in Mid- and North Argyll (Amar *et al.* 2006, RSPB unpubl. data), confirming earlier findings (Williamson 1974, Averis & Martin 1985). Although Thom said they were uncommon in conifer plantations, these surveys in Argyll found Dunnocks quite frequently in pre-thicket and thicket crops.

The BBS 1-km squares surveyed annually in Argyll have shown little variation in overall numbers since 1994. However, results from the Taynish CBC showed a slight increase over the 14 years since 1990. An average of 3.4 territories was found during 1990–1996 and 4.8 during 1997-2003, with a maximum of nine in 2002. This slight increase could have been due in part to the recent run of mild winters.

Records since the Second Atlas indicate that Dunnocks have bred on Coll (3-5 pairs in 2003), Colonsay, Oronsay and probably on Jura, but that they have been only a scarce annual visitor to Tiree, mostly in autumn and winter. They have bred occasionally on Sanda, the last record being in 1999. One on Cairn na Burgh More on 28 June 2001 was the only recent record for the Treshnish Isles, and a bird was present on Scarba in July 2004 (ABR, Argyll Database).

Dunnocks are highly sedentary in Britain and Ireland, although it has been suggested that they may undergo a sporadic partial migration in late autumn (Migration Atlas). The race breeding in the Inner Hebrides, the Outer Hebrides and Ireland, is considered to be *hebridium*. This has darker, more richly coloured upperparts than *occidentalis*, which occupies most of mainland Britain. Birds breeding on the mainland of western Scotland are reported to be *hebridium* (B&R, McGowan *et al.* 2003) or *hebridium/occidentalis* intergrades (BWP). Four Argyll ringing recoveries have been

A familiar garden bird, Dunnocks can also do well in other habitats with dense ground cover. *John McAvoy*

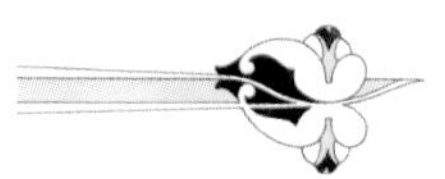

close to the ringing site, so there is no evidence at present for any immigration of *occidentalis* into Argyll from further east or south. Nevertheless, some movement does occur. B&R reported that Dunnocks, like Robins, wintered "in numbers" on Sanda and exhibited some degree of seasonal migration on the mainland. More recently, apparent migrants have been noted in autumn on Colonsay and Tiree as well as at the Mull of Kintyre. Thirty-four birds at the north end of Gigha on 17 October 2002 must also have been migrants. Most such records have been in October, but immigrants have also been reported recently from Tiree in winter and spring.

The possibility that some migrants in Argyll might belong to the Continental race *modularis* was raised by B&R. This form is highly migratory, with noticeable movements down the east coast of Britain, in both spring and autumn. The migration is particularly obvious on Fair Isle, where there are few breeding Dunnocks (Migration Atlas). However, while B&R stated that Continental Dunnocks occurred annually at the Butt of Lewis, the only evidence that they have reached Argyll appears to be the statement in Elliott (1989) that two birds ringed at Bridgend (Islay) in March 1977 had wing lengths corresponding to *modularis*. Further evidence is required before admitting this race to the Argyll list.

Paul Daw

Robin

Erithacus rubecula

A widespread and common resident, with small numbers breeding on Coll but none on Tiree. There is a noticeable autumn passage with some migrants staying for the winter.

The Robin nests throughout mainland Scotland. It is adaptable and uses a wide variety of habitats, provided that there is a shrub layer. Although less common, it breeds on all the main island groups apart from Shetland (Thom). Large scale immigration from continental Europe occurs in autumn when flocks, occasionally in the hundreds, arrive in the Northern Isles and along the east coast (SBR). Most migrants move further south, but some remain for the winter, boosting numbers in areas where Robins are scarce at other times. The native population is largely sedentary although there is some local dispersal, mainly of females in winter, with a few making longer journeys (Winter Atlas).

In the 19th century H&B said that Robins were so common everywhere that details about their distribution were unnecessary. They had no evidence of historical changes in numbers. They described Robins as common, although not abundant, on Mull and Jura and common in winter on Tiree.

In the mid-20th century the Robin was reported to breed fairly commonly on Islay and Mull (including at least one pair on Iona) as well as in woods on Jura. It also nested on Lismore and was widespread on Gigha and Colonsay. On Coll and Tiree it was chiefly a winter visitor, although it bred there occasionally (B&R) However, according to Boyd (1958) there were no records of breeding on Tiree and, although MacDougall (1938) said it 'breeds occasionally', it was not reported there by five observers over seven summers during 1939-55 (Boyd 1958).

With the exception of a few coastal 10-km squares where presence only was noted, the First Atlas showed confirmed breeding almost everywhere in Argyll. However, Robins were only shown as present on Iona and there were no records for Coll, Tiree, the Garvellachs, Scarba or the Treshnish Isles. However, Robins were present during the breeding season on the Garvellachs and Lunga (near Scarba) when these islands were visited in 1975 and 1976 respectively (T.D.H. Merrie pers. comm.).

In the mid 1980s, Thom gave no recent breeding records for Coll (although small numbers were present in June 1984) and none for Tiree. By 1989 Robins were described as breeding in small numbers in and around the gardens at Arinagour on Coll (Stroud 1989).

The Winter Atlas showed Robins in most of the Argyll 10-km squares, sometimes in relatively large numbers (e.g. in Cowal, Mull and Mid-Argyll). There were also records for all 10-km squares on both Coll and Tiree.

Robins were found in all 38 broadleaved woods surveyed in 1985, where they were the ninth most numerous species (Averis & Martin 1985). This compares to a ranking of sixth in deciduous woodland in Glen Nant (Williamson 1974). In spruce plantations on Cowal, they were the second most numerous species in the spring of 1991 and most numerous of all in 1992. Although numbers were lower in winter, they were the fourth most numerous species in 1990/1991 and third in 1991/1992 (Patterson *et al.* 1995).

The distribution of Robins in the Second Atlas is broadly similar to that of the First Atlas, except confirmed breeding was now shown for two of the three 10-km squares covering Coll and birds were present on Tiree. There were confirmed breeding records from 79% of the Argyll 10-km squares and the abundance map showed areas of high density in parts of Cowal and Kintyre. A pair bred on Eileach an Naoimh, Garvellachs, in 1991 (ABR 8).

Recent surveys have confirmed the Robin as one of the most numerous species in both broadleaved and coniferous woodlands in Argyll. In 14 randomly selected 1-km squares containing mainly coniferous woodland, Robins were found at 12 sites and were the fifth most numerous species with an average of 11.6 registrations per site (Wilson & Fuller 2001, P. Daw unpubl. data). During one visit to a 1-km square containing mainly recently-felled conifers, 33 individuals were recorded.

Robins were found in all 16 broadleaved woods surveyed during 2003 (Amar *et al.* 2006, P. Daw unpubl. data), but

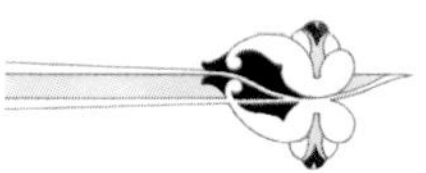

at lower densities (average of 8 registrations per site) than in coniferous woodlands (Wilson & Fuller 2001, P. Daw unpubl. data). Robins were found all 29 broadleaved woods in Mid- and North Argyll during the Second Woodland Bird Survey 2003/4 and had increased in numbers by 50% since the similar survey in 1985 (Amar *et al.* 2006, RSPB unpubl. data).

Scarba during a visit by the Argyll Bird Club in 2004.

Immigrants arrive on Tiree from August onwards and sometimes quite large numbers remain during the winter (over 100 estimated in January 2001). However, although a few individuals may linger as late as May, there have still been no confirmed breeding records from Tiree. Large numbers of migrants also appear on other islands. At least 100 were

Robin populations decline sharply after harsh winters, but in favourable conditions, numbers build up again quickly. *John McAvoy*

present on Sanda on 14 September 2002 (Sanda Island Bird Report 2002, ABR). Data from the CES site at Aros Moss, Kintyre, indicate that after a period of low productivity following the nationally poor year of 1996, the percentage of juveniles increased and has remained stable since 1999 (Brown 2002).

No clear trend is evident in the 1-km squares regularly surveyed in Argyll for the BBS since 1994 although, in one square in Kintyre, a high total of 32 Robins were recorded during a single visit in 1998. The species was found in 70% of BBS squares surveyed in 2003. The Taynish CBC found a gradual increase from an average of 21.7 territories during 1990-1995 to 25.7 during 2001-2006, possibly due in part to the recent run of mild winters (see Figure in account for Wren). In 2003 the Robin was the fifth most numerous breeding species at Taynish.

Records since the Second Atlas indicate Robins breed on only some Argyll islands. Breeding has occurred on Sanda Island in most years (two pairs fledged young in 2002) and was confirmed on Iona in 1999. Seven territories were identified at the RSPB's Loch Gruinart Reserve in June 1997, and in 2003 birds were present in the breeding season on Jura. They bred on the RSPB Reserve and elsewhere on Coll, but there was no recent estimate of numbers. However, Robins are only irregular visitors to the Treshnish Isles where single birds were found in June 2001 and 2002. They were not recorded on

Robins breeding in the British Isles belong to the race *melophilus*, which on average has darker, warmer-toned upperparts and a darker, more rufous breast than the Continental race *rubecula*. However, differences are subtle and few individuals can be confidently identified to subspecies, making ringing an essential tool for studying movements (Migration Atlas).

Most British Robins are sedentary, but a few winter as far afield as Spain (Migration Atlas). Although relatively few, ringing recoveries involving Argyll suggest that long-distance movements are not unusual. Only six of 26 recoveries were less than 30km from the ringing site. While some of the longer movements might relate to *rubecula* (see below), others certainly involve *melophilus* since they were ringed as chicks

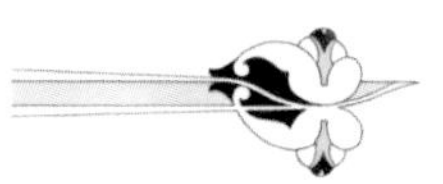

in the British Isles. For example, a chick ringed at Kinlochewe, Highland, on 24 May 1996 was recovered 254km to the south at Southend, Kintyre, on 11 September 1996. Another chick, ringed at Barcaldine, North Argyll, on 29 June 1983, was recovered 227km away in Antrim, Northern Ireland, the following winter. Also likely to be of Argyll origin was a juvenile ringed at Achnacree, North Argyll, on 4 August 1984 and recovered in Avon on 7 February 1985. At 594km, this is the longest recorded movement of an Argyll-ringed Robin, though it exceeds by just 1km the distance covered by another juvenile ringed on Sheep Island, Kintyre, on 27 August 1984 and recovered in Cornwall on 19 November 1985.

Falls of continental *rubecula* occur regularly on the east coast of Britain in autumn, especially in October, and are thought to be mainly from Fennoscandia. Most are on passage, but a few may remain in the British Isles for the winter (Migration Atlas). Some may reach the west coast of Scotland, occasionally if not regularly, though there are no ringing recoveries to support this. It is worth noting that the British *melophilus* is believed to be rare on passage in Ireland, where most coastal movements in autumn are thought to involve *rubecula* (Migration Atlas). On the other hand, Thom believed that autumn passage on the west coast of Scotland could involve the dispersal of native birds to winter in Ireland. In fact, four of the 21 recoveries of Argyll-ringed Robins were in Northern Ireland, although only one (see above) definitely involves the race *melophilus*. Similarly, short-distance movements are thought likely to be responsible for the appearance of Robins at sites in the Hebrides where the species rarely breeds (Migration Atlas). B&R were uncertain which race was responsible for the increase of Robins in the Inner Hebrides in winter. Thus, it appears that despite occasional claimed sightings of *rubecula*, including a bird at the Mull of Kintyre on 5 November 2000, the occurrence of this race in Argyll has yet to be confirmed.

Paul Daw

Common Nightingale

Luscinia megarhynchos

Vagrant.

Although the Nightingale breeds in some numbers in southern England, there are relatively few Scottish records. Indeed, away from the Northern Isles and the Isle of May, it is a major rarity. Two Argyll records relate to individuals heard singing by observers very familiar with the characteristic song. One was at Loch Skerrols on Islay on 28 April 1973 (SB 9:235) and another at West Loch Tarbert in Kintyre on 25 May 1989 (SBR 1997:57, ABR 14:73). The most recent record concerns one seen well, feeding in a garden at Balephuil on Tiree on 2 May 2004. It was seen again nearby on 4 May (Argyll Database).

Tristan ap Rheinallt

Bluethroat

Luscinia svecica

Vagrant.

Although the Bluethroat is a regular migrant on the east coast of Scotland and in the Northern Isles, especially in spring, it is rarely recorded on the west coast. There have been two records in Argyll: a female was at Ugadale, near Saddell in Kintyre, on 29 May 1975 (SB 9:224), and a male was at Arinagour on Coll on 16 May 1994 (ABR 12:64). The latter was of the red-spotted race *L. s. svecica*, which breeds from Scandinavia eastwards and accounts for most Scottish records.

Tristan ap Rheinallt

Black Redstart

Phoenicurus ochruros

Rare spring and late autumn visitor.

The Black Redstart is mainly a passage migrant to Scotland, where it is much scarcer on the west coast than in the east and the Northern Isles (Thom). H&B knew of no records from Argyll, the first occurrence apparently being at Scarinish on Tiree on 4 November 1910 (ASNH 1911:137). There are a few additional published records from the first half of the 20th century, B&R including "mainland Argyll", Sanda, Tiree and Skerryvore among the list of locations where birds had been seen.

The claim made by Greenleas (1953) that this species was seen nearly every autumn at Southend in Kintyre is based on unpublished information and thus difficult to assess. In fact, published records continued to be few and far between until the latter half of the 1970s, when sightings began to increase. Between 1981 and 2006, birds were reported in 17 of 26 years, with a total of 31 records, including a previously unpublished record of one at Balevullin on Tiree on 11 November 1998 (J. Bowler pers. comm.). All these records involved lone individuals, most of which were seen in Kintyre (including Sanda) (13 records) or Islay (eight records). In addition, four birds were reported from Tiree, one from Mull and two from Coll, with further mainland records from Ganavan, Castle Sween and Kilmichael of Inverlussa.

The seasonal distribution of 30 dated records during 1981-2006 shows that most records occur in spring (early March

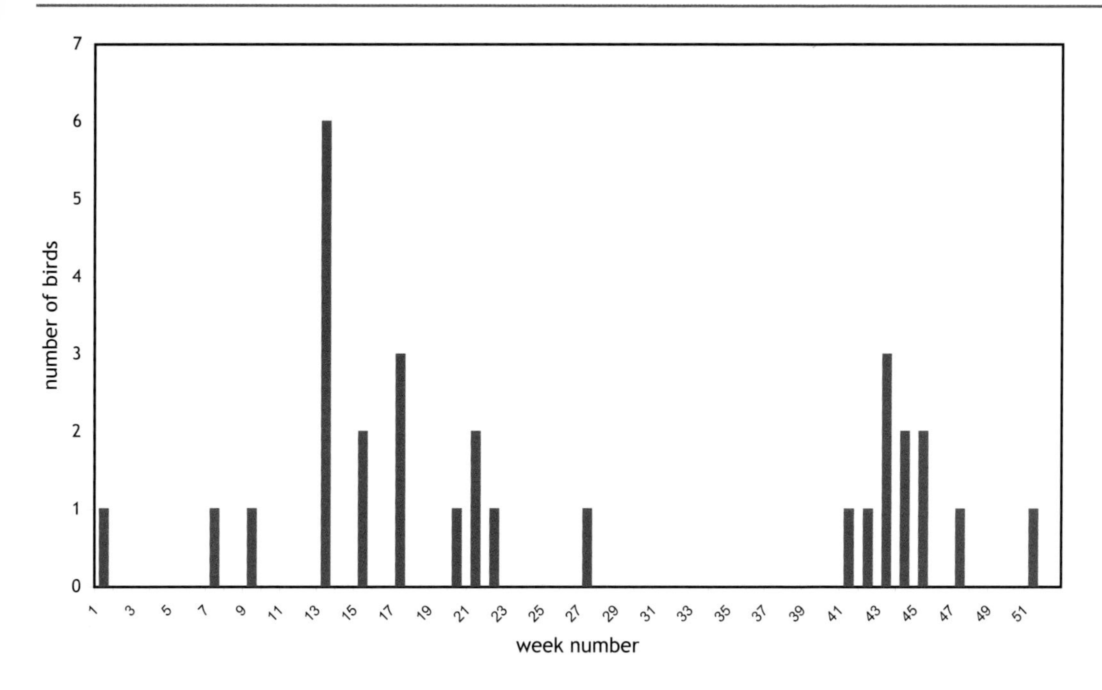

Seasonality of dated records of Black Redstart, 1981-2006.

to late May) or autumn (early October to late November) (Figure). Outside these periods, a female was on Sanda on 7 July 1989 and a male at the Mull of Kintyre on 19 December the same year (SBR 1989:35: ABR 6:47). More recently, singles were at Port Charlotte on Islay for three weeks in January 2002, and at Ganavan on 16 February 2003 (Argyll Database). The Port Charlotte bird was one of the few to have been seen on more than one day. Breeding has never been suspected, but a singing male held territory in Campbeltown from 25 April to 15 May 2003 (Argyll Database).

Tristan ap Rheinallt

Common Redstart

Phoenicurus phoenicurus

A summer visitor, locally common in open woodland. It is a scarce passage migrant on Colonsay, Islay, Tiree and Coll.

This summer visitor to Scotland breeds in open woodland on the mainland and on some larger islands. It does not breed in the Outer Hebrides or the Northern Isles and is now scarce or absent throughout much of the central lowlands, the east coast and the far north-west. Passage migrants, presumably from northern Europe, occur in spring and autumn at localities where they do not breed (Thom, Second Atlas).

Early sources described Redstarts as nowhere very common in Scotland (B&R) and they were not mentioned in Argyll parishes in the NSA. However, they were said to have spread greatly during the latter part of the 19th century, so that by the 1890s they could be described as "exceedingly common" in mainland Argyll, although there were still few if any records from the islands (H&B).

By the mid-20th century there was a reversal in population growth, with a decrease in both England and Scotland. However, Redstarts were still described as common in parts of the West Highlands and they bred fairly frequently on Mull. There were also breeding records for Islay and Jura (B&R). The only records for Tiree were of migrants at Skerryvore lighthouse just before and after the start of the 20th century (Boyd 1958). There were no authenticated records from Coll or Colonsay.

The First Atlas confirmed breeding over much of mainland Argyll and on Mull, apart from the south-west. However, there were few records for Kintyre and, while probable or confirmed breeding was shown for four 10-km squares covering Jura, on Islay only two south-eastern squares

The Redstart is one of the most distinctive birds of Argyll oakwoods in summer. *Philip Snow*

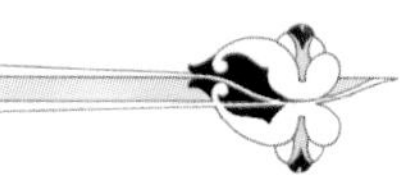

had breeding records. There were no records at all for most of the other islands including Gigha, Colonsay, Coll, Tiree and Scarba.

Williamson (1974) found the density of Redstarts at Glen Nant, Mid-Argyll, in 1973 to be higher than in any other western oakwood he had surveyed in Scotland in the previous five years, although breeding numbers are known to vary considerably from year to year. In the mid-1980s, Redstarts were said to breed only in small numbers or sporadically on Mull, Islay and Jura (Thom). In Mid- and North Argyll, they were found in all 38 broadleaved woods surveyed in 1985, being the seventh most numerous species (Averis & Martin 1985).

Two migrants were reported from Colonsay, in 1973 and 1974 (both in May) (Jardine *et al.* 1986) and there were four records of migrants on Tiree between 1985 and 1988, all in April or May (Stroud 1989).

On the mainland and Mull, the distribution in the Second Atlas was broadly similar to that of 1968-72, except that there was a notable extension of confirmed breeding records in Kintyre. However, there was only one 10-km square with confirmed breeding on Islay and two on Jura. There were confirmed breeding records from 37% of Argyll's 10-km squares. The highest densities were in parts of Mid- and North Argyll.

Recent survey work has confirmed the Redstart's preference for broadleaved (mainly oak) woodlands. They were found in only two of the 14 randomly selected 1-km squares containing mainly coniferous woodland (Wilson & Fuller 2001, P. Daw unpubl. data). In conifer forests in Cowal, they occasionally bred in Tawny Owl nestboxes (Petty 1992), although they were not recorded by Patterson *et al.* (1995) in the same forests. In contrast, Redstarts were found in all but four of 29 broadleaved woods surveyed during the Second Woodland Bird Survey 2003/4 in Mid- and North Argyll, but numbers had decreased by 28.7% since the 1985 survey (Amar *et al.* 2006, RSPB unpubl. data). The results from the Taynish CBC show a very stable population over the 14 years since the census started in 1990 with an annual average of 6.0 territories, apart from two years (1992 and 1994) when numbers were low. Redstarts were found in too few of the 1-km BBS squares in Argyll for any trend to be evident.

Records of singing males since the Second Atlas suggest that Redstarts currently breed quite widely in Mid-Argyll and on Mull. Fewer have been reported in Cowal and North Argyll, and just one singing male in Kintyre, but there have been no confirmed breeding records on any other islands. Results from the long running nest-box scheme at Blarcreen Wood in North Argyll indicate that Redstarts, like other species nesting in boxes, are vulnerable to predation by Pine Martens. In 2001, eggs or young of three pairs using boxes were predated by Pine Martens and no young fledged. In 2002, only one of eight pairs that nested fledged young, the eggs or young in the others nests having been depredated. In 2003, no Redstarts attempted to breed in boxes (ABR, Argyll Database). Elsewhere in Argyll, Redstarts have been reluctant to use nestboxes provided for hole-nesting passerines in broadleaved woods (Petty 1989, 1990).

The main arrival in Argyll is usually during the second or third week of April. One at Taynish NNR on 9 April 2002 was the earliest reported since at least 1980. Most seem to have left by the end of August, although there are a few October records, and the latest in recent years was at Barr Glen, Kintyre on 1 November 1980.

Outwith its breeding range, this species is very scarce as a passage migrant on the islands. During 1994-2003, there were six records on Islay (three autumn and three spring), two on Colonsay (one autumn and one spring), two on Tiree in autumn and one on Sanda in spring. A female seen at the RSPB Reserve on 6 May 2003 was apparently the first ever record for Coll (ABR, Argyll Database).

There is only one ringing recovery. An adult female ringed in Glenbranter Forest, Cowal, in June 1996 was controlled on passage at Gibraltar Point (481km) in August 1997.

Paul Daw

Whinchat

Saxicola rubetra

Widespread and fairly common summer visitor.

The Whinchat is a summer visitor breeding widely in mainland Scotland and on all the main island groups apart from Orkney and Shetland. Its preferred habitat, of rough grassland with gorse bushes, occurs most commonly in the Southern Uplands and Western Scotland. Here it is more numerous than on mountainous terrain or the tidier farmland of the east coast (Thom, Second Atlas).

Early sources described Whinchats as generally distributed in Scotland (B&R) and they were recorded in many parishes in the NSA, including two in Argyll. However, Gray said they were not nearly as numerous as Stonechats. By contrast, in the 1890s they were described as "much more general and abundant, and less sporadic" than Stonechats and they could apparently be "extremely abundant in some localities" (H&B). This pattern was said to be repeated on the larger islands, such as Islay and Jura, although they were only autumn migrants on Tiree.

By the mid-20th century, Whinchats were apparently plentiful in certain districts, including around Oban. On the Argyll islands they bred commonly on Mull and Jura, but only locally on Colonsay and Islay (B&R). Although breeding was reported on Coll before 1899 and several pairs were said to have nested during 1945-49, none were seen there between April and June in both 1954 and 1955. There were records on Tiree in the 1890s, including two at Skerryvore lighthouse, but none were reported by Boyd (1958).

In view of these earlier records, it is perhaps surprising that the First Atlas shows breeding confirmed in almost all 10-km squares on mainland Argyll, Islay and Mull. Breeding was also confirmed on Colonsay and Tiree and there were probable breeding records for Coll and the Treshnish Isles.

In the mid-1980s there was thought to be a population of 6-20 birds on Colonsay (Jardine *et al.* 1986) and in 1987 two pairs were found on Tiree and small numbers bred between Arinagour and Breachacha on Coll (Stroud 1989). Also, Whinchats were found in five of 38 broadleaved woods surveyed in 1985 (Averis & Martin 1985).

The Whinchat is typically associated with unimproved grasslands. *David Palmar*

Despite a significant contraction of range in south and east England and in parts of eastern Scotland, the distribution in Argyll in the Second Atlas was very similar to that in the First. Breeding was confirmed in 74% of 10-km squares and the abundance map showed high densities in Knapdale and parts of Kintyre and on Islay, Jura and Mull.

The preferred open habitat of Whinchats has not been adequately covered by recent survey work, but a survey of the Rinns of Islay in 1994 found 53 pairs, including birds just inside the forestry edge (ABR 11:74). However, they were found in only two of 14 randomly selected 1-km squares in 2000 (Wilson & Fuller 2001, P. Daw unpubl. data). Not surprisingly, Whinchats were absent from the Taynish CBC. The evidence from the few BBS 1-km squares regularly surveyed in Argyll implies a recent decline in numbers, with very few recorded during 2000–2003, possibly reflecting a more general decline in upland Britain over the last 20 years (Henderson *et al.* 2004).

Since the Second Atlas, records of singing males and pairs on territory during the breeding season have suggested that numbers either fluctuate from year to year or have fallen. For example, over ten years (1994-2003) numbers varied between two and nine pairs on Colonsay and between three and 27 pairs at Loch Gruinart, Islay. At both, the peak year was 1997 and numbers at Loch Gruinart have been considerably lower since 2003. Good numbers are still reported from Islay, Mid-Argyll and Mull, with smaller numbers from Cowal, Kintyre and North Argyll. Although breeding pairs in double figures were noted around the airfield at Machrihanish in 1997 and 1998, only four pairs were found breeding on Aros Moss in 2001. Three pairs were breeding on Tiree in 2002, but none have been recorded since. The only recent records for Coll concerned two individuals in May 2002. Although around six birds were noted on Jura in early May 2003, there have been no confirmed breeding records subsequently (ABR, Argyll Database).

The main arrival of Whinchats in Argyll is usually during the second or third week of April. However, in 2000 there were exceptionally early birds on Islay on 19 March and on Oronsay on 5 April. Most breeding birds have left by the end of August, but passage migrants appear widely throughout September and into October. The latest record in recent years was one on Tiree on 20 October 1996. Whinchats are recorded regularly outwith their breeding range as passage migrants, especially in autumn. They are seen frequently on Sanda Island, where they have not bred for some years (ABR, Argyll Database).

There are only two ringing recoveries. A chick ringed at Easdale, Mid-Argyll, in June 1960 was found dead in the Algarve, Portugal in September 1962 (2,124 km), and a full-grown male ringed at Dungeness in August 1954 was found dead at Kilmelford in May 1956.

Paul Daw

Common Stonechat

Saxicola torquatus

A widespread resident, but some leave breeding areas during winter. Numbers can decline dramatically after severe winters.

Stonechats frequent areas of rough grassland with gorse or other shrubby growth, habitats similar to those used by Whinchats. They breed in all the island groups in Scotland apart from Shetland and tend to have a more coastal distribution than Whinchats. Numbers are highest in the

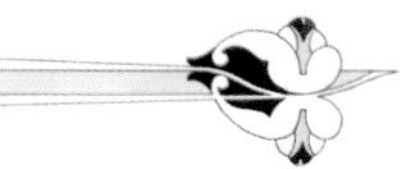

west. Here they occur more frequently inland and may occupy heather and grass moors with just an occasional shrub as a song post (Thom). It is chiefly a resident although emigration occurs from certain areas and some birds travel as far as the Mediterranean. Small numbers occur on passage. The eastern races *maura* and *stejnegeri* are recorded in some years in Scotland (SBR).

The OSA mentioned the Stonechat in Kilfinan parish in the late 18th century. In the NSA, it was recorded at Inveraray in 1845. Although described by Graham as common on Mull and Iona in the 19th century, H&B considered it to have been far more local and scarce than the Whinchat. They mentioned its occurrence on Jura, and said it was found at Balephetrish, Tiree, only in summer, although there were reports of it being commoner there in winter.

Numbers were much reduced following the severe winters of 1939/40 and 1940/41 and the 'great storm' in spring 1947. However, by 1950 the species had recovered and was again said to be common in mainland Argyll. Distribution on the islands was patchy, and while common on Islay, it was not as plentiful as the Whinchat on Jura. Considering how numerous it is there now, it is astonishing that B&R found only one pair on Mull during May 1948. It was locally common on Colonsay and Oronsay, and many bred on Coll, but there was only one record on Tiree, of a pair breeding in 1899 (B&R). In contrast, Boyd (1958) quotes observers who found males and pairs during the breeding season at seven sites on Tiree between 1950 and 1955. Together these reports reflect a slow recovery in numbers following a series of harsh winters. Autumn passage was noticed at the time, although many remained during winter and ringing returns indicated that some movements were relatively local.

The First Atlas showed Stonechats as widely distributed in Argyll, but with a coastal emphasis. There were gaps in some inland areas of north Cowal and North Argyll. On Colonsay, Coll and Tiree, they appeared to be more widespread than Whinchats and were probably breeding on the Treshnish Isles. The species was present during the breeding season on Lunga (near Scarba) when the island was visited in 1976 (T.D.H. Merrie pers. comm.).

In the mid 1980s, numbers on Colonsay were high and they were breeding in non-optimum habitats such as reed beds (Jardine *et al.* 1986). Some 15-25 pairs were thought to be breeding on Tiree in 1987, mainly in heather and gorse, while at least 25 pairs were breeding on Coll at this time (Stroud 1989).

The Winter Atlas showed Stonechats present in much the same areas as during the breeding season, although with a pronounced coastal bias. They were particularly numerous along the western coasts of Knapdale, Mid-Argyll, Coll, Islay and Mull.

The Argyll distribution in the Second Atlas was similar to that found in 1968-72, but with breeding records lacking for a few more inland 10-km squares. There were confirmed breeding records from 70% of Argyll 10-km squares and the abundance map showed high densities in south Kintyre, Islay and Jura.

A survey of the Rinns of Islay in 1994 found 82 pairs, including birds just inside young forest, and 15 pairs bred on moorland at the RSPB's Loch Gruinart Reserve (ABR 11:74). Wilson & Fuller (2001) found Stonechats in four of the 14 randomly selected 1-km squares surveyed in 2000, and they were found in most of the 1-km squares regularly surveyed in Argyll for the BBS, but the species was only recorded in the Taynish CBC as an occasional visitor.

Numbers of singing males/pairs on territory during the breeding season since the Second Atlas have fluctuated from year to year. During 1994-2003, numbers in the breeding season varied between eight and 40 pairs on Colonsay, and between three and 15 pairs on moorland at the RSPB's Loch Gruinart Reserve, Islay. The lowest counts occurred after the cold winter of 1995/96. In contrast, 2002 was a peak year with 40 pairs on Colonsay and three on Oronsay, and 26 pairs in a whole reserve count at Loch Gruinart. Stonechats were widespread and quite common on Coll in 1998 (ABR, Argyll Database).

Stonechats advertise their presence by perching prominently on shrubs and bushes. *David Palmar*

Records of singing males/pairs received since 2000 indicate that the Argyll population is currently at a high level, in agreement with monitoring in other areas of upland Scotland (Sim *et al.* 2005). They were well distributed on high ground away from the coast, widespread and numerous on Islay and Mull (including Iona), and frequent in the south and east of Jura. At least eight pairs were noted on territories on Tiree in April 2004, and 36 pairs were found on Colonsay and five on Oronsay in June 2004. Eight territories were located along the road at Aros Moss, Machrihanish in 2000. Four pairs were found breeding on Sanda in 2003, but Stonechats are only rare visitors to the Treshnish Isles (ABR, Argyll Database).

Most Stonechats in Argyll apparently make local movements away from high ground in winter, at which time they are still numerous in coastal areas. At least some travel further. A young bird ringed on Sanda on 9 August 1980 was killed in Spain (1,373km) on 18 October 1980. Another young bird ringed near Tayvallich in August 1990 was found dead in Berkshire in March 1992.

Stonechats in Argyll belong to the race *hibernans*. Older authorities (e.g. B&R) assigned birds breeding in much of western Scotland, including most of the Argyll islands, to the race *theresae* (Hebridean Stonechat). This race is now considered insufficiently distinct and it is no longer accepted by the BOURC. There are no accepted Argyll records of the races *maura* or *stejnegeri*, both of which occur elsewhere as rare visitors in Scotland in some years.

Paul Daw

Northern Wheatear

Oenanthe oenanthe

A common summer visitor and passage migrant.

This is a widely distributed summer visitor breeding in open grassy country, often with heather and rocky outcrops. Wheatears are common throughout mainland Scotland and on all island groups, apart from near the east coast and in the Central Lowlands where they breed sparsely (Thom, Second Atlas). They are among the first migrants to arrive in spring.

In the mid-19th century, Wheatears were mentioned in the parishes of Inveraray and Killean, Kintyre (NSA). Writing later, Gray said "it takes up its abode on many of the uninhabited islets and rocks" of the Inner Hebrides and this is borne out by Graham who described a nest in the enlarged mouth of a Storm-petrel's burrow on the islet of Soay, near Iona. According to H&B, the Wheatear was universally distributed on all the islands, although somewhat local on the mainland.

In the mid-20th century, Wheatears were found in "all the wilder parts" including moors, links and rough grassy hills, from sea level to altitudes of over 900m asl (B&R). They also bred on the larger islands including Coll, Colonsay, Islay, Jura, Mull and Tiree as well as on many smaller islands such as Cara, Gigha, Iona, Lismore and the Treshnish Isles.

The First Atlas confirmed breeding almost throughout Argyll, including the Treshnish Isles, apart from three 10-km squares in Cowal and one in Kintyre. Wheatears were present during the breeding season on the Garvellachs and Lunga (near Scarba) when these islands were visited in 1975 and 1976 respectively (T.D.H. Merrie pers. comm.).

The distribution in the Second Atlas was broadly similar to that in the First, except that confirmed breeding records were lacking for more inland 10-km squares, especially in northern Argyll. This was borne out by the abundance map, which showed highest densities in coastal areas and on islands.

Wheatear habitat has not been fully covered by recent survey work, but a study of the Rinns of Islay in 1994 found 245 pairs, with a bias toward the west side, particularly along the coast (ABR 11:74). On the other hand, Wheatears were found in only two of the 14 randomly selected 1-km squares surveyed in 2000 Survey (the squares on Colonsay and Tiree) (Wilson & Fuller 2001). In the Taynish CBC, none were found in most years, but single territories were found in four of 14 years. The evidence from the few BBS 1-km squares regularly surveyed in Argyll suggests a decline in numbers since the late 1990s.

Little information on population levels has been gathered since the Second Atlas. The last count at the RSPB's Loch Gruinart Reserve was in 1997 when 33 territories were located. Around 15 pairs bred on Sanda Island in each of the years 1998-2003 and a thorough census there in 2002 found 18 pairs on the main island and a single pair on Sheep Island. A minimum of 22 pairs were found at 17 locations on Iona in June 2000, and 15 singing males were found along the west coast of Jura, in the Loch Tarbert area, on 2 May 2002. Elsewhere, Wheatears breed commonly on Coll, Colonsay, Mull and Tiree. They are widely, although more thinly, distributed in Kintyre and Mid-Argyll. Birds were reported on Lismore in late May 2002, but there have been no recent breeding records from Cowal (ABR, Argyll Database).

Wheatears on the Treshnish Isles have been ringed and monitored regularly since 1997. A concerted effort in 2000 located 13 pairs on the main body of Lunga (excluding the south end) and around 10 pairs breed there in most years. Breeding has also been recorded on the south end of Lunga, on Fladda and on Sgeir an Eirionnaich. Most retraps on Lunga have been of birds hatched on the island, but an adult male re-trapped on Lunga in June 2001 had been ringed as a juvenile on Fladda on 3 July 1997 (TIARG Reports).

Leaving their winter quarters in sub-Saharan Africa as early as January, Wheatears are among the earliest passerines to arrive in the spring. The first males arrive on territory in Argyll around mid-March, and a widespread arrival often takes place about the second week of April. The earliest record in recent years was of a male at Ulva Lagoons, Loch Sween, on 9 March 1997 and there were several other early records that year (Argyll Database). There was an old record of one on 5 February 1898 at Skerryvore Lighthouse (Boyd 1958). The only Argyll ringing recovery of a spring migrant involved a bird that was trapped on Guernsey on 31 March 2000 and

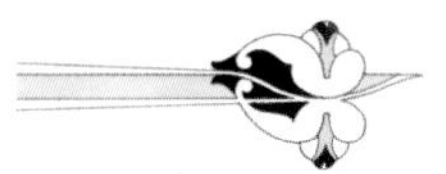

found on Lismore seven days later. Wheatears seen in Argyll in spring presumably include passage birds on their way to other Scottish locations as well as local breeders.

Departure from breeding territories in Britain may begin as early as mid-July (Migration Atlas). This is illustrated by a chick ringed at Loch na Keal (Mull) on 25 May 1984 and recovered in the Arcachon area of south-west France on 23 July the same year. Most British breeders have moved away by early September, passing through France, Spain, Portugal, Morocco and Algeria (Migration Atlas). One of the few recoveries of Argyll-ringed Wheatears involves a bird ringed on Sanda, Kintyre, on 28 July 1994 and recovered 2,600km to the south in Morocco in October 1994.

Wheatears may be very numerous in autumn, especially on the islands. Large numbers can be seen on Colonsay in late July and early August when young are still present and the first migrants are passing through (Jardine *et al.* 1986). Migrants are still moving through in October with a few into November. A very late bird was at Loch Gruinart, Islay, on 29 November 1985 (ABR).

Wheatears breeding in Argyll, the rest of the British Isles and most of northern Europe, belong to the nominate race *oenanthe*. Birds of the race *leucorhoa* (Greenland Wheatears) are larger and have more uniformly coloured underparts than *oenanthe*. These pass through Scotland on their way to and from their breeding grounds in Iceland, Greenland and perhaps northern Canada.

Passage of race *oenanthe* through the British Isles can continue until the end of October or even later (Migration Atlas). Thus, many Wheatears passing through Argyll, particularly later in the autumn, presumably originate from Scandinavia or other areas to the north and east of Britain.

Greenland Wheatears do not leave their breeding grounds until late August, and the main autumn passage through the British Isles does not take place until most local birds have departed. Some apparently migrate directly from Greenland to mainland Europe, usually moving south over the sea to the west of the British Isles. However, in some weather conditions large falls may occur (Migration Atlas). Such a fall was presumably responsible for the report of about 100 Greenland Wheatears on Tiree on 8 October 1910 (B&R). However, autumn records in Argyll typically involve single birds or small numbers. Most are in late September or October, with a few as early as mid-September. An unusually late bird at Kilnaughton Bay (Islay) on 24 November 1999 was thought to be of this race. Almost all reports come from the islands, but a single bird was at Ledaig Point (North Argyll) on 5 October 1988.

The spring passage of Greenland Wheatears is believed to follow a more overland route, with birds passing through

A summer visitor to unimproved grassland and moorland, the Wheatear nests in dry-stone walls, ruins, natural rock crevices and rabbit burrows. *Margaret Staley*

Britain and Ireland before heading for Iceland and Greenland. Protracted passage occurs through outlying Scottish islands (BWP), with a peak between late April and mid-May, later than the main passage of *oenanthe* (Migration Atlas). Judging by recent records, numbers of Greenland Wheatears passing through Argyll in spring are small. As in autumn, most reports come from Kintyre and the islands, though there are isolated records from Cowal, Mid-Argyll and North Argyll. Most are seen in May, but late April records include 18 on Tiree on 27 April 2000, while a few stragglers have lingered into early June. On the whole, it seems likely that Greenland Wheatears are under-recorded in Argyll, and perhaps especially so in spring.

Paul Daw

Blue Rock Thrush

Monticola solitarius

Vagrant.

A first-summer male of unknown race was on Skerryvore during 4 to 7 June 1985, and was found dead on 8 June; it is retained in the Natural History Museum at Tring. Although originally placed in Category D of the British list (BB 79:585), a BOURC review resulted in its acceptance as the first British record of a genuinely wild bird (Ibis 135:221, BB 86:510-511). Full details of the record were published by Hume (1995), an extract of which is presented here:

"On 14th June 1985, Mrs Elizabeth McConnell wrote to the British Trust of Ornithology from Girvan, Ayrshire. The first lines of her letter caused immediate excitement: 'Enclosed please find 'bird'; we think it is a Blue Rock Thrush."

The letter gave brief details, and John Marchant responded with considerable interest: it was, indeed, a Blue Rock Thrush *Monticola solitarius* and, as such, potentially the first record for Britain. The specimen had arrived safely, but had begun to decay.

"...The weather was fine, occasionally sunny, during the bird's stay, and it hopped about on the rocks of the small island... There were five or six birds present at the time the Blue Rock Thrush appeared, but it remained separate from them; it was not heard to call. A dish of fresh water was ignored by all the birds, and the rock thrush spent its time picking insects from the rocks. It was nervous when approached, always flying off out of sight behind the rocks when it realised it was being watched. It appeared to seek a crack in the rocks at night."

Until 1999, there was only one other accepted British record of this species, which breeds no closer than southern France. In late 1999 and early 2000, however, there was a remarkable series of three records from south-west England.

Tristan ap Rheinallt

Ring Ouzel

Turdus torquatus

A summer visitor breeding very locally in upland areas. Declining in numbers. More widespread, though still very scarce, on migration.

The Ring Ouzel is on the Red List of species of high conservation concern in the UK due to a rapid decline (more than 50%) in breeding numbers over the last 25 years (RSPB web page). In addition, it has shown a moderate (25-49%) contraction of UK breeding range over the last 25 years (Wotton *et al.* 2002), which represents an additional 'Amber-listing' criterion. In Scotland, B&R noticed there had been a "serious decrease" in the breeding population of this species during the first half of the 20th century. That decline has continued through the second half of the 20th century, both in Scotland (Thom), and elsewhere in Britain and Ireland (Second Atlas), and is still continuing (Henderson *et al.* 2004, Sim *et al.* 2005).

Many hypotheses have been put forward to explain the decline, including (i)increased access of people onto the hills causing disturbance to breeding birds (ii) climate change leading to drier soils making feeding on earthworms more difficult in late summer (iii) increased numbers of Blackbirds leading to more interspecific competition (iv) afforestation of moorland habitat (v) changes in the species composition of upland grassland and (vi) possible changes in the winter area, especially montane areas of Morocco and southern Spain where juniper habitat may have been lost; juniper berries appear to be important winter food (Migration Atlas). But although support has been found for some of these ideas, none of the hypotheses has yet been shown to be the key reason for the decline (Buchanan *et al.* 2003).

Ring Ouzels breed widely but thinly in moorland and mountainous areas of Scotland, chiefly at altitudes between 250m and 500m asl. Now they are virtually restricted to the southern uplands and the central and north-west Highlands, with sporadic breeding on the Clyde Islands and Inner Hebrides (Thom, SBR). Very few are now found in Argyll, which is clearly on the periphery of the species' distribution in Britain. Highest densities of Ring Ouzels are generally found in the eastern uplands rather than in the west, and declines appear to have been especially pronounced in western areas such as Ireland, Wales and Argyll. However, the species has bred recently and may well still do so in a few mountainous areas of North Argyll and possibly on Mull. It may also breed in small numbers on Islay and Jura, although there are no recent records. Many potential breeding localities are seldom visited by birders, so isolated pairs could easily go undetected. Otherwise it occurs widely but in very small numbers on the mainland and islands as a passage migrant in spring and autumn. In Scotland and in Argyll, the first Ring Ouzels arrive in March, sometimes early in the month, and the majority have taken up territories by early May. The main

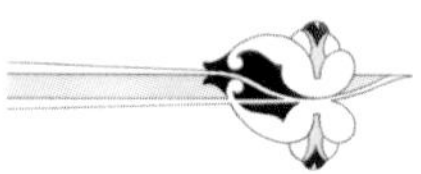

autumn passage takes place in late September and October but stragglers occur in November and there have been a few winter records (SBR), including one at Cruachan reservoir in the winter of 1998-99 (ABR).

Bob Furness

Blackbird

Turdus merula

This is a common and locally abundant resident. There is a noticeable autumn passage in most years, with some birds staying for the winter.

Blackbirds are most numerous in gardens, towns and villages (relatively uncommon habitats in Argyll), farmland and mature woodland. They are widely distributed on the mainland of Argyll wherever there are trees. In oak woods they are relatively scarce and recent surveys have found only small numbers in conifer forests. Blackbirds are absent from moorland and montane habitats (Thom).

The NSA mentioned the Blackbird in lists from all over Scotland and in many places there were reports of recent increases. However, it has probably always been locally common. Graham says "a few pairs breed wherever they can find a suitable spot; but the greater numbers come to us only to pick up a winter subsistence". At the end of the 19th century H&B considered it was "not generally so numerous as the Common (Song) Thrush and requires better shelter and more of it". It occurred on Jura, Islay and the larger wooded islands. It was rare on Tiree in winter, but occurred in considerable numbers in autumn. Nevertheless, in the 1950s the Blackbird was said to outnumber the Song Thrush by at least four to one in the Oban area. At the same time it bred apparently abundantly on Islay and in suitable woods on Jura and Gigha, but was reportedly not very common on Colonsay. It also nested on Coll and commonly on Iona and Mull (B&R).

The First Atlas showed Blackbirds as probably or definitely breeding in almost every 10-km square in Argyll. The exceptions were one square in western Jura and those covering smaller off-shore islands such as the Garvellachs and Scarba, although even here individuals were seen. As with other species, the scale of mapping did not reveal detailed local distribution.

A survey of 38 broadleaf woodlands in 1985 found Blackbirds in all but ten; they were less numerous than Song Thrushes by a ratio of 2:3 (Averis & Martin 1985).

By the time of the Second Atlas a slight contraction in range was evident, with confirmed breeding records from

Recoveries of ringed birds suggest that Argyll Blackbirds are more migratory than was once thought. *David Palmar*

only 77% of Argyll's 10-km squares. The losses appeared to have occurred in an area (three 10-km squares) around the north end of Loch Awe and Glen Kinglass (North Argyll), on Islay and Tiree and on some of the smaller islands, where there were not even sight records. The losses on Tiree may have been more apparent than real as Stroud (1989) estimated there were 6–20 pairs in 1987. The abundance map showed that, apart from a few scattered localities on the mainland with moderate densities, Blackbirds were fairly thinly distributed in Argyll, especially on the islands.

During a study of Sitka Spruce plantations in Cowal, Blackbirds were the ninth most numerous species in the spring of 1992, although relatively few were found in spring 1991. Only small numbers were present in the two winters of fieldwork (Patterson *et al.* 1995). A survey of the Rinns of Islay in 1994 found 31 territories, although gardens, where this species is likely to be more common, were not surveyed (ABR 11:75).

Records since the Second Atlas have indicated recent increases on some islands. On Tiree it was estimated that 20+ pairs were breeding in 1998, but a more thorough survey in June 2000 found a minimum of 49 singing males. Records from Mull also suggested that Blackbirds were relatively common in suitable habitat. There were regular breeding records from Coll and Colonsay and one or two pairs have bred annually on Oronsay and Sanda. Although Blackbirds have been seen on Jura, there have been no recent breeding records and there are no recent records (even of presence) from Scarba. A single male on Lunga in June 2003 was the first record for the Treshnish Isles since the late 1970s (ABR, Argyll Database). According to Fraser Darling 'hundreds' wintered on the Treshnish Isles, at least in the first half of the 20th century (B&R).

Results from the Taynish CBC showed an increase in the number of territories over the 15 years since the census started in 1990 (Figure). Blackbird territories outnumbered Song Thrush territories in just two of the years. There was a significant positive relationship between Blackbird and Song Thrush numbers, indicating that some common factor influenced numbers.

In 14 randomly selected 1-km squares (containing mainly coniferous woodland) surveyed in 2000, 19 Blackbirds were found in seven squares, compared to 33 Song Thrushes in 12 squares (Wilson & Fuller 2001, P. Daw unpubl. data). They were found in all but three of the 29 broadleaved woods surveyed during the Second Woodland Bird Survey 2003/4 and numbers had more than doubled since the same woods were surveyed in 1985 (128.3% increase) (Amar *et al.* 2006, RSPB unpubl. data).

The arrival of immigrants in autumn has been noted since at least the 19th century (H&B). Winter recoveries in Scotland of birds ringed on their breeding grounds suggest the majority come from Fennoscandia and Denmark (Thom). A young male ringed in Glenbranter, Cowal, in October 1990 was controlled in Norway in October 1991. There are three records of birds ringed in Argyll in spring or autumn being recovered in Ireland, suggesting that some, at least, of our Blackbirds may winter there. Recoveries of birds ringed elsewhere in Scotland tend to reinforce this picture (Thom).

Most migrant Blackbirds arrive from mid-October to mid-November, usually with flocks of other thrushes. Compared to Fieldfares and Redwings, the numbers involved are small; the highest recent counts were of 150 birds on Tiree on 3 November 2000 and 63 together on Mull in November 2002. B&R comment on the preponderance of males among these immigrants (mentioning Argyll and Mull) and this phenomenon has often been noted in the county in recent years, in particular involving first-winter birds (Argyll Database).

Paul Daw

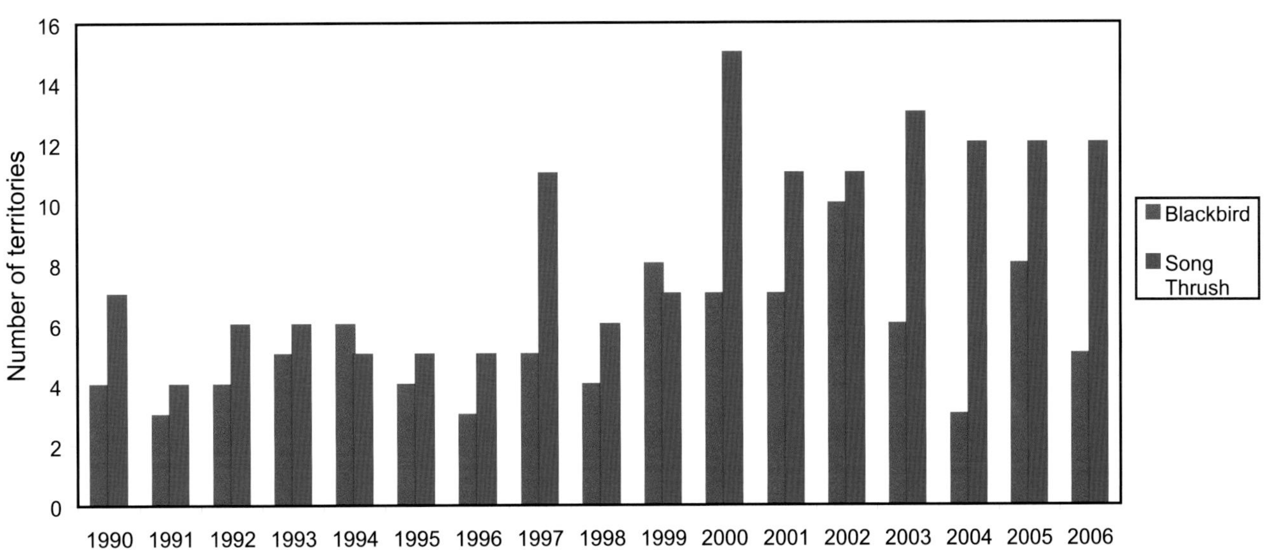

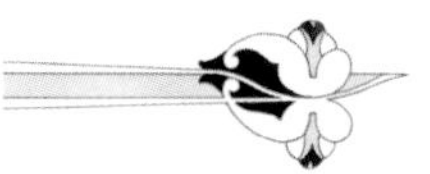

Fieldfare

Turdus pilaris

A passage migrant and winter visitor. Abundant in autumn but relatively few remain in winter or pass through in spring.

The Fieldfare is an abundant passage migrant and winter visitor to Scotland from Fennoscandia. Although a few early individuals often appear in August, the main influx is usually in mid-October, when flocks may run into thousands in good years (Thom). In part the variation in numbers arriving in Scotland from year to year may reflect fluctuations in numbers in Scandinavia, as these are very strongly influenced by autumn and winter temperatures and rowanberry production, which together explain 80% of the variation in abundance of Fieldfares on spring migration into southern Norway (Hogstad *et al.* 2003). They are apparently less able to withstand severe winter weather than Blackbirds. While many Fieldfares arrive in autumn, many move on south, although some remain in Scotland throughout the winter, but usually in smaller flocks (Winter Atlas).

Exceptionally, Fieldfares may be recorded in Argyll in late August, and there are also records in September in some years. However, peak passage is from mid-October to mid-November, at which time flocks may be seen throughout Argyll, including the islands. Numbers seen vary from year to year. Flocks often exceed 500 birds during late October, but flock sizes fall quickly as the autumn progresses; groups of more than a few dozen birds are unusual by late November. Winter flocks tend to be particularly frequently seen in Islay, Tiree, and Kintyre, although the species can be found throughout most of Argyll in small groups during winter. How long birds stay in Argyll appears to depend on the severity of the winter and the abundance of berry crops. The latter provide alternative food, as Fieldfares are unable to forage for earthworms and other grassland invertebrates when the ground is frozen. There is no clear spring migration peak, but rather the wintering birds gradually disappear. Most are gone by the end of April, but odd individuals have been seen in May in some years. Probably most migration in spring is by a more southern and easterly route such that few birds pass through Argyll.

Breeding in Scotland was first recorded in Orkney in 1967 and scattered pairs bred in other parts of Scotland over the following years. However, colonisation has not progressed as initially expected and breeding now appears to occur only sporadically (Second Atlas, SBR). The colonisation of Scotland reflects a general range expansion of the Fieldfare over the last 150 years, which has spread as a breeding species south into Germany and France, east into Russia, and west even into Greenland and North America (Thom). However, breeding has not been recorded in Argyll, possibly because there is so little spring migration through Argyll. It seems likely that many cases of breeding in Scotland are a consequence of spring migrants being delayed by late cold weather and eventually remaining to breed.

Bob Furness

Large flocks of migrating Fieldfares and Redwings can be seen in Argyll in autumn. *Philip Snow*

Song Thrush

Turdus philomelos

A widespread and common resident, with some locally bred birds departing in the autumn. There is a noticeable autumn passage, with other birds arriving for the winter.

Song Thrushes occur in almost any habitat with shrubs and trees. They are widely distributed on both the mainland and islands of Argyll. Although surveys quoted in Thom indicate that Blackbirds are twice as numerous as Song Thrushes in some Scottish woodlands, survey work in Argyll shows Song Thrushes are more numerous in both broadleaved and coniferous woods. Birds arrive from the continent in autumn and some of these continue further south. At the same time there is probably some southward movement of local birds, especially to Ireland.

There were records of the Song Thrush in Scotland from at least the 17th century and by the late 18th century it was mentioned in the NSA as increasing in numbers. At the end of the 19th century, H&B described it as common in most districts and resident, especially near the coast. They also noted that Song Thrushes disappeared from Islay for more than a year following the severe winter of 1879/80. They were found breeding on all the larger islands during the mid-20th century, although described as only local on Colonsay (B&R).

The First Atlas showed a very similar distribution to Blackbird, with Song Thrushes probably or definitely breeding in most of Argyll's 10-km squares. There were no records for Scarba or the Treshnish Isles, but they probably bred on the Garvellachs. The species was found on Lunga (near Scarba) during a visit in 1976 (T.D.H. Merrie pers. comm.). A survey of 38 broadleaf woodlands in 1985 found Song Thrushes in all but five and more numerous than Blackbirds by a ratio of 3:2 (Averis & Martin 1985).

A slight contraction in range was evident from the Second Atlas, with confirmed breeding records from only 72% of 10-km squares in Argyll. The losses mainly related to coastal areas of Islay and Jura and, more surprisingly, two 10-km squares near Taynuilt. The abundance map showed that, unlike Blackbirds, Song Thrushes occurred in moderate or high densities in Kintyre, Mid-Argyll and parts of Cowal and Mull. They were less numerous on the remaining islands and in North Argyll.

Song Thrushes usually outnumber Blackbirds in Argyll's woodlands. *Philip Kirkham*

In June 2001 a Song Thrush was heard singing regularly at The Village on Lunga, and one was seen on Cairn na Burgh. These were the first records for the Treshnish Islands in 30 years (TIARG Reports). None were seen or heard there

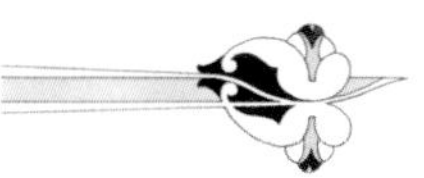

in 2002 or 2003. There are no other indications of recent changes in distribution.

During a study of spruce plantations in Cowal, the Song Thrush was the eleventh most numerous species in the spring of 1991 and the twelfth in 1992 (cf. Blackbird). Although numbers were considerably lower in winter, it was the eighth most numerous species in 1990/1991 and the seventh in 1991/1992 (Patterson *et al.* 1995). A survey of the Rinns of Islay in 1994 found 25 territories, although gardens, where this species is likely to be more common, were not surveyed (ABR 11:75).

Recent survey work has confirmed that Song Thrushes are still more numerous than Blackbirds in both broadleaved and coniferous woodlands in Argyll. In the 14 randomly selected 1-km squares (containing mainly coniferous woodland) surveyed in 2000, 33 Song Thrushes were found in 12 squares, compared to 19 Blackbirds in seven squares (Wilson & Fuller 2001, P. Daw unpubl. data). Song Thrushes were found in all 29 broadleaved woods during the Second Woodland Bird Survey 2003/4 in Mid- and North Argyll and had more than doubled in numbers (147.5% increase) since the similar survey in 1985 (Amar *et al.* 2006, RSPB unpubl. data).

Records since the Second Atlas have indicated good breeding populations on some of the islands. A survey at the RSPB's Loch Gruinart Reserve in 1997 found an estimated 38 territories. In June 2000, at least 22 singing birds were found on Tiree, 12 pairs bred on Oronsay and three or more pairs bred on Sanda (ABR). Results from the Taynish CBC showed a slight increase in number of territories during 1990-2006 (Figure in Blackbird account). Song Thrush territories outnumbered Blackbird territories in 15 of the 17 years and there was a significant positive relationship between Song Thrush and Blackbird numbers, indicating some common influence.

The pattern of Song Thrush movements in Argyll is complex, and only limited ringing data are available. Immigrants arrive with other winter thrushes from late September onwards, but in relatively small numbers (no recent counts exceed 25 birds). While some birds may move on further south, counts on Tiree in December and January indicate that some at least remain for the winter (ABR, Argyll Database). The Winter Atlas showed the highest numbers along the west coast and on the islands. An adult ringed on Sanda Island in July was found dead near Belfast in October of the same year, and a first-year bird ringed in County Donegal in December was found dead near Benderloch in September two years later. Some birds in Argyll may be from further north in Scotland. A juvenile ringed near the Dornoch Firth (Highland) in July was found dead on Luing the following March. Ringing recoveries from birds ringed on passage elsewhere in Scotland confirm that some travel as far south as Iberia and Italy (Thom).

Song Thrushes in Europe represent a cline of increasingly pale plumage from west to east, with the darkest (*hebridensis*) in the Hebrides and Skye and the palest (nominate *philomelos*) in Scandinavia, Poland and eastwards (BWP). Most Song Thrushes found in mainland Argyll are presumed to belong to the race *clarkei* found in most of Britain and the near Continent. However individuals occurring on the islands, especially Islay and Tiree have been reported as showing at least some of the characteristics (dark, heavy spotting, greyish rump and upper tail coverts and smokey brown flanks) of *hebridensis*. When E.V. Baxter visited Coll, Iona and Mull in the 1930s she noted that Song Thrushes there were heavily spotted (B&R). A recent review concluded (supporting earlier authorities) that birds from the Inner Hebrides and parts of western Scotland are probably intermediate between *hebridensis* and *clarkei* (McGowan *et al.* 2003). It is possible that some *hebridensis* move to the Argyll islands in winter, although there is no empirical evidence to support this. As the authors say, we are still largely ignorant of the status, distribution and movements of the 'Hebridean' Song Thrush.

Most of the Song Thrushes arriving here in autumn are likely to be of the continental race *philomelos* although there are no ringing recoveries to confirm this. However, birds seen recently on Islay, and a bird trapped and ringed on Sanda, showed characteristics of this race (ABR). Many of these birds move further south to southern Europe or Ireland (Thom).

Paul Daw

Redwing

Turdus iliacus

A passage migrant and winter visitor. Abundant in autumn but relatively few remain during winter. Occasional individuals may be recorded in late spring or summer. The species bred on Mull in 1991, but there have not been any subsequent breeding records.

The Redwing is an abundant passage migrant and winter visitor. Migrants to Scotland originate from two areas; the race *coburni* breeds in Iceland and the Faeroes while the race *iliacus* breeds mainly from Fennoscandia eastwards to Siberia.

The first known nesting in Scotland was in Sutherland in 1925, but although they now breed regularly, numbers are still very small and there has been no sign of extensive colonisation (Second Atlas, SBR). Redwings nesting in Scotland belong to the nominate race, so originate from continental birds that remained in Scotland rather than returning north to breed. In Scotland, breeding tends to occur in scrubby woodland of birch, Alder, Rowan and willow, close to water or damp grassland or even in conifer plantations, habitats that are available in many parts of Argyll. So, it is perhaps surprising that there is only a single breeding record for Argyll.

The wintering range of *iliacus* includes Britain and much of western and southern Europe, while *coburni* winters mainly in Ireland, Scotland and north-west Iberia (Migration Atlas, Milwright 2002). Field observations demonstrate that Redwings of both races occur in Argyll as passage migrants, and this is confirmed by the very small number of ringing recoveries in Argyll. Three Icelandic-ringed chicks (*coburni*) have been recovered in Argyll in the month of November, while a Redwing ringed in Belgium in October 1998 and recovered in Tarbert on 1 November 2000 almost certainly belonged to the race *iliacus*. Unfortunately, although the two races are, with care, separable in the field, there is relatively little comparative information about their occurrence in Argyll in autumn, winter or spring.

It is possible that Icelandic Redwings pass through earlier than birds of the race *iliacus*, many of which are thought to move into western Britain from November onwards, having first made landfall on the North Sea coast (Migration Atlas). The highly synchronised autumn departure from Iceland in October (Migration Atlas) fits in neatly with the observed mass arrival of birds in Argyll during the same month. On the other hand, the neatest explanation for the arrival of large mixed flocks of Redwings and Fieldfares in Argyll at this time of year would be that they have a common origin in Scandinavia, as Fieldfares do not breed in Iceland.

The huge flocks of Redwings that pass through in autumn often leave the rowan and hawthorn trees stripped bare of fruit. *Philip Kirkham*

It is clear from ringing recoveries that Scotland and Ireland are major wintering areas for *coburni*, and it is interesting to note that no individuals of the Icelandic subspecies have been recovered in England or Wales (Migration Atlas) although many spend the winter in Iberia. It is likely that a substantial proportion of the Redwings that remain in Argyll for the winter are Icelandic birds, though the numbers wintering in Argyll are very small in relation to the numbers arriving in autumn. Many Redwings move on further south and birds ringed in Scotland during autumn passage, which presumably include large numbers of birds of each subspecies, have been recovered in France, Spain and Portugal (Thom). However, the species' nomadic habits and its capacity to make long hard-weather movements could mean that relatively more *iliacus* occur in Argyll in some winters than in others.

Numbers remaining in Argyll may also be influenced by berry crops, particularly rowanberries, which represent an essential food resource for Redwings both during migration and in winter (Guitian *et al.* 1994). Swann (1983) observed that migrating Redwings appeared to head for Highland glens because they contained many Rowan trees and few other birds that ate berries. A similar pattern occurs in upland Argyll, but only when Rowan fruits are plentiful. Redwings locate sources of ripe fruit based on the strong ultraviolet reflectance of these berries, which is visible to birds though

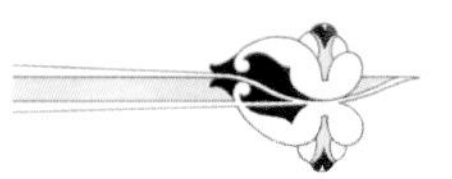

not to humans (Siitari *et al.* 1999).

Icelandic Redwings certainly account for many if not all of the small flocks seen on spring migration in Argyll. Many *iliacus* apparently return to their breeding grounds in Scandinavia to Siberia via eastern England, bypassing Scotland completely (Thom, Migration Atlas).

Bob Furness

Mistle Thrush

Turdus viscivorus

A widespread but thinly distributed resident breeding species. Flocks are sometimes seen on passage. On Coll and Tiree it is only an occasional visitor.

The Mistle Thrush is 'Amber-listed' in the UK due to a moderate (25-49%) decline in the UK breeding population over the last 25 years (RSPB web page). However, this period of decline follows a long phase of population range expansion and increase in numbers. Before 1800, Mistle Thrushes were extremely rare in most of Britain outside the southern parts of England, and were almost unknown in Scotland (Thom, Historical Atlas). H&B recorded the species as occurring in most parts of Argyll by the 1870s, but almost becoming extinct during the severe winter of 1879-80, and in many places only seen as a non-breeding visitor where it seemed "likely before long to become resident and breeding". They also reported "the Fieldfare arrives just as the Mistle Thrush leaves certain districts...and thus a very considerable confusion occurs in their names amongst the natives".

By the 1950s, the species had colonised every mainland county, including Argyll. Over recent decades Mistle Thrushes have bred on most of mainland Scotland, including most of mainland Argyll with mature woodland and parkland, and in most of the Inner Hebrides, but they are still only sporadic on the Outer Hebrides and Orkney, and do not breed in Shetland (Thom, Second Atlas, Pennington *et al.* 2004). In Argyll, areas of oak woodland can hold about nine pairs km^{-2} (Williamson 1974), although densities of 2-4 pairs km^{-2} may be more typical of old conifer plantations and other forms of woodland and farmland (Thom).

Although the First Atlas showed Mistle Thrushes breeding throughout most of mainland Argyll, by the time of the Second Atlas there were apparent losses in some parts of Mid- and North Argyll and there were also some blank 10-km squares on Islay and Jura. Confirmed breeding was recorded in only 43% of Argyll's 10-km squares.

Other information about Mistle Thrushes in Argyll comes from a number of studies. A survey of 38 broadleaf woodlands in Argyll in 1985 found Mistle Thrushes in 29, but at a lower density than Song Thrushes (Averis & Martin 1985). However, no territories were found during The Rinns

Mistle Thrushes start to breed very early in the year, sometimes even during the winter months. *Philip Kirkham*

of Islay survey in 1994 (cf. 25 Song Thrush territories) (ABR 11:75). The results from the Taynish CBC showed that Mistle Thrushes were much less numerous than Blackbirds or Song Thrushes with an average of only 1.4 territories over the 14 years since the census started in 1990. They were found in 13 of the 16 broadleaved woods surveyed for the Second Woodland Bird Survey 2003, but again at much lower densities than the other two thrush species (Amar *et al.* 2006, RSPB unpubl. data).

A few pairs have bred on Colonsay since the first half of the 20th century (Jardine *et al.* 1986, ABR) but, contrary to the distribution map in Thom, there are no breeding records for Coll or Tiree. Boyd (1958) described Mistle Thrushes as occasional autumn and spring visitors to Coll and Tiree, and in recent years they have been less than annual visitors, mainly in winter (Argyll Database).

Mistle Thrushes can breed very early in the year, and there have been records in recent years of birds breeding during winter (SBR). They defend large territories, usually containing mature trees, though often in areas with grassland where they can forage. They feed chicks mostly on insects, but also on fruit. Fruit crops, including Hawthorn, Holly, Ivy and Yew berries, may be defended through the winter (Snow & Snow 1984, Skorka & Wojcik 2005), and local distribution of Mistle Thrushes in Argyll may be influenced by availability of such berry crops. Mistle Thrushes are often sedentary, relying on such winter resources, but some migrate. In Argyll, post-breeding flocks of 30 or more birds occur from July onwards but passage migrants are usually irregular and few in number, though in some years flocks of dozens or even hundreds of birds may pass by during late September to November. A loose flock of 153 flying east along the Crinan Canal on 29 September 2000 was by far the largest number seen together in Argyll in recent years.

It seems unlikely that many continental Mistle Thrushes migrate through Argyll, as even Shetland receives very few Mistle Thrushes during migration seasons. However, a few birds ringed in Scotland have been recovered in Ireland, so a partial migration of this species into Ireland from, or through, Argyll is a possibility. Rather few Mistle Thrushes have been ringed in Argyll, or elsewhere in Scotland, so the extent of such movements is unclear (Migration Atlas). It may well vary from year to year depending on a combination of fruit production, numbers of birds (especially young birds) in the population, and severity of the weather, as has been reported in the more extremely fluctuating conditions of east Europe (Skorka & Wojcik 2005).

Bob Furness

John Halliday (far left), Reserves Manager for SNH, leads a visit by the Argyll Bird Club to Taynish NNR in May 2007. John has carried out Common Bird Census work at this internationally important oakwood since 1990. His dataset, unique in Argyll, has informed many of the accounts in this book. *Louise Wood*

A fine-grained mix of habitats, including improved pasture, coniferous and broad-leaved woodland, moorland, low-density settlement and running fresh water. This pattern of land use is typical of low-altitude valleys in mainland Argyll, and hosts a diverse range of birds including Dipper, pipits, Sky Lark, Grey Wagtail, Stonechat, thrushes, finches, tits, crows, Tawny Owl and Sparrowhawk. This example shows the River Awe in Mid-Argyll, looking south-east. The Arrochar Alps lie beyond. *John Anderson*

Grasshopper Warbler

Locustella naevia

A summer visitor that breeds locally in open habitats with dense ground vegetation, including young conifer plantations. Numbers fluctuate from year to year.

With its distinctive song and skulking habits, the Grasshopper Warbler is more often heard than seen. *Gordon Yates*

The Grasshopper Warbler is a summer visitor to Scotland. While breeding has occurred at some time in all mainland counties, distribution is patchy and it is only really numerous in western counties from Dumfries and Galloway north to Argyll. The species does not breed in the Outer Hebrides or the Northern Isles (Thom, Second Atlas). It prefers areas of thick ground cover, and often thrives among recently planted conifers, a trait first recorded in Argyll by Gray.

Possibly because of its skulking habits, this species received little attention in the earlier accounts and is not mentioned in the Argyll parish lists in either of the Statistical Accounts of Scotland. Gray, who said it was more local in distribution in Scotland than any other warbler except the Lesser Whitethroat, mentioned Bonawe, North Argyll, as the furthest north that he had encountered it. H&B simply say it was included in a list from Jura, while B&R listed records from across Argyll, including a bird killed at Skerryvore lighthouse in May 1907. Taken together, these sparse historic records suggest that the species has been widely distributed across Argyll since at least the mid-19th century.

Since the 1960s, the species has shown large and rapid changes in distribution and abundance across most of Britain, including a decline of 37% between the First and Second Atlases. There were further large fluctuations between 1994 and 2003, but little overall change (Second Atlas, BTO Trend). These rises and falls are difficult to explain. Some may be due to the loss of breeding habitat, but unidentified factors affecting the African wintering grounds are also likely to be involved (Second Atlas, Migration Atlas). However, the species has continued to do well in Argyll, with no reduction in range between the two Breeding Atlases. There was even some range expansion in Kintyre and Islay over this period. During 1988-91, it bred in 26% of 10-km squares in the county.

Today, it nests across Argyll wherever there is suitable habitat, including Coll and Tiree (ABR). It occurs widely on Islay. During a survey of the Rinns in 1994, 39 singing males were recorded, mostly associated with young conifer plantations. It regularly nests on Colonsay (maximum counts during 1982-2005 were of 10 singing males in 2002 and 2005) and Jura (five singing males at Ardfernal in 1990). There were 15 territories on Moine Mhor NNR in 1991. In all areas, numbers fluctuate widely from year to year. At the RSPB's Loch Gruinart Reserve, Islay, there were four or five pairs during surveys from 1985 to 1992. This increased to

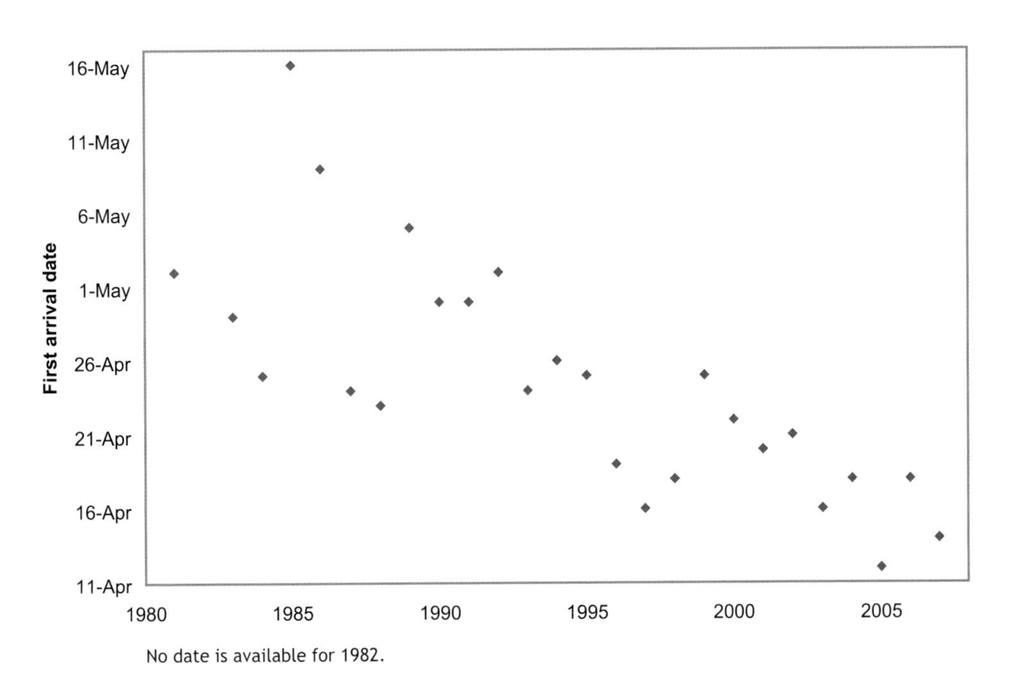

No date is available for 1982.

First arrival records of Grasshopper Warblers in Argyll, 1981-2007.

ten pairs in 1994 and 28 in 1997, dropping to two in 2000. Counts for 2001, 2002, 2003 and 2006 were 13, 10, 10 and 22 respectively. In the Taynish CBC plots, numbers fluctuated between zero and six pairs between 1990 and 2006, but with no clear trend. The mean count over these years was 2.4 pairs. In the best year (1990), Taynish NNR as a whole supported 14 pairs at a density of 4.2 pairs km^{-2}.

Birds begin to arrive in Argyll in mid-April with the main influx in early May. At this time, passage birds are often heard 'reeling' in places where they do not stay to breed. There is a significant negative correlation between year and first arrival date, with Grasshopper Warblers now arriving earlier than they did in the early 1980s. The latest recorded date for Argyll is of a single bird at Bruichladdich on 15 September 2003. Very few are recorded as passage migrants (SBR 1998-2001).

David Wood

Sedge Warbler

Acrocephalus schoenobaenus

A summer visitor that is common in suitable wet habitats.

Sedge Warblers are widely distributed summer visitors. They breed throughout mainland Scotland and on most of the larger islands, apart from Shetland. They are characteristic of lowland marsh and riparian habitats, but sometimes breed in drier scrubland. For this reason they are most numerous in southern Scotland, the Central Lowlands, Argyll and eastern counties north to Inverness, but are scarce in the north-west (Thom, Second Atlas). Sedge Warblers arrive relatively late, the first birds not appearing until late April or early May. After a short breeding season they depart in late July or early August and may congregate in suitable reed-beds prior to departure (SBR).

Like the Grasshopper Warbler, this species gets little mention in the earlier accounts, although it is listed as occurring in Killean parish, Kintyre, in the NSA. Gray said they were especially abundant in the western counties of Scotland extending to the north of Argyll and that they were found in limited numbers on Islay and Mull. One was seen at Skerryvore Lighthouse on 13 May 1898 (Boyd 1958).

They were said to be breeding commonly and fairly abundantly in all Scottish counties in the mid-20th century (B&R). Distribution on the islands at this time was patchier. They were reportedly common on Islay, but uncommon on Jura and there were only two records for Colonsay. Only one or two were found on Coll and Lismore, and they were uncommon on Mull. There had been no breeding records for Coll or Tiree prior to 1937-38 when two possible pairs were on Coll. However, in 1955 at least six singing males were heard on Tiree in July, and three singing males were on Coll on 2-3 June 1955 (Boyd 1958).

Distribution in Argyll in the First Atlas was rather patchy, with more towards the west coast. They were largely absent from eastern Kintyre and from many 10-km squares in Cowal, Mid- and North Argyll. On the islands they were widespread only on Islay, absent from much of Jura and Mull, and present with probable or confirmed breeding records in at least one 10-km square on each of Coll, Colonsay and Tiree. Nationally, the species was in decline at this time according to the CBC.

Subsequently, the population seems to have increased on Tiree, where an estimated 25-30 pairs were breeding in May-June 1986. In 1987, the estimated total there was over 45 pairs (Stroud 1989). In 1986 a minimum of four pairs were on Coll, singing males were found at a minimum of seven sites on Mull, 22 pairs bred at Loch Gruinart, five pairs bred at Taynish NNR (ABR 4:34) and about 20-25 pairs bred annually on Colonsay (Jardine *et al.* 1986).

Sedge Warblers arrive in Argyll later than most other summer visitors. *Philip Kirkham*

Both gains and losses in distribution were in evidence by the time of the Second Atlas. Several new squares in Kintyre and Mull were occupied and breeding was confirmed in all three 10-km squares on Coll and Tiree. Birds were found in the 1991 breeding season on the Garvellachs and on the McCormaig Isles, Mid-Argyll. At the same time there was some range contraction in Mid- and North Argyll. The abundance map showed high densities on Islay and Tiree, and in parts of Kintyre.

A survey of the Rinns of Islay in 1994 found 196 territories including birds inside young forests, with high densities in areas of scrub and reed as well as along the forest edge (ABR). In contrast, in 2000 they were found in only two 1-km squares (one each on Colonsay and Tiree) of the 14 such squares randomly selected in Argyll (Wilson & Fuller 2001, P. Daw unpubl. data).

The results from the Taynish CBC show considerable annual fluctuations, with numbers peaking in 1998-1999 (13 territories) but no clear trend was evident (see Figure in the Common Whitethroat account). The few 1-km squares regularly surveyed in Argyll for the BBS show a similar pattern, with annual fluctuations but no obvious trend.

Since the Second Atlas, records of adults feeding young and of singing males during the breeding season reflect the same picture of fluctuating numbers, not only from year to year but from locality to locality. In ten years (1994-2003) breeding season numbers on Colonsay (including Oronsay) varied between 17 and 63 pairs. The latter figure was in 2000 when there were also high numbers on Sanda (five pairs), but relatively few territories (eight) in the Taynish CBC and low numbers on Tiree. In contrast, in 1998 only 29 singing birds were located on Colonsay but a record 13 territories were found at Taynish. However, 2002 seems to have been a good year almost everywhere. An estimated 100 or more males were singing on Tiree, 53 were on Colonsay and there were casual records of at least 50 singing on Islay. Nor was it just the larger islands that did well. There were good numbers on Gigha, at least two singing males on Cara, and singing birds on Lismore. One was even heard singing on Lunga, Treshnish Isles, for the first time since 1999. There were records from all the Argyll recording areas apart from Cowal. However, there were noticeably fewer in most places the following year (2003) (Argyll Database).

Results from the Constant Effort Ringing Site at Aros Moss, Kintyre, indicate a stable breeding population of 15 to 20 pairs annually, although breeding success may have declined recently (Brown 2002).

Three Sedge Warblers ringed in Argyll have been recovered elsewhere. A juvenile ringed on Sanda on 27 July 1995 was controlled near Fishguard (Dyfed) on 14 August 1995, an adult ringed at the Mull of Kintyre in May 1984 was controlled 963km away in France (at St Philbert de Grand Lieu in Loire-Atlantique) in August 1986, and a juvenile ringed on Islay on 4 August 1975 was controlled in Dorset on 1 September 1975. Five birds recovered in Argyll had been ringed 1-3 years previously in Finistère (France) (840km), Dorset, Sussex, Glamorgan (Wales) and Newshot Island (Strathclyde). An adult ringed at Aros Moss, Kintyre, on 21 May 1997 was re-trapped at the same site on 26 May 2002.

Sedge Warblers are one of the later arrivals among our migrants, the first birds usually appearing in the last week in April or first week in May. The earliest in recent years was one at Loch Leathan, Mid-Argyll, on 18 April 1993. Most have left the breeding areas by early August, but a few birds, presumably migrants, are seen in September, including birds at Loch Gruinart, Islay, on 26 September 1993 and at Balemartine, Tiree, on 29 September 2006.

Paul Daw

Reed Warbler

Acrocephalus scirpaceus

A rare spring-summer vagrant.

There are only five accepted records of this species in Argyll, all from the islands and all involving single birds (Table).

In addition, unstreaked *Acrocephalus* warblers, perhaps this species or Marsh Warbler *A. palustris*, were reported from Tiree on 3 June 1987 (ABR 5:11), the Mull of Kintyre on 7 June 1989 (ABR 6:50) and Loch Finlaggan on Islay on 1 July 2004 (Argyll Database) .

Although a common breeder in England and Wales, the Reed Warbler only became established as a breeding species in mainland Scotland in 1993. With breeding now apparently regular in Dumfries & Galloway and elsewhere, it seems likely that Reed Warblers will be recorded increasingly in Argyll. Indeed, it is possible that they are being overlooked at the moment.

Tristan ap Rheinallt

Date	Location	Reference
1 July 1976	Foreland Marsh (Islay)	SB 10:108
Early August 1980	Bridgend (Islay)	ABR 1:65, SBR 1980:46
26 June 1981	Loch Gorm (Islay)	ABR 1:65, SBR 1981:43
3 May 1997	Colonsay Hotel	ABR 14:77, SBR 1997:62
2 May 2004	Carnan Mor (Tiree)	Argyll Database

All records of Reed Warblers in Argyll up to the end of 2006.

Booted Warbler

Hippolais caligata

Vagrant.

The Booted Warbler is a rare but more or less annual visitor to the British Isles, breeding from northern Russia eastwards. The first Argyll record concerned an individual at Balemartine on Tiree on 20 September 1998 (BB 92:596). This was the first record for western Scotland and only the fifth Scottish record away from the Northern Isles. On 31 August 2006 a second bird was found on Tiree, feeding in weedy pasture at Balephetrish. It remained there until 2 September 2006 (record accepted by BBRC).

Tristan ap Rheinallt

Icterine Warbler

Hippolais icterina

Vagrant.

Although it is a regular passage migrant through the Northern Isles and along parts of the east coast of Scotland, this Northern European breeder is infrequently recorded in the west of the country. The four Argyll records to the end of 2006 compare with 11 from the Outer Hebrides (to the end of 2001). Predictably, most of these records (three out of four) come from the islands. All concern single birds (Table).

All records of Icterine Warblers in Argyll up to the end of 2006.

Date	Location	Reference
28 Aug 1978	Mull of Oa (Islay)	SBR 1978:39
12/13 to 28 Jun 1984	Taynuilt	ABR 2:43
2 Jun 1987	Scarinish (Tiree)	SBR 1988:47, ABR 5:11
4 to 5 Sep 1993	Portnahaven (Islay)	SBR 1993:50, ABR 10:68

Early June dates are typical for spring migrants in Scotland. Although the 1984 record was not published in SBR, this singing bird was tape-recorded by the owner of the garden in which it set up its territory. Singing males have been reported from Highland Region in several recent years, with breeding confirmed for the first time in Britain at Creag Meagaidh NNR in 1992.

Tristan ap Rheinallt

Blackcap

Sylvia atricapilla

This is a scarce but increasing summer visitor and a regular passage migrant, especially in autumn. An increasing number of birds winter in Argyll.

In Scotland, Blackcaps breed thinly in counties north of the central lowlands and very locally to Caithness. There are occasional records of singing birds in Orkney, but they are otherwise absent from the Northern Isles. They breed in similar habitat to Garden Warblers, but are less inclined to occupy continuous scrub (Thom, Second Atlas). The number of birds wintering in Scotland is increasing.

In the mid 19th century the NSA mentioned Blackcaps in both the Inveraray and Killean (Kintyre) parishes, and Gray said they were widely distributed in western Scotland, although nowhere numerous. Even at that early date Gray recognised how unusual the Blackcap's wintering habit was compared with other warblers. Later H&B said it occurred sparingly and, while mentioning records from Ledaig, North Argyll, and from Jura, added the surprising comment that they had never met with Blackcaps themselves.

By the middle of the 20th century B&R described Blackcaps breeding in Kintyre and west of Loch Fyne, including Inveraray, but said they were rarer to the east. There were no recent records from Jura and none from any other islands, apart from a sight record on Colonsay quoted by Loder (1935). Blackcaps were considered less common than Garden Warblers, and were common as passage migrants only on the east coast. B&R gave several winter records from Scotland, including one at Skerryvore Lighthouse on 16 November 1885.

The First Atlas showed relatively few records for Argyll, with breeding confirmed or suspected in only about twenty 10-km squares. Two of these were on Mull, one on Jura and the remainder on the mainland, mostly in Kintyre and the Loch Fyne/Loch Awe area, with two squares each in Cowal and North Argyll.

Surprisingly, the Winter Atlas found Blackcaps to be more widespread in Argyll during November-February than in the breeding season. Birds were found on Coll, Tiree, Colonsay, Islay and Mull, and in Mid- and North Argyll, while a remarkable four individuals were feeding at a bird table in Kintyre during 14-15 November 1983.

Blackcaps were not recorded breeding in either of the broadleaved woods in Argyll censused by Williamson (1974). However, in 1985 they were found in 12 of 38 similar woodlands surveyed, although only in small numbers (1.25 per occupied wood) (Averis & Martin 1985). During the 1980s, there were singing birds in spring on Colonsay, but breeding was not confirmed (Jardine *et al.* 1986). In 1987 and 1988 single males were seen in spring on Tiree and one was there on 10 November 1983 (Stroud 1989). In the late 1980s, there were territorial birds on Islay and Mull, and in

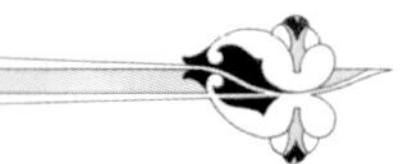

1986 several pairs were said to be breeding on Gigha (ABR).

The Second Atlas confirmed a considerable extension of the Blackcap's range in Argyll. Similar to the Garden Warbler, it was now breeding throughout Kintyre and in the Oban area. There were gains in Cowal and on Mull, and breeding was confirmed in three 10-km squares on Islay and one on Jura. Birds were present on Colonsay, but breeding was not proved. However, there were some losses in Mid-Argyll. Breeding was confirmed in only 23% of 10-km squares in the county, and Blackcaps were nowhere very numerous.

More recent surveys have shown that, although numbers may vary from year to year, there is evidence of a gradual increase. At Taynish NNR, Mid-Argyll, there has been a slow increase since census work began in 1990, but there were six years with no Blackcaps (Taynish CBC). In contrast, Garden Warblers exhibited a quite different trend (Figure in Garden Warbler account).

Although Blackcaps were recorded in only one of the 14 randomly selected 1-km squares (containing mainly coniferous woodland) surveyed in 2000 (Wilson & Fuller 2001, P. Daw unpubl. data), they were found in 14 of 29 broadleaved woods surveyed for the Second Woodland Bird Survey 2003/4 in Mid- and North Argyll, where numbers had trebled since 1985 (Amar *et al.* 2006, RSPB unpubl. data). Too few 1-km squares were regularly surveyed in Argyll for the BBS to reveal significant trends for this species, but it was found in four of the 25 squares visited at least twice during 1994-2003.

Since the Second Atlas, singing males have been reported during the breeding season from several sites in Cowal (including the eastern side of Loch Fyne) where they were often associated with *Rhododendron ponticum* thickets amongst broadleaved woodland, from several sites in North Argyll, including Lismore, and from many places in Kintyre (nine singing males were noted at Torrisdale in June 2001) including Gigha. In Mid-Argyll singing birds have been noted regularly along the west side of Loch Fyne, around Lochgilphead, in the Oban area, in Knapdale and around Loch Awe. The main concentration on Islay was in Bridgend Woods, where six or more singing males have been heard recently. There have been several records from Ballygrant Woods and Port Askaig, and scattered individuals elsewhere on Islay. Since at least 1997, one or more have been heard singing every year on Colonsay and five were reported there in 2004. There have been occasional reports of singing birds at Jura House on Jura. In 2003, a singing male was heard at The Lodge on Coll in both May and July. Recently, birds have been reported with increasing frequency in April and May on Tiree, presumably migrants (Argyll Database).

Blackcaps are unique among migrant passerines in Argyll, in that there are records for every month of the year. For this reason, it is difficult to be certain when our breeding birds arrive or depart. However, there is evidence that many breeding Blackcaps arrive around mid-April. The earliest

The Blackcap is the only warbler that regularly spends the winter in Argyll. *Margaret Staley*

singing bird at Taynish NNR was on 15 April 2003. As there are continuous records through summer into October, it is not easy to be sure when our breeding birds depart. Birds seen during September and October are generally thought to be migrants, probably from Scandinavia. There are widespread records through November and December and there is evidence that these are mainly winter visitors from central Europe (Bearhop *et al.* 2005). Although there are frequent records for the last two months of the year, the occurrence of birds from January to March seems to vary from year to year. There were many records during this period in 2001, but none in 2000 or 2002. Allowing for observer bias, it would appear that winter birds are much more widespread than those in summer, since there are recent records from mid-November to end of February for every Argyll recording area including the islands (Argyll Database). However, winter records are generally of birds in gardens, mostly at bird feeders and not necessarily in typical breeding habitat.

Only one Argyll-ringed Blackcap has been recovered elsewhere. An adult female ringed on Islay on 29 September 1976 was captured and released in Sussex on 28 October 1976 (716km). A first-year female ringed on Lundy (Bristol Channel) on 2 November 1995 was found dead near Campbeltown on 16 July 1998; and another first-year female ringed in Lot-et-Garonne (France) on 30 September 1995 was found dead near Ford, Lochgilphead, on 8 November 1995 (1,375km).

Paul Daw

Garden Warbler

Sylvia borin

A summer visitor and scarce breeding species in woodland and scrub habitats.

The Garden Warbler is a summer visitor that breeds widely, but sparsely, in southern and eastern Scotland. In recent years it has spread westwards in Argyll and northwards to the Great Glen. It breeds in deciduous woodland, scrub and young conifer plantations, wherever there is dense ground cover for nesting, but it is absent from high ground. It is one of the latest migrants in spring (Thom).

Among the earlier authors, only Gray mentions this species, saying he was "disposed to think that it is not commonly distributed" although he adds that it was difficult to judge its comparative numbers due to its shy habits. There were sight records of migrants at Skerryvore Lighthouse on 8 September and 20 October 1897 (Boyd 1958).

By the middle of the 20th century, there were indications that Garden Warblers were gradually spreading north. They were nesting in the south of Argyll, especially around Loch Fyne, but there were no confirmed breeding records from the north of the county, although birds had been seen or heard in both the Oban area and at the northern end of Loch Awe. Nor were they known to breed on any of the Argyll islands. Although the breeding range of the Blackcap was more extensive, it was considered that Garden Warblers were more plentiful (B&R).

The First Atlas showed very few records for Argyll, with breeding confirmed or suspected in only two or three 10-km squares each in Cowal, Knapdale and North Argyll. Birds were also present in three 10-km squares around Loch Awe, but there were no records for the Loch Fyne area or for any islands. With a scattered population of an elusive species, it is possible that some were overlooked.

Garden Warblers were not recorded as breeding in either of the Argyll woods surveyed by Williamson (1974). In 1985 a survey of 38 broadleaf woodlands found them in ten, although only in small numbers (1.6 per occupied wood) (Averis & Martin 1985). Eight were heard in song at six sites in Kintyre in May 1989 (ABR 6). A pair bred on Colonsay in 1974 and since then there have been intermittent records there of pairs or singing birds (Jardine *et al.* 1986). Birds were singing at two locations on Mull in May 1980, one was seen singing at Gallanach, Coll, in July 1984 and two pairs were reported at Loch Gruinart, Islay, in 1987 (ABR).

That a considerable range extension had taken place in Argyll by the late 1980s was clearly shown in the Second Atlas. This was most noticeable in Kintyre, where there were now confirmed breeding records for most 10-km squares, and in the Oban area. There were gains also on the islands with confirmed breeding on Colonsay and in three squares on Mull, although, despite earlier breeding records, only presence was shown on Islay. The species was nowhere very abundant and there were confirmed breeding records from only 14% of the Argyll 10-km squares.

Recent survey work has shown that, although numbers may vary from year to year, there is evidence that Garden Warblers may now be more numerous. The Taynish CBC found an average of 1.7 territories during 1990–1996,

Over the last 30 years, Garden Warblers have significantly expanded their range in Argyll. *John Robinson*

Fluctuation in the numbers of Garden Warblers and Blackcaps breeding in Taynish CBC plots, 1990-2006.

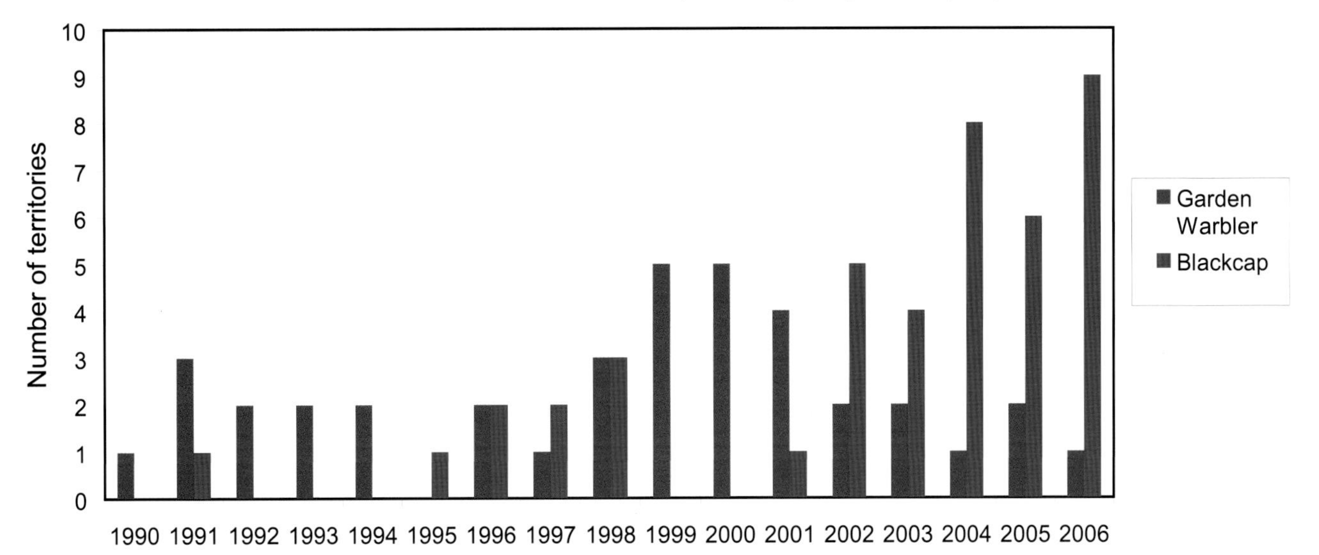

increasing to 3.1 territories during 1997-2003. Numbers peaked in 1991 and again in 1999/2000 (Figure).

Although Garden Warblers were not found in any of the 14 randomly selected 1-km squares (containing mainly coniferous woodland) surveyed in 2000 (Wilson & Fuller 2001, P. Daw unpubl. data), they were recorded in 15 of 29 broadleaved woods surveyed for the Second Woodland Bird Survey during 2003/4 in Mid- and North Argyll and numbers had increased five-fold (Amar *et al.* 2006, RSPB unpubl. data). Too few 1-km squares are regularly surveyed in Argyll for the BBS to reveal significant trends, but the species was found in five of the 25 squares visited at least twice since 1994.

Since the Second Atlas, singing males have been reported during the breeding season from several sites in Cowal, from Kintyre (birds at five locations in 1998) and from the northern part of North Argyll. However, most records have come from Mid-Argyll, particularly the woods around Loch Sween, Loch Awe and Loch Fyne, and from the Oban area (ABR).

On Colonsay, single singing birds were heard in Colonsay House gardens during the breeding season in 2000 and during 2002-2004, and an autumn migrant was found there in September 2000. Although there have been occasional records in May during the past ten years of birds singing on Islay, these may have been migrants. In recent years, birds have been reported only twice on Islay in autumn (ABR). Migrants have been seen occasionally on other islands, including two on Coll (September 1992 and October 2003), two on Sanda (May 2001 and September 2002) and several on Tiree in May and in September-October (ABR).

Garden Warblers rarely appear in Argyll until early May, but in recent years there have been a few records during the last week of April, including birds at Appin, North Argyll, on 23 April 2006 and in Mid-Argyll on 27 April in 2000 and 2002. Departure goes largely unnoticed, but there are regular records of migrant birds in September, usually on the islands. There have also been records in October, on Tiree in 1997, on Coll in 2003 and in Mid-Argyll in 2005, and a late bird was on Islay on 4 November 1997 (ABR, Argyll Database).

Paul Daw

Barred Warbler

Sylvia nisoria

Vagrant.

The Barred Warbler was first recorded in Argyll in 1896, when a first-year bird was killed at the Dubh Artach light on 8 or 9 September (ASNH 1897:140,142, B&R). It was only the second Scottish record of this species, which in Europe breeds mainly in the east and south-east. Nowadays it is recorded regularly in autumn in the Northern Isles and, to a lesser extent, along the east coast. However, sightings in western Scotland remain rare, and there are only five

Records of Barred Warblers in Argyll from 1897 to the end of 2006.

Date	Location	Comment	Reference
9 September 1913	Tiree	Flushed from a plot of cabbages	SN 1914:44, SN Extra Publication No. 3:12,52, B&R
21 August 1983	North Connel	First-year trapped and ringed	SBR 1983:35, ABR 1:65
30 September 1992	Arinagour (Coll)	First-year	SBR 1992:55, ABR 9:47
28 August 2006	Scarinish (Tiree)	Juvenile	Argyll Database
3 October 2006	Balephuil (Tiree)	Juvenile, accompanied by Lesser Whitethroat	Argyll Database

additional accepted records from Argyll. All concern single birds (Table).

Unlike most other migrant warblers, Barred Warblers are extremely rare in spring in Britain. The spread of dates for the Argyll records is typical.

Tristan ap Rheinallt

Lesser Whitethroat

Sylvia curruca

Rare passage migrant.

It is difficult to draw conclusions about the past status of the Lesser Whitethroat in Argyll. Although Gray claimed that its distribution extended north to the middle of Argyllshire, Paterson (1899) disputed this, believing that its status in Argyll was "more a matter of opinion that of actual knowledge." Gray's claim was also regarded as unsatisfactory by B&R, while H&B regarded the Lesser Whitethroat as of "extremely doubtful occurrence" in Argyll. In the first half of the 20th century, Walter Stewart recorded at least one pair nesting in Inveraray in 1921 (SN 1922:73; see BB 15:208), and the same record was quoted by B&R, although McWilliam questioned its validity. In 1948, a nest was said to have been found in an Oban garden (B&R). The only other published record for this period concerned a bird at Peninver in Kintyre on 22 May 1928 (SN 1929:144), which could have been a migrant.

Reviewing the Scottish records, Thom believed it possible that sporadic breeding had occurred in the country throughout the 20th century, and the Argyll records could be seen as part of this pattern. Be that as it may, the apparent recent expansion of the species' range in Scotland (Second Atlas) has not been accompanied by confirmed breeding records from Argyll, although there have been several occurrences in both spring and autumn. A bird on Iona on 13 September 1965 (the first since the 1948 Oban record) was the first of 20 recorded to the end of 2006. Of these, eight were in spring (4 May to 3 June), one in summer (24 June) and 11 in autumn (14 August to 12 November). As with many other scarce migrants, the majority of the records came from the islands (Islay, Coll, Tiree, Colonsay, Iona, Sanda) with only three from the mainland.

Birds at Connel on 26 August 1983 (ABR 1:65) and 14 August 1990 (SBR 1990:54, ABR 7:46), and a singing male nearby at Achnacairn, North Connel, on 5 to 11 May 1985 (SB 14:118, ABR 3:50), could have been migrants. On the other hand, three records in such a small area of the mainland suggest breeding, as does a record from Easter Ellister on Islay on 24 June 1992 (ABR 9:47).

Tristan ap Rheinallt

Common Whitethroat

Sylvia communis

A summer visitor, with numbers fluctuating from year to year. Breeding is most widespread in low-lying areas, particularly in coastal scrub.

The Whitethroat breeds throughout mainland Scotland in scrub, woodlands and hedgerows, although more sparsely in the north and west. It also breeds on many of the Inner Hebrides, but is scarce and sporadic in the Outer Hebrides and the Northern Isles (Thom, Second Atlas).

Although Inveraray was the only Argyll parish in which Whitethroats were listed in the NSA, Gray said they were common in the western counties of Scotland. H&B mentioned it in the Ledaig/Barcaldine area, as well as on Mull and Jura and they quote Graham saying Whitethroats were present on Iona. There were records of nesting on Coll in 1891 and of a pair there in 1903 (Boyd 1958).

In the mid-20th century, this species was described as well distributed and common on the Scottish mainland north to Ross-shire, and common on many of the islands including Islay, Jura, Colonsay, Gigha and Mull (B&R). There were breeding records for Iona, and birds were present in the breeding season on Lismore. Although widespread, Whitethroats were not found at any great altitude and were

Numbers of Whitethroats in the UK have been rising slowly since the early 1980s. *Philip Kirkham*

only numerous as migrants on the east coast.

Following a severe drought in their African wintering grounds, there was a major crash in numbers in 1969, when only about a quarter of the British breeding population returned (Winstanley *et al.* 1974). Little fieldwork for the First Atlas had been done in Scotland before the crash, and its effects were evident in the patchy confirmed breeding distribution shown for Argyll. This was most noticeable on islands such as Islay and Mull, but gaps were also apparent in Cowal, Kintyre and North Argyll. There were no records at all for Tiree, but breeding was confirmed on Coll.

In 1985 a survey found Whitethroats in seven of 38 broadleaf woodlands in Argyll but, as expected in this habitat, only in small numbers (1.3 per occupied wood) (Averis & Martin 1985). In the mid-1980s about ten pairs were breeding annually on Colonsay (but none on Oronsay) (Jardine *et al.* 1986) and there were confirmed breeding records for Coll, but birds seen on Tiree in May were probably migrants (Stroud 1989a). One was present on the Garvellachs on 6 June 1986.

Although there was some recovery in numbers from 1974 onwards, another sharp decline occurred following the winter of 1983/84, and by the time of the Second Atlas a noticeable contraction in range had taken place in Argyll. This almost exclusively affected inland areas of Mid- and North Argyll. The abundance map still showed areas of relatively high density in Knapdale and parts of Kintyre, and breeding was confirmed in 59% of Argyll's 10-km squares.

A survey of the Rinns of Islay in 1994 found 49 territories, with most birds in moorland scrub, roadside bushes and even forest edges, but very few were found in the northern Rinns (ABR 11:77). Whitethroats were found in five of the 14 randomly selected 1-km squares (containing mainly open country and coniferous woodland) surveyed in 2000 (Wilson & Fuller 2001, P. Daw unpubl. data).

Recent survey work shows that numbers vary considerably from year to year, with no obvious trend in the Taynish CBC (Figure). In some years numbers almost mirror those of Sedge Warblers, but in other years they differ. An increase was more apparent on Colonsay where an average 13.5 singing males were found in the years 1990-1996 increasing to 19.8 during 1997-2003, and an impressive 35 in 2004 (ABR). The few 1-km squares regularly surveyed in Argyll for the BBS that cover suitable habitat show no obvious trend in numbers. The species was found in 10 of 25 squares visited at least twice since 1994.

Survey work for other species has found Whitethroats to be widespread in low-growing shrubs and tangled undergrowth close to the sea. During the 2002 Peregrine Survey, Whitethroats were widely distributed on Jura, especially along the west coast raised beaches, at least 30 singing males being recorded in late May. They were frequently found in similar habitats on Mull and in Knapdale and Kintyre. Recent records have also shown a coastal bias in North Argyll (Argyll Database) and along the west coast of Cowal to the Ardlamont peninsula (S.J. Petty pers. comm.).

Recently, there have been breeding season records from some of the smaller islands including Ulva, Gigha and Iona (all in 2002) and Scarba in 1999 and 2004. Up to six pairs bred on Sanda Island in 2002 and 2003 (Morton 2002, 2004). In late June 2002, a male in song on Fladda was the first record for the Treshnish islands in over 30 years. Recent records indicate that Whitethroats are currently widespread and fairly numerous on Mull, but rather less so on Islay (Argyll Database).

Singing birds have been regularly recorded on Coll since the First Atlas and, in early June 2005, an estimated seven pairs were present between Arinagour and Uig. On Tiree there were records of singing birds in May in both 2002 and 2003, and a pair was present at Heylipol in June 2004, when alarm calls were noted and breeding was suspected.

Whitethroats are one of the latest summer visitors to

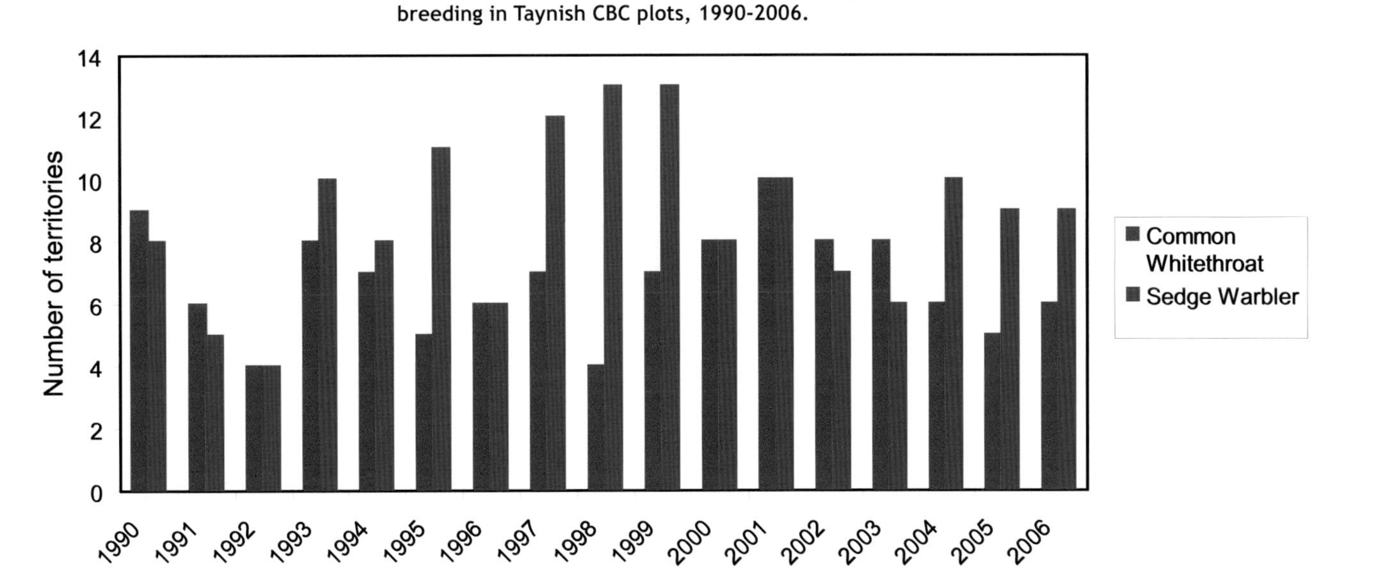

arrive, most not appearing until the first week of May or later but a few arriving in late April. One on Islay on 13 April 1989 was the earliest in recent years, and one was seen on Tiree on 14 April 2003. Most have left by the end August, but a trickle of birds appears during September, especially on the islands, and a late juvenile was on Islay on 4 October 1998 (Argyll Database).

Three birds ringed outside Argyll have been recovered within the county. A young bird ringed in Sussex in September 1968 was found dead near Campbeltown in August 1969 (654km) and another young bird ringed at Hounslow Heath (Greater London) in August 1992 was found dead near Connel in July 1993 (641km). A male ringed at the Calf of Man in May 1987 was controlled on Sanda (145km) in June 1987 and again in May 1988.

Paul Daw

Greenish Warbler

Phylloscopus trochiloides

Vagrant.

One was found dead at the Mull of Kintyre lighthouse on 27 May 1983 and the corpse retained by the RSPB Scottish Office (BB 78:576). According to the finder, the bird was trapped in gradually deteriorating condition on 25, 26 and 27 May, dying on the last date (E. J. Maguire pers. comm.). An exceptionally early autumn individual, aged as a first-winter, was trapped on Sanda on 31 July 1987 (BB 81:583). These are the only two Argyll records of this northern European and Asiatic species, which otherwise had not been recorded in western Scotland to the end of 2003. However, one was trapped on Tory Island, Donegal, on 21 September 1998 (BB 94:491).

Tristan ap Rheinallt

Yellow-browed Warbler

Phylloscopus inornatus

Vagrant.

Although its nearest breeding grounds are close to the Urals, this attractive *Phylloscopus* warbler is not unfamiliar in autumn along the Scottish east coast and in the Northern Isles. However, it is a much scarcer visitor to the west of the country. In Argyll, there have been six records, all in September and October. The first was a bird killed at the Skerryvore lantern on 21 September 1906 (Tomison 1907, B&R). Tomison described the occurrence as follows:

"One was captured on the night of the 20th Sept. 1906, or, to be more particular, at 2 A.M. of 21st. On the same night there was a great rush of Pipits, Wheatears, White Wagtails, and amongst the dead on the trimming-path this rare and interesting visitor was found. It was identified by Mr. Eagle Clarke."

Many years went by before the next occurrence, but there were five accepted records during the period 1988-2003, all from Islay or Tiree. The first and last of these coincided with exceptionally good years for this species in Britain, 2003 being the best ever and 1988 the next best (Fraser & Rogers 2006b) (Table).

Hume's Leaf Warbler *Phylloscopus humei*, previously treated as a race of Yellow-browed Warbler, is now regarded as a separate species. It is much rarer than Yellow-browed and tends to turn up later in the autumn. The details of the four most recent Argyll records indicate that the birds were *P. inornatus*. The early date of the Skerryvore bird would make *P. humei* unlikely.

Tristan ap Rheinallt

Records of Yellow-browed Warblers in Argyll from 1907 to the end of 2006.

Date	Location	Reference
20 October 1988	Kilchoman (Islay)	ABR 5:28, 7:7
2 October 1998	West Hynish (Tiree)	ABR 15:85
13-14 October 1999	Gleannagaoidh, nr Port Charlotte (Islay)	ABR 16:89
27 September - 1 October 2001	Kilkenneth (Tiree)	ABR 18:91
24-26 September 2003	Loch Gruinart (Islay)	Argyll Database

Western/Eastern Bonelli's Warbler

Phylloscopus bonelli/orientalis

Vagrant.

A singing male was at Easter Ellister on Islay from 21 to 22 May 1976 (BB 71:522). This was the second Scottish record of this closely related species pair. Unfortunately, like many other British records, it cannot be assigned with confidence to either Western or Eastern Bonelli's Warbler. However the former, which breeds from northern France southwards, is the more likely.

[At the time of writing, a record of a Western Bonelli's Warbler seen and photographed on Tiree on 8 September 2006 is being considered by BBRC].

Tristan ap Rheinallt

Wood Warbler

Phylloscopus sibilatrix

A scarce but widely distributed summer visitor to mature broadleaved woods.

The Wood Warbler is a summer visitor that breeds in closed canopy deciduous woods with little understorey. Thus, it is most abundant in western oakwoods and only thinly distributed in eastern Scotland (Thom). It has been slowly extending its range in Scotland and now breeds north to Caithness and Sutherland, but sparsely. Apart from Mull and Arran, where they have recently become more abundant, Wood Warblers are scarce or absent on most of the islands, although there are occasional records of singing birds on Skye and the Western Isles (Second Atlas, SBR 1982-2001).

In the mid-nineteenth century, Gray said the Wood Warbler's range extended to the north of Argyll and mentions a nest at Minard on Loch Fyne. Somewhat later, H&B described it as spreading, and said that many could be heard in the woods around Poltalloch, Mid-Argyll, in June 1889.

Wood Warblers were breeding in every mainland county of Scotland by the middle of the 20th century, although more commonly in the west than east. In Argyll they were found in many places on Mull and had been recorded from Islay and Jura (B&R). There were occasional records from Colonsay (Jardine *et al.* 1986), and single sightings on Coll and Tiree, both in May 1954 (Boyd 1958).

A patchy distribution was shown in the First Atlas, with gaps evident on the mainland in parts of Cowal and south Kintyre. Breeding was confined to a cluster of 10-km squares in the east of Islay and south of Jura and in two squares on Mull, but there were no records for Colonsay, Coll or Tiree. To a certain extent this reflects the availability of suitable habitat. There were confirmed records of breeding in a wood on Colonsay in 1977 and 1982, and in 1983 birds were heard singing in two woods on the island (Jardine *et al.* 1986).

Wood Warblers were found in moderate numbers in two broadleaved woodlands in Argyll censused by Williamson (1974). In 1985, they were found in all 38 similar woodlands surveyed, being the sixth most numerous species with a mean of 10.2 individuals per occupied wood (Averis & Martin 1985). Birds were heard singing in several deciduous woods on Jura in early June 1985 (ABR 3:51) and one was found on Scarba in 1987 (ABR 5:11).

The Second Atlas depicted a considerable range extension in Argyll. This was most noticeable on Mull where they were found in almost every 10-km square. There were also gains on Jura and Lismore, and in Cowal and Kintyre. They were missing from 3-4 of the squares in Mid- and North Argyll where they had been found breeding in the First Atlas. Breeding was confirmed in only 49% of 10-km squares in the county, with areas of high density in parts of Knapdale and Cowal.

Recent surveys have indicated a decline in numbers, and possibly a contraction in range in Argyll. At Taynish NNR, where the CBC started in 1990, numbers peaked at around six pairs in 1998 and subsequently declined (see Figure in Willow Warbler account).

Wood Warblers were recorded in only three of 14 randomly selected 1-km squares (containing mainly coniferous woodland) surveyed in 2000 (Wilson & Fuller 2001, P. Daw unpubl. data). In contrast, they were found in 27 of the 29 broadleaved woods surveyed for the Second

The Wood Warbler's song, often delivered from high in the canopy, is a characteristic sound of Argyll oakwoods in spring. *Philip Snow*

Woodland Bird Survey 2003/4 in Mid- and North Argyll, although numbers had decreased by 38.1% since the similar survey in 1985 (Amar *et al.* 2006, RSPB unpubl. data), a trend that was reflected in western oakwoods in Wales (Amar *et al.* 2005).

Since the Second Atlas, singing males have been reported during the breeding season from several sites in Cowal, North Argyll and Kintyre (mostly in the west). On Islay in the late 1990s, singing males were reported from several sites, mainly in the east. Since 2000, Islay records have been few and far between, and recently they have been heard regularly only in the Port Askaig area. There have been occasional reports of singing birds on Colonsay (but none since 2000) and on Jura (but not since 1997). The only substantial island population is now on Mull, where they are still widely distributed in suitable habitat. Most recent records on the mainland have come from Mid-Argyll, where they are apparently still widespread and fairly numerous in suitable woodlands (Argyll Database). Changes in grazing pressure affecting the growth of understorey vegetation in deciduous woodlands may influence the future distribution and numbers of Wood Warblers in Argyll.

This is one of the most punctual of summer visitors. In recent years, the first singing Wood Warblers have always been heard between 20 and 30 April. However, departure goes largely unnoticed and there are no Argyll records after August, the latest being on Kerrera on 18 August 2001 (Argyll Database). Migrants have occasionally been seen on islands where Wood Warblers do not breed, including one on Coll (May 1994) and two on Tiree (May 1998 and April 2002) (Argyll Database).

Paul Daw

Common Chiffchaff

Phylloscopus collybita

A summer visitor and scarce breeding species that is occasionally recorded in winter. On passage, it occurs more frequently on some islands than others.

The Chiffchaff is a scarce summer visitor to most of Scotland and only in parts of the south and west it is locally numerous. It prefers tall, especially broadleaved, trees with a shrub layer often of rhododendrons, a habitat frequently found in policy woodlands. Chiffchaffs are absent from much of northern Scotland away from the Great Glen, and they breed only sporadically on most of the islands apart from Arran (Thom, Second Atlas). They are one of the earliest migrants, the first often being heard in mid-March (SBR).

Despite the fact that Gray mentioned a few Chiffchaffs occurring in the Loch Lomond area, H&B record this species only on Jura, and even this they appear to doubt. It was only a very local breeding species in Scotland in the mid-20th century and, although B&R said it nested regularly as far north as Argyll, the only localities cited in the county were near Oban (where "a few" bred) and at Aros House and Gruline on Mull. Migrants (of unknown race) were mentioned on Islay and Tiree.

Thus, it was something of a surprise that the First Atlas showed Chiffchaffs nesting widely on mainland Argyll, although most 10-km squares showed probable rather than confirmed breeding. There were also records for at least two or three squares each on Islay, Jura and Mull.

Chiffchaffs were not recorded breeding in either of the broadleaved woods censused in 1974 (Williamson 1974) and were found (all single birds) in only three of 38 similar woodlands in 1985 (Averis & Martin 1985). In the 1980s, there were records of singing birds in the breeding season in at least three woods on Colonsay and breeding was thought to have taken place (Jardine *et al.* 1986), but occasional singing birds in spring on Coll and Tiree were probably migrants (ABR).

The Second Atlas presents a mixed picture for Argyll. Breeding was confirmed on Coll and Colonsay, and new squares with confirmed breeding were shown for Islay, Jura and Mull. However, gaps had appeared on the mainland, especially in Kintyre and Mid-Argyll. Stricter criteria for proof of breeding may have accounted for some of these changes. Breeding was confirmed in only 25% of 10-km squares in the county. Nowhere was it abundant, although 95 territories were found in Kintyre in 1989 (ABR 6:50).

Chiffchaffs have shown up poorly in recent surveys, although this may in part be because their habitats (especially policy woodlands) have not been well covered. In the Taynish CBC, one singing male was recorded in just one of 16 years. Nor were they found in any of the 14 randomly selected 1-km squares (containing mainly coniferous woodland) surveyed in 2000 (Wilson & Fuller 2001, P. Daw unpubl. data). Chiffchaffs were found in only five of 29 broadleaved woods surveyed for the Second Woodland Bird Survey 2003/4 in Mid- and North Argyll (Amar *et al.* 2006, RSPB unpubl. data). Too few 1-km squares were regularly surveyed in Argyll for the BBS to reveal significant trends, although it has recently been recorded in good numbers in at least one square in Cowal.

Since the Second Atlas, singing males have been reported during the breeding season from several sites in Cowal, including three singing at Castle Toward School in 2004, several woods in Kintyre, especially in the Carradale area, and

In Argyll, the Chiffchaff is a localised summer visitor, but occurs regularly at certain sites every year. *David Palmar*

a few localities in North Argyll. In Mid-Argyll they have been reported from the Oban, Connel and Lochgilphead areas and from around Loch Sween and the western shores on Loch Fyne. They have become scarce on Islay, having been heard recently only in the Kildalton area. On Jura, the few singing early in the year could well have been migrants, as there have been no breeding season records there since 1997. They still occur annually on Colonsay (five were singing there during the breeding season in 2003) and in several parts of Mull, including Iona. On Coll, single birds were heard singing near The Lodge in June in both 2002 and 2003 and the odd pair may have bred (Argyll Database).

Some evidence suggests that Chiffchaffs may be declining in Argyll, but the truth is difficult to ascertain as the readily identifiable song is often heard from migrants.

Chiffchaffs are often heard singing as early as late March. They were particularly early in 1997, when at least three were on Islay on 13 March and one was on Tiree on 16 March. Most have left the breeding areas by early August, but dates of departure are obscured by the widespread appearance of migrants later in the season. Passage migrants often occur on islands where they do not breed, including Tiree, and they have been regularly ringed on Sanda (Argyll Database).

Chiffchaffs of the race *collybita* breed not only in the British Isles, but over most of west and central Europe as far north as Denmark and southern Sweden. Some Continental *collybita* occur on passage in Britain, as do birds of the race *abietinus*, which breeds in northern Fennoscandia and parts of eastern Europe. In addition, birds of the race *tristis* (Siberian Chiffchaffs) from east of the Urals are believed to occur as scarce visitors in autumn and winter. However, the picture is obscured by identification difficulties and by the fact that some authorities assign birds occupying a zone between the breeding ranges of *abietinus* and *tristis* to yet another race, *fulvescens*. At the time of writing, *fulvescens* appears on the Scottish list, but was included within *tristis* by BWP and was not mentioned in the Migration Atlas. Although there are no relevant ringing recoveries, most non-*collybita* migrants in Argyll are presumably *abietinus*. The occurrence of *tristis*, whose plumage almost completely lacks yellow tones, is still a matter for debate. Indeed, many rarities committees only accept records of this race if they are based on individuals examined in the hand. Also, whilst some recent late-autumn birds on the islands have given the thin piping call often associated with *tristis* (J. Bowler, C.R. McKay, S. Wellock, pers. comm.), there is disagreement over whether this call is diagnostic.

In late autumn, well after local breeders have departed, Britain receives a wave of migrant Chiffchaffs from the Continent. This is most apparent on the east coast in the second half of October, but it also occurs in the west, where it typically continues into early November (Migration Atlas). In Argyll as elsewhere, some of the birds occurring at this time of year have less olive and yellow in the plumage than *collybita*, and may call differently. Judging by the relatively small number of published records, they occur mostly on the islands between the last few days of October and the end of December, with occasional sightings in January and February.

According to the Winter Atlas, three or more Chiffchaffs were found in winter in the 10-km square that covers western Scarba and southern Luing, although there is no mention of these records in the relevant ABR. Single records for Coll and Islay were also shown. In addition, a bird apparently showing the characteristics of the race *tristis* was present in Tobermory, Mull, on two dates in December 1984 (ABR 2). From 1985 to 1991 there were fairly frequent winter (mid-November to end February) records, mostly on Islay but also on Colonsay and Mull and in the Oban area. Many of these showed the characteristics of the races *abietinus* or *tristis*. Since then, reports of wintering birds have been few. There were records on Tiree on 17 November 1996, 2 December 1997, three dates in December 2001, on 19 and 26 November 2004, 23 November and 6 December 2005, 17 and 22 November 2006 and 16 January 2007. On Islay, a bird was present on 22 November 1998, and on Coll there were records on 16 January 2002, 16-21 November 2003, 18 and 23 November 2004 and 23 November 2006. On the mainland, records came from Loch na Cille (Loch Sween) on 5 December 2004, and from Taynuilt (Mid-Argyll) on 16 February 2007. Again, many of these birds showed the characteristics of *abietinus*/*tristis* and most were probably just late migrants (Argyll Database).

Paul Daw

Willow Warbler

Phylloscopus trochilus

A widespread and abundant summer visitor.

Willow Warblers are the most abundant summer migrant in Scotland. They breed in open/young woodland with some kind of shrub/grass layer, even isolated clumps of birch and willow, to at least 700m asl. Among conifers they are most abundant prior to canopy closure. Willow Warblers breed throughout the Scottish mainland and on all the larger islands except Tiree and Shetland, although they are scarcer in the Outer Hebrides and Orkney (Thom, Second Atlas). The first birds arrive in early April, with the main influx later in the month.

Doubtless because of the familiar song, this was one of the few warblers mentioned in the NSA, where it was listed for Inveraray and Killean (Kintyre) parishes. H&B said Willow Warblers were common in summer wherever there was natural cover, including on Islay, and they mentioned one on Tiree in May 1889. In the mid-20th century B&R described them as Scotland's commonest breeding warbler, nesting in every mainland county and being found even near stunted

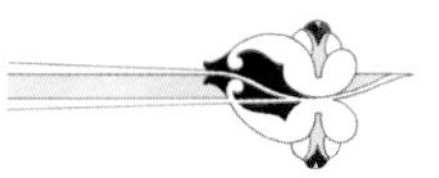

bushes among heather at up to 500m asl. They also nested on many of the islands including Colonsay, Gigha, Islay, Jura, Lismore and Mull, and a few were thought to breed on Coll (B&R). Three pairs were possibly breeding on Coll in 1938 (Boyd 1958).

Willow Warblers were almost ubiquitous on mainland Argyll in the First Atlas, with probable or confirmed breeding in every 10-km square apart from one bare coastal fringe in southern Kintyre. There were also probable or confirmed breeding records from most squares on Islay (except the far west), Jura and Mull and from two squares on Colonsay (but not Oronsay). Coll had one square with probable breeding, but there were none on Tiree.

Surveys in 1973 found that Willow Warblers were the fourth most numerous species in the oak/ash dominated woodland at Glen Nant, but only the seventh most numerous in the ash/hazel/oak woodland at Glasdrum (Williamson 1974). They were found on the Garvellachs and on Lunga (near Scarba) in the summers of 1975 and 1976 respectively recorded breeding in 81% of 10-km squares in the county. The abundance map showed areas of high density in parts of Cowal, Kintyre and Mid-Argyll. In a study of Sitka Spruce forests in Cowal, Willow Warblers were the fifth most numerous species in the spring of 1991 and fourth most numerous in 1992 (Patterson *et al.* 1995).

A survey of the Rinns of Islay in 1994 found 163 territories, including birds along the forest edge, but excluding those inside the forest where higher densities occurred (ABR 11:79). In contrast to England and Wales, recent surveys have indicated that numbers are on the increase in Argyll, as elsewhere in Scotland (Raven *et al.* 2005).

In the Taynish NNR, the population has almost doubled since census work commenced in 1990 when there were 54 pairs (Figure). In 2006 there were 106 pairs. The Figure also shows how much more abundant Willow Warblers are than Wood Warblers (Taynish CBC).

Willow Warblers were recorded in 12 of the 14 randomly selected 1-km squares (containing mainly coniferous woodland) in 2000, being the second most numerous species after Meadow Pipit (Wilson & Fuller 2001. P. Daw unpubl. data). They were found in all 29 broadleaved woods censused for the Second Woodland Bird Survey 2003/4 in Mid- and North Argyll, and numbers had increased by 19.2% since the similar survey in 1985 (Amar *et al.* 2006, RSPB unpubl. data). This contrasts sharply with an overall decline nationally, found in similar surveys elsewhere in Britain, of 68.8% (Amar *et al.* 2006). In contrast, results from the Constant Effort Ringing Site at Aros Moss, Kintyre, indicated a steady decline in the number of adults ringed from 1997 to 2002, although at least some of these may have been migrants from outwith Argyll (Brown 2002). No clear trends emerge from the 1-km squares visited in Argyll for the BBS, partly because many of them have not been continuously covered since the survey

Fluctuation in the numbers of Willow Warblers and Wood Warblers breeding in Taynish CBC plots, 1990-2006.

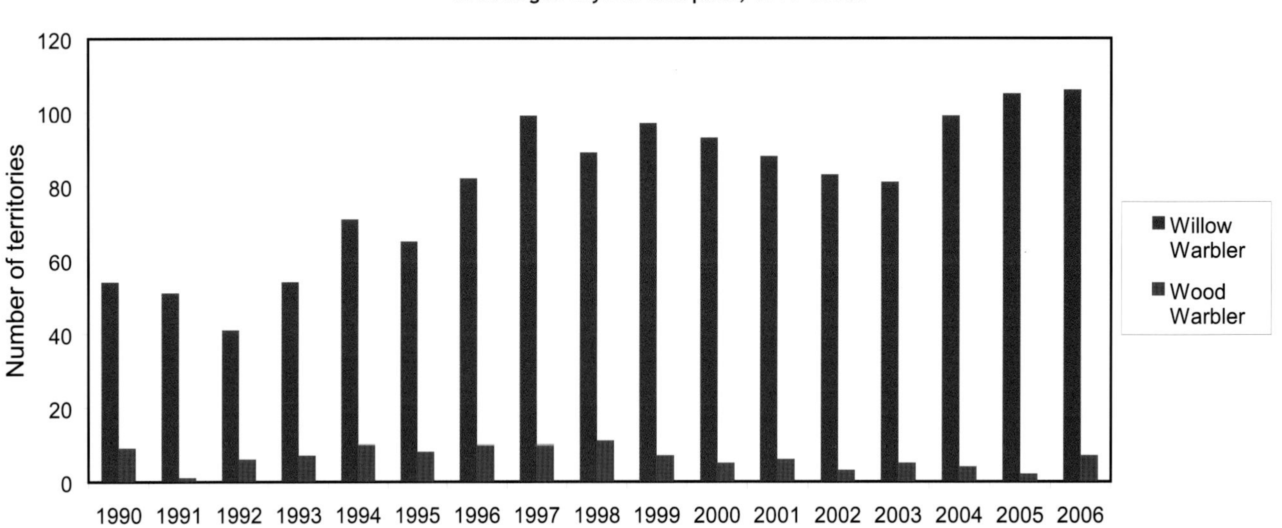

(T.D.H. Merrie pers. comm.). The Winter Atlas lists a single record on Coll, of a single bird seen at Arnabost on 28 November 1983 and described as a very late migrant (ABR 1).

A survey of broadleaf woodlands in 1985 found Willow Warblers at all 38 sites surveyed and, with 24.9 individuals per wood, they were the second most numerous species after Chaffinch (Averis & Martin 1985). At the RSPB's Loch Gruinart Reserve, Islay, 64 pairs were considered to have bred in 1986 (ABR 4:34-35), and in 1987-88 they were breeding in small numbers (10-30 pairs) on Coll, but there was no evidence of breeding on Tiree (Stroud 1989).

The Second Atlas indicated little overall change since the First, except for confirmed breeding in the far west of Islay and in two 10-km squares on Coll. Willow Warblers were

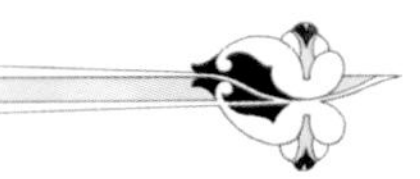

began in 1994.

Since the Second Atlas, singing males have been reported regularly during the breeding season on Coll and an estimated 28 were in song around the island in 2004 (Argyll Database, S. Wellock pers. comm.). Although singing birds had been heard fairly regularly over the years during April and May, a pair that reared three young at Moss in June 1997 was the first recorded breeding on Tiree. Breeding was confirmed again in 1998, and in 1999 up to five pairs were thought to be breeding in the Moss area. However, in 2001 a pair apparently on territory was not seen after 6 June, and few if any were thought to have bred in 2002. Nevertheless at least one pair bred in the Heylipol/Moss area in both 2003 and 2004. So, it appears that irregular breeding by a few pairs now occurs on Tiree (Argyll Database, J. Bowler pers. comm.).

Willow Warblers usually arrive during the second or third week in April. In some years odd birds may be seen in late March, and one on Colonsay on 27 March 1989 was the earliest in recent years. There appears to have been a trend towards slightly earlier first dates and birds were found during the first week of April at several sites in 2000-2003. Most have left the breeding areas by early August, but a few migrants are seen in September and occasionally well into October. Apart from the bird on Coll in November (above), the latest was one on Tiree on 26 October 1999 (Argyll Database).

The Willow Warbler is by far the most abundant breeding warbler in Argyll. *Philip Kirkham*

Willow Warblers that breed in Britain winter in sub-Saharan Africa, mainly in the Gulf of Guinea region. Although autumn movements through Britain are mainly on a south to south-east bearing, there is a change of direction to south to south-west on departure from England (Migration Atlas). Data from Argyll reflect this general picture. Most birds ringed in Argyll have been juveniles in early autumn, and these have been recovered in autumn in the Isle of Man, Lancashire, Lincolnshire, Dorset and Devon as well as further afield, in The Netherlands, western France and Portugal. Although there are no recoveries from the winter quarters, autumn-ringed juveniles from Argyll have been recovered in spring in South Wales, southern Spain, and Morocco. Birds ringed in spring in the Channel Islands, Dorset, Merseyside, the Isle of Man and Gwynedd (Wales) have been recovered in Argyll in spring or summer. This suggests that birds breeding in or migrating through Argyll follow roughly the same route in spring as in autumn, though there is one clear exception; a juvenile ringed in Fife on 12 August 1982 and recovered at Ceann an t-Sailein (Mid-Argyll) on 2 May 1983.

Most Willow Warblers are known to return to the general vicinity of their natal site in subsequent years (Lawn 1982). This is supported by the recovery on 22 June 1985 on Luing (Mid-Argyll) of a bird ringed at the same location on 7 August 1984. Also, a juvenile ringed on Sheep Island (Kintyre) on 2 August 1983 was trapped there on 6 May 1988. However, both these birds may have been on passage when ringed, and the only recovery of an Argyll-ringed nestling comes from the Atlantic coast of Spain.

Birds breeding from northern Scandinavia eastwards are assigned to the race *acredula* which, although very variable in coloration, is paler and browner on average than the western European race *trochilus*. However, the two forms are seldom distinguishable in the field (BWP). Individuals of *acredula* move south or south-east in autumn (Migration Atlas), and although they occur regularly on the east coast of Britain, they are likely to be rare in Argyll. Nevertheless, they are said to have occurred at the Mull of Galloway and Ailsa Craig (B&R). A complicating factor is the fact that some of the birds breeding in Scotland apparently resemble *acredula* (Thom), and indeed occasional individuals seen on Islay during the breeding season have been strikingly brown-and-white (T. ap Rheinallt pers. comm.).

Paul Daw

Goldcrest

Regulus regulus

A common resident of coniferous forests and to a lesser extent broadleaved woods. Numbers are augmented by passage birds in spring and especially in autumn, when remarkable "falls" sometimes occur.

The Goldcrest is one of several species to have benefited from widespread reforestation. Surprisingly, this is not a new development. As long ago as 1871 Robert Gray wrote that, in the previous 60-70 years, Goldcrests had increased from "very scarce" to "widely resident" in response to the numerous new "fir plantations" (Gray). The Goldcrest's small, needle-like bill is adapted to reach between the bases of conifer needles to extract prey, mainly small insects and spiders that are not so easily caught by other woodland birds such as tits. The disadvantage of this specialisation is that its food becomes unavailable when conifer leaves are coated in ice or snow. But, although Goldcrest numbers may crash during hard winters, they are (unlike Blue and Great Tits in Scotland) double-brooded and their numbers recover rapidly.

This is, of course, the smallest British bird, smaller than a large moth and weighing less than a 10p coin (5g and 6.5g). Its minute size, its skulking habit and its high-pitched call, inaudible to many older people, all make it inconspicuous. The Goldcrest is the eleventh most abundant breeding passerine in British woodlands, occurring in 85% of woods (Second Atlas). During that survey, breeding was recorded in 53% of 10-km squares in Argyll, a slight increase since the First Atlas, probably due to an increase in conifer plantations.

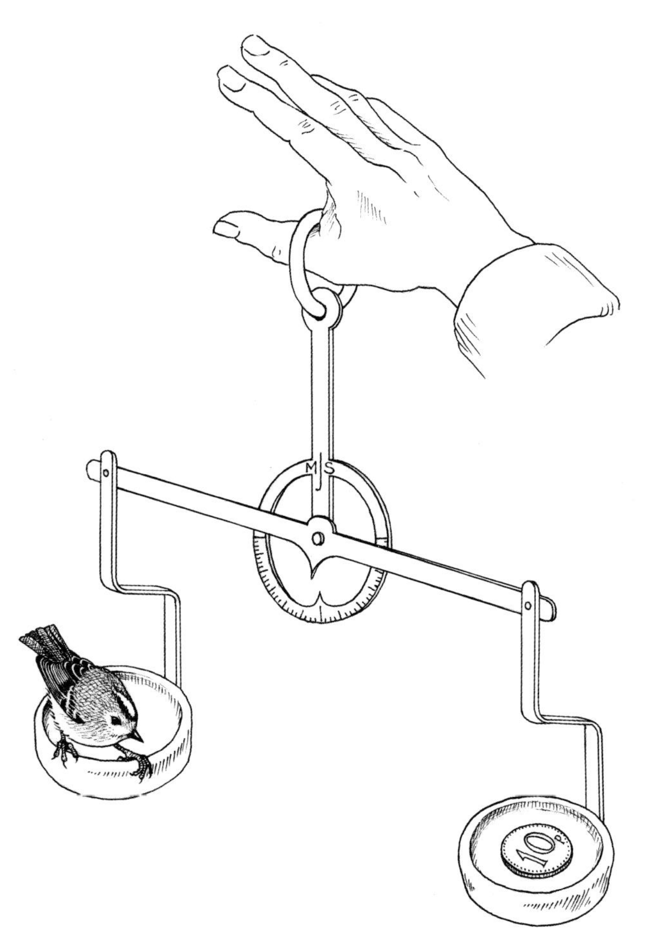

The Goldcrest is Britain's smallest bird, weighing less than a 10p coin. *Margaret Staley*

The Goldcrest is primarily a resident of coniferous woodland but it also occurs in other woods. Its highest breeding density in Scotland recorded by Thom was 26 pairs km^{-2} in the mixed woodlands of Glen Nant. It was found in 25 of 29 broadleaved woods in North and Mid-Argyll during the Second Woodland Bird Survey in 2003/4 and, although numbers had more than doubled since the similar survey in 1985, Goldcrests were relatively scarce in this kind of woodland (Amar *et al.* 2006, RSPB unpubl. data). Thus, in the Taynish CBC, an average of only one territory was found each year over a ten-year period (*cf.* 72 for Willow Warbler and 20 for Blue Tit). By contrast, two of the 1-km squares of the BBS covering conifer woods held averages of 18 and 20 Goldcrests in recent years (ABR, Argyll Database). Patterson *et al.* (1995) found in Sitka Spruce forests in Cowal that it was present in 20-47% of plots in spring and 19-24% of plots in winter (over two years), suggesting that some birds moved out of this habitat during winter.

Breeding has been recorded not only on the mainland and Mull but also on islands such as Islay, Coll and Colonsay and it probably occurs in most wooded areas of Argyll. Parties of ten, twenty or more are not uncommon in midsummer, usually in mixed flocks with tits and Treecreepers (ABR).

Goldcrests become much more conspicuous when on passage in spring and, particularly, in autumn. In March and April, migrants appear in numbers in places such as Sanda, Coll and Tiree. B&R recorded a fall of 60 at Skerryvore Lighthouse on 24 March 1904. In 1990 there were "hundreds" at the Mull of Kintyre lighthouse around midnight on 15-16 March. There was another large fall in late April that year, and similarly large numbers were counted there in April 1981 and April 1983 (ABR). On Tiree, some 123 birds were counted during falls in late March-early April 2005 (J. Bowler, pers. comm.).

Autumn passage peaks in late September and early October. Notable passages were recorded on Colonsay and Gigha in mid-September to mid-October 1987 and on Islay on 15-20 October 1990. There were again records of "hundreds" at the Mull of Kintyre Light around midnight on 5-6 September 1988, followed by smaller numbers there the next night and again on 11 and 13 October. There were remarkable counts of 150 at Glen Kerran and 65 at Macharioch on 23 September 1990 (ABR). That may well have been the same day that a spectacular fall of Goldcrests occurred in the centre of Oban, when dead and dying birds were being scattered like leaves by moving traffic and exhausted survivors were resting in flocks on ledges, window sills and garden gates (Mrs M.R. Craik, pers. obs.). Such events echo Robert Gray's record that, one day in autumn 1847, Goldcrests were "like a swarm of bees" with "six or more on every plant". He caught some with a butterfly net and kept them in captivity, but all died during the first frost a fortnight later (Gray).

Ringing has shown that some Goldcrests from northern Europe and Russia migrate to the British Isles for the winter (Migration Atlas) and spectacular falls of continental Goldcrests on the east coast of Britain are well known. However, the origins of birds arriving on the west coast of Scotland are less clear and, while most are likely to be British-bred, some may come from further afield. There have only been three ringing recoveries that involve Argyll, but they show the remarkable distances that this tiny bird can fly. The most interesting was a rapid movement of an adult male ringed

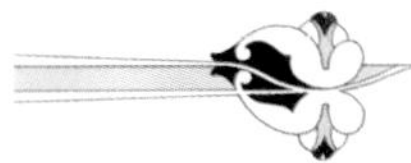

on the Calf of Man on 6 September 1981 and controlled on Sanda the next day (145km). A male ringed on Islay on 13 September 1976 was controlled in Staffordshire on 5 February 1977 (456km); and a young male ringed near Morecambe (Lancashire) on 25 September 1983 was controlled near the Mull of Kintyre on 21 April 1984 (227km).

Goldcrests are present throughout the winter but are less conspicuous. There are fewer records in midwinter than at other times of year, *e.g.* records of six in December 1985 and nine in January 1986 at Loch Gruinart, flocks of 20 on Colonsay in "winter" in late 1986, one at Arinagour on Coll on 14 December 1991 and 10-15 at the Lodge Plantation, Coll, in December 2004 where they now winter regularly (ABR). A winter record from Tiree of historical interest was given by H&B - a Goldcrest was caught in Mr MacQuarrie's shop at Scarinish on 12 November 1887. This is an unusually late date for Tiree, and there are no records from the island between December and February (J. Bowler pers. comm.).

Clive Craik

Firecrest

Regulus ignicapilla

Vagrant.

Although now well established as a breeder in southern England, the Firecrest remains a rare bird in Scotland. As with so many other scarce and rare passerines, most records come from the east coast and the Northern Isles. Most records are in autumn, with a few individuals in winter and even fewer in spring. However, the dates of the seven accepted Argyll records, all involving single birds, do not reflect this seasonal pattern (Table).

Interestingly, five of the seven records come from the mainland, and two of them involve birds seen in winter. As Thom suggested, the chances of wintering birds in woodland being overlooked must be high.

[A record of one on Islay in October 1990 (SBR 1990:56, ABR 7:48) was later rejected (ABR 9:10).]

Tristan ap Rheinallt

All records of Firecrests in Argyll to the end of 2006.

Date	Location	Comment	Reference
23 to 24 January 1980	Saddell (Kintyre)		SBR 1980:48, ABR 1:67 with incorrect date
16 May 1980	Sanda	Trapped	SBR 1980:48, ABR 1:67
25 May 1981	Mull of Kintyre	Male trapped	SBR 1981:45, ABR 1:67
4 November 1982	Mull of Kintyre		SBR 1982:41, ABR 1:67
30 December 1999	Dalmally		SBR 1999:105, ABR 16:91
12 March 2002	Loch na Cille, near Tayvallich	Possibly present since *c.*6 March	Argyll Database
22 October 2004	RSPB Loch Gruinart		Argyll Database

Small areas of ancient broad-leaved woodland, such as this one at Crinan Ferry, are widely distributed across Argyll. They are one of the county's most important habitats for biodiversity. *David Wood*

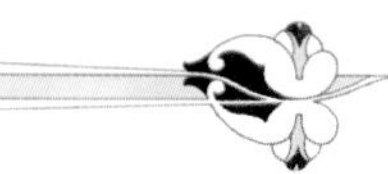

Above: Crinan Wood, by the Crinan Canal, Mid-Argyll. This Woodland Trust reserve supports a bird assemblage typical of western oak woods, including Wood Warbler, Common Redstart and Eurasian Jay.

Both photos: David Wood

Below: Even very steep ground can support ancient woodland, and some woods survived because they were remote and inaccessible. This 'hanging' oak woodland is on Eilean Righ, Loch Craignish.

Spotted Flycatcher

Muscicapa striata

A summer visitor, breeding widely but sparsely in mature woodlands, particularly where there are canopy gaps or along edges.

The Spotted Flycatcher is widely distributed across mainland Scotland, though at greatly reduced abundance in Caithness, Sutherland and much of the west Highlands. It is almost absent from Orkney, Shetland and the Outer Hebrides. It is a species of woodland gaps and edges, and frequently occurs in riparian habitats, so long as there are some large trees present. It has adapted well to nesting in gardens, especially those with some mature trees, from which it can hawk for large flying insects, its preferred food.

Gray recorded that this species was "very generally distributed", but gave no further indication of distribution or abundance in Argyll. H&B described it as "common" on Mull and in most other wooded areas, including the islands of Kerrera and Jura. They asserted that it was a rapidly spreading species, but unfortunately provided no justification for this claim. Records of its distribution in Argyll remained sparse through the first half of the 20th century, with B&R simply confirming that it bred sparingly on Islay, and around Ardlussa and Craighouse on Jura. Its status as a widespread breeding species in Argyll, including Coll, Mull, Colonsay, Jura and Islay, was confirmed by the First Atlas. In the Second Atlas, breeding was recorded in 53% of 10-km squares. This survey suggested a slight contraction in range in mainland Argyll, but some limited expansion in Islay since the First Atlas. Abundance was very variable, with hotspots in parts of mid and south Kintyre, Mid-Argyll, south-east Islay and North Argyll.

Information on trends in breeding numbers in Argyll is limited. A total of 84 individuals were recorded from 30 out of 38 broadleaved woodlands surveyed in North and Mid-Argyll in summer 1985 (ABR 3). The species is only occasionally recorded in BBS squares in Argyll. Its weak, unobtrusive song may lead to under-recording. Numbers breeding in the Taynish CBC fluctuated between one and eight pairs per year during 1990-2005. This gave a maximum breeding density of 20 pairs km^{-2} in woodland areas at Taynish in 2000, when eight pairs were present. This compares to 0-20 pairs km^{-2} found in six western oakwoods in Scotland by Williamson (1974).

There are few reliable estimates of the breeding populations of individual islands. Elliott (1989) estimated that 15-30 pairs breed on Islay most years, and there are up to four pairs each year on the RSPB's Loch Gruinart Reserve. There were at least four pairs on Colonsay in 1992, and the species keeps a foothold on Coll, with one pair in 1989 and two pairs in 2004 (ABR).

Across Britain, Spotted Flycatcher numbers have been in decline since the late 1960s. This decline accelerated during

The Spotted Flycatcher has declined over most of Britain since the late 1960s. *John McAvoy*

1983-1996, when CBC data indicated a reduction of 75% in the breeding population (Freeman & Crick 2003). Although breeding success varied from year to year, this did not appear to be related to the decline. Instead, falling survival rates of first-year birds were the most likely cause. It was unclear where this increased mortality occurred; in Britain post-fledging, on migration or in the winter quarters. Argyll does not seem to have been immune from this decline. Spotted Flycatchers were found in only nine of 29 broadleaved woods in Mid- and North Argyll during the Second Woodland Bird Survey 2003/4 (cf. 30 of 38 in 1985) and numbers had decreased by 68% since the similar survey in 1985 (Amar *et al.* 2006, RSPB unpubl. data).

The species is one of our last summer migrants to arrive. First and last dates for Argyll are 28 April and 1 October (1980-2002 data), with no indications that arrival and departure dates have changed during this period. The main influx occurs in mid to late May, and most birds leave by mid-September (Thom, ABR). In spring and autumn, small numbers of migrants can be seen on islands such as Tiree and Sanda where breeding does not occur, and in open habitats elsewhere (Argyll Database). Autumn gatherings apparently occur on Islay (Booth 1975), but elsewhere records of more than two individuals together are rare and invariably relate to family groups.

There have been no ringing recoveries from Argyll, and few from Scotland overall. Recoveries of birds ringed in England indicate that British birds migrate through western France and Iberia before reaching the wintering grounds in Africa. The return migration may be more directly north

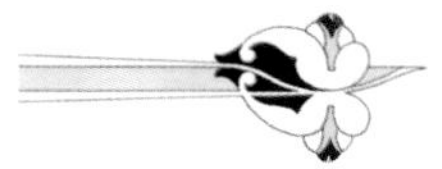

(Migration Atlas). Most recoveries in Europe are due to birds being deliberately killed by man.

David Wood

Red-breasted Flycatcher

Ficedula parva

Vagrant.

This attractive migrant, which breeds from Germany eastwards, is an annual visitor to the Northern Isles and the east coast of Scotland. However, records in western Scotland are rather few and far between, and there have been just two occurrences in Argyll. Birds aged as first-winters were at Easter Ellister on Islay on 1 November 1974 (SB 8:458) and 10 to 17 October 1975 (SB 9:228, Elliott 1989).

Tristan ap Rheinallt

Pied Flycatcher

Ficedula hypoleuca

Pied Flycatchers breed, as single pairs or in small colonies, in mature deciduous woodland in scattered parts of mainland Argyll and possibly on Mull, but they are scarce passage migrants elsewhere. The known breeding total has never exceeded nineteen pairs.

This is a summer visitor to much of Europe. In the British Isles its breeding strongholds are mature broadleaved woods in the west, particularly in Wales and northern England, but it extends south to Cornwall and Devon and more patchily north to Skye and the Great Glen. The British population has been estimated at 35,000-40,000 pairs (Second Atlas). In Scotland, its main concentrations are in the Borders, Dumfries & Galloway, and just outside Argyll in the Loch Lomond area. The fragmentary population in Argyll is thus a minor outpost. It is known to have bred in all four mainland areas (North Argyll, Mid-Argyll, Cowal and Kintyre) and breeding was suspected on Mull when a male and female were seen in late May 2002.

The first record from potential breeding habitat in the Argyll area seems to have been a pair seen by Bruce Campbell in Glen Etive in 1945. He also recorded a number of singing males, and one unsuccessful nesting, in North Argyll in 1945-1951 (Campbell 1954). In 1985, Pied Flycatchers were found at twelve woodland sites during the breeding season. Most of these records came from an RSPB survey of woodland birds in North and Mid-Argyll and in Kintyre, during which Pied Flycatchers were found in eight of 38 suitable woods (Averis & Martin 1985). Breeding was confirmed at four of these, including a pair feeding newly fledged young on the shores of Loch Etive on 1 July (the first known successful breeding for Argyll), and a pair entering a hole in a dead alder at Kennacraig (Kintyre) on 11 May. There is, however, much suitable breeding habitat for this species in Argyll and the paucity of records before 1985 may reflect a lack of organised surveys as much as a genuine absence, although Williamson (1974) did not record it during census work in broadleaved woodlands in Mid-Argyll in 1973.

Interest in the species took on a new dimension in 1987, when Argyll Bird Club's Nestbox Scheme began (Petty 1989, 1990, 1993). By 1989, around 20-80 boxes had been placed at each of twelve suitable woodland sites. In that year Pied Flycatchers laid at four of these - Bonawe

Uncommon but unmistakeable, in Argyll the Pied Flycatcher is at the edge of its European range. *Philip Snow*

(8 boxes), Ardgenavan, near Inverarary (3), Glenbranter (1) and Dalavich (1); Loch Lomond, just over the Argyll border, where a tantalising 19 boxes were occupied, was also in the scheme (all from Petty 1990). Boxes were placed at more sites in later years. By 2003 Pied Flycatchers had bred in boxes at 16 sites, all in North Argyll, Mid-Argyll or Cowal, but breeding was annual or near-annual only at two of these (Bonawe and Ardgenavan). Birds at most sites were ringed, revealing interesting aspects of breeding behaviour. A bigamous male bred with two females in different boxes and successfully raised young in both at Bonawe in 1994; another did so there in 1995; and yet another male did this at Ardgenavan in 1997. This behaviour is well known in the species (Lundberg & Alatalo 1992). A male ringed as a chick at Loch Katrine in 1989 raised young in boxes at Bonawe in each of the years 1991-1994; and a female ringed as a chick at Ellary (Knapdale) in 1996 bred in boxes at Bonawe in each of the years 1997-2000.

The largest number of boxes occupied by Pied Flycatchers in the county in any year was 19 in 1996; and the largest number at any one site was 12 at Bonawe in 2000 (although some of these may have been replacement clutches after predation of five clutches or broods by Pine Marten). Predation by Pine Martens of eggs, chicks and adults of all the species using boxes became an annual problem in at least one area (Craik 2002b) and had all but eliminated Pied Flycatcher as a nestbox-breeding species at Bonawe by 2003.

There are scattered records in May and June of Pied Flycatchers in suitable habitat in parts of North Argyll, Mid-Argyll, Cowal and Kintyre where there are no nestboxes and where breeding has never been confirmed, suggesting a wider breeding distribution than is known at present (see ABR Systematic Lists for years 1986, 1989-92, 1995-98 and 2000). Equally, there are apparently suitable areas with adequate nestboxes where Pied Flycatchers are absent. The environmental factors causing this patchy breeding distribution in the county are unknown.

The earliest arrivals in spring (up to 2002) were on 7 April 2001 at Torran (Loch Awe) and 12 April 1997 at Minard Castle (Loch Fyne). Spring passage birds have been recorded from Mull of Kintyre Lighthouse (18 May 1982), Colonsay (12 May 1985), Tiree (21 May 2002, 6 May 2004 and 25 May 2004) and Islay (four records in late May and early June). In autumn, migrants have been recorded between early August and late October, the first such record involving a bird seen on Skerryvore on 21 September 1906 (Tomison 1907). Apart from single birds at Ardentinny, Strath of Appin and Tighnahoran, by Loch Caolisport, all the remaining autumn records have come from the islands. Islay (7 records) and Tiree (4 or 5) accounted for most sightings, with birds also reported from Coll (2) and Colonsay (1). The seven autumn records from Islay included a possible family party of six birds on 15 August 1980 and a very late bird at Gruinart on 28 October 1989 (M.A.Ogilvie, pers. comm., ABR, Argyll Database).

British-ringed Pied Flycatchers have been recovered in the Ivory Coast region of western Africa, which seems to be the main wintering area (Clark *et al.* 2002, Migration Atlas).

Only one foreign recovery is on record from birds ringed in Argyll. A chick ringed at Bonawe on 15 June 1995 was recovered dead in Morocco (2,747km) on 15 September of the same year. A female ringed as a chick at Bonawe on 8 June 2001 was controlled (caught and released) at Dungeness Bird Observatory, Kent, on 3 May 2002 (738km). The same bird was found breeding in a box at Brenchoile, Katrine, Central Region, in May 2005.

The subspecies found from France to Scandinavia, including Britain, is *F. h. hypoleuca*. Other subspecies are found in adjacent parts of Europe.

Clive Craik

Long-tailed Tit

Aegithalos caudatus

A widespread and fairly common resident, scarce on Colonsay and a rare visitor to Coll and Tiree.

During the breeding season, the Long-tailed Tit is confined mainly to broadleaved woodland, particularly areas with a mix of tree species and ages. It also frequents woodland edges, wooded riparian habitats and large gardens. At other times of the year it wanders more widely, often in flocks that occasionally forage in scrub and coniferous woodland. Gray noted that it was "tolerably common in many parts of the West of Scotland, but is more noticeable in winter" and that "it is found also on some of the inner islands, being rather common on Islay". H&B report that it was "occasionally common in most districts of the mainland" and that "it occurs commonly in the larger and wooded islands", presumably meaning Mull and Islay, as they say that it was "not on our list for Jura". B&R record it as common in Argyll and give records for Islay and Mull, but not Jura. Thom says that breeding was sporadic on Jura and "a small group which bred on Colonsay in the 1970s is apparently now extinct" (in the mid 1980s). The Second Atlas shows that it is widely distributed in mainland Argyll, Mull and Islay, with birds also present in woodlands on the east side of Jura. Comparing the First and Second Atlases indicates very little change in distribution during the intervening years. The Scottish population is estimated at 36,890 pairs (BTO data), but the size of the Argyll population is unknown. Long-tailed Tits were found in 16 of 29 broadleaved woods during the Second Woodland Bird Survey 2003/4 but numbers had decreased by 46.3% since the similar survey in 1985 (Amar *et al.* 2006).

Long-tailed Tits are known to suffer heavy mortality in prolonged cold spells and can at times become virtually extinct in some localities (Second Atlas, Perrins 1979).

Long-tailed tits come to peanuts in some gardens, but are usually seen as foraging flocks in winter. *Philip Snow*

Populations along the Argyll coast, with its oceanic climate, may be less affected. However, populations on small islands are susceptible to periodic extinctions after severe storms or prolonged cold periods because of small numbers and limited resources. This may explain events on Colonsay, which was recolonised soon after the turn of this century. Up to three pairs bred there during 2001/02 and over 70 birds were counted in 2002, but then numbers declined substantially (Argyll Database). The species is a vagrant to Coll and Tiree, but autumn records there are increasing (J Bowler pers. comm.). The first record for Tiree was of two at Lower Vaul on 2 September 1996 and one to two were seen in the autumns of 1993, 1997 and 2001. The first record for Coll was on 25 October 1981 with five at Arinagour, after which one to eight were seen in the autumns/winters of 1992 and 2002 to 2004. All records on Coll and Tiree occurred during October to February.

During the breeding season, the Long-tailed Tit is mainly insectivorous, obtaining most of its food from the outer twigs, leaves and buds of broadleaved trees and scrubs (BWP, Perrins 1979). It builds an intricate, domed nest that is camouflaged with lichens on the outside and lined inside with hundreds or even thousands of small feathers. The nest is sometimes placed quite high up, often in the fork of a birch tree, so that it blends in with the trunk. Nests are also built in a wide range of lower sites, including bramble patches, gorse bushes, other low scrubs and, sometimes, even in a conifer, providing there are some broadleaved trees or bushes nearby. It is one of the earliest birds to breed, often laying in March, long before the true tits. Many early nests are lost to predators, but the parents often re-build and lay again. There is a complex social system, with failed breeders frequently becoming helpers at nests of relatives (Hatchwell *et al.* 2001).

Even in broadleaved woods this species is far less abundant than Blue and Great Tit. In the Taynish oakwoods it was a scarce breeding species with just 0-3 territories occupied annually during 1990-2005, an average density of just 2.5 pairs km^{-2} (Taynish CBC). Williamson (1974) also found it was scarce in the mixed broadleaved woods of Glen Nant (Mid Argyll), but here densities were 13.6 pairs km^{-2}, although data were only available for one year. The higher densities in Glen Nant may have been due to a greater diversity of tree ages and species compared with Taynish.

Its reliance on insects, combined with a small body mass, is the main reason why this species is so susceptible to severe winter conditions (Perrins 1979). It may eat a few small seeds during winter and it is increasingly visiting garden bird feeders. During 2004, in gardens in Argyll and Bute, this was the 24th most frequent visitor, with a reporting rate of 10.6% (Garden BirdWatch). Soon after breeding, close relatives gather together in flocks, and the groups persist until nest building the following spring (Glen & Perrins 1988). In the south of England, the size of flock territories was 20-30ha, but no information is available from further north. Flocks roost together in a tight cluster, usually in a dense thicket, a useful survival strategy in cold weather. Once the flock breaks up in spring, males form separate breeding territories within the winter flock territory, whereas the females move to breed in nearby flock territories, thus avoiding close inbreeding. Winter flocks usually comprise five to 20 birds, and this seems to be the normal range in Argyll also, although some flocks of over 30 birds have been recorded (Argyll Database).

The British race *rosaceus* is highly sedentary and, although quite a number have been ringed in Argyll, none have been recovered, apart from a few close to the ringing site. Birds of the Scandinavian race *caudatus*, which have a white head, are very rare vagrants to the east coast of Britain, including the Northern Isles (Migration Atlas, Pennington *et al.* 2004), but none have been reported in Argyll.

Steve J. Petty

Blue Tit

Cyanistes caeruleus

A widespread and common resident, but only an infrequent visitor to Coll and Tiree.

In Argyll, this is a widespread and common breeding species in broadleaved woodland, particularly where oak trees (*Quercus* spp.) are present. It also breeds in a wide range of semi-wooded habitats including gardens. It does not breed in treeless landscapes or on Coll and Tiree. Outside the breeding season it often occurs in areas where it does not breed, including Coll and Tiree.

The OSA recorded it as plentiful on the mainland of Lorn and Lower Argyll and H&B said that "records are universal from most areas, including the larger isles, such as Mull, Jura, etc.". B&R considered it to have increased in Scotland during the 19th century and noted that it was common or plentiful on Islay, Jura, Gigha and Mull, with some records from Colonsay and Lismore. More recent range expansion has included the Outer Hebrides, where breeding was first recorded in 1963 (Thom). The Second Atlas showed that Blue Tits were widespread in Argyll, being absent only from the more mountainous areas and from Coll and Tiree, and that little alteration in breeding range had occurred since the First Atlas. Birds were present on Coll during the spring and summer of 1983-84, but were not proved to have bred (Stroud 1989). There is more suitable habitat on Coll than Tiree, so it is surprising that most recent records come from Tiree, all outwith the breeding season. Here there were 14 records during 1997-2005, including one bird that successfully wintered in a garden at Sandaig between November 2003 and March 2004 (J. Bowler pers. comm.).

Blue Tits were found in all of the 29 broadleaved woods surveyed for the Second Woodland Bird Survey 2003/4 and numbers had increased by 54% since 1985 (Amar *et al.* 2006). The Scottish population has been estimated at 601,000 pairs (BTO source), but there is no estimate for Argyll. BTO Trend indicates a 46% increase in Scotland during 1994-2003. The only long-term data from Argyll come from the Taynish CBC (Mid-Argyll). Here, the population has more than doubled, increasing from 14 territories in 1990 to 34 territories in 2005 (Figure). In contrast, Great Tits had fewer territories and increased less (Figure). Interestingly, the populations of both species fluctuated in synchrony, suggesting that breeding numbers were not influenced by interspecific competition, but by some common environmental factor/s.

Blue Tits were one of the main species in the Argyll Bird Club's nest box project. *John McAvoy*

The Blue Tit is a bird of temperate deciduous and Mediterranean evergreen forests (BWP). Therefore, it is not surprising that the highest breeding densities in Argyll occur in mature broadleaved woodland, particularly where oak and birch are abundant. It was the fourth most abundant breeding bird in an oakwood in Mid-Argyll during 1990-2004 (Taynish CBC). During the breeding season, Blue Tits feed mainly on caterpillars from the tree canopy, and their breeding season is timed so that peak energy demands of the chicks coincide with the greatest abundance of caterpillars (Perrins 1979). Breeding also occurs in a wide range of semi-open habitats as long as some broadleaved trees are present, but breeding densities are much lower than in oak woodland. Breeding only occurs in upland spruce forests when broadleaved trees are interspersed within the forest or are present nearby. In Glenbranter Forest (Cowal), 88 spruce plots of varying ages were censused for breeding birds twice each spring during 1991-92 (Patterson *et al.* 1995). Blue Tits were recorded only in one of the plots, and then only in early spring 1992.

Blue tits nest mainly in tree holes (BWP, Perrins 1979). Surprisingly, these are often in short supply in many broadleaved woodlands, or are commandeered by the more dominant Great Tit. However, Blue Tits can use cavities with entrance holes too small for Great Tits. Blue Tits breed also in cavities in stone walls, crags and buildings, and in suitable nest boxes. However, in some areas of Argyll, nests in boxes may be prone to attack by predators, including Great Spotted Woodpecker, Pine Marten and Weasel. The only published study from Argyll comes from an ABC project involving nestboxes in eight areas of broadleaved woodlands in 1988 (Petty 1989, 1990). The timing of breeding varied among areas, with laying starting earlier nearer the coast (mean = 27 April in Knapdale) than further inland (mean = 8 May at Loch Lomond). The only other study in the west of Scotland was on the Isle of Rum (Love 1981). Here, the mean first egg and clutch and brood sizes were similar to those in Argyll (Table).

Blue Tit reproductive data from Argyll (Petty 1989) and the Isle of Rum (Love 1981) (n=sample size).

Mean breeding parameter	Argyll	Isle of Rum
Date of first egg	3 May (n=97)	4 May (n=30)
Clutch size	10.12 (n=101)	9.13 (n=30)
Fledged brood size	8.53 (n=100)	8.00 (n=30)

Outside the breeding season they often form mixed foraging flocks with other species of tit, which sometimes include Treecreeper and Goldcrest (Perrins, 1979). They regularly visit gardens for food. In Argyll & Bute in 2004, the Blue Tit was the second most frequent visitor to garden

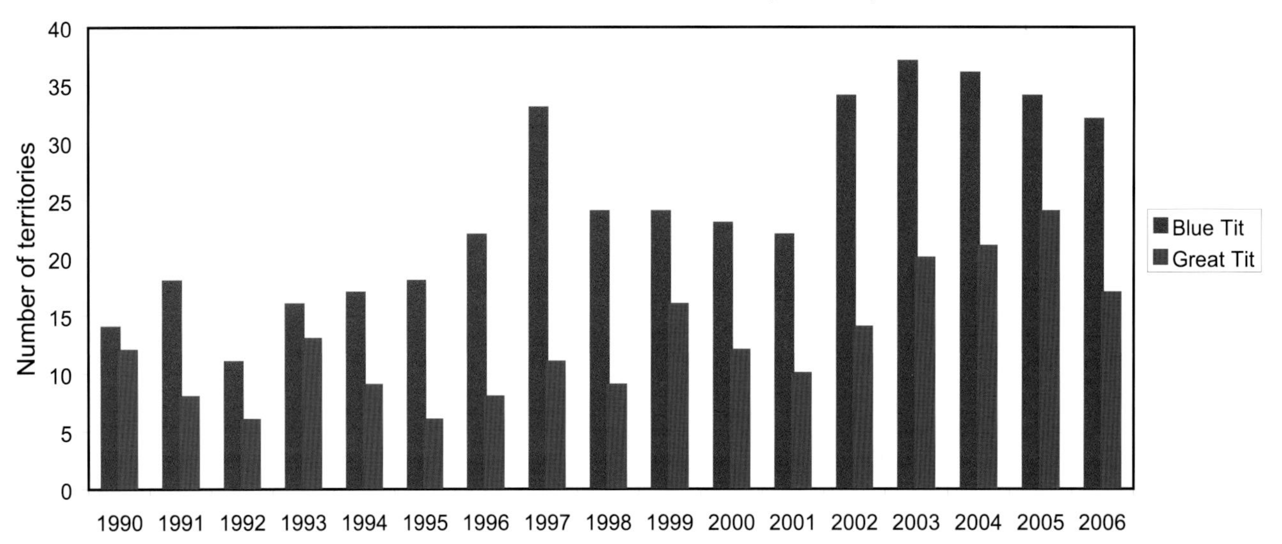

bird feeders. Overall, reporting rates were 97.6%, and were highest during December-April and lowest during June-August (BTO Garden BirdWatch).

There are no obvious threats to Blue Tit populations in Argyll. In fact, with more interest in indigenous woodlands, including the creation of new areas of native woodlands, the future seems good. Climate warming may pose a future problem, as it is not yet clear how Blue Tits will adjust their breeding to match the earlier flushing of broadleaved trees, which triggers the appearance of defoliating caterpillars on which adults feed their chicks (Visser *et al.* 2003).

The British race *obscurus* is mainly sedentary, but a few long distance movements occur, particularly when population levels are high (Migration Atlas). Generally, they are more mobile than Great Tits (Perrins 1979, Figure in Great Tit account). Many birds have been ringed in Argyll, but few (33) recovered. Twelve (36%) were found less than 10km from the ringing site, 21 (64%), 10-99km from the ringing sites, with no birds travelling more than 100km. Most recoveries occurred during February-March. The longest distance recorded (90km) was from a bird ringed outside Argyll (Jordanhill, Glasgow) and recovered in Glen Shira (Mid-Argyll). Sometimes quite rapid movements can occur. A bird ringed on Sanda Island on 18 September 2002 was trapped and released at Kames (Cowal) on 29 September; a distance of 72km in 11 days.

The Scandinavian sector of the continental race *caeruleus* are more prone to migrate/irrupt, but there have been no confirmed records in Argyll, although this race does occasionally reach the Northern Isles during October-December (Pennington *et al.* 2004) and south-east England (Cramp *et al.* 1960).

Steve J. Petty

Great Tit

Parus major

A widespread and common resident, but only an infrequent visitor to Coll and Tiree.

The Great Tit is a widespread and common breeding species in wooded habitats throughout mainland Argyll and the islands, except Coll and Tiree. It is most abundant in mature broadleaved woodland, but breeds also in parks, gardens, farmland and occasionally in low-lying conifer plantations. Outside the breeding season, it occurs in a wider range of habitats, and infrequently on Coll and Tiree.

H&B noted that it was "observed commonly in most suitable localities, where it also breeds", but that it was "rather more local than other tits in the north of our area". They also recorded it "in the wooded isles of Islay, Jura and Mull" (presumably meaning in woods on these islands). B&R recorded it breeding on Islay, Mull and Jura, and mentioned one on Lismore in July 1942. They noted that it had extended its range northwards in Scotland during the first half of the 20th century, a point reinforced by Thom. This expansion included the Outer Hebrides, where the first breeding attempt was on Lewis in 1962, after which numbers increased but then declined to six pairs by the early 1980s (Thom).

Thom stated that "small numbers have been recorded recently on Coll and Colonsay". Currently, it is an uncommon breeding species on Colonsay, being much scarcer than the Blue Tit (Jardine 2002), but it has never bred on Coll or Tiree (ABR, Argyll Database). Birds were present on Coll in spring and summer 1984, but no proof of breeding was obtained. There were single records on Coll in 1958, in April 1987 and in November 2002 (Stroud 1989, Argyll Database). The first record for Tiree was on 21 October 1997 when two were seen, after which one to two were reported on 11 occasions up to 5 April 1998, all probably the same individuals. Single birds were seen at Crossapol on 5 December 1999 and at Mannal on 3 April 2005 (J Bowler pers. comm.). Fewer Great Tits than Blue Tits are recorded on these two islands.

The Second Atlas indicates a very similar distribution in Argyll for both Blue and Great Tit, with Great Tit showing little change in distribution between the Atlases. On the other hand, numbers appear to be increasing throughout most of Scotland, with the BBS indicating an increase of 64% during 1994-2004. This may be linked to increases in suitable breeding habitat and milder winters, resulting in better overwinter survival. Currently, the Scottish population is estimated at 340,095 pairs (BTO source), but there is no estimate for Argyll.

Taynish CBC (Mid-Argyll) provides the only long-term data on numbers in Argyll. Here, the population doubled from 12 territories in 1990 to 24 in 2005. During the same period, Blue Tits increased more than Great Tits, but the populations of both species fluctuated in synchrony (see Figure in Blue Tit account). However, a quite different trend emerged during the Second Woodland Bird Survey of broadleaved woods in Mid- and North Argyll during 2003/4.

Although common in most broadleaved woods, Great Tits may be limited in some habitats by a lack of nesting cavities. *David Palmar*

Great Tits were found in all 29 woods, but numbers had decreased by 31.2% since a similar survey in 1985 (Amar *et al.* 2006).

While predominantly a bird of broadleaved woodland, Great Tits occupy a wider range of habitats than Blue Tits, including farmland and gardens providing they contain some trees (Perrins 1979). In many Atlantic oakwoods in Argyll they are less abundant than Blue Tits. In Taynish CBC it was the sixth most abundant species, while Blue Tit was the fourth. However, in areas with a mixture of woodland types, Great Tits sometimes outnumber Blue Tits as was found in mixed broadleaved woods at Glen Nant, Mid-Argyll (Williamson 1974).

They are scarce in spruce forests. In Cowal, they were recorded only once from 88 plots, with trees of varying ages, which were censused for breeding birds twice each spring during 1991-1992 (Patterson *et al.* 1995). However, other data from Cowal indicate that they are slightly more abundant in conifer forests than this study suggests, particularly in low-lying parts with nearby broadleaved trees. Here they were often found breeding in Tawny Owl nest boxes, while Blue Tits were not (S.J. Petty, unpubl. data).

Great Tits feed on a wide range of arthropods during the breeding season, including those caterpillars found abundantly on the foliage of oak and birch (BWP). Generally they feed lower down than Blue Tits, often amongst the understorey and even on the ground. Like Blue Tits, their breeding season is timed so that peak energy demand of chicks coincides with the greatest abundance of caterpillars (Van Noordwijk *et al.* 1995).

They require a larger entrance hole to a nest site than Blue Tits, and this may well limit breeding densities in many otherwise suitable habitats (Perrins 1979). Support for this comes from nest box studies, which show they use boxes more readily than Blue Tits. The latter often persist in using natural cavities when available (Perrins 1979). Great Tits also breed in suitable cavities in stone walls, buildings and crags. Eggs and chicks, particularly in nest boxes, are sometimes predated by Great Spotted Woodpecker, Pine Marten or Weasel.

In Argyll, Great Tits are single brooded, whereas in southern England they occasionally rear two broods (Perrins 1979). The only published information on breeding performance in Argyll comes from eight nestbox sites in broadleaved woodlands in 1988 (Petty 1989, 1990). Overall, Great Tits were less abundant than Blue Tits. Breeding was three days later than in Blue Tits (Table) and varied among areas, but this was not related to the timing of breeding in Blue Tits, suggesting that some areas were better for Great Tits than for Blue Tits and *vice versa*. Generally, clutch and brood sizes were smaller than in Blue Tits (Table).

Outwith the breeding season, Great Tits sometimes forage in mixed flocks comprising other tit species, Goldcrests and Treecreepers. Besides arthropods, they exploit a succession of seasonally available seeds including Hazel nuts, which they are able to open, and Beech mast (Perrins 1979). In 2004,

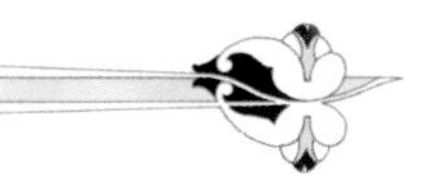

Breeding performance of Great and Blue Tits from eight nestbox study areas in broadleaved woods in Argyll in 1988 (Petty 1989).

Mean breeding parameter	Great Tit	Blue Tit
Date of first egg	6 May	3 May
Clutch size	8.24 (n=54)	10.12 (n=101)
Fledged brood size	7.83 (n=52)	8.53 (n=100)

it was the fifth most frequent bird using garden feeders in Argyll and Bute, with a reporting rate of 90.6% (BTO Garden BirdWatch). Most reports were during November-January and least during June-September.

The Great Tit is abundant in Argyll and faces no threat. Many oakwoods have regenerated since the cessation of charcoal-making in the 19th and early 20th centuries and will become better breeding habitats for Great Tits as they age and develop more holes suitable for nesting. The establishment of many new areas of native woodland in Argyll, plus an increasing interest in existing broadleaved woodlands, ensure a secure future for this species.

The Great Tit is even more sedentary than the Blue Tit (Migration Atlas, Perrins 1979) (Figure). Compared

Distance moved by Great Tits (n=17) and Blue Tits (n=33) that had been ringed in Argyll.

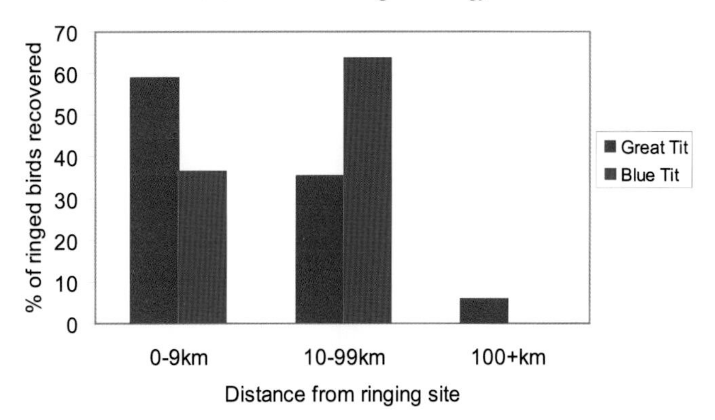

to Blue Tits, fewer have been ringed in Argyll and fewer recovered. There has been only one long distance movement; a chick ringed at Succoth (near Dalmally) in June 1994 was controlled near Glenurquhart (Highland) on 12 November 1994 (106km). In addition, 19 birds recovered in Argyll had been ringed elsewhere. Most (53%) had moved less than 10km, but three (16%) had moved over 100km. One male ringed in Darnaway Forest (Grampian) on 9 March 1983 was controlled at Barcaldine (near Oban) on 3 April of that year (152km) while another young male ringed at Drumnadrochit (Highland) on 14 December 1979 killed itself on a window at Barcaldine on 5 March 1980 (103km). These recoveries, together with the one from Dalmally to Glenurquhart, suggest that the Great Glen provides a wooded dispersal corridor from east to west and *vice versa*. However, the blue riband for this species belongs to an adult female ringed in Cheshire in March 1976 and controlled at Blairmore (near Dunoon) in December 1978 (332km).

Birds of the continental race *major* from northern Europe are prone to migrate/irrupt and occasionally reach the east coast of Britain (Migration Atlas), but there has been no confirmed record in Argyll. Examples of this race have been identified in the hand on the Isle of May and in Shetland (Thom, Pennington *et al.* 2004). They are smaller than the British race *newtoni*.

Steve J. Petty

Crested Tit

Lophophanes cristatus

Vagrant.

One was said to have been shot by a Mr A. Campbell at Barcaldine House, North Argyll, in January 1838, the occurrence being reported by Macgillivray (Gray, H&B). H&B, while accepting the record, commented that the specimen could not be traced. B&R also injected a note of doubt by remarking that the value of old records from Argyll and elsewhere was difficult to appraise, while Thom made no mention of Argyll in her review of the Crested Tit's distribution. As with old records of Willow Tit, therefore, it

The Crested Tit has been recorded only twice in Argyll. *Margaret Staley*

seems best to regard the 1838 record as unproven.

Thus there are only two acceptable Crested Tit records from Argyll. The first concerns an individual seen in native pinewood at Doire Darach, near Water of Tulla, on 9 November 1991 (SBR 1991:67, ABR 8:59, 9:9). This record represents an isolated outlier, the nearest occupied wood being 45 km to the north at Gairlochy (Summers & Canham 2001). However, the occurrence is by no means as remarkable as that of an individual seen intermittently and photographed at a bird table in Tobermory, Mull, between 19 October and 9 November 2002 (Argyll Database). These two records are among only a handful of extralimital sightings in Scotland.

Tristan ap Rheinallt

Coal Tit

Periparus ater

An abundant resident that is widely distributed throughout most of Argyll, but not on Coll or Tiree. Found almost exclusively in woodland, especially in conifers.

Despite being our smallest tit species and not migratory, the Coal Tit is one of the most abundant and widely distributed birds in Argyll, breeding in most 10-km squares. The Second Atlas shows the Coal Tit differs from the Blue and Great Tit in breeding at higher densities in Scotland than in England, making it a particularly Scottish bird. The BTO estimates that there are around 210,000 pairs of Coal Tits in Scotland, so it is one of the five or six most abundant birds in the country. Although numbers in Argyll are not known, the Second Atlas shows this species is particularly common in the west of Scotland, and it must be one of the most numerous birds in Argyll.

Although on the continent the Coal Tit can occasionally show winter 'irruptive' movements in relation to variation in food supplies, ringing data from the British Isles indicate Coal Tits rarely move more than a few kilometres from their place of birth (Migration Atlas). This sedentary nature seems to be especially evident in Scotland and Ireland, where there are no records of Coal Tits moving more than 10km from the location of ringing. There are no resident Coal Tits on Coll or Tiree; on those islands this species is a rare vagrant.

Whereas highly mobile birds tend to be monotypic, it is a common feature of bird species that are highly sedentary that populations are separable into distinct geographical races. This is the case with the Coal Tit, which has been divided into 12 subspecies. The continental race *ater* is a rare vagrant to Britain. In Britain the race is *britannicus* and in Ireland *hibernicus*. Since few continental Coal Tits even reach Shetland and Orkney, it is extremely unlikely that any of the continental subspecies of Coal Tits get as far as Argyll. However, vagrants from the Irish subspecies might very rarely reach Argyll. Irish birds have distinctly more yellow cheeks than British birds, but British birds can vary quite a lot and juveniles tend to be more yellow-cheeked as well as more likely to disperse. So identification of Irish Coal Tits in Argyll will be a major challenge. Elliott (1989) states that "Two birds with the pale primrose-yellow cheeks of the Irish race (*P. a. hibernicus*) were shot in 1913 along with a third having white cheeks as found in the British race (*P. a. britannicus*). It is likely that there is a periodic movement between Ireland and Scotland in response to food shortages, and Irish birds may be overlooked on Islay." However, *hibernicus* is not accepted on the Scottish list, as the identification based on cheek colour alone is probably unsound. The best chance of finding an Irish Coal Tit would be to scrutinise the vagrant Coal Tits that occasionally arrive on the islands of south-western Argyll, since some of these sites are not much further from Irish forests than from Scottish ones, but at the moment there is no clear evidence to support Elliott's suggestion that Irish Coal Tits may move to Scotland as a result of food shortages.

The Coal Tit is almost exclusively found in woodland; especially in confer forests. In broadleaved woodland it is subordinate to the larger Blue and Great Tits, but the Coal Tit is much better adapted to feeding and breeding in conifers than these larger tits. Not only is the Coal Tit more agile because its smaller weight allows it to feed on the tips of conifer branches, but its longer and narrower bill is better suited than those of the Blue and Great Tit to probing into partly open cones to extract seeds, and is probably more suitable for picking caterpillars, aphids and spiders from between conifer needles.

The massive expansion of spruce forests in Argyll since the 1930s has provided Coal Tits with the opportunity to increase in numbers. As a result, the species must be much more numerous now than before reforestation. Numbers will have increased, particularly when the Sitka Spruce plantations matured and began to produce cones, as Coal Tits seem to feed extensively on spruce seeds in winter. But in summer they are predominantly insectivorous, and chicks are reared on a diet dominated by caterpillars. Coal Tits can breed in conifer forests long before the trees reach cone-bearing age because they are not dependent on tree cavities for nest sites. Instead, they often nest in ground holes, often amongst tree roots and buttresses. Census work in Sitka Spruce forests in Cowal showed that Coal Tits were the most widespread species in winter, but by spring three other passerines were more abundant (Fig. 1). The relatively small change between the winter and spring distribution of Coal Tit suggests that most birds overwinter in the forest (see below) in contrast to Wrens, Robins and Chaffinches.

Nevertheless, Coal Tits do occur in broadleaved woodlands, and in some locations they can be surprisingly abundant (Fig. 2). Over a sixteen-year period in Taynish CBC they were almost as abundant as Great Tits, and in four of these years they outnumbered Great Tits, but not Blue Tits. In five census plots in Glen Nant, Williamson (1974) showed that Coal Tits actually outnumbered both Blue and Great Tits. He suggested this might be due to the lack of

Coal tits are common visitors to peanut feeders in gardens, particularly in mid-winter. *John McAvoy*

suitable tree cavities for the latter two species. Coal Tits were found in all 29 broadleaved woods in the Second Woodland Bird Survey in 2003/4 but numbers had decreased by 30% since the similar survey in 1985 (Amar *et al.* 2006, RSPB unpubl.data).

BTO survey data show no clear evidence of abundance decreasing after cold winters. This may seem surprising given that the Coal Tit weighs only 9g, and does not migrate to avoid harsh weather. In fact, remaining resident in the same spot all year round may be one reason why the Coal Tit can cope with hard weather. Unlike Blue and Great Tits, the Coal Tit hoards food in autumn to help it survive the winter (Brotons & Haftorn 1999). Food hoarding obviously only works if the birds stay in one place and gain intimate knowledge of the small home range in which they have stored food for later use. Despite this food hoarding behaviour, Coal Tits are not territorial in winter, and many individuals may share overlapping home ranges. Indeed, they frequently form winter foraging flocks with other small birds such as Treecreepers, Long-tailed and Blue Tits.

Another reason for a lack of correlation between Coal Tit numbers and winter weather may be that feeding conditions for Coal Tits in winter depend on the amount of seed set by conifers. Sitka Spruce shows considerable variation from year-to-year in the amount of seed it produces. Good years for spruce seem to be synchronous throughout Britain, but independent of winter weather. So, Coal Tits have large supplies of spruce seeds in some winters and not in others. In Argyll, Coal Tits can often be seen in winter extracting seeds from spruce trees, particularly in sunny weather when the cone scales open.

They will also visit gardens to take peanuts and seeds. The BTO's Garden BirdWatch study shows that Coal Tits occur in rather few gardens in England, but are fairly common in Scottish gardens. Their presence in gardens peaks in mid-winter, whereas most species show highest use of garden feeders in late winter or early spring. In Argyll, Coal Tits are even more frequent garden birds than in the rest of Scotland, probably because most Argyll gardens are not far from conifer forests, so Coal Tits can easily reach gardens despite their sedentary nature. At garden feeders Coal Tits are subordinate to larger birds, but tend to be the first species to hop onto feeders after disturbances by cats, Sparrowhawks or people. The Coal Tit seems to accept a high risk of predation in order to exploit feeder food, before being displaced by larger

Fig. 1. Relative abundance of five common passerines over two seasons (mean of two winter and four spring counts) in Sitka Spruce forests in Cowal (Patterson *et al.* 1995).

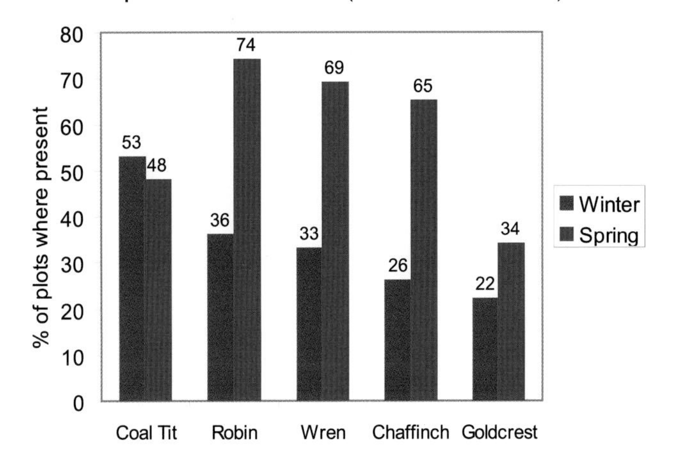

Fig. 2. Abundance of tit territories in broadleaved woodlands at Taynish NNR (mean 1990-2005) and Glen Nant (Williamson 1974).

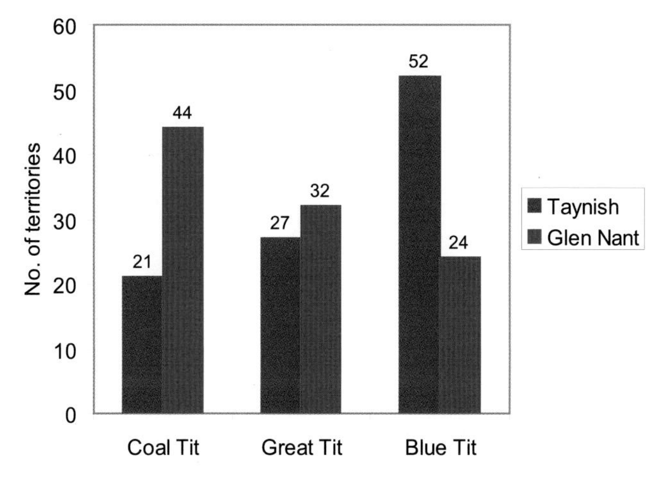

birds. Analysis of numbers of Coal Tits visiting a garden on the eastern edge of Argyll shows that the species was more frequent in years when the Sitka Spruce cone crop was poor, suggesting that Coal Tits prefer to feed on spruce seeds when available, but resort to feeding in gardens when winter food is in short supply (McKenzie *et al.* 2007).

Bob Furness

Willow Tit

Poecile montanus

Vagrant.

The Willow and Marsh Tits were not recognised as separate species in Britain until 1897 (Perrins 1979). Therefore, early statements about the species are difficult to interpret. For example, H&B suggest that "Marsh Tits", possibly of the "northern form – *P. borealis*" [= the northern race of Willow Tit, *Parus montanus borealis*] "swarmed in the glens of Mull before the severe winter of 1878-9". B&R made no reference to this claim, but stated: "There are several records in the breeding season from Argyll, but so far no nest has been found." However, it is not possible to be certain from this statement that any of the records refer to the present Argyll recording area. At least one derives from Walter Stewart, who claimed to have heard a bird in Glen Shira during 1919-1921 (Stewart 1938).

Stewart also noted that: "Fifty years or more ago the then Duke of Argyll knew the bird well in Inveraray woods. Then known as the Marsh Tit." If this is the case, then it is difficult to understand why Harvie-Brown, who received records regularly from the Duke of Argyll, did not mention the fact. Given these uncertainties and the fact that Stewart did not actually see the Glen Shira bird, none of the historical records is considered fully acceptable.

This leaves only one confirmed Willow Tit record in Argyll: a bird seen at Crannach, Water of Tulla, on 1 June 1991 by Bob McGowan, who submitted full details of the sighting (SBR 1991:66, ABR 8:59).

[A "Marsh/Willow Tit" was reported from Port Ellen on Islay on 15 November 1974 (SB 8:449), but there appear to be few details to support this unlikely occurrence.]

Tristan ap Rheinallt

Eurasian Nuthatch

Sitta europaea

Vagrant.

The status of the Nuthatch in Argyll is perhaps best described as obscure. Its name appears without qualification in a list of birds compiled for the Parish of Inveraray in the early part of the 19th century (NSA). H&B commented that the inclusion of Nuthatch on this list was "curious", using square brackets to indicate that they were not convinced of its occurrence in Argyll as a wild bird. Gray made no mention of it.

H&B also briefly discussed the Duke of Argyll's efforts to introduce Nuthatches to Inveraray in 1879. In a letter dated 5 February 1889, the Duke of Argyll described to Harvie-Brown his failure to introduce Red-winged Blackbirds to Inveraray, and he continued:

"I may mention that I have failed also in, perhaps, a more likely attempt which was to introduce into the large woods of this place the Common English Nuthatch. I got from a Dealer in birds at Brighton a good many couple [sic] of these birds and turned them out in most suitable tracts of old timber. Not one of them was ever seen again".

More than half a century later, B&R had nothing new to say about this species in Argyll, and indeed could quote only a few scattered records from the whole of Scotland. In the mid-

The distinctive Nuthatch may be less rare in Argyll than previously thought. *Philip Kirkham*

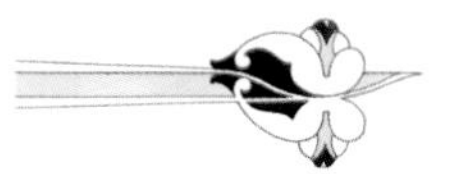

1970s, however, two Argyll records were published in SBR. One concerned a bird in a garden at Dalmally on 22 June 1975 (SB 9:219), and the other an individual in Lochgilphead in January and February 1976 (SB 10:105). The latter was also reported in 1975 and later in 1976, and the observer believed that the species bred in the area. Although never published, there were also several other reports around the same time. The Argyll Bird Recorder wrote in 1976 that "there do seem to be rather persistent scattered Nuthatch records from about six different independent observers, e.g. Taynuilt, Dalmally, Lochgilphead, Loch Riddon, Loch Caolisport, over the last five years or so" (unpublished information from Recorder's files). Furthermore, unconfirmed reports from Mid-Argyll extend back as far as the mid-1950s (Rainier 1975).

In the broader Scottish context, a similar pattern of scattered reports over a long period was also seen in Perth in the 1960s and 1970s (Thom), who commented that the scatter of dates of the Scottish records suggested that "occasional irruptive movements may take place in autumn and winter, with some birds first being noticed when they come near habitations in hard weather." It is also conceivable that a small resident population could persist, largely undetected, to the north and/or west of the Central Lowlands. Murray (1991b), in a historical review, observed that prior to the 1980s, most Scottish records occurred in two bands, one near the border with England and the other following the line of the Highland Boundary Fault from Argyll to Angus. He referred to "attempted, and possibly failed, colonisation of the southern Highlands in the late 1960's [sic] and 1970's."

After the mid-1970s, there were no further accepted records in Argyll for more than 20 years. However, scattered birds continued to be reported, mostly from gardens on the mainland. These reports are difficult to evaluate because they come from casual birdwatchers who, understandably, are unable to back up their sightings with sufficient detail to satisfy a rarities committee. Yet because the Nuthatch is such a distinctive bird, many if not all are likely to be genuine, as may also be the case for the earlier unpublished records.

In the meantime, the Nuthatch became established as a breeding species in the south of Scotland and then underwent a rapid expansion from about 1995 onwards, with reports coming from as far north as Highland and Caithness (Maxwell 2004a, b). Thus the sighting of a bird feeding on peanuts in a Glenbranter garden on 6 April 1999 (ABR 16:92) forms part of a pattern of increase that might result in the Nuthatch (again?) becoming an established member of the Argyll avifauna. One was again seen feeding on peanuts in Glenbranter on 20 and 22 April 2006 (Argyll Database).

Tristan ap Rheinallt

Eurasian Treecreeper

Certhia familiaris

A widespread and fairly common resident, but rare on Tiree and Coll.

The Treecreeper breeds in woodland throughout Argyll, preferring broadleaved or mixed broadleaved/coniferous habitats with some old and dead trees. It occurs at lower density in coniferous forests, parks and large gardens. Outside the breeding season it forages more widely and often joins parties of tits and Goldcrests, but avoids treeless landscapes.

Prior to the mid-19th century, its range would have been greatly reduced by deforestation. It was unknown from southern Scotland at the time of the OSA (Historical Atlas). Subsequently, it would have benefited from the establishment of new woodland on many large estates in Argyll in the 19th century and from extensive reforestation from the 1920s. Gray described it as common in the west of Scotland, but he failed to find it on the islands. H&B noted that it was "generally abundant in the suitable wooded districts from Torcastle in the north, southward" and that it "occurs also in the larger islands wherever sufficiency of wood affords shelter and attraction, such as Mull and Jura". They also said that it "appears to have become much rarer in many places within our district since the severe winter of 1886". In 1948, B&R "found it not uncommon in the woods on Islay". Thom remarked on its range expansion since 1950 in the Hebrides.

Treecreepers were found in 27 of 29 broadleaved woods during the Second Woodland Bird Survey 2003/4 but numbers had decreased by 27.1% since the similar survey in 1985 (Amar *et al.* 2006). Generally, there appears to have been little change in status in Argyll between the First and Second Atlases. The latter shows it to be well distributed on mainland Argyll and on the large islands of Mull, Jura and Islay, except in more hilly areas. It breeds on Colonsay, but is uncommon (Jardine 2002). The first record for Coll was of two birds at Lodge Plantation on 6 May 1989 (J. Bowler pers. comm.). A single bird was seen later the same year at Crossapol, Tiree on 10 September. There were records on Coll in October 1992, November 1998 and November 2003. The last bird remained and was joined by another in May 2004. Breeding was thought likely at Lodge Plantation in May 2004 when two adults were observed carrying faecal sacs. In 2005, one pair was present in each of two plantations, although it is not known if either bred.

Treecreepers feed largely on insects and spiders and are known to suffer heavy mortality in severe winters, a common feature of small insectivorous birds. They forage mainly on trunks and larger branches of trees, where they extract prey from crevices in the bark with their long, curved beaks (BWP). Thus, in the early 21st century, numbers are likely to be high due to a run of mild winters, and birds in Argyll may well benefit from the mild, oceanic climate. Nevertheless, Treecreepers only occur at low densities in Argyll, even in the

Like other small insectivores, Treecreepers spend most of the day searching for food. *Margaret Staley*

best habitats. For example, in the Taynish oakwoods, this was only the 15th most abundant bird, fluctuating between three and eight pairs during 1990-2005, with no obvious trend (Taynish CBC).

The Treecreeper is even scarcer in spruce forests. It was not recorded at all in Glenbranter Forest (Cowal) where 88 spruce plots of varying ages were censused for breeding birds twice in spring and once in winter during 1991-92 (Patterson *et al.* 1995). However, birds do breed in conifer forests, but usually in older parts of the forest, particularly where there is a mixture of tree species (S.J. Petty pers. obs.). The botanical gardens and policy woodland of Argyll are good places to find Treecreepers, particularly when they contain Giant Redwoods. The dry spongy bark of this tree provides ideal sites for birds to excavate hemispherical roosting chambers (Mackenzie 1957, 1959). This habit is widespread in Scotland, and good examples can be seen in the avenue of Giant Redwoods in Benmore Gardens (Cowal). Typical nest sites are behind the loose bark of dead trees, and occasionally nestboxes are used, particularly those designed for the species (Mackenzie 1957). They breed earlier than most of the tits, the first eggs being laid in early April (Flegg 1973). The majority of pairs are single-brooded, but occasionally a second brood is raised, although it is not clear if this happens in Argyll. Elsewhere, second broods are more frequent in conifers.

This species rarely takes food from bird feeders. It was only the 32nd most abundant bird species to visit gardens in Argyll and Bute in 2004, with a reporting rate of just 7.4% (Garden BirdWatch). The Scottish population is estimated at 40,414 pairs, but there is no estimate for Argyll. Due to an increase in suitable woodlands, Treeceeper numbers may continue to increase in the future, albeit tempered by the occasional severe winter.

Outside the breeding season Treecreepers are found in a wider range of wooded habitats, where they often join flocks of tits and Goldcrests (BWP). This association appears to be more beneficial to Treecreepers than to other flock members, as it allows them to increase their foraging rate by having to spend less time on the lookout for predators, particularly Sparrowhawks (Henderson 1989, Arévalo & Gosler 1994).

The British race (*britannicus*) is highly sedentary and, once settled, birds often remain in their territories for life (Migration Atlas). Few are ringed and very few recovered. The only recovery in Argyll was of a chick ringed at Loch Katrine (Central Region) in June 1989 and found dead at Ardgartan (near the head of Loch Long) in July 1990 (18km).

There are occasional irruptions of the nominate race (*familiaris*) from Scandinavia and eastern Europe, and a small number of these have been identified along the east coast of Britain (Migration Atlas). Those in Shetland arrived mainly during September-October (Pennington *et al.* 2004). None are known to have reached Argyll.

Steve J. Petty

Golden Oriole

Oriolus oriolus

Rare migrant, mainly in spring.

The Golden Oriole is an annual visitor to Scotland in small numbers; despite its mainly southerly breeding distribution on the Continent, most recent records have come from the Northern Isles. However, there have been scattered occurrences all over the country.

In Argyll, this species was first recorded in September 1938, when one was seen on Coll (B&R, Boyd 1958). The next records were not until 1965, when single males were seen on Iona on 27 May (SB 3:374), Coll on 31 May and 1 June (SB 3:374) and Kildalton on Islay on 22 September (SB 4:113). These springtime occurrences coincided with the first record for the Outer Hebrides on 29 May (SB 4:290). With the exception of a bird, stated to be a first-year male, on Tiree on 27 May 1969 (SB 6:108), there were no further records until the 1980s. Then, there was a total of 14 records in nine of the 15 years between 1983 and 1997. With the exception of two males seen at Port Askaig on Islay on 15 April 1987 (SBR 1987:43, ABR 5:11), all involved single birds. Nine of the 14 records came from the islands (four on Islay, three on Mull, one on Coll and one on Shuna, near Luing). Of the remaining five, two came from Kintyre and three from Taynish NNR, where males were recorded on 26 May 1992 (SBR 1992:61, ABR 9:50), 14 May 1993 (SBR 1993:56, ABR 10:71) and 10 June 1997 (SBR 1997:69, ABR 14:81). The remarkable series of records at Taynish must have involved at least two different birds, since the singing 1997 individual was apparently an immature male.

Thus during 1938 to 1997, there was a total of 19 records in Argyll, all but two during spring (15 April to 11 June), with a peak in late May. Interestingly, there were no further records during the five years 1998 to 2002. On 31 May 2003, however, a male sang briefly once again at Taynish NNR. On 31 May 2004 a male was seen singing and feeding in oak trees at a location near Connel. It was seen singing there again on 7 June 2004, and on 1 July 2005, a pair was reported nearby (Argyll Database).

Tristan ap Rheinallt

Red-backed Shrike

Lanius collurio

Vagrant.

Although it has declined almost to the point of extinction as a breeding bird in Britain, the Red-backed Shrike is a regular migrant through the Northern Isles and along parts of the east coast of Scotland. Like several other species that breed

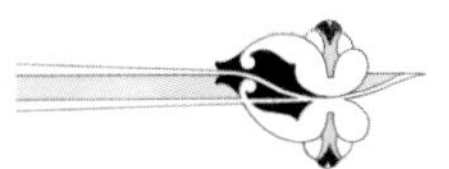

Records of Red-backed Shrikes in Argyll from 1977 to the end of 2006.

Date	Location	Comment	Reference
10 Jun 1977	Ballochgair (Kintyre)	Male	SB 10:150
27 Sep 1979	Kilmartin	Female or immature, found dead	SBR 1979:45
19 - 25 Sep 1986	Lagg (Jura)	Juvenile/first-winter, photographed	ABR 5:14
31 Oct 1987	Port Ellen (Islay)	Female or immature	SB 1987:43, ABR 5:11, 14:81
29 May - 12 Jun 1992	Mull	Male; sightings at three separate locations were probably the same bird	ABR 9:50
5 Jul 1994	Dalrannoch, Loch Creran	Male	SBR 1994:58 (with incorrect dates), ABR 12:71
15 May 1998	Aros Moss (Kintyre)	Male, trapped	ABR 15:88
1 Jun 1998	Pennyghael (Mull)	Female	ABR 15:88
27 Sep 2004	Kiloran (Colonsay)	First-winter	Argyll Database

on the Continent, however, it is much scarcer in the west. Neither Gray nor H&B made any reference to its occurrence in Argyll, and although B&R stated that it had occurred in the county, they did not provide any locations or dates.

The first dated Argyll record is that of a male near Portnahaven on Islay on 5 June 1954; this was said to be the first record for the Inner Hebrides (Meiklejohn & Stanford 1954, SN 68:7). Since then there have been nine more records, all since 1977. Of these, eight were in spring and autumn (Table).

Tristan ap Rheinallt

Lesser Grey Shrike

Lanius minor

Vagrant.

Although most Scottish records of this rare visitor come from the Northern Isles, Lesser Grey Shrikes have occurred at widely scattered locations throughout the country. The first individual to be seen in Argyll was at Salen on Mull on 5 September 1974 (BB 68:329, SB 8:461). More than a decade later, a first-winter bird was at Arileod on Coll from 26 October to 2 November 1988 (BB 83:486, ABR 5:28).

Tristan ap Rheinallt

Great Grey Shrike

Lanius excubitor

Increasingly rare passage migrant and winter visitor.

In Scotland, the Great Grey Shrike occurs most often in the east and in the Northern Isles (B&R, Thom). Like many other migrants that breed in Northern Europe, it is much scarcer on the west coast and rare in Ireland. In Argyll, the species features on the list given in the NSA for Inveraray, and H&B quoted two records from the same location. It was also said to have occurred in Barcaldine, while Gray referred to specimens collected in Argyll during the winter of 1865/66. B&R described it as uncommon on the islands, but quoted two records from Mull in 1907 and one from Islay in 1909. In addition, a bird was reported from Mull in February 1908 (ASNH 1909:202).

The next records come from the 1960s, when there were two mainland records and two from Islay. At the beginning of the following decade, a large autumn influx into Scotland resulted in five birds being seen in Argyll and the Clyde towards the end of 1970 (SB 6:396-7) and four in Argyll in early 1971 (SB 7:158). Since then, there have only been 16 records, with none between 1997 and 2002, though one was seen in the upper reaches of the Barr Water in Kintyre on 10 January 2003 (Argyll Database). In contrast to the usual situation with rarities, all but three of these records were on the mainland, the exceptions being two birds on Islay in 1976 (Elliott 1989), and one at Duart Bay on Mull in 1993 (SBR 1993:57, ABR 10:71). Most of the mainland records were in Mid-Argyll, but birds also occurred in Kintyre (Largybaan, Machrihanish, Barr Water) and Cowal (Strachur). Nine of the 16 recent records were in winter (December to February), two in autumn and five in spring, the earliest arrival date being

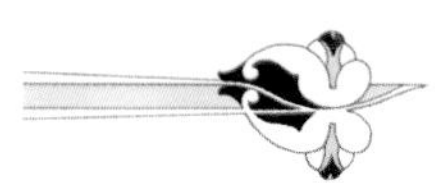

24 October and the latest departure date 23 May.

In addition to the large arrival in Scotland in autumn 1970, there were also influxes in 1976 and 1982 (Thom). The last of these was presumably responsible for the four Argyll records in early 1983 (ABR 1:69). In Britain as a whole, numbers have declined since the 1980s, and this may explain the lack of recent records from Argyll.

Tristan ap Rheinallt

Woodchat Shrike

Lanius senator

Vagrant.

A juvenile was at Kilnaughton Bay, near Port Ellen on Islay, on 16 September 1996 (SBR 1996:62, ABR 13:81). It represents the sole Argyll record of this species, which is a common summer visitor to southern Europe. A full account was published by Cronin & ap Rheinallt (1997).

Spring migration accounts for the majority of Scottish records, but autumn juveniles are not infrequently reported, mostly from the Northern Isles. However, the Woodchat Shrike is a major rarity in the west of the country: for example, only two have been seen in the Outer Hebrides.

Tristan ap Rheinallt

Ardfern, Mid-Argyll, looking west towards Jura and Scarba. Small coastal settlements like this, surrounded by farmland and woodland, support a wide range of common bird species. The wider landscape contains diverse additional habitats, including islands, sheltered intertidal mudflats, rocky shores, freshwater lochs and moorland. *John Anderson*

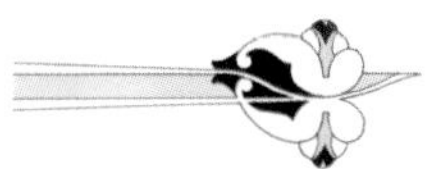

Eurasian Jay

Garrulus glandarius

A widely distributed but scarce woodland resident in most of mainland Argyll. Rarely reported on the islands.

The Jay is one of our most obvious woodland birds that is mentioned regularly in historic accounts. Gray recorded it as present in many parts of Argyll and as common in the woods of upper Loch Fyne, while H&B stated that it was formerly common around Benderloch and Loch Sween. One of Scotland's first systematic bird distribution studies (Lumsden 1876b) described Jays as "very common" along Loch Lomond and "not uncommon" in central Argyll, on Loch Fyne and in Cowal, but they were not recorded in Kintyre. Records from the 20th century begin with two shot at Stonefield in January 1903 and one in 1904; these are probably the first Argyll specimen records (ASNH 1904: 125-6). Thereafter, Jays were occasionally seen around West Loch Tarbert, at Stonefield and at Dunmore (McWilliam).

Jays were heavily persecuted by gamekeepers in the 19th century, and they still are on some game estates. Alston (1913) observed Jays coming to food provided in a garden in Argyll and remarked "the Jay is still to be found, if only sparsely and locally, in suitable localities in Argyll; and were it not for incessant persecution, would doubtless soon be noted as an increasing species". As predicted by Alston, the general reduction in corvid persecution after the First World War allowed a UK-wide increase in Jay abundance and range (Historical Atlas), but the extent of this expansion in Argyll was not quantified.

The Jay plays an important role in the regeneration of native woodlands. *Philip Kirkham*

By the early 1970s, Jays had further extended their breeding range to include most of mainland Argyll (except for south Kintyre). Thom reported that Argyll had a fair-sized and widely scattered population, estimated at over 100 pairs. By the time of the Second Atlas, more squares were occupied in Cowal, but fewer in Kintyre and North Argyll; Jays were now found breeding in 6% of 10-km squares in Argyll and had continued their northwards expansion along the Great Glen. Further increase in numbers was confirmed in the Second Woodland Bird Survey of 2003-2004 when Jays were found in 12 of 29 broadleaved woods in Mid- and North Argyll; numbers had increased by 50% since the similar survey in 1985 (Amar *et al.* 2006, RSPB unpubl. data).

Today, the Jay's distribution across Scotland is still patchy, but Argyll is one of its few Scottish 'hotspots'. Here it can be found in most woods on the mainland, with concentrations in Cowal and Mid-Argyll. However, records from the islands are rare, reflecting the Jay's reluctance to cross open water. There were six records from Islay during 1969-1998, some of which may refer to the same bird, but apparently none since (Ogilvie 2003, Argyll Database). Up to 2006, Mull had 13 or 14 records, and one was seen on Jura in October 2002 (ABR, Argyll Database).

All Jays found in the British Isles belong to the race *rufitergum*. Normally this race is regarded as very sedentary (Migration Atlas). Nevertheless, the species is often found more widely in Argyll from mid-September onwards, particularly in Cowal and Mid-Argyll, with records from up to ten sites per year. Parties often gather around good food sources in autumn, particularly where there are large acorn crops. These autumn gatherings may be local birds attracted to good feeding locations rather than immigrants. However, there are no ringing recoveries from Argyll to cast light on such movements. The nominate race of Scandinavia and most of temperate Europe is prone to irruptions but, even though continental birds have occasionally reached Britain, most were recorded in southern England, even in the large irruption of 1983 (John & Roskell 1985). It is unlikely that migrants from Scandinavia ever reach Argyll considering their scarcity in Shetland, where there have only been two records, both in the 19th century (Pennington *et al.* 2004).

Essentially woodland birds, Jays have a close association with oakwoods. In mast years, Jays seem to spend most of their day flying to their favourite oak tree and leaving with crops bulging with acorns. These are buried for use during winter, some of them a considerable distance away. Because not all acorns are retrieved, some grow into trees. Thus, Jays assist with the dispersal of oak seed, sometimes into woods that lack oaks, so playing an important role in woodland regeneration (Bossema 1979). Jays can also be found in well-wooded gardens and in conifer plantations. Changes in land

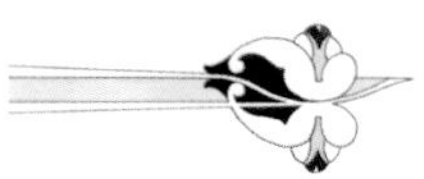

use in Argyll, including the restructuring of conifer forests, the shift to continuous-cover forestry and the gradual increase in broadleaved woodland, will undoubtedly be of long-term benefit to Jays.

David Wood & Michael Thomas

Magpie

Pica pica

Breeds only on the Cowal peninsula, with sporadic records elsewhere, particularly in spring.

In Argyll, the Magpie is restricted as a breeding species to the Cowal peninsula. Here the resident population is largely restricted to the low ground extending from the southern tip of Cowal along the Clyde/Loch Long coast as far north as Blairmore. Small flocks sometimes occur in this area; the total population appears to be around 50 individuals (Peter Staley, pers. comm. to Paul Daw). Ten birds were observed in a single tree at Dalriada Grove, Innellan, in 1999 and nine birds were present in a garden in Blairmore in 2002 (ABR). Elsewhere in Argyll, it is rare.

Excluding a single bird that was resident year-round at Ronachan House, Kintyre (1991-1993), 63 individual Magpies were recorded in Argyll outside Cowal between 1981 and the end of 2005 (ABR). There was no obvious trend in the yearly frequency of these records. In 1983 and 2000 none were recorded outside Cowal, but there were eight such records in each of the years 1999, 2002 and 2005. However, there was a marked seasonal pattern, with the most frequent sightings in April and a smaller peak in autumn (Figure). During four years (1995-1998) there were records from Barcaldine in North Argyll. Whether these all involved the same individual is unknown, but there have been no records from Barcaldine since. On 4 February 2006, an unusual sighting was made of two birds together in Glen Fyne; and in October that year, there were two or three individuals in the Slockavullin-Barsloisnoch area, Mid-Argyll.

On Islay, records of 22 birds between 1965 and 2002 showed a similar seasonal pattern (Elliott 1989, ABR). Extra-limital sightings have come from all parts of Argyll, although records from the islands are sparse. Apart from the Islay records, there have been four on Mull and one on Tiree since 1981. These vagrants may end up staying for several days or weeks, or exceptionally longer, in the same general area. For example, a first-year bird was recorded at Ardtalla, Islay, on 22 May 2002, and was seen at various locations around the island until early 2003. The seasonal pattern and wide geographic distribution of these records are difficult to interpret. Research elsewhere suggests that British Magpies are highly sedentary, with short post-fledging dispersal distances (Birkhead 1991, Migration Atlas), but these findings are somewhat at odds with the distribution of records in Argyll. Unfortunately there are no ringing records from the county, although a bird ringed just outside Argyll at Tarbet (Loch Lomond) was subsequently shot by a gamekeeper in Aberdeenshire.

Older records suggest a wider historic distribution in Argyll. Gray noted that it was occasionally seen on Mull and Islay but did not nest on those islands. A pair bred at Calgary on Mull in the 1870s, but these were eventually killed by keepers. It was 'commoner' around Ardchattan and Bonawe, and was also present on the north side of the River Awe (H&B). By the 1930s it was reported to be almost extinct in Argyll (Duncan 1938). However, Brackenridge (1968) found a nest in lower Glen Fyne in 1947 and as far as he knew there had always been a small breeding population around Toward, Cowal. In 1965 and 1966 up to eight birds were regularly seen at Asknish, Lochgair, and Merrie (1967) suggested that they were spreading west and north from Renfrewshire. Thom thought there were about ten pairs in Cowal but none elsewhere in Argyll. In 1988-1991, Magpies were recorded in only 2% of 10-km squares in Argyll (Second Atlas). Despite the regularity of records from across Argyll, and the two records of more than one individual in 2006, there is no firm evidence that Magpies have nested outside Cowal since the late 1960s.

UK-wide, Magpies increased by 108% between 1967 and 2002, while in Scotland, there was a 59% increase between 1994 and 2003. The population expanded rapidly until

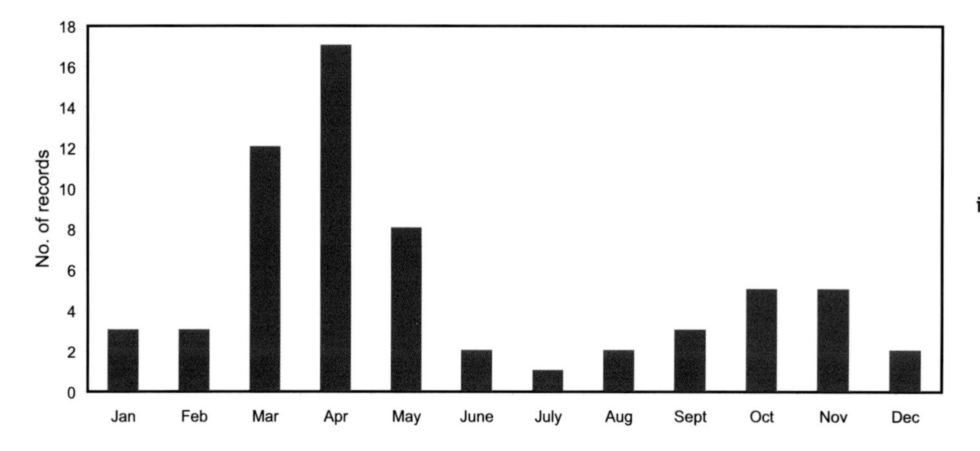

Monthly distribution of records of individual Magpies in Argyll, excluding records from Cowal, 1981-2005.

the late 1980s and now appears to have stabilized (CBC & BBS data, Baillie *et al.* 2005). Nesting success improved dramatically with the relaxation of keepering, and Magpies have colonised suburban and urban areas, which provide

Away from Cowal, the Magpie is an Argyll rarity. *Philip Kirkham*

a favourable mix of open ground for feeding and trees for cover, roosting and nesting. In Scotland, range expansion has not been as extensive as might have been expected, given the availability of apparently suitable habitat and the abundance of Magpies in the urban and suburban sprawl of the central belt.

David Wood & Michael Thomas

Red-billed Chough

Pyrrhocorax pyrrhocorax

Resident and sedentary on Islay, Colonsay and Oronsay but more mobile as sub-adults. Flocks occur throughout the year, often close to communal roosts.

In recent years, breeding Choughs have been associated with the western coasts of Islay, Jura and Colonsay where they mostly nest in caves and recesses in cliffs or in suitable buildings. Breeding pairs defend a home range of varying size and remain there for most of the year, roosting at or close to the nest. Pre-breeders (sub-adults) form flocks that roost communally both on cliffs and in buildings.

Choughs feed predominantly on arthropods, principally soil-living, surface-active and dung-associated invertebrates, their preferred foraging areas generally being grasslands of various types. Those particularly favoured are sand dunes, sand grasslands and machair as well as agricultural grasslands including leys, old pastures and meadows, permanent grasslands, both acidic and calcareous, as well as a range of rough grazing areas, moorland grassland and dwarf shrub heaths. During the winter on both Colonsay and Islay, Choughs are also found foraging along the strand line of sandy beaches, especially where seaweed has been covered by sand, and in places where arable silage or grains have been fed to livestock. Also utilised are silage and hay aftermath during late summer and cereal stubble in autumn. Clearly, most of these foraging preferences are associated with farming, especially the rearing of sheep and cattle.

Historical records indicate that it was during the early part of the 20th century that Choughs in Scotland became virtually restricted to Argyll. The last records came from Iona in 1890, Skye in 1918, South Uist in 1902, Ayrshire in 1929 and Wigtownshire in 1922 (B&R). Prior to this, Choughs were more widely distributed in Scotland, occurring in more northern areas, farther inland and on the east coast (Bishop Leslie reported them at St Abbs in 1578, but they were reduced to a single pair there in 1867). Although their abundance during this early period remains obscure, it is clear that there was a significant reduction in distribution during the 19th century, which appears to have been in two stages. First, a contraction to the (mostly) western coasts and islands by about 1835 and second, to the Argyll islands of Islay, Jura and Colonsay by the end of the century (see Rolfe 1966 and Warnes 1983 for summaries). Various theories have been suggested to explain this contraction, the most plausible being a combination of persecution and severe winter weather.

Over the last 40 years, there have been more complete population estimates. In 1963 the Scottish Chough population was estimated at 70 individuals confined entirely to Argyll, including 11 breeding pairs and a flock of 47 on Islay (Rolfe 1966). In 1976 the number in Islay was estimated as 153-158 birds including 39-41 breeding pairs (Ogilvie 1992a). Since 1982, censuses have been carried out at ten-year intervals (Table).

Other surveys in 1986 (Bignal *et al.* 1988) and 1998 (Cook *et al.* 2001) revealed that numbers peaked in 1986 (at 105 pairs and 150 others) and fell to a low point in 1998 (66 pairs, no complete estimate of the number of 'others'). The recent losses from Kintyre, Mull and Jura left the entire Scottish population restricted to Islay and Colonsay (except one mainland pair outside Argyll).

There are many enigmas associated with the Chough, not least its demography. For instance, whilst numbers in Islay

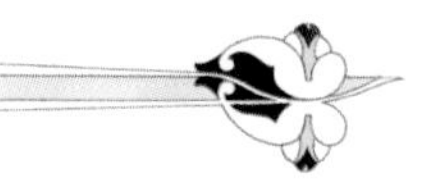

have fluctuated those in Colonsay have steadily increased; and although Colonsay must have been re-colonised in the early 1980s from Islay, Gray suggested that Islay was colonised in the late 19th century from Colonsay, where at the time they were "very numerous".

Between 1982 and 2006, over 1,200 Chough nestlings were individually colour-ringed in Islay resulting in several thousand re-sightings, which have been used to describe the annual cycle of behaviour (e.g. Bignal *et al.* 1997). Most birds spend their first two years as members of a flock with other sub-adults, foraging together and using the main communal roost that draws birds from all parts of Islay. Once established as breeders, the pair stay close to their nest site and home range throughout the year, roosting at or close to the nest. During January and February, adjacent breeding pairs join together in small foraging flocks, apparently sharing home ranges. The function of these pre-breeding "alliances" is not clear but, with the onset of egg-laying, the behaviour changes and pairs become strongly territorial and intolerant of other Choughs, both in the home range and near the nest site.

Choughs nest in caves, rock-crevices and recesses in cliffs, as well as in farm outbuildings, deserted buildings and mineshafts. Rolfe (1966) mentioned Choughs nesting in buildings in Islay in 1963. In 1986, 27% of pairs in Scotland were nesting in buildings, with 62% of inland nests in Islay in such sites (Bignal *et al.* 1987). In 2002, 33 of the 62 pairs in Islay were breeding in buildings (Finney & Jardine 2003). Nest building begins in March and egg-laying starts in early April. The most frequent clutch size is five (smaller in first-time breeders). Between 1992 and 2004, breeding success (the number of young fledged from nests where eggs were laid) in Islay varied from 1.29 to 2.62. The average was 1.76 for 1992-1997 and 2.29 for 1998-2004. Eggs hatch asynchronously after 21 days and the first young leave the nest after six weeks, but the fledglings generally stay in the cave or building for another week before joining the parents on the home range. Within three or four weeks the parents escort the young to the communal roost. It is at this time of the year (late July-early August) that the largest flocks are seen and the highest numbers recorded at the roost, although breeding pairs soon return to their home ranges and leave fledglings to fend for themselves. Most pairs mate for life and several birds are still breeding in their teens, although breeding success declines with age after about ten years. The oldest known successfully breeding birds are a male aged 17 years and a female aged 16 (at different sites). The oldest known birds are paired, a 20 year-old male and a 23 year-old female.

The Chough's bill is specialised for digging and probing for invertebrates, and habitat preferences reflect this. It requires a range of habitats where invertebrates can thrive and can be available year-round. In Argyll, these places are associated with relatively low-intensity pastoral livestock farming in areas of high natural diversity, mostly near the coast. The resulting vegetation and land-use mosaics produce a wide variety of feeding opportunities and prey items. Some of these are natural, such as rocky outcrops in pastures, sand dunes with larvae of the Mining Bee, ant-hills in old grasslands and fly larvae in rotting kelp on sandy shores. Others are anthropogenic, such as cereal stubble and long-rotation unfertilised pastures, as well as the "micro-habitats" and untidy features associated with the agricultural landscape. The latter include earth banks, field clearance cairns, old walls, middens and even livestock burial areas. Such features have been lost in the more intensively farmed parts of Scotland. The importance of extensive livestock rearing is difficult to over-emphasise; it restricts vegetation growth and so provides the access to bare ground that foraging Choughs need. In certain situations, particularly on sand dunes and limestone grassland, cattle dung can provide a rich source of easily located invertebrate food. Cultivation of animal fodder, especially cereals and arable silage (and their aftermath) can provide supplementary feeding opportunities during winter.

Changes in distribution and numbers in recent years are difficult to attribute to land management. The low-intensity, extensive pastoral farming and the abundance of natural and man-made nesting sites are crucial to Choughs in Western Scotland. However, these do not explain why so much apparently suitable habitat is unoccupied, for example on Mull. Neither can it explain the recent increases in Colonsay. Nor can the expansion, contraction and then recovery in Islay

The estimated Red-billed Chough population in Argyll from three censuses (Warnes 1983, Bignal *et al.* 1992, Finney & Jardine 2003).

	Islay	Jura	Colonsay	Kintyre	Mull	Total
Number of breeding pairs						
1982	61	8	1	2	0	72
1992	74	3	9	0	1	87
2002	64	0	18	0	0	82
Number of other individual birds						
1982	53	7	0	7	0	67
1992	54	0	8	0	0	62
2002	77	0	30	0	0	107

A recently fledged Chough. Almost all of the Choughs in Scotland breed on Islay, Colonsay and Oronsay. *Eric M. Bignal*

be explained by land-use change, management practices or nest site availability. Why have Choughs gone from Jura and Mull?

Choughs are highly social birds and it seems that "Choughs need other Choughs". For the young, the limiting factor for survival may be not just the availability of resources but also the opportunity to learn survival and foraging skills from others. This may partly explain why persecution and severe winters had such an impact during the historical period. Moreover, such social factors may explain why isolated breeding pairs, both historically and recently, never developed into larger breeding groups. We know from colour-ringing that the early increases on Colonsay were the result of immigration from Islay, Colonsay being close enough for recruits from Islay to have raised numbers above a critical threshold. In effect Islay, Jura, Colonsay and Oronsay are inter-dependent sub-populations that sometimes provide emigration, yet at other times require immigrants. Choughs in Kintyre were probably linked in a similar way with Rathlin Island and the Antrim coast, but numbers at all three places declined at the same time, probably for different reasons.

Eric M. Bignal

Western Jackdaw

Corvus monedula

A common resident on the Argyll mainland and some islands wherever there is improved grassland for foraging and suitable cavities for nests. Breeding colonies are often located in towns and villages.

The Jackdaw is one of the most adaptable of Argyll's breeding birds, equally at home on crags of the wild Atlantic coast and in town centres. It is widely distributed and common across much of the county, although less abundant than in other parts of its British range, including west coast strongholds in Wales, Cornwall and the Isle of Man. To the north of Argyll, the species becomes much sparser. Its breeding distribution across Argyll's islands is an odd mixture. It is absent from Coll and Tiree, uncommon over much of Mull, but plentiful on Islay, Gigha, Colonsay and Iona (Second Atlas). Jackdaws were recorded from 40% of 10-km squares in Argyll during 1988-1991, but are recorded from only 10% of BBS squares.

Nineteenth century accounts point to a rapid northwards expansion of the breeding range throughout Scotland, including Argyll, from around 1800 (Gray, H&B). The OSA mentioned that Jackdaws were numerous on Gigha.

Jackdaws occur in a wide range of habitats: from rugged sea cliffs to town centres. *David Palmar*

H&B stated that in Argyll they were "quite too numerous to catalogue". They reported colonies at Castle Sween and at five additional sites at the head of Loch Sween, each of 30-40 pairs. The same authors reported Jackdaws on Gigha "in great numbers", on the adjacent island of Cara, "very common" on Islay where increasing numbers were recorded from the Rinns of Islay coastline, and from Lochbuie on Mull. On Iona in the late 1800s, there was a long-established colony of around 30 pairs nesting in the ruins of the Abbey (Graham) and by 1948 there were also six to eight pairs in the ruins of the Nunnery (B&R). Jackdaws spread progressively on Islay from around 1850 to 1937, beginning with wintering birds and becoming common as a breeding species by 1888 (B&R).

More recently, the species has continued to do well in Britain. During 1972-1996, the CBC index increased by 117%, with most gains occurring in open habitats (Gregory & Marchant 1996, Crick *et al.* 1998). Breeding distribution and abundance were probably linked to the availability of grassland for foraging and suitable sites for nesting (O'Connor & Shrubb 1986). However, Scottish studies in the 1980s indicated that a wide range of habitats are used at different phases of the breeding season (Thom). Afforestation and the near-extinction of mixed farming are both likely to have reduced numbers in Argyll.

Relatively few Jackdaws have been ringed in Argyll and the few recoveries indicate that the species is remarkably sedentary year round, which is consistent with the national pattern (Migration Atlas). Large winter flocks occur across Argyll, often in mixed groups with Rooks; the largest such flock was of 750 birds at Gruinart on Islay in October 2000 (ABR).

David Wood & Michael Thomas

Rook

Corvus frugilegus

A widely distributed species across lowland Argyll wherever improved grassland and suitable woods for nesting occur. Rookeries are used over many years.

The Rook is one of the few common species with reliable Argyll-wide data on breeding distribution, abundance and trends. Its conspicuous nesting colonies, and the ease with which individual nests can be identified, allows rapid survey by non-specialist birdwatchers. Counts are accurate if they coincide with maximum colony development in the second half of April (Griffin 1999). There was near-complete Argyll coverage in the national Rook censuses of 1943-46 and 1975. There have also been repeated and near-complete surveys in strongholds on Islay and Kintyre.

Rooks are rather less adaptable than other British corvids. Feare *et al.* (1974) showed that Scottish Rooks have a strong preference for lowland agricultural areas and a heavy dependence on grass fields for foraging during the breeding season. This effectively determines their breeding distribution.

Breeding numbers of Rooks fluctuated widely through the 20th century (Nicholson 1951, Sage & Vernon 1978, Sage & Whittington 1985, Marchant & Gregory 1999). Recent BBS results suggest some regional differences in trends, with numbers in Scotland continuing to rise, while those in England have fallen (Baillie *et al.* 2005). Rooks are considered to be sensitive to changes in agricultural practice,

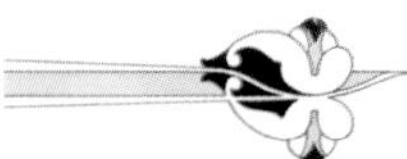

Rooks are closely associated with improved grasslands, and are sensitive to agricultural changes. *Louise Wood*

yet the reasons for these population changes are not fully understood. In 1996, the Scottish population was about 376,600 pairs (Marchant & Gregory 1999).

In the Loch Lomond catchment, there was a 20% decline between 1945 and 1975 (Mitchell 1976), but elsewhere in Argyll the story has been one of population growth. In 1945 there were estimated to be 1,050 nests in Kintyre, but in just seven years, between 1989 and 1996, this increased by 80%, from 1,397 to 2,514, (Maguire *et al.* 1996/1997). The single largest Argyll colony in 1996 was at Glenbarr, Kintyre (500 nests), and there was a separate cluster of 15 rookeries in and around Campbeltown, totalling 732 nests. On Islay, numbers of nests increased by 89% over a slightly longer period; from 211 in 1985 to 399 in 2002 (Figure).

Numbers of Rook nests in Islay and Kintyre, 1985-2002.

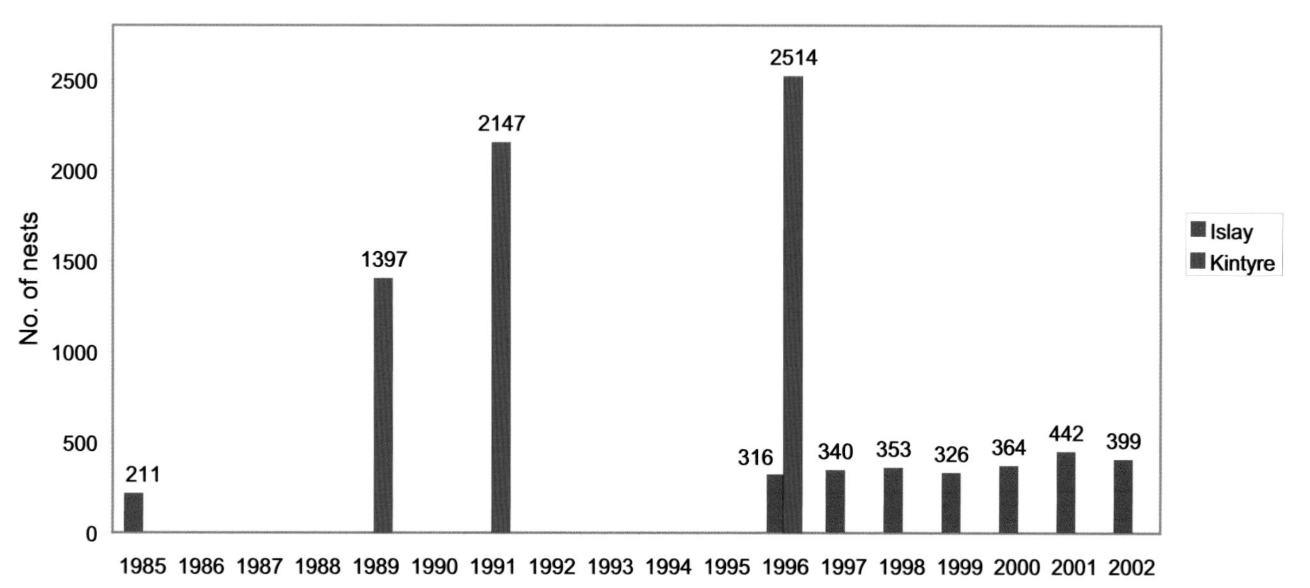

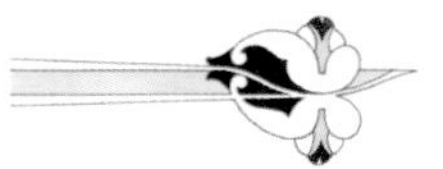

Outside Kintyre and Islay, rookeries are widely distributed across lowland Argyll, but breeding numbers are much smaller. Traditional colonies include one of up to 35 nests on Iona, and one of around 15 nests at Connel. In 1985, a new rookery of about 40 nests was established at the SWT's Ballachuan Reserve, displacing a well-established heronry (ABR). The 1975 Rookery Survey recorded 3,217 nests in 78 rookeries across Argyll, equivalent to 0.40 nests km^{-2}, one of the lowest densities in Scotland (Castle 1977).

In the Second Atlas, Rooks were recorded breeding in 25% of 10-km squares in Argyll. Nesting Rooks are scarce on Mull, and the species does not breed on Colonsay, Tiree or Coll. However, there is a marked post-breeding influx of juveniles to some islands. For example, on Mull a flock of 80 roosted at Dervaig on 27 June 1997. On Oronsay and Tiree, there are almost annual records of between one and three birds; these records have occurred in all seasons. Winter flocks of up to several hundred birds regularly occur on Islay and in Kintyre, with maxima of around 500 at Gruinart on 2 September 2000, 750 at Neriby on 28 October 2000, and 200 at Ballure on 19 December 1999.

Historical attitudes towards the Rook were, at best, ambivalent (B&R). H&B say that "to give a complete list of all rookeries in the limits of the area would be in itself a heavy piece of work, and with such a universally spreading species scarcely deserving of the trouble .... of late years Rooks have decidedly become more rapacious, carnivorous and destructive than they were formerly...". The species was widely persecuted in Argyll, but some rookeries were remarkably persistent despite this. Elliott (1989) stated that the Islay rookeries of Gruinart and Cornabus date back to 1857 and 1818 respectively.

Today, the interaction between Rooks and agriculture is known to be complex (summary in Eaton & Bradbury 2003). Earthworms and leatherjackets are the most important foods for chicks and fledglings, but many other invertebrates are also taken, including agricultural pests. At other times of year the diet is more varied and may include vegetable items such as grass, root crops and legumes. In Campbeltown, they regularly scavenge for discarded food items in the main street, often walking almost under the feet of pedestrians (P. Daw pers. obs.). The Rook may still be legally killed under a general licence, but this is no longer carried out extensively in Argyll.

David Wood & Michael Thomas

The all-black Carrion Crow is most often seen in southern parts of Argyll. *David Palmar*

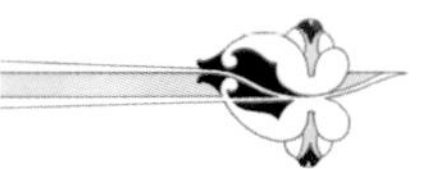

Carrion Crow

Corvus corone

A sedentary resident, mainly in Cowal and parts of Mid-Argyll in a variety of habitats, but mainly on low ground. It hybridises with the Hooded Crow in areas where the distribution of the two species overlap.

Carrion Crows have been present across the southern parts of Argyll since at least the middle of the 19th century. Gray recorded them from Loch Eck, while H&B noted they were 'abundant on parts of the mainland' but almost absent from the Argyll islands. Pre-1960s records from more northern parts of Argyll were sporadic, and the breeding status of the birds was seldom noted. A nest was claimed to have been found on Islay (Scot Skirving 1895) and Gray observed two pure black crows with a Hooded Crow at Loch Melfort. Carrion Crows were said to turn up occasionally on Tiree (Anderson 1913). There was one at Skerryvore on 13 March 1913 (SN Extra Publication no. 3:32) and at least two at Port Ellen, Islay in May 1955 (SN 69:182). They were apparently absent from Iona and Mull (Graham). Elliott (1989) considered them to be annual vagrants to Islay, with three-quarters of all records "from the low ground between Port Ellen and Island House, around Bridgend Bay or in the Gruinart or Loch Gorm districts".

Approximate centre of the Carrion Crow/Hooded Crow hybrid zone in mainland Scotland, 1928-1991.

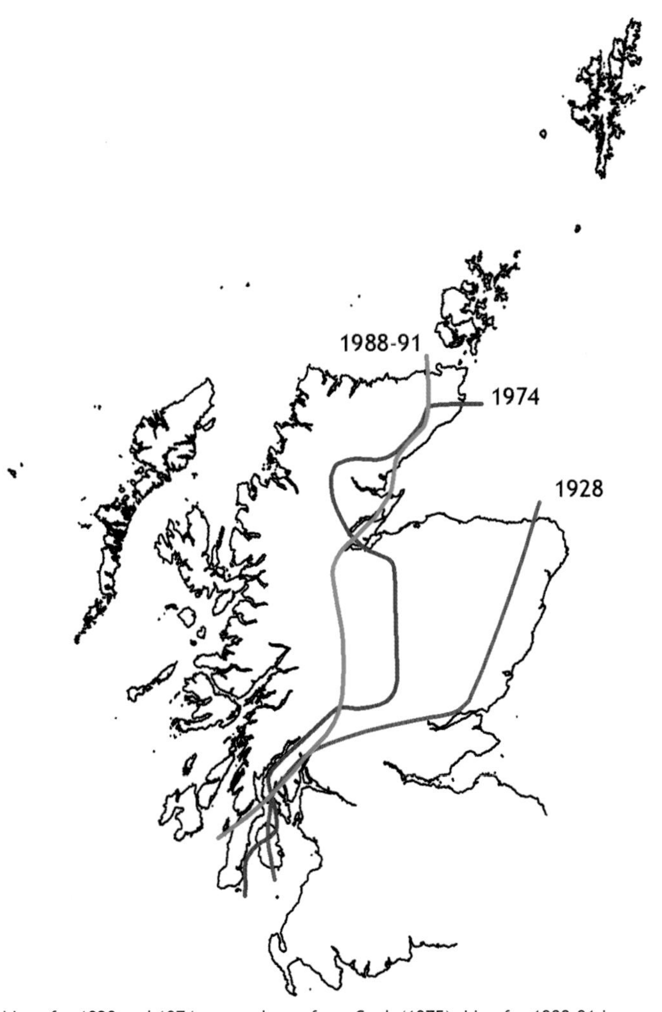

Lines for 1928 and 1974 are re-drawn from Cook (1975). Line for 1988-91 is based on the highest densities of hybrid Crows from the Second Atlas.

Carrion and Hooded Crows were for many years regarded as the same species, because they can interbreed and produce fertile offspring (with intermediate plumage). Their relative distributions and zones of contact across Scotland and mainland Europe have fascinated naturalists and biologists for many years. The extent of the hybrid zone in Scotland was first mapped by Meise (1928) and re-examined by Cook (1975) using data from the First Atlas, surveys of the Scottish Ornithologists' Club and personal records. He found that in east Scotland the zone had moved significantly to the north and west over this period, but had remained almost static in Argyll (Figure).

The Second Atlas allowed the movement of the zone to be plotted once again. Its width had not altered between 1968-1972 and 1988-1991, but, along most of its length, Carrion Crows had moved about 30km north and west into areas previously dominated by Hooded Crows, with a corresponding change in the distribution of hybrids. The shift was most pronounced in parts of Argyll, the central highlands and Caithness. In Argyll, Carrion Crows had extended their range in Cowal and Mid-Argyll, and hybrids had started to appear in Kintyre, but they apparently lost some ground in south Kintyre (Second Atlas). Today, most crows at lower altitudes in Cowal have an all-black appearance, with regular reports of Carrion Crows from the Dunoon area (ABR). In 1988-1991, Carrion Crows nested in 13% of 10-km squares in Argyll, and hybrids in 11%. More than 10% of crows around Loch Fyne appear to be wholly black and at least 20% are hybrids. Each year, individual all-black crows are recorded in all seasons across Argyll, including Tiree and Islay (ABR).

The fact that the width of the hybrid zone remained almost unchanged between studies interested biologists, as no mechanism had been identified to prevent hybrid birds from expanding their range (Mayr 1942). Habitat differences were examined as a potential separating mechanism between Hooded and Carrion Crows (Cook 1975, Second Atlas). Within the Scottish hybrid zone, Hooded Crows were found more often on poorer quality land at higher altitude, while Carrion Crows became widespread on low-lying grasslands. Two separate studies in the Italian hybrid zone confirmed that the two species prefer different foraging habitats (Saino 1992, Rolando & Laiolo 1994). Other European studies have shown a number of other small but significant differences between Hooded and Carrion Crows, including vocal differences, evidence for non-random mating and reduced fitness of hybrids. Taken together, these differences have led to recommendations that the two crows should be regarded as separate species (Parkin *et al.* 2003).

Like Hooded Crows, Carrion Crows are found either as

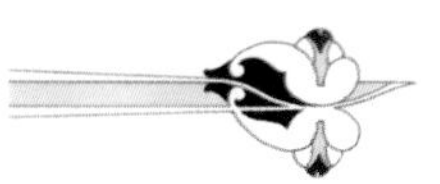

territorial pairs or as non-breeding members of a flock. When a territorial bird dies, it is replaced by one of the flock; thus territorial behaviour effectively limits the size of the breeding population (Charles 1972). During 1994-2005, Carrion Crow numbers in England increased by 21% whereas in Scotland they declined by 8% (Raven & Noble 2006). Carrion Crows in Scotland are highly sedentary, with no evidence from ringing recoveries of winter influx from other parts of Scotland (Migration Atlas). The only Argyll ringing recovery is of a hybrid bird on Kintyre, recovered four km away 11 years later.

David Wood & Michael Thomas

Hooded Crow

Corvus cornix

The most abundant crow in Argyll, occurring in a wide range of habitats, including most of the islands. It hybridises with the Carrion Crow where their ranges overlap.

The Hooded Crow is a familiar and common species across Argyll, able to utilise an extremely wide range of habitats including mountains, heather moorland, farmland, forest edges, gardens and coasts. Its abundance despite centuries of organised persecution indicates its extreme resilience and adaptability.

The Hooded Crow is possibly the most heavily controlled species in Argyll, being one of 12 species that may be killed under a general licence. 'Hoodies' have a notorious reputation for causing economic damage to sheep farmers and rearers of gamebirds. They are also blamed for reducing the populations of more 'attractive' wildlife species. As early as 1457, James II directed that 'Crawys' should be destroyed, although this reference might equally have been intended for Carrion Crows. Control measures on Scotland's west coast grew with the development of the large Victorian estates, the expansion of sheep farming and game rearing, and a large increase of dedicated gamekeepers. Crows were vilified in 19th century natural history accounts (Graham, Gray, H&B) and were avidly killed by trapping, shooting and poisoning with strychnine. The dedication of some estates to this cause was remarkable. For example, between 1872 and 1882 2,111 were killed in Ardnamurchan and between 1877 and 1887, 600 were killed on the Ardfin estate on Jura (H&B). Control on this scale declined during the early 20th century, but patchy and sporadic attempts still continue. For example, Hoodies were controlled on Colonsay for several years in the mid-1990s. This appears to have reduced the size of the non-breeding flock, which exceeded 100 birds before culling began, but a breeding population of up to eight pairs persisted (ABR, Jardine 2002). On Islay, Elliott (1989) noted that persecution had resulted in virtual extinction by 1939, but that numbers started to increase during the war years.

Hooded Crows are omnivorous and intelligent, and they readily exploit new food sources. This explains much of their success. During the early 1970s, in a 2000ha area south of Oban, Hooded Crows living at low altitude fed mainly on cattle food (spilled oats) in winter and on insects in summer (Houston 1977a). Birds living at higher altitude fed on carrion and some cattle food in winter and on insects in summer. Territory-holding birds found enough food year round to maintain at least some fat reserves, whereas some non-territorial birds living in flocks starved during winter. Houston suggested that the availability of oats in winter maintained flock numbers at artificially high levels. Winter flocks in Houston's study frequently visited the shoreline and the Oban landfill site, but they found little food at either. However, during the late 1970s in Ardnamurchan, most crow nests were at low altitude (<150m) and close to the coast, possibly because of the amount of food along the shoreline (Hewson & Leitch 1982). The Hooded Crow's habit of dropping crustaceans and molluscs onto rocks to break the shells, which is widespread in north-west Scotland, was observed on Iona as early as the 1880s (Graham).

Houston (1977a, 1977b) examined the level of crow predation on ewes and lambs. Crow attacks on trapped ewes caused only slight economic damage, because at lambing time there was normally a glut of other foods. Nearly all lambs scavenged by crows were already dead, or 'at the point of starvation'. However since these studies, winter stock-feeding practices have changed significantly, which may have reduced the food available to crows. On the other hand, the availability of carrion as road kills has increased. It would be interesting to examine how crow foraging behaviour has adapted to these changes.

During 1988-1991, Hooded Crows bred in 87% of 10-km squares in Argyll (Second Atlas). They nested on all islands larger than a few hectares, including Lunga in the Treshnish Isles, Sanda and Iona. In the 19th century they were also recorded from Staffa (H&B). An analysis of Scotland-wide BBS results (Baillie *et al.* 2005) suggested that breeding numbers had declined by 36% between 1994 and 2003, although the population index showed wide year-to-year fluctuations, so any long-term trend remains unclear.

Although Hooded Crows occur across all of north and west Scotland, their abundance peaks on the western and northern coasts, on the Inner and Outer Hebrides, and in the Northern Isles. Their abundance in parts of Kintyre, Mid-Argyll, North Argyll and Mull matches other 'hotspots' on the Isle of Man, Skye, the Outer Hebrides, Caithness, Orkney and Shetland (Second Atlas). In Ardnamurchan, breeding density was 0.026 nests per ha in the coastal zone comprising coastal pasture, birch scrub and other woodland (Hewson & Leitch 1982). This was comparable to densities

The 'Hoodie' is one of the most conspicuous and widely distributed birds of Argyll. *Philip Snow*

in north-east Scotland (Picozzi 1975), but lower than densities in Cumbernauld and Kilsyth (A. Wood, quoted in Thom). Elliott (1989) estimated that 200-300 pairs nested on Islay. Typical winter flock size is 20-35 birds, but larger aggregations do occur. There were 40 at Machair Bay on Islay in November 1997, 84 between Heylipol and the Reef on Tiree in October 1998 and 136 at the head of Loch Feochan in September 2004 (ABR, Argyll Database). An exceptional single flock of over 500 birds was reported by H&B on Jura.

Hooded Crows in Argyll are largely sedentary. Most ringing recoveries are local, the most distant being a bird ringed in Oban and recovered in Cowal a year later (38km). Although there are some old records of large winter movements in western Scotland (B&R), there is no evidence of regular or substantial movements into Argyll during winter.

David Wood & Michael Thomas

Common Raven

Corvus corax

A resident that is widely distributed throughout the mainland and islands of Argyll. Numbers are increasing.

Historical accounts suggest that the Raven was common and widely distributed across Scotland, even in towns, up to the end of the 18th century (summary in B&R). However, in common with other corvids, Ravens were intensively persecuted on many estates in the 19th and early 20th centuries, reducing numbers significantly. Populations in western Scotland probably suffered less than in more populous and accessible counties like Perthshire, and Ratcliffe (1962) considered there was little evidence for a decrease "in the wilder regions which are now their main stronghold". Nonetheless, in Ardnamurchan, 107 were killed between 1862 and 1882, with a maximum of 13 in 1868 (H&B). In Argyll, H&B recorded that Ravens were 'common' in many parts of Mull, and on Islay and Jura, with a single pair on Tiree. Graham stated that there was one pair on Iona, and B&R listed it as a breeding species on Sanda. Whilst acknowledging their pest status, the early Scottish naturalists also admitted a grudging admiration for Ravens, considering them 'noble', 'resilient', 'cunning' and 'vigilant'. For many writers, the species seemed

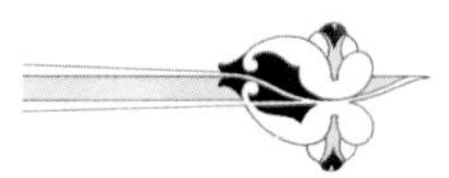

to embody the notion of the romantic Scottish wilderness that was so fashionable in the 19th century.

Perhaps the earliest objective descriptions of Ravens on Scotland's west coast were made in 1830 by Macgillivray (quoted in Gray). He noted their varied diet of carrion, fish, poultry, eggs, grain and grass, as well as the coherence of family groups and the development of larger post-breeding flocks. He recorded their feeding behaviour around carrion, marvelling at how quickly Ravens flocked to stranded cetaceans, while a freshly dead horse would attract 30-50 Ravens. His description of the Raven's preferred feeding sequence on a dead sheep makes grisly reading, and is consistent with reports from farmers in Argyll today.

In the 20th century, two world wars allowed some respite from persecution. Numbers remained fairly stable until the 1960s when conifer afforestation in Argyll began in earnest (Ratcliffe 1962). This led to reduction in sheep carrion, but at the same time persecution was reduced. Although some foraging habitat was lost to conifer forest, there is little evidence that numbers declined as a result, unlike south-west Scotland (Marquiss *et al.* 1978). In fact, during a 1989-91 study in Argyll it was considered that lack of recruits was the main factor limiting the population to well below the potential for the area. In other words, there was much suitable habitat that lacked breeding birds but few non-breeders to fill the gaps (Thomas 1993). By contrast, more recent surveys suggest that most suitable habitat in Argyll is now occupied by territorial Ravens (see below).

In the latter part of the 20th century, the expansion of large landfill sites in Argyll provided extra food, particularly for non-breeding flocks. The provision of winter food for sheep and cattle was also exploited by this adaptable corvid. Nonetheless, numbers appear to have been held down by human interference until the early 1990s, probably because of widespread illegal use of poisons, to which wide-ranging, non-breeding flocks of Ravens were susceptible (Weir 1978). Publicity campaigns in the 1980s and 1990s highlighting the danger of poisons to birds of prey, together with some high-profile prosecutions, may have been catalysts in reducing this mortality and so triggering population growth. By the time of the Second Atlas, 75% of 10-km squares in Argyll were occupied by breeding Ravens, including gains since the First Atlas of about ten squares in Cowal, Kintyre and on the islands.

Recent surveys, and monitoring by the Argyll Raptor Study Group, have built up a better picture of the breeding status of Ravens in Argyll. Almost all areas have shown increases since the early 1990s, with numbers in coastal locations showing the largest rises. Populations have more than doubled on Coll and Tiree, and recent monitoring on Kintyre has indicated substantial increase there (Urquhart *et al.* 2007). Currently, the minimum estimated population for Argyll is 360-372 pairs (Table 1). However, estimates for some areas, notably North Argyll and Jura, are little more than informed guesses, and the early 1990s figure from Mid-Argyll is also likely to be low as it covered only part of this area. The total territorial population in the county probably exceeds 400 pairs, making Argyll a stronghold for the species in Scotland. Ratcliffe (1997) estimated the Argyll breeding population at 335 pairs (170 coastal and 165 inland pairs). These figures exclude a large non-breeding population (see below).

Established pairs use traditional nesting sites year after year. For example, in 1920 Ravens nested on Eilean nam Ban near Fionnphort on Mull (Gordon 1920) and the site was still in regular use in 2006. Most nests are on crags, often beneath an overhang to give shelter. Many such sites are inaccessible, but on some islands with few suitable crags, lower and more accessible ledges are being used by the expanding population. Unlike the situation in central Wales, Ravens in Argyll have, until quite recently, shown a marked reluctance to build nests in trees. However, this may now be changing. On Mull at least four pairs are successfully nesting in Scots Pine, Ash and Larch. On Islay, five pairs now breed in Scots Pine, Beech and

Table 1. Estimated number of territorial Raven pairs in Argyll.

Area	No. of occupied territories	Area surveyed (km^2)	Density (occupied territories km^{-2})	Date	Trend	Source
Mid-Argyll[1]	40	unknown	-	Early 1990s	increasing	P. Haworth (unpub.)
Kintyre[2]	47 (minimum)	238	0.060	2006	increasing	Urquhart *et al.* 2007
Cowal	52	925	0.056	2002	increasing?	ABR
North Argyll	25-30			2006	increasing	P. Daw pers. comm.
Tiree	12	79.5	0.150	2006	increasing	J. Bowler pers.comm.
Coll	21	74.1	0.283	2005	increasing	J. Bowler pers.comm.
Colonsay & Oronsay	15	49.1	0.305	2006	increasing	D. Jardine pers. comm.
Mull	85	910	0.093	1998	increasing	Haworth (1999)
Islay	35-37	715	0.050	1996/7	increasing	Madders & Leckie (1999)
Jura	15-20	365	0.048	2006	increasing	P. Daw pers. comm.
Small islands[3]	13	-	-	2006	Stable/increasing	Numerous sources
Total	360-372					

[1]Oban to Lochgilphead only.
[2]Survey of optimal habitat only (238ha). Density of 0.060 is based on area of all of Kintyre (785ha).
[3]Gigha (1), Gunna (1), Lismore (1), Luing (2), Lunga (1), Kerrera (3), Seil (3), Staffa (1).

Argyll is a stronghold for the Raven in Scotland. *Philip Kirkham*

Oak, and in Kintyre, three of the 12 new sites found in 2006 were in trees. In Cowal, tree-nesting has been recorded in Oak, Douglas Fir and other conifers. Tree-nesting pairs can be hard to find, particularly in conifers, so this habit may be more widespread than records suggest.

Relationships with other birds, especially raptors, are intriguing. Ravens and Peregrines often nest surprisingly close together on the same crag, the Peregrines sometimes breeding in disused Raven nests. A recent study in Europe has suggested that Peregrines benefit from this association, as the Ravens give excellent warning of approaching predators, such as Golden Eagles (Sergio *et al.* 2004). Ravens are surprisingly good at detecting distant Golden Eagles, giving alarm calls often followed by a chase in which they mob and harass the intruder until it departs. Ratcliffe (1997) noted that it was "unusual for Ravens to breed within one km of an active eagle nest, and the distance is often several km". The mean distance between occupied nests of the two species in Argyll was 2.1km (n=13, minimum 0.6km) (Thomas 1993, also see Fielding *et al.* 2003). In some parts of Mull, Ravens have ousted Buzzards from favoured crags and trees, the Buzzards usually moving a short distance to another site.

The Raven is one of the first birds to breed in spring. In an Argyll study, Thomas (1993) estimated that during 1989-1990 laying began in the second or third week in February and peaked during the last week in February or first week in March. Productivity was high, with 83% of 86 breeding attempts producing at least one fledgling. Median clutch was five (n=23), median successful brood size was three (n=59) and median brood per pair laying was two (n=79). Breeding success was higher nearer the coast and at low altitude and, not surprisingly, it tended to decline with the amount of conifer forest within one km. Recent productivity of Ravens in Argyll has been variable (Table 2), but in a good year several

Table 2. Breeding data for Ravens in Argyll in 2004 (ARSG, Broad 2005)

Area	Sites checked	Sites occupied	Sites where eggs laid	Sites successful	Outcome unknown	Minimum number of young fledged	Young per successful site
Colonsay	13	12	10	8	2	26	3.25
Islay	2	2	2	2	0	10	5.00
Cowal	25	25	23	12	10	34	2.83
Bute	14	12	9	8	2	35	4.37
Total	54	51	44	30	14	105	3.50

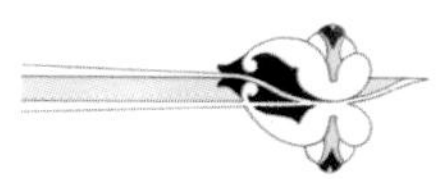

hundred fledged young can be added to the population by June.

Communal roosting is a widespread phenomenon of Raven populations (Heinrich 1990, Ratcliffe 1997). Such roosts draw in birds from a large area and are often sited in woodlands, occasionally on crags. These gatherings appear to comprise largely non-breeding birds and may allow individuals to gradually increase their dominance within the flock and to pair, so they can move quickly into a vacant territory. In the morning, small flocks disperse in different directions in search of food. One advantage of being in a flock is the ability to exploit food in areas defended by territorial Ravens, something single birds are unable to do.

Communal roosts in Argyll can be large and are sometimes associated with refuse dumps. A roost near the landfill site at Lochgilphead held over 100 birds (Argyll Database). More than 200 have been counted at sites on Islay and Mull. Ratcliffe (1997) mentioned a roost of 245 in Mid-Argyll on 31 August 1994 and up to 100 in 1991 at the landfill site at Moleigh, near Oban. Recently, three roosts with a minimum total of around 300 birds have been located on Kintyre: the Ronachan roost held more than 130 during March, the highest count at Skeroblin Loch was 59 in early April and the Glen Kerran roost held a maximum of 82 in early May (Urquhart *et al.* 2007). Roosting numbers have also increased on Coll and Tiree. The flock at Gott rubbish tip on Tiree grew from 32 on 26 May 1988 to 95 on 17 June 2005. On Coll, 80 were roosting at Ballyhaugh on 16 April 1997, over 20 at Ballyhaugh Hill on 24 March 1999 and 40 at Ben Feall in November 2002 (J. Bowler pers. comm.). These observations show that communal roosting is not restricted to winter.

Ravens quickly exploit new feeding opportunities. For example, deer stalkers often remark that Ravens appear soon after a rifle is fired, to feed on the gralloch left behind by the shooting party. On 12 November 2000, in a particularly good mast year, over 60 were seen collecting acorns from the ground in an oakwood at the side of Loch Nell, near Oban (S.J. Petty pers. comm.). Ravens are commonly blamed for attacking livestock and it seems clear that some farms suffer significant losses of calves, ewes and lambs. Licences to control them have recently been granted in Kintyre and elsewhere in Argyll. Ravens are not covered by the general licence which permits the killing of some other British corvids, so those wishing to control Ravens must apply for a specific licence and show that economic damage is being caused. However, the wariness of Ravens means that few birds are actually shot.

Fourteen Ravens, all ringed as chicks in Argyll, have been recovered; six in Argyll (including a movement from Colonsay to Kintyre and another from Kintyre to Islay), seven elsewhere in Scotland and one in Ireland. For a species considered "relatively sedentary" (Migration Atlas), this high proportion outside Argyll is perhaps surprising. The most distant were near Wanlockhead (Dumfries and Galloway) (103km), in Sma' Glen (Tayside) (141km), near Boat of Garten (Highland) (186km) and near Tomintoul (Grampian) (178km). The only Argyll recovery originating from outside the county was a chick ringed on the Copeland Islands (Co. Down, Ireland) in April 1956 and killed near Campbeltown in March 1957. This is one of only two recorded movements of a Raven across the Irish Sea (Grantham 2004).

Paul F. Haworth

Common Starling

Sturnus vulgaris

A common resident on Islay, Coll, Tiree and part of Kintyre, but less common on most of the mainland. Flocks containing juveniles appear in many parts of the county in late summer, and numbers increase in winter by immigration from north-west Europe.

During his stay on Iona from 1848 to1854, Graham found many Starlings feeding in the fields and nesting and roosting in the Abbey ruins. Likewise, H&B describe Starlings on Tiree as abundant about 1860 and becoming more so during 1870-1890. However, early in the 19th century Starlings are thought to have been scarce or extinct on the mainland of Scotland following an earlier contraction in range. As evidence of recovery and spread on the mainland, H&B cite the appearance of Starlings at Benderloch (where they became "very numerous and troublesome" by 1892), at the Loch Awe Hotel in 1890 and at Inveraray about 1870 (the Duke of Argyll "never saw a Starling until he went to England in 1836"). They concluded that Argyll and the Inner Isles were populated by an invasion from the north and west. By 1870 Starlings were spreading fast through the Scottish mainland, colonising both town and country (Gray). Like Wood Pigeons half a century earlier and Collared Doves a century later, their range and numbers grew rapidly until they became one of our most familiar birds.

This increase, which continued well into the 20th century, has been ascribed to new crops and to changes in climate, as well as to persecution of raptors (Thom, First Atlas). About 1950, B&R described the Starling as an abundant resident on Islay, very common on Coll and "superabundant" on Tiree, where numbers had doubled between 1893 and 1913. It was known to nest on Colonsay, Lismore and Mull, including Treshnish and Iona; however, it was "not plentiful" on Jura or Gigha.

Two of the Starling's main needs are holes or crevices for nesting and year-round availability of invertebrates, such as leatherjackets and earthworms on pastureland and small crustaceans and insects on the shore. Where numerous crevices are available, small breeding colonies may form. B&R gave an intriguing description of "a great boulder on the west side of the Mull of Kintyre...honeycombed with holes in every one of which a pair of Starlings was nesting". H&B (1892) described how Starlings nested "in dwarf stone walls" on Tiree. Almost a century later, on Coll there were 18 nests in holes along a 50m stretch of wall in 1985, and six in 200m of wall at Gallanach and five in 400m of wall at Achamore

Starlings in rural areas are closely associated with permanent pasture and livestock rearing. *Philip Kirkham*

in 1990. Holes in trees are used quite often and, at Scalasaig (Colonsay) in 1986, a pair nested below ground at the base of an Ash tree. They may also nest on sea cliffs, as on the Treshnish Islands where several pairs breed each year. Thirty pairs bred at the RSPB's Loch Gruinart Reserve in 1986; and 145 birds were found in a single 1-km square on Tiree in late May 2000. In Taynish CBC, there was an average of two territories during 1990-2000 (maximum 4). One or a few pairs breed on Sanda Islands in most years, although not in 2003 (ABR). These and other figures (below) emphasise the importance of the agriculture and habitats of Coll, Tiree, Islay and Kintyre for this species, as for so many others.

The First Atlas found Starlings to be the fifth most widespread species in Britain and Ireland with about 3.5 million pairs and confirmed breeding in more 10-km squares than any other species. In Argyll breeding was proved in almost every square except for two small gaps in the south of Mull and the north of Jura. In summer 1985, Starlings were found in four of 38 broadleaf woods surveyed in Mid- and North Argyll, when 14 were seen and it was the 32nd most numerous species (Averis & Martin 1985).

The Second Atlas found numbers in the British Isles had more than halved to 1.5 million pairs and that the range had contracted, the species disappearing particularly from the north-west mainland of Scotland. In Argyll breeding was recorded in 65% of 10-km squares, the main absences being in the mountains of Jura, Mull and North Argyll. The highest breeding densities in Argyll were on Coll, Tiree and part of west Islay, but over on the mainland Starlings were much more thinly and locally distributed. The Migration Atlas reported that this decrease continued during 1982-2002. In the summers of 1995-2001, Starlings were recorded breeding in 4/17, 3/21, 4/16, 3/16, 3/15, 2/12, 1/6 BBS squares, and in 2/14 Countryside 2000 squares (ABR).

Ringing has established that Starlings breeding in the British Isles are sedentary, most remaining close to their breeding sites in winter. However, huge numbers arrive here in autumn from north-west Europe and winter numbers in Britain and Ireland are estimated at 37 million, some ten to twenty times the breeding population. Those wintering in north-west Scotland come mainly from Denmark, Norway, Sweden and Finland (Migration Atlas, Winter Atlas).

Argyll ring recoveries reflect this NE-SW flyway. Starlings ringed here have been recovered in the following countries (one each unless stated). The most distant was 2,318km away in Russia (in the Karelian Republic, just east of Finland), and others were in Finland (1,834 km), Norway (7) (779-1,209km), Denmark (922km), Ireland, northern England (6), southern England (2) and elsewhere in Scotland (9). Similarly, Starlings recovered in Argyll had been ringed (one each) in Norway, at Tarbat Ness (Highland Region), Banff, Balmuir (Dundee, Tayside), and Chester-le-Street (Co. Durham).

As in summer, the main concentrations in winter are on Islay, Coll, Tiree and south Kintyre and, as in Scotland generally, the species is absent from mountainous areas such as those of Jura, Mid- and North Argyll (Winter Atlas). Favoured sites for nightly roosts are reedbeds and man-made structures with ledges or beams, as well as the more usual woods and plantations. Numbers at individual roosts in the county rarely exceed 4,000 birds, not nearly approaching the hundreds of thousands often found at roosts elsewhere in the British Isles. Notable roost sites have included Bruichladdich Pier on Islay (1,200 in July 1988 and 1991, and 1,000 in July 1990) and old distillery buildings in Campbeltown (where 5,000 in January 1989 and 4,500 in October-December 2000 were the largest ever reported in Argyll). Other large roosts have been recorded at the RSPB's Loch Gruinart Reserve and Ardnave on Islay, and at Crossapol, Loch a'Phuill, The Manse and Heylipol on Tiree with some 3,000-4,000 birds roosting in a barn at Heylipol in February 2006 (ABR). Much earlier on Tiree, H&B recorded them roosting "in numbers on the rigging of fishing smacks at Scarinish harbour"; and if a shot was fired into a cave at Ceann a' Mhara at about 4 pm on a

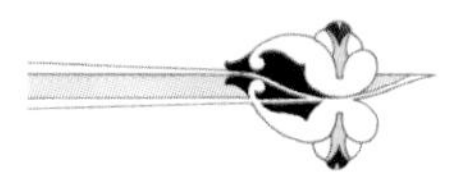

winter's evening "...a solid stream of Starlings several feet deep will come out, and will continue for some minutes". Nowadays in late summer, flocks of up to a hundred, sometimes more, are often found roosting in shrubs and trees on small islands in mainland sealochs.

During 1980-2001 there were 182 reports of gatherings of 100 or more Starlings (67 on Islay, 55 on Tiree, 23 in Kintyre, 14 on Colonsay, nine in Mid-Argyll, seven on Mull, six on Coll and one in Cowal, but none from Jura or North Argyll). These included 34 of 1,000 or more (14 on Islay, 11 in Kintyre, eight on Tiree and one on Coll). Compare these flock sizes with of a flock of 60 feeding on the shore at Taynish NNR on 11 November 1997, the largest ever recorded there (ABR, Argyll Database).

Two temporary summer roosts of adults only were reported on Tiree in early June 1987 (500+ at Crossapol and 900+ at Middleton) and another of *c.*300 adults and young formed in reedbeds at Loch Seil on 17 July 1988. Passage flocks moving south, often mainly juveniles, appear in many parts of the county in late summer and autumn, for example on Mull in 1985, 1988 and 1990, at the Mull of Kintyre in 1988, 1989 and 1990, and at Ledaig Point in 1990. The Starling was one of the species recorded "throughout the year" during 1982-1994 at Ledaig Point by Jennings (1995). An unusual site was The Dutchman's Cap, where 23 were seen on 25 June 2000. There are records of spring passage on Colonsay in 1985 and 1986 and at the Mull of Kintyre in 1983 (ABR).

The subspecies found in most of the British Isles is *S. v. vulgaris*. Another subspecies, *S. v. zetlandicus*, occurs in Shetland and its occurrence in the Outer Hebrides has been claimed. The juveniles of both Shetland and Outer Hebridean Starlings are sooty black, unlike the light brown juveniles of the mainland. Interestingly, juveniles on Tiree and Coll, and occasionally on Islay, are also this black colour. However, despite this similarity in juvenile plumage, biometric evidence suggests that the Outer Hebridean birds are closer to *vulgaris* than to *zetlandicus* (McGowan *et al.* 2003).

Clive Craik

Rose-coloured Starling

Sturnus roseus

Rare migrant in the summer and autumn months.

Although the Rose-coloured Starling rarely breeds closer to Britain than Hungary, it is well known for its eruptive behaviour, with large flocks often moving westwards in late spring and early summer. Despite the species' south-eastern origin, Scotland accounts for a significant proportion of British records. Although most Scottish records come from the Northern Isles, the Rose-coloured Starling has, like other conspicuous species, been reported from all parts of the country.

In Argyll, the first known record was in July 1852, when a bird was shot at Eredine (H&B). This was followed in the first half of the 20th century by two further occurrences: a male found dead at Bonawe on Loch Etive in August 1907 (ASNH 1908:49,195) and a first-summer bird on Iona on 11 July 1932 (SN 1932:152). Since then, there were 23 additional accepted records to the end of 2004, all involving single birds, though one on Coll in August 1983 joined a bird already present on the island (BB 78:580, ABR 1:71). Two of the records were considered to relate to individuals seen earlier. A bird on Islay in late summer 1988, for example, was thought to be a returning individual from 1987 (BB 82:554). The Figure shows the seasonal distribution of the 22 dated records, discounting these two probable repeat sightings.

There are scattered records from late May to mid-October, with a peak in June. Like most vagrants, most sightings (16 out of 24, including undated) come from the islands, Islay having the lion's share with eight records. Only three of the records involve juveniles, which were first seen on 28 August, 1 October and 21 October.

In 2002, there was a widespread invasion that resulted in record numbers in Europe, in the UK, and in Scotland. This was reflected in Argyll, which had its best year ever with six accepted sightings. Numbers were again high nationally in 2003, when Argyll produced five records. Being so conspicuous, adult Rose-coloured Starlings are often

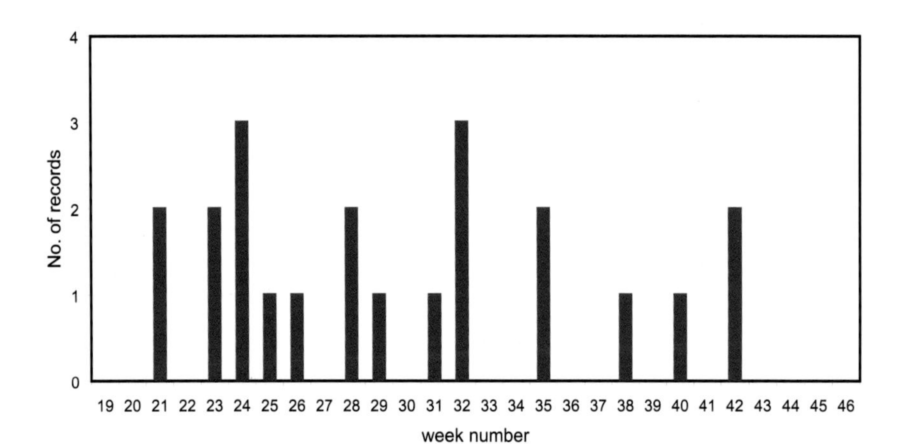

Weekly distribution of Rose-coloured Starling records to 2004.

Record numbers of Rose-coloured Starlings appeared in Argyll in 2002 and 2003. *Jim Dickson*

reported by casual birdwatchers. Often these reports are not accompanied by details and thus fail to gain acceptance even though most if not all are undoubtedly genuine. There were several such reports from Argyll in 2002.

Tristan ap Rheinallt

House Sparrow

Passer domesticus

A common resident near human habitation and on agricultural land in many parts of the county. Small to moderate-sized colonies occur in rural and urban gardens, but larger flocks gather in late summer and autumn where traditional methods of agriculture persist.

House Sparrows are colonial and commensal with humankind, and the contempt bred by this familiarity has taken several forms. The damage that sparrow flocks can cause to seedling plants and flowers has made them the enemy of gardeners and farmers. Most birders consider House Sparrows so insignificant that few ever bother to count or report them; thus most records in the Argyll Database each year come from relatively few sites, usually those covered by RSPB wardens. Similarly, although House Sparrows are caught regularly in mist nets, for many years ringers were not permitted to ring them, mainly on the grounds that expensive rings should not be wasted on such an abundant and well-known species.

However, the idea that the House Sparrow is well-studied is mistaken. Data are so sparse that in some books the section on the much less familiar Tree Sparrow is longer (e.g. Thom). Our ignorance has been highlighted, and all these negative feelings have been somewhat blunted, by the alarming discovery that since the 1970s numbers have been in sharp decline. Sparrows on farms decreased by 60% between 1979 and 1995, while urban sparrows declined gradually up to about 1990, then much more rapidly, becoming almost extinct in some cities. However, House Sparrows in suburbs and small towns have decreased much less. The reasons are unknown, but the decrease seems to be taking place in all habitats, although it has been more severe in the south of Britain than in the north (Migration Atlas, Summers-Smith 2003).

In contrast, records from the 19th century show that the species was then increasing in numbers and extending its range north through the British Isles, reaching the north-west mainland of Scotland by 1900 (First Atlas). Gray found small colonies on farm steadings on the inner isles and also on the west mainland from Sutherland to Argyll, but the species was nowhere numerous. In some parts if Argyll he described how "of late years, towns of considerable size have sprung up as watering places, and the sparrow has multiplied in a corresponding degree".

H&B found it "abundant as a breeding species among the ruins of Iona" and elsewhere on Mull, and common in all suitable places on the mainland, although varying considerably in numbers. It was "very numerous in Benderloch", "nesting in an old ruined church on Tiree" and "found in Jura".

B&R considered it "common, in fact too common" in most parts of mainland Scotland wherever there were houses or cultivation. They described it as abundant on Islay, present on Jura, local on Gigha and Colonsay, nesting on Coll and common locally on Mull and Iona. In an interesting set of records, they reported that James Fisher had found it breeding on Lismore in 1942, and that there had been none on Tiree in 1888, but that it had become a nuisance by 1913 and was common round farms and buildings there by 1942. It was said to be "a visitor for a few hours in summer" at Skerryvore Lighthouse; and there had been interbreeding with Tree Sparrow on Tiree. Numbers in many parts of Scotland had crashed in 1928-29 because of disease, and hard winters had also reduced numbers.

Although its commensalism makes it scarce in areas uninhabited by humans, both Breeding Atlases showed the House Sparrow to be widespread in the British Isles and present in most parts of Argyll. There were a few empty squares in uninhabited parts of Jura, Mull and Mid- and North Argyll, but no major change between the two surveys. During work for the Second Atlas (1988-91), House Sparrows were found breeding in 57% of the 10-km squares in Argyll. During the years 1995-2001, they were found in 1/17, 1/21, 1/16, 1/16, 1/15, 0/12, and 1/6 BBS squares and in 3/14 Countryside

Although it is still a familiar bird, House Sparrow numbers have declined significantly since the 1970s. *John McAvoy*

2000 squares (ABR).

The Winter Atlas showed little difference from the breeding distribution of this highly sedentary species, although there were fewer occupied squares than in summer in the north-west Highlands generally, including areas such as Jura and Mull.

Some still breed in natural holes and cavities or deep inside shrubs and creepers, but most now nest in buildings. They ingeniously find even the smallest holes into lofts or other spaces under roofs or behind walls, and the large and untidy nests sometimes block ducts and immobilise extractor fans. Each pair may raise two, three or even four broods between April and August and this fecundity can give rise to large flocks, mainly of juvenile birds, by late summer.

Most reports during the year are of flocks of well under 100 birds. In the Argyll Database, the numbers of reports in each of the years 1997-2003 were as follows (brackets give numbers of those reports that concerned flocks of 10-99 and 100+ birds): 16 (2,1); 46 (7,1); 50 (24,1); 82 (33, 4); 67 (16, 1); 49 (19, 2); 44 (11,0). All the flocks of over 100 birds were on farms during July-October and almost all were on Coll, Tiree, Islay or Iona. Notable flock sizes reported in earlier years included 120 at Keil Hotel, Southend, Kintyre on 14 August 1990. Perhaps the largest flocks ever recorded in Argyll were of 210 birds at Whitehouse, Tiree, on 6 September 1989 (ABR) and 240 at Arileod, Coll, on 6 September 2004.

Ringers' lack of interest in the species is perhaps justified by the ringing data. Most recoveries are at less than 1km and very few indeed have been recovered at more than 20km. There have been only three recoveries of British-ringed birds abroad – all just across the Channel in France or the Netherlands – and no recoveries within the British Isles of foreign-ringed birds. In Argyll, there have been no recoveries from more than 4km. Indeed, the House Sparrow has been well described as "one of the most sedentary species of wild bird" (Migration Atlas).

Clive Craik

Tree Sparrow

Passer montanus

Former breeder, now a rare migrant.

Describing a visit to Kirkapol on Tiree in 1889, H&B wrote that "we inspected the old church ruins and kirk-yard, and found both Common and Tree Sparrows far from uncommon among the old buildings." They added that: "In Oronsay, Harvie-Brown discovered a pair or two amongst ivy- and honeysuckle-covered cliffs behind Oronsay House, which may have been nesting either in the cliffs or in the ruins of St. Oran's Chapel, which was close at hand, in 1888. Their feeble chirp was first recognised, and then they were seen perched high up among the rocks or flitting about the cliff face in the strong sunlight."

Sadly, sights such as these now belong to the past. At the end of the 19th century, its distribution was described as "curious and sporadic" by H&B, who referred to a colony of about 20 pairs at Kilchoan on Loch Melfort, and to records from Iona, Jura and several locations on Tiree. Earlier, Gray referred to the species' occurrence at Arrochar, just outside the Argyll boundary. Anderson (1898) described the Tree Sparrow as "numerous and resident" on Tiree, where it was once regarded as a serious pest of barley. It also apparently bred on Coll (Irby 1899). Some years later, however, Anderson (1913) implied that Tree Sparrows had declined to extinction on Tiree, whilst MacDougall (1938) recorded none on Coll in 1937 or 1938.

B&R also referred to the species' habit of breeding in small isolated colonies, complaining that this made its distribution hard to map accurately. At the time they wrote (1953), none of the colonies referred to by earlier writers were known to survive. At Kilchoan, the colony apparently became extinct between 1931 and 1941, whilst birds had apparently disappeared from both Iona and Jura. By the second half of the 1960s, Tree Sparrows were regarded as "very unusual" in Argyll (recorder's files), though small colonies were said to have been found on the mainland at Keills in 1956 and at Kilmartin in 1963 (Rainier 1975). Work for the First Atlas in 1968-72 produced several new records, with breeding confirmed at two sites on the Ross of Mull and in the west of Islay, though the latter record does not appear to be referred to anywhere else and may be an error. Birds were also seen at Dalmally, at Achnamara by Loch Sween and at Port Ellen on Islay; and, according to the Atlas maps, breeding probably occurred in NR64 (Gigha and the adjacent mainland). This apparent increase may have been due to increased observer effort during the survey. On the other hand, there is evidence that population levels in Scotland and the UK generally were at a low point around 1950, temporarily recovering after this (Thom, Second Atlas).

Subsequent to the First Atlas survey, there were several records from Islay in the early 1970s (Booth 1975), followed by a period of scarcity; Elliott (1989) implied the existence of a small breeding population on Islay "not likely to have exceeded ten breeding pairs." However, he pointed out that seven of the 13 records known to him were in April or September, suggesting that migrants could have been responsible for many of the Islay sightings. The only other island record during this period involved four birds present for several weeks at Tobermory in autumn 1978 (SBR 1978:42).

On the mainland, a small colony of less than ten pairs occupied nestboxes at Kilchrist, south of Campbeltown, in the late 1970s and early 1980s (E. J. Maguire pers. comm.). Other records from south Kintyre included one of a bird at Southend on 4 November 1972 (D. Merrie pers. comm.) and one in NR61 (perhaps again Kilchrist) during the first winter (1981/82) of the Winter Atlas survey. This survey also found birds in four contiguous 10-km squares centred on West Loch Tarbert. Records came from Kilberry, Skipness and Tarbert (ABR 1:71, ABR 2:48). It is possible that breeding occurred in this area, since two birds were seen at Stonefield, just north of Tarbert, on 6 June 1984 (ABR 2:48). In addition, four were at Minard on 15 May 1983 (ABR 1:71).

There were no records between mid-1984 and the New Atlas survey of 1988-91. This showed probable breeding in one 10-km square and sightings in three scattered 10-km squares, two of which (NR64 and NR78) were shared with the First Atlas, the third apparently deriving from a sighting of a single bird at Claggain Bay on Islay on 25 April 1989 (ABR 6:54). The record of probable breeding refers to a bird seen at the site of the former colony at Kilchrist on 15 June 1990 (ABR 7:51). However, some other records from this period appear to have been omitted, perhaps because they were taken to refer to migrants. This would certainly apply to the remarkable record of 14 in the garden of the Mull of Kintyre lighthouse, with five nearby at Balnamoil, on 3 May 1990 (ABR 7:51). However, there would seem to be no reason to exclude records of single birds at Knock on Mull on 5 May 1991 and Loch Gruinart on Islay on 18 May 1991 (ABR 8:62) while incorporating the Claggain Bay record above. Outwith the spring and summer months, one was seen on The Laggan in Kintyre on 3 October 1989 (ABR 6:54) and one at Gruinart on 31 October 1990 (ABR 7:51).

Between 1992 and 1996, there were nine further records, including a sighting of two birds at Lagg on Jura on 12 July 1992 (ABR 9:53). The remaining records concerned single birds seen on Islay (five), Mull (two) and Iona (one). Most of these, like those in 1990 and 1991, were in spring (April/May) or autumn (October) and probably referred to migrants. From 1996 to 2005 there were no records at any season. However, one was at Totronald on Coll on 27 March 2006, and another (possibly the same bird) was on Tiree at Balephuil on 21 April and at Moss (where it was photographed) on 22 April 2006. On the morning of 3 June 2006, a flock of 18 Tree Sparrows was watched for ten minutes at Balnahard on Colonsay (D.C. Jardine). This was the first record for Colonsay since 1899 and the largest flock recorded in Argyll for many years. Despite these recent records, it seems likely that the Tree Sparrow is extinct as a breeder in Argyll, as indeed it appears to be in the Outer Hebrides (e.g. SBR 1992:63), while populations in areas such as the Clyde are declining. Over the UK as a whole, the breeding population suffered a 95% decline during 1974-1999 (Gregory *et al.* 2002), and although productivity has been increasing across Britain since the late 1990s, the long-term prospects for this species do not look good.

Tristan ap Rheinallt

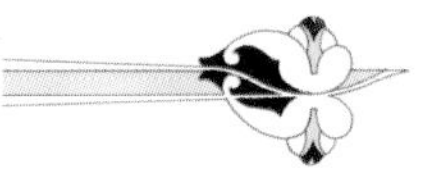

Red-eyed Vireo

Vireo olivaceus

Vagrant.

One was seen at Arinagour on Coll on 3 October 1992 (BB 86:525). This was the fifth Scottish occurrence of Red-eyed Vireo, which is the most frequently recorded North American passerine in Britain and Ireland. Further records in 2000 and 2003 brought the Scottish total to seven: three in the Outer Hebrides, two in Caithness, one in Argyll and one in Lothian. All but one of these birds occurred in October.

Tristan ap Rheinallt

Designed landscapes and botanic gardens such as Benmore (seen here) were established across Argyll in the 19th century. Today, they provide suitable conditions for a wide range of species associated with mature, open woodland.

Above: David Wood
Below: Steve Petty

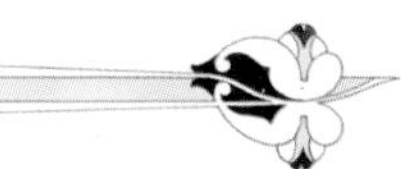

Chaffinch

Fringilla coelebs

An abundant resident except on Tiree and Coll. Foraging flocks gather outwith the breeding season, when numbers are augmented by winter visitors.

The Chaffinch is the most widespread and common finch in Scotland, breeding throughout the mainland and on most of the Inner Hebrides, apart from Tiree. It breeds in a wide variety of rural and urban habitats, wherever there are trees or bushes (Thom). A lack of suitable woodland explains the small breeding populations on the Outer Hebrides and Orkney (SBR), and the lack of regular breeding on Shetland (Pennington *et al.* 2004).

Surprisingly, Chaffinches were mentioned in only two Argyll parishes in the NSA, but perhaps they were too familiar to mention? Later in the 19th century, Gray described them as widely distributed throughout Scotland and mentioned a female found near the summit of Beinn a' Chaolais on Jura, at over 700m asl. He also provided two pages of charming anecdotes regarding their tameness, including one concerning a lady in Ayrshire who had kept a male as a pet for 17 years. Its longevity might have had something to do with the fact that it was fed a more varied diet than many local labourers received at the time!

Curiously, Graham never met with Chaffinches on Iona or Mull, but H&B writing not much later in the 19th century reported it as one of the commonest birds on Mull. Indeed, they described it as one of the most abundant birds throughout the west of Scotland and mentioned "enormous flocks" seen in Benderloch. Only on Tiree was it less well known, with just a few appearing in winter.

In the mid-20th century, B&R again described it as one of the most abundant birds in Scotland, commonly breeding wherever there were trees and bushes, even above 450m asl. It was considered locally common on Islay, Jura, Gigha and Mull, but they made no mention of its status on Coll or Tiree. Boyd (1958) noted a total of five individuals seen in winter on Tiree in 1949, 1952 and 1953, but gave no records for Coll. It was present, presumably breeding, on Colonsay in the 1930s (Loder 1935).

The First Atlas showed Chaffinches breeding throughout mainland Argyll, apart from the coastal fringes of southern Kintyre. They also bred throughout most of Islay and in the south and east of Jura. On Mull confirmed breeding records were lacking only for three 10-km squares on the Ross of Mull, and they bred on Colonsay, but not Oronsay. There were no records for Coll or Tiree and only presence was indicated for the Garvellachs. Williamson (1974) found Chaffinches to be the most numerous species in 1973 in both the oak/ash dominated woodland at Glen Nant and the ash/hazel/oak woodland at Glasdrum.

A similar distribution to the First Atlas was shown in the Winter Atlas, except for small numbers on Coll, Tiree and Oronsay. The dot shown for Dubh Artach, the tiny islet 26km south-west of Mull is presumably a mapping error!

The Chaffinch is one of the most abundant birds in Argyll. *John McAvoy*

On Coll, a pair with a juvenile at Arinagour on 24 June 1985 was the first recorded evidence of breeding on the island (Argyll Database). By 1987, at least two pairs were breeding in The Lodge Plantation and one pair at Gallanach Plantation (Stroud 1989). On Colonsay, a short study in an oakwood at A' Choille Mhor in May 1983 found Chaffinches to be the most numerous species, and in January 1984 a flock of 200 was noted at Druim Clach (Jardine *et al.* 1986).

A survey of broadleaf woodlands in Mid- and North Argyll during 1985 found Chaffinches at all 38 sites, and with an average of 26.7 individuals per wood, they were most numerous species (Averis & Martin, 1985). In Sitka Spruce forests in Cowal, they were the third most numerous species in the spring of 1991 and second in 1992. Although numbers were considerably lower in winter, Chaffinches were the second most numerous species in 1990/1991 and fifth in 1991/1992 (Patterson *et al.* 1995).

The Second Atlas indicated little overall change since the First, except for one additional 10-km square each on Islay and Jura and confirmed breeding on Coll. They were found breeding in 80% of all 10-km squares in the county and the abundance map shows patches of high density in parts of

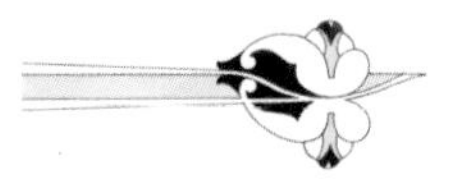

Cowal, Kintyre and Mid-Argyll, but lower numbers on most of the islands.

Recent surveys have indicated that the Chaffinch population in Argyll may be increasing. At Taynish NNR it was the third most abundant species. Here the population has increased, albeit in a fluctuating manner (Figure). The Figure also shows how much more abundant Chaffinches are than Bullfinches. Chaffinches were recorded in 11 of 14 randomly selected 1-km squares (containing mainly coniferous woodland) surveyed in 2000 (Wilson & Fuller 2001, P. Daw unpubl. data), where they were the third most numerous species after Meadow Pipit and Willow Warbler. Chaffinches were found in all 29 broadleaved woods during the Second Woodland Bird Survey 2003/4, but at slightly lower levels (3.7% decrease) than during a similar survey in 1985 (Amar *et al.* 2006, RSPB unpubl. data). Elsewhere in Scotland, the Chaffinch population seems to be relatively stable (Raven *et al.* 2005).

As in the past, large flocks appear in some winters. In 1983, 1,200 were at Kilmichael Glassary, Mid-Argyll, on 30 December and a maximum of 1,800 were at Loch Gruinart RSPB Reserve during January 1985. Large numbers were seen in the autumn and winter of 1999, when approximately 2,000 were at three sites on the Laggan, near Campbeltown, on 30 September, *c.*1,000 were at Tayinloan, Kintyre, on 11 November and 600 were at Mulindry, Islay, on 29 December. The largest flock reported since then was 450 at Loch Crinan, Mid-Argyll, on 25 December 2002.

Chaffinches breeding in the British Isles belong to the race *gengleri*, which is on average smaller and more brightly coloured than the widespread northern European race *coelebs*. On the whole, British Chaffinches tend to be sedentary. Thus, of 49 recoveries of Chaffinches ringed in or on the borders of Argyll, 44 (90%) were within 20km and 34 (69%) within 10km of the ringing site. Where dispersal does take place, birds from northern Britain tend to move longer distances than those from the south (Migration Atlas). As ringing data from Argyll demonstrate, some movements can exceed 100km. A first-winter female ringed in Cowal in December 1978 was recovered in Grampian (159km to the north-east) in late June 1979. Another ringed in Kintyre in early March 1977 was recovered in Mid-Argyll (109km to the north) in late June 1980. The fact that these recoveries involved females is illustrative of a general trend, the median recovery distance for female Chaffinches ringed in Argyll being 21 km, compared to 2km for males. Sexual difference in the movements of Chaffinches has long been recognised (Newton 1972b).

Although it is reasonable to assume that Chaffinches recovered in June in Scotland belong to the native breeding population, some other long-distance recoveries of birds ringed in Argyll probably relate to Continental birds. In fact, the Chaffinch population of the British Isles is estimated to roughly double following the autumn arrival of birds from the Continent, mainly from Fennoscandia. Most of these immigrants appear to arrive in southern England, some then moving north and west within the British Isles. Only a few cross the North Sea directly, though the proportion is higher when the return movement occurs in spring (Migration Atlas).

The proportions of native and immigrant birds in Argyll outwith the breeding season are unknown. However, the number of immigrants may be small, given that there are only four Argyll recoveries of Chaffinches ringed outside the area and its immediate surroundings. One of these recoveries provides the only firm evidence of the occurrence of the race *coelebs* in Argyll; a bird ringed in Norway on 6 August 1983 was found 1,127km away at Kilkenzie, Kintyre, on 2 April 1984.

Numbers of two finches breeding at Taynish NNR (Mid-Argyll), 1990-2006.

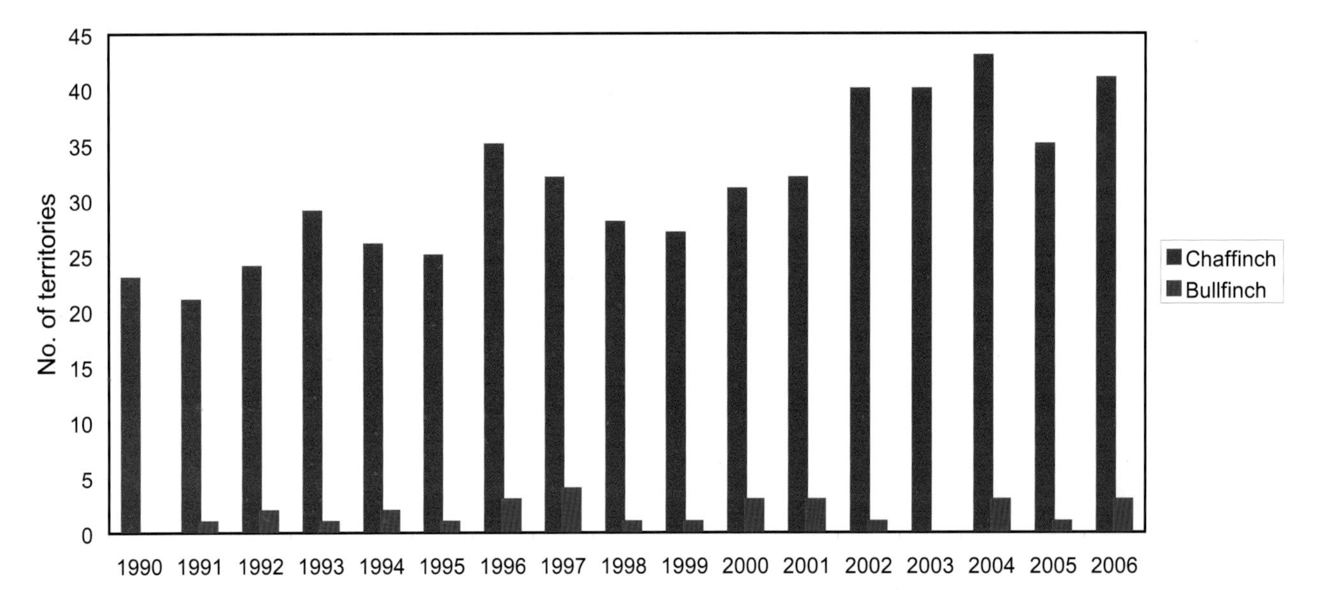

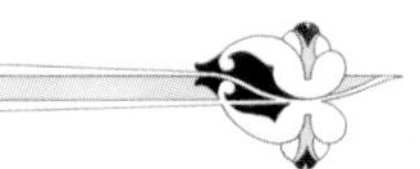

Three other birds may also be *coelebs*, two ringed in the Isle of Man during autumn and one in Antrim in winter. Wintering flocks of Chaffinches over most of mainland Scotland appear to be composed largely of local birds rather than Continental immigrants as is the case in southern England (Migration Atlas). However all migrants to Shetland are considered to be of the nominate race (Pennington *et al.* 2004).

Paul Daw

near Taynuilt in March 1984. Since 1983/84, there have been only four winters when flocks of more than 20 birds have been seen in Argyll (Table).

Since March 1997, the only reports of more than 10 birds have been of 14 or more with Chaffinches at Slockavullin on 26 December 1998 and 20 flying over the RSPB's Reserve at Creag Mhor, Islay, on 27 October 2003 (Argyll Database).

According to the Winter Atlas, Bramblings are always found in flocks. However, more than two thirds of Brambling records in the Argyll Database relate to just one or two birds. They are quite frequently seen in gardens with Chaffinches and there are records for every year since at least 1983. During 1995-2004, Bramblings were seen in every Argyll recording area, including the islands. In fact, although earlier authorities stress how scarce Bramblings were on the Inner Hebrides, there are more than twice as many records in the database for Islay as there are for any other recording area, although this could be due in part to observer bias. In contrast, there are only a handful of records for Cowal.

The first birds are usually seen in October, but there is one record of an individual at Ledaig Point, North Argyll, on 13 September 1988. Most have left by the end of March, but there are several April-May records including two singing males near Carsaig, Mull, on 13 May 1999. There are only two summer records, an adult male in song at Moine Mhor during 15-27 June 1995 and another male seen near the Crinan Canal on 28 June 1999 (ABR).

Paul Daw

Brambling

Fringilla montifringilla

An uncommon winter visitor. Numbers vary from winter to winter, but with fewer birds in recent years. There are a few summer records.

Bramblings are often found feeding under beech trees in good mast years. *Margaret Staley*

Bramblings occur in Scotland, as winter visitors and as passage migrants, in numbers that vary considerably from year to year. Migrants appear in the Northern Isles from August onwards, but the main arrival is generally in October. Their favoured winter food is seeds from Beech trees. In "mast years", they are frequently seen with Chaffinches feeding on the ground beneath large Beeches. In years of abundance, they are distributed throughout much of Scotland apart from the north-west. In other years, most records come from eastern counties (Thom, Winter Atlas). They have occasionally bred in Scotland, but not in Argyll, and widespread colonisation is unlikely (BS3).

Bramblings were mentioned in the NSA in the parish list for Inveraray, and from comments in Gray, it seems the pattern of occurrence in the 19th century was similar to today, with 'immense flocks in some winters'. Gray noted that they appeared only sparingly on the 'inner islands', with none in some years. This pattern was confirmed by H&B, who said they occurred to the west of the watershed in Argyll only in excessively severe winters. They mentioned 'considerable flocks' around Inveraray in the severe winter of 1890/91.

In the mid-20th century, B&R said Bramblings were scarce visitors to the Inner Hebrides. Although Boyd (1958) quoted records for Tiree from the turn of the 19th/20th centuries, including a 'large flock' in December 1898, he could find no recent records for Coll or Tiree. Bramblings were supposedly 'quite common' in winter on Colonsay in the 1930s (Loder 1935).

Survey work for the Winter Atlas included the winter of 1983/84 when unusually high numbers appeared in Argyll. Counts of 40 or more birds were shown for 10-km squares around Oban and Connel and at the head of Loch Fyne. The ABR listed flocks of up to 300 around Connel from November 1983 onwards, and in January 1984 there were 120 near Oban, up to 200 in the Benderloch area and 80 at Cairndow. There were approximately 50 at Loch Tromlee

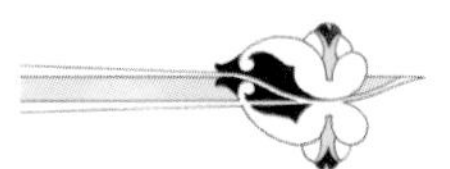

Date	Grid reference	Location	Comment
1992/93			
12/10/1992	NR2664	Foreland House, Islay	1 male - first arrival
18/10/1992	NR7559	Ardpatrick House, Mid-Argyll	10
15/11/1992	NR8297	Slockavullin, Mid-Argyll	30
18/01/1993	NR7518	Kildalloig (near Campbeltown), Kintyre	300 - present since December 1992
02/03/1993	NR7518	Kildalloig, Kintyre	50 - last seen locally
16/04/1993	NR8298	Nether Largie, Mid-Argyll	4 - last of winter
1993/94			
11/10/1993	NR1752	Gleann na Rainich, Islay	1 - first of winter
26/10/1993	NR3964	Knocklearoch, Islay	20
09/11/1993	NR6823	Rhoin Farm (near Campbeltown), Kintyre	30
23/03/1994	NR3968	Finlaggan, Islay	15 - last of winter
1995/96			
08/11/1995	NR2464	Sunderland Farm, Islay	2 - first arrivals
25/12/1995	NR8297	Slockavullin, Mid-Argyll	100 or more with Chaffinches
05/01/1996	NR3362	Bridgend, Islay	20
25/01/1996	NM9038	Benderloch, North Argyll	4 - last reported
1996/97			
12/10/1996	NN1213	Kilblaan, Glen Shira, Mid-Argyll	1 - first arrival
19/12/1996	NM9035	Connel Airfield, North Argyll	*c.*120 with Chaffinches
29/12/1996	NM9038	Benderloch, North Argyll	*c.*40
01/01/1997	NM9035	South Ledaig, North Argyll	*c.*40 throughout January
02/02/1997	NM9741	Barcaldine, North Argyll	200 with Chaffinches
22/02/1997	NM9035	South Ledaig, North Argyll	*c.*25
13/03/1997	NR4863	Jura House, Jura	2
18/03/1997	NS1676	Dunoon, Cowal	1 - last reported

Winters with more than 20 Brambling records between 1983/84 and 2006/07 (Argyll Database)

Greenfinch

Carduelis chloris

This fairly common resident and partial migrant is present all year round, but fewer breed on the islands than on the mainland. Small groups are widespread outside the breeding season.

The Greenfinch is a familiar species in gardens on the mainland, both as a pugilist at the winter bird table and as a widespread breeder in conifer hedges. Locally, its bell-like song and twanging alarms are one of the most characteristic sounds of spring. On the outer islands it breeds more sparsely but occurs at all times of year. There are many fewer reports in the Argyll Database from Coll, Jura and North Argyll than from the other seven areas. In the case of North Argyll, this is probably due to under-recording.

Gray described it as permanently resident from north to south in west Scotland but made no mention of Argyll. Graham's five-word description from Iona and Mull ("Is common all the year") was the shortest of all 124 of his species accounts. H&B said that in 1890 it was common in most wooded districts, mentioning Benderloch, and that it was present on larger wooded islands such as Mull and Jura. B&R also regarded this as a common bird wherever there were trees or bushes.

However, a survey of broadleaved woods in mainland Argyll in summer 1985 showed that it was scarce in mature deciduous woodland. Thirty-eight woods were surveyed but only a single Greenfinch was seen. It was the 51st most numerous species, decidedly less common in this habitat than Spotted Flycatcher (84 birds), Common Crossbill (42), Yellowhammer (16), Goldfinch (13) and Pied Flycatcher (12) (ABR 3:11, Averis & Martin 1985). Yet, in a survey of 67 gardens in Argyll (two on Mull, the rest on the mainland) from November 1985 to February 1987, the Greenfinch was the tenth most frequently recorded species, found in 22% of gardens in spring-summer and 24% of gardens in autumn-winter (Thompson 1989). Such data reflect the fact that the Greenfinch is mainly a bird of gardens, hedges and seed-rich farmland.

Boyd (1958) recorded breeding at Scarinish on Tiree in 1954. B&R mentioned breeding on Islay (both in 1913 and around 1950) and on Colonsay, Jura, Gigha, Mull and Lismore, but they gave breeding status on Coll and Tiree as "uncertain". As early as 1953, they described how the species had turned to gardens in both town and country after stackyards had been discontinued in agriculture. Since then the Greenfinch, like many seed-eating birds, has continued to be affected by a succession of changes in farming methods. The Second Atlas gave the loss of "weeds" through use of herbicides, together with less wasteful methods of harvesting cereal seeds and the change from spring to autumn ploughing of stubble fields, as causes of the decline, continuing: "Over much of the country, the large flocks of Greenfinches, which were once so common on farmland, are now seldom seen".

Nevertheless, both First and Second Atlases showed confirmed or suspected breeding in most parts of the county, but with noticeably empty areas in Jura and east Mull. Breeding was recorded in 31% of 10-km squares during 1988-1991. The highest densities were around Oban and in certain parts of Islay, Kintyre and Cowal but, as throughout north and west Scotland, even the highest densities were much lower than in central and southern England or in the agricultural parts of east Scotland (Second Atlas). During 1980-2005, breeding was recorded in all areas of the county but was scarce although annual on Coll (one pair in 1985 increasing to nine pairs in 2005) and only occasional on Tiree (bred successfully only in 1991, 1992 and 1999). About 25 pairs bred on Colonsay in 1990, probably a typical number. At least five pairs bred at the RSPB's Loch Gruinart Reserve in 1996, the first-ever record at Taynish NNR was a pair on 28 May 2000, and a single bird at Moine Mhor NNR on 4 May 1993 was the second record for the reserve. Only two territories were found in the Rinns Survey on Islay in 1994. During 1994-2001, the species was identified in 0/17, 1/17, 0/21, 2/16, 2/16, 3/15, 0/12 and 1/6 of the 1-km squares of the BBS (ABR, Argyll Database) and in 2/14 of the 1-km squares of the Countryside 2000 Survey (ABR).

Breeding starts early in April, and the earliest date that fledged young have been recorded in the county is 9 May 2002 at Kintallan, Tayvallich. A pair with two recently fledged young, a second or possibly third brood, were at Tullochgorm, Minard on 23 August 2000. Breeding success varies noticeably from year to year, as judged by the numbers and sizes of autumn and winter flocks in the Argyll Database. For example, there were "unusually large flocks" in the late summer and early autumn of 2001. That autumn and winter there were 15 records of flocks with ten or more birds, the largest four holding 140, 100, 60 and 60 birds; while in 1998-1999 there were five such flocks and the largest held only 17 birds.

The Winter Atlas showed only minor changes in distribution compared with the breeding season. There were more occupied squares on Tiree and Islay, consistent with the fact that Greenfinches become more numerous on the islands in winter. In general, flocks are widespread outside the breeding season. Most are small, usually up to 40 birds, but flocks of 100 to 200 have been recorded, especially where farming methods provide abundant grain or other food. The largest eight flocks during the years 1980-2005, all of 100 or more, were reported from Islay, Kintyre and Mull.

The largest three of these flocks were 200 at Kentallen, Mull, on 22 August 1981, 180 at Homeston, Kintyre, on 24 August 1991, and 140 at the RSPB's Loch Gruinart Reserve on 23 August 2001; the other five came from Tayinloan (2), Islay (2) and Salen, Mull (1). The biggest flocks are in August and September, but large flocks can also occur in midwinter (e.g., 100 Greenfinches in flock with Chaffinch and Twite at Mulindry, Islay, on 20 December 1995, and 80 at Braigo, Islay, on 20 January 2002). On Colonsay, the Greenfinch winter population increased from about ten in the early 1980s to 80-100 in 1993-1994 after the provision of garden bird-feeders. B&R described how "Large flocks arrive on Tiree in autumn and early winter, and a few remain in the stackyards until spring". More recently, the largest flock on Tiree was 78 at Crossapol Farm on 14 February 2005 and the largest on Coll was 40 at Arinagour on 23 October 2004. On both islands, Greenfinches are now widespread at garden bird-tables in winter (ABR, Argyll Database).

Sixteen Greenfinches were counted flying south from the Mull of Kintyre between 28 October and 5 November 1989 (ABR). Such movements can cause birds to appear suddenly offshore. Thus Boyd (1958) gave records from the Skerryvore Lighthouse in October-November 1897 and 1906, while B&R related how, on 10 October 1911, "a few" reached even as far as St Kilda. Ringing has shown that most British Greenfinches are sedentary, moving less than 20km between breeding season and other times of year. However, a small minority make longer movements, sometimes 100-200 km or more, usually south and west after breeding. However, it can be difficult to distinguish near-random post-breeding dispersal of this species from directed seasonal movement (Migration Atlas).

Greenfinches have adapted well to living in gardens. *John McAvoy*

In at least some parts of mainland Argyll, Greenfinches are scarce at bird tables in late autumn and midwinter but become

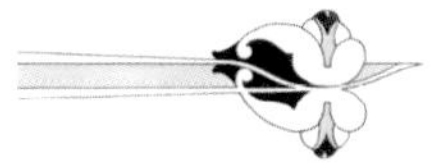

numerous around February (Argyll Database). This spring return probably explains the more distant ringing recoveries, which are mostly of birds ringed outside the breeding season that then fly north and east to breeding areas. Birds ringed in the county have been recovered near Buckie (Grampian) (291km), near Dingwall (Highland) (132km), at Glencaple (Dumfries & Galloway) (167km), and one ringed at the Mull of Kintyre was recovered near Appin (140km). Birds recovered in Argyll had been ringed in Tayside (1), Dumfries & Galloway (2) and Ireland (one each from Co. Londonderry and Co. Down).

Clive Craik

European Goldfinch

Carduelis carduelis

This bird of open ground and farmland occurs in all areas of Argyll, but nowhere in great numbers. Autumn flocks of 100-400 have sometimes been reported, but most flocks hold fewer than ten birds.

The sight of a "charm" of Goldfinches foraging among thistles is surely one of the great pleasures of modern birdwatching. In the 19th century, however, Goldfinches were much prized as cage birds because of their highly attractive red and yellow plumage, and their numbers became dangerously low.

The NSA (quoted by B&R) described how, around the year 1834 on the Argyllshire coast, Goldfinches were "very numerous, coming to the shore in large flocks during frosty weather". By about 1870 Gray ascribed their scarcity in western Scotland to the bird trade but said they were "still sparingly distributed in... some parts of Argyll". Twenty years later, H&B stated that the Goldfinch "used to occur in flights in the district of Benderloch, but it has been cleared out by professional bird-catchers". Although it had become "decidedly local and rare", it had recently occurred at Barcaldine and had "certainly bred at Ledaig on Loch Creran, as we are assured by Mr Anderson Smith, who saw a young bird in the hands of a bird-catcher near that place". Graham often described how he supplied others with specimens of various bird species from Iona and Mull but, surprisingly, he made no mention of the Goldfinch in his accounts of 124 species from that area.

Goldfinch numbers recovered slowly after laws made in 1881 banned the trapping of wild birds. Secondary legislation affecting this and other species was passed as recently as 1954 (Second Atlas). By 1950, B&R described the Goldfinch as a local resident in south-west Scotland as far north as Argyll, mentioning its presence on Islay and Jura but stating that none had been seen near Oban since the severe winter of 1941. Goldfinch numbers are indeed reduced by long cold spells, just as they increase during warm, dry summers with good harvests of seeds, particularly from plants of the family *Compositae* such as thistles, Dandelion, Groundsel and Common Ragwort. Its thin bill allows the Goldfinch to extract seeds of some other plants, such as Teasel and Common Knapweed, which are less easily exploited by larger-billed finches (First Atlas, Thom). However, this greater dependence on certain seeds confines it to weed-rich areas more than, for example, adaptable relatives such as Greenfinch and Chaffinch. The Goldfinch has been more affected than other finches by loss of its prime food through herbicide use and habitat destruction. However, it seems to be adapting to other foods, as there are reports of Goldfinches feeding on peanuts in gardens at Tullochgorm (a flock of eight in January 2005) and at Barcaldine in January and May 2001 and in February 2003 (two birds at each time). However, the Goldfinch was not among the 12 top species in the garden bird survey in Argyll (Thompson 1989). Natural foods have included Beech seeds at Tullochgorm in September 2004 and seeds of burdock at Hynish, Tiree, in February 2003 (Argyll Database). Elsewhere in Scotland, Goldfinches are known to extract seeds from cones of Sitka Spruce (Shaw & Livingstone 1991), and they may well do so in Argyll.

The First Atlas confirmed breeding in most 10-km squares in Britain south of the Highland boundary but showed an absence from most of north-west Scotland. Within Argyll, which straddles this borderline, breeding was widespread on much of the mainland but sparse in North Argyll and on Islay. Only one square was shown occupied on Mull but none on Coll, Tiree or Colonsay. In the Second Atlas, breeding was recorded in 32% of squares in the county. Many formerly empty squares were occupied on Islay and Mull, and breeding was suspected in one square on Colonsay but was still unrecorded on Coll and Tiree. The highest breeding densities were in small areas around Oban and in south-east Islay, but this density was much lower in most of Argyll than over most of central and southern Britain.

Regular annual surveys have confirmed this low breeding density. Thus in the years 1996-2000, Goldfinches were recorded in 0/16, 1/16, 0/16 1/15 and 0/12 of the 1-km squares of the BBS, and in none of 14 one-km squares in the Countryside 2000 survey (ABR). In the Taynish CBC, the average number of territories over 1990-2000 was one, with a maximum of four in 1998. Goldfinches were reported in only five of 38 deciduous woods surveyed in North and Mid-Argyll in summer 1985, when a total of 13 were seen, making this the 33rd most numerous species encountered (ABR 3:11, Averis & Martin 1985). Only two Goldfinches were recorded in the Rinns Survey on Islay in 1994.

Breeding was first confirmed on Coll in 2004, when several pairs bred in the Aringour area, and breeding occurred there again in 2005 and 2006 (J. Bowler pers. comm.). Breeding remains unconfirmed on Tiree and Colonsay, although nine or more pairs were present on Colonsay in June 2004 and the species is an annual visitor to Tiree in May.

Outside the breeding season, Goldfinches are widespread but nowhere abundant, and the largest numbers are seen in late summer. During 1980-2005, most flocks recorded in the Argyll Database and ABR were in single figures, and almost all contained fewer than 50 birds. There were only five records of more than 60: a flock of 400 at Aros Moss, Kintyre, on 27 August 2001, and 300 there in early September 2001 (possibly the same birds); 250 at Loch Creran on 7 September 1988; 122 at Aros Moss, Kintyre, on 1 September 2000; and 120 at the RSPB's Loch Gruinart Reserve in September 1986.

Small numbers are now recorded annually at most times of year on Coll, Tiree and Colonsay. The largest number on Coll was 19 at Arileod on 14 October 2002, the largest on Tiree was 13 at Balemartine on 20 October 2001, although 40 headed south over Ruaig on 21 October 2005 (J. Bowler pers. comm.), and the largest on Colonsay was 20 at Machrins on 17 Oct 1992 (ABR, Argyll Database).

Goldfinches are much more abundant in some autumns than in others, probably as a result of variable breeding success. In the Argyll Database for 1997-2005, the numbers of flocks of more than nine birds in the second half of each year varied enormously between years (as did the size of the biggest flock, given in brackets): 3 (30); 2 (20); 3 (28); 16 (122); 19 (400); 24 (40); 17 (40): 5 (38) and 2 (22). In August-October 2000, when there were many more flocks than usual with 25-55 Goldfinches, mostly in Kintyre, Cowal, Islay and Mid-Argyll, ABR records show that Linnets also appeared in high numbers, presumably also after a successful breeding season.

Goldfinches have only recently started feeding on peanuts in gardens. This one was at Kilmelford on 10 December 2005. *John McAvoy*

Many Goldfinches, perhaps as many as 80% of the breeding population, leave the British Isles in winter, when overseas ring recoveries come mainly from France, Belgium and Spain. Most emigration takes place in September and October (Migration Atlas). Passage counts at the Mull of Kintyre between 15 October and 5 November 1989 recorded a total of 20 flying south (ABR). However, very few Goldfinches are ringed in Argyll and there are no recoveries to cast light on the movements of local birds. Survey work for the Winter Atlas found the largest numbers on Islay and Mull and in Mid-Argyll, with comparatively few in Kintyre.

Clive Craik

Siskin

Carduelis spinus

A locally common partial migrant. Numbers fluctuate from year to year depending on cone crops.

During the 19th century the Siskin was an extremely rare bird in Argyll and was not recorded breeding (Historical Atlas). H&B reported its appearance only in the Benderloch area. At this time, breeding was confined mainly to north-east Scotland.

With the formation of the Forestry Commission in 1919, conifer plantations were established in increasing areas of Argyll following both the First and Second World Wars. The long narrow bill of the Siskin was well adapted for extracting the small seeds found in the papery cones of Sitka Spruce, which had become the predominant tree species in the county. Therefore, it was not surprising that the Siskin colonised Argyll during the 20th century. However, even in the first half of the 20th century it was not a common bird, with only small numbers breeding in Argyll, but it was noted to be increasing (B&R).

Numbers of Siskins increased enormously during the 20th century with the growth of coniferous forests. *John McAvoy*

It is now a locally common breeding species, but absent from Tiree and Coll. Numbers fluctuate from year to year in response to variations in conifer cone crops. The date of first breeding in Argyll was not recorded, but by the time of the First Atlas of 1968-72 it was fairly widespread in Mid- and North Argyll and on Mull. At this time it was scarcer in the younger plantations in Kintyre, and on Jura and Islay. By the time of the Second Atlas, the Siskin was recorded breeding in 54% of 10-km squares in the county, perhaps the most widespread colonisation of any bird given its complete absence during the 19th century. Breeding has now been recorded on Islay, Jura, Mull and Colonsay, but Siskins remain scarce on some of the other islands. There are no records from Coll and Tiree in some years, and none prior to 1988.

In a study of forest birds based in Glenbranter Forest, Cowal, Patterson *et al.* (1995) demonstrated annual variation in the wintering population in response to the availability of conifer seed. They found Siskins were more abundant in mature trees than in young trees and estimated the maximum number at 12,400 birds in 7600ha during April-May 1991, indicating that Siskins were now one of the most abundant birds in Argyll, at least in years with good cone crops.

Most groups of Siskins in Argyll are relatively small, comprising fewer than 50 birds, but in late summer and autumn larger flocks of between 100 and 300 can gather in areas where food is abundant. At such times they feed on the seeds of birch (July and August) and conifers and alder (autumn-winter) (ABR). More birds spend the winter in Argyll when conifers produce large crops of cones, particularly Sitka Spruce.

In spring, groups are smaller and are often found feeding on peanuts provided in gardens. Ringing studies have shown there is a high turnover of birds at these sites, and very large numbers of migrants can be involved. More birds visit garden bird feeders in springs with few cones than when cones are abundant (McKenzie 2007). When cones are plentiful, most birds feed on conifer seed as soon as they arrive in Argyll. In such years, breeding is earlier than in poor cone years (Shaw 1990).

More Siskins are ringed in Argyll than any other finch due to the large numbers attracted to garden bird feeders during early months of the year. Not surprisingly, there have been many recoveries. Siskins ringed in Belgium (6), Ireland (5), Wales (2), southern England (82) northern England (21) and elsewhere in Scotland (46) have been caught in Argyll, while birds ringed in Argyll have subsequently been retrapped in the Netherlands (1), Belgium (2) and Malta (1) as well as in many locations in Britain.

David Jardine

Linnet

Carduelis cannabina

This partial migrant breeds at low altitudes on heath and scrub, mainly on Islay and Kintyre, more sparsely elsewhere. It becomes less widely distributed in winter when most reports come from Islay, Kintyre and Colonsay.

Early writers give few hard facts about this species. Gray's account is almost entirely lyrical – indeed, much of it is a poem. One of his few factual statements, that Linnets were "very common over the whole of the inner islands", contradicts the able and meticulous Graham, who did not even mention the species during his 1848-1854 residence on Iona. However, H&B found it with Twite on Iona in 1888 and 1891; they also reported it breeding occasionally on Tiree and occurring at many sites on the mainland and probably on Jura.

B&R described the Linnet in Argyll as "local though widespread". It nested "pretty commonly" on Islay and Gigha but they found none on Coll in 1938, Jura in 1939 or Colonsay in 1942. In 1948 they saw only one on Mull and none on Iona.

Thom recognised that some contradictions may have arisen from confusion with the similar Twite. She described the Linnet as scarce or local in Argyll, except in the south half of Kintyre, and as breeding sporadically on Mull, Colonsay, Coll, Tiree and possibly on Jura, but as "widespread and quite common" on Islay.

Flocks disband and birds return to breeding sites in March and April, and breeding lasts from May to July. There may be more than one brood a year. Linnets breed singly or in small colonies in gorse bushes, hedges and other shrubs, usually in open country and scrubland, and low vegetation is needed for roosting throughout the year. Their required food is the seeds of plants that are often described as "weeds" growing on "waste ground". In recent decades, as hedges have been destroyed, ground has been reclaimed, and both "waste ground" and crops have been sprayed unselectively with "selective" herbicides, Linnets have declined noticeably over much of the British Isles.

Nevertheless, both the First and Second Atlases showed that most 10-km squares in Britain were occupied, except for a large area of Scotland north-west of a fairly sharp border from Tay to Clyde and passing roughly through Argyll. Breeding was recorded in 37% of 10-km squares in the county, including most of Islay and Kintyre, these two areas also holding the highest densities. Many squares on Colonsay, Coll and Tiree were occupied, but many or most squares in Mull, Cowal, North Argyll, Mid-Argyll and Jura were empty. As expected, the lowest densities were in the more mountainous parts of the county.

The highest breeding counts have come from Islay, e.g. 55 territories at the RSPB's Loch Gruinart Reserve in 1997, and 71 on The Rinns in 1994. Some idea of density on Colonsay was given by counts of 13 individuals on Oronsay in a survey on 24 May 1998, and 20 near Milbuie on 17 May 1991. On Tiree 28-30 pairs bred in 2002, 40-50 pairs in 2003 and 70 pairs in 2005 – an increase possibly linked to increasing amounts of nesting cover in gardens. Two pairs bred on Coll's RSPB Reserve in 1999 and Coll held an estimated island total of 20 pairs in 2003 (J. Bowler pers. comm.). On Sanda Islands there were four pairs in 1997 and 1998, *c.*10 in 1999, 10-15 in 2000, 26 in 2001 and 15 in 2003. On the Taynish CBC, the 1990-2000 average was two territories, with three in each of the years 1997-1999 and 2001, five in 2000 and a record six in 2002. Six to eight pairs bred at Aros Moss (Kintyre) in 2002. During 1995-2001, Linnets were recorded in 3/17, 3/21, 2/16, 4/16, 3/15, 2/12 and 2/6 BBS squares and in 1/14 Countryside 2000 squares (ABR, Argyll Database).

Flocks start to form in August, and in the west of Scotland these tend to be smaller than in eastern or southern Britain. Some British breeders winter locally, while others move south or south-west to winter in France and Spain. Very few are ringed in the Argyll area, and recovery maps show the whole of west Scotland blank for both breeding and winter seasons (Migration Atlas). The only Argyll recovery is of a bird ringed on Sanda in 1984 and controlled there in 1988, presumably showing breeding site fidelity. We do not know how far our

Linnets are scarce birds in much of Argyll, but more numerous on the islands. *David Palmar*

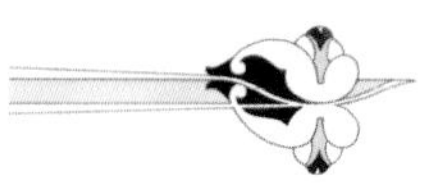

breeding birds travel or how many of our wintering birds breed here.

Many breeding areas are vacated in winter as birds move between good feeding sites, such as stubble fields and saltmarshes. The Winter Atlas showed a general absence in north-west Scotland including most of Argyll, where the main wintering concentrations were in the west of Islay and the south of Kintyre. Smaller numbers were found on Coll, Tiree, Mull and Cowal but Linnets were absent from Jura, North and Mid-Argyll and Colonsay. In more recent years, Linnets have been absent from both Tiree and Coll between mid-November and mid-March (J. Bowler pers. comm.).

This is reflected to some extent by the distribution of flocks recorded outside the breeding season during 1980-2003; 82 were on Islay, 26 on Kintyre, 17 on Tiree, 16 on Colonsay, 11 on Mull, three in Mid-Argyll, two in North Argyll, one on Coll, and none on Jura or Cowal (compiled from flocks reported in ABR and Argyll Database: the flocks reported in ABR were usually only those of more than 50 birds, but flocks of more than 20 were given in some years). These included 52 flocks with more than 100 birds (35 on Islay, six on Colonsay, five in Kintyre, three on Tiree, two on Mull and one on Coll). The largest flocks recorded in the Argyll Database were 550 at Clachan (Tiree) on 28 September 2004, 400 on Islay in autumn 1983, 350 at Corsapol (Islay) on 22 September 2001, 350 at Rockside (Islay) on13 August 2002, and 300+ at Southend (Kintyre) on 18 July 2001. Up to 2003, the largest flocks were generally reported from Islay, but more recently post-breeding flock-sizes have increased on Tiree in line with an increase in the number of breeding pairs on the island; thus in August-September 2004, in addition to the largest flock above, there were six reports of flocks of 100-250 on Tiree (J. Bowler pers. comm.).

Both numbers of flocks and numbers of birds peak in September. In some autumns Linnets are more numerous than in others; for example, in 2000, 2003 and 2004 there were many reports of flocks with more than 100 birds, while in 1997 there were none over 100 and only two over 50. There are many fewer records in December. Numbers start to increase in January and most birds return in March, but the flocks are considerably smaller and fewer than in autumn (ABR).

Linnets breeding throughout Scotland belong to the poorly defined race *C. c. autochthona*. They are slightly darker than the race *C. c. cannabina* breeding in the rest of the British Isles and in continental Europe. However, this is only an average difference and it is almost impossible to assign individuals to one race or the other, or to draw a geographical boundary between them. The only Scottish-bred chick to have been recovered outside Scotland moved from Dumfries & Galloway to Cumbria. From this and other evidence, it is thought that *autochthona* is largely sedentary (Migration Atlas, McGowan *et al.* 2003).

Clive Craik

Twite

Carduelis flavirostris

A local resident, mainly in coastal areas on the mainland and islands; winter flocks may comprise resident birds and migrants.

The Twite breeds mainly in coastal habitats on the mainland and islands. Thus, in Argyll the most important areas for Twite are at low elevation, unlike England and some other areas in Scotland where breeding occurs at higher elevation (Langston *et al.* 2006). In Argyll, flocks can be found on low-lying arable and coastal areas from August onwards. There is evidence to indicate some birds emigrate from Argyll in autumn and return in spring. There may also be an influx into Argyll of wintering birds from other areas.

H&B noted that the Twite was not universal in Argyll and mention that it was common on the moors of Benderloch and was also found in Tiree and the other islands. B&R were more specific and describe Twite as locally common in Argyll. They recorded it from Kintyre, Point of Knap, near Kilberry, on Islay (at Port Ellen, the Oa and Kildalton), Texa, Jura, Colonsay, Tiree and Coll.

The First Atlas provided the earliest comprehensive survey of this species in Argyll. It showed that it was well distributed on islands and in coastal areas (except parts of Kintyre), but largely absent from Cowal and large parts of inland Mid- and North Argyll. The breeding distribution has not changed greatly in recent years, with the Second Atlas recording it in 36% of 10-km squares in Argyll. There was some evidence of a decline, with birds not being reported breeding from eighteen 10-km squares where it was found in the First Atlas, but conversely it was found in eleven new 10-km squares.

There appears to have been a long-term decline in Twite populations in Scotland, but mainly away from the coastal population in Argyll (Langston *et al.* 2006). Estimates of breeding populations on Colonsay and Sanda during the last ten years have shown little overall change, but numbers in some years can be significantly lower, and then recover over a number of years (ABR).

The main threats to Twite in Argyll are agricultural changes which lead to (i) a reduction in the area of arable crops and weedy fields and (ii) increases in grazing pressure. Such changes reduce natural weed seeds upon which Twite are dependent. Reforestation has resulted in a loss of Twite habitat elsewhere in the UK, but this appears to have been largely avoided in Argyll, where most of the population breed at low elevation, areas least likely to be planted with trees.

In autumn, post-breeding flocks are a common sight in weedy fields and coastal habitats (Clark & Sellers 1998). In winter they are found mainly on Coll, Tiree, the Ross of Mull, Colonsay and Oronsay, the Rinns of Islay and the Kintyre coast. Smaller numbers are found in coastal areas of Mid- and North Argyll, but in the Winter Atlas they were absent from Cowal. Most winter flocks are under 100 birds, but each winter larger flocks with between 100 and 300 birds have been reported regularly from Islay and occasionally from Colonsay, Iona, Coll and Tiree. The largest number recorded was 800 in a mixed flock of finches feeding at Mulindry, Islay, on 20 December 1995.

Until recently the Argyll population was believed to be relatively sedentary; the only ringing recovery on record was of an adult male ringed on the Copeland Isles (Co. Down) on 7 April 1983 and controlled at the Mull of Kintyre on 29 May 1983. Passage was reported on Oronsay in April in the late 1980s and at Uisaed Point, Kintyre, in late September during the early 1990s. More recently, a colour-ringing study has shown that some birds from the west of Scotland winter on the shores of Morecambe Bay near Heysham in Lancashire (Raine *et al.* 2006). Birds ringed there in winter have been seen on Oronsay in April (2), Colonsay in May, Mull in June and Sanda in July (2). The main breeding population in England, in the south Pennines, winters predominantly on the east coast of England (Raine *et al.* 2006).

David Jardine

The Twite is mainly restricted to coastal areas on the islands and parts of mainland Argyll. *Philip Kirkham*

Lesser Redpoll

Carduelis cabaret

A partial migrant that breeds locally, with numbers fluctuating from year to year. Post-breeding flocks gather from July and most birds move south for the winter.

The Lesser Redpoll was previously regarded as the race *cabaret* of the Common Redpoll *Carduelis flammea*. Since 2000, the Lesser Redpoll has been treated as a full species *C. cabaret* (BOURC 2000). The Common Redpoll now comprises three races (Mealy, Greenland and Iceland Redpolls – see next species). Many older Argyll records did not distinguish between races; thus some winter records below might have involved Common Redpolls. Only birds that were clearly identified at the time as belonging to races other than *C. flammea cabaret*, as this species was then known, have been mentioned under Common Redpoll.

The Lesser Redpoll is a partial migrant breeding throughout most of mainland Scotland, on the Clyde islands and on most of the Inner Hebrides. It is associated particularly with birchwoods, scrub and the pre-thicket stage of conifer forests, and it feeds primarily on small seeds that are abundant on trees and plants in these habitats. It is capable of extracting seeds from the cones of Sitka Spruce and other conifers. When available, conifer seed is an important food in early spring.

Many recent changes in the breeding distribution of Lesser Redpolls in Scotland can be linked to reforestation (B&R, BS3). They breed in young forests for a very short period just prior to canopy closure, when trees are large enough to nest in, but still open enough to allow a proliferation of ground vegetation. Between the First and Second Atlases there was a significant contraction of range, especially in Grampian (Second Atlas). At the same time, a small population was established on the Outer Hebrides and in Caithness. Redpolls breed intermittently in Shetland and Orkney, but there is some doubt about their species (SBR 1998-2001). Both Lesser and Common Redpolls have been recorded breeding on Shetland (Pennington *et al.* 2004). Between 1994 and 2003, numbers declined in England, but this was balanced to some extent by a 17% increase in Scotland (BTO Trend).

In Argyll, the Lesser Redpoll breeds widely across the mainland and on most of the islands. It was recorded in 41% of 10-km squares during the Second Atlas. In two CBC plots at Taynish NNR, numbers fluctuated between one and eight pairs between 1990 and 2006 (mean 4.2 pairs), with peak numbers around the turn of the century (Figure). It was found in 21 of 29 broadleaved woods in Mid- and North Argyll during the Second Woodland Bird Survey in 2003-04, where numbers had increased by 90% since a similar survey in 1985 (Amar *et al.* 2006, RSPB unpubl. data). The reasons for such a large increase are unclear. Census work in Sitka Spruce forests in Cowal provides evidence of seasonal changes in

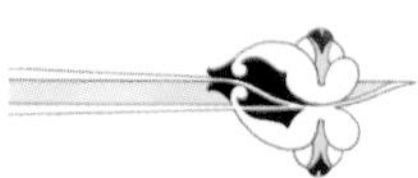

Lesser Redpolls breed widely across Argyll in broadleaved and young conifer woodlands. *Roy Blewitt*

abundance (Patterson *et al.* 1995). Here, only 5% of plots held birds in winter, but this increased to 9-15% by early spring (mid April-mid May) and to 18-28% by late spring (mid May-mid June), suggesting that, in most years, Redpolls were arriving back in breeding areas quite late.

The Lesser Redpoll breeds on most of the larger islands in Argyll. It was first recorded breeding on Sanda in 2001, when three pairs nested in a new broadleaved plantation and raised 15 young. There were again three pairs on Sanda in 2003. The first breeding record on Coll was in 1989, when a pair nested successfully at The Lodge, and there have been regular breeding season records since, with between four and eight birds on the island in 2003. It was reported to be 'extremely abundant' on Shuna in late May 1994. In 2005, up to four pairs were on Tiree in June, at Carnan Mor. Two broods of fledged young were found there on 16 July, the first confirmed breeding record for Tiree. On Islay, new areas were colonised following afforestation; there were seven separate

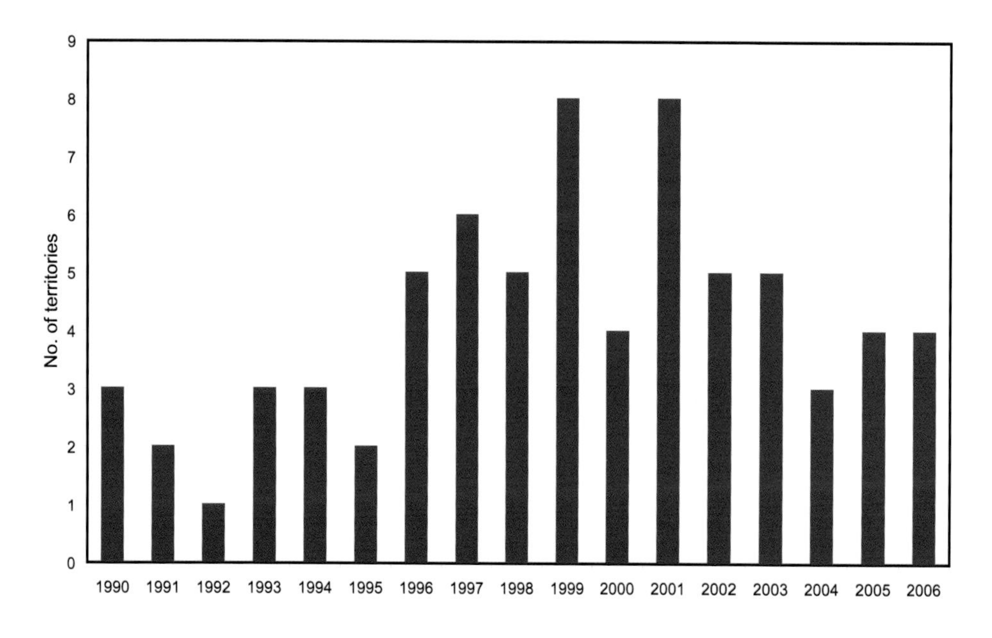

Numbers of Lesser Redpolls breeding at Taynish NNR (Mid-Argyll), 1990-2006.

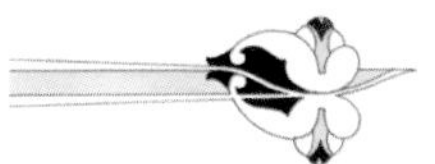

breeding locations on the Rinns in 1994, compared with none up to 1989. There were 5-10 pairs on Colonsay in 1999, the maximum recorded from that island. Nineteen males were recorded at separate sites on Jura in May 2002, and there were eight on Scarba on 21 June 2003. Breeding has not been recorded on Iona, but there are occasional spring records, presumably of birds migrating north from their wintering quarters (e.g. three on 30 April 2003; ABR).

In the NSA the Lesser Redpoll was recorded from Argyll and five other Scottish counties, but otherwise there were few early records. Its preference for birch woodlands in western Scotland was first recorded by Gray. H&B said that it was "included amongst the nesting species of Benderloch" and "that of late years it has not been infrequent (1887)". B&R noted that it "breeds locally on Islay, and is fairly well distributed in the woods on Jura". In 1948 they found a pair "up Glen Gorm (Mull) and a pair at Torosay Castle". Generally, there appears to have been an increase throughout the 20th century until around the mid-1980s (Historical Atlas, B&R, Thom).

In most years, post-breeding flocks of 20 to 30 birds are reported from across Argyll in August and September. In winter, most of the breeding population move south. The Winter Atlas suggests that few remain in the north and west of Scotland, but winter flocks of up to 60 birds are recorded in Argyll in most years (Argyll Database). However, in the 1970s and 1980s, large flocks of 100-250 birds were recorded from Mull, Mid-Argyll, Islay and Kintyre (ABR, Elliott 1989). These large flocks occurred at a time when extensive areas of forest were suitable for breeding and they may have been post-breeding aggregations. There were no such records after 1986, when many of the forests established in the 1960s and 1970s would have become unsuitable for breeding.

There have been two ringing recoveries. A young bird ringed in Kent in October 1974 was killed near Grogport in Kintyre in July 1975 (677km). An adult male ringed on Bute in September 1971 was found dead near Dunoon in October 1972.

David Wood

Common Redpoll

Carduelis flammea

Scarce migrant; status rather uncertain.

Recently split from Lesser Redpoll, the Common Redpoll breeds across northern Europe, Asia and North America.

Three races of this species occur in Britain on migration and in winter: *C. f. rostrata* (Greenland Redpoll) breeding in Greenland, *C. f. islandica* (Iceland Redpoll) breeding in Iceland, and *C. f. flammea* (Mealy Redpoll) breeding in the remainder of the species' European range. The Mealy Redpoll is a regular visitor to eastern Britain in the winter months, its numbers varying from year to year (Migration Atlas). In Scotland, peak numbers usually occur in October, with the largest numbers in Fair Isle (Thom). Its status in Argyll is obscure and, although it is perhaps unlikely to be a regular visitor, the few published records may not reflect its true abundance (ap Rheinallt & Daw 2000).

The 1910 records (Table) were associated with the most recent large-scale irruption of Mealy Redpolls into Britain (Migration Atlas).

Greenland Redpolls are thought to reach north-west Scotland in most years, with large influxes on occasion (Migration Atlas). Again, this form may well be under-recorded in Argyll. Although B&R stated that there had been records from Tiree, Mull and mainland Argyll, ap Rheinallt & Daw (2000) could only trace four confirmed records: a male and a female procured on Tiree on 12 and 27 September 1913 respectively (SN 1914:44, SN Extra Publication No. 3: 9, 36), and singles at Roundhouse on Coll on 8 October and 18 December 1992 (SBR 1992:66, ABR 9:54). In addition, one was at Balemartine on Tiree on 15 September 2001 (accepted by SBRC).

More recently, a bird on Tiree on 1 November 2003, and four birds on Tiree in October 2004 were accepted as Common Redpolls of uncertain race (Argyll Database). There is increasing recognition that Iceland Redpolls of variable appearance, whose taxonomic status is still subject to debate, occur as migrants in north and north-west Scotland (e.g. Pennington & Maher 2005), thus racial identification of

Date	Location	No. of birds	Reference
21 October 1910	Mull	1	ASNH 1911:114
22 November 1910	Craignish	?	ASNH 1911:209
December 1910	Skerryvore	?	ASNH 1911:209
October-November 1933	Oronsay	1	Jardine et al. 1986
9 October 1976	Bridgend (Islay)	5	SB 10:114
17 February 1986	Connel	6	SB 14:253, ABR 4:38
13 February 1987	Gruinart (Islay)	1	SBR 1987:45, ABR 5:12
December 1992 to March 1993	Killdalloig (Kintyre)	1	E. J. Maguire pers. comm.
28 September 2002	Loch Gorm (Islay)	1	Argyll Database
1 November 2003	Balephuil (Tiree)	1	Argyll Database
25-29 October 2004	Tiree	4	Argyll Database

Records of Common Redpolls in Argyll from 1910 to the end of 2006.

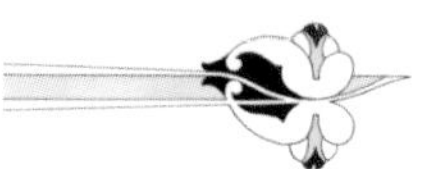

Common Redpolls seems less straightforward today than it did in the past. It is entirely possible that some of the Mealy Redpolls listed in the Table were in fact Iceland or indeed Greenland Redpolls.

It also appears that Greenland and/or Iceland Redpolls breed in the Outer Hebrides, at least in some years (Stevenson 2005). They might occur in Argyll during the breeding season, and indeed pale redpolls have been seen recently on Islay in late spring (ap Rheinallt pers. obs.).

Tristan ap Rheinallt

Arctic Redpoll

Carduelis hornemanni

Vagrant.

The first Argyll record of this species concerns a first-winter bird associating with a flock of Linnets at Loch Gruinart on Islay from 22 to 24 September 2001 (BB 96:602). Although it was thought at the time to belong to the race *exilipes* (Coues's Redpoll) (ap Rheinallt 2002), it seems more likely to have been a Hornemann's Redpoll (*C. h. hornemanni*), which breeds in eastern Canada and Greenland, and typically occurs in Britain earlier in the autumn than *exilipes* (Pennington & Maher 2005). On 23 October 2004 a splendid white male (considered to be an adult *exilipes*) was watched at The Manse, Scarinish on Tiree (BB 100:95). It was accompanied by an immature bird that showed some characteristics of Arctic Redpoll, but Common Redpoll could not be conclusively ruled out (J. Bowler, pers. comm.).

Most Scottish records of Arctic Redpoll come from the Northern Isles and it is a major rarity elsewhere, although occurrences were considerably more widespread than usual during the invasion of winter 1995/96. Interestingly, the Islay record coincided with reports of single Arctic Redpolls from Aughris Head (Co. Mayo) on 15 September and Tory Island (Co. Donegal) on 18 September (Birding World 14:363).

[Arctic Redpoll was formerly on the Argyll list on the strength of a specimen procured on Mull on 10 October 1920 by Meinertzhagen (B&R). However, Knox (1993) showed clearly that this record was the result of deliberate fraud, the specimen in question probably having been collected in Greenland in 1936.]

Tristan ap Rheinallt

Common Crossbill

Loxia curvirostra

An irruptive species with large numbers breeding in good cone years, but few staying when cones are scarce.

Numbers, distribution and breeding season of Crossbills in Argyll vary depending on the masting of coniferous trees, particularly spruces. It is a highly irruptive species and, when cone crops are depleted, large flocks gather, usually in June-July, before departing to locate new seed sources (Newton 1972b).

During the 19th century, Crossbills were scarce visitors to Argyll. H&B did not record them breeding and they were sufficiently rare to report an invasion of birds in July 1888 when they were reported from Appin, Mull and Jura. Neither Gray nor Graham mentioned Crossbills in Argyll. B&R also gave few references; they noted small numbers in the autumn of 1927 in the Inner Hebrides, but provided no evidence of breeding.

During the 20th century, particularly following the Second World War, large areas of Argyll were reforested, mainly with Sitka Spruce and Norway Spruce. As these forests matured, they provided a habitat that was quickly colonised by Crossbills.

It is not known when breeding first occurred in Argyll, but by the time of the First Atlas breeding was proven in

Boom and bust: Crossbills are much commoner in years with bumper crops of spruce cones. *Philip Snow*

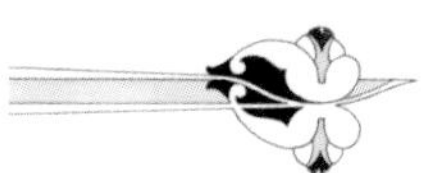

three 10-km squares and possible breeding in a further four squares. The population continued to increase with birds being reported from fourteen 10-km squares in the Winter Atlas. These records may well have been of breeding birds, as Crossbills are one of the earliest birds to breed. Autumn and winter breeding has been reported in forests comprising trees whose cones ripen early, such as Sitka Spruce. Indeed, territorial pairs have been found in Argyll in November and December, but breeding has yet to be proved in these months.

Crossbills have been recorded annually in Argyll since 1980 (ABR). In the Second Atlas they were recorded in 16% of 10-km squares in the county. However, this probably over-represented their breeding status, for one of the largest invasion of Crossbills recorded in Britain occurred in 1990 (Jardine 1992) and many birds stayed to breed in 1991. In a study of forest birds in Glenbranter Forest it was estimated that there were 24,200 Crossbills in 7600ha during April–June 1991. The following spring there were none, as Crossbills had moved on due to lack of cones.

Most counts of Crossbills in Argyll have been of flocks of fewer than 25 birds. Outside the major invasion of 1990/91, counts of over 50 were unusual. Following the good breeding winter of 1984/85, 250 were recorded feeding on defoliating caterpillars in the oakwood at Stonefield, Loch Etive, on 18 June 1985. These birds may well have been moulting and have sought out this unusual food to gain proteins required for feather growth.

In addition to the mainland, breeding has also been recorded in conifer forests on Mull and Islay. On Islay, evidence of breeding was first reported in the early 1980s (Elliott 1989). The records from Jura, Colonsay and Tiree were thought to be of transitory birds. On the outer islands, where conifers are not readily available, other foods are utilised, such as Thrift seed, on which ten birds were feeding at West Hynish, Tiree, on 15 July 2001.

Summers *et al.* (2002) showed that, on the basis of call types, there were various forms of Common Crossbills in Scotland. Their study identified 3 types (1A, 2B, and 4E); but only the widespread type 1A was found in Argyll. However, it should be noted that the proportions of various call types vary among years, as a result of immigrants arriving in Scotland from different areas of mainland Europe. Therefore, it is possible that other call types may occur in years that lack tape recording data.

The study of Crossbill call types in Scotland led to a re-appraisal of records of Scottish Crossbill in Argyll (Jardine & ap Rheinallt 1997). As previous records lacked biometric data or call note recordings, they were considered unsound, and this species was removed from the County list.

There have been no ringing recoveries of Common Crossbills to or from Argyll.

David Jardine

Common Rosefinch

Carpodacus erythrinus

Vagrant; may have bred.

Long known in Scotland as a scarce passage visitor, mainly to the Northern Isles, the Common Rosefinch bred in Highland Region in 1982 (Thom). The number of birds recorded annually in Britain increased greatly through the 1980s and 1990s, with spring birds becoming noticeably widespread in Scotland and turning up in several areas where they had not previously been recorded (Wallace 1999, Fraser & Rogers 2001). This increase was considered by Wallace (1999) to be associated with a much-increased breeding population in southern Fennoscandia. This population may account for most or all of the nine Argyll records to date, seven of which have been in late spring (late May-June).

The first two records came from Iona, where an adult female was seen on 14 June 1989 (SBR 1990:62, ABR 8:67). A pair was seen at the same (undisclosed) location a year later, from 12 June to 15 July 1990, and the female was seen

Records of Common Rosefinch in Argyll from 1994 to the end of 2006.

Date	Location	Comment	Reference
11 to 21 June 1994	Colonsay House Gardens	Singing male, with a probable second singing bird on 11 June	SBR 1994: 64, ABR 11: 86
21 and 22 September 1996	Balemartine (Tiree)	Female	SBR 1996: 66, ABR 14: 88
7 November 1996	Oronsay	Juvenile female [sic]	SBR 1996: 66, ABR 14: 88
7 June 1998	Balemartine (Tiree)	Adult male, in song	SB 1998: 104, ABR 15: 95
10 June 1999	Arduaine Gardens, near Loch Melfort	Adult male, in song	SBR 1999: 117, ABR 16: 99
23 and 25 June 1999	Seafield Farm, near Bowmore (Islay)	First-summer male, in song	SBR 1999: 117 (with second date incorrect), ABR 16: 99
27 May 2004	Jura House (Jura)	Adult male, in song	Argyll Database

to gather nest material on 16 June (SBR 1990:62, ABR 7:54). Breeding was not proven, however, but there was a confirmed breeding record in Sutherland in 1990, and a further four in England in 1992 (Wallace 1999).

The remaining seven Argyll records occurred during the period 1994 to 2004 (Table).

As with so many other rarities, the majority of Argyll records come from the islands, with only the one mainland sighting.

Tristan ap Rheinallt

Common Bullfinch

Pyrrhula pyrrhula

A widely distributed resident, albeit at low density. It is most often found in woods with a well-developed scrub layer and in young conifer forests. Flocks occur in winter.

The Bullfinch was said to be rare in Scotland at the end of the 18th century and was not recorded in Argyll in the OSA. However, over the past 200 years it appears to have extended its range northward in Britain. It was mentioned in three Argyll parishes in the NSA and was common in mainland Argyll by the second half of the 19th century (Gray). It also occurred on larger and more wooded islands, such as Islay, Jura, Mull and Kerrera (H&B), with further records from Islay, Jura and Gigha in the first half of the 20th century (B&R).

Bullfinches are probably seen more often in young forestry plantations than anywhere else in Argyll. *Philip Kirkham*

In recent years there has been a marked increase in Bullfinches in the new forests of south-west Scotland (Thom). A comparison between the First and Second Atlases showed a contraction in range on Mull and an extension in Kintyre. The latter may be attributable to an increase in conifer forests at the appropriate stage of development. The Second Atlas showed breeding records for 42% of 10-km squares in Argyll. The species bred for the first time at Taynish NNR in 1991, and has since averaged 1.9 pairs per year (see Figure in Chaffinch account). Bullfinches were found in seven of 38 broadleaved woods surveyed in Mid- and North Argyll in 1985 (Averis & Martin 1985).

The Winter Atlas showed Bullfinches as absent from many parts of Argyll, especially the islands and coastal areas. However, a few inland areas held larger numbers.

More recently, on the larger islands only Islay and Mull have held significant numbers. On Islay there are records of pairs or family parties from all the main woodlands, while on Mull most records come from the western half of the island (Argyll Database). On Colonsay breeding was recorded in 1976, and there were intermittent records of pairs during the breeding season from 1980 to 1991, but no records since (Jardine *et al.* 1986). On Jura, apart from a single bird in July 1994, there have been no records since the confirmed breeding in the north of the island shown in the Second Atlas. Two individuals were reported on the Garvellachs in June 1991. A female at An Airidh during 16-18 April 2000 was apparently the first recorded on Tiree. The only record from Coll was in 1899 (Irby 1899). One was also recorded on Skerryvore in April 1888 (H&B).

Bullfinches were found in only two of 14 randomly selected 1-km squares (containing mainly coniferous woodland) surveyed in 2000 (Wilson & Fuller 2001, P. Daw unpubl. data) and in nine of the 16 broadleaved woods in Mid- and North Argyll surveyed in 2003 (Amar *et al.* 2006, P. Daw unpubl. data).

Large flocks sometimes occur outside the breeding season. The largest number reported since 1980 was of 70 feeding in birch at Glenbranter, Cowal, on 3 January 1994. During the winter, flocks of 20 or more have been seen at Loch Caolisport, Balinoe Forest (Mid-Argyll), Cologin (near Oban), Doire Darach (North Argyll) and Knap (Cowal). These flocks presumably comprised local birds, as there were no reports of 'Northern' Bullfinches in Scotland at the same time (see below). A flock of 50 feeding on a forestry track in pre-thicket Sitka Spruce at Cruach Eachd (North Argyll) on 23 January 2000 was at least 350m asl. Birds are not infrequently seen in this type of habitat or even on open moorland (Argyll Database). In the latter habitat, they often feed on Heather seeds.

The noticeably larger and brighter-coloured nominate race *pyrrhula* from Northern Europe is migratory and occurs in Scotland, mainly in the Northern Isles and usually in small numbers. Until 2004 there had been sight records of

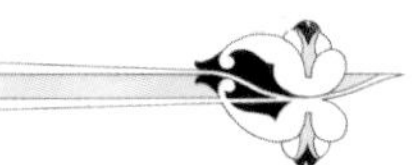

birds in Argyll probably belonging to this race, but none had been confirmed. In autumn 2004 an influx occurred in Scotland (Pennington & Meek 2006). On Tiree, a male was at Mannal on 16 October and a female was at The Manse on 16 November. More were reported on Coll, including four females at Lodge Plantation on 23 October, seven (including two males) at The Lodge on 30 October and single birds on two dates in November. A pair was reported at Creag Mhor, RSPB Loch Gruinart, on 8 November 2004. On 25 April 2005, two males and a female were sighted at the Lodge Plantation, Coll, presumably returning birds (J. Bowler & S. Wellock pers. comm.).

Paul Daw

Hawfinch

Coccothraustes coccothraustes

Vagrant.

Although Hawfinches have bred within some 40 km of the borders of Argyll (First and Second Atlases), they remain rare and irregular visitors to our area. Indeed, there are only 14 Argyll records in total, with no marked seasonal pattern. They are divided more or less equally between the mainland and islands.

The first record concerns a young male killed at the lantern at Skerryvore on 28 April 1904, the corpse being preserved in the Royal Scottish Museum (Tomison 1907, ASNH 1905:207). Another was caught there two-and-a-half years later, on 11 November 1906 (Tomison 1907: ASNH 1907:139). Following a lengthy gap, a pair was seen at Dunstaffnage in winter 1945; according to B&R, this was at the time the only record from the western Scottish mainland north of Dunbartonshire. Between 1953 and 2005, there were 11 further Argyll records (Table).

Some of the above records were associated with more widespread influxes. The 1985 Loch Awe bird, for example, occurred at the same time as birds in Shetland, Orkney and Wick. Similarly, there was a widespread arrival of migrant Hawfinches in Scotland in mid-April 2000 (Birding Scotland 3:144).

Tristan ap Rheinallt

Date	Location	Comment	Reference
4 June 1953	Glendaruel	Male	SN 69:43
August 1959	Lochgilphead	One	SB 1:206
25 October 1959	Kennovay (Tiree)	One, dead	SB 1:154
5 September 1976	Saddell (Kintyre)	One	SB 10:114
7 April 1985	Ardanaiseig, Loch Awe	One	ABR 3:59
23 February 1986	Gruinart (Islay)	Four	SB 14:254
28 to 31 March 1988	Arinagour (Coll)	One, probably present for several days prior to 28th	ABR 5:30
22 to 24 April 2000	Achnacreebeag, North Connel	Male	ABR 17:102
19 January 2004	Benderloch (North Argyll)	Adult male	Argyll Database
12 May 2004	Heylipol (Tiree)	Adult eating sunflower seeds at bird table	Argyll Database
28 to 29 October 2005	Oban	In a garden	Argyll Database

Records of Hawfinches in Argyll, 1953-2005.

American Redstart

Setophaga ruticilla

Vagrant.

A female or first-winter bird was at Portnahaven on Islay on 1 November 1982 (BB 76:525). This was the second British record of this attractive North American vagrant and the only Scottish record to date.

Full details were published by Dawson & ap Rheinallt (2001). The bird was first seen in their garden by local residents Mr and Mrs Donald MacLeod, who thought that it might be an escape. Jane Dawson, when she arrived in response to their telephone call, did not recognise the bird but suspected that it might be a transatlantic vagrant. It was extremely tame but very active, feeding in bushes and sometimes descending to the lawn and pathway. It spent most of the day in the same garden, where it was photographed. Remarkably, an apparently different individual turned up in Lincolnshire a few days later.

Tristan ap Rheinallt

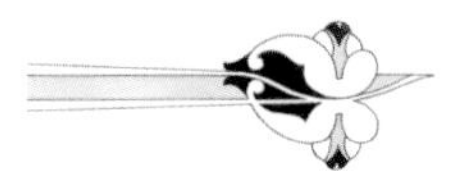

Lapland Bunting

Calcarius lapponicus

Scarce migrant, recorded most frequently in autumn.

Although it has nested in Scotland in the past, the Lapland Bunting is normally seen on migration, with most records coming from the east coast and Northern Isles. It also winters in small numbers on the east coast. Birds migrating through western Scotland in autumn are considered to come from Greenland (Thom, Migration Atlas), although strangely the race *calcaratus* that breeds in Greenland is not on the British list (Dudley *et al.* 2006). Neither H&B nor B&R provided any records of this species from Argyll, and indeed the first record was apparently not until 1974, when two were seen at Ardnacross on Mull on 5 September and two at Ardnave on Islay on 15 October (SB 8:45).

Since then the species has been recorded with increasing regularity in the county, with two records in the late 1970s, 13 in the 1980s, 12 in the 1990s, 12 in 2000-03 and 18 in 2004-spring 2007. All but ten of the 59 records have come from Islay, Tiree and south Kintyre, the exceptions being a bird found dead at Skerryvore on 2 December 1986 (SB 14:254), three records on Coll, and two each on Colonsay, Mull and Oronsay (ABR/Argyll Database).

The seasonal distribution of records shows that Lapland Buntings are almost exclusively migrants in Argyll, with more than twice as many records in autumn as in spring. There is one rather unusual summer record, of a male at Heylipol on Tiree on 18 June 1985 (ABR 3:59), and there have recently been four records in the midwinter period (4 December to 20 February). The presence of a flock at Kilchoman on Islay in autumn 1987, numbering 14 on 31 October and seven on 6 November (SBR 1987:46, ABR 5:12) and followed by sightings elsewhere on the island on 20 February and 7 March (ABR 5:30), was very unusual. This is the only flock to have been recorded in Argyll. Other than a sightings of four birds at Kilchoman on 6 April 1988 (ABR 5:30), and four at Upper Killeyan, Islay on 13 November 2004, all other records have involved between one and three birds.

Tristan ap Rheinallt

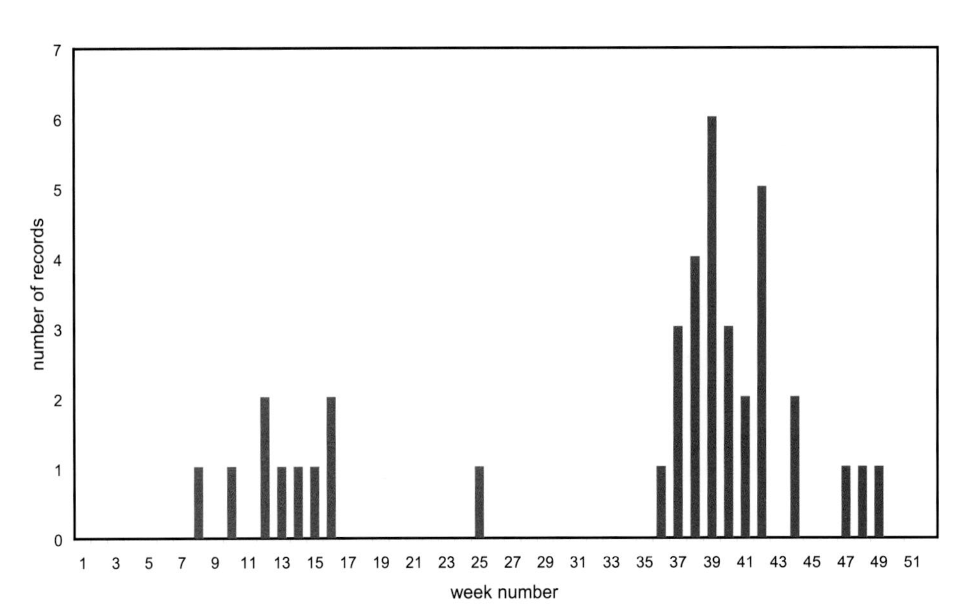

Weekly variation in Argyll records of Lapland Bunting, 1974-2003.[1]

[1]The dates of two September records are unknown.

Snow Bunting

Plectrophenax nivalis

Occurs annually in varying numbers on passage and in winter, both along the coast and in the hills. Has probably bred in North Argyll.

As a breeding species in Britain, the Snow Bunting is confined to the highest Scottish mountains. The core breeding area is the Cairngorms, with sporadic breeding elsewhere in the Highlands. It seems highly probable that Snow Buntings have bred in North Argyll, but proof seems to be lacking, even though they have certainly nested close to the border of the Argyll recording area.

Although H&B discussed breeding by this species, their records originated from Ben Nevis, which is no longer part of Argyll. B&R listed a sighting of a pair on Ben Cruachan in North Argyll on 1 July 1901, suggesting strongly that breeding occurred. However, they knew of no other relevant records. The First Atlas included no records within or even close to Argyll, although a pair was reported from one Argyll site in late May or early June 1979 (SBR 1979:44). Also, Snow Buntings were said by Thom to have been seen in suitable habitat in Argyll during the breeding season in the period 1966-75.

The Second Atlas produced confirmation of breeding

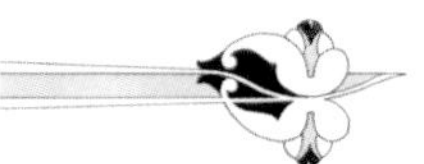

in grid square NN24 on the northern boundary of Argyll, near Loch Tulla, but the nest was apparently situated a few metres inside Highland Region (ABR). However, birds were also reported from three nearby 10-km squares, two of which were entirely within Argyll, in the Glen Kinglass and Ben Cruachan area. Within this area, a singing bird was above Glen Noe on 3 June 1989. These records were associated with a more general extension of the species' range in the western Highlands, although it is possible that this was an artefact of increased observer activity (Second Atlas). Since then, there appear to have been no published records of Snow Buntings on the high tops of Argyll during the summer months. It has been suggested that the small Scottish population is at risk from climatic amelioration (Migration Atlas), and it may be that breeding outside the core area will become less frequent over time.

The Snow Bunting is much more familiar to birdwatchers in Argyll as a migrant and wintering species. Although H&B and Graham regarded it as an irregular or rare visitor, it was described by Gray as very common throughout the western counties and by B&R as very common on migration in the western islands. Its status today lies somewhere between these two extremes. There are scattered records of small numbers of birds every winter and sometimes a few larger flocks, although Argyll does not harbour the flocks of many hundreds, or even thousands, sometimes seen in the north and east of Scotland. Most birds seen are females and immatures, which are more migratory than adult males (Migration Atlas).

few records in some winter periods. Arrival dates of the first autumn migrants also vary considerably from year to year, ranging from mid-September to mid- or even late October. The earliest in recent years seem to have been singles at Saligo Bay on Islay on 15 September 1994 and at Moine Mhòr in Mid-Argyll on 15 September 1995. While most early-autumn records concern lone individuals or small numbers of birds, 20 were at Balnahard on Colonsay on 21 September 1983, and there were two flocks of 70 at Portnahaven and Kilchoman on Islay on 6 October 1985 and a flock of 52 at West Parkfergus in Kintyre on 11 October 1997. These flocks are among the largest recorded in Argyll at any season, exceeded in recent years only by 90 at Lussa Loch in Kintyre on 31 January 1975 (SBR) and around 100 at Glen Aray in Mid-Argyll on 22 March 1987.

It appears that many Snow Buntings in Argyll in autumn are passage migrants, presumably on their way to wintering grounds further south. Migration probably continues through November, very few birds remaining after this date in some years. In winter, as on migration, most records come from stubble fields, coastal grassland (including machair), sand dunes or seashore. The islands, especially Islay, account for a high proportion of records, particularly early in autumn. However, birds also occur widely on high ground, both on the islands and on the mountains of Cowal, Mid-Argyll and North Argyll. Numbers wintering at high altitude appear to be small, though no doubt there is substantial under-recording. A flock of 50 at Beinn a' Bhuiridh in North Argyll

North Argyll is at the southern edge of the Snow Bunting's breeding distribution in Europe. *Philip Snow*

The migratory habits of Snow Buntings appear to be influenced by climatic factors, with the result that there are large variations in numbers reaching the British Isles each year. This is certainly the case in Argyll, where there are very

on 8 and 9 November 1986 was exceptional.

The Winter Atlas survey has been the only attempt to date to map the distribution of wintering Snow Buntings in Argyll. During these three winters (1981-84), birds were

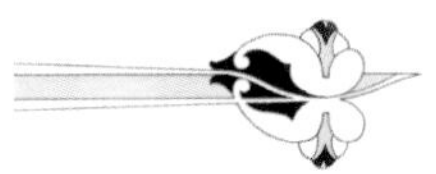

found to be rather local. They were reported from some of the major islands (Islay, Jura, Mull, Tiree) but not from others (Colonsay, Coll). On the mainland, their distribution reflected their ability to winter both in lowland coastal areas and on high ground. Most records came from the southern tip of Kintyre, the area around West Loch Tarbert, and the eastern boundary of the Argyll recording area from the head of Loch Long north to Ben Lui. Otherwise, they were found at very few locations.

Snow Buntings are known to be nomadic during the winter months (Migration Atlas). This may explain the appearance of flocks in Argyll in midwinter, as in 1997/98. The last record in 1997 was on 8 November, suggesting that the scattered sightings earlier that autumn all referred to passage migrants. However, three flocks of more than 30 birds were seen on Islay between January and March 1998, when birds also occurred on Mull, Oronsay and Tiree. More direct evidence of nomadism was given by a first-winter Snow Bunting seen at Duich Moss on Islay on 28 January 1996, only a month after it had been colour-ringed on the Norfolk coast.

There is a return passage of birds through Scotland in the spring, normally from late February or early March to the second week of May, with stragglers into June (B&R, Migration Atlas). In Argyll, the most obvious manifestation of this migration is the appearance of single birds at widely scattered locations, from sea-level to the summits of the highest hills. With one or two possible exceptions, such as the Glen Aray record above, large flocks do not appear to be involved. Indeed, the highest reported count during April to June seems to be four birds, on Beinn Narnain in Cowal on 7 May 1988. Many of the birds seen in late spring are males. Not infrequently, they remain at exactly the same location for several days. There are very few records after mid-May, but on Islay one was at Laggan Bay on 10 June 1992 and two were at Kilchoman on 22 June 1964 (SB 3:207).

Snow Buntings of two races, *insulae* and *nivalis*, are likely to occur in Argyll. The Scottish breeding population is apparently composed almost entirely of birds showing characteristics of the darker race *insulae*, whose main stronghold is in Iceland. Icelandic birds also account for the majority of wintering Snow Buntings in northern Scotland, although in Scotland as elsewhere in Britain a significant number of *nivalis* also occur. Their origin is currently unknown, but some may come from Greenland via Iceland. It also appears that *insulae* departs earlier in the spring than *nivalis* (Migration Atlas), so that migrants passing through Argyll in April and May are more likely to belong to the latter race. However, there are no relevant ringing recoveries and no published information on the occurrence of either race in Argyll.

Tristan ap Rheinallt

Yellowhammer

Emberiza citrinella

A local resident, which appears to be declining. Currently, most birds breed near the coast.

Yellowhammers are widely distributed as a breeding species on the Scottish mainland, typically in farmland. They occur in varying numbers on the Clyde Islands and Inner Hebrides, but are absent from the Outer Hebrides and Northern Isles. In recent years their range has contracted over much of western Scotland and they no longer occur in previously occupied areas of higher ground (Second Atlas). Flocks form in winter, although numbers involved have declined recently. There is some evidence of small-scale immigration in winter from breeding areas to the north (Thom).

The NSA lists Yellowhammers in the parishes of Inveraray and Killean, Kintyre. Gray described it as generally distributed throughout western Scotland, including nearly all the 'inner islands'. He also mentioned two unusually bright yellow individuals shot on Gometra, Mull. It was resident on Iona and not very numerous, according to Graham, but plentiful in the Calgary area of Mull. H&B said it was a rare straggler to Tiree, and quoted the then Duke of Argyll as saying they were decreasing rapidly around Inveraray Castle. Even at this time, agricultural changes were suggested as a possible cause of the decline.

Yellowhammers have declined across Britain since the 1970s, at the same time as winter stubbles and weedy field edges became much rarer. *David Palmar*

In the mid-20th century, B&R could still say that Yellowhammers were common birds on the Scottish mainland, breeding in every county, although not to any great altitude. They were locally distributed on Colonsay, Islay and Jura, but were occasional winter visitors in small numbers on Tiree. Although there were breeding records early in the 20th century for Coll, none were found there in the 1930s and 1940s. On Mull, they were reported as sparsely distributed in 1948, and several were seen on Lismore in 1942. B&R thought that breeding numbers fluctuated from year to year, but that after a considerable period of decline, they were on the increase. Boyd (1958) recorded two pairs on Coll in late April 1955, but said that there were no breeding or recent winter records for Tiree. Five or six pairs were breeding on Colonsay in 1939 (Jardine *et al.* 1986).

The breeding distribution shown for Argyll in the First Atlas was patchy. Probable or confirmed breeding was shown for most of Kintyre, for the western half of Cowal and for the coastal areas of Mid- and North Argyll. There were similar records for south and east Islay, north and west Jura, Scarba and much of Mull. Only probable breeding was indicated for the single occupied 10-km square on Colonsay. There were no records for Coll or Tiree. However, numbers on Colonsay recovered and five pairs were recorded breeding in 1983 (Jardine *et al.* 1986).

The Winter Atlas showed Yellowhammers absent from most of Mid-Argyll and Cowal, from the southern half of Mull and from much of Jura. Although this may be due in part to lack of coverage, it may have been an early indication of range contraction.

In 1985, Yellowhammers occurred occasionally in open woodland, particularly in young trees, and were found in eight of 38 broadleaf woodlands surveyed in Mid- and North Argyll (Averis & Martin 1985).

By the time of the Second Atlas, range contraction had led to noticeable losses in much of Cowal and parts of Mid-Argyll. Yellowhammers were still breeding in much of Kintyre and on Colonsay, Islay and Jura. On Mull, there were additional records for three coastal 10-km squares. Breeding was shown for two squares that cover most of Tiree, but, as there had been no other published records of Yellowhammers on Tiree since the early 20th century, this was almost certainly an error. The species was found breeding in 46% of 10-km squares in the county, but the abundance map shows they occurred at very low densities, apart from the northern half of Jura where they were more plentiful.

None of the recent systematic surveys have adequately covered the habitat in which Yellowhammers now occur in Argyll. Although one territory was found in the first year (1990) of the Taynish CBC, none have been recorded there since. Neither were they found in any of the 14 randomly selected 1-km squares (containing mainly coniferous woodland) surveyed in 2000 (Wilson & Fuller 2001, P. Daw unpubl. data) or in any of the 16 broadleaved woods censused in 2003 (Amar *et al.* 2006, P. Daw unpubl. data). They were recorded regularly in only one 1-km square visited in Argyll for the BBS.

However, Yellowhammers were found during surveys of other species. During the Peregrine Survey in 2002, birds were located quite frequently at remote coastal sites on Jura and Mull. At least 10 singing males were located in the vicinity of Peregrine eyries on Mull in June 2002. The habitat comprised small crags with low scrubby vegetation, bracken and heather with isolated small trees. Yellowhammers occurred in similar haunts on Islay where 14 were found at 12 coastal sites north of Gortantaoid Point on 16 May 1999.

Since the Second Atlas, singing males have been reported during the breeding season from Scarba, from several sites on Islay, from The Laggan, Kintyre (where numbers have declined in recent years), and from the Connel/Oban/Kerrera/Seil Island and Carsaig/Tayvallich areas of Mid-Argyll. Yellowhammers seem to be relatively numerous on Mull with singing males still reported regularly from many locations, chiefly coastal. There have been very few recent breeding season records from Cowal or North Argyll, none from Gigha and no records from Colonsay (where at least seven males were found in 1989) since 2000. Apart from a single male reported at Acha Mill on 27 April 2004, there have been no recent records from Coll. No Yellowhammers have been seen on Tiree since the early 20th century (Argyll Database). A widespread decline has been noted elsewhere in upland Britain (Henderson *et al.* 2004).

In the past, quite large flocks were noted in some winters, for example *c.*80 at Sunipol, Mull, in November 1981 and 40 at a roost at Aros Moss, Kintyre, in February 1994. Although no flock as large as this has been reported recently, groups of 20 or so birds may still be found at favoured locations. At Loch Skerrols, Islay, 28 were seen in a stubble field in February 2001, 23 were at Lerags, Mid-Argyll, in April 2001 and up to 20 in a garden at Penmore, Mull, in January 2003 (ABR, Argyll Database).

Apart from a locally ringed bird recovered at Ford, Loch Ederline, in 1981-1982, the only recovery is of an adult male ringed at Tobermory in January 1978 and controlled at Ederline in April 1979 (63km).

Paul Daw

Cirl Bunting

Emberiza cirlus

Vagrant.

Although it breeds in the UK, the Cirl Bunting is perhaps one of the most unlikely species to feature on the Argyll list. The sole record concerns a pair seen at St Catherine's on Loch Fyne on 6 June 1920, with the male seen again on 10 June (SN 1921:107). The observer, Walter Stewart, was a well-

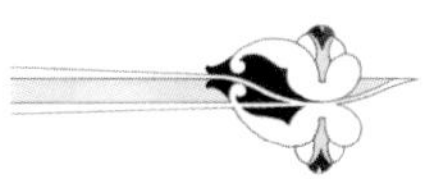

known ornithologist in his day and published full details of the sighting (Stewart 1920):

"On June 6th, 1920, at St. Catherines, Upper Loch Fyne, Argyll, I had the good fortune to see a pair of Cirl Buntings (*Emberiza cirlus*). They both rose from a bramble-covered bank between the road and shore, and alighted on the other side of the road under some large trees, chestnut and lime. I had ample time and opportunity to examine them minutely with binoculars at about fifteen yards' distance. The greenish-coloured head and black marking on the throat rendered the male bird very conspicuous, compared with the more sombre-coloured female. The male bird also hopped about in a lively manner, while the female was inclined to squat on the ground. ...However, on the 10th I again saw the male a little bit farther along, hopping about on the road, but this time it seemed much more shy and soon flew up amongst the high branches of a chestnut tree... I may remark that I had previously seen Cirl Buntings in Dorsetshire. It may seem very improbable to find the Cirl Bunting so far to the north, but it was quite impossible to mistake the bird at such close range."

With B&R casting doubt on all earlier records, this became the first acceptable occurrence of Cirl Bunting in Scotland. It was followed soon afterwards by a sighting of two birds at Eglington (Ayrshire) on 8 May 1928 and one trapped at Parkhill (Angus) on 27 November the same year. A further six records followed to the end of 2001, all of these coming from recognised migration sites (Andrews & Naylor 2002).

Not all authors have been inclined to accept the Argyll record: McWilliam considered that it could not be "regarded as beyond the possibility of doubt." However, a recent SBRC review concluded that the record should stand (R. Forrester pers. comm.). Certainly, it predates the substantial contraction that has occurred in the species' British breeding range since the 1930s. It is also noteworthy that breeding was recorded in Cumbria and Lancashire in the first half of the 20th century, although the Lancashire records were later rejected (A. Murray pers. comm.).

Tristan ap Rheinallt

Rustic Bunting

Emberiza rustica

Vagrant.

This northern European species has been recorded twice in Argyll, both times in spring. A male was at Easter Ellister on Islay on 23 May 1980 (BB 74:492, ABR 1980:74) and another was at Hynish on Tiree on 4 June 1987 (BB 81:591). Most Scottish records come from the Northern Isles, but this species differs from several other rare buntings in that spring records normally outnumber autumn records.

Tristan ap Rheinallt

Little Bunting

Emberiza pusilla

Vagrant.

A first-winter bird was found dead at Skerryvore Lighthouse on or around 27 September 1985 (BB 79:582). This is the only Argyll record of a northern European and Siberian species that occurs regularly in autumn in the Northern Isles but is scarce elsewhere in Scotland.

Tristan ap Rheinallt

Yellow-Breasted Bunting

Emberiza aureola

Vagrant.

The only Argyll record of this northern European and Siberian species, which is an annual autumn visitor to the Northern Isles, involves a female or immature seen at Kenovay on Tiree on 5 September 1981. The record was initially rejected by BBRC (BB 75:532) but later accepted (BB 78:585).

Tristan ap Rheinallt

Reed Bunting

Emberiza schoeniclus

This is a local resident that breeds in dense, tall vegetation growing in marshy areas or by water, and occasionally in drier habitats such as young conifer plantations. It is nowhere abundant in winter but flocks of up to 100 birds occur in moist habitats or on stubble and other seed-rich farmland.

Although Graham did not mention this species during his time on Iona, Gray described the "Black-headed Bunting" as a resident of many parts of the mainland of west Scotland and some of the inner islands. H&B found it "not rare, but generally local in summer" and recorded it breeding "not numerously" near Ledaig and Culcherran mosses in North Argyll; they also reported it on Jura. B&R recorded it from Islay, Jura, Gigha, Colonsay, Coll, Iona and Mull.

The spread to breed in drier habitats, such as farmland and young conifer plantations, was recognised as early as the 1930s and may have been caused by the drainage of wetlands (Thom). The distribution map in the First Atlas showed Reed Buntings breeding in nearly all 10-km squares of the British Isles, the largest gaps being in the north-west of Scotland. In Argyll, most squares in Coll, Tiree, Islay, Kintyre and the south of Jura were occupied, but there were empty areas in the mountainous parts of Mid-Argyll, Cowal, the north of Jura and the centre and south of Mull.

Work in the early 1980s found that numbers in Britain had more than halved since about 1970. This decrease occurred at the same time as declines of Linnet and Tree Sparrow, probably all for the same reason - destruction by herbicides of farmland "weeds" on which these seed-eaters depend (Second Atlas). In areas such as Argyll, overgrazing by multitudes of free-ranging sheep and increasing numbers of wild deer may have had a similar destructive effect on the flora and hence on this suite of bird species. At about the same time Reed Buntings began feeding in gardens in winter, a habit that has recently been observed on both Tiree and Coll (J. Bowler pers. comm.).

Despite these losses, work for the Second Atlas recorded breeding in 56% of 10-km squares in the county. Densities were highest on Islay, slightly lower on Coll, Tiree and in parts of Jura, Kintyre, Mid-Argyll and Cowal, and much lower in North Argyll, Mull and Colonsay. During BBS work in the years 1995-2001, Reed Buntings were found in 1-km squares as follows: 3/17, 3/21, 2/16, 4/16, 2/15, 2/12 and 2/6 (Argyll Database), and also in 3/14 Countryside 2000 squares (ABR).

Reed Buntings breed regularly in all ten areas of the county. The more important counts have included the following. On Islay, 72 pairs were counted in a survey of the Rinns in 1994, and at the RSPB's Loch Gruinart Reserve, 65 pairs were counted in 1997, 30 pairs in 2002 and 59 pairs in 2003. On Tiree, an estimated 20-25 pairs bred in 1986, 30 pairs in 1987, at least ten pairs in 1999, and 15-20 pairs in 2003. On Coll, an estimated 15 pairs bred in 1987,12-15 pairs in 1990 and 10-20 pairs in 2003; and on the RSPB's Coll Reserve, four pairs bred in 1996, two pairs in 1999 and one pair in 2001. On Colonsay/Oronsay during 1986-2003, numbers varied between a minimum of six pairs in 1991 and a maximum of 15 pairs in 1996, with a recent run of higher-than-usual counts of 10, 12, 11, 13 and 17 pairs in 2000-2004. On Sanda Islands, the average for 1997-2003 was 3.9 pairs, varying between two pairs in 1999 and six pairs in 2001. In the Taynish CBC the 1990-2000 average was two pairs, varying between one pair in 2000 and 2001 and six pairs in 1992 (ABR, Argyll Database).

Reed Buntings have not declined in Argyll to the same extent as other seed-eating birds. *Philip Kirkham*

Ringing has shown that almost all Reed Buntings that breed in Britain also winter there, perhaps moving 100km from their breeding area but usually much smaller distances. Less than 1% move abroad, mainly to northern France. In autumn, birds are found on passage at places such as Fair Isle and along the east coast of Britain. The British population is joined in winter by small numbers of migrants, mostly from Scandinavia, Finland, Holland and Germany. Most of these winter in the south and east of Britain. There is little evidence that they reach Argyll but, as so few are ringed or recovered here, it is not surprising that the migration maps show no points at all in west Scotland (Migration Atlas).

Reed Buntings become much less widely distributed in winter as they leave areas such as north-west Scotland, the Lake District and north Wales. During work for the Winter Atlas, they were found to be absent from most of Mull, Jura, Colonsay, Cowal, Mid-Argyll and North Argyll. They were present in small numbers on Coll and Tiree, but the largest numbers were on parts of Kintyre and Islay. Here the small winter flocks, sometimes with finches and Yellowhammers, feed on seed-rich farmland during the day and spend the night in communal roosts, often in reedbeds.

Reed Buntings are strongly affected by temperature, especially by winter cold. In countries where the mean January temperature is below zero centigrade, the entire population leaves for the winter; but in countries such as Britain and Ireland where this temperature exceeds 5°C, almost all are resident. For reasons not fully understood, the sex ratio is unequal in winter and varies from 1.5 male per female in warm winters to 3.0 in cold winters. Numbers fall noticeably after long cold winters, such as those of 1962-63 and 1981-82, but recover after runs of good breeding seasons and mild winters.

These characteristic year-to-year changes in abundance are illustrated by winter records from well-counted sites on Islay and Kintyre. The largest flocks on record in Argyll seem to be 100 on 23 January 1995 and 80 on 25 January 1993, both at Loch Gruinart, and 80 on 4 January 1997 at Portnahaven (Islay). However, in poor years the numbers wintering at Loch Gruinart peak at 20-40 or even fewer. Smaller winter flocks are widespread locally in the county and in good winters, such as that of 1999-2000, flocks in double figures are regular at several other sites, notably Tayinloan, Kames Golf Course and the stubble fields of Tiree and Coll (ABR, Argyll Database).

Clive Craik

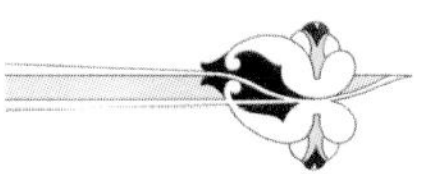

Black-headed Bunting

Emberiza melanocephala

Vagrant.

Although this species breeds in south-east Europe and south-west Asia, Scotland accounts for a large proportion of British records. In the past, many of these records were thought to refer to escaped cage-birds, but nowadays most Black-headed Buntings are regarded as genuine vagrants. Eight birds have been seen in Argyll, their arrival dates varying between 27 May and 21 June. Reflecting the overall pattern in Scotland and the UK, all but one were males (Table). These eight individuals represent nearly one in three of all Scottish records away from the Northern Isles, where most birds occur. The Highland area accounts for another ten records and the Outer Hebrides for four (to the end of 2003), underlining the northern and western distribution of the species.

Tristan ap Rheinallt

All records of Black-headed Buntings in Argyll to 2006.

Date	Location	Comment	Reference
11 Jun 1968	Ardnave (Islay)		BB 62:488
21 Jun 1974	Seil		BB 68:331
27 - 30 May 1989	Kilmore, near Oban		BB 83:492
7 Jun - 4 Jul 1993	Bruichladdich (Islay)		BB 87:566
3 - 8 Jun 1999	Kirkapol (Tiree)		BB 93:564
8 Jun 2000	Colonsay	Female	SBR 2001:130, ABR 18:105[1]
15 Jun 2000	North Connel		BB 94:500
12 June 2005	Kiloran (Colonsay)	Male	BB 100:102

[1]Both references give the year incorrectly as 2001.

Corn Bunting

Emberiza calandra

Recently extinct as a breeding bird in Argyll, but there are occasional records of wandering birds.

The Corn Bunting in Scotland has been in long-term decline (BS3). It is typically associated with arable farmland and machair on the islands. Since its extinction on Tiree in the late 1990s, the only surviving island populations in Scotland are on the southern Outer Hebrides, and these are in decline. The only mainland populations of any size are in Fife, north-east Scotland and Tayside, where numbers are also falling (BS3). Elsewhere, there are a few in Dumfries & Galloway and a lone singing male in the Borders. Occasional wandering birds turn up away from breeding areas.

In the 19th century this species was often known as the 'Common Bunting' and Gray said it was nowhere more plentiful than in Argyll, Ayrshire and Wigtownshire, although in the NSA it is mentioned only in the parish of Inveraray. According to Graham it was abundant in winter in the stockyards of Iona and relatively numerous in summer. It was common on Tiree, especially in the northwest of the island, but more local on the mainland (H&B).

A decline in numbers had already been noticed by the mid-20th century. In the 1930s it was no longer found in Knapdale, but was still relatively common on Coll and Tiree. By the late 1940s it had disappeared from Iona and Mull. It was considered to be a summer visitor to nesting areas, dispersing in autumn and becoming more gregarious during winter (B&R). In 1955, there were thought to be more than 50 singing birds on Tiree in June-July, and up to four on Coll (Boyd 1958). On Islay there have been no breeding records since the 1940s, although there were sporadic records of birds until the 1980s (Elliott 1989). The last breeding record for Colonsay/Oronsay was a pair near the Priory on Oronsay in 1974 (Jardine *et al.* 1986).

By the time of the First Atlas, Corn Buntings had virtually disappeared from the western mainland of Scotland and from most of the Inner Hebrides. In Argyll, there was still a breeding population on Tiree and probable breeding was indicated in two 10-km squares on Coll. Probable breeding was also shown for the 10-km square covering the north of Gigha, but there was no other information to support this, although there was anecdotal evidence of singing birds until at least the mid-1970s (V. Tulloch pers comm.).

On Tiree, a census in 1971 found 95 singing males, and counts in 1973-1977 found similar numbers, but only 60 were located in early July 1979. A crash seems to have occurred between 1979 and 1983, when only an estimated 19 birds could be found. In the years following, a slight recovery occurred and a census in 1987 located 34 singing males (Cadbury 1989). The possibility of a climatic factor being involved in the suddenness of the decline after 1979 was examined, but no evidence emerged to support this theory (Cadbury 1989). A survey in 1989 revealed a further drop in numbers with only 19 pairs located (ABR 6:57). On Coll, there were fewer data although breeding was confirmed there in 1971 (Cadbury 1989). The three singing males found between Arnabost and Sorisdale in June 1984 appear to have been the last recorded on the island (ABR 2:51).

The Second Atlas showed a further serious contraction in range in Scotland, with breeding occurring in Argyll only on Tiree, although there was still a record from Gigha. Suggested reasons for this decline are diminished seed supplies in winter due to changing agricultural practices and a reduction in invertebrate numbers in summer due to pesticide use.

Numbers on Tiree continued to decline rapidly in the 1990s. A comprehensive survey in June 1995 found only 6-10 territories and in 1996 only a single male was found, at Ruaig. This may have been the only Corn Bunting on the island, as several of the 1995 territories were unoccupied. The only bird seen during the 1997 breeding season was also at Ruaig, but a single bird was seen elsewhere on the island later in the year. There were records of single birds at several sites on Tiree between February and May 1998, but these were all thought to be the same individual. The last record of a singing bird on Tiree was at the Ruaig/Salum crossroads on 15 and 20 June 1999. A single bird on 4 March 2000 could have been on passage and was, at the time of writing (2006), the last sighting on Tiree (ABR).

In memoriam: the Corn Bunting now appears to be extinct in Argyll. *Philip Kirkham*

That very small numbers do occur on passage or as winter visitors is demonstrated by a series of winter records on Islay between 1985 and 1993 and by odd birds seen in spring and autumn on Mull and in the Tayinloan/Gigha area. In 2001, a singing male was found on Gigha on 16 July, which could have been an early migrant (ABR).

In 2002, for the first time since regular recording began, there were no reports of Corn Buntings in Argyll. However, in 2003 a single bird was seen several times during January and February feeding on arable land at Smaull, Islay, and another individual was seen feeding on spilt grain at the farm on Oronsay for several days in early January (Argyll Database). Despite these occasional wanderers, the chances of this undramatic, rather charming bird re-establishing itself as a breeding species in Argyll must be considered slim.

Paul Daw

Brown-headed Cowbird

Molothrus ater

Vagrant

A male Brown-headed Cowbird was at Ardnave Point on Islay on 24 April 1988 (BB 86:536). As the first and only British record of this North American species, and the second for the Western Palearctic following a female found dead in Norway in 1987, it is one of Argyll's most notable rarities.

Full details were published by the finder (McKay 1994). The bird was seen in an area of heavily grazed dune pasture, where it associated closely with grazing cattle. It was watched for some 30 minutes at close range as it fed on insects and seeds, but unfortunately it disappeared shortly afterwards. Although this species is a relatively short-distance migrant, the record was accepted into Category A of the British and Irish list on the basis that natural occurrence was more likely than escape from captivity.

Tristan ap Rheinallt

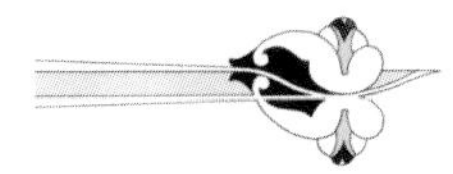

Appendix 1: Status of Argyll bird species

Gaelic names of Argyll birds are provided where suitable names exist. Thanks are due to Tristan ap Rheinallt who has consulted the appropriate authorities to ensure that these are correct.

The races of Greater and Lesser Canada Goose ($) have been claimed many times on Islay but are not, as yet, officially accepted by BOURC.

The non-native races of Common Chiffchaff and Willow Warbler (#) have been claimed many times in Argyll but there is still some doubt as to how reliably they may be identified in the field - see text.

'Conservation status' refers to the lists contained in Gregory *et al.* 2002.

'NBAP species' refers to the list of UK National Biodiversity Action Plan species, as updated in 2007.

Paul Daw

Argyll species number	BTO code	Euring number	*British Birds* vernacular name	Scientific name	Gaelic Name	BOURC status category	Conservation status	NBAP species
0001.0	MS	0152.0	Mute Swan	*Cygnus olor*	Eala	AC2		
0002.0		0152.1	Black Swan	*Cygnus atratus*		E*		
0003.0	BS	0153.0	Bewick's Swan	*Cygnus columbianus*	Eala-bheag	A	Amber list	
0004.0	WS	0154.0	Whooper Swan	*Cygnus cygnus*	Eala-fhiadhaich	AE*	Amber list	
0005.0	BE	0157.0	Bean Goose	*Anser fabalis*	Muir-ghèadh	AE	Amber list	
0006.0	PG	0158.0	Pink-footed Goose	*Anser brachyrhynchus*	Gèadh-gorm	AE*	Amber list	
0007.0	EW	0159.1	European White-fronted Goose	*Anser albifrons albifrons*	Gèadh-bhlàr	A	Amber list	
0007.1	NW	0159.2	Greenland White-fronted Goose	*Anser albifrons flavirostris*	Gèadh-bhlàr	AE*	Amber list	yes
0009.0	LC	0160.0	Lesser White-fronted Goose	*Anser erythropus*	Gèadh-bhlàr-beag	A		
0010.0	GJ	0161.0	Greylag Goose	*Anser anser*	Gèadh-glas	AC2C4E*	Amber list	
0011.0	HD	0162.0	Bar-headed Goose	*Anser indicus*		E*		
0012.0	SJ	0163.0	Snow Goose	*Anser caerulescens*	Gèadh-bàn	AC2E*		
0013.0	RJ	0164.0	Ross's Goose	*Anser rossi*		E		
0014.0	EM	0165.0	Emperor Goose	*Anser canagicus*		E*		
0015.0	CG	0166.0	Greater Canada Goose	*Branta canadensis*	Gèadh-dubh (Canada Goose)	C2E*		
0015.1	CGP	0166.4	Greater Canada Goose race *parvipes*	*Branta canadensis parvipes*		$		
0016.0	CG	0166.1	Lesser Canada Goose race *minima* 'Cackling'	*Branta hutchinsii minima*		$		
0016.1	CGH	0166.2	Lesser Canada Goose race *hutchinsii* 'Richardson's'	*Branta hutchinsii hutchinsii*		$		
0017.0	BY	0167.0	Barnacle Goose	*Branta leucopsis*	Cathan	AC2E*	Amber list	
0018.0	PB	0168.2	Brent Goose (Pale-bellied)	*Branta bernicla hrota*	Gèadh-got	A	Amber list	
0018.1	DB	0168.1	Brent Goose (Dark-bellied)	*Branta bernicla bernicla*	Gèadh-got	A	Amber list	yes
0018.2	BB	0168.3	Brent Goose (Black Brant)	*Branta bernicla nigricans*		A		
0019.0	EB	0169.0	Red-breasted Goose	*Branta ruficollis*		AE		
0020.0	UD	0171.0	Ruddy Shelduck	*Tadorna ferruginea*		BDE*		
0021.0	SU	0173.0	Common Shelduck	*Tadorna tadorna*	Crà-ghèadh	A	Amber list	
0022.0	MY	0174.1	Muscovy Duck	*Cairina moschata*		E*		
0023.0	MN	0178.0	Mandarin Duck	*Aix galericulata*		C1E*		
0024.0	DC	0177.0	Wood Duck	*Aix sponsa*		E*		
0025.0	WN	0179.0	Eurasian Wigeon	*Anas penelope*	Glas-lach	AE*	Amber list	
0026.0	AW	0180.0	American Wigeon	*Anas americana*		AE		
0027.0	GA	0182.0	Gadwall	*Anas strepera*	Lach-ghlas	AC2	Amber list	
0028.0	T	0184.0	EurasianTeal	*Anas crecca*	Crann-lach	A	Amber list	
0029.0	TA	0184.1	Green-winged Teal	*Anas carolinensis*		A		
0030.0	MA	0186.0	Mallard	*Anas platyrhynchos*	Lach-riabhach	AC2C4E*		
0031.0	BD	0187.0	Black Duck	*Anas rubripes*		A		
0032.0	PT	0189.0	Pintail	*Anas acuta*	Lach-stiùireach	AE	Amber list	
0033.0	GY	0191.0	Garganey	*Anas querquedula*		A	Amber list	
0034.0	TB	0192.0	Blue-winged Teal	*Anas discors*		AE		
0035.0		0193.0	Cinnamon Teal	*Anas cyanoptera*		E*		
0036.0	SV	0194.0	Shoveler	*Anas clypeata*	Lach-a'-ghuib-leathainn	A	Amber list	
0037.0	RQ	0196.0	Red-crested Pochard	*Netta rufina*		AC2E*		
0038.0	PO	0198.0	Common Pochard	*Aythya ferina*	Lach-mhàsach	AE*	Amber list	
0039.0	NG	0200.0	Ring-necked Duck	*Aythya collaris*		A		
0040.0	FD	0202.0	Ferruginous Duck	*Aythya nyroca*		AE		

Argyll species number	BTO code	Euring number	*British Birds* vernacular name	Scientific name	Gaelic Name	BOURC status category	Conservation status	NBAP species
0041.0	TU	0203.0	Tufted Duck	*Aythya fuligula*	Lach-thopach	A		
0042.0	SP	0204.0	Greater Scaup	*Aythya marila*	Lach-mhara	A	Amber list	yes
0043.0	AY	0205.0	Lesser Scaup	*Aythya affinis*		A		
0044.0	E	0206.0	Common Eider	*Somateria mollissima*	Lach-Lochlannach	A	Amber list	
0045.0	KE	0207.0	King Eider	*Somateria spectabilis*		A		
0046.0	HQ	0211.0	Harlequin Duck	*Histrionicus histrionicus*		A		
0047.0	LN	0212.0	Long-tailed Duck	*Clangula hyemalis*	Eun-buchainn	A	Amber list	
0048.0	CX	0213.0	Common Scoter	*Melanitta nigra*	Lach-bheag-dhubh	A	Red list	yes
0049.0	FS	0214.0	Surf Scoter	*Melanitta perspicillata*		A		
0050.0	VS	0215.0	Velvet Scoter	*Melanitta fusca*	Lach-dhubh	A	Amber list	
0051.0	GN	0218.0	Common Goldeneye	*Bucephala clangula*	Lach-bhreac	A	Amber list	
0052.0	SY	0220.0	Smew	*Mergus albellus*	Sìolta-bhreac	A		
0053.0	RM	0221.0	Red-breasted Merganser	*Mergus serrator*	Sìolta-dhearg	A		
0054.0	GD	0223.0	Goosander	*Mergus merganser*	Sìolta	A		
0055.0	RY	0225.0	Ruddy Duck	*Oxyura jamaicensis*		C1E*		
0056.0	RG	0329.0	Red (Willow) Grouse	*Lagopus lagopus scotica*	Coileach-fraoich	A	Amber list	yes
0057.0	PM	0330.0	Ptarmigan	*Lagopus muta*	Tàrmachan	A		
0058.0	BK	0332.0	Black Grouse	*Tetrao tetrix*	Caoileach-dubh	AE	Red list	yes
0059.0	CP	0335.0	Capercaillie	*Tetrao urogallus*	Capall-coille	BC3	Red list	yes
0060.0	RL	0358.0	Red-legged Partridge	*Alectoris rufa*	Cearc-thomain-dhearg-chasach	C1E*		
0061.0	P	0367.0	Grey Partridge	*Perdix perdix*	Cearc-thomain	AC2E	Red list	yes
0062.0	Q	0370.0	Common Quail	*Coturnix coturnix*	Gearradh-gort	A	Red list	
0062.1		0393.0	Reeve's Pheasant	*Syrmaticus reevesii*		E*		
0063.0	PH	0394.0	Common Pheasant	*Phasianus colchicus*	Easag	C1E*		
0064.0	GF	0396.0	Golden Pheasant	*Chrysolophus pictus*		C1E*		
0065.0		0399.1	Indian Peafowl	*Pavo cristatus*		E		
0066.0	RH	0002.0	Red-throated Diver	*Gavia stellata*	Learga-ruadh	A	Amber list	
0067.0	BV	0003.0	Black-throated Diver	*Gavia arctica*	Learga-dhubh	A	Amber list	yes
0068.0	ND	0004.0	Great Northern Diver	*Gavia immer*	Muir-bhuachaill	A	Amber list	
0069.0	WV	0005.0	White-billed Diver	*Gavia adamsii*	Learga-bhlàr	A		
0070.0	PJ	0006.0	Pied-billed Grebe	*Podilymbus podiceps*		A		
0071.0	LG	0007.0	Little Grebe	*Tachybaptus ruficollis*	Spàg-ri-tòn	A		
0072.0	GG	0009.0	Great Crested Grebe	*Podiceps cristatus*	Gobhlachan-laparan	A		
0073.0	RX	0010.0	Red-necked Grebe	*Podiceps grisegena*	Gobhlachan-ruadh	A	Amber list	
0074.0	SZ	0011.0	Slavonian Grebe	*Podiceps auritus*	Gobhlachan-mara	A	Amber list	
0075.0	BN	0012.0	Black-necked Grebe	*Podiceps nigricollis*	Gobhlachan-dubh	A	Amber list	
0076.0	F	0020.0	Fulmar	*Fulmarus glacialis*	Eun-crom	A	Amber list	
0077.0	CQ	0036.0	Cory's Shearwater	*Calonectris diomedea*		A		
0078.0	GQ	0040.0	Great Shearwater	*Puffinus gravis*	Fachach-mòr	A		
0079.0	OT	0043.0	Sooty Shearwater	*Puffinus griseus*	Fachach-dubh	A		
0080.0	MX	0046.0	Manx Shearwater	*Puffinus puffinus*	Fachach-bàn	A	Amber list	
0081.0	BM	0046.3	Balearic Shearwater	*Puffinus mauretanicus*		A		yes
0082.0		0048.0	North Atlantic Little Shearwater	*Puffinus baroli*		A		
0083.0		0050.0	Wilson's Storm-petrel	*Oceanites oceanicus*		A		
0084.0		0051.0	White-faced Storm-petrel	*Pelagodroma marina*		B		
0085.0	TM	0052.0	European Storm-petrel	*Hydrobates pelagicus*	Pàraig	A	Amber list	
0086.0	TL	0055.0	Leach's Storm-petrel	*Oceanodroma leucorhoa*	Gobhlan-mara	A	Amber list	
0087.0	GX	0071.0	Northern Gannet	*Morus bassanus*	Sùlaire	A	Amber list	
0088.0	CA	0072.0	Great Cormorant	*Phalacrocorax carbo*	Sgarbh	A	Amber list	
0089.0	SA	0080.0	Shag	*Phalacrocorax aristotelis*	Sgarbh-an-sgumain	A	Amber list	
0090.0		0093.1	Ascension Frigatebird	*Fregata aquila*		A		
0091.0	BI	0095.0	Eurasian Bittern	*Botaurus stellaris*	Corra-ghràin	A	Red list	yes
0092.0	AM	0096.0	American Bittern	*Botaurus lentiginosus*		A		
0093.0	NT	0104.0	Night Heron	*Nycticorax nycticorax*		AE*		
0094.0		0115.0	Snowy Egret	*Egretta thula*		A		
0095.0	ET	0119.0	Little Egret	*Egretta garzetta*	Corra-gheal-bheag	A	Amber list	
0096.0	HW	0121.0	Great White Egret	*Ardea alba*	Corra-bhàn-mhòr	A		
0097.0	H	0122.0	Grey Heron	*Ardea cinerea*	Corra-ghritheach	A		
0098.0	OR	0134.0	White Stork	*Ciconia ciconia*		AE		
0099.0	IB	0136.0	Glossy Ibis	*Plegadis falcinellus*		AE		
0100.0	NB	0144.0	Eurasian Spoonbill	*Platalea leucorodia*		A	Amber list	
0101.0	HZ	0231.0	Honey Buzzard	*Pernis apivorus*		A	Amber list	
0102.0	KB	0238.0	Black Kite	*Milvus migrans*		A		
0103.0	KT	0239.0	Red Kite	*Milvus milvus*	Clamhan-gobhlach	AC3	Amber list	
0104.0	WE	0243.0	White-tailed Eagle	*Haliaeetus albicilla*	Iolaire-mhara	AC3E	Red list	
0105.0	MR	0260.0	Marsh Harrier	*Circus aeruginosus*	Clamhan-lòin	A	Amber list	

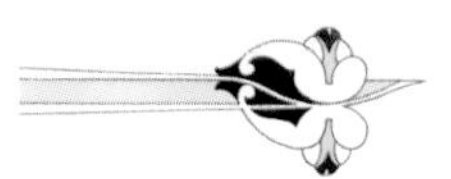

Argyll species number	BTO code	Euring number	*British Birds* vernacular name	Scientific name	Gaelic Name	BOURC status category	Conservation status	NBAP species
0106.0	HH	0261.0	Hen Harrier	*Circus cyaneus*	Brèid-air-tòin	A	Red list	
0107.0	GI	0267.0	Northern Goshawk	*Accipiter gentilis*	Glas-sheabhag	AC3E*		
0108.0	SH	0269.0	Eurasian Sparrowhawk	*Accipiter nisus*	Speireag	A		
0109.0	BZ	0287.0	Common Buzzard	*Buteo buteo*	Clamhan	AE*		
0110.0	RF	0290.0	Rough-legged Buzzard	*Buteo lagopus*	Bleidir-molach	A		
0111.0	EA	0296.0	Golden Eagle	*Aquila chrysaetos*	Iolaire	A	Amber list	
0112.0	OP	0301.0	Osprey	*Pandion haliaetus*	Iolaire-iasgaich	AE*	Amber list	
0113.0	K	0304.0	Common Kestrel	*Falco tinnunculus*	Clamhan-ruadh	A	Amber list	
0114.0	FV	0307.0	Red-footed Falcon	*Falco vespertinus*		A		
0115.0	ML	0309.0	Merlin	*Falco columbarius*	Mèirneal	A	Amber list	
0116.0	HY	0310.0	Hobby	*Falco subbuteo*	Gormag	A		
0117.0	YF	0318.0	Gyr Falcon	*Falco rusticolus*	Seabhag-mhòr-na-seilg	AE		
0118.0	PE	0320.0	Peregrine Falcon	*Falco peregrinus*	Seabhag	AE	Amber list	
0119.0	WA	0407.0	Water Rail	*Rallus aquaticus*	Snagan-allt	A	Amber list	
0120.0	AK	0408.0	Spotted Crake	*Porzana porzana*	Traon-breac	A	Amber list	
0121.0		0409.0	Sora	*Porzana carolina*		A		
0122.0	JC	0410.0	Little Crake	*Porzana parva*		A		
0123.0	CE	0421.0	Corn Crake	*Crex crex*	Traon	A	Red list	yes
0124.0	MH	0424.0	Moorhen	*Gallinula chloropus*	Cearc-uisge	A		
0125.0	CO	0429.0	Common Coot	*Fulica atra*	Lach-a'-bhlàir	A		
0126.0	AN	0433.0	Common Crane	*Grus grus*		A	Amber list	
0127.0	OC	0450.0	Oystercatcher	*Haematopus ostralegus*	Gille-Brìghde	A	Amber list	
0128.0	AV	0456.0	Avocet	*Recurvirostra avosetta*		A	Amber list	
0129.0	TN	0459.0	Stone-curlew	*Burhinus oedicnemus*		A	Red list	yes
0130.0	LP	0469.0	Little Ringed Plover	*Charadrius dubius*		A		
0131.0	RP	0470.0	Ringed Plover	*Charadrius hiaticula*	Trìlleachan-tràghad	A	Amber list	
0132.0	KL	0474.0	Killdeer	*Charadrius vociferus*		A		
0133.0	DO	0482.0	Dotterel	*Charadrius morinellus*	Amadan-mòintich	A	Amber list	
0134.0	ID	0484.0	American Golden Plover	*Pluvialis dominica*		A		
0135.0	IF	0484.2	Pacific Golden Plover	*Pluvialis fulva*		A		
0136.0	GP	0485.0	European Golden Plover	*Pluvialis apricaria*	Feadag	A		
0137.0	GV	0486.0	Grey Plover	*Pluvialis squatarola*	Feadag-ghlas	A	Amber list	
0138.0	L	0493.0	Northern Lapwing	*Vanellus vanellus*	Curracag	A	Amber list	yes
0139.0	KN	0496.0	Red Knot	*Calidris canutus*	Luatharan-gainmhich	A	Amber list	
0140.0	SS	0497.0	Sanderling	*Calidris alba*	Luatharan-glas	A		
0141.0	PZ	0498.0	Semipalmated Sandpiper	*Calidris pusilla*		A		
0142.0	LX	0501.0	Little Stint	*Calidris minuta*	Luatharan-beag	A		
0143.0	TK	0502.0	Temminck's Stint	*Calidris temminckii*		A	Amber list	
0144.0	WU	0505.0	White-rumped Sandpiper	*Calidris fuscicollis*		A		
0145.0	BP	0506.0	Baird's Sandpiper	*Calidris bairdii*		A		
0146.0	PP	0507.0	Pectoral Sandpiper	*Calidris melanotos*		A		
0147.0	CV	0509.0	Curlew Sandpiper	*Calidris ferruginea*	Luatharan-crom	A		
0148.0	PS	0510.0	Purple Sandpiper	*Calidris maritima*	Luatharan-rìoghail	A	Amber list	
0149.0	DN	0512.0	Dunlin	*Calidris alpina*	Graillig	A	Amber list	
0150.0	OA	0514.0	Broad-billed Sandpiper	*Limicola falcinellus*		A		
0151.0	BQ	0516.0	Buff-breasted Sandpiper	*Tryngites subruficollis*		A		
0152.0	RU	0517.0	Ruff	*Philomachus pugnax*	Gibeagan	A	Amber list	
0153.0	JS	0518.0	Jack Snipe	*Lymnocryptes minimus*	Gobhrag-bheag	A		
0154.0	SN	0519.0	Common Snipe	*Gallinago gallinago*	Naosg	A	Amber list	
0155.0	DS	0520.0	Great Snipe	*Gallinago media*		A		
0156.0	LD	0527.0	Long-billed Dowitcher	*Limnodromus scolopaceus*		A		
0157.0	WK	0529.0	Woodcock	*Scolopax rusticola*	Coileach-coille	A	Amber list	
0158.0	BW	0532.0	Black-tailed Godwit	*Limosa limosa*	Cearra-ghob	A	Red list	yes
0159.0	BA	0534.0	Bar-tailed Godwit	*Limosa lapponica*	Roid-ghuilbneach	A	Amber list	
0160.0	WM	0538.0	Whimbrel	*Numenius phaeopus*	Eun-Bealltainn	A	Amber list	
0161.0	CU	0541.0	Eurasian Curlew	*Numenius arquata*	Guilbneach	A	Amber list	yes
0162.0	DR	0545.0	Spotted Redshank	*Tringa erythropus*	Gearradh-breac	A	Amber list	
0163.0	RK	0546.0	Common Redshank	*Tringa totanus*	Cam-ghlas	A	Amber list	
0164.0	GK	0548.0	Greenshank	*Tringa nebularia*	Deoch-bhuidhe	A		
0165.0	LZ	0550.0	Greater Yellowlegs	*Tringa melanoleuca*		A		
0166.0	LY	0551.0	Lesser Yellowlegs	*Tringa flavipes*		A		
0167.0	GE	0553.0	Green Sandpiper	*Tringa ochropus*	Luatharan-uaine	A	Amber list	
0168.0	OD	0554.0	Wood Sandpiper	*Tringa glareola*	Luatharan-coille	A	Amber list	
0169.0	CS	0556.0	Common Sandpiper	*Actitis hypoleucos*	Luatharan	A		
0170.0	PQ	0557.0	Spotted Sandpiper	*Actitis macularius*		A		
0171.0	TT	0561.0	Turnstone	*Arenaria interpres*	Trìlleachan-beag	A	Amber list	

Argyll species number	BTO code	Euring number	*British Birds* vernacular name	Scientific name	Gaelic Name	BOURC status category	Conservation status	NBAP species
0172.0	NK	0564.0	Red-necked Phalarope	*Phalaropus lobatus*	Deargan-allt	A	Red list	yes
0173.0	PL	0565.0	Grey Phalarope	*Phalaropus fulicarius*	Liathag-allt	A		
0174.0	PK	0566.0	Pomarine Skua	*Stercorarius pomarinus*	Fasgadair-donn	A		
0175.0	AC	0567.0	Arctic Skua	*Stercorarius parasiticus*	Fasgadair	A		yes
0176.0	OG	0568.0	Long-tailed Skua	*Stercorarius longicaudus*	Fasgadair-stiùireach	A		
0177.0	NX	0569.0	Great Skua	*Stercorarius skua*	Fasgadair-mòr	A	Amber list	
0178.0	MU	0575.0	Mediterranean Gull	*Larus melanocephalus*		A	Amber list	
0179.0	LF	0576.0	Laughing Gull	*Larus atricilla*		A		
0180.0	LU	0578.0	Little Gull	*Larus minutus*	Crann-fhaoileag	A		
0181.0	AB	0579.0	Sabine's Gull	*Larus sabini*		A		
0182.0	ON	0581.0	Bonaparte's Gull	*Larus philadelphia*		A		
0183.0	BH	0582.0	Black-headed Gull	*Larus ridibundus*	Faoileag-a'-chinn-duibh	A	Amber list	
0184.0	IN	0589.0	Ring-billed Gull	*Larus delawarensis*		A		
0185.0	CM	0590.0	Common Gull	*Larus canus*	Faoileag-chumanta	A	Amber list	
0186.0	LB	0591.0	Lesser Black-backed Gull	*Larus fuscus*	Farspag-bheag	A	Amber list	
0187.0	YG	0592.6	Yellow-legged Gull	*Larus michahellis*		A		
0188.0	HG	0592.0	Herring Gull	*Larus argentatus*	Faoileag-an-sgadain	A	Amber list	yes
0189.0	IG	0598.0	Iceland Gull	*Larus glaucoides*	Faoileag-liath	A		
0190.0	GZ	0599.0	Glaucous Gull	*Larus hyperboreus*	Muir-mhaighstir	A		
0191.0	GB	0600.0	Great Black-backed Gull	*Larus marinus*	Farspag	A		
0192.0	QG	0601.0	Ross's Gull	*Rhodostethia rosea*		A		
0193.0	KI	0602.0	Kittiwake	*Rissa tridactyla*	Ruideag	A	Amber list	
0194.0	IV	0604.0	Ivory Gull	*Pagophila eburnea*		A		
0195.0		0622.0	Bridled Tern	*Onychoprion anaethetus*		A		
0196.0	AF	0624.0	Little Tern	*Sternula albifrons*	Steàrnag-bheag	A	Amber list	
0197.0	CJ	0606.0	Caspian Tern	*Hydroprogne caspia*		A		
0198.0	BJ	0627.0	Black Tern	*Chlidonias niger*	Steàrnag-dhubh	A		
0199.0	WJ	0628.0	White-winged Black Tern	*Chlidonias leucopterus*		A		
0200.0	TE	0611.0	Sandwich Tern	*Sterna sandvicensis*	Steàrnag-mhòr	A	Amber list	
0201.0	FO	0618.0	Forster's Tern	*Sterna forsteri*		A		
0202.0	CN	0615.0	Common Tern	*Sterna hirundo*	Steàrnag-chumanta	A		
0203.0	RS	0614.0	Roseate Tern	*Sterna dougallii*	Steàrnag-stiùireach	A	Red list	yes
0204.0	AE	0616.0	Arctic Tern	*Sterna paradisaea*	Steàrnag	A	Amber list	
0205.0	GU	0634.0	Common Guillemot	*Uria aalge*	Eun-dubh-an-sgadain	A	Amber list	
0206.0	TZ	0635.0	Brünnich's Guillemot	*Uria lomvia*		A		
0207.0	RA	0636.0	Razorbill	*Alca torda*	Falc	A	Amber list	
0207.1		0637.0	Great Auk	*Pinguinus impennis*		B1		
0208.0	TY	0638.0	Black Guillemot	*Cepphus grylle*	Gearra-breac	A	Amber list	
0209.0	LK	0647.0	Little Auk	*Alle alle*	Colcach-bheag	A		
0210.0	PU	0654.0	Puffin	*Fratercula arctica*	Buthaid	A	Amber list	
0211.0		0663.0	Pallas's Sandgrouse	*Syrrhaptes paradoxus*		A		
0212.0	DV	0665.0	Rock Dove / Feral Pigeon	*Columba livia*	Calman-creige (Rock Dove)	AC4E*		
0212.9	FP	0665.1	Feral Pigeon	*Columba livia*		AC4E*		
0213.0	SD	0668.0	Stock Dove	*Columba oenas*	Calman-gorm	A	Amber list	
0214.0	WP	0670.0	Wood Pigeon	*Columba palumbus*	Calman-fiadhaich	A		
0215.0	CD	0684.0	Collared Dove	*Streptopelia decaocto*	Calman-a'-chrios	A		
0216.0	TD	0687.0	Turtle Dove	*Streptopelia turtur*	Calman-tùchan	A	Red list	yes
0217.0	CK	0724.0	Common Cuckoo	*Cuculus canorus*	Cuthag	A	Amber list	yes
0218.0		0727.0	Black-billed Cuckoo	*Coccyzus erythrophthalmus*		A		
0219.0		0728.0	Yellow-billed Cuckoo	*Coccyzus americanus*		A		
0220.0	BO	0735.0	Barn Owl	*Tyto alba*	Comhachag	AE*	Amber list	
0221.0		0739.0	Eurasian Scops Owl	*Otus scops*		A		
0222.0	SO	0749.0	Snowy Owl	*Bubo scandiacus*		AE		
0223.0		0744.0	Eagle Owl	*Bubo bubo*		E*		
0224.0	TO	0761.0	Tawny Owl	*Strix aluco*	Comhachag-dhonn	A		
0225.0	LE	0767.0	Long-eared Owl	*Asio otus*	Comhachag-adharcaiche	A		
0226.0	SE	0768.0	Short-eared Owl	*Asio flammeus*	Comhachag-chluasach	A	Amber list	
0227.0	NJ	0778.0	European Nightjar	*Caprimulgus europaeus*	Sgraicheag-oidhche	A		yes
0228.0	SI	0795.0	Common Swift	*Apus apus*	Gobhlan-mòr	A		
0229.0	AI	0798.0	Alpine Swift	*Apus melba*	Gobhlan-monaidh	A	Red list	
0230.0	KF	0831.0	Common Kingfisher	*Alcedo atthis*	Biorra-crùidein	A	Amber list	
0231.0	MZ	0840.0	European Bee-eater	*Merops apiaster*		A		
0232.0		0841.0	European Roller	*Coracias garrulus*	Cuairsgean	A		
0233.0	HP	0846.0	Hoopoe	*Upupa epops*	Calman-cathaidh	AE		
0234.0	WY	0848.0	Wryneck	*Jynx torquilla*	Geocair	A	Red list	yes
0235.0	G	0856.0	Green Woodpecker	*Picus viridis*	Snagardach	A	Amber list	

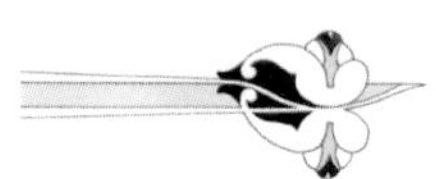

Argyll species number	BTO code	Euring number	*British Birds* vernacular name	Scientific name	Gaelic Name	BOURC status category	Conservation status	NBAP species
0236.0	GS	0876.0	Great Spotted Woodpecker	*Dendrocopos major*	Snagan-daraich	A		
0237.0	S	0976.0	Sky Lark	*Alauda arvensis*	Uiseag	A	Red list	yes
0238.0	SX	0978.0	Shore Lark	*Eremophila alpestris*		A		
0239.0	SM	0981.0	Sand Martin	*Riparia riparia*	Gobhlan-gainmhich	A	Amber list	
0240.0	SL	0992.0	Barn Swallow	*Hirundo rustica*	Gobhlan-gaoithe	AE	Amber list	
0241.0	HM	1001.0	House Martin	*Delichon urbicum*	Gobhlan-taighe	A	Amber list	
0242.0	VR	0995.0	Red-rumped Swallow	*Cecropis daurica*		A		
0243.0	PR	1002.0	Richard's Pipit	*Anthus richardi*		A		
0244.0	TP	1009.0	Tree Pipit	*Anthus trivialis*	Riabhag-choille	A	Amber list	yes
0245.0	MP	1011.0	Meadow Pipit	*Anthus pratensis*	Snàthag	A	Amber list	
0246.0	VP	1012.0	Red-throated Pipit	*Anthus cervinus*		A		
0247.0	RC	1014.1	Rock Pipit	*Anthus petrosus*	Gabhagan	A		
0248.0	YW	1017.0	Yellow Wagtail	*Motacilla flava*	Breacan-buidhe	A	Amber list	yes
0248.1		1017.1	Blue-headed (Yellow) Wagtail	*Motacilla flava flava*		A		
0248.2		1017.3	Grey-headed (Yellow) Wagtail	*Motacilla flava thunbergi*		A		
0249.0	GL	1019.0	Grey Wagtail	*Motacilla cinerea*	Breacan-baintighearna	A	Amber list	
0250.0	PW	1020.0	Pied Wagtail	*Motacilla alba yarellii*	Breac-an-t-sìl	A		
0250.1	WZ	1020.1	White Wagtail	*Motacilla alba alba*		A		
0251.0	WX	1048.0	Waxwing	*Bombycilla garrulus*	Canarach-dearg	A		
0252.0	DI	1050.0	Dipper	*Cinclus cinclus*	Gobha-uisge	A		
0253.0	WR	1066.0	Wren	*Troglodytes troglodytes*	Dreathann-donn	A		
0254.0	D	1084.0	Dunnock	*Prunella modularis*	Gealbhonn-nam-preas	A	Amber list	yes
0255.0	R	1099.0	Robin	*Erithacus rubecula*	Brù-dhearg	A		
0256.0	N	1104.0	Common Nightingale	*Luscinia megarhynchos*	Spideag	A	Amber list	
0257.0	BU	1106.0	Bluethroat	*Luscinia svecica*		A	Amber list	
0258.0	BX	1121.0	Black Redstart	*Phoenicurus ochruros*	Ceann-dubhan	A	Amber list	
0259.0	RT	1122.0	Common Redstart	*Phoenicurus phoenicurus*	Ceann-dearg	A	Amber list	
0260.0	WC	1137.0	Whinchat	*Saxicola rubetra*	Gocan	A		
0261.0	SC	1139.0	Common Stonechat	*Saxicola torquatus*	Clacharan	A	Amber list	
0262.0	W	1146.0	Northern Wheatear	*Oenanthe oenanthe oenanthe*	Brù-gheal	A		
0262.1	W	1146.2	'Greenland' Wheatear	*Oenanthe oenanthe leucorhoa*		A		
0263.0		1166.0	Blue Rock Thrush	*Monticola solitarius*		AE		
0264.0	RZ	1186.0	Ring Ouzel	*Turdus torquatus*	Dubh-chreige	A	Red list	yes
0265.0	B	1187.0	Blackbird	*Turdus merula*	Lon-dubh	A		
0266.0	FF	1198.0	Fieldfare	*Turdus pilaris*	Liath-thruisg	A	Amber list	
0267.0	ST	1200.0	Song Thrush	*Turdus philomelos*	Smeòrach	A	Red list	yes
0268.0	RE	1201.0	Redwing	*Turdus iliacus*	Sgiath-dhearg	A	Amber list	
0269.0	M	1202.0	Mistle Thrush	*Turdus viscivorus*	Smeòrach-mhòr	A	Amber list	
0270.0	GH	1236.0	Grasshopper Warbler	*Locustella naevia*	Ceileiriche-leumnach	A	Red list	yes
0271.0	SW	1243.0	Sedge Warbler	*Acrocephalus schoenobaenus*	Uiseag-oidhche	A		
0272.0	RW	1251.0	Reed Warbler	*Acrocephalus scirpaceus*		A		
0273.0		1256.0	Booted Warbler	*Hippolais caligata*		A		
0274.0	IC	1259.0	Icterine Warbler	*Hippolais icterina*		A		
0275.0	BC	1277.0	Blackcap	*Sylvia atricapilla*	Ceann-dubh	A		
0276.0	GW	1276.0	Garden Warbler	*Sylvia borin*	Ceileiriche-gàraidh	A		
0277.0	RR	1273.0	Barred Warbler	*Sylvia nisoria*		A		
0278.0	LW	1274.0	Lesser Whitethroat	*Sylvia curruca*	Gealan-coille-beag	A		
0279.0	WH	1275.0	Common Whitethroat	*Sylvia communis*	Gealan-coille	A		
0280.0	NP	1293.0	Greenish Warbler	*Phylloscopus trochiloides*		A		
0281.0	YB	1300.0	Yellow-browed Warbler	*Phylloscopus inornatus*	Ceileiriche-buidhe	A		
0282.0	IW	1307.0	Bonelli's Warbler sp.	*Phylloscopus bonelli/orientalis*		A		
0283.0	WO	1308.0	Wood Warbler	*Phylloscopus sibilatrix*	Ceileiriche-coille	A	Amber list	yes
0284.0	CC	1311.0	Common Chiffchaff	*Phylloscopus collybita*	Caifean	A		
0284.1		1311.3	'Siberian' Chiffchaff #	*Phylloscopus collybita tristis*		A		
0284.2		1311.4	'Scandinavian' Chiffchaff #	*Phylloscopus collybita abietinus*		A		
0285.0	WW	1312.0	Willow Warbler	*Phylloscopus trochilus*	Ceileiriche-giuthais	A	Amber list	
0285.1		1312.2	'Scandinavian' Willow Warbler #	*Phylloscopus trochilus acredula*		A		
0286.0	GC	1314.0	Goldcrest	*Regulus regulus*	Crìonag-bhuidhe	A	Amber list	
0287.0	FC	1315.0	Firecrest	*Regulus ignicapilla*	Crìonag	A	Amber list	
0288.0	SF	1335.1	Spotted Flycatcher	*Muscicapa striata*	Breacan-glas-sgiobalta	A	Red list	yes
0289.0	FY	1343.0	Red-breasted Flycatcher	*Ficedula parva*		A		
0290.0	PF	1349.0	Pied Flycatcher	*Ficedula hypoleuca*	Breacan-glas	A		
0291.0	LT	1437.0	Long-tailed Tit	*Aegithalos caudatus*	Ciochan	A		
0292.0	BT	1462.0	Blue Tit	*Cyanistes caeruleus*	Cailleachag-cheann-ghorm	A		
0293.0	GT	1464.0	Great Tit	*Parus major*	Currac-bhaintighearna	A		
0294.0	CI	1454.0	Crested Tit	*Lophophanes cristatus*	Gulpag-stuic	A		

Argyll species number	BTO code	Euring number	*British Birds* vernacular name	Scientific name	Gaelic Name	BOURC status category	Conservation status	NBAP species
0295.0	CT	1461.0	Coal Tit	*Periparus ater*	Smutag	A		
0296.0	WT	1442.0	Willow Tit	*Poecile montanus*	Currac-ghiuthais	A		yes
0297.0	NH	1479.0	Eurasian Nuthatch	*Sitta europaea*		A		
0298.0	TC	1486.0	Eurasian Treecreeper	*Certhia familiaris*	Snaigear	A		
0299.0	OL	1508.0	Golden Oriole	*Oriolus oriolus*	Buidheag-Eòrpach	A	Amber list	
0300.0	ED	1515.0	Red-backed Shrike	*Lanius collurio*		A	Red list	yes
0301.0		1519.0	Lesser Grey Shrike	*Lanius minor*		A		
0302.0	SR	1520.0	Great Grey Shrike	*Lanius excubitor*	Feòladair-glas	A		
0303.0	OO	1523.0	Woodchat Shrike	*Lanius senator*		A		
0304.0	J	1539.0	Eurasian Jay	*Garrulus glandarius*	Sgraicheag	A		
0305.0	MG	1549.0	Magpie	*Pica pica*	Pioghaid	A		
0306.0	CF	1559.0	Red-billed Chough	*Pyrrhocorax pyrrhocorax*	Cathag-dhearg-chasach	AE	Amber list	
0307.0	JD	1560.0	Western Jackdaw	*Corvus monedula*	Cathag	A		
0308.0	RO	1563.0	Rook	*Corvus frugilegus*	Ròcas	A		
0309.0	C	1567.0	Carrion Crow	*Corvus corone*	Feannag-dhubh	A		
0309.1	HB	1567.2	Hybrid Crow	*Corvus corone x cornix*		A		
0310.0	HC	1567.3	Hooded Crow	*Corvus cornix*	Feannag-ghlas	A		
0311.0	RN	1572.0	Common Raven	*Corvus corax*	Fitheach	A		
0312.0	SG	1582.0	Common Starling	*Sturnus vulgaris*	Druid	A	Red list	yes
0313.0	OE	1584.0	Rose-coloured Starling	*Sturnus roseus*	Druid-dhearg	A		
0314.0	HS	1591.0	House Sparrow	*Passer domesticus*	Gealbhonn	A	Red list	yes
0315.0	TS	1598.0	Tree Sparrow	*Passer montanus*	Gealbhonn-nan-craobh	A	Red list	yes
0316.0		2044.0	Zebra Finch	*Poephila guttata*		E		
0317.0		1620.0	White-rumped Munia	*Lonchura striata*		E		
0318.0	EV	1633.0	Red-eyed Vireo	*Vireo olivaceus*		A		
0319.0	CH	1636.0	Common Chaffinch	*Fringilla coelebs*	Breacan-beithe	AE		
0320.0	BL	1638.0	Brambling	*Fringilla montifringilla*	Breacan-caorainn	A		
0321.0	GR	1649.0	Greenfinch	*Carduelis chloris*	Glaisean-daraich	AE		
0322.0	GO	1653.0	Goldfinch	*Carduelis carduelis*	Lasair-choille	A		
0323.0	SK	1654.0	Siskin	*Carduelis spinus*	Gealag-bhuidhe	AE		
0324.0	LI	1660.0	Linnet	*Carduelis cannabina*	Gealan-lìn	A	Red list	yes
0325.0	TW	1662.0	Twite	*Carduelis flavirostris*	Gealan-beinne	A	Red list	yes
0326.0	FR	1663.0	Common Redpoll	*Carduelis flammea*		A		
0326.1		1663.1	'Mealy' Redpoll	*Carduelis flammea flammea*		A		
0326.2		1663.2	'Greenland' Redpoll	*Carduelis flammea rostrata*		A		
0327.0	LR	1663.4	Lesser Redpoll	*Carduelis cabaret*	Dearcan-seilich (Redpoll)	A	Amber list	yes
0328.0	AL	1664.0	Arctic Redpoll	*Carduelis hornemanni*		A		
0329.0	CR	1666.0	Common Crossbill	*Loxia curvirostra*	Cam-ghob	A		
0329.1	SQ	1679.0	Common Rosefinch	*Carpodacus erythrinus*		A	Amber list	
0330.0	BF	1710.0	Bullfinch	*Pyrrhula pyrrhula*	Corcan-coille	A	Red list	yes
0330.1		1710.1	'Northern' Bullfinch	*Pyrrhula pyrrhula pyrrhula*		A		
0331.0	HF	1717.0	Hawfinch	*Coccothraustes coccothraustes*	Gobach	A	Amber list	yes
0332.0	AD	1755.0	American Redstart	*Setophaga ruticilla*		A		
0333.0	LA	1847.0	Lapland Bunting	*Calcarius lapponicus*		A		
0334.0	SB	1850.0	Snow Bunting	*Plectrophenax nivalis*	Gealag-an-t-sneachda	A	Amber list	
0335.0	Y	1857.0	Yellowhammer	*Emberiza citrinella*	Buidheag-bhealaidh	A	Red list	yes
0336.0	CL	1858.0	Cirl Bunting	*Emberiza cirlus*		A	Red list	yes
0337.0		1873.0	Rustic Bunting	*Emberiza rustica*		A		
0338.0	LJ	1874.0	Little Bunting	*Emberiza pusilla*		A		
0339.0		1876.0	Yellow-breasted Bunting	*Emberiza aureola*		A		
0340.0	RB	1877.0	Reed Bunting	*Emberiza schoeniclus*	Gealag-lòin	A	Red list	yes
0341.0		1880.0	Red-headed Bunting	*Emberiza bruniceps*		D		
0342.0		1881.0	Black-headed Bunting	*Emberiza melanocephala*		AE		
0343.0	CB	1882.0	Corn Bunting	*Emberiza calandra*	Gealag-bhuachair	A	Red list	yes
0344.0		1899.0	Brown-headed Cowbird	*Molothrus ater*		A		

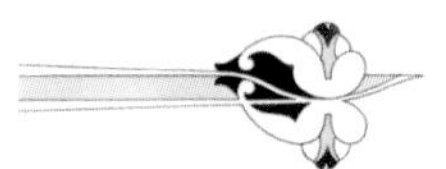

Appendix 2: Category D and E bird species

The following species in categories D and E of the British List have been officially recorded in Argyll. Species in category E were apparently not recorded in the county before 1993 and have only been noted haphazardly since. As these birds do not form part of the British List 'proper', there has been an element of ornithological snobbery about recording them! However, as there are several well known instances (e.g. Mandarin Duck) of escaped/released species becoming established as self-sustaining populations it is important to document them.

The British Ornithologists Union's official view is: "The BOU encourages all observers to report records of non-native species to the relevant local bird recorder. Local recorders and those producing local, county or regional publications are encouraged to publish these records and to make these records available to the Rare Breeding Birds Panel (RBBP), which publishes an annual report of non-native species breeding in Britain each year in *British Birds*. The BOU is responsible for maintaining the British List. Part of this responsibility is to monitor the occurrence of non-native species which may qualify for addition to Category C of the British List. To undertake this we require published information from which to work and which we can quote as reference."

The majority of these species found in Argyll have been wildfowl and most will have escaped from ornamental collections in the county or nearby. Category E* species have been recorded breeding with their own kind outside captivity.

Paul Daw

Black Swan

Cygnus atratus

Category E*. Infrequent visitor to Argyll, often seen with Mute Swans.

A few pairs have bred in various parts of Britain (including in Scotland) in most years recently (Ogilvie *et al.* 1999a, 1999b, 2000, 2001, 2002, 2003, 2004). In Argyll, one was present, often with Mute Swans, in the Dunstaffnage/Loch Etive area from early July to mid-October 1994 and one was with Mute Swans in Balvicar Bay, Mid-Argyll, on 6 June 1996. There were several reports in 2000, some of which must have been of the same bird(s). One was reported in Small Isles Bay, Jura, on 10 April, on 23 July, two were at Peninver, Kintyre, during the second two weeks in June, one was in the Ardrishaig/Loch Gilp area of Mid-Argyll during the last week of August and one (presumably the Loch Gilp bird) was at Achnamara (Loch Sween), Mid-Argyll, on 28 August. The last was reportedly a juvenile (ABR).

Bar-headed Goose

Anser indicus

Category E*. Reported with increasing frequency.

Although widely recorded in Britain, with 85 individuals reported in 27 localities in 1991 (Delaney 1993), breeding success appears to be low. In Argyll, two were on Loch Ederline (near Ford), Mid-Argyll, on 24 July 1998 and three were on Loch Finlaggan, Islay, on 23 June 1999. Since 2000 there have been regular reports of birds at the head of Loch Feochan (near Oban), including 15 with Greylag Geese on 14 August 2000, five with Canada Geese on 11 August 2004 and four on 14 September 2006. One was seen with Greylag Geese at Connel, Mid-Argyll, on 24 July 2006 (ABR, Argyll Database).

Ross's Goose

Anser rossii

Category DE. Two records of a single bird.

No recent records of feral breeding attempts in Britain (Ogilvie *et al.* 1999a, 1999b, 2000, 2001, 2002, 2003, 2004). One was seen with Snow and Bar-headed Geese at the head of Loch Feochan on 14 August 2000. Presumably the same individual was seen at both Loch Feochan and Loch Nell (near Oban) during December 2001 (ABR).

Emperor Goose

Anser canagicus

Category E. Three records of single birds.

First reported breeding in the wild in Britain in 2001 (Ogilvie *et al.* 2003). One was on Loch Fyne near the Wildlife Park at Inveraray on 16 April 1999 and one was seen at the head of

Loch Feochan and on Loch Nell in September 2000 (ABR).

Ruddy Shelduck

Tadorna ferruginea

Category BE*. Only two recent records.

Although genuine wild vagrants may have occurred in Scotland in the past, all recent records are assumed to refer to escapes. There are many reports of single birds and small flocks, mainly in southern England and occasionally in Scotland, but there are few breeding attempts (Ogilvie *et al.* 1999a, 1999b, 2000, 2001, 2002, 2003, 2004). An adult female was at Bridgend Merse, Islay, on 4 May 1997 and two birds were present at Loch a' Phuill, Tiree, on 6 and 7 July 1997 (ABR).

Muscovy Duck

Cairina moschata

Category E*. Widespread and probably under-recorded in Argyll.

Quite large feral populations of Muscovy Ducks have become established in Britain to the extent that they are regarded as a pest species in some places (Dudley 2005). They are kept widely as farmyard birds, but often survive independently. Recent Argyll records have included a single at Innellan, Cowal, in June 2000, a pair in the harbour at Tarbert, Kintyre, in spring and summer 2001 and three at Achnamara, Mid-Argyll, in November 2001 (ABR).

Wood Duck

Aix sponsa

Category E*. Only one recent record.

A pair or two are reported breeding in the wild somewhere in Britain in most years and non-breeding birds are reported more widely (Ogilvie *et al.* 1999a, 1999b, 2000, 2001, 2002, 2003, 2004). A female was present in Balgie Burn and on the foreshore at West Bay (Dunoon), Cowal, from at least October 2000 to May 2001 (ABR).

Cinnamon Teal

Anas cyanoptera

Category E*. Only one recent record.

No recent records of feral breeding attempts in Britain (Ogilvie *et al.* 1999a, 1999b, 2000, 2001, 2002, 2003, 2004). A male seen in the Aros Estuary, Mull, on 22 September 2001 was presumed to be an escape, although it is possible that the species could occur as a vagrant from North America (ABR).

Reeve's Pheasant

Syrmaticus reevesii

Category E*. Recent releases in Cowal.

In the past this has been a favoured gamebird for release in Scotland because it frequents hilly, densely wooded country usually shunned by other species of pheasant. Birds released in Speyside in the early 1970s were apparently breeding in the wild in 1974 (First Atlas, Thom). At present, small numbers are to be found at a few sites in the south of England (Ogilvie *et al.* 2004).

Males were seen on several occasions in late April/early May of both 2006 and 2007 near the head of Loch Striven, Cowal. On 8 May 2007 two males were seen in the same area fighting with a male Common Pheasant and a dead male was picked up nearby, later the same day (S. Petty pers. comm.). A male seen at Ballimore, Cowal, on 8 May 2007 was reportedly one of several released on the estate in 2006 (T. Callan pers. comm.).

Golden Pheasant

Chrysolophus pictus

Category C1E*. The introduced population on Mull may now be extinct.

Apparently self-sustaining populations occur in Britain, mainly in south-east England. For Argyll (Thom) mentions a record from Kintyre but gives no date. From at least the early 1980s a small feral population was present at Gruline, Mull. In 1988 there were approximately 30 individuals here and birds were reportedly introduced to two other estates on Mull (ABR). In 1991 there were 17 birds at Gruline and two were reported from Gleann Seilisdeir. Two females were seen at Gruline in Feb 1993 and two males were there in 1994. The last definite report of these birds was in 1996 when the population numbered about 12 birds; it was apparently not self-sustaining, requiring winter feeding and periodic

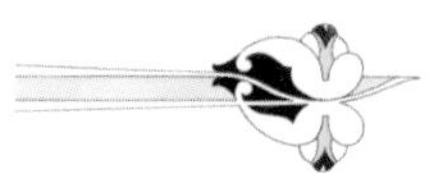

reintroduction to maintain numbers (ABR). Since then there have been no definite records from Mull. The only other record was of two at Achamore Gardens, Gigha, in March 1988 (ABR).

Indian Peafowl

Pavo cristatus

Category E. Only one recent record.

It has occasionally bred in the wild in southern England in the past (Ogilvie *et al.* 2001). A male was wandering along the main A83 road at Dalchenna (near Inveraray), Mid-Argyll, on 22 September 2004 (Argyll Database).

Pelican sp.

Pelecanus sp.

Category E. Only one recent record.

No recent records of feral breeding attempts in Britain (Ogilvie *et al.* 1999a, 1999b, 2000, 2001, 2002, 2003, 2004), but escapes are reported fairly frequently. A Pelican of undetermined species was reported on the golf course at Southend, Kintyre, in June 1998 by several local people (ABR).

Flamingo sp.

Phoenicopterus sp.

Category E. Only one recent record.

No recent records of feral breeding attempts in Britain (Ogilvie *et al.* 1999a, 1999b, 2000, 2001, 2002, 2003, 2004), but presumed escapees are regularly reported. Two Flamingos of undetermined species were seen flying north past Machrihanish SBO on 28 July 1993 (ABR).

Feral Pigeon

Columba livia

Category E*.

See under Rock Dove in main sequence.

Eurasian Eagle Owl

Bubo bubo

Category E*. Two recent records, one of a long staying bird.

A pair has bred regularly in northern England for some years and another pair bred in Moray & Nairn in the 1980s (Ogilvie *et al.* 1999a, 1999b, 2000, 2001, 2002, 2003, 2004). Single birds are occasionally reported elsewhere. All British records are currently believed to be escaped or released birds. A bird seen frequently in the Arduaine, Mid-Argyll, area during 1989-1991 and again in June 1997 was reportedly released from captivity in the vicinity (ABR). An escaped bird belonging to a local keeper was seen in a garden at Benderloch, North Argyll, in early April 2007 (Argyll Database).

Red-headed Bunting

Emberiza bruniceps

Category DE. At least eight Argyll records, but none since 1994.

Because this species is widely kept in captivity there is always the suspicion that birds occurring in Britain are escapes, although vagrancy is possible. Six Argyll records in the 1970s may have involved as few as two birds. There was then a long gap until one was seen on Iona on 10 June 1993 followed by one present at Arnabost Farm, Coll, during 16-17 June 1994 (ABR).

Zebra Finch

Poephila guttata

Category E. Only one recent record.

Frequently recorded in Britain as an escaped cage bird. One was found dead in a garden at Blairmore, Cowal, on 29 May 1994 (ABR).

White-rumped Munia

Lonchura striata

Category E. Only one recent record.

Occasionally recorded in Britain as an escaped cage bird. One photographed in a garden in Dunoon was present during 14-16 April 2005 (Argyll Database).

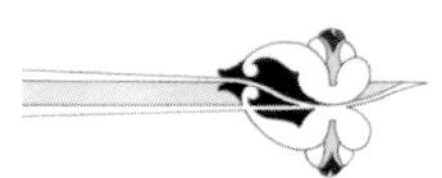

Appendix 3: Scientific names

This Appendix gives the scientific names of non-bird species mentioned in the book. Also listed are four bird species which are referred to in the text, but which do not appear on the Argyll bird list.

Bob Furness

Plants

Alder (Black or Common) *Alnus glutinosa*
Ash *Fraxinus excelsior*
Beech (European) *Fagus sylvatica*
Birch *Betula* spp. (Downy *B. pubescens* and Silver *B. pendula*)
Bog Bean *Menyanthes trifoliata*
Bramble (Common Blackberry) *Rubus fruticosus*
Burdock *Arctium lappa*
Chestnut (Horse) *Aesculus hippocastanum*
Chestnut (Sweet) *Castanea sativa*
Crab (Siberian) *Malus baccata*
Crowberry *Empetrum nigrum*
Dandelion *Taraxacum officinale*
Elm (Wych) *Ulmus glabra*
Fir (Douglas) *Pseudotsuga menziesii*
Gorse (Common) *Ulex europaeus*
Groundsel *Senecio vulgaris*
Hawthorn *Crataegus monogyna*
Hazel *Corylus avellana*
Heather *Calluna vulgaris*
Holly *Ilex acquifolium*
Honeysuckle *Lonicera periclymenum*
Ivy (Common) *Hedera helix*
Juniper *Juniperus communis*
Kelp (=Tangle) *Laminaria* spp.
Knapweed (Common) *Centaurea nigra*
Larch *Larix* spp. (European *L. decidua*, and Japanese *L. kaempferi*)
Lime *Tilia* spp.
Lovage (Scots) *Ligusticum scoticum*
Oak *Quercus* spp. (Sessile *Q. petraea*, and Common *Q. robur*)
Pine (Scots) *Pinus sylvestris*
Ragwort (Common) *Senecio jacobaea*
Rape (Oilseed) *Brassica napus*
Reed (Common) *Phragmites australis* (syn. *communis*)
Rhododendron *Rhododendron* spp., especially *R. ponticum*
Rowan *Sorbus aucuparia*
Spruce *Picea* spp. (Norway *P. abies*, and Sitka *P. sitchensis*)
Teasel *Dipsacus fullonum*
Thrift (=Sea Pink) *Armeria vulgaris*
Willow *Salix* spp.
Wrack (Knotted) *Ascophyllum nodosum*
Yew (Common) *Taxus baccata*

Invertebrates

Anemone (Fireworks) *Pachycerianthus multiplicatus*
Bee (Mining) *Andrena* spp.
Cockle (Common) *Cerastoderma edule* (formerly *Cardium edule*)
Drinker Moth *Euthrix potatoria*
Eggar (Northern) *Lasiocampa quercus callunae*
Eggar (Oak) *Lasiocampa quercus*
Fox Moth *Macrothylacia rubi*
Fritillary (Marsh) *Euphydryas aurinia*
Lobster (Common) *Homarus gammarus*
Lobster (Norway) *Nephrops norvegicus*
Mussel (Blue) *Mytilus edulis*
Mussel (Horse) *Modiolus modiolus*
Mussel (Zebra) *Dreissena polymorpha*
Scallop (King) *Pecten maximus*
Scallop (Queen) *Aequipecten opercularis*
Winkle (or Periwinkle) *Littorina* spp.

Fish

Charr (Arctic) *Salvelinus alpinus*
Cod *Gadus morhua*
Eel (European) *Anguilla anguilla*
Halibut (Atlantic) *Hippoglossus hippoglossus*
Herring *Clupea harengus*
Mackerel *Scomber scombrus*
Minnow *Phoxinus phoxinus*
Powan (Common Whitefish) *Coregonus clupeoides,* also known as *C. lavaretus*
Salmon *Salmo salar*
Shark (Basking) *Cetorhinus maximus*
Sprat *Sprattus sprattus*
Stickleback (Three-spined) *Gasterosteus aculeatus*
Trout (Brown) *Salmo trutta*

Amphibians

Frog (Common) *Rana temporaria*

Mammals

Badger *Meles meles*
Deer (Red) *Cervus elaphus*
Deer (Roe) *Capreolus capreolus*
Deer (Sika) *Cervus nippon*
Ferret (domesticated mustelid) *Mustela furo*

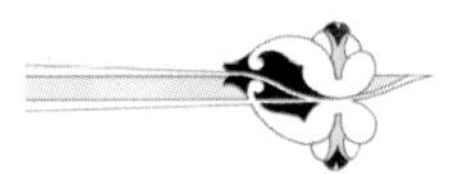

Fox *Vulpes vulpes*
Hare (Mountain) *Lepus timidus*
Hedgehog *Erinaceus europaeus*
Marten (Pine) *Martes martes*
Mink (American) *Mustela vison*
Mouse (Wood = Long-tailed Field) *Apodemus sylvaticus*
Otter *Lutra lutra*
Porpoise (Harbour) *Phocoena phocoena*
Rabbit *Oryctolagus cuniculus*
Rat (Brown = Common) *Rattus norvegicus*
Squirrel (Red) *Sciurus vulgaris*
Vole (Bank) *Clethrionomys glareolus*
Vole (Field) *Microtus agrestis*
Weasel *Mustela nivalis*
Whale (Minke) *Balaenoptera acutorostrata*

Birds (not on the Argyll bird list)
Blackbird (Red-winged) *Agelaius phoeniceus*
Courser (Cream-coloured) *Cursorius cursor*
Curlew (Eskimo) *Numenius borealis*
Ptarmigan (Willow) (=Willow Grouse) *Lagopus lagopus*

Appendix 4: Useful addresses

Organisation	Postal address	Phone/fax/e-mail/website
Argyll and Bute Biodiversity Partnership	Marina Curran-Colthart, Local Biodiversity Officer, Kilbowie House, Gallanach Road, Oban PA34 4PF	Tel: 01631 562125 Fax: 01631 570861 E-mail: marina.curran-colthart@argyll-bute.gov.uk Website: http://www.argyll-bute.gov.uk/biodiversity/
British Trust for Ornithology	The Nunnery, Thetford, Norfolk IP24 2PU	Tel: 01842 750050 Fax: 750030 E-mail: info@bto.org Website: http://www.bto.org/
British Trust for Ornithology (Scotland)	School of Biological and Environmental Sciences, Cottrell Building, University of Stirling, Stirling FK9 4LA	Tel: 01786 466560 Fax 01786 466561 E-mail: scot.info@bto.org Website: http://www.bto.org/regional/btoscotland.htm
Forest Enterprise Scotland (offices covering parts of Argyll)	Cowal & Trossachs Forest District, Aberfoyle, Stirling FK8 3UX	Tel: 01877 382383 E-mail: cowal.trossachs.fd@forestry.gsi.gov.uk
	West Argyll Forest District, Whitegates, Lochgilphead, Argyll PA31 8RS	Tel: 01546 602518 E-mail: west.argyll.fd@forestry.gsi.gov.uk
	Lorne Forest District, Millpark Road, Oban, Argyll PA34 4NH	Tel: 01631 566155 E-mail: lorne.district@forestry.gsi.gov.uk
Hebridean Whale and Dolphin Trust	Hebridean Whale and Dolphin Trust, 28 Main Street, Tobermory, Isle of Mull PA75 6NU	Tel: 01688 302620 E-mail: info@hwdt.org Website: http://www.whaledolphintrust.co.uk/
Islay Natural History Trust	Main Street, Port Charlotte, Isle Of Islay PA48 7TX	Tel: 01496 850288 E-Mail: inht@islaywildlife.freeserve.co.uk Website: http://www.islaywildlife.freeserve.co.uk
Islay Bird Group	J.S.Armitage, Airigh Sgallaidh, Portnahaven, Isle of Islay PA47 7SZ	Tel: 01496 860396 E-mail: jsa@ornquest.plus.com Islay Birds blog site: http://www.islaybirds.blogspot.com

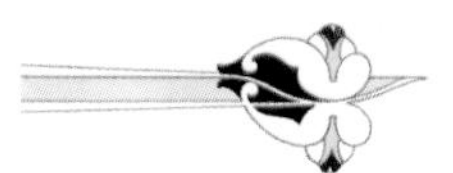

Organisation	Postal address	Phone/fax/e-mail/website
Machrihanish Seabird and Wildlife Observatory	Eddie Maguire (Warden), Machrihanish Seabird/Wildlife Observatory, Lossit Park, Machrihanish, Argyll PA28 6PZ	Tel: 07919 660 292 E-mail: machrihanishbirds@btinternet.com Website: http://www.machrihanishbirds.org.uk/
Isle of Mull Bird Club	Janet T Hall (Membership Secretary), Druim Mhor, Craignure, Isle of Mull, Argyll PA65 6AY	Membership Secretary Tel: 01680 812441 E-mail: oystercatcher@dee-emm.co.uk Website: http://www.mullbirdclub.org.uk/
Royal Society for the Protection of Birds (Scotland)	Scotland Headquarters, Dunedin House, 25 Ravelston Terrace, Edinburgh EH4 3TP	Tel: 0131 311 6500 E-mail: rspb.scotland@rspb.org.uk Website: http://www.rspb.org.uk/scotland/
Royal Society for the Protection of Birds, South &West Scotland Regional Office	10 Park Quadrant, Glasgow G3 6BS	Tel: 0141 331 0993
Scottish Natural Heritage (offices covering parts of Argyll)	1 Kilmory Estate, Lochgilphead, Argyll PA31 8RR	Tel: 01546 603611 Website: http://www.snh.org.uk
	Glencruitten Road, Oban, Argyll PA34 4DN	Tel: 01631 567228
	Main Street, Bowmore, Isle of Islay, Argyll PA34 7JJ	Tel: 01496 810711
	Ballochyle, Sandbank, Dunoon, Argyll PA23 8RD	Tel: 01369 705377
Scottish Ornithologists' Club	Waterston House, Aberlady, East Lothian EH32 0PY	Tel: 01875 871 330 E-mail: mail@the-soc.org.uk Website: http://www.the-soc.org.uk/
Scottish Wildlife Trust	Cramond House, Kirk Cramond, Cramond Glebe Road, Edinburgh EH4 6NS	Tel: 0131 312 7765 (switchboard) Website: http://www.swt.org.uk/

Appendix 5: Gazetteer

This Gazetteer lists all of the place names referred to in this book. For larger geographical features, the grid reference gives the approximate centre of the site.

There are two Loch Tallants on Islay. Most records relate to the loch near Laggan Bridge.

Many place names occur more than once in Argyll (e.g. Fearnoch and variations) and a qualifier is usually inserted to establish the site referred to.

Paul Daw

Place name	Recording Area	Grid ref.
A' Choille Mhor	Colonsay	NR4196
Acha	Coll	NM1854
Achanadriane	Kintyre	NR7250
Achnacairn	North Argyll	NM9235
Achnacloich	Mid-Argyll	NM9533
Achnacreebeag	North Argyll	NM9336
Achnacreemore	North Argyll	NM9236
Achnamara	Mid-Argyll	NR7786
Add Estuary	Mid-Argyll	NR8093
Ailsa Craig	Ayrshire Recording Area	NX0199
Airds Bay (Loch Etive)	Mid-Argyll	NN0032

Place name	Recording Area	Grid ref.
Airthrey Loch (Stirling)	Forth Recording Area	NS8196
Allt Mhoille	North Argyll	NN1131
Amod	Kintyre	NR6412
An Carn	Jura	NR6893
An Fhaodhail	Tiree	NM0144
Aoradh	Islay	NR2767
Appin	North Argyll	NM9346
Ardalanish Bay	Mull	NM3718
Ardanaiseig	Mid-Argyll	NN0824
Ardchattan	North Argyll	NM9734
Ardchonnel	Mid-Argyll	NM9032

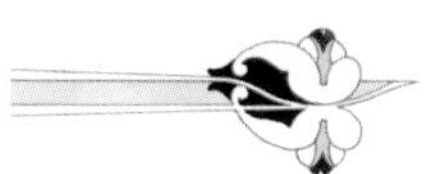

Place name	Recording Area	Grid ref.
Ardentallen Point	Mid-Argyll	NM8222
Ardentinny	Cowal	NS1887
Ardfernal	Jura	NR5671
Ardfin	Jura	NR4763
Ardgartan	Cowal	NN2703
Ardgenavan (Loch Fyne)	Mid-Argyll	NN1711
Ardilistry Bay	Islay	NR4448
Ardkinglass House (Loch Fyne)	Cowal	NN1710
Ardlamont Point	Cowal	NR9963
Ardlarach	Islay	NR2958
Ardmucknish Bay	North Argyll	NM8937
Ardnacross	Mull	NM5449
Ardnamurchan (area to the N & W of Morvern -formerly part of Argyll)	Highland Recording Area	NM56
Ardnave	Islay	NR2873
Ardnave Loch	Islay	NR2873
Ardpatrick House	Mid-Argyll	NR7559
Ardpatrick Point	Mid-Argyll	NR7357
Ardrishaig	Mid-Argyll	NR8585
Ardross	Highland Recording Area	NH6174
Ardskenish	Colonsay	NR3491
Arduaine	Mid-Argyll	NM8010
Arduaine Gardens	Mid-Argyll	NM7910
Ardyne	Cowal	NS1068
Ardyne Point	Cowal	NS0968
Arileod	Coll	NM1654
Arinagour	Coll	NM2257
Arnabost	Coll	NM2060
Aros Estuary	Mull	NM5644
Aros House	Mull	NM5545
Aros Moss	Kintyre	NR6721
Arrochar	Clyde Recording Area	NN2904
Ashfield	Mid-Argyll	NR7685
Asknish (Loch Gair)	Mid-Argyll	NR9391
Bach Island (Kerrara)	Mid-Argyll	NM7726
Backpacker's Lodge	Colonsay	NR3996
Balemartine	Tiree	NL9841
Balephetrish	Tiree	NM0046
Balephetrish Bay	Tiree	NM0047
Balephuil	Tiree	NL9540
Balephuil Bay	Tiree	NL9440
Balevullin	Tiree	NL9546
Balgie Burn, Dunoon	Cowal	NS1676
Balinoe	Tiree	NL9742
Balinoe Forest	Mid-Argyll	NM8722
Ballachuan Hazel Wood (SWT Reserve)	Mid-Argyll	NM7614
Ballachuan Loch (Seil)	Mid-Argyll	NM7615
Ballard	Coll	NM1655
Ballinaby	Islay	NR2267
Ballochgair	Kintyre	NR7727
Ballochroy	Kintyre	NR7252
Ballure	Kintyre	NR7149
Ballure (coast)	Kintyre	NR7050
Ballygrant	Islay	NR3966
Ballygrant Woods	Islay	NR4066
Ballyhaugh	Coll	NM1757
Balnabraid Glen	Kintyre	NR7515
Balnahard	Colonsay	NR4199
Balnamoil (Mull of Kintyre)	Kintyre	NR6306
Balvicar (Seil)	Mid-Argyll	NM7616
Balvicar Bay	Mid-Argyll	NM7717
Barcaldine	North Argyll	NM9541
Barnashaig	Mid-Argyll	NR7286
Barr Glen	Kintyre	NR6736
Barrapol	Tiree	NL9543
Baugh	Tiree	NM0243
Bealachandrain	Cowal	NR9983
Beinn a' Bhuiridh	North Argyll	NN0928
Beinn a' Chaolais	Jura	NR4873
Beinn Bhàn	Islay	NR3956
Beinn Chreagach Mhor	Mull	NM6338
Beinn Dorain	North Argyll	NN3237
Beinn Luibhean	Cowal	NN2407
Beinn Narnain	Cowal	NN2706
Beinn Sgulaird	North Argyll	NN0545
Beinn Talaidh	Mull	NM6234
Bellochantuy	Kintyre	NR6632
Bellanoch	Mid-Argyll	NR7992
Belnahua (Sound of Luing)	Mid-Argyll	NM7112
Ben Buie	Mull	NM6127
Ben Cruachan (summit)	North Argyll	NN0630
Ben Lui	Mid-Argyll	NN2626
Ben More (summit)	Mull	NM5233
Benderloch	North Argyll	NM9038
Benmore	Cowal	NS1485
Benmore Botanic Garden	Cowal	NS1385
Black Mount (Loch Tulla)	North Argyll	NN2842
Blackrock (Loch Indaal)	Islay	NR3062
Blairmore (Loch Long)	Cowal	NS1981
Blarcreen	North Argyll	NM9935
Blarghour (Loch Awe)	Mid-Argyll	NM9913
Bolsay	Islay	NR2257
Bonawe	North Argyll	NN0033
Bousd	Coll	NM2563
Bowmore	Islay	NR3159
Braevallich (Loch Awe)	Mid-Argyll	NM9507
Braigo	Islay	NR2369
Breachacha	Coll	NM1553
Bridgend	Islay	NR3362
Bridgend Merse	Islay	NR3262
Bridgend Woods	Islay	NR3462
Bruichladdich	Islay	NR2661
Brunerican Bay	Kintyre	NR6907
Bunessan	Mull	NM3821
Burg	Mull	NM3745
Burnt Islands (Kyles of Bute)	Cowal	NS0175
Cairn na Burgh (Treshnish Isles)	Mull	NM3044
Cairnbaan	Mid-Argyll	NR8390
Cairndow	Cowal	NN1810
Calgary	Mull	NM3751
Caliach Point	Mull	NM3454
Campbeltown	Kintyre	NR7120
Campbeltown Loch	Kintyre	NR7220
Canna (Island)	Highland Recording Area	NG2406
Cara (Island)	Kintyre	NR6343
Carnan Mor	Tiree	NL9640
Carradale	Kintyre	NR8138
Carraig an Daimh (Sound of Jura)	Mid-Argyll	NR6678
Carrick Castle	Cowal	NS1994

Place name	Recording Area	Grid ref.
Carsaig	Mull	NM5321
Carskey Bay	Kintyre	NR6607
Carskiey	Kintyre	NR6507
Castle Sween	Mid-Argyll	NR7178
Castle Toward School	Cowal	NS1168
Ceann a' Mhara	Tiree	NL9340
Ceann an t-Sailein	Mid-Argyll	NR7079
Ceannivara = Ceann a' Mhara		
Chiscan Farm	Kintyre	NR6718
Clachan	Kintyre	NR7656
Clachan Burn	Kintyre	NR7556
Clachan Mor	Tiree	NL9847
Claddach	Islay	NR1653
Cladville	Islay	NR1754
Claggain Bay	Islay	NR4653
Cliad	Coll	NM2059
Cluniter	Cowal	NS1572
Cnoc Bhirceapol	Tiree	NL9644
Coilessan	Cowal	NN2601
Coire Allt Achadh Luirginn	Mull	NM6437
Colintraive	Cowal	NS0374
Cologin	Mid-Argyll	NM8526
Colonsay Golf Course	Colonsay	NR3593
Colonsay Hotel	Colonsay	NR3894
Colonsay House	Colonsay	NR3996
Conie Glen	Kintyre	NR6910
Connel	Mid-Argyll	NM9134
Cornabus	Islay	NR3346
Cornaigbeg	Tiree	NL9846
Cornaigmore	Tiree	NL9847
Corpach Bay	Jura	NR5691
Corr Eilean (McCormaig Islands - Sound of Jura)	Mid-Argyll	NR6775
Corsapol	Islay	NR2966
Coul Point	Islay	NR1864
Coull Farm	Islay	NR2064
Coulport	Clyde Recording Area	NS2087
Craig (Glen More)	Mull	NM5829
Craigens	Islay	NR2967
Craigfad	Islay	NR2355
Craighouse	Jura	NR5267
Craignish Castle	Mid-Argyll	NM7701
Crannach (Water of Tulla)	North Argyll	NN3545
Crannich	Mull	NM5244
Crarae Gardens	Mid-Argyll	NR9897
Craro Island (off Gigha)	Kintyre	NR6247
Creag Island (off Lismore - Lynn of Lorn)	North Argyll	NM8337
Creag Mhor	Islay	NR2769
Creggans	Cowal	NN0802
Crinan	Mid-Argyll	NR7894
Crinan Canal	Mid-Argyll	NR8589
Crinan Ferry	Mid-Argyll	NR7993
Crinan Moss	Mid-Argyll	NR8093
Croggan	Mull	NM7027
Croig	Mull	NM4053
Crossapol	Coll	NM1253
Crossapol	Tiree	NL9943
Crossapol Bay	Tiree	NM0043
Cruach Eachd, North Argyll	North Argyll	NN2232
Cuil Bay	Highland Recording Area	NM9754
Culcharron	North Argyll	NM9139
Culcherran = Culcharron		
Cumbernauld	Forth Recording Area	NS7574
Dalavich	Mid-Argyll	NM9612
Dalchenna	Mid-Argyll	NN0705
Dalintober	North Argyll	NM9140
Dalmally	Mid-Argyll	NN1527
Dalnahasaig (Dalnahassoch)	Mid-Argyll	NR8293
Dalrannoch	North Argyll	NM9341
Danna (island)	Mid-Argyll	NR6978
Darnaway Forest	Moray & Nairn Recording Area	NH9751
Derryguaig	Mull	NM4835
Dervaig	Mull	NM4352
Doire Darach	North Argyll	NN2841
Druimdrishaig (Ormsary)	Mid-Argyll	NR7370
Drumnadrochit	Highland Recording Area	NH5029
Drumgarve	Kintyre	NR7226
Duart Bay	Mull	NM7434
Dubh Artach (26 km SW of Mull)	Mull	NM1203
Duich Moss	Islay	NR3254
Dùn Bàn	Kintyre	NR5914
Dunderave Point (Loch Fyne)	Mid-Argyll	NN1409
Dunmore (West Loch Tarbert)	Kintyre	NR7861
Dunoon	Cowal	NS1776
Dunoon, West Bay	Cowal	NS1776
Dunrostan (Loch Sween)	Mid-Argyll	NR7381
Dunstaffnage	Mid-Argyll	NM8834
Dunstaffnage Bay	Mid-Argyll	NM8833
Duntrune Castle	Mid-Argyll	NR7995
Dutchman's Cap (Treshnish Isles)	Mull	NM2438
Easdale	Mid-Argyll	NM7417
East Kames (Loch Fyne)	Mid-Argyll	NR9289
East Loch Fada	Colonsay	NR3995
East Loch Tarbert	Kintyre	NR8768
Easter Ellister	Islay	NR2053
Ederline	Mid-Argyll	NM8702
Edrachillis	Highland Recording Area	NC1138
Eileach an Naoimh (Garvellachs)	Mid-Argyll	NM6409
Eilean Annraidh (Iona)	Mull	NM2926
Eilean Aoghainn (Loch Fyne)	Mid-Argyll	NR9894
Eilean Balnagowan, Highland	Highland Recording Area	NM9553
Eilean Beag	Jura	NM6801
Eilean Buidhe (off Ardmarnock - Loch Fyne)	Cowal	NR9071
Eilean Buidhe (off Portavadie - Loch Fyne)	Cowal	NR9169
Eilean Dubh (Lynn of Lorn)	North Argyll	NM8438
Eilean Fraoich (Sound of Jura)	Mid-Argyll	NR7186
Eilean Inshaig (Loch Craignish)	Mid-Argyll	NM8104
Eilean Loch Oscair (off Lismore - Lynn of Lorn)	North Argyll	NM8645
Eilean Mor	Jura	NM6701
Eilean nam Ban (Sound of Iona)	Mull	NM2924
Eilean nan Coinean (Sound of Jura)	Mid-Argyll	NR7186
Eleraig	Mid-Argyll	NM8616
Ellary	Mid-Argyll	NR7375
Eredine (Loch Awe)	Mid-Argyll	NM9609
Eriska	North Argyll	NM9042
Escart	Kintyre	NR8466

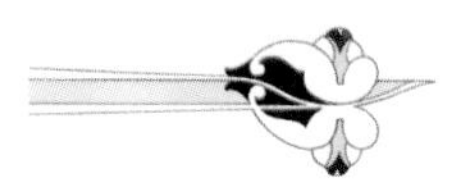

Place name	Recording Area	Grid ref.
Esknish	Islay	NR3664
Fairlie	Ayrshire Recording Area	NS2054
Farne Islands	Northumberland	NU2338
Faslane	Clyde Recording Area	NS2489
Feall Bay	Coll	NM1354
Fellonmore (Loch Spelve)	Mull	NM6827
Fidden	Mull	NM3021
Finlaggan	Islay	NR3968
Firth of Lorn	Mid-Argyll	NM7527
Fladda (Sound of Luing)	Mid-Argyll	NM7212
Fladda (Treshnish Isles)	Mull	NM2943
Ford	Mid-Argyll	NM8603
Foreland	Islay	NR2764
Frenchman's Rocks	Islay	NR1554
Furnace	Mid-Argyll	NN0200
Gairletter	Cowal	NS1984
Gairletter Point	Cowal	NS1984
Gairlochhead	Clyde Recording Area	NS2391
Gairlochy	Highland Recording Area	NN1784
Gallanach	Coll	NM2160
Ganavan	Mid-Argyll	NM8632
Garmony	Mull	NM6640
Garvellachs	Mid-Argyll	NM6510
Gigha (island)	Kintyre	NR6449
Glas Bheinn	Islay	NR4259
Glas Eilean (Loch Fyne)	Mid-Argyll	NR9185
Glasdrum	North Argyll	NN0146
Glassary see Kilmichael Glassary		
Gleann na Rainich	Islay	NR1853
Gleann Seilisdeir	Mull	NM4730
Gleannagaoidh	Islay	NR2153
Glen Aray	Mid-Argyll	NN0913
Glen Finart	Cowal	NS1691
Glen Forsa	Mull	NM6237
Glen Fyne	Mid-Argyll	NN2316
Glen Kerran	Kintyre	NR7113
Glen Kinglass	North Argyll	NN1335
Glen Lochy	Mid-Argyll	NN2529
Glen Lonan	Mid-Argyll	NM9328
Glen Nant	Mid-Argyll	NN0227
Glen Noe	North Argyll	NN0733
Glen Orchy	North Argyll	NN2432
Glen Shira	Mid-Argyll	NN1213
Glenbarr	Kintyre	NR6636
Glenbranter	Cowal	NS1197
Glenbranter Forest	Cowal	NS1096
Glencarse	Forth Recording Area	NO1921
Glendaruel	Cowal	NR9983
Glengorm	Mull	NM4355
Glenkinglass Lodge	North Argyll	NN1638
Glenramskill House	Kintyre	NR7319
Glunimore Island (Sanda)	Kintyre	NR7405
Gortantaoid Point	Islay	NR3374
Gott Bay	Tiree	NM0546
Grasspoint	Mull	NM7430
Gribun	Mull	NM4533
Grishipoll	Coll	NM1959
Gruline	Mull	NM5440
Gunna (Island)	Coll	NM0951
Hawes Bank	(off) Coll	NM2675

Place name	Recording Area	Grid ref.
Helensburgh	Clyde Recording Area	NS3181
Heylipol	Tiree	NL9743
Holy Loch	Cowal	NS1681
Homeston	Kintyre	NR6715
Horse Island	Clyde Recording Area	NS2142
Hough Bay	Tiree	NL9346
Hunter's Quay	Cowal	NS1879
Hynish	Tiree	NL9839
Inch Kenneth	Mull	NM4335
Innnellan	Cowal	NS1570
Inver	Jura	NR4471
Inveraray	Mid-Argyll	NN0908
Inverinan (Loch Awe)	Mid-Argyll	NM9917
Inverneil	Mid-Argyll	NR8481
Iona	Mull	NM2625
Iona Abbey	Mull	NM2824
Islandadd Bridge	Mid-Argyll	NR8092
Islay Airport	Islay	NR3251
Islay House	Islay	NR3362
Jura House	Jura	NR4863
Kames Bay (Loch Melfort)	Mid-Argyll	NM8211
Kames Golf Course	Cowal	NR9670
Keil Point (Southend)	Kintyre	NR6707
Keills (Loch na Cille)	Mid-Argyll	NR6980
Kennacraig	Kintyre	NR8262
Kennacraig-Islay Ferry Crossing	Islay	NR6955
Kenovay	Tiree	NL9946
Kerrara (Island)	Mid-Argyll	NM8128
Kilberry	Mid-Argyll	NR7164
Kilblaan (Glen Shira)	Mid-Argyll	NN1213
Kilbrannan Sound	Kintyre	NR8953
Kilbride Bay	Cowal	NR9566
Kilbride Farm	Cowal	NR9668
Kilchattan	Colonsay	NR3695
Kilchenzie	Kintyre	NR6724
Kilchiaran	Islay	NR2060
Kilchoan House	Mid-Argyll	NM7913
Kilchoman	Islay	NR2163
Kilchrist	Kintyre	NR6917
Kilchurn Castle	Mid-Argyll	NN1327
Kildalloig	Kintyre	NR7518
Kildalton	Islay	NR4550
Kildalton House	Islay	NR4347
Kilfinan	Cowal	NR9378
Kilfinichen	Mull	NM4928
Kilkenneth	Tiree	NL9444
Killean	Kintyre	NR6944
Killellan	Kintyre	NR6815
Killinallan	Islay	NR3171
Killinallan Dunes	Islay	NR3172
Killinallan Point	Islay	NR3072
Kilmaronag	Mid-Argyll	NM9334
Kilmartin	Mid-Argyll	NR8398
Kilmartin Burn	Mid-Argyll	NR8296
Kilmartin Glen,	Mid-Argyll	NR8398
Kilmelford	Mid-Argyll	NM8413
Kilmichael Glassary	Mid-Argyll	MR8593
Kilmichael Glen	Mid-Argyll	NR8694
Kilmichael of Inverlussa	Mid-Argyll	NR7785
Kilmore	Mid-Argyll	NM8725

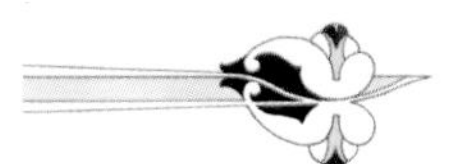

Place name	Recording Area	Grid ref.
Kilmory	Mid-Argyll	NR8786
Kilmun	Cowal	NS1781
Kilnaughton Bay	Islay	NR3445
Kilninian	Mull	NM3945
Kiloran Bay	Colonsay	NR4098
Kiloran Village	Colonsay	NR3996
Kilsyth	Forth Recording Area	NS7178
Kilvecuen	Mull	NM4019
Kingussie, Highland	Highland Recording Area	NH7500
Kintaline Mill	North Argyll	NM8939
Kintallan	Mid-Argyll	NR7487
Kinuachdrachd	Jura	NR7098
Kirkconnel	Dumfries & Galloway Recording Area	NS7311
Kirkapol	Tiree	NM0447
Knap	Cowal	NS2090
Knapdale (area between Lochgilphead and Tarbert)	Mid-Argyll	NR7869
Knock	Mull	NM5438
Knocklearoch	Islay	NR3964
Knockstapplebeg	Kintyre	NR6912
Kyles of Bute - East	Cowal	NS0472
Kyles of Bute - West	Cowal	NR9870
Lagg	Jura	NR5978
Laggan	Islay	NR2856
Laggan Bridge	Islay	NR3457
Langa Quarry	Kintyre	NR6524
Langamull	Mull	NM3853
Largie Castle (site)	Kintyre	NR7048
Largie Farm	Kintyre	NR7046
Largybaan	Kintyre	NR6114
Leac a' Chaoruinn (Eredine)	Mid-Argyll	NM9605
Lealt	Jura	NR6690
Ledaig	North Argyll	NM9037
Ledaig Point,	North Argyll	NM8935
Lerags	Mid-Argyll	NM8324
Liath Eilean (Sound of Jura)	Mid-Argyll	NR6878
Liath Eilein (Loch Caolisport)	Mid-Argyll	NR7172
Linne Mhuirich	Mid-Argyll	NR7284
Lismore (island)	North Argyll	NM8038
Little Colonsay	Mull	NM3736
Little Eachaig River	Cowal	NS1281
Loch a' Chlair	Tiree	NL9844
Loch a' Chnuic Bhric	Jura	NR4473
Loch a' Phuill	Tiree	NL9541
Loch Airigh Dhaibhaidh	Islay	NR3155
Loch Allan	Islay	NR4267
Loch an Eilein	Tiree	NL9843
Loch an Eilein Beg	Kintyre	NR7953
Loch an Eilein Mor	Kintyre	NR8053
Loch an Torr	Mull	NM4552
Loch Arail	Mid-Argyll	NR8079
Loch Assapol	Mull	NM4020
Loch Avich	Mid-Argyll	NM9314
Loch Awe (mid)	Mid-Argyll	NN0219
Loch Awe (head)	Mid-Argyll	NN1125
Loch Ba	Mull	NM5638
Loch Ba head	Mull	NM5836
Loch Ballygrant	Islay	NR4066
Loch Beg	Mull	NM5229
Loch Bhasapol	Tiree	NL9747
Loch Bhirceapol	Tiree	NL9644
Loch Buie	Mull	NM6023
Loch Caolisport	Mid-Argyll	NR7475
Loch Craignish	Mid-Argyll	NM7800
Loch Creran	North Argyll	NM9543
Loch Crinan	Mid-Argyll	NR7994
Loch Cuin i.e. Loch a' Chumhainn	Mull	NM4251
Loch Don	Mull	NM7332
Loch Earblaig	Tiree	NL9446
Loch Eck	Cowal	NS1390
Loch Eck (head)	Cowal	NS1296
Loch Ederline	Mid-Argyll	NM8602
Loch Eighinn	Islay	NR3350
Loch Etive (Outer)	North Argyll	NM9434
Loch Etive (Upper)	North Argyll	NN0536
Loch Fada	Colonsay	NR3895
Loch Feochan	Mid-Argyll	NM8623
Loch Finlaggan	Islay	NR3867
Loch Frisa	Mull	NM4848
Loch Fyne	Mid-Argyll	NR9386
Loch Gair	Mid-Argyll	NR9290
Loch Garradh nan Capull	Tiree	NL9741
Loch Gilp	Mid-Argyll	NR8685
Loch Gorm	Islay	NR2365
Loch Gruinart	Islay	NR2868
Loch Indaal	Islay	NR2961
Loch Katrine	Forth Recording Area	NN4209
Loch Laich	North Argyll	NM9246
Loch Leathan	Mid-Argyll	NR8798
Loch Linnhe	North Argyll	NM9251
Loch Long (head)	Cowal	NN2904
Loch Lussa	Kintyre	NR7129
Loch Meldalloch	Cowal	NR9374
Loch Melfort	Mid-Argyll	NM8112
Loch na Beiste	Kintyre	NR7654
Loch na Cille (Danna)	Mid-Argyll	NR6980
Loch na Keal	Mull	NM5038
Loch nan Druimnean	Mid-Argyll	NM8414
Loch nan Gad	Kintyre	NR7857
Loch Nell	Mid-Argyll	NM8927
Loch Peallach	Mull	NM4852
Loch Poit na h-I (= Loch Pottie)	Mull	NM3122
Loch Restil	Cowal	NN2208
Loch Riaghain	Tiree	NM0347
Loch Riddon	Cowal	NS0077
Loch Romain	Kintyre	NR8253
Loch Ryan	Dumfries & Galloway Recording Area	NX06
Loch Scammadale	Mid-Argyll	NM8920
Loch Scridain	Mull	NM4525
Loch Seil	Mid-Argyll	NM8020
Loch Shira	Mid-Argyll	NN1009
Loch Skerrols	Islay	NR3463
Loch Spelve	Mull	NM6927
Loch Staoisha	Islay	NR4071
Loch Striven	Cowal	NS0777
Loch Sween	Mid-Argyll	NR7484
Loch Tallant (Kildalton)	Islay	NR4450
Loch Tallant (Laggan)*	Islay	NR3357

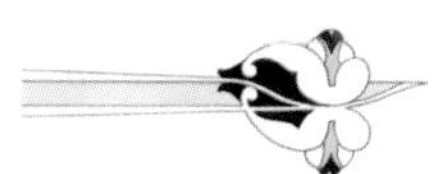

Place name	Recording Area	Grid ref.
Loch Tarbert	Jura	NR5681
Loch Tromlee	Mid-Argyll	NN0424
Loch Tuath	Mull	NM3743
Loch Tulla	North Argyll	NN3043
Lochaber (area N from Loch Leven to Glen Garry)	Highland Recording Area	
Lochan Luing	Kintyre	NR6948
Lochawe Village	North Argyll	NN1126
Lochbuie	Mull	NM6025
Lochdon	Mull	NM7233
Lochdonhead	Mull	NM7233
Lochgair	Mid-Argyll	NR9190
Lochgilphead	Mid-Argyll	NR8688
Lochgoilhead	Cowal	NN2001
Lochorodale,	Kintyre	NR6615
Lodge Plantation	Coll	NM2257
Lonban	Coll	NM1756
Lossiemouth	Moray & Nairn Recording Area	NJ2371
Lossit Point	Islay	NR1756
Lough Neagh	Northern Ireland	
Lower Vaul	Tiree	NM0547
Lowlandsman's Bay	Jura	NR5672
Luing (island)	Mid-Argyll	NM7310
Lunga (near Scarba)	Mid-Argyll	NM7008
Lunga (Treshnish Isles)	Mull	NM2741
Lusragan Burn	Mid-Argyll	NM9032
Lussa Bay	Jura	NR6486
Lussa Loch	Kintyre	NR7129
Macharioch	Kintyre	NR7309
Machir Bay	Islay	NR2062
Machrie Hotel	Islay	NR3249
Machrie River	Islay	NR3250
Machrihanish Airfield	Kintyre	NR6622
Machrihanish Bay	Kintyre	NR6322
Machrihanish Links	Kintyre	NR6522
Machrihanish SBO (Seabird Observatory)	Kintyre	NR6220
Machrihanish Water	Kintyre	NR6720
Mannal	Tiree	NL9840
McCormaig Isles	Mid-Argyll	NR6776
Mid Loch Fada	Colonsay	NR3895
Middleton	Tiree	NL9443
Milton	Tiree	NM0847
Minard	Mid-Argyll	NR9796
Minard Castle	Mid-Argyll	NR9794
Mishnish Lochs	Mull	NM4752
Moine Mhor (National Nature Reserve)	Mid-Argyll	NR8192
Morvern (area to the W of Loch Linnhe - formerly part of Argyll)	Highland Recording Area	NM75
Moss	Tiree	NL9544
MSBO = Machrihanish Seabird Observatory	Kintyre	NR6220
Muckairn	Mid-Argyll	NM9733
Mulindry	Islay	NR3559
Mull of Kintyre	Kintyre	NR5906
Mull of Kintyre Lighthouse	Kintyre	NR5808
Mull of Oa	Islay	NR2641
Na h-Urrachann (Scarba)	Mid-Argyll	NM6703
Nerabus	Islay	NR2255
Neriby	Islay	NR3660
Nether Largie	Mid-Argyll	NR8298
North Connel	North Argyll	NM9034
North Ledaig	North Argyll	NM9036
Oa Peninsula	Islay	NR2844
Oban	Mid-Argyll	NM8529
Oban - Craignure, Mull Ferry	Mull	NM7934
Octovullin	Islay	NR3464
Oronsay	Colonsay	NR3489
Orsay	Islay	NR1651
Otter Ferry	Cowal	NR9284
Otter House	Cowal	NR9278
Outer Loch Etive (i.e. Connel Bridge to Taynuilt)	North Argyll	NM9434
Paps of Jura	Jura	NR4973
Pass of Brander	Mid-Argyll	NN0527
Peninver	Kintyre	NR7524
Penmore	Mull	NM4052
Pennyghael	Mull	NM5126
Pennygown	Mull	NM5942
Pentire Head	Cornwall	SW9380
Peterculter	North-east Scotland Recording Area	NJ8000
Pigs Paradise	Colonsay	NR3697
Pitlochry	Perth & Kinross Recording Area	NN9458
Point of Knap	Mid-Argyll	NR6972
Poltalloch	Mid-Argyll	NR8196
Port Askaig	Islay	NR4369
Port Charlotte	Islay	NR2558
Port Ellen	Islay	NR3645
Port Mor	Colonsay	NR3594
Port Wemyss	Islay	NR1651
Portnahaven	Islay	NR1652
Portsonachan	Mid-Argyll	NN0520
Proaig	Islay	NR4557
Rainberg Mor	Jura	NR5687
Rannoch Moor	Highland Recording Area	NN3550
Reisa Mhic Phaidean (Sound of Jura)	Mid-Argyll	NM7500
Rhinns of Islay - see Rinns of Islay		
Rhoin Farm	Kintyre	NR6823
Rhu	Clyde Recording Area	NS2683
Rhugarbh	North Argyll	NM9340
Rhunahaorine	Kintyre	NR7048
Rhunahaorine Point	Kintyre	NR6949
Rinns of Islay	Islay	NR2256
River Dearg	North Argyll	NM9739
River Eachaig	Cowal	NS1484
River Massan	Cowal	NS1087
River Ruel	Cowal	NS0080
River Shira	Mid-Argyll	NN1212
River Sorn	Islay	NR3462
Rockside	Islay	NR2263
Ronachan Point	Kintyre	NR7455
Ronnachmore	Islay	NR3058
Rosneath	Clyde Recording Area	NS2583
Ross of Mull	Mull	NM3620
Roundhouse	Coll	NM1554
Ruaig	Tiree	NM0747
Rubha Chraiginis	Tiree	NL9245
Rubha nan Eoin (Loch Long)	Cowal	NS2192
Ruddon's Point, Fife	Fife Recording Area	NO4500
Saddell	Kintyre	NR7832

Place name	Recording Area	Grid ref.
Salen	Mull	NM5743
Saligo	Islay	NR2166
Saligo Bay	Islay	NR2066
Salum	Tiree	NM0748
Salum Bay	Tiree	NM0649
Sanaig Cliffs	Islay	NR2371
Sanaigmore	Islay	NR2370
Sanda Islands	Kintyre	NR7204
Sandaig	Tiree	NL9343
Scalasaig	Colonsay	NR3994
Scallastle	Mull	NM6938
Scallastle Bay	Mull	NM6939
Scar Rocks	Dumfries & Galloway Recording Area	NX2533
Scarba (Island)	Mid-Argyll	NM7004
Scarinish	Tiree	NM0444
Scarisdale Point	Mull	NM5137
Scoor	Mull	NM4119
Seafield (Bowmore)	Islay	NR3159
Seil Island	Mid-Argyll	NM7518
Sgat Beag (Loch Fyne)	Cowal	NR9466
Sgat Mor (Loch Fyne)	Cowal	NR9366
Sgeir an Eirionnaich (Treshnish Isles)	Mull	NM2843
Sgeir an Eitich (off Ganavan)	Mid-Argyll	NM8532
Sgeir na h-Iolaire (Treshnish Isles)	Mull	NM2843
Sheep Island (Sanda)	Kintyre	NR7305
Shian Bay	Jura	NR5287
Shuna (Island)	Mid-Argyll	NM7607
Silver Craigs	Mid-Argyll	NR8984
Singing Sands	Islay	NR3444
Skeroblin Loch	Kintyre	NR7026
Skerryvore Lighthouse (17km SW of Tiree)	Tiree	NL8426
Skervuile Lighthouse (Sound of Jura)	Jura	NR6071
Skipness	Kintyre	NR9057
Slockavullin	Mid-Argyll	NR8297
Small Isles Bay	Jura	NR5368
Smaull	Islay	NR2168
Soa (Island)	Mull	NM2419
Soa (Island)	Tiree	NM0746
Soa Point	Tiree	NM0745
Sorisdale	Coll	NM2763
Sorobaidh Bay	Tiree	NL9942
Sound of Gigha	Kintyre	NR6749
Sound of Jura (sea area between Jura and the mainland)	Mid-Argyll	NR6480
South Ledaig	North Argyll	NM9035
South Shian	North Argyll	NM9041
Southend	Kintyre	NR6908
St Catherines	Cowal	NN1207
Stac Mhic Mhurchaidh (off Iona)	Mull	NM2426
Staffa	Mull	NM3235
Stonefield (West Loch Tarbert)	Kintyre	NR8568
Stonefield Castle Hotel	Mid-Argyll	NR8671
Strachur	Cowal	NN0901
Strachur Bay	Cowal	NN0801
Strath of Appin	North Argyll	NM9445
Stronchullin	Cowal	NS1884
Strone Glen	Kintyre	NR6409
Stronvar (Uig)	Coll	NM1654
Succoth (nr. Dalmally)	Mid-Argyll	NN2125

Place name	Recording Area	Grid ref.
Sunderland Farm	Islay	NR2464
Sunipol	Mull	NM3753
Tangy Loch	Kintyre	NR6928
Tarbert	Kintyre	NR8668
Taychreggan (Loch Awe)	Mid-Argyll	NN0421
Tayinloan (jetty)	Kintyre	NR6946
Taynish NNR (National Nature Reserve)	Mid-Argyll	NR7384
Taynuilt	Mid-Argyll	NN0031
Tayvallich	Mid-Argyll	NR7487
Tenga	Mull	NM5145
Tervine	Mid-Argyll	NN0825
Texa (Island)	Islay	NR3943
The Laggan	Kintyre	NR6624
The Lodge	Coll	NM2157
The Manse (Scarinish)	Tiree	NM0445
The Reef	Tiree	NM0045
The Roundhouse	Coll	NM1554
The Strand (Oronsay/Colonsay)	Colonsay	NR3690
Tighnabruaich	Cowal	NR9772
Tighnahoran	Mid-Argyll	NR7675
Tobermory	Mull	NM5055
Torcastle	Highland Recording Area	NN1378
Torlochan	Mull	NM5540
Tormisdale	Islay	NR1958
Torosay	Mull	NM7335
Torran (Loch Awe)	Mid-Argyll	NM8704
Torran Rocks	Mull	NM2614
Torrans	Mull	NM4825
Torrisdale	Kintyre	NR7936
Totronald	Coll	NM1656
Toward	Cowal	NS1368
Toward Point	Cowal	NS1367
Traigh nam Barc	Colonsay	NR3591
Treshnish Isles	Mull	NM2842
Treshnish Point	Mull	NM3348
Trudernish	Islay	NR4652
Tullochgorm	Mid-Argyll	NR9695
Turnalt	Mid-Argyll	NM8407
Tynacoille	Islay	NR2763
Ugadale	Kintyre	NR7728
Uisaed Point	Kintyre	NR6220
Ulva Ferry	Mull	NM4439
Ulva (Island)	Mull	NM3939
Ulva Lagoons (Loch Sween)	Mid-Argyll	NR7182
Vaul	Tiree	NM0448
Water of Tulla	North Argyll	NN3546
West Ardhu	Mull	NM4251
West Hynish	Tiree	NL9639
West Loch Tarbert	Kintyre	NR7759
West Machrihanish	Kintyre	NR6520
West Parkfergus	Kintyre	NR6621
Westport Marsh	Kintyre	NR6525
Whitehouse	Tiree	NL9947
Whitehouse Bay	Mid-Argyll	NR8581
Wildlife Park Inveraray	Mid-Argyll	NN0705

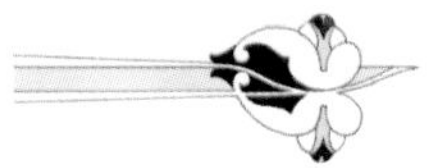

References

Alexander DR 1979. *The birds of Colonsay and Oransay*. Privately published.

Allen WH 1957. Review of a book by Acworth. *Bird-Banding* 28:55-56.

Alston JH 1913. The Jay in Argyllshire. *Scott Nat* :43-44.

Amar A, Smith K, Lindsell J 2005. Population changes of some bird species in Scottish and Welsh Atlantic oakwoods between 1980s and 2003/4 using data from the Repeat Woodland Bird Survey. *Bot J Scotl* 57:179-185.

Amar A, Hewson CM, Thewlis RM, Smith KW *et al.* 2006. *What's Happening to our Woodland Birds? Long-term changes in the populations of woodland birds.* Sandy/Thetford: RSPB/BTO (RSPB Research Rept 19/BTO Research Rept 169).

Anderson DIK & Petty SJ 1996. Population growth and breeding of Mandarin *Aix galericulata* in Cowal, Argyll. *Argyll Bird Rept* 12:82-84.

Anderson P 1894. Bird notes from the island of Tiree. *Ann Scott Nat Hist* 23:146-153, 212-224.

Anderson P 1898. On birds observed on the island of Tiree. *Ann Scott Nat Hist* 27:153-161.

Anderson P 1911. Increase of Mute Swans in Tiree. *Ann Scott Nat Hist* 1911:246-247.

Anderson P 1913. The birds of the island of Tiree. *Scott Nat* 1913:73-78, 169-172, 193-200, 217-224, 241-245.

Anderson Smith W 1882. *Benderloch: or Notes from the West Highlands.* Alexander Gardner, Paisley.

Anderson Smith W 1887. *Loch Creran: Notes from the West Highlands.* Alexander Gardner, Paisley.

Andrews IJ & Naylor KA 2002. Records of species and subspecies recorded in Scotland on up to 20 occasions. *Scott Birds* 23:61-116.

Annual reports of the National Census of Greenland White-fronted Geese in Britain. *Greenland White-fronted Goose Study*, c/o Department of Wildlife Ecology, Ronde, Denmark.

Anon 1953. Magnificent Frigatebird in Scotland. *Scott Nat* 65:193-194.

Anon 1954. Magnificent Frigate-bird in Tiree, Inner Hebrides: a new British Bird. *Brit Birds* 47:58-59.

Anon 1995. Article in "The Oban Times" 31st August 1995, page 9.

Anon 1999. *National Planning Policy Guideline 14: Natural Heritage.* Scottish Office, Edinburgh.

Anon 2003. The status of Baird's Sandpiper in Scotland. *Birding Scotl* 6:155.

Anon 2005a. *An Agricultural Strategy for the Argyll Area.* Published by the Argyll Agricultural Forum, July 2005.

Anon 2005b. *Report of the National Goose Management Review Group: Review of the National Policy Framework for Goose Management in Scotland. Response by the Scottish Executive.* Scottish Executive paper 2005/12.

Anon 2006. *The Scottish Forestry Strategy 2006.* Forestry Commission Scotland, Edinburgh.

ap Rheinallt T 1999. A Checklist of the Birds of Argyll. *Argyll Bird Rept* 15:100-110.

ap Rheinallt T 2001. White-rumped Sandpiper *Calidris fuscicollis* on Islay, 13 August 2000 – the first Argyll record. *Argyll Bird Rept* 17:118-120.

ap Rheinallt T 2002. Arctic Redpoll *Carduelis hornemanni* on Islay, 22 September 2001 – the first Argyll record. *Argyll Bird Rept* 18:115-120.

ap Rheinallt T & Daw P 2000. Argyll Bird Checklist – 2000 Update. *Argyll Bird Rept* 16:105-108.

Arévalo JE & Gosler AG 1994. The behaviour of Treecreepers *Certhia familiaris* in mixed-species flocks in winter. *Bird Study* 41:1-6.

Ascherson N 2002. *Stone Voices: The Search for Scotland.* Granta Books, London.

Austin G & Houston DC 1997. The breeding performance of the Buzzard *Buteo buteo* in Argyll, Scotland and a comparison with other areas in Britain. *Bird Study* 44:146-154.

Averis B & Martin J 1985. *Argyll Woodland Survey: A Survey of Broadleaf Woodlands in Argyll, Spring 1985.* RSPB Rept.

Bagworth T 2000. Rare and unusual birds on the Calf of Man 1996-1999. *Peregrine: The Manx Bird Report 1996* Vol.8 No. 1:48.

Baillie SR, Marchant JH, Crick HQP, Noble DG *et al.* 2005. *Breeding Birds in the Wider Countryside: their Conservation Status 2004.* BTO Research Rept 385.

Baines D & Summers RW 1997. Assessment of bird collisions with deer fences in Scottish forests. *J Appl Ecol* 34:941-948.

Baker H, Stroud DA, Aebischer NJ, Cranswick PA, Gregory RD, McSorley CA, Noble DG, Rehfisch MM 2006. Population estimates of birds in Great Britain and the United Kingdom. *Brit Birds* 99:25-44.

Band W, Madders M, Whitfield DP 2006. Developing field and analytical methods to assess avian collision risk at wind farms. In: de Lucas M, Janss G, Ferrer M (eds). *Birds and Wind Power.* Lynx Edicions, Barcelona.

Banks AN, Coombes RH, Crick HQP 2002. The Peregrine breeding population of the UK & Isle of Man in 2002. *BTO Research Rept* 330.

Bannerman DA 1953-1963. *The Birds of the British Isles.* 12 vols. Oliver & Boyd, Edinburgh.

Barne JH, Robson CF, Kaznowska SS, Doody JP, Davidson NC, Buck AL eds. 1997. *Coasts and seas of the United Kingdom. Region 14 South-west Scotland: Ballantrae to Mull.* Joint Nature Conservation Committee. (Coastal Directories Series), Peterborough.

Bartoszewicz M & Zalewski A 2003. American Mink, *Mustela vison* diet and predation on waterfowl in the Slonsk Reserve, western Poland. *Folia Zool* 52:225-238.

Baxter EV & Rintoul LJ 1928. *Geographical Distribution and status of Birds in Scotland.* Oliver & Boyd, Edinburgh.

Baxter EV & Rintoul LJ 1953. *The Birds of Scotland.* Oliver & Boyd, Edinburgh.

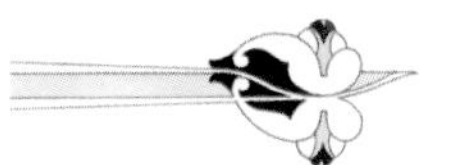

Bearhop S, Fiedler W, Furness RW, Votier SC *et al.* 2005. Assortative mating as a mechanism for rapid evolution of a migratory divide. *Science* 310:502-504.

Berry J 1939. *The Status and Distribution of Wild Geese and Wild Duck in Scotland.* Cambridge University Press, Cambridge.

Bibby H, Fojt W, Burd F 1987. Saltmarsh survey of Great Britain. Scotland Regional Report - South West. Unpublished report to Nature Conservancy Council.

Bignal E Bignal S, McCracken D 1997. The social life of the Chough. *Brit Wildl* 8:373-383.

Bignal E, Bignal S, Moore P, Clarke J, Clarke P 1992. *The Second International Chough Census in Scotland 1992.* Scottish Chough Study Group, unpublished report.

Bignal E, Curtis DJ, Matthews JL 1988. *Islay: Land Types, Bird Habitats, and Nature Conservation. Part 1. Land Use and Birds in Islay.* NCC Chief Scientists Directorate, Report No. 809, Part 1. Nature Conservancy Council, Peterborough.

Bignal E, Monaghan P, Benn S, Bignal S *et al.* 1987. Breeding success and post fledging survival in the Chough *Pyrrhocorax pyrrhocorax. Bird Study* 34:39-42.

Birkhead TR 1991. *The Magpies: the Ecology and Behaviour of Black-billed and Yellow-billed Magpies.* T & AD Poyser, London.

Bishop AH 1913. An Oronsay shell-mound – A Scottish pre-neolithic site. *Proc Scot Arch Soc* 48:52-108.

Blatchford JG 1971. Breeding birds of Coll 1969-70. *Scott Birds* 6:271-274.

Booth C 1975. *Birds in Islay.* Argyll Reproductions Ltd. Port Charlotte, Islay.

Booth C 1981. *Birds in Islay,* 2nd edn. Argyll Reproductions Ltd. Port Charlotte, Islay.

Bossema I 1979. Jays and oaks: an eco-ethological study of a symbiosis. *Behaviour* 70:1-117.

BOURC 2000. Twenty-seventh Report (October 2000) *Ibis* 143:171-175.

Bowler JM 2003. A Tiree taster, spring 2003. *Birding Scotl* 6:126-127.

Boyd JM 1958. The birds of Tiree and Coll. *Brit Birds* 51:41-56,103-118.

Brackenridge W 1968. The Magpie in western Scotland. *Scott Birds* 5:65.

Broad R 2005. Argyll Raptor Study Group – monitoring survey for 2004. *Eider* (June 2005):6-9.

Broad RA & Cadbury CJ 1989. Breeding seabirds of Tiree & Coll. In: *The Birds of Coll & Tiree: status, habitats and conservation.* Ed. D.A. Stroud. NCC/SOC. Edinburgh.

Broad RA, Seddon AJE, Stroud DA 1986. The waterfowl of fresh water lochs in Argyll: May-June 1985. *Argyll Bird Rept* 3:77-91.

Brotons L & Haftorn S 1999. Geographic variation of the storage behaviour in the Coal Tit *Parus ater*: role of winter residency and environmental conditions. *Ibis* 141:587-595.

Brown AW & Brown LM 1985. The Scottish Mute Swan census 1983. *Scott Birds* 13:140-148.

Brown AW & Brown LM 1993. The Scottish Mute Swan census 1990. *Scott Birds* 17:93-102.

Brown AW & Brown LM 2005. The 2002 census of the Mute Swan in Scotland. *Scott Birds* 25:1-16.

Brown N 2002. *An Ornithological Survey of the Constant Effort Site at Aros Moss, Kintyre 1997-2002.* Privately Published Report.

Brown P & Waterston G 1962. *The Return of the Osprey.* Collins, London.

Buchanan GM, Pearce-Higgins JW, Wotton SR, Grant MC, Whitfield DP 2003. Correlates of the change in Ring Ouzel *Turdus torquatus* abundance in Scotland from 1988-91 to 1999. *Bird Study* 50:97-105.

Buckley TE 1893. Goshawk in Mull. *Ann Scott Nat Hist* 5:45.

Burton H Evans TL & Weir DN 1970. Wrynecks breeding in Scotland. *Scott Birds* 6:154-6.

Burton NHK, Armitage MJS, Musgrove AJ, Rehfisch MM 2002. Impacts of man-made landscape features on numbers of estuarine waterbirds at low tide. *Environ Mgmt* 30:857-864.

Butter R 1999. *Kilmartin: Scotland's richest prehistoric landscape.* Kilmartin House Trust, Kilmartin, Argyll.

Cadbury CJ 1980. The status and habitats of the Corncrake in Britain 1978-79. *Bird Study* 27:203-218.

Cadbury CJ 1989. Corncrake and Corn Bunting status and habitats on Tiree and Coll, Inner Hebrides. In: *Birds on Coll and Tiree: Status, Habitats and Conservation* (ed. DA Stroud) pp. 51-66. NCC/SOC, Edinburgh.

Campbell B 1947. Nesting Season of Common Buzzard. *Brit Birds* 40:182-183.

Campbell B 1954. The breeding distribution and habitats of the Pied Flycatcher in Britain. Part I: Historical and present distribution. *Bird Study* 1:81-101.

Campbell JW 1937. Scottish bird notes. *Scott Nat* 1937: 175-177.

Campbell LH & Talbot TR 1987. Breeding status of Black-throated Divers in Scotland. *Brit Birds* 80:1-8.

Campbell M 2001. *Argyll: the enduring heartland.* House of Lochar, Colonsay.

Carss DN 1989. Sawbill ducks at fish farms in Argyll, western Scotland. *Scott Birds* 15:145-150.

Carss DN 1994. Killing of piscivorous birds at Scottish fin fish farms 1984-1987. *Biol Conserv* 68:181-188.

Carss DN & Marquiss M 1996. *The feeding behaviour and impact of Grey Herons on fisheries: A literature review.* ITE, Banchory.

Castle ME 1977. Rookeries in Scotland-1975. *Scott Birds* 9:327-334.

Charles JK 1972. *Territorial behaviour and the limitation of population size in crows* Corvus corone *and* Corvus cornix. PhD Thesis, University of Aberdeen.

Charles WN 1981. Abundance of the Field Vole (*Microtus agrestis*) in conifer plantations. In: *Forest and Woodland Ecology* (ed. FT Last) pp. 135-137. Institute of Terrestrial Ecology, Cambridge.

Chisholm 2007. History of the Wood Sandpiper as a breeding bird in Britain. *Brit Birds* 100:112-121.

Clark H & Sellers RM 1998. Winter habitats of Twite in Scotland. *Scott Birds* 19:262-269.

Clark JA, Balmer DE, Adams SY 2002. Bird ringing in Britain and Ireland in 2001. *Ring & Migr* 21:80-143.

Cook A 1975. Changes in the Carrion/Hooded Crow hybrid zone and the possible importance of climate. *Bird Study* 22:165-168.

Cook AS, Grant MC, McKay CR, Peacock MA 2001. Status, distribution and breeding success of the Red-billed Chough in Scotland in 1998. *Scott Birds* 22:82-91.

Corbet GB & Harris S 1991. *The Handbook of British Mammals,*

3rd edn. Blackwell, Oxford.

Covey R, Fortune F, Nichols DM, Thorpe K 1998. *Marine Nature Conservation Review Sectors 3, 4, 13 & 15. Lagoons in mainland Scotland and the Inner Hebrides: area summaries.* Joint Nature Conservation Committee. (Coasts and seas of the United Kingdom. MNCR series), Peterborough.

Craik JCA 1992. Exceptional mortality of auks, terns and kittiwakes in west Scotland in July 1985. *Sula* 6:125-138.

Craik JCA 1997. Long-term effects of North American Mink on seabirds in western Scotland. *Bird Study* 44:303-309.

Craik JCA 1998. Recent mink-related declines of gulls and terns in west Scotland and the beneficial effects of mink control. *Argyll Bird Rept* 14:98-110

Craik JCA 1999. Breeding success of Common Gulls in west Scotland I. Observations at a single colony. *Atlantic Seabirds* 1:169-181.

Craik JCA 2000. Breeding success of Common Gulls in west Scotland II. Comparisons between colonies. *Atlantic Seabirds* 2:1-12.

Craik JCA 2002a. Increasing numbers of Greylag and Canada Geese breeding in mainland sealochs. *Argyll Bird Rept* 18:123-124.

Craik JCA 2002b. Pine Martens and Pied Flycatchers at Bonawe. *Eider* (September 2002):10.

Cramp S, Bourne WRP, Saunders D 1974. *The Seabirds of Britain and Ireland.* Collins. London.

Cramp S, Pettet R, Sharrock JTR 1960. The irruption of tits in autumn 1957. *Brit Birds* 53:49-77,99-117,176-192.

Cramp S. (ed.) 1977. *The Birds of the Western Palearctic*, vol 1. Oxford University Press, Oxford.

Cramp S & Simmons KEL (eds). 1985. *The Birds of the Western Palearctic*, vol 4. Oxford University Press, Oxford.

Crick HQP & Ratcliffe DA 1995. The Peregrine *Falco peregrinus* breeding population of the UK in 1991. *Bird Study* 42:1-19.

Crick HQP, Baillie SR, Balmer DE, Bashford RI *et al.* 1998. *Breeding Birds in the Wider Countryside: their Conservation Status (1972-1996).* BTO Research Rept 198. BTO, Thetford.

Cronin C & ap Rheinallt T 1997. Woodchat Shrike *Lanius senator* on Islay, 16 September 1996 – the first Argyll record. *Argyll Bird Rept* 13:92-95.

Davies AK 1988. The distribution and status of the Mandarin Duck *Aix galericulata* in Britain. *Bird Study* 35:203-207.

Davies J 1999. *Broad scale remote survey and mapping of the sublittoral habitats and their associated biota in the Firth of Lorne.* SNH Research, Survey and Monitoring Report No. 157.

Daw P 2000. Systematic List for 1999. *Argyll Bird Rept* 16:6-104.

Dawson J & ap Rheinallt T 2001. Blast from the past. American Redstart, Islay, November 1982. *Birding Scotl* 4:186-188.

Dayton N 2000. *An evaluation of selected upland vegetation sites within Kintyre, Mid-Argyll and Cowal.* Quadrat: Unpublished report to SNH.

Delaney S 1993. Introduced and escaped geese in Britain in summer 1991. *Brit Birds* 86:591-599.

De Leon A, Minguez E, Harvey P, Meek E, Crane JE, Furness RW 2006. Factors affecting breeding distribution of Storm-petrels *Hydrobates pelagicus* in Orkney and Shetland. *Bird Study* 53:64-72.

Del Hoyo J, Elliott A, Christie DA (eds.) 2004. *Handbook of the Birds of the World: Volume 9 Cotingas to Pipits and Wagtails.* Lynx Edicions, Barcelona.

Dennis RH 1968. Sea Eagles. *Fair Isle Bird Observ Rept* 21:17-21.

Dennis R. 1995. Ospreys *Pandion haliaetus* in Scotland – a study of recolonization. *Die Vogelwelt* 116:193-195.

Dickson J & Daw P 2005. Record influx of white-winged gulls. *The Eider* (June 2005):10.

Dipper FA & Beaver R 1999. *Marine Nature Conservation Review Sector 12. Sealochs in the Clyde Sea: area summaries.* Joint Nature Conservation Committee. (Coasts and seas of the United Kingdom. MNCR series), Peterborough.

Donald PF 2004. *The Skylark.* T&AD Poyser, London.

Dudley SP 2005. Changes to Category C of the British List. *Ibis* 147:803-820.

Dudley SP, Gee M, Kehoe C, Melling TM & the British Ornithologists' Union Records Committee 2006. The British list – a checklist of birds of Britain (7th edition). *Ibis* 148:526-563.

Duncan A. 1938. *Report on the Investigation of the Magpie in Scotland.* Scottish Ornithologists' Club, Edinburgh.

Eaton M & Bradbury R 2003. Review of species-specific and generic resource requirements. In: *Predicting the Response of Farmland Birds to Agricultural Change* (eds. NJ Aebisher, R Bradbury, M Eaton, IG Henderson, GM Siriwardena & J Vickery). BTO, Thetford.

Edlin HL 1976. *Argyll Forest Park.* 5th Edition. HMSO, Edinburgh.

Elliott RE 1989. *Birds of Islay.* Christopher Helm, London.

Environmental Resources Management. 1996. *Landscape assessment of Argyll and the Firth of Clyde.* Scottish Natural Heritage Review No 78.

Etheridge B, Summers RW & Green RE 1997. The effects of illegal killing and destruction of nests by humans on the population dynamics of the Hen Harrier *Circus cyaneus* in Scotland. *J Appl Ecol* 34:1081-1105.

Evans LGR 1994. *Rare Birds in Britain 1800-1990.* LGRE Publications Ltd, Amersham.

Evans RJ 2000. Wintering Slavonian Grebes in coastal waters of Britain and Ireland. *Brit Birds* 93:218-226.

Everett MJ 1967. Waxwings in Scotland, 1965/66 and 1966/67. *Scott Birds* 4:534-548.

Everett MJ 1971. Breeding status of Red-necked Phalarope in Britain and Ireland. *Brit Birds* 64:293-302.

Everett M 1982. Breeding Great and Arctic Skuas in Scotland in 1974-75. *Seabird Rept* 6:50-58.

Feare CJ, Dunnet GM, Patterson IJ 1974. Ecological studies of the Rook *Corvus frugilegus* L. in north-east Scotland. Food intake and feeding behaviour. *J appl Ecol* 11:867-896.

Fielding AH, Haworth PF, Morgan DH, Thompson DBA, Whitfield DP 2003. The impact of Golden Eagles (*Aquila chrysaetos*) on a diverse bird of prey assemblage. In: *Birds of Prey in a Changing Environment* (ed. DBA Thompson, SM Redpath, AH Fielding, M Marquiss & CA Galbraith) pp. 221-243. The Stationery Office, Edinburgh.

Finney SK & Jardine DC 2003. The distribution and status of the Red-billed Chough in Scotland in 2002. *Scott Birds* 24:11-17.

Fisher J 1952. *The Fulmar.* Collins, London.

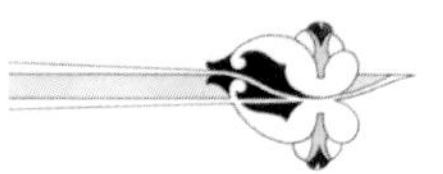

Fisher J 1966. The Fulmar population of Britain and Ireland, 1959. *Bird Study* 13:334-354.

Flegg JJM 1973. A study of Treecreepers. *Bird Study* 20:287-302.

Flowerdew JR & Ellwood SA 2001. Impacts of woodland deer on small mammal ecology. *Forestry* 74:277-287.

Forestry Commission 2005. *Forestry Statistics 2005.* Forestry Commission, Economics and Statistics Unit, Edinburgh.

Forrester RW, Andrews IJ, McInerny CJ, Murray RD *et al.* 2007 (in press). The Birds of Scotland. Scottish Ornithologists' Club, Aberlady.

Fox AD, Norris DW, Stroud DA, Wilson HJ 1994. Greenland White-fronted Geese in Ireland and Britain 1982/83 – 1993/94. *Greenland White-fronted Goose Study Research Rept* No. 8.

Fraser PA & Rogers MJ 2001. Report on scarce migrant birds in Britain in 1999. *Brit Birds* 94:560-589.

Fraser PA & Rogers MJ 2006a. Report on scarce migrant birds in Britain in 2003. Part 1: American Wigeon to Wryneck. *Brit Birds* 99:74-91.

Fraser PA & Rogers MJ 2006b. Report on scarce migrant birds in Britain. Part 2: Short-toed Lark to Little Bunting. *Brit Birds* 99:129-147.

Fraser PA, Lansdown PG & Rogers MJ 1999. Report on scarce migrant birds in Britain in 1996. *Brit Birds* 92:3-35.

Fraser PA, Lansdown PG & Rogers MJ 2000. Report on scarce migrant birds in Britain in 1998. *Brit Birds* 93:588-641.

Fraser Darling F 1940. *Island Years.* Bell, London.

Freeman SN & Crick HQP 2003. The decline of the Spotted Flycatcher *Muscicapa striata* in the UK: an integrated population model. *Ibis* 145:400-412.

Fuller RJ 1982. *Bird Habitats in Britain.* T & AD Poyser, Calton.

Furness RW 1987. *The Skuas.* T & AD Poyser, Calton.

Galbraith H, Furness RW, Fuller RJ 1984. Habitats and distribution of waders breeding on Scottish agricultural land. *Scott Birds* 13:98-107.

Galeotti P 2001. *Strix aluco* Tawny Owl. *BWP Update* 3:43-77.

Garden EA 1958. The national census of heronries in Scotland 1954, with a summary of the 1928/29 census. *Bird Study* 5:90-109.

Gathorne-Hardy AE 1914. *My Happy Hunting Grounds.* Longmans, Green & Co., London.

Gibbons DW, Reid JB, Chapman RA 1993. *The New Atlas of Breeding Birds in Britain and Ireland: 1988-1991.* T & AD Poyser, London.

Gibson JA 1958. The breeding birds of the Clyde area. *Glasgow Bird Bull* 7:133-169.

Gibson JA 1969. Population studies of Clyde seabirds part I. *Trans Buteshire Nat Hist Soc* 17:79-95.

Gibson JA 1970. Population studies of Clyde seabirds part II. *Trans Buteshire Nat Hist Soc* 18:21-30.

Gibson JA 1976. Population studies of Clyde seabirds part III. *Trans Buteshire Nat Hist Soc* 20:53-67.

Gibson JA 1979. The breeding birds of the Clyde area: supplementary notes. *Western Nat* 8:27-45.

Gibson JA 1985. Population studies of Clyde seabirds part IV (Lesser Black-backed and Herring Gulls). *Trans Buteshire Nat Hist Soc* 22:85-105.

Gibson JA 1990. Population studies of Clyde seabirds part V. *Trans Buteshire Nat Hist Soc* 23:81-107.

Gibson JA & McWilliam JM 1959. *A Supplement to the 'Birds of the Firth of Clyde'.* Glasgow.

Gilbert G 2002. The status and habitat of Spotted Crakes *Porzana porzana* in Britain in 1999. *Bird Study* 49:79-86.

Glen NW & Perrins CM 1988. Cooperative breeding by Long-tailed Tits. *Brit Birds* 81:630-641.

Gomersall CH 1986. Breeding performance of the Red-throated Diver *Gavia stellata* in Shetland. *Holarct Ecol* 9:277-284.

Gordon AC & Merrie TDH 1964. Goshawk in North and South Argyll. *Scott Birds* 3:27.

Gordon S 1920. *The Land of the Hills and Glens.* Cassel, London.

Graham HD 1890. *The Birds of Iona and Mull, 1852-1870.* David Douglas, Edinburgh.

Grantham M 2004. Ringing in January. *Birding World* 17:527.

Gray R 1871. *The Birds of the West of Scotland, including the Outer Hebrides.* Murray, Glasgow.

Green RE 1995. The decline of the Corncrake *Crex crex* in Britain continues. *Bird Study* 42:66-75.

Green RE & Stowe TJ 1993. The decline of the Corncrake *Crex crex* in Britain and Ireland in relation to habitat change. *J Appl Ecol* 30:689-695.

Green RE & Williams G 1994. The ecology of the Corncrake *Crex crex* and action for its conservation in Britain and Ireland. In: *Third European Forum on Birds and Pastoralism* (ed. E Bignal & DJ Curtis).

Greenleas J 1953. The birds of Southend, Argyll. *Glasgow and West Scotland Bird Bull* 2:33-37.

Greenwood JD, Crick HQP, Bainbridge IP 2003. Numbers and international importance of raptors and owls in Britain and Ireland. In: *Birds of Prey in a Changing Environment* (ed. DBA Thompson, SM Redpath, AH Fielding, M Marquiss, CA Galbraith), pp. 25-50. The Stationery Office, Edinburgh.

Greenwood S 1960. Goshawks in Islay. *Scott Birds* 1:186.

Gregory RD & Marchant JH 1996. Population trends of Jays, Magpies, Jackdaws and Carrion Crows in the UK. *Bird Study* 43:28-37.

Gregory RD, Wilkinson NI, Noble DG, Robinson JA *et al.* 2002. The population status of birds in the United Kingdom, Channel Islands and Isle of Man: an analysis of conservation concern 2002-2007. *Brit Birds* 95:410-448.

Gribble FC 1983. Nightjars in Britain and Ireland in 1981. *Bird Study* 30:165-176.

Grieve S 1923. *The book of Colonsay and Oronsay.* Oliver & Boyd, Edinburgh.

Griffin LR 1999. Colonization patterns at Rook *Corvus frugilegus* colonies: implications for survey strategies. *Bird Study* 46:170-173.

Guitian J, Munilla I, Guitian P, Lopez B 1994. Frugivory and seed dispersal by Redwings *Turdus iliacus* in southwest Iceland. *Ecography* 17:314-320.

Gunnis FG 1902. On the occurrence of the Carolina Crake [*Porzana carolina* (Linn.)] in the island of Tiree. *Ann Scott Nat Hist* 1902:9-10.

Hagemeijer WJM and Blair MJ 1997. *The EBCC Atlas of European Breeding Birds.* T & AD Poyser, London.

Hancock M 2000. Artificial floating islands for nesting Black-throated Divers *Gavia arctica* in Scotland: construction, use and effect on breeding success. *Bird Study* 47:165-175.

Hancock M, Baines D, Gibbons D, Etheridge B, Shepherd M 1999. Status of male Black Grouse *Tetrao tetrix* in Britain in 1995-96. *Bird Study* 46:1-15.

Harris MP 1984. *The Puffin.* T & AD Poyser, Berkhamstead.

Harris MP, Wanless S, Rothery P, Swann RL, Jardine D 2000. Survival of adult Common Guillemots *Uria aalge* at three Scottish colonies. *Bird Study* 47:1-7.

Harvie-Brown JA 1879. *The Capercaillie in Scotland.* Edinburgh.

Harvie-Brown JA 1880. On the decrease in Scotland of the Great Spotted Woodpecker. *Proc Nat Hist Soc Glasgow* 4:6.

Harvie-Brown JA 1892. The Great Spotted Woodpecker in Scotland. *Ann Scott Nat Hist* 1892:4-17.

Harvie-Brown JA 1895. *Atlas of Scotland.* Edinburgh.

Harvie-Brown JA 1908. The Great Spotted Woodpecker's resuscitation in Scotland since 1841 or 1851. *Ann Scott Nat Hist* 1908:210-216.

Harvie-Brown JA & Buckley TE 1892. *A Vertebrate Fauna of Argyll and the Inner Hebrides.* David Douglas, Edinburgh.

Hatchwell BJ, Anderson C, Ross DJ, Fowlie MK, Blackwell PG 2001. Social organization of cooperatively breeding Long-tailed Tits: kinship and spatial dynamics. *J Anim Ecol* 70:820-830.

Haworth PF 1999. A *Population Study of Ravens on the Isle of Mull.* Scottish Natural Heritage Contract No: HT/97/98/91.

Haworth PF, McGrady MJ, Whitfield DP, Fielding AH, McLeod DRA 2006. Ranging distance of resident Golden Eagles *Aquila chrysaetos* in western Scotland according to season and breeding status. *Bird Study* 53:265-273.

Hayman P Marchant J & Prater A 1986. *Shorebirds: An Identification Guide to the Waders of the World.* Croom Helm, London.

Haysom SL 2001. *Aspects of the ecology of Black Grouse (*Tetrao tetrix*) in plantation forests in Scotland.* PhD Thesis, University of Stirling.

Heinrich B 1990. *Ravens in winter.* Barry & Jenkins Ltd, London.

Helander B & Stjerberg T 2002. *Action plan for the conservation of White-tailed Sea Eagle.* Birdlife International, Sweden.

Henderson IG 1989. The exploitation of tits *Parus* species, Long-tailed Tits *Aegithalos caudatus* and Goldcrests *Regulus regulus* by Treecreepers *Certhia familiaris*: a behavioural study. *Bird Study* 36:99-104.

Henderson IG, Fuller RJ, Conway GJ, Gough SJ 2004. Evidence for declines in populations of grassland-associated birds in marginal upland areas of Britain. *Bird Study* 51:12-19.

Hewson R & Leitch A 1982. The spacing and density of Hooded Crow nests in Argyll (Strathclyde). *Bird Study* 29:235-238.

Hogstad A, Selås V, Kobro S 2003. Explaining annual fluctuations in breeding density of Fieldfares *Turdus pilaris* – combined influences of factors operating during breeding, migration and wintering. *J Avian Biol* 34:350-354.

Holloway S 1996. *The Historical Atlas of Breeding Birds in Britain and Ireland: 1875-1900.* T & AD Poyser, London.

Holmes M 1986. The Barn Owl: its current status in Argyll. *Argyll Bird Rept* 3:100-102.

Houston D 1977a. The effect of Hooded Crows on hill sheep farming in Argyll, Scotland: the food supply of Hooded Crows. *J appl Ecol* 14:1-15.

Houston D 1977b. The effect of Hooded Crows on hill sheep farming in Argyll, Scotland: Hooded Crow damage to hill sheep. *J appl Ecol* 14:17-29.

Hudson AV, Stowe TJ, Aspinall SJ 1990. Status and distribution of Corncrakes in Britain. *Brit Birds* 83:173-186.

Hudson R 1972. Collared Doves in Britain and Ireland during 1965-1970. *Brit Birds* 65:139-155.

Hume RA 1995. Blue Rock Thrush in Strathclyde: new to Britain and Ireland. *Brit Birds* 88:130-132.

Ingold P 1991. Competition for feeding areas and dominance relationships among Shelducks *Tadorna tadorna* with broods. *Ornis Scand* 22:27-32.

Irby LH 1899. Observations on the birds of Tiree and Coll. *Ann Scott Nat Hist* 32:206-210.

Jackson B 2003. Forster's Tern, an Argyll first, 8th-11th January 2003. *Birding Scotl* 6:39-41.

Jackson DG 2003. Between-lake differences in the diet and provisioning behaviour of Black-throated Divers *Gavia arctica* breeding in Scotland. *Ibis* 145:30-44.

Jackson DB 2005. Environmental correlates of lake occupancy and chick survival of black-throated divers *Gavia arctica* in Scotland. *Bird Study* 52:225-236.

Jackson B 2003. Forster's Tern, an Argyll first, 8th-11th January 2003. *Birding Scotl* 6:39-41.

Jackson W 2001. The Snowy Egret in Argyll – a new British bird. *Birding World* 14:460-464.

Jackson W 2004. Snowy Egret in Argyll & Bute: new to Britain. *Brit Birds* 97:270-275.

Jardine DC 1989. How many Buzzards are there in Argyll? An estimate based upon the 1988 Atlas returns. *Argyll Bird Rept* 5:46-47.

Jardine DC 1992. Crossbills in Scotland 1990 - an invasion year. *Scott Bird Rept* 23:65-69.

Jardine DC 1998. Increases in Fulmars on Colonsay 1975-1997 *Argyll Bird Rept* 14: 94-97.

Jardine DC 2002. *The Birds of Colonsay and Oronsay.* House of Lochar, Isle of Colonsay.

Jardine DC 2003. Buzzards (*Buteo buteo*) on Colonsay 1990-2000: Numbers and breeding performance. in Thompson DBA, Redpath, SM, Fielding AH, Marquiss M & Galbraith CA (eds.) *Birds of Prey in a Changing Environment* pp179-182. The Stationery Office, Edinburgh.

Jardine DC & ap Rheinallt T 1997. The status of the Scottish Crossbill *Loxia scotica* in Argyll. *Argyll Bird Rept* 13:96-100.

Jardine DC, Clarke J, Clarke PM 1986. *The Birds of Colonsay & Oronsay.* Stornoway Gazette Ltd, Stornoway.

Jardine DC & Jardine JA 1994. American Golden Plover on Colonsay – a new species in Argyll. *Argyll Bird Rept* 10:81-83.

Jardine DC, How J, Clarke J, Clarke PM 2002. Seabirds on Colonsay and Oronsay, Inner Hebrides. *Scott Birds* 23:1-9.

Jardine Sir W 1866. The Naturalist's Library vols. III and IV. Lizars, Edinburgh.

Jenkins D 2003. *Of Partridges and Peacocks and things about which I know nothing.* TLA Publications, Philadelphia..

Jennings AR 1995. Birds recorded in the area around Ledaig Point, near Oban, in the years 1982-1994. *Argyll Bird Rept* 11:98-101.

John AWG & Roskell J 1985. Jay movements in autumn 1983. *Brit Birds* 78:611-637.

Johnstone GW 1967. Blackgame and Capercaillie in relation to forestry in Britain. *Forestry*, Suppl. "Wildlife in the Forest", 68-77.

Jones D 2004. *Argyll and Bute Profile 2004.* Argyll and Bute Council, Kilmory, Lochgilphead.

Klomp NI & Furness RW 1992. The dispersal and philopatry of Great Skuas from Foula, Shetland. *Ring & Migr* 13:73-82.

Knox AG 1993. Richard Meinertzhagen – a case of fraud examined. *Ibis* 135:320-325.

Lack P 1986. *The Atlas of Wintering Birds in Britain and Ireland*. T & AD Poyser, Calton.

Laidlaw TG 1900. Report on the movements and occurrence of birds in Scotland during 1899. *Ann Scott Nat Hist* 33:70-87.

Laidlaw TG 1902. Report on the movements and occurrence of birds in Scotland during 1901. *Ann Scott Nat Hist* 35:193-199.

Laidlaw TG 1903. Report on the movements and occurrence of birds in Scotland during 1902. *Ann Scott Nat Hist* 36:205-210.

Laidlaw TG 1904. Report on the movements and occurrence of birds in Scotland during 1903. *Ann Scott Nat Hist* 37:207-217.

Langston RHW, Smith T, Brown AF, Gregory RD 2006. Status of breeding Twite *Carduelis flavirostris* in the UK. *Bird Study* 53:55-63.

Lawn MR 1982. Pairing systems and site tenacity of the Willow Warbler *Phylloscopus trochilus* in southern England. *Ornis Scand* 13:193-199.

Lawrie AD 1891. Fork-tailed Petrel in Argyllshire. *The Field* 17 Oct 1891.

Lees AC & Gilroy JJ 2004. Pectoral Sandpipers in Europe: vagrancy patterns and the influx of 2003. *Brit Birds* 97:638-646.

Linton E & Fox AD 1991. Inland breeding of Shelduck *Tadorna tadorna* in Britain. *Bird Study* 38:123-127.

Little B & Furness RW 1985. Long-distance moult migration by British Goosanders *Mergus merganser*. *Ring & Migr* 6:77-82.

Lloyd C, Tasker ML, Partridge K 1991. *The Status of Seabirds in Britain and Ireland*. T & AD Poyser, London.

Loder J de V 1935. *Colonsay and Oronsay in the Isles of Argyll: their history, flora, fauna and topography*. Oliver & Boyd, Edinburgh.

Love JA 1981. An island population of Blue Tits. *Bird Study* 28:63-64.

Love JA 1983. *The Return of the Sea Eagle*. Cambridge University Press, Cambridge.

Lowe P 1916. *Our Common Sea Birds*. Country Life Books.

Lumsden J 1876a. Notes regarding the occurrence of the American Bittern, *Botaurus lentiginosus*, in Islay. *Proc Nat Hist Soc Glasgow* 3:43-44.

Lumsden J 1876b. Notes on the distribution of the Common Jay in Scotland. *Scott Nat* 1876:233-240.

Lundberg A & Alatalo RV 1992. *The Pied Flycatcher*. T & AD Poyser, London.

Lyster IHJ 1971. Waxwings in Scotland, 1970/71. *Scott Birds* 6:420-438.

MacDougall H 1938. Notes on the birds of Coll. *Scott Nat* 1938:139-144.

Macgillivray W 1836. *Descriptions of the rapacious birds of Great Britain*. MacLachlan & Stewart, Edinburgh.

McGowan RY 2003. The Ascension Frigatebird from Tiree, 1953. *Birding Scotl* 6:103-106.

McGowan RY, Clugston DL, Forrester RW 2003. Scotland's endemic subspecies. *Scott Birds* 24:18-35.

McKay CR 1994. Brown-headed Cowbird in Strathclyde: new to Britain and Ireland. *Brit Birds* 87:284-287.

McKenzie A, Petty SJ, Toms MP, Furness RW 2007. The importance of Sitka Spruce *Picea sitchensis* seed and garden bird feeders for Siskins *Carduelis spinus* and Coal Tits *Periparus ater*. *Bird Study* 54:236-247.

Mackenzie JMD 1956. Treecreepers using nest boxes and other artificial sites. *Scott Nat* 68:84-91.

Mackenzie JMD 1957. Treecreepers roosting in Wellingtonias. *Bird Study* 4:94-97.

Mackenzie JMD 1959. Roosting of Treecreepers. *Bird Study* 6:8-15.

McLaren C & Murray G 1985. *The Birds of Mid-Argyll, Kintyre & Cowal*. Droineach Press, Cumbernauld.

McLeod DRA, Whitfield DP, Fielding AH, Haworth PF, McGrady MJ 2002. Predicting home range use by golden eagles *Aquila chrysaetos* in western Scotland. *Avian Sci* 2: 183-198.

Macmillan AT 1959. The invasion of Waxwings *Bombycilla garrulus*. December 1958. *Scott Birds* 1:102-106.

Macmillan AT 1960. The invasion of Waxwings *Bombycilla garrulus* in Scotland in October and November 1959. *Scott Birds* 1:241-251.

Macmillan AT 1962. The Waxwing invasion of November 1961. *Scott Birds* 2:85-89.

Macmillan AT 1964. The Waxwing invasion of October and November 1963. *Scott Birds* 3:180-194.

Macmillan AT 1965. The Collared Dove in Scotland. *Scott Birds* 3:292-301.

Macmillan AT 1967. Cranes in North Argyll. *Scott Birds* 4:556.

McNeill M 1910. *Colonsay, One of the Hebrides*. Douglas, Glasgow.

McSorley CA, Dean BJ, Webb A, Reid JB 2003. *Seabird use of waters adjacent to colonies:Implications for seaward extensions to existing breeding seabird colony Special Protection Areas*. JNCC Report, No. 329.

McWilliam JM 1931. On the breeding of the Black-throated and Red-throated Divers in south Argyllshire. *Scott Nat* 1931:161-164.

McWilliam JM 1936. *The Birds of the Firth of Clyde*. HF & G Witherby, London.

Madders M 1992. Wintering and breeding greylag geese on Coll and Tiree. *Argyll Bird Rept* 8:13-18.

Madders M 1997. *A Population and Behavioural Study of Ravens on Islay (Argyll & Bute)*. Report to SOAEFD and SNH. Project no. MMA/001/96.

Madders M 2000. Habitat selection and foraging success of Hen Harriers *Circus cyaneus* in west Scotland. *Bird Study* 47:32-40.

Madders M 2003. Hen Harrier *Circus cyaneus* foraging activity in relation to habitat and prey. *Bird Study* 50:55-60.

Madders M & Moser M 1986. Winter wader populations in Argyll. *Argyll Bird Rept* 3:93-94.

Madders M & Leckie FM 1999. Raven population size and distribution on the Isle of Islay in winter. *Scott Birds* 20:49-62.

Madders M & Snow P 1987. *Birds of Mull*. Saker Press, Islay.

Madders M, Snow P, Welstead J 1992. *Birds of Mid-Argyll*. Saker Press, Islay.

Madsen J, Cracknell G, Fox T (eds.) 1999. Goose populations of

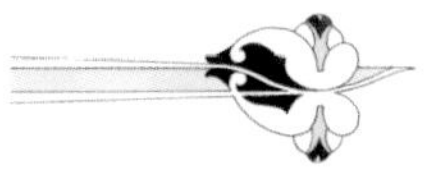

the Western Palearctic: a review of status and distribution. *Wetlands International Publication* No. 48. NERI, Denmark.

Maguire E 1978. Breeding of Storm Petrel and Manx Shearwater in Kintyre, Argyll. *Western Nat* 7:63-66.

Maguire EJ 1979. Notes on the breeding of the Buzzard in Kintyre. *Western Nat* 8:3-13.

Maguire E 1995. *Machrihanish Seabird Observatory 1994 Report.* Kintyre Bird Club, Campbeltown.

Maguire EJ 2001. Flight identification of Grey and Red-necked Phalarope. *Birding Scotland* 4:19-24.

Maguire E 2003. *Birds of Kintyre.* Peninsula Wildlife Publications, Oban.

Maguire E 2005. French Kittiwakes at Machrihanish. *Eider* (June 2005):5.

Maguire E 2006. Machrihanish Seabird and Wildlife Observatory: spring news 2006 (March to 24th-May). *Eider* (June 2006):5-6.

Maguire EJ, McGlynn J, Morans L 1996/1997. Rookeries in Kintyre, 1996. *Machrihanish Seabird Obs Rept 1996/1997*: 49-50.

Marchant JH & Gregory RD 1999. Numbers of nesting Rooks *Corvus frugilegus* in the United Kingdom in 1996. *Bird Study* 46:258-273.

Marion L & Le Gentil J 2006. Ecological segregation and population structuring of the Cormorant *Phalacrocorax carbo* in Europe, in relation to the recent introgression of continental and marine subspecies. *Evolut Ecol* 20:193-216.

Marquiss M 1989. Grey Heron *Ardea cinerea* breeding in Scotland – Numbers, distribution and census techniques. *Bird Study* 36:181-191.

Marquiss M, Newton I, Ratcliffe DA 1978. The decline of the Raven *Corvus corax* in relation to afforestation in southern Scotland and northern England. *J appl Ecol* 15:129-144.

Marquiss M & Newton I 1981. A radio-tracking study of the ranging behaviour and dispersion of European Sparrowhawks *Accipiter nisus*. *J Anim Ecol* 51:111-115.

Marquiss M, Carss DN, Armstrong JD, Gardiner R 1998. *Fish-eating Birds and Salmonids in Scotland.* Report on fish-eating birds research (1990-1997) to the Scottish Office Agriculture, Environment and Fisheries Department. 156 pp.

Marquiss M, Madders M, Carss DN 2003. White-tailed Eagles *Haliaeetus albicilla* and lambs *Ovis aries*. pp 471-479. In: *Birds of Prey in a changing environment*. Ed. Thompson DBA, Redpath SM, Fielding A H, Marquiss M, Galbraith CA, The Stationery Office, Edinburgh.

Martin A 1996. *The Ring-Net Fishermen.* 2nd Edition. John Donald Publishers Ltd., Edinburgh.

Martin MWA 1988. Colonial nesting Red-breasted Mergansers. *Scott Bird News* 9:8.

Mavor RA, Parsons M, Heubeck M, Schmitt S 2006. *Seabird numbers and breeding success in Britain and Ireland, 2005.* Joint Nature Conservation Committee, Peterborough.

Maxwell J 2004a. The Nuthatch in Scotland – part 1. *Scott Bird News* 71:7.

Maxwell J 2004b. The Nuthatch in Scotland – part 2. *Scott Bird News* 72:9.

Mayr E 1942. *Systematics and the Origin of Species.* Columbia University Press, New York.

Mead CJ 1985. Will they return? *BTO News* 137:4.

Meiklejohn MFM & Stanford JK 1954. June notes on the birds of Islay. *Scott Nat* 129-145.

Meise W 1928. Die Vertbreitung der Aaskrähe (Formenkreis *Corvus corone* L.). *J Ornithol* 76:1-203.

Merrie TDH 1967. The Magpie in western Scotland. *Scott Birds* 4:449.

Merrie TDH 1978. Relationship between spatial distribution of breeding divers and the availability of fishing waters. *Bird Study* 25:119-122.

Merrie TDH 1979. Success of artificial island nest-sites for divers. *Brit Birds* 72:32-33.

Merrie TDH 1996. Breeding success of raft-nesting divers in Scotland. *Brit Birds* 89:306-309.

Millais JG 1913. *British Diving Ducks* (two volumes). Longmans, London.

Milwright RDP 2002. Redwings *Turdus iliacus* migration and wintering areas as shown by recoveries of birds ringed in the breeding season in Fennoscandia, Poland, the Baltic Republics, Russia, Siberia and Iceland. *Ring & Migr* 21:5-15.

Mitchell J 1976. The breeding status of the Rook in the Loch Lomond area. *Loch Lomond Bird Rept* 4:8-15.

Mitchell PI, Newton SF, Ratcliffe N, Duncan TE 2004. *Seabird Populations of Britain and Ireland.* T & AD Poyser, London.

Morris FO 1893. *A History of British Birds.* 4th Edition, Nimmo, London.

Morris FO 1903. *A History of British Birds.* 5th Edition, Nimmo, London.

Morton K 2001. 1998 and 1999 raptor round up. *Scott Birds* 22 (Suppl.).

Morton R 2002. *Sanda Island Bird Observatory Report for 2002.* Privately Published.

Morton R 2004. *Sanda Island Bird Observatory Report for 2003.* Privately Published.

Moss D 1979. Even-aged plantations as a habitat for birds. In: *The Ecology of Even-Aged Plantations* (ed. ED Ford, DC Malcolm & J Atterson) pp. 413-427. Institute of Terrestrial Ecology, Cambridge.

Moser ME, Broad RA, Dennis RH, Madders M 1986. The distribution and abundance of some coastal birds on the west and north-west coasts of Scotland in winter. *Scott Birds* 14:61-67.

Mudge GP, Dennis RH, Talbot TR, Broad RA 1991. Changes in the breeding status of Black-throated Divers in Scotland. *Scott Birds* 16:77-84.

Mudge GP & Talbot TR 1993. The breeding biology and causes of nest failure of Scottish Black-throated Divers *Gavia arctica*. *Ibis* 135:113-120.

Murray RD 1991a. Quail in Scotland, 1989. *Scott Bird Rept 1989* :45-50.

Murray RD 1991b. The first successful breeding of Nuthatch in Scotland. *Scott Bird Rept 1989* :51-55.

Murray S & Wanless S 1997. The status of the Gannet in Scotland in 1994-95. *Scott Birds* 19:10-27.

Musgrove AJ 2002. The non-breeding status of the Little Egret in Britain. *Brit Birds* 95:62-80.

Naylor KA 1996. A Reference Manual of Rare Birds in Great Britain and Ireland. Nottingham. Vol. 1. Nottingham (published privately).

Nethersole-Thompson D & Nethersole-Thompson M 1979. *Greenshanks.* T & AD Poyser, Berkhamsted.

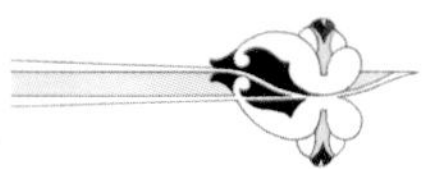

New Statistical Account – see Society for the Benefit of the Sons and Daughters of the Clergy.

Newton I 1972a. Birds of prey in Scotland: some conservation problems. *Scott Birds* 7:5-23.

Newton I 1972b. *Finches*. Collins, London.

Newton I 1986. *The Sparrowhawk.* T & AD Poyser, Berkhamsted.

Newton I 1992. Recovery of a Sparrowhawk population in relation to declining pesticide contamination. *J Appl Ecol* 29:476-484.

Newton I & Haas MB 1984. The return of the Sparrowhawk. *Brit Birds* 77:47-70.

Newton SF & Newton AV 1991. Wintering wildfowl in Argyll 1989-1990. *Argyll Bird Rept* 7:67-74.

Nicholson EM 1951. *Birds and Men*. Collins, London.

Norman RK & Saunders DR 1969. Status of Little Terns in Great Britain and Ireland in 1967. *Brit Birds* 62:4-13.

Norris CA 1947. Report on the distribution and status of the Corncrake *Crex crex*. *Brit Birds* 40:226-244.

O'Brien M, Beaumont D, Smith M, Suddaby D In prep. Changes in the breeding status of Red-necked Phalaropes in Britain and Ireland since 1970.

O'Connor RJ & Shrubb M 1986. *Farming and Birds*. Cambridge Univ Press, Cambridge.

Ogilvie MA 1981. The Mute Swan in Britain, 1978. *Bird Study* 28:87-106.

Ogilvie MA 1983. Wildfowl of Islay. *Proc Roy Soc Edin B* 84:473-489.

Ogilvie M 1992a. *The Birds of Islay – Including when and where to find them*. Lochindaal Press, Bruichladdich.

Ogilvie MA 1992b. Barn Owls on Islay. *Argyll Bird Rept* 8:4-9.

Ogilvie MA 1992c. Recent status change of some birds in Islay. *Scott Birds* 16:240-259.

Ogilvie M 2003. *The Birds of Islay: Including When and Where to Find Them, With Notes on Other Fauna and Flora (Third Edition)*. Lochindaal Press, Bruichladdich.

Ogilvie MA & Atkinson-Willes GL 1983. Wildfowl of the Inner Hebrides. *Proc Roy Soc Edin* 83B:491-504.

Ogilvie M, & the Rare Breeding Birds Panel. 1999a. Non-native birds breeding in the United Kingdom in 1996. *Brit Birds* 92: 176-182. (*NNBB 96*)

Ogilvie M, & the Rare Breeding Birds Panel. 1999b. Non-native birds breeding in the United Kingdom in 1997. *Brit Birds* 92: 472-476. (*NNBB 97*)

Ogilvie M, & the Rare Breeding Birds Panel 1999c. Rare breeding birds in the UK in 1997. *Brit Birds* 92:389-428.

Ogilvie M, & the Rare Breeding Birds Panel. 2000. Non-native birds breeding in the United Kingdom in 1998. *Brit Birds* 93: 428-433. (*NNBB 98*)

Ogilvie M, & the Rare Breeding Birds Panel. 2001. Non-native birds breeding in the United Kingdom in 1999. *Brit Birds* 94: 518-522. (*NNBB 99*)

Ogilvie M, & the Rare Breeding Birds Panel. 2002. Non-native birds breeding in the United Kingdom in 2000. *Brit Birds* 95: 631-635. (*NNBB 00*)

Ogilvie M, & the Rare Breeding Birds Panel. 2003. Non-native birds breeding in the United Kingdom in 2001. *Brit Birds* 96: 620-625. (*NNBB 01*)

Ogilvie M, & the Rare Breeding Birds Panel. 2004. Non-native birds breeding in the United Kingdom in 2002. *Brit Birds* 97: 633-637. (*NNBB 02*)

Old Statistical Account – see Sinclair J.

Onley D & Scofield P 2007. *Albatrosses, Petrels and Shearwaters of the World*. Christopher Helm, London.

Owen M, Atkinson-Willes GL, Salmon DG 1986. *Wildfowl in Great Britain*, 2nd Edition. Cambridge University Press, Cambridge.

Paisley O 2001. *The Marine Natural Heritage of Argyll and Bute*. Unpublished report to the Argyll & Bute Coastal Zone Management Project.

Parkin DT, Collinson M, Helbid AJ, Knox AG, Sangster G 2003. The taxonomic status of Carrion and Hooded Crows. *Brit Birds* 96:274-290.

Paterson J 1899. Notes on the Lesser Whitethroat (*Sylvia curruca*, Linn.) as a Clyde species. *Ann Scott Nat Hist* 1899: 210-214.

Paterson J & Renwick J 1900. Narrative of a cruise in Loch Fyne, June 1899. *Trans Nat Hist Soc Glasgow* 5:366-372.

Patterson IJ, Ollason JG, Doyle P 1995. Bird populations in upland spruce plantations in northern Britain. *Forest Ecol Mgmt* 79:107-131.

Pennant T 1776. *A Tour in Scotland and voyage to the Hebrides*. 2nd Edition. Benjamin White, London.

Pennant T 1789. *A tour of Scotland and voyage to the Outer Hebrides, 1771-1776. Caledonian Zoology (2nd Edition).*

Pennie ID 1950. The history and distribution of the Capercaillie in Scotland: Part 1. *Scott Nat* 62: 65-87, 157-178.

Pennie ID 1951. The history and distribution of the Capercaillie in Scotland: Part 2. *Scott Nat* 63:4-17.

Pennington M & Maher M 2005. Greenland, Iceland and Hornemann's Redpolls in Britain. *Birding World* 18:66-78.

Pennington MG & Meek ER 2006. The 'Northern Bullfinch' invasion of autumn 2004. *Brit Birds* 99:2-24.

Pennington M, Osborn K, Harvey P, Riddington R *et al.* 2004. *The Birds of Shetland*. Christopher Helm, London.

Percival SM 1991. The population structure of Greenland Barnacle Geese *Branta leucopsis* on the wintering grounds on Islay. *Ibis* 133:357-364.

Perrins CM 1979. *British Tits*. Collins, London.

Pettifor RA, Percival SM, Rowcliffe JM 1999. *Greenland population of the Barnacle Goose - the collation and statistical analysis of data and Population Viability Analyses*. Report to Scottish Natural Heritage 137, 45 pp.

Petty SJ 1985. Counts of some breeding birds in two recently afforested areas of Kintyre. *Scott Birds* 13:258-262.

Petty SJ 1989. Nestbox project: second year results. *Argyll Bird Rept* 5:40-45.

Petty SJ 1990. A nestbox study of Blue Tit, Great Tit and Pied Flycatcher: third-year results. *Argyll Bird Rept* 6:72-77.

Petty SJ 1992. *Ecology of the Tawny Owl* Strix aluco *in the Spruce Forests of Northumberland and Argyll*. PhD Thesis, Open University.

Petty S 1993. Some results from the nestbox project in 1993. *Eider* (winter 1993):6-7.

Petty SJ 1996. Adaptations of raptors to man-made forests in the British uplands. In: *Raptors in human landscapes* (Ed. Bird DM Varland DE & Negro JJ) pp. 201-214. Academic Press, London.

Petty SJ 1999. Diet of Tawny Owls (*Strix aluco*) in relation to Field Vole (*Microtus agrestis*) abundance in a conifer forest in northern England. *J Zool, Lond* 248:451-465.

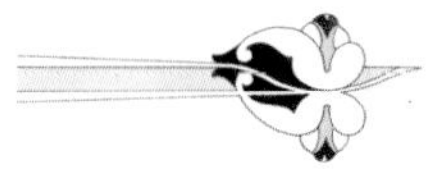

Petty SJ 2004. Black grouse on Mull. *Eider* (June 2004):8-9.

Petty SJ 2007. An unsuccessful attempt to establish Northern Goshawks in Argyll. *Scott Birds* 27:41-45.

Petty SJ & Anderson D 1986. Breeding by Hen Harriers (*Circus cyaneus*) on restocked sites in upland forest. *Bird Study* 33:177-178.

Petty SJ & Avery MI 1990. *Forest Bird Communities: A Review of the Ecology and Management of Forest Bird Communities in Relation to Silvicultural Practices in the British Uplands.* Forestry Commission Occasional Paper 26. Forestry Commission, Edinburgh.

Petty SJ & Anderson DIK 1994. First breeding records of the Mandarin in Argyll. *Scott Birds* 17:164-165.

Petty SJ, Shaw G, Anderson DIK 1994. Value of nest boxes for population studies and conservation of owls in coniferous forests in Britain. *J Raptor Res* 28:134-142.

Petty SJ, Patterson IJ, Anderson DIK, Little B, Davison M 1995. Numbers, breeding performance and diet of the Sparrowhawk *Accipiter nisus* and Merlin *Falco columbarius* in relation to cone crops and coniferous seed-eating finches. *Forest Ecol Mgmt* 79:133-146.

Petty SJ, Anderson DIK, Davison M, Little B *et al.* 2003. The decline of Common Kestrels *Falco tinnunculus* in a forested area of northern England: the role of predation by Northern Goshawks *Accipiter gentilis*. *Ibis* 145:472-483.

Petty SJ & Thomas CJ 2003. Distribution, numbers and breeding performance of Tawny Owls (*Strix aluco*) in relation to clear-cutting in a conifer forest in northern England. In: *Birds of Prey in a Changing Environment* (ed. DBA Thompson, SM Redpath, AH Fielding, M Marquiss, CA Galbraith), pp. 111-129. The Stationery Office, Edinburgh.

Petty S & Lambin X 2004. Relationships between clearcutting, Field Vole abundance and the breeding performance of Tawny Owls in upland spruce forests in northern Britain. In: *Managing Woodlands and their Mammals: Proceedings of a Symposium Organised Jointly by the Mammal Society and the Forestry Commission* (ed. C Quine, R Shore, R Trout), pp. 91-93. Forestry Commission Edinburgh.

Picozzi N 1975. A study of the Carrion/Hooded Crow in north-east Scotland. *Brit Birds* 68:409-419.

Plaza J & Sanderson WG 1997. Chapter 5.4 Rare sea-bed species. In: *Coasts and seas of the United Kingdom. Region 14 South-west Scotland: Ballantrae to Mull*, ed. by JH Barne, CF Robson, SS Kaznowska, JP Doody, NC Davidson, AL Buck, 95-100. JNCC. (Coastal Directories Series), Peterborough.

Radford MC 1960. Common Gull movements shown by ringing returns. *Bird Study* 7:81-93.

Raine AF, Sowter DJ, Brown AF, Sutherland WJ 2006. Migration patterns of two populations of Twite *Carduelis flavirostris* in Britain. *Ring & Migr* 23:45-52.

Rainier, I 1975. Notes on the birds of Mid-Argyll. *Western Nat* 4:95-113.

Rainier I 1983. Additional notes on the birds of Mid-Argyll. *Scott Nat* :103-107.

Ratcliffe DA 1962. Breeding density in the Peregrine *Falco peregrinus* and Raven *Corvus corax*. *Ibis* 104:13-39.

Ratcliffe DA 1984. The Peregrine breeding population of the United Kingdom in 1981. *Bird Study* 31:1-18.

Ratcliffe DA 1993. *The Peregrine Falcon*, 2nd Edition. T & AD Poyser, Calton.

Ratcliffe DA 1997. *The Raven: a Natural History in Britain and Ireland.* T & AD Poyser, London.

Ratcliffe N, Pickerell G, Brindley E 2000. Population trends of Little and Sandwich Tern *Sterna albifrons* and *S sandvicensis* in Britain and Ireland from 1969-1998. *Atlantic Seabirds* 2:211-226.

Raven MJ, Noble DG, Baillie SR 2005. *The Breeding Bird Survey 2004.* BTO Research Report 403. BTO, Thetford.

Raven MJ, Noble DG 2006. *The Breeding Bird Survey 2005.* BTO Research Report 439. BTO, Thetford.

Rawcliffe CP 1958. The Scottish Mute Swan census 1955-56. *Bird Study* 5:45-55.

Redpath S, Madders M, Donnelly E, Anderson B *et al.* 1998. Nest site selection by Hen Harriers in Scotland. *Bird Study* 45:51-61.

Rintoul LJ & Baxter EV 1927. On the decrease of black game in Scotland. *Scot Nat* 163:5-13, 164:45-52, 165:69-75.

Ritchie J 1920. *The Influence of Man on Animal Life in Scotland.* Cambridge University Press. Cambridge.

Rivers SL 2002. High counts of Sooty Shearwaters in Scotland. *Birding Scotl* 5:163.

Robel RJ 1969. Movements and flock stratification within a population of Blackcocks in Scotland. *J Anim Ecol* 38:755-763.

Rolando A & Laiolo P 1994. Habitat selection of Hooded and Carrion Crows in the alpine hybrid zone. *Ardea* 82:193-200.

Rolfe R 1966. The status of the Chough in the British Isles. *Bird Study* 66:221-236.

Ross A 1913. Birds of Islay. *Glasgow Nat* 6:7-32.

Ross BP & Furness RW 2000. *Minimising the impact of Eiders on mussel farms.* University of Glasgow, Glasgow.

Ross BP, Lien J, Furness RW 2001. Use of underwater playback to reduce the impact of Eiders on mussel farms. *ICES J Mar Sci* 58:517-524.

Ruttledge RF & Ogilvie MA 1979. The past and present status of the Greenland White-fronted Goose in Ireland and Britain, *Irish Birds* 1:293-363.

Sage BL & Vernon JDR 1978. The 1975 national survey of Rookeries. *Bird Study* 25:64-86.

Sage BL & Whittington PA 1985. The 1980 sample survey of Rookeries. *Bird Study* 32:77-81.

Saino N 1992. Selection of foraging habitat and flocking by crow *Corvus corone* phenotypes in a hybrid zone. *Ornis Scand* 23:111-120.

Sandeman P 1965. Attempted reintroduction of White-tailed Eagle to Scotland. *Scott Birds* 3:411-412.

Saunders H and Eagle Clarke W 1927. *Manual of British Birds.* Gurney & Jackson, London.

Scot Skirving R 1892. Grey Phalarope on Islay. *Ann Scott Nat Hist* 1892:72.

Scot Skirving R 1895. Carrion Crow, Hen Harrier and eagles in Islay. *Ann Scott Nat Hist* 1895:53-54.

Selby PJ 1833. *Illustrations of British Ornithology*. Vol 1.

Sergio F, Rizzolli F, Marchesi L, Pedrini P 2004. The importance of interspecific interactions for breeding-site selection: Peregrine Falcons seek proximity to Raven nests. *Ecography* 27:818-826.

Sharrock JTR 1976. *The Atlas of Breeding Birds in Britain and Ireland.* T & AD Poyser, Berkhamsted.

Shaw G 1990. Timing and fidelity of breeding for Siskins *Carduelis spinus* in Scottish conifer plantations. *Bird Study* 37:30-36.

Shaw G & Livingstone J 1991. Goldfinches and other birds eating Sitka Spruce seed. *BTO News* 174:8-9.

Shepherd KB, Green M, Knight AC, Stroud DA 1988. *The Breeding Birds of Tiree and Coll in 1987/88 with Special Emphasis on Breeding Waders.* NCC Chief Scientists Directorate Report 827.

Shrubb M 2003. Farming and birds: an historic perspective. *Brit Birds* 96:158-177.

Shutes JCB & ap Rheinallt T 1995. Little Ringed Plover on Islay, 16 May 1983 - the sole Argyll record. *Argyll Bird Rept* 11:92-94.

Siitari H, Honkavaara J, Viitala J 1999. Ultraviolet reflection of berries attracts foraging birds. A laboratory study with Redwings (*Turdus iliacus*) and bilberries (*Vaccinium myrtillus*). *Proc Roy Soc Lond B* 266:2125-2129.

Sim IMW, Gibbons DW, Bainbridge IP, Mattingley WA 2001. Status of the Hen Harrier *Circus cyaneus* in the UK and the Isle of Man in 1998. *Bird Study* 48:341-353.

Sim IMW, Gregory RD, Hancock MH, Brown AF 2005. Recent changes in the abundance of British upland breeding birds. *Bird Study* 52:261-275.

Sim IMW, Dillon IA, Eaton MA, Etheridge B, et al. 2007. Status of the Hen Harrier *Circus cyaneus* in the UK and the Isle of Man in 2004, and a comparison with the 1988/89 and 1998 surveys. *Bird Study* 54:256-267.

Sinclair J 1754-1835. *The statistical account of Scotland, 1791-1799.* William Creech, Edinburgh.

Skorka P & Wojcik JD 2005. Population dynamics and social behavior of the Mistle Thrush *Turdus viscivorus* during winter. *Acta Ornithol* 40:35-42.

Smith GC, Henderson IS, Robertson PA 2005. A model of Ruddy Duck *Oxyura jamaicensis* eradication for the UK. *J appl Ecol* 42:546-555.

Snow BK & Snow DW 1984. Long-term defence of fruits by Mistle Thrushes *Turdus viscivorus*. *Ibis* 126:39-50.

Society for the Benefit of the Sons and Daughters of the Clergy 1845. *The new statistical account of Scotland.* William Blackwood & Sons, Edinburgh.

Sohle I, Wilson LJ, Dean BJ, O'Brien SH, Webb A & Reid JB 2006. *Surveillance of wintering seaducks, divers and grebes in UK inshore areas.* JNCC Rept 392. Joint Nature Conservation Committee, Peterborough.

Southern HN 1970. The natural control of a population of Tawny Owls (*Strix aluco*). *J Zool, Lond* 162:197-285.

Southern HN & Lowe VPW 1982. Predation by Tawny Owls (*Strix aluco*) on Bank Voles (*Clethrionomys glareolus*) and Wood Mice (*Apodemus sylvaticus*). *J Zool, Lond* 198:83-103.

Stanbury A & Campbell S 1994. *Survey of the breeding waders and other species on the Rhinns of Islay.* Unpublished RSPB Report.

Stevenson A 2004. Scottish Pacific Golden Plovers – an addendum. *Birding Scotl* 7:115.

Stevenson A 2005. Redpolls in the Outer Hebrides. *Birding World* 18:124.

Stewart AG 1970. The seabird wreck – autumn 1969. *Scott Birds* 6:142-149.

Stewart W 1920. Cirl Bunting in Argyllshire. *Brit Birds* 14:89-90.

Stewart W 1938. Bird notes from Upper Loch Fyne. *Scott Nat*: 81.

Stone CJ, Webb A, Barton C, Ratcliffe N *et al.* 1995. *An Atlas of Seabird Distribution in North-West European Waters.* JNCC, Peterborough.

Stroud DA (ed.) 1989. *The Birds of Coll and Tiree: Status, Habitats and Conservation.* NCC/SOC, Edinburgh.

Stroud DA & Newton SF 1986. 1985 Argyll Mute Swan census – preliminary results. *Argyll Bird Rept* 3:73.

Stroud J 1986. The status of the Corncrake on Islay 1985. *Argyll Bird Rept* 3:89-92.

Stowe TJ & Becker D 1992. The status and conservation of the Corncrake *Crex crex* outside the breeding grounds. *Tauraco* 2:1-23.

St. John C 1924. *The Wild Sports and Natural History of the Highlands.* Gurney & Jackson, London.

Stewart AG 1970. The seabird wreck - autumn 1969. *Scott Birds* 6:142-149.

Suddaby D, Shaw KD, Ellis PM & Brockie K 1994. King Eiders in Britain and Ireland in 1958-90: occurrences and ageing. *Brit Birds* 87:418-430.

Summers RW & Canham M 2001. The distribution of Crested Tits in Scotland during the 1990s. *Scott Birds* 22:20-27.

Summers RW, Jardine DC, Marquiss M, Rae R 2002. The distribution and habitats of Crossbills *Loxia* spp. in Britain, with specific reference to the Scottish Crossbill *Loxia scotica*. *Ibis* 144:393-410.

Summers-Smith JD 2003. The decline of the House Sparrow: a review. *Brit Birds* 96:439-446.

Svärdson G 1957. The "invasion" type of bird migration. *Brit Birds* 50:314-343.

Swann RL 1983. Redwings in a Highland Glen. *Scott Birds* 12:260-261.

Tait AM 1969. Roller on Islay. *Scott Birds* 5:391.

Thom VM 1986. *Birds in Scotland.* T & AD Poyser, Calton.

Thomas CJ 1993. *Modelling the distribution and breeding performance of the Raven* Corvus corax *in relation to habitat: an application using satellite remote sensing and geographical information systems.* PhD Thesis, University of Glasgow.

Thompson PS 1989. The Argyll Garden Bird Survey. *Argyll Bird Rept* 5:36-39.

Thompson WA 1849-1851. *The natural history of Ireland. Vols 1-3. Birds.* Reeve, Benham & Reeve, London.

Tomison J 1907. Bird-life as observed at Skerryvore lighthouse. *Ann Scott Nat Hist* 1907:20-31.

Urquhart B & Maguire E 2006. A population study of Common Ravens in Kintyre during 2006. Report to SNH

Urquhart B, Maguire E, Petty S 2007. Ravens in Kintyre - 2006 survey. *Eider* (March 2007):16-17.

Ussher RJ & Warren R 1900. *The Birds of Ireland.* Gurney & Jackson, London.

Van Noordwijk AJ, McCleery RH, Perrins CM 1995. Selection for the timing of Great Tit breeding in relation to caterpillar growth and temperature. *J Anim Ecol* 64:451-458.

Vernon JDR 1969. Spring migration of the Common Gull in Britain and Ireland. *Bird Study* 16:101-107.

Verrall K 1977a. Little Shearwater in Argyllshire. *Scott Birds* 9:380-381.

Verrall K 1977b. Laughing Gull in Argyllshire. *Scott Birds* 9:381-382.

Verrall K & Bourne WRP 1982. Seabird movements around

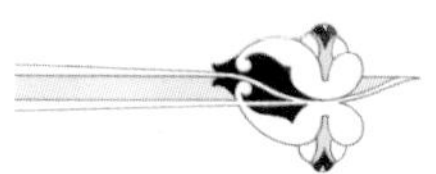

western Islay. *Scott Birds* 12:3-11.

Village A 1981. The diet and breeding of Long-eared Owls in relation to vole numbers. *Bird Study* 28:215-224.

Village A 1990. *The Kestrel.* T & AD Poyser, Calton.

Village A 1992. *Asio* owls and Kestrels *Falco tinnunculus* in recently-planted and thicket plantations. In: *The Ecology and Conservation of European Owls* (ed. by CA Galbraith, IR Taylor, S Percival) pp. 11-15. JNCC, Peterborough.

Visser ME, Adriaensen F, van Balen JH, Blondel J *et al.* 2003. Variable responses to large-scale climate change in European *Parus* populations. *Proc Roy Soc Lond B* 270:367-372.

Votier SC, Harrop AHJ & Denny M 2003. A review of the status and identification of American Wigeon in Britain & Ireland. *Brit Birds* 96:2-22.

Waldbridge G, Small B & McGowan RY 2003. From the Rarities Committee's files: Ascension Frigatebird on Tiree – new to the Western Palearctic. *Brit Birds* 96:58-73.

Walker D, McGrady M, McCluskie A, Madders M, McLeod DRA 2005. Resident Golden Eagle ranging behaviour before and after construction of a windfarm in Argyll. *Scott. Birds* 25:24-40.

Wallace DIM 1999. History of the Common Rosefinch in Britain and Ireland, 1869-1996. *Brit Birds* 92:445-471.

Wallace DIM, Bradshaw C & Rogers MJ 2006. A review of the 1950-57 British rarities. *Brit Birds* 99:460-464.

Waltho C 2001. *Firth of Clyde Eider news.* No. 1. 4pp. Report produced by Chris Waltho, Carluke.

Waltho C 2002. *Firth of Clyde Eider news.* No. 2. 8pp. Report produced by Chris Waltho, Carluke.

Warnes JM 1983. The status of the Chough in Scotland. *Scott Birds* 12:238-246.

Watson A 1965. Research on Scottish Ptarmigan. *Scott Birds* 3:331-349.

Watson D 1977. *The Hen Harrier.* T & AD Poyser, Berkhamsted.

Watson J, Leitch AF, Broad R 1992. The diet of the Sea Eagle *Haliaeetus albicilla* and Golden Eagle *Aquila chrysaetos* in Western Scotland. *Ibis* 134:27-31.

Weir DN 1978. Effects of poisoning on Raven and raptor population. *Scott Birds* 10:31.

Wellock S 2004. *Coll Birds.* Internal RSPB report.

Wernham CV, Toms PM, Marchant JH, Clark JA, Siriwardena GM, Baillie SR (eds). 2002. *The Migration Atlas: Movements of the Birds of Britain & Ireland.* T & AD Poyser, London.

Whitfield DP, McLeod DRA, Fielding AH, Broad RA, Evans RJ, Haworth PF 2001. The effects of forestry on Golden Eagles on the island of Mull, western Scotland. *J appl Ecol* 38:1208-1220.

Whitfield DP, Evans RJ, Broad RA, Fielding AH, Haworth PF, Madders M & McLeod DRA 2002. Are reintroduced white-tailed eagles in competition with golden eagles? *Scott Birds* 23:36-45.

Whitfield DP, Fielding AH, Gregory MJP, Gordon AG, McLeod DRA, Haworth PF 2007. Complex effects of habitat loss on Golden Eagles *Aquila chrysaetos. Ibis* 149:26-36.

Whyte C, Hancock M, Bainbridge I, Jackson D 1995. *The joint RSPB SNH 1994 Black-throated Diver* Gavia arctica *survey.* Unpublished RSPB Report.

Williamson K 1974. Breeding birds in the deciduous woodland of mid-Argyll, Scotland. *Bird Study* 21:29-44.

Willis SG 2000. Effects of disturbance by ecotourism on breeding distributions of Shag *Phalacrocorax aristotelis*, Puffin *Fratercula arctica* and Fulmar *Fulmarus glacialis* on the Treshnish Isles, Argyll, UK. *Treshnish Isles Auk Ringing Group Rept 2000*:44-49.

Wilson AM & Fuller RJ 2001. *Bird Populations and Environmental Change: Countryside Survey 2000, Module 5.* BTO Research Rept 263.

Wilson LJ, Dean BJ, Webb A, McSorley CA & Reid JB 2006. *Wintering seaducks, divers and grebes in UK inshore areas: aerial surveys and shore-based counts 2004/05.* JNCC Rept No. 371. Joint Nature Conservation Committee, Peterborough.

Winstanley D, Spencer R, Williamson K 1974. Where have all the whitethroats gone? *Bird Study* 21:1-14.

Witherby HF, Jourdain FCR, Ticehurst NF, Tucker BW 1945. *The Handbook of British Birds.* HF & G Witherby, London.

Wotton SR, Langston RHW, Gregory RD 2002. The breeding status of the Ring Ouzel *Turdus torquatus* in the UK in 1999. *Bird Study* 49:26-34.

Wyllie I 1981. *The Cuckoo.* Batsford, London.

Wynne-Edwards VC 1953. Leach's Petrels stranded in Scotland in October-November 1952. *Scott Nat* 65:167-189.

Yates G 2005. Unusual nest sites of Sparrowhawks and Tawny Owls on Islay. *Eider* (December 2005):4-5.

Yates MG, Goss-Custard JD, Rispin WE 1996. Towards predicting the effect of loss of intertidal feeding areas on overwintering shorebirds (Charadrii) and Shelduck (*Tadorna tadorna*): Refinements and tests of a model developed for the Wash, east England. *J appl Ecol* 33:944-954.

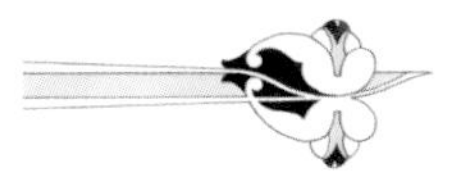

Birds of Argyll: Index to species accounts

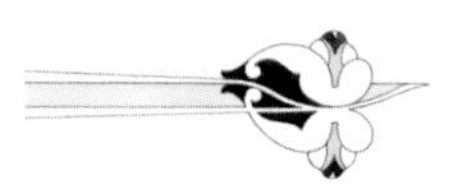

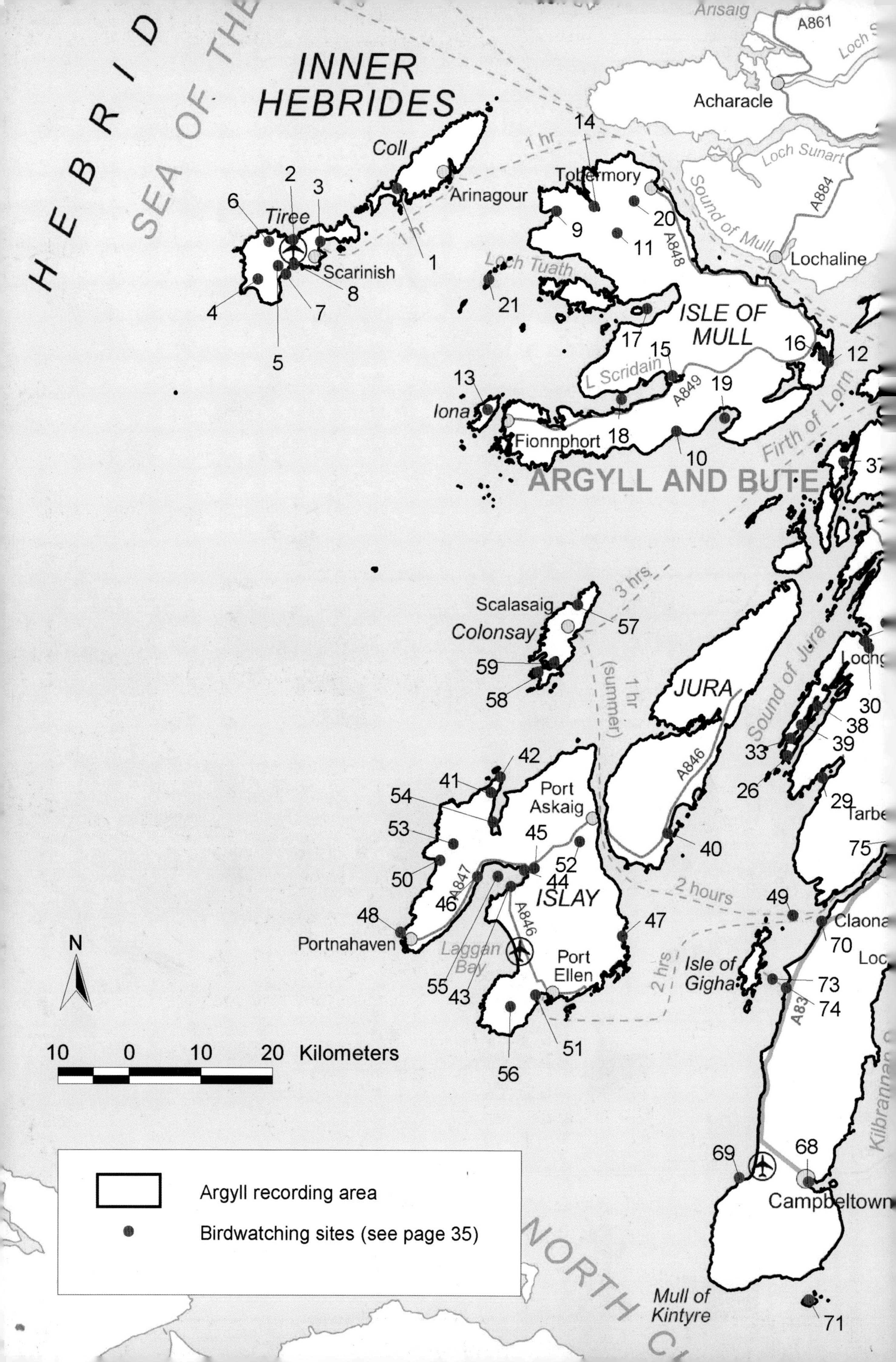

INNER HEBRIDES
HEBRID
SEA OF THE
Arisaig
A861
Acharacle
Loch Sunart
Sound of Mull
A884
Lochaline
Coll
Arinagour
Tiree
Scarinish
Tobermory
A848
Loch Tuath
ISLE OF MULL
L Scridain
A849
Iona
Fionnphort
Firth of Lorn
ARGYLL AND BUTE
1 hr
3 hrs.
Scalasaig
Colonsay
1 hr (summer)
JURA
A846
Sound of Jura
Port Askaig
ISLAY
A847
Laggan Bay
Port Ellen
Portnahaven
2 hours
2 hrs
Isle of Gigha
Campbeltown
Mull of Kintyre
NORTH
N
10 0 10 20 Kilometers
Argyll recording area
Birdwatching sites (see page 35)
1 2 3 4 5 6 7 8 9 10 11 12 13 14 15 16 17 18 19 20 21
26 29 30 33 38 39 40 41 42 43 44 45 46 47 48 49 50 51 52 53 54 55 56 57 58 59
68 69 70 71 73 74 75